Course	Engineering Graphics and Design I and II Vol. 1
Course Number	**ENGR1211 and 1212**
Professors	Yoon duk Kim Anant Honkan Valerie Bennett GEORGIA PERIMETER COLLEGE **MCSE**

http://create.mheducation.com

ISBN-10: 1308091370 ISBN-13: 9781308091372

Contents

Credits

Preface

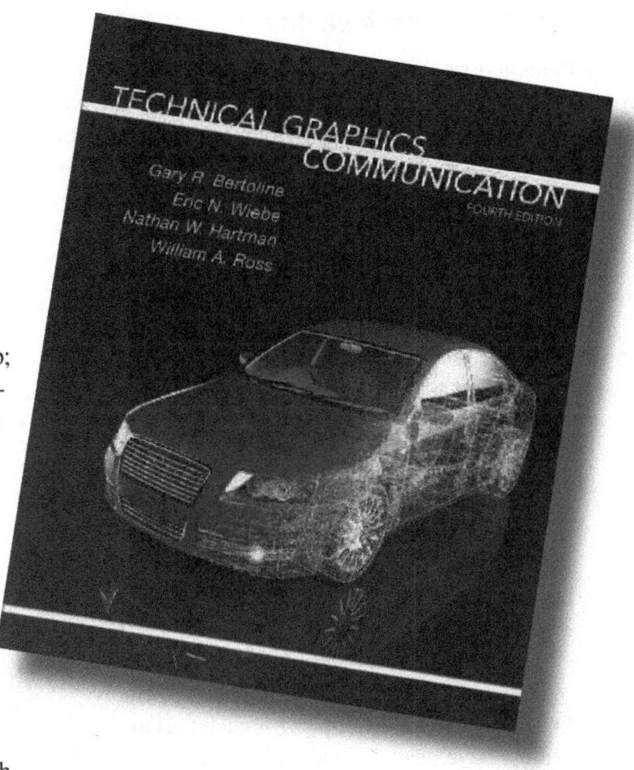

To the authors of this text, teaching graphics is not a job; it is a "life mission." We feel that teaching is an important profession and that the education of our engineers and technologists is critical to the future of our country. Further, we believe that technical graphics is an essential, fundamental part of an engineer and technologist's education. We also believe that many topics in technical graphics and the visualization process can be very difficult for some students to understand and learn. For these and other reasons, we have developed this text, which addresses both traditional and modern elements of technical graphics, using what we believe to be an interesting and straightforward approach.

Engineering and technical graphics have gone through significant changes as a direct result of the use of computers and CAD software. Although these changes are important to the subject of technical graphics, there is much about the curriculum that has not changed. Engineers and technologists still find it necessary to communicate and interpret designs, using graphics methods such as drawings or computer models. As powerful as today's computers and CAD software have become, they are of little use to engineers and technologists who do not fully understand fundamental graphics principles and 3-D modeling strategies or do not possess high-level visualization skills.

This graphics text is therefore based on the premise that there must be some fundamental changes in the content and process of graphics instruction. Although many graphics concepts remain the same, the fields of engineering and technical graphics are in a transition phase from hand tools to the computer, and the emphasis of instruction is changing from drafter to 3-D geometric modeler, using computers instead of paper and pencil.

Goals of the Text

This text was written to help the engineering and technology student learn the techniques and standard practices of technical graphics so that design ideas can be adequately communicated and produced. The text concentrates on the concepts and skills necessary to use both hand tools and 2-D or 3-D CAD. The primary goals of the text are to show how to

1. Clearly represent mental images.
2. Graphically represent technical designs, using accepted standard practices.
3. Use plane and solid geometric forms to create and communicate design solutions.
4. Analyze graphics models, using descriptive and spatial geometry.
5. Solve technical design problems, using traditional tools or CAD.
6. Communicate graphically, using sketches, traditional tools, and CAD.
7. Apply technical graphics principles to many engineering disciplines.

The authors of this text have gone to great lengths to truly integrate traditional and modern engineering design graphics theory and practice into a single text.

Features of the Fourth Edition

Much thought has gone into designing a complete instructional approach to teaching and learning of technical graphics. The instructor is provided with a number of tools to assist in the instruction aspects, and the student is provided with tools to assist in the learning process.

This text was specifically written using techniques that will prepare students to use technical graphics concepts, practices, and modern tools, to solve design problems and communicate graphically. One goal was to provide to the students a textbook that was clear, interesting, relevant, and contemporary.

Some of the distinguishing features of this text include the following:

1. *New Feature—Supplemental Solid Modeling Exercises*—A series of new problems focusing on 3-D solid modeling for parts and assemblies have been developed and are included in a special section at the ends of Chapter 10 Multiview Drawing, Chapter 13 Auxiliary Views, Chapter 16 Section Views, and Chapter 20 Working and Assembly Drawings. Visual examples for each part and assembly have been created with various solid modeling software packages and are included with engineering sketches to aid students in visualizing part geometry and the modeling process. In addition to supplementing traditional subjects in each of the chapters, these problems also provide a logical extension to the chapter on 3D Modeling by furnishing students a new series of software independent solid modeling exercises that may be modeled with any of the popular parametric based solid modeling software packages currently in use. In addition to 3-D solid modeling experience, it is also intended that these problems may serve as a basis for students to; 1) explore basic property analysis of solid models, 2) develop variable parametric models based on design intent, 3) generate detail and working assembly documentation drawings, 4) create intelligent spread sheet driven bills of material for managing the product development process and 5) explore methods of relational bottom up and top down assembly modeling.
2. *Design Problems*—The new design problems in Chapter 3 were developed to provide students an opportunity to exercise the various stages of the design process outlined in this chapter. They provide an ideation stage, a decision-making stage, design creation stage, and a documentation stage. Each problem includes provisions for sketching, 3D modeling, and documentation of the student's final solution to the problem. In addition, the problems were deliberately designed in an open-ended fashion to promote creativity in the solution process, and to provide a context in which the student can work to develop a 3D model that addresses the required criteria.
3. *Integration of CAD*—CAD concepts and practices have been integrated through all the chapters when they are relevant to the topic. They are not simply "tacked onto" the end of a chapter.
4. *Visualization chapter* (chapter 5)—This *unique* chapter, devoted exclusively to visualization, assists the student in understanding the concepts and importance of visualization and offers techniques for reading and visualizing engineering drawings.
5. *3-D modeling chapter* (chapter 9)—This *unique* chapter is devoted exclusively to the theory and practice of 3-D modeling with an emphasis in constraint-based CAD.
6. *Modern topics*—The book is filled with modern examples, illustrations, and industry examples so students can relate to the material being presented and get excited about the subject.
7. *Integration of design*—Design concepts are integrated through the text to give relevance and understanding of the relationship of design to technical graphics. This is visually reinforced throughout the text through the use of an icon located in the margin of the text whenever a design concept is covered. The icon is a smaller version of the Concurrent Engineering Design Process figure first introduced in Chapter 2. Figure 2.8 breaks design into three major components: ideation, refinement, and implementation. Whenever one of these topics is discussed in the text, a smaller version of Figure 2.8 is placed in the margin with ideation, refinement, or implementation highlighted. This lets the student know that the topic being covered is relevant to the engineering design process and constantly reinforces design as the underlying theme for engineering and technical graphics.

Ideation

Refinement

Implementation

Coverage of Modern Topics

One of the primary reasons we wrote the text is that many modern topics are either not found or not covered in sufficient detail in traditional texts. Examples of contemporary topics covered in this book include:

Computer simulation
Human factors
Product data management (PDM)
Virtual reality (VR)
NURBS
Data exchange standards
3-D modeling problems
3-D modeling concepts and practices

Extensive Coverage of Traditional Topics

Even though we firmly believe our coverage results in the most modern text available, we have been very careful to include all the traditional topics normally found in a technical drawing textbook. The authors fully understand that students must learn the fundamentals whether using hand tools or CAD to communicate graphically. Therefore, coverage of traditional topics is comprehensive and in many cases includes step-by-step procedures and enhanced color illustrations to facilitate teaching and learning. The text includes the latest ANSI standard practices used in industry.

Chapter Overviews and Features

Every chapter has been carefully planned and written with a consistent writing, illustration, design style, and pedagogy. The book was written as a part of a more global instructional approach to engineering and technical graphics and will serve as a starting point for instructor and student.

To accomplish these goals, the text is divided into 4 parts and 25 chapters. Each part has a brief introduction with a listing of chapters in the part so the instructor and student understand the logical sequencing of topics and chapters. Each chapter has a logical sequence and organization that is easily navigated. Each chapter contains these features:

Relevant Quotes Each chapter opens with a quote that is relevant to the chapter material being covered or the topic of graphics in general. These quotes, many by famous historical figures, reinforce the importance of graphics in industry and society.

Objectives Each chapter has a list of measurable objectives that can be used as a guide when studying the material presented in the text. Instructors can also use the objectives as a guide when writing tests and quizzes.

Introduction A brief overview of the chapter contents prepares the student for the material to be presented. The introduction sets the stage for the relevancy and importance of the material to be covered for the engineer or technologist. The introduction includes a rationale explaining why it is important to learn the material in the chapter.

Color Is Important in a Modern Engineering and Technical Graphics Textbook This was the first technical graphics textbook to use four-color illustrations throughout to better present the material and improve learning. The selection and use of color in the text is consistent to enhance learning and teaching. *Many of the color illustrations are also available to the instructor in the image library found in the Instructor Resources to supplement lectures, as explained in detail later in this Preface.*

The use of color in the text was done specifically to enhance teaching, learning, and visualization. Workplanes are represented as a light pink (Figure 9.30). Projection and picture planes are a light purple color (Figure 10.10).

Important information in a figure is shown in red to highlight the feature and draw the attention of the reader (Figure 8.6). Color shading is often used on pictorial illus-

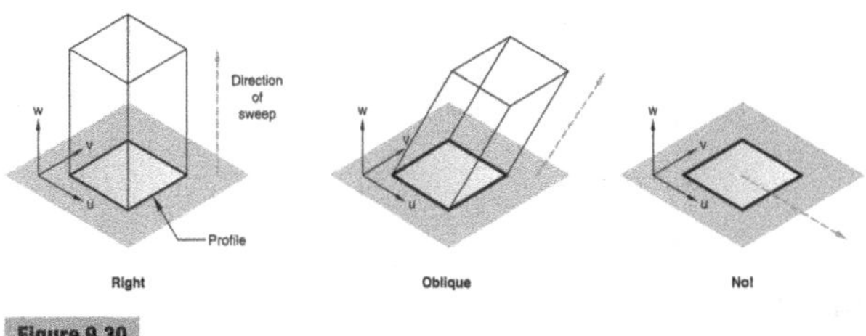

Figure 9.30

Types of linear sweeping operations
In some systems, linear sweeps are restricted to being perpendicular to the workplane.

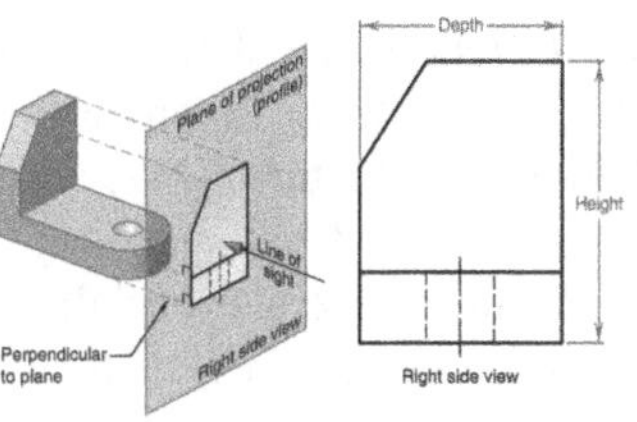

Figure 10.10

Profile view
A right side view of the object is created by projecting onto the profile plane of projection.

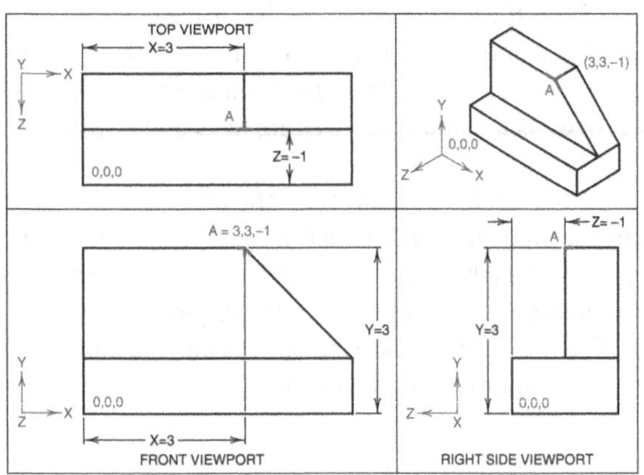

Figure 8.6

Display of coordinate axes in a multiview CAD drawing
Only two of the three coordinates can be seen in each view.

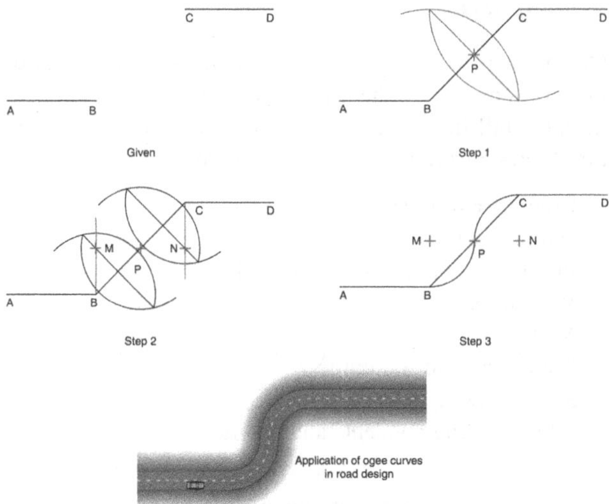

Figure 8.48

Constructing an ogee curve between two parallel lines

trations so the user can better visualize the 3-dimensional form of the object (Figure 10.43). This is especially important for most students who are being asked to use their visual mode to think and create. Color shading highlights important features, more clearly shows different sides of objects, and adds more realism to the object being viewed.

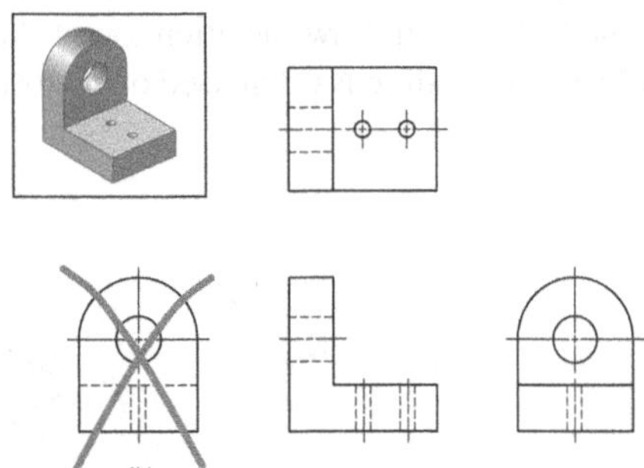

Figure 10.43

Most descriptive views
Select those views which are the most descriptive and have the fewest hidden lines. In this example, the right side view has fewer hidden lines than the left side view.

Frequently, different shades of color are used on objects to highlight various features, improve visualization of objects, and better describe them (Figure 8.48). Different shades of color are also used on a single object to highlight surface features, which is useful especially when trying to draw attention to certain features, such as holes, oblique planes, and surfaces to be projected onto a picture plane. **Some texts use two colors, which are adequate for some illustrations, but our research with students clearly demonstrates that having the ability to display objects and text illustrations in many different colors provides a considerable advantage when teaching engineering and technical graphics.** Effective use of color improves the pedagogy and can greatly enhance an instructor's lecture and ability to teach complicated or hard to understand concepts. Being limited to one or two colors as in other texts is an unnecessary obstacle to effective teaching and learning.

Photographs and screen captures are much more interesting and show much more detail when in color (Figure 3.40). In some aspects of engineering design, such as

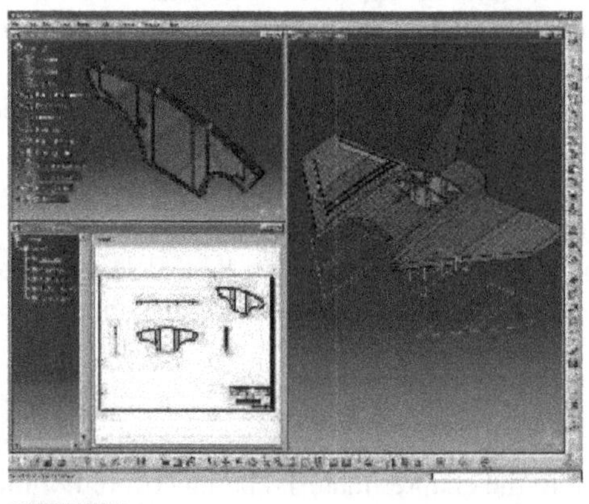

Figure 3.40

Production drawing
A production drawing showing views of a welded body part.
(Courtesy of Dassault Systemes.)

finite element analysis, color is the method used to communicate or highlight areas of stress or temperature. Showing a black and white illustration to explain finite element analysis is just short of being useless. CAD systems are capable of displaying millions of colors and can create photographic realistic models of designs and assemblies. Full-color illustrations in engineering and technical graphics are prerequisite for a modern text.

Practice Exercises A unique feature of the text is the use of practice exercises, which cause the student to pause and actively engage in some activity that immediately reinforces their learning. For example, Practice Exercise 7.1 in Chapter 7, "Sketching and Text," asks the student to find a few familiar objects and begin making isometric sketches.

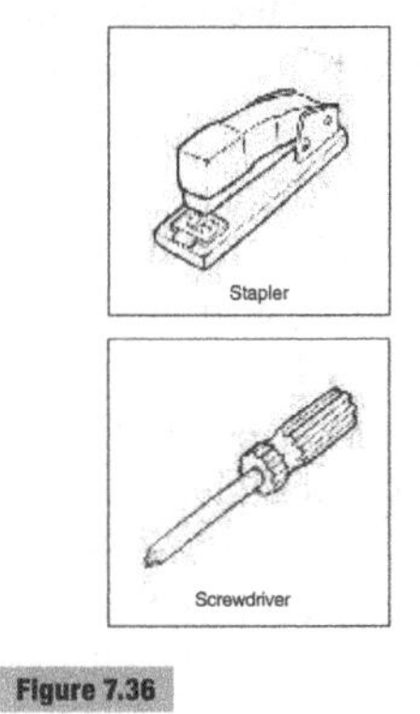

Figure 7.36
Isometric sketches of common objects

Step-by-Step Illustrated Procedures Most chapters include many drawing examples that use step-by-step procedures with illustrations to demonstrate how to create graphics elements or to solve problems. These step-by-step procedures show the student in simple terms how a drawing is produced. Most of the illustrations accompanying the step-by-step procedures are in multiple parts so the student can see how the drawing is created. In many cases the color red is used in each step of the illustration to show what is being added or created.

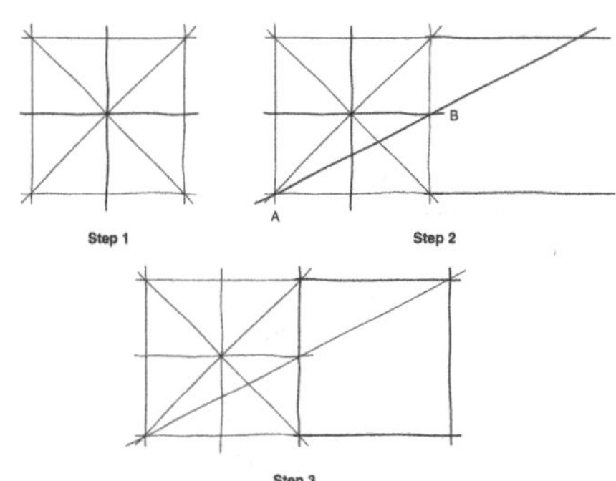

Figure 7.21
Sketching identically proportioned squares
An identically proportioned square is created by extending both top and bottom horizontal lines and constructing diagonals across the existing box.

Integration of CAD Every chapter includes specific references to CAD rather than simply adding them to the end of the chapter. By integrating the references in the text, the student learns how CAD is used in the context of the topic being explained. In some cases whole sections or chapters deal with CAD topics. For example, Chapter 9, "Three-Dimensional Modeling," covers the use of CAD to create 3-D models. Students begin to understand that CAD is another tool used by the engineer and technologist to communicate. Traditional topics and CAD topics are seamlessly integrated because the text was written that way from the outset. CAD is not an add-on or afterthought. It is fully integrated and embraced as a means of creating graphics for engineers and technologists (Figure 10.35).

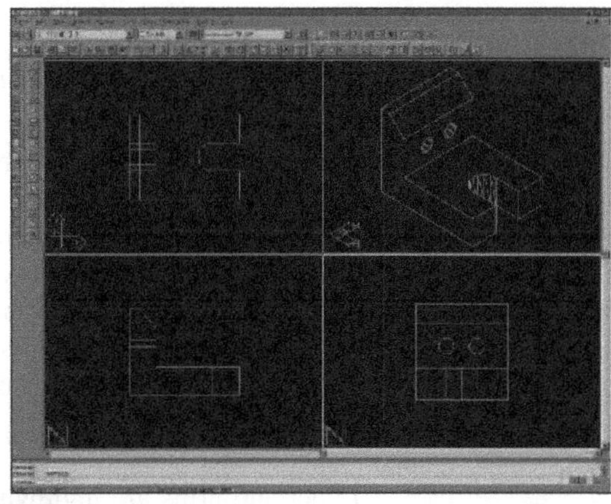

Figure 10.35
Predefined multiviews on a CAD system

Historical Highlights Many of the chapters include information about important events and people in the history of graphics. This is an extension of the history of graphics first introduced to the students in Chapter 1. Historical Highlights are presented as a special boxed feature that contains an overview of the person or event along with photographs and drawings. They are used as a means of giving the student an historical context to graphics.

Dream High Tech Jobs This feature is included in many chapters and describes interesting jobs that are available to engineers and technologists who have mastered technical communications.

Dream High Tech Job

Designing Snowboards

Design in Industry Most chapters includes a special feature covering some aspect of design as practiced in industry. This Design in Industry feature covers design in many types of industries so that students with varied engineering interests can see how design is used to solve problems. Many feature quotes from engineers working in industry explaining how they solved problems or used CAD tools to enhance the design process. All the Design in Industry items include figures to supplement the information presented.

Highlighting Key Terms Important terms are highlighted in each chapter with bold or italicized text. All boldfaced terms are included in the extensive glossary found at the end of the text for easy reference. Italicized text draws the attention of the reader to highlighted important terms or phrases.

Summary Each chapter ends with a summary as a means to pull everything covered in the chapter together for the student. The summary is a brief overview of the most important topics covered in the chapter. In some cases, the summary also includes important information listed in tables or bulleted lists.

Questions for Review Each chapter includes an extensive list of questions for review. Included are questions meant to measure whether students learned the objective listed at the start of each chapter. Other questions are used to reinforce the most important information presented in the chapter. The types of questions used require students to answer through writing or through sketching and drawing.

Further Reading Many of the chapters include a list of books or articles from periodicals relevant to the content covered in the text. The Further Reading list can be useful for the instructor to find additional information about a topic.

Problems Every chapter in the text includes an extensive number and variety of problem assignments. Most chapters include text-based problems that describe a problem to solve or drawing to create. Most chapters include problems with figures that students are to solve or replicate using traditional tools and CAD. The figure-based problems are very extensive and range from the very simple to complex. This arrangement allows the instructor to carefully increase the complexity of the problems as students learn and progress. The most complex drawings can be used to supplement assignments given to the most talented students or for group-based projects.

Most of the problems are of real parts made of plastic or light metals, materials commonly found in industry today. There are many examples of *unique* problems that

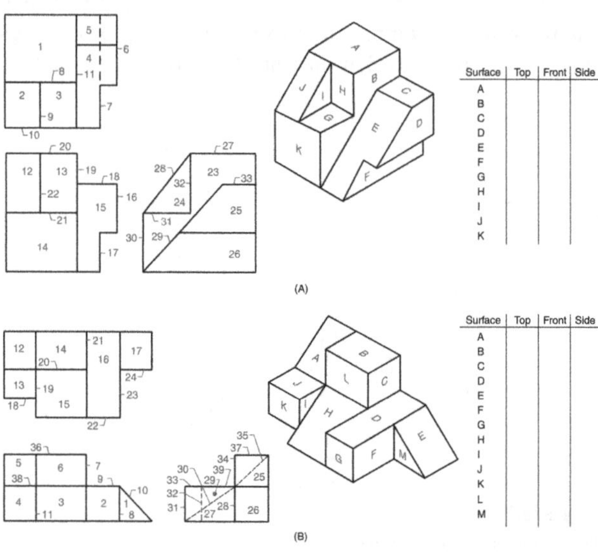

Figure 5.55

are not found in other textbooks. For example, many of the problems in Chapters 5 and 9 are not found in other engineering and technical graphics texts. These problems reinforce student learning and give them experience that will be of great value in industry.

The wide range and numerous problems allow the instructor to frequently change assignments so that fresh problems are used from semester to semester. Additional problems are available on the website and through our workbooks.

Classic Problems Many chapters include Classic Problems, which are additional problems that can be assigned. They have been taken from the seminal technical graphics textbooks by Thomas E. French, published by McGraw-Hill. Many of the problems are castings with machined surfaces giving the student experience with additional materials and machining processes.

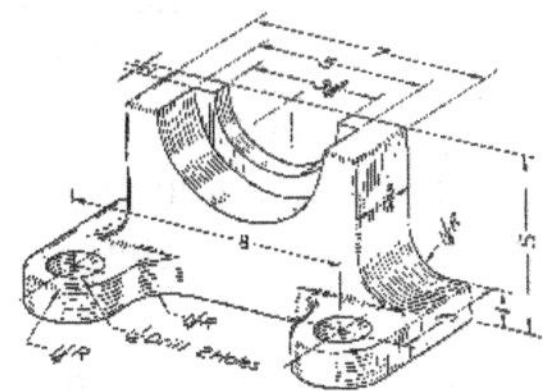

Figure 10.156
Bearing rest

Part 1
Global Implementation for Technical Graphics

This section contains four chapters that introduce the student to engineering design graphics. It includes an explanation of the importance of graphics instruction for engineers and technologists, has a brief overview of the engineering design process, explains the tools used to communicate graphically, and shows how to create simple sketches.

- Chapter 1, "Introduction to Graphics Communications," explains the role and importance of graphics communications in engineering design. The concept of visualization is first introduced to the student so they can begin to relate its importance to design graphics. There is a strong emphasis on communications so students begin to understand that graphics is a powerful form of human communications. One *unique* feature of the chapter is Practice Exercise 1.1, which shows through a simple exercise why graphics communication is the only useful method of describing design and the power of graphics over the written or spoken word.
- Chapter 2, "The Engineering Design Process," was significantly changed for the 3rd and 4th editions. Much of the original content was moved to a new Chapter 3, and new material was added. Chapter 2 is a brief introduction to traditional and modern technical design methodologies with more emphasis on concurrent engineering and product lifecycle management. One *unique* aspect of this chapter is the explanation of the modern practices used in engineering design, in which engineers interact and communicate with other professionals in the company.
- Chapter 3, "Design in Industry," is an in-depth overview of modern engineering design practice in industry. Before the 4th edition this was chapter 4. It was moved adjacent to Chapter 2 to provide a more comprehensive view of the processes and artifacts of the technical graphics processes as utilized in industry. Engineering design is explained in context with 3-D CAD modeling and the sharing of design information across the enterprise. The design process is covered in detail and includes important topics, such as ideation, the designer's notebook, computer simulation, design analysis, and design review meetings.
- Chapter 4, "The Role of Technical Graphics in Production Automation and Manufacturing Processes," is an introduction to modern manufacturing and production processes. The chapter explains in contemporary terms the general manufacturing and production process and its relationship to technical design and drawing, including 3-D models. In addition, quality management, automation, and design for manufacturability (DFM) are explained.

Part 2
Fundamentals of Technical Graphics

This part explains visualization in the context of engineering design and shows students how to construct 2-D and 3-D geometry and create multiview and pictorial technical drawings.

- Chapter 5, "Design Visualization," is a *unique* chapter aimed at helping students improve their visualization abilities, which are fundamental to understanding and creating technical graphics. This chapter is unlike anything found in other technical graphics texts. The chapter briefly explains the human visual systems so students understand the complexity and power of human visualization.

The chapter quickly moves into the very basics of visualization as it related to engineering design graphics. The nomenclature and techniques used to describe objects are explained in detail so students understand the language of engineering and technical graphics. This leads into extensive coverage of the visualization techniques employed for technical drawings, such as image planes and orientation. Students get their first introduction into inclined, normal, and oblique lines and planes.

Integrated into the chapter is information about data visualization and the use of graphs and charts to describe and visualize engineering data. Another *unique* feature of this chapter is the extensive coverage of VR in Section 5.8, "Virtual Reality and Visualization."

- Chapter 6, "Technical Drawing Tools," is an introduction to the traditional and modern tools used to create sketches, drawings, and computer models. Traditional tools are described, with step-by-step instructions on how to use them. The instructions also cover how CAD is used to supplement traditional tools. This is the first chapter employing one of the major features of this text: step-by-step instructions.
- Chapter 7, "Sketching and Text," is an introduction to the creation of sketches and their use to support the design process. Traditional sketching tools are described, along with important sketching techniques. Step-by-step procedures guide the student through simple sketching activities.

  The additional sketching techniques are similar to those found in the classic text, *Drawing on the Right Side of the Brain* by Betty Edwards, and includes contour sketching, negative space sketching, and upside-down sketching. All of these techniques can dramatically improve a person's ability to make sketches.
- In Chapter 8, "Engineering Geometry and Construction," the student is shown how to create and edit 2-D geometry, using both traditional tools and CAD. More advanced technical geometry that can be created with 3-D CAD is also introduced. This chapter includes an extensive explanation of coordinate space which is especially useful for 3-D CAD. Another *unique* aspect of this chapter is the extensive coverage of geometric principles, such as parallelism, intersections, tangencies, and comprehensive coverage of 2-D and 2-D geometry.
- Chapter 9, "Three-Dimensional Modeling," is an extensive coverage of 3-D modeling theory, techniques, and applications. The chapter shows how computers are used to create all types of 3-D models, using various construction techniques. Coverage includes wireframe, surface, and solid modeling, constraint modeling, constructive solid geometry modeling CSG, and boundary representation modeling. Feature analysis is explained so students begin to understand design intent which is so important when concerned with modern engineering design. A section on feature definition explains how to build models using various features defined by the user. Virtually every method and technique used to create 3-D models with CAD is covered in the chapter, giving the student the understanding necessary to use any 3-D modeling system. Chapter 9 has more modern topic coverage, including more material on constraint-based modeling.
- Chapter 10, "Multiview Drawings," introduces standard multiview drawings for technical design and production. The chapter begins by explaining projection theory in general and multiview projections in particular. Standards and conventional practices for multiview drawings are then introduced. Integrated into the chapter are explanations and the use of illustration to assist the learner in visualizing the principles of orthographic projection. These visualization techniques provide a solid foundation and understanding of orthographic projection and how it relates to creating multiview drawings.
- Chapter 11, "Axonometric and Oblique Drawings," is an introduction to such drawings and contains an in-depth discussion of pictorial projections and drawings, building on the material covered in Chapter 7, "Sketching and Text." Through step-by-step instructions, the student is shown how to create pictorial drawings, using traditional instruments or CAD. This chapter also goes to great lengths to explain the theory and technique of axonometric and oblique drawings so students understand at a very fundamental level how these projection techniques are created.
- Chapter 12, "Perspective Drawings," is an introduction to perspective projection and drawings. This chapter again builds on the information presented in Chapter 7, "Sketching and Text." Step-by-step instructions describe how to create one- and two-point perspective drawings. Extensive background material is provided so students understand the concepts underlying perspective projections.
- Chapter 13, "Auxiliary Views," introduces the theory of auxiliary views and the techniques for drawing them. The fold-line and reference plane methods are explained using step-by-step instructions. Auxiliary view techniques are then applied to the solutions of problems concerning reverse construction, views in a spec-

ified direction, dihedral angles, and the true size of an oblique plane.

Part 3
Descriptive Geometry

Part 3 is a basic introduction to the theory and practice of descriptive geometry, intersections and developments.

- Chapter 14, "Fundamentals of Descriptive Geometry," is an introduction to the application of descriptive geometry to the solution of spatial problems. There is extensive coverage of the underlying concepts and projection theory related to auxiliary views. One *unique* feature of this chapter is the five principles of descriptive geometry, which summarize the important concepts in the solution of spatial geometry problems. Another feature is the list of tips and axioms useful in solving such problems.
- Chapter 15, "Intersections and Developments," introduces two concepts: (1) the intersections between geometric forms and (2) 3-D geometric developments. The chapter presents the standards and techniques for drawing these important elements through detailed step-by-step illustrated procedures. One *unique* aspect of the illustrations used in the step-by-step procedures includes 3-D pictorial color illustrations of the intersecting objects, making it easier for the student to visualize the problem being solved.

Part 4
Standard Technical Graphics Practices

Part 4 includes ten chapters which describe the standard practices commonly used to create technical drawings to support the engineering design process. In this part students learn how to create section views, dimension and tolerance a drawing, and represent fasteners on drawings. Modern manufacturing practices are covered as well as working drawings.

- Chapter 16, "Section Views," is an introduction to the techniques and standards used to create all types of section views. One important concept is section view visualization, which is explained early in the chapter. Each section view type is examined in terms of its visualization, the applicable standards practices, and the techniques useful in its construction. A Summary of Important Practices is included at the end of this chapter to assist the student in making section views.
- Chapter 17, "Dimensioning and Tolerancing Practices," introduces the techniques and standards for adding dimensions to technical drawings. There is extensive coverage of standard practices used for nearly any feature found on drawings, and they are explained using illustrations which sometimes include color rendered pictorial views useful in visualizing the dimensioning or tolerancing concept being explained. The need for tolerancing is discussed in great detail so that the student will understand and appreciate the importance of tolerancing in technical design. The summary includes two tables that condense important dimensioning and tolerancing information useful for students in developing their own technical drawings.
- Chapter 18, "Geometric Dimensioning and Tolerancing Basics," introduces the standards, techniques, and practices associated with ASME Y14.5M-1994 standard geometric dimensioning and tolerancing. The chapter explains each type of geometric dimension, how it is measured, and how its associated symbols are used in technical drawings. There is extensive use of illustrations with rendered pictorial views of the principle being explained.
- Chapter 19, "Fastening Devices and Methods," introduces the student to various types of fasteners and their representation on technical drawings. Step-by-step procedures demonstrate how to read a thread table, create simplified and schematic internal and external thread forms, and draw bolts and springs. One *unique* feature of this chapter is the many references to the *Machinery Handbook* to familiarize students with this important guide to information on fasteners. Another is the very detailed explanation of how to read an ANSI standard thread table.
- Chapter 20, "Working Drawings," describes how to create a standard set of drawings that specify the manufacture and assembly of a product based on its design. All of the important features of a set of working drawings are described and illustrated, along with engineering change orders (ECO) and reprographic practices, including digital technologies.
- Chapter 21, "Technical Data Presentation," describes how to create technical illustrations and represent data using both traditional techniques and computers. The chapter covers such modern illustration techniques as color theory, lighting, animation, and multimedia. Students learn the basic concepts used to represent data graphically followed by examples of charts and graphs produced from data. One *unique* feature of this chapter is the representation of 3-D graphs and charts to represent data.

- Chapter 22, "Mechanisms: Gears, Cams, Bearings, and Linkages," is an introduction to the standard technical drawings for gears, cams, bearings, and linkages. In this chapter students learn the theory and practice used to represent mechanisms. Included in this chapter are a number of step-by-step procedures used to read mechanism catalogs and draw the mechanism using standard practices.
- Chapter 23, "Electronic Drawings," is an introduction to the symbols and applications of electronic drawings in industry.
- Chapter 24, "Piping Drawings," explains the fundamentals of piping, as well as the symbols used to create standard piping drawings.
- Chapter 25, "Welding Drawings," is an introduction to welding processes and the symbols used to represent welded assemblies in technical drawings.

Glossary, Appendixes, and Index

At the end of the text is an extensive glossary containing the definitions of all key terms shown in bold in the text. This glossary contains over 600 terms related to engineering and technical drawing, engineering design, CAD, and manufacturing.

The appendixes contain supplementary information useful to the student, such as an extensive listing of abbreviations commonly used in technical graphics; geometric dimensioning and tolerancing information; materials properties, useful when creating a materials library for CAD solid modelers; properties of geometric forms, useful for 3-D modeling; ANSI standard tolerancing tables; and standard fastener tables for drawing and specifying various fasteners, keys, washers, and pins.

An extensive index is included at the end of the text to assist the reader in finding topics quickly. This index is carefully cross-referenced so related terms can easily be found by the user.

Supplements

A number of supplements have been developed to assist in the instruction of technical graphics.

Instructor's Manual

This supplement is available on the instructor's web site and it contains

Chapter objectives
Chapter outlines
Chapter summaries
Key terms
Questions for review with answers
True-false questions with answers
Multiple-choice questions with answers
Teaching tips and suggestions

Solutions Manual

This solutions manual contains answers to the end-of-chapter word problems, as well as many of the end-of-chapter drawing problems. Solutions are available on the instructor's web site.

Workbooks

A workbook with additional drawing problems is available. *Graphics Drawing Workbook* contains many of the problems found in the text in workbook form. This workbook has many traditional and nontraditional types of problems that are useful for visualization exercises and 3-D modeling.

Online Learning Center (OLC)

The OLC website follows the textbook chapter by chapter. As students study, they can refer to the OLC website for learning objectives, a chapter summary, flashcards, animations, and more. Before taking an exam, students will know if they're ready thanks to interactive exercises and taking self-grading quizzes.

A secured Instructor Center stores your essential course materials to save you prep time before class. The Instructor's Manual and presentation materials are now just a couple of clicks away. You will also find additional problem material and exercises (some are Internet-specific).

OLC Supplements

Many supplements for each chapter are found on the online learning center, including the following;

Learning Objectives A listing of all learning objectives for each chapter in the text.

Chapter Outline An extensive outline of each chapter.

Multiple-Choice Quiz An interactive online quiz covering important topics in the chapter. Answers are submitted for automatic and immediate grading for review by the student.

Questions for Review The questions include a hint button if a student cannot answer the question. The hint button refers the student to the chapter page where the material relevant to answering the question can be found.

True or False Questions An interactive online true and false test covering important topics in the chapter. Answers are submitted for automatic and immediate grading for review by the student.

Flashcards Interactive exercises to assist students in learning important terms from each chapter of the text.

Web Site Links Many chapters include numerous web site links that can be used by students and faculty to supplement the textbook material.

Animations Many chapters include animations that can be downloaded and played on a computer showing how to visualize and understand concepts.

Related Readings A listing of additional books that can be used as references or further reading on topics covered in the chapter.

Image Library The image library, available to instructors, contains all the images in each chapter that can be viewed, printed, or saved.

AutoCAD Problems Some chapters contain additional mechanical, civil, and architectural AutoCAD problems in PDF format for viewing and printing hard copies. These problems include step-by-step procedures useful in drawing the problem using AutoCAD software.

Stapler 3-D Modeling Project The 3-D stapler modeling project was removed from the 4th edition, but it can be found on the Online Learning Center. The purpose of the integrated 3-D modeling project is to further assist and motivate students to learn engineering and technical graphics concepts through a real project. The 3-D modeling project uses a real product, a stapler made by Swingline. The stapler is a fairly simple device with some challenging surfaces. The range of complexity allows students to begin with simple parts and move on to increasingly sophisticated graphics and models as they become more knowledgeable and experienced in using computer graphics.

Old Drawing Problems Many of the drawing problems that were in the 3rd edition but not replaced with new problems in the 4th edition can be found on the Online Learning Center.

Geometric Forms Patterns of simple geometric forms are patterns that can be cut out by the student and formed into their 3-D shape. Instructors can use them to supplement their lectures, as visualization aids, and for additional problem assignments.

Acknowledgments

The authors wish to thank the reviewers for the numerous editions, focus groups, and industrial advisory board members for their contribution to the content, organization, and quality of this book and its supplements.

Reviewers/Survey Respondents for the Fourth Edition

Douglas C. Acheson, *Purdue School of Engineering and Technology at IUPUI*

Mark W. McK. Bannatyne, *Purdue University, IUPUI Campus*

Christina Barsotti, *Clark College*

Tom Bledsaw, *ITT Educational Services*

Joel Brodeur, *Montana State University-Northern*

Perry Carmichael, *Linn-Benton Community College*

Ralph Dirksen, *Western Illinois University*

Yaomin Dong, *Kettering University*

Dale P. Eddy, *Kettering University*

Howard M. Fulmer, *Villanova University*

Mohammad Ghaffarpour, *University of Illinois-Chicago*

Joseph P. Greene, *California State University, Chico*

Karen Groppi, *Cabrillo College*

Bruce A. Harding, *Purdue University*

Hong–Tae Kang, *University of Michigan-Dearborn*

Edward J. Nagle, *Tri-State University*

Alan D. Papendick, *Central Michigan University*

Anne Perry, *Kankakee Community College*

Rex Pierce, *Southern Illinois University Edwardsville*

George Platanitis, *University of Ontario*

Anthony A. Roberts, *Southwest Virginia Community College*

Alexei V. Saveliev, *University of Illinois-Chicago*

Bert A. Siebold, *Murray State University*

Nancy E. Study, *Virginia State University*

Slobodan Urdarevik, *Western Michigan University*

Ken Youssefi, *University of California-Berkeley, San Jose State University*

John A. Zaner, *University of Southern Maine*

Illustrators

A text of this type would be useless without good, accurate graphics. We have had the good fortune to have some of the best young illustrators in the country work on this text. Joe Mack and James Mohler led a team of illustrators that worked many months on the illustrations. The authors are indebted to these two individuals, both of whom have enormous talent. Joe Mack has since moved on to a very successful career in multimedia software development, and James Mohler has started his own multimedia company. In addition, the authors would like to thank the other illustrators on the team: Rob Cumberland, Jonathan Combs, Doug Acheson, Doug Bailen, Aaron Cox, Brad Johnson, Steve Adduci, Clark Cory, Trent Mohr, Keith Huggins, Dale Jackson, Jonathan Humphries, Sue Miller, Andy Mikesell, Travis Fuerst, Jason Bube, and Kevin Bertoline.

Other Contributors

Accuracy checking of end-of-chapter problems was done by Ted Branoff, North Carolina State University; Ed Nagle, Tri-State University; Jim Hardell, Virginia Polytechnic Institute; and Murari Shah, Purdue University. Special thanks to Peter Booker for the use of historical figures found in his text, A History of Engineering Drawing. We would like to thank Gary Lamit for permission to adopt some figures from his text, Technical Drawing and Design (West Publishing Company), that were used in Chapter 25 and Appendix 6.

The authors would also like to thank the publisher, McGraw-Hill, for its support of this project. Special thanks to Kelley Butcher for all the work she put into this project. She is simply the best developmental editor with whom the authors have ever worked. Our thanks to Bill Stenquist and Darlene Schueller who have given us the support and direction needed to complete the project and stay focused. Our thanks also to the production staff at McGraw-Hill, especially Rose Kernan, who pulled the graphics and text together into a beautifully designed and easy-to-use textbook.

Gary Bertoline would like to especially thank his wife, Ada, and his children, Bryan, Kevin, and Carolyn, for the support they have given so that he might fulfill this important mission in his life. His thanks also go to Caroline and Robert Bertoline, who encouraged him to pursue his studies. He would also like to thank all his colleagues, especially those at Purdue University, his instructors at Northern Michigan University who inspired him to pursue graphics as a discipline, and Wallace Rigotti who taught him the basics.

Finally, we would like to know if this book fulfills your needs. We have assembled a "team" of authors and curriculum specialists to develop graphics instructional material. As a user of this textbook, you are a part of this "team," and we value your comments and suggestions. Please let us know if there are any misstatements, which we can then correct, or if you have any ideas for improving the material presented. Write in care of the publisher, McGraw-Hill, or E-mail Gary R. Bertoline at bertoline@purdue.edu.

Gary R. Bertoline
Eric N. Wiebe
Nathan W. Hartman
William A. Ross

"If I have seen further . . . it is by standing upon the shoulders of Giants." Isaac Newton

This book is dedicated to the pioneers in graphics, and our teachers, colleagues, family, and students from whom we have learned so much and to whom owe our gratitude.

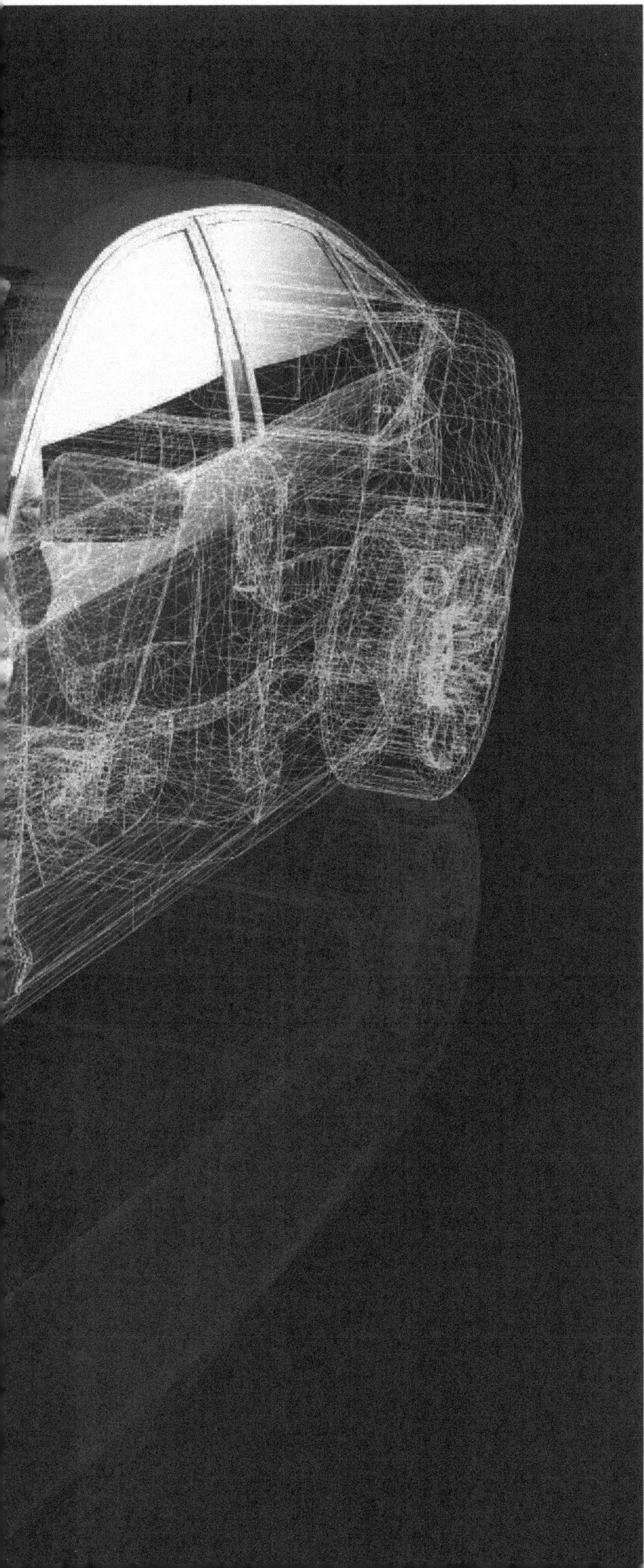

Chapter One

Introduction to Graphics Communications

A drawing acts as the reflection of the visual mind. On its surface we can probe, test, and develop the workings of our peculiar vision.

—Edward Hill

Objectives

After completing this chapter, you will be able to:

1. Describe why technical drawings are an effective communications system for technical ideas about designs and products.
2. Discuss the historical development of technical graphics.
3. Define important terms related to graphics communications for technology.
4. Define standards and conventions as applied to technical drawings.
5. Describe the difference between artistic and technical drawings.
6. List six areas in engineering technology that are important to creating and using graphics communications.

Introduction

Chapter 1 is an introduction to the graphics language of the engineer and technologist. The chapter explains why technical drawing is an effective way to communicate engineering concepts, relating past developments to modern practices, and examines current industry trends, showing why engineers and technologists today have an even greater need to master graphics communication. Concepts and terms important to understanding technical drawing are explained and defined, and an overview of the tools, underlying principles, standards, and conventions of engineering graphics is included.

1.1 Introduction

What is graphics communications? For one thing, it is an effective means of communicating technical ideas and problem solutions.

Look at what happens in engineering design. The process starts with the ability to visualize, to see the problem and the possible solutions. Then, sketches are made to record initial ideas. Next, geometric models are created from those sketches and are used for analysis. Finally, detail drawings or three-dimensional (3-D) models are made to record the precise data needed for the production process. Visualizing, sketching, modeling, and detailing are how engineers and technologists communicate as they design new products and structures for our technological world.

Actually, graphics communications using engineering drawings and models is a language, a clear, precise language, with definite rules that must be mastered if you are to be successful in engineering design. Once you know the language of graphics communications, it will influence the way you think, the way you approach problems. Why? Because humans tend to think using the languages they know. Thinking in the language of technical graphics, you will visualize problems more clearly and will use graphic images to find solutions with greater ease.

In engineering, it is estimated that 92 percent of the design process is graphically based. The other 8 percent is divided between mathematics and written and verbal communications. Why? Because graphics serves as the primary means of communication for the design process. Figure 1.1 shows a breakdown of how engineers spend their time. Drafting and documentation, along with design modeling, comprise more than 50 percent of the engineer's time and are purely visual and graphical activities. Engineering analysis depends largely on reading technical graphics, and manufacturing engineering and functional design also require the production and reading of graphics.

Why do graphics come into every phase of the engineer's job? To illustrate, look at the jet aircraft in Figure 1.2.

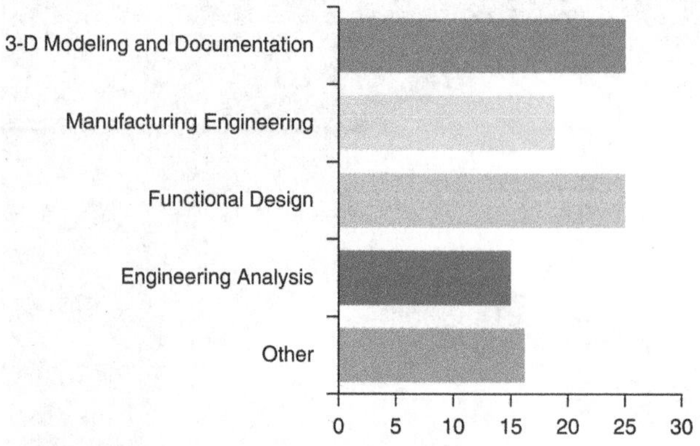

Figure 1.1

A total view of engineering divided into its major activities

Graphics plays a very important role in all areas of engineering, for documentation, communications, design, analysis, and modeling. Each of the activities listed is so heavily slanted toward graphics communications that engineering is 92 percent graphically based.

Figure 1.2

Aircraft designed using graphics

This jet aircraft would be impossible to create without computer graphics models and drawings. Drawings are the road maps which show how to manufacture or build products and structures.

(© The Boeing Company.)

Like any new product, it was designed for a specific task and within specified parameters; however, before it could be manufactured, a 3-D model and engineering drawings like that shown in Figure 1.3 had to be produced. Just imagine trying to communicate all the necessary details verbally or in writing. It would be impossible!

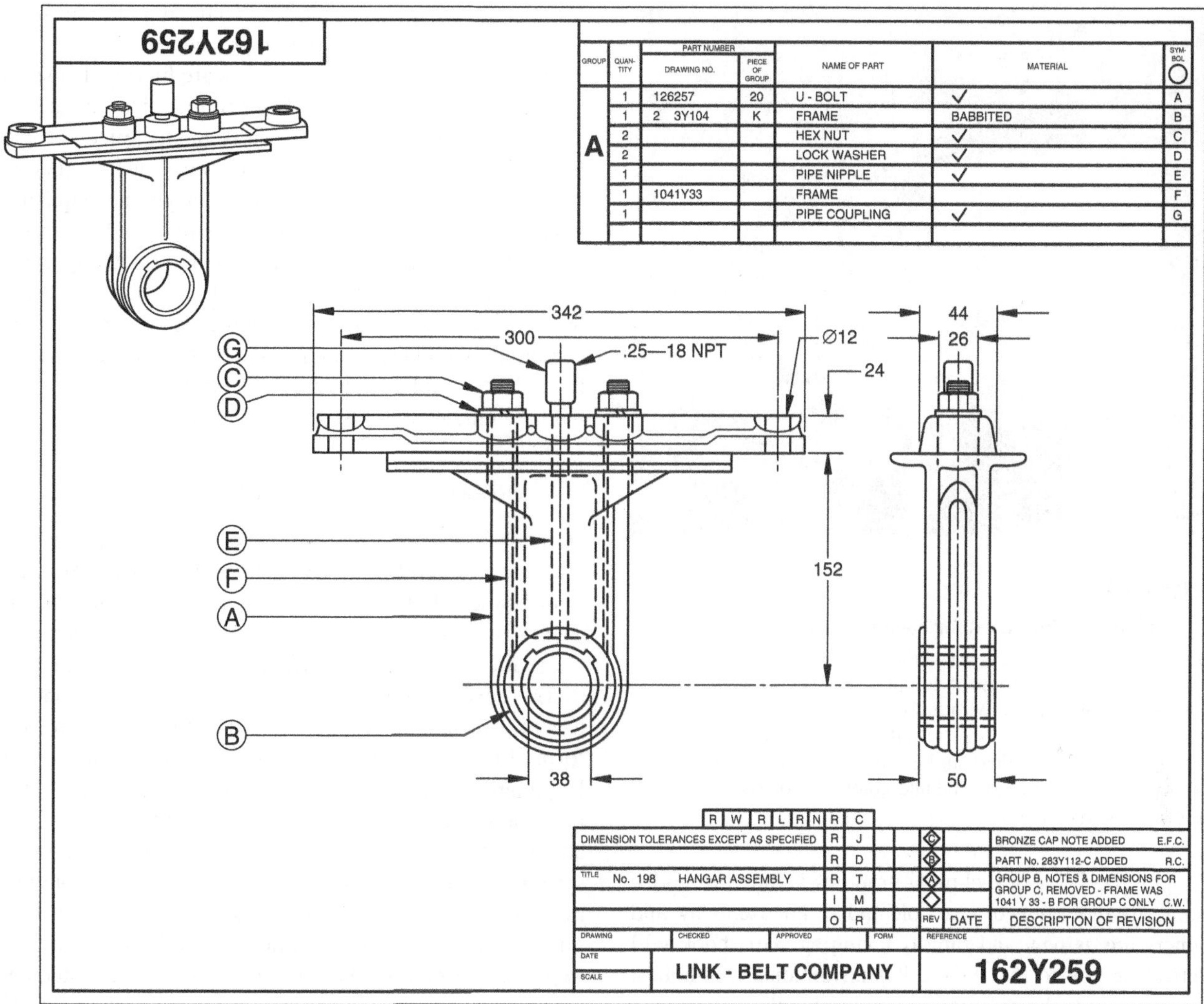

162Y259
PART NUMBER
GROUP
QUANTITY
DRAWING NO.
PIECE OF GROUP
NAME OF PART
MATERIAL
SYMBOL
A
1 126257 20 U - BOLT ✓ A
1 2 3Y104 K FRAME BABBITED B
2 HEX NUT ✓ C
2 LOCK WASHER ✓ D
1 PIPE NIPPLE ✓ E
1 1041Y33 FRAME F
1 PIPE COUPLING ✓ G
342
300
.25—18 NPT
Ø12
24
44
26
152
38
50
G
C
D
E
F
A
B
R W R L R N R C
DIMENSION TOLERANCES EXCEPT AS SPECIFIED
R J
R D
R T
I M
O R
TITLE No. 198 HANGAR ASSEMBLY
BRONZE CAP NOTE ADDED E.F.C.
PART No. 283Y112-C ADDED R.C.
GROUP B, NOTES & DIMENSIONS FOR GROUP C, REMOVED - FRAME WAS 1041 Y 33 - B FOR GROUP C ONLY C.W.
REV DATE DESCRIPTION OF REVISION
DRAWING
CHECKED
APPROVED
FORM
REFERENCE
DATE
SCALE
LINK - BELT COMPANY
162Y259

Figure 1.3

Engineering drawing

Engineering drawings and computer models such as these were needed to produce the hangar assembly shown. The 3-D model is used to design and visualize the hangar. The engineering drawings are used to communicate and document the design process.

A designer has to think about the many features of an object that cannot be communicated with verbal descriptions (Figure 1.4). These thoughts are dealt with in the mind of the designer using a visual, nonverbal process. This "visual image in the mind" can be reviewed and modified to test different solutions before it is ever communicated to someone else. As the designer draws a line on paper or creates a solid cylinder image with a computer, he or she is translating the mental picture into a drawing or model that will produce a similar picture in the mind of anyone who sees the drawing and shares the same mastery of language. This drawing or graphic representation is the medium through which visual images in the mind of the designer are converted into the real object.

Technical graphics can also communicate solutions to technical problems. Such technical graphics are produced according to certain standards and conventions so they can be read and accurately interpreted by anyone who has learned those standards and conventions.

Figure 1.4

Technical drawings used for communications

Technical drawings are a nonverbal method of communicating information. Descriptions of complex products or structures must be communicated with drawings. A designer uses a visual, nonverbal process. A visual image is formed in the mind, reviewed, modified, and ultimately communicated to someone else, all using visual and graphics processes.

(© Charles Thatcher: Stone.)

The precision of technical graphics is aided by tools; some are thousands of years old and still in use today, and others are as new and rapidly changing. This book will introduce you to the standards, conventions, techniques, and tools of technical graphics and will help you develop your technical skills so that your design ideas become a reality.

Engineers are creative people who use technical means to solve problems. They design products, systems, devices, and structures to improve our living conditions. Although problem solutions begin with thoughts or images in the mind of the designer, presentation devices and computer graphics hardware and software are powerful tools for communicating those images to others. They can also aid the visualization process in the mind of the designer. As computer graphics have a greater impact in the field of engineering, engineers will need an ever-growing understanding of and facility in graphics communications.

Technologists assist engineers and are concerned with the practicable aspects of engineering in planning and production. Technologists must be able to communicate quickly and accurately using graphics by sketching design problems and solutions, analyzing design solutions, and specifying production procedures.

Both engineers and technologists are finding that sharing technical information through graphical means is becoming more important as more nontechnical people become involved in the design/manufacturing process. As Figure 1.5 illustrates, the circle of people requiring technical information is rapidly widening, and engineering and technical information must be effectively communicated to many other people who are not engineers or technologists, such as marketing, sales, and service personnel. Computer graphics can assist in the process. It can be the tool used to draw together many individuals with a wide range of visual needs and abilities.

1.2 Human Communications

Humans have developed a number of different ways to communicate both technical and nontechnical information. **Spoken language** is a highly refined communications system that humans use to express thoughts, emotions, information, and other needs. **Writing** is another highly developed communications system based on the use of a formal system of symbols. Writing began as a form of picture communications, as shown in the ancient Egyptian hieroglyphics in Figure 1.6. With the development of alphabets, the written symbols became more abstract, creating an extremely sophisticated and versatile system of communication. Nonetheless, written communications have all the same weaknesses as spoken language when describing technical ideas. The old saying, "a picture is worth a thousand words," is an understatement when it comes to technical concepts because it is simply impossible to communicate some ideas with only words.

Mathematics is an abstract, symbol-based communications system built on formal human logic. Chemistry also has its own communications systems based on symbols, as do other sciences. It is important to realize that mathematics plays a very important role in engineering design; in fact, all human communications systems discussed here are needed. A successful engineer is one who can effectively use all of these forms of communication, especially technical drawings.

A communications system is selected according to the human need to be communicated. For example, you would not attempt to use mathematics to express human emotion. Instead, you would use a verbally based communications system, whether oral or written, whether sign language, Braille, or even Morse Code. However, for solving the technical problems of engineering, the visual language of technical graphics is the most efficient.

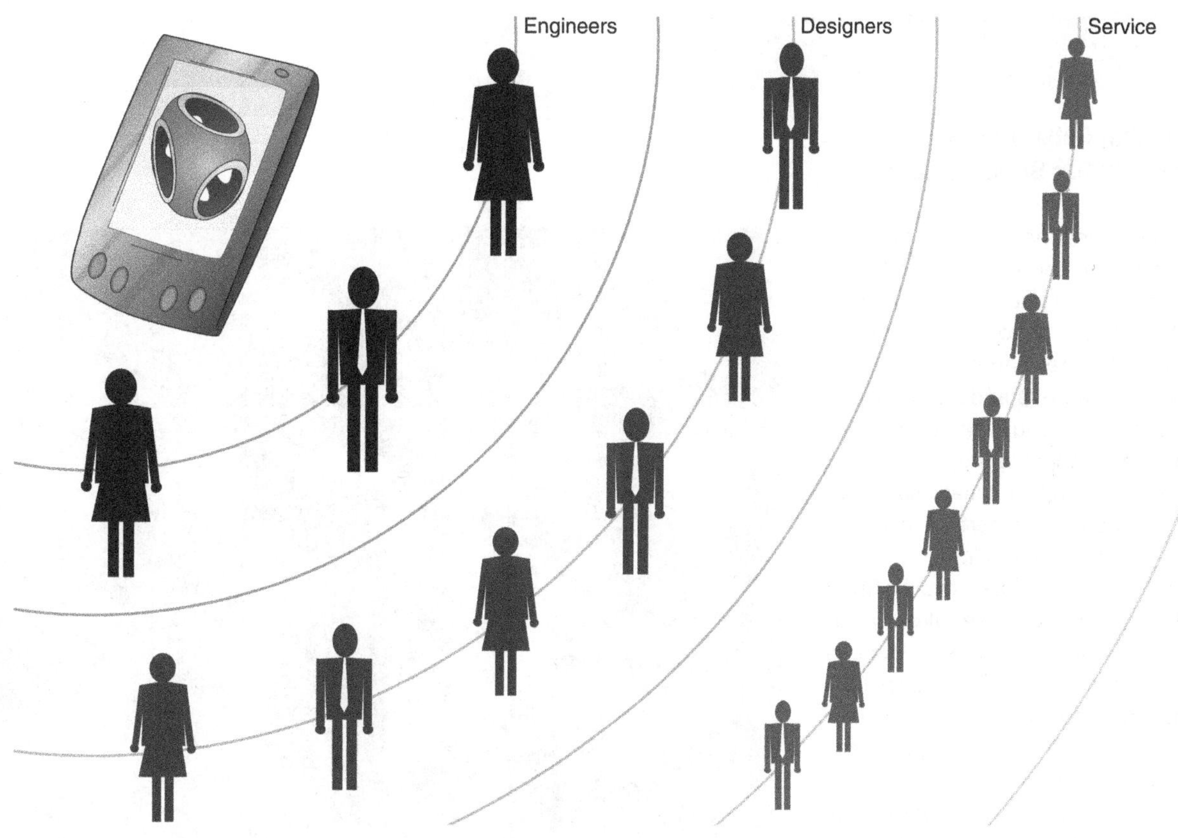

Figure 1.5

Users of graphics

The circle of people requiring technical information is growing rapidly.

Graphics is a visual communications language incorporating text, images, and numeric information. Graphics includes everything from the more traditional types of engineering drawings to sophisticated computer models, such as the solid model of a mechanical part or the display in the goggles of a virtual reality system, and all follow the rules or laws of visual science.

Figure 1.6

Egyptian hieroglyphics are pictures that were used for communication.

Practice Exercise 1.1

1. Attempt to describe the part shown in Figure 1.27 using written instructions. The instructions must be of such detail that another person can make a sketch of the part.
2. Now try verbally describing the part to another person. Have the person make a sketch from your instructions.

These two examples will help you appreciate the difficulty in trying to use written or verbal means to describe even simple mechanical parts. Refer to Figure 1.7 and others in this text to get an idea of how complicated some parts are compared with this example. It is also important to note that air and water craft have thousands of parts. For example, the nuclear powered *Sea Wolf* class submarine has more than two million parts. Try using verbal or written instructions to describe that!

Dream **High Tech** Job

Designing Robots to Explore Planets in Our Solar System

The engineering design process is used in many types of jobs—from the design of consumer product packaging to the design of robots used to explore planets in our solar system. An understanding of the design process along with strong skills in a field of engineering can lead to exciting job opportunities, such as the one described here of a young engineer working at NASA.

NASA's twin Mars rovers, Spirit and Opportunity, have already rewritten the book on the Red Planet's history, their amazing discoveries transmitted to an audience of millions. But Ayanna Howard is not content to let NASA rest on its laurels. She's designing future generations of robotic explorers to bring back even more science for the buck. Her goal: a robot that can be dropped off on a planet and wander around on its own, eliminating the kind of intense supervision from Earth that Spirit and Opportunity require—their every move must be meticulously choreographed in advance and on a daily basis.

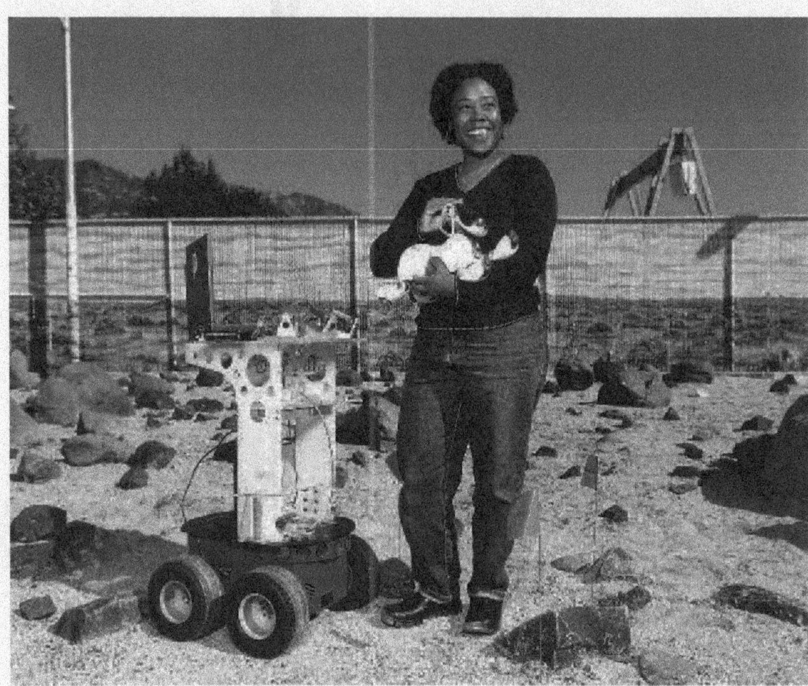

MARS ON EARTH

Ayanna Howard cradles a Sony AIBO robot used to test new software approaches in JPL's Mars Yard. Here, prototype Mars rover designs are put through their paces in a simulated Martian landscape.

(© Henry Blackham)

"I want to plop a rover on Mars and have it call back when it finds interesting science," Howard says. "Like a geologist, it should wander around until it sees something that might be interesting. Then it should be able to investigate further and decide if it's really interesting or just another rock."

Howard works as a senior robotics engineer at NASA's Jet Propulsion Laboratory in Pasadena, Calif. The laboratory has dominated the robotic

1.3 The Importance of Technical Graphics

Technical graphics is a real and complete language used in the design process for

1. Visualization
2. Communication
3. Documentation

A **drawing** is a graphical representation of objects and structures and is done using freehand, mechanical, or computer methods. A drawing serves as a graphic model or representation of a real object or idea. Drawings may be abstract, such as the multiview drawings shown in Figure 1.7, or more concrete, such as the very sophisticated computer model shown in Figure 1.8. Even though draw-

exploration of the solar system since the earliest days of the Space Age.

Space exploration, however, is only a test bed for Howard's ultimate technical objective: making robots better at helping people. "It's bigger than space exploration—it's robots assisting people," she says. "But space exploration is definitely one of the prime ways that robots assist people."

The 1970s TV show *The Bionic Woman* sparked Howard's interest in human-robot interaction and inspired her to become an engineer. The TV series depicted a severely injured woman who was given superhuman powers, courtesy of bionics; artificial replacements for human parts. "But around the 10th grade, I took biology—and I hated it!" Howard says.

She was stuck, because she knew she'd need medical training if she were going to attach limbs to people. Then someone suggested she check out robots. "I could still build limbs and figure out how to make them move, and as long as I didn't work on people, I didn't have to go to med school," Howard remembers thinking.

So she studied computer engineering—at Brown University in Providence, R.I., because her parents insisted she leave her native California for her undergraduate education. "They felt California was too laid back!" she says, laughing. She returned to the West Coast for her school-break vacations, and she was accepted to JPL's summer program for students.

"When I first got here, I was designing a database. I didn't even really know that JPL had robotics until I started talking to people. Then I realized all these spacecraft, like the Voyager probes, were robots," she recalls. Howard kept working at the laboratory during summers, nurturing her growing interest in artificial intelligence. After graduating from Brown, she earned a master's degree and then a doctorate in electrical engineering from the University of Southern California, in Los Angeles, while working at JPL.

Ayanna Howard (SM)

Age: 33

What she does: Develops autonomous robots

For whom: NASA's Jet Propulsion Laboratory

Where she does it: Pasadena, Calif.

Fun factors: Her robots could end up exploring Mars and beyond

What Howard likes best about her job is integrating diverse hardware and software elements into a working robot. "Problem shooting with a device that you have to touch and interact with is the hardest part of developing a robot, but it's the most fulfilling," she says.

Howard also mentors disadvantaged girls and frequently addresses elementary and high school students, often in poor neighborhoods. Although a lack of computers and other resources can be a big problem, she finds that simply showing up and explaining that you can make a good living as an engineer can widen a child's horizons. "They haven't talked to somebody who's a professional, except for teachers," Howard says. "They look at TV, and it's all acting and sports, so that's what they want to be. But when you meet children, it's surprisingly easy to get them excited about engineering."

"My hobby is my job," she adds. And if the first mission to use technology she invented departs for Mars early next decade, as planned, Howard will be among the select few who count exploring planets as one of their hobbies.

—Stephen Cass

ings may take many forms, the graphics method of communication is universal and timeless.

It may seem to be a very simple task to pick up a pencil and start drawing three-dimensional images on two-dimensional paper. However, it takes special knowledge and skill to be able to represent complex technical ideas with sufficient precision for the product to be mass-produced and the parts to be easily interchanged (Figure 1.9). This special knowledge is called **technical drawing**.

The projection techniques used to represent 3-D images on 2-D paper or flat computer screens took many years to develop. Actually, it has taken millennia for the techniques needed for graphics communications to evolve into the complex and orderly systems we have today.

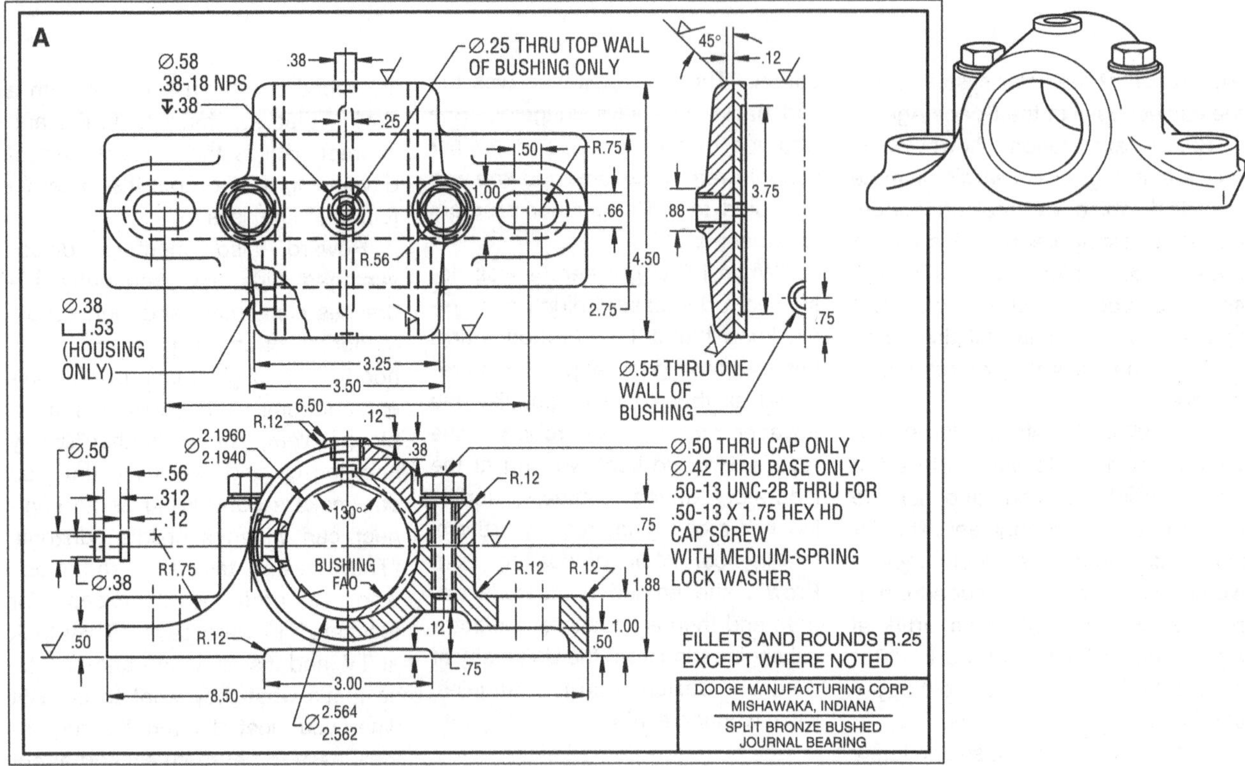

Figure 1.7

Multiview drawing of a journal bearing

Only experienced users of technical drawings can interpret the various lines, arcs, and circles sufficiently to get a clear mental picture of what this part looks like three-dimensionally.

Figure 1.8

3-D computer model of the interior of an automobile

This computer rendering of a 3-D computer model is more easily understood because more detail is given through the use of colors, lights, and shades and shadows.

(Courtesy of Burrows, rendered on Render Drive.)

The volumes of standards developed by the American National Standards Institute (ANSI) will quickly convince you that technical drawing is a precise, formal language.

1.3.1 Visualization

A powerful tool for design engineers is the ability to see in their minds the solution to problems. **Visualization** is the ability to mentally picture things that do not exist. Design engineers with good visualization ability not only are able to picture things in their minds, but are able to control that mental image allowing them to move around the image, change the form, look inside, and other movement as if they were holding the object in their hands. Some of the greatest engineers and scientists throughout history have had powerful visualization ability, such as Albert Einstein, James Clerk Maxwell, Leonardo DaVinci, and Thomas Edison.

In his book titled *Engineering and the Mind's Eye,* Eugene Ferguson summarizes the importance of visual-

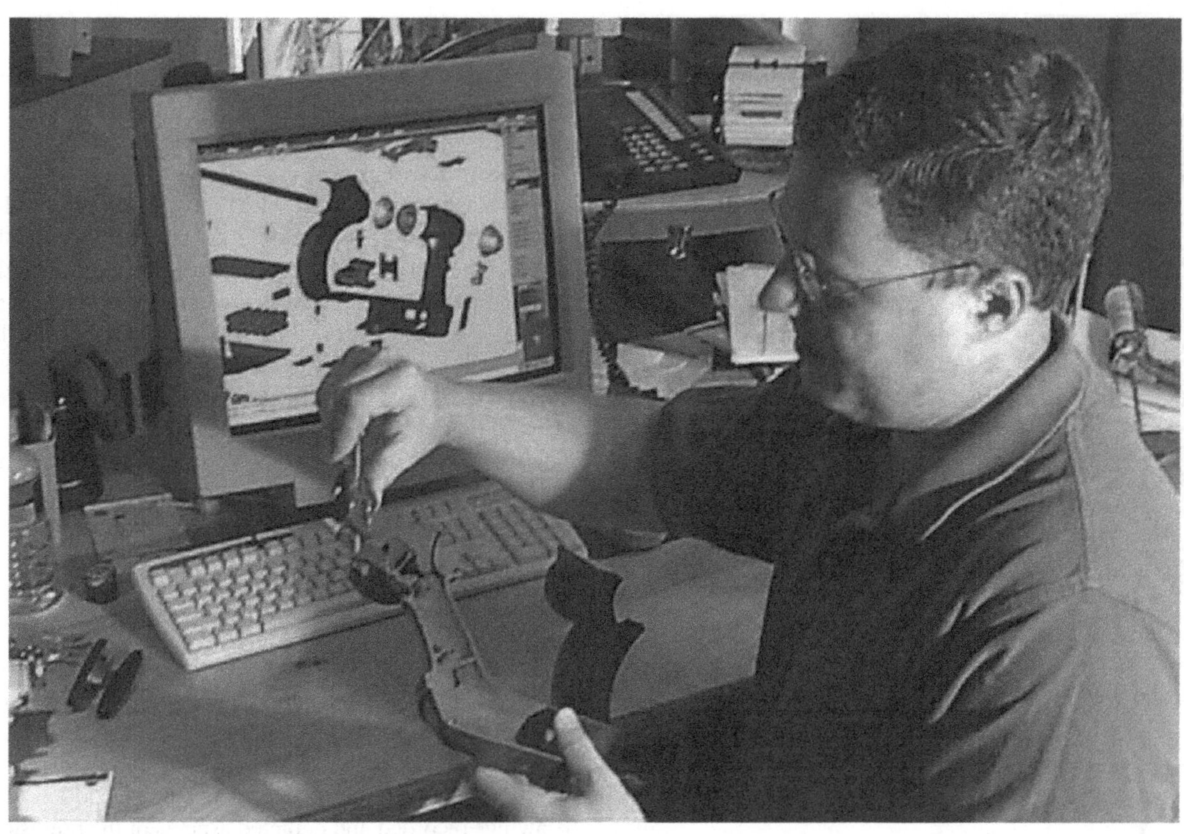

Figure 1.9

Technical drawings are used to communicate complex technical information.
(Courtesy of Priority Designs (www.prioritydesigns.com).)

ization to the design process. "It has been nonverbal thinking, by and large, that has fixed the outlines and filled in the details of our material surroundings for, in their innumerable choices and decisions, technologists have determined the kind of world we live in, in a physical sense. Pyramids, cathedrals, and rockets exist not because of geometry, theory of structures, or thermodynamics, but because they were first a picture—literally a vision—in the minds of those who built them."

Most designers will initially capture their mental images by sketching them on paper. Sometimes these sketches are very rough and quickly done to capture some fleeting detail in the mind of the designer. When communicating one's sketch to others, the sketches must be refined (Figure 1.10).

Your ability to visualize should improve as you solve the problems located at the end of every chapter in this book. Visualization and the resulting sketch is the first phase in the whole process of graphics being used in the

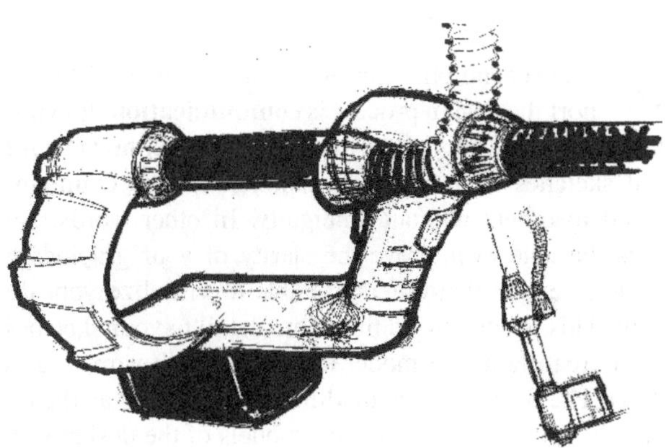

Figure 1.10

Design sketch of a hand digitizing tool

This type of sketch allows designers to quickly explore and communicate design ideas.
(Courtesy of Priority Designs (www.prioritydesigns.com).)

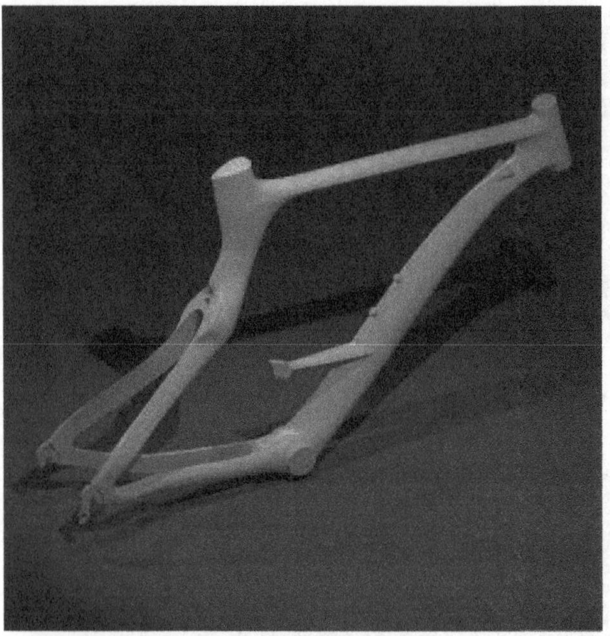

Figure 1.11

A refined 3-D model of a bicycle used to communicate the design without ambiguity.

(Courtesy of IDE, Inc.)

design process. You will find that as a professional engineer or technologist, the ability to visualize problem solutions and communicate them through your sketches will be one of your most important skills.

1.3.2 Communication

The second phase in the graphics produced to support the design process is **communication** drawings and models. In this phase your goal is to refine your initial sketches so your design solution can be communicated to others without ambiguity. In other words, you must be able to improve the clarity of your graphics to such an extent that others are able to visualize your design. This is done by adding more detail to your sketches, then creating a 3-D model using CAD software (Figure 1.11). The 3-D model is modified and changed as the design is refined. In the past real models of the design were created; however, many industries use rendered 3-D computer models to replace real models. Sometimes it is necessary to have real models, which can be easily produced from the 3-D model through a process called rapid prototyping, which will be explained later.

1.3.3 Documentation

After the design solution is finalized, graphics is the most effective way to permanently record that solution. Before 3-D modeling, **documentation** drawings were 2-D detail drawings that were copied through a process called blueprinting. These blueprints were then used to produce the design. Although few companies still use this process, the trend is for companies to refine the 3-D model, which is then used directly by machine tools to create the design. 2-D detail drawings may still be created, but their primary purpose is for legal and archival purposes (Figure 1.12). 2-D documentation drawings follow very strict standard practices so everyone in the engineering field can "read" the drawings. These standards are the "language" used to communicate graphically.

1.4 A Brief History of Graphics Communications

Drawing is so old that its history is virtually that of humanity, and it closely parallels human technological progress. Drawing may be called a "universal language." It is the natural method for humans to communicate visual images of the mind. As far back as 12,000 B.C., cave drawings recorded and depicted aspects of the prehistoric human experience. Drawings to communicate technical ideas may even predate the advent of written language, as shown in Figure 1.13. This Bronze Age diagram of a plow dates from 1500 B.C. Figure 1.14 is a timeline showing significant accomplishments in graphics.

The earliest evidence of drawing instruments can be found in the Museum of the Louvre, Paris, on two headless statues of Gudea (2130 B.C.). Gudea was an engineer and governor of the city/state of Lagash in the country later known as Babylon. On the knees of the statue, the sculptor modeled two contemporary drawing boards. The drawing boards are inscribed with the plan view of the temple of Ningirsu and with some kind of scribing instrument and scales (Figure 1.15).

The ancient Greeks had a great deal of influence on drawing through their work in geometry. Many of the tools used in engineering, such as the compass and triangles, were developed at this time. Around the year 450 B.C., the architects of the Parthenon, Ictinus and Callicrates, made a type of *perspective drawing* by foreshortening and converging parallel lines in their drawings. (See Chapter 10 for more information about perspectives.)

There was very little development in art and drawing from Christ's time until the Renaissance (1300–1500).

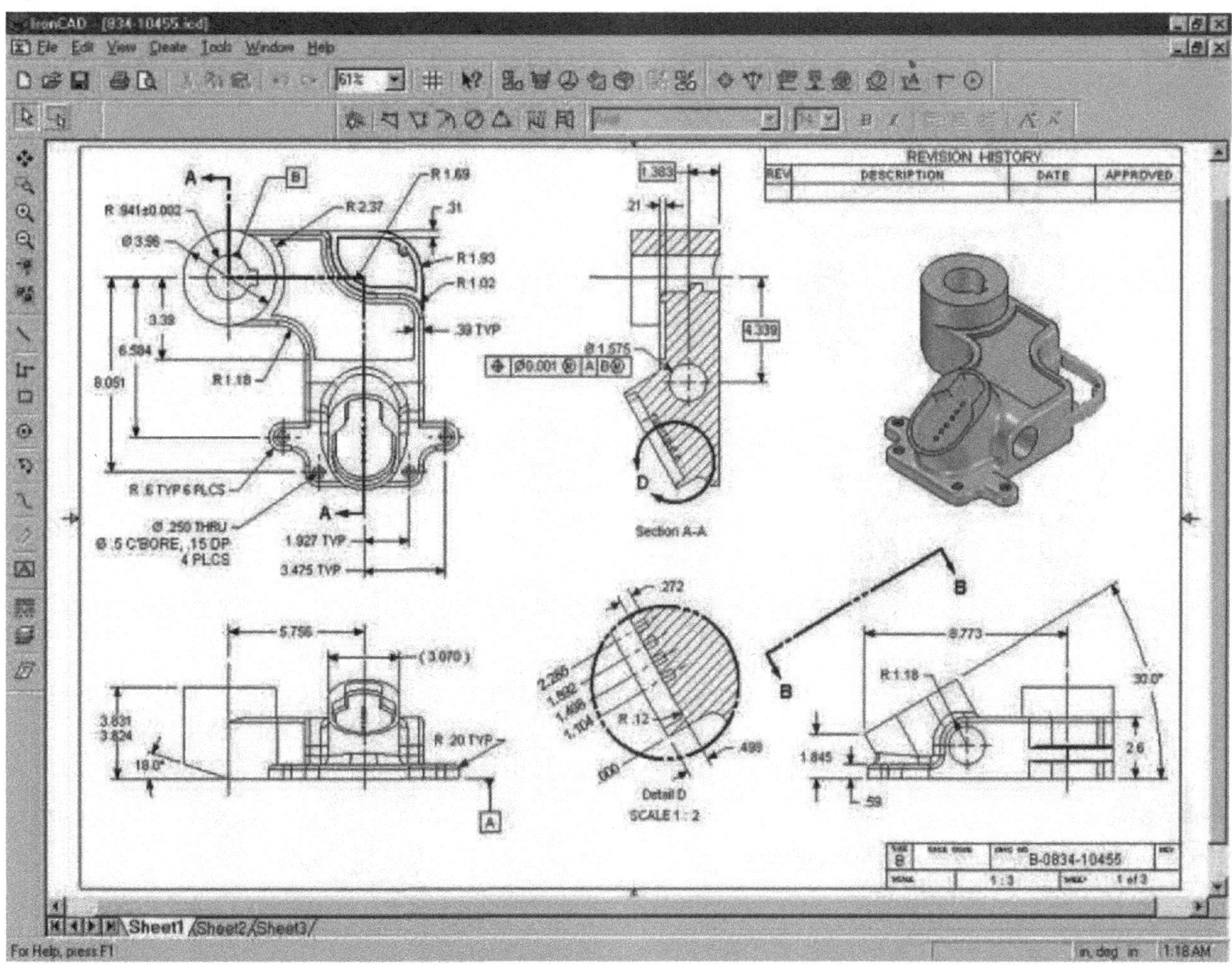

Figure 1.12

A detail drawing used in the documentation process

(Courtesy of IronCAD, LLC. and Simon Floyd Design Group.)

Two approaches to drawing developed during the Renaissance, the nonmathematical and the mathematical. In the nonmathematical approach, Giotto and Duccio advanced the clarity of perspective drawings with the use of symmetry, converging lines, and the technique of foreshortening. Masaccio improved the techniques for the proper shading and coloring of a drawing by developing a method called *aerial perspective drawing.*

The mathematical approach to drawing was advanced by the Italian architect Brunelleschi (1377–1446). He demonstrated the theoretical principles of perspective drawing. Brunelleschi was followed by Alberti, who wrote the treatise *della Pittura* (1435), which defined in mathematical terms the principles of perspective drawing in paintings.

Others who advanced the mathematical approach to drawing were Francesca (1420–1492), who developed theoretical works on perspective drawings and made three-view drawings using orthogonal projection methods; da Vinci (1453–1516), who wrote a treatise on the theory of perspective drawings (Figure 1.16); and Durer (1471–1528), whose book *Vier Buchen von Menschlicher Proportion,* published in 1528, used orthographic projection techniques in many of the illustrations. Durer also developed a method of more easily creating perspective drawings by using a perspective picture window, as shown in Figure 1.17. Orthographic projection was used in Durer's book on the geometry of drawing, published in 1525. Isometric drawing, a type of pictorial drawing,

Figure 1.13

A Bronze Age plow from a rock engraving of about 1500 B.C. from Fontanalba, Italian Alps

This probably was not a work of art, but a crude technical drawing showing the arrangement of oxen and harness.

(From P. Booker, *A History of Engineering Drawing.* London: Chatto & Windus, 1962.)

Figure 1.15

The drawing plan and scribing instruments inscribed into the statue of Gudea dated 2130 B.C.

The upper board displays the ground plan of a building, and both have representations of a scribing instrument and scale.

(From P. Booker, *A History of Engineering Drawing.* London: Chatto & Windus, 1962.)

Figure 1.16

Perspective drawing created by da Vinci

(From P. Booker, *A History of Engineering Drawing.* London: Chatto & Windus, 1962.)

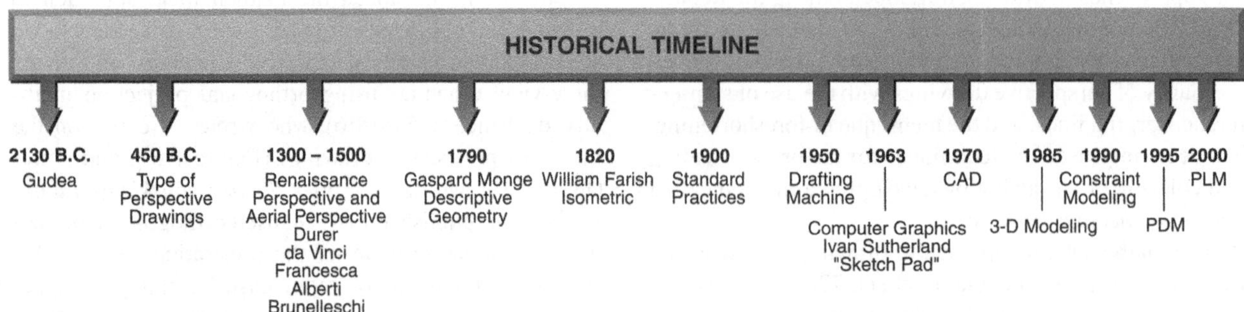

Figure 1.14

Historical timeline of major events in graphics over the last four millennia

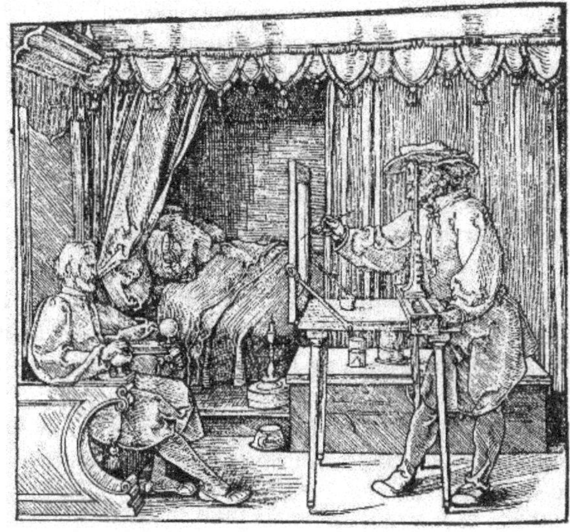

Figure 1.17

A reproduction of a woodcut by Durer from 1500 A.D. showing perspective drawing using a glass screen

(From P. Booker, *A History of Engineering Drawing*. London: Chatto & Windus, 1962.)

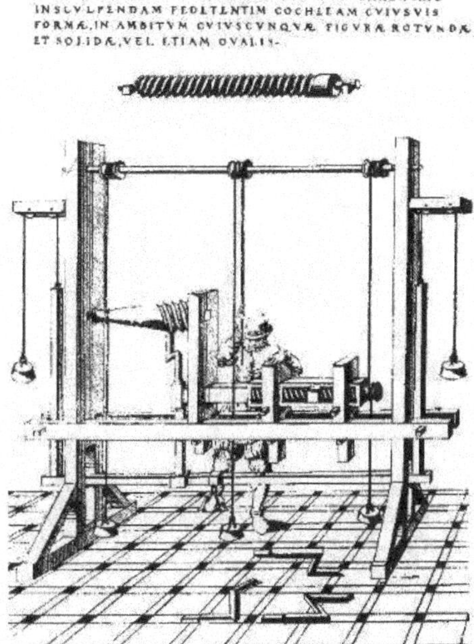

Figure 1.18

Perspective drawing of a screw lathe from 1568

Although the perspective drawing visually represents the machine accurately, dimensionally the drawing does a very poor job. Dimensionally accurate drawings are important in the design and production of products; therefore, some other type of drawing must be used.

(From P. Booker, *A History of Engineering Drawing*. London: Chatto & Windus, 1962.)

was introduced in the early 19th century by an Englishman named William Farish. The ordinary graph or curve used to represent the variation of quantities plotted along two coordinates was developed in the 19th century. (See Chapter 8 for more information about orthographics drawings, and Chapter 9 for isometric drawings.)

It is clear that from the earliest recorded times humans have struggled with trying to communicate 3-D objects using images on 2-D surfaces. Most of the efforts of these pioneer artists and artisans were aimed at developing a drawing technique that closely related what they saw or perceived. Both artistic and technical applications of drawings used the developments of the early graphics pioneers for their own purposes. From the 1400s on, the perspective technique has been the primary method used to communicate graphically. However, people have realized that perspective drawings have limitations in presenting true conditions, especially for technical purposes (Figure 1.18).

1.4.1 Descriptive Geometry

It took a brilliant young mathematician, Gaspard Monge (1746–1818), to organize and develop the science of technical drawing called *descriptive geometry*. Monge was faced with designing a complicated fortress in a star shape (Figure 1.19). He used orthographic projection and the revolution method to solve the complicated fortress problems graphically instead of mathematically, which was the traditional technique.

Gaspard Monge developed the science of descriptive geometry in the late 1700s. It is the basis of all of today's types of three-dimensional representations on two-dimensional media. The fundamentals of graphic projection have not changed significantly since Monge's time, although the methods and tools, as well as the standards and conventions, have changed drastically, evolving from instruments such as the T-square to the drafting machine to **computer-aided design/drafting (CAD)**.

1.4.2 Computer Graphics

The computer has had a major impact on the methods used to design and create technical drawings. In 1950, the first computer-driven display attached to MIT's Whirlwind I

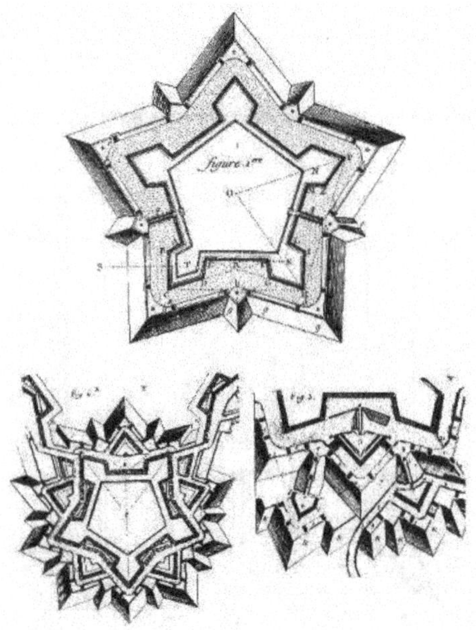

Figure 1.19

Type of fortification Gaspard Monge worked on while developing descriptive geometry

Monge used orthographic projection and the revolution method in designing this star-shaped fortress. Monge advanced graphics communications by organizing and developing the science of descriptive geometry.

(From P. Booker, *A History of Engineering Drawing*. London: Chatto & Windus, 1962.)

computer was used to generate simple pictures. In the late 1950s MIT's TX-0 and TX-2 computers were used to create interactive computing, and interest in computer graphics began to increase rapidly.

In 1963, Ivan Sutherland, a graduate student at MIT, published his doctoral thesis, which led to the development of interactive computer graphics, which in turn evolved into CAD.

In the mid-1960s, large computer graphics research projects were begun at MIT, GM, Bell Telephone labs, and Lockheed Aircraft. D. T. Ross of MIT developed an advanced compiler language for graphics programming. Steven A. Coons, also at MIT, and J. C. Ferguson at Boeing began work in sculptured surfaces. GM developed their DAC-1 system, and other companies, such as Douglas, Lockheed, and McDonnell, also made significant developments in computer graphics.

In the 1970s, research began to produce interactive computer graphics systems. Developments in the mathematics of parametric geometry were initiated by Coons (bicubic patches) and Bezier (special surfaces). Wireframe and polygonal modeling schemes began to develop.

About 1980, Apple and IBM PCs popularized the use of bitmap graphics. This resulted in an explosion of easy-to-use and inexpensive graphics-based applications.

In the early 1980s PC-based software programs began to emerge, with Versa CAD and AutoCAD being the leaders. In the mid-1980s a proliferation of CAD software programs began to flood industry. The 1990s saw a consolidation of CAD software companies into a few strong vendors and the development and implementation of 3-D modeling. Further consolidation is expected in the decade of 2000 with further development and common use of 3-D modeling to support the design of products and structures.

1.5 Visual Science

Approximately eighty percent of our sensory input comes from our visual system. Studies have shown that one-half of the population has a preference for visual rather than verbal learning style. Much of what we learn and experience is through our visual sense. Much of our technological world could not exist without the use of graphics to plan, produce, market, and maintain goods and services.

Visual science is defined as the study of the processes that produce images in the mind. Visual science has at least three major categories: spatial cognition, imaging, and geometry (Figure 1.20). These three categories form the foundation for any field of study related to the visual sciences. For example, an engineering design graphics course should have elements of all three areas.

Spatial cognition is the mental process used to perceive, store, recall, create, edit, and communicate spatial images. It is generally agreed that the ability to think quickly and to recognize complex mental models are signs of intelligence and important prerequisites to learning. **Imaging** is the process of producing, and reproducing ideas. A knowledge of imaging processes is used to create graphics that are easily visualized or recognized by the user. **Geometry** is the branch of mathematics that deals with the properties, relationships, and measurements of points, lines, planes, and solids. There are three primary areas of geometry: plane, solid, and descriptive. Plane geometry is concerned with planar figures, such as circles and polygons, and their relationships. Solid geometry is concerned with three-dimensional objects, such as cylinders, cones, and cubes, and their relationships.

Design in Industry

Going Virtual

Virtual reality and simulation software tools hold the promise of drastically slashing product development costs through the elimination of expensive physical prototypes. With costs for the latest virtual reality (VR) tools and simulation systems coming down, automotive and aerospace manufacturers increasingly are seeking to deploy sophisticated, collaborative visualization systems throughout their product development planning organizations, as well as using virtual simulations for designing overall plant layouts and within manufacturing cells.

Although VR tools historically have been the domain of researchers, commercial applications in automotive, aerospace, and medical device manufacturing are becoming much more common. Using VR systems like the CAVE (Computer Automated Visualization Environment), developed in the early 1990s by the Electronic Visualization Laboratory at the University of Illinois at Chicago (EVL, UIC), automakers and aircraft manufacturers can review realistic virtual model prototypes, avoiding the expense of $200,000 for a fiberglass auto prototype to upwards of $3 million for an aircraft prototype.

Over the past few years, the addition of more realistic visualization software also has furthered VR's acceptance, with efforts like the partnership between software developer Engineering Animation Inc. (Ames, IA), workstation supplier Silicon Graphics Inc. (Mountain View, CA), and General Motors Corp. (Detroit) offering EAI's VisConcept, a software suite providing a true 1:1, or human-scale, immersive visualization environment. In addition, projection and display technologies have improved to the point where it's possible to easily create high-resolution stereoscopic images—seeing an image in each eye with depth and volume just as in the real world.

Collaborative visualization may represent a new opportunity to manufacturers, particularly in the automotive industry where many major auto manufacturers are trying to persuade their top suppliers to adopt visualization technology. Large-scale displays like the WorkWall enable manufacturing teams to collaborate in much the same way they used to work around drafting tables, but with realistic, full-scale 3-D models.

With Fakespace Systems' WorkWall, teams can view realistic stereoscopic images during product development team design reviews.

(Image courtesy of Fakespace Systems Inc.)

Users of the Fakespace wall can review styling and component changes on virtual models before committing to final product designs.

(Image courtesy of Fakespace Systems, Inc.)

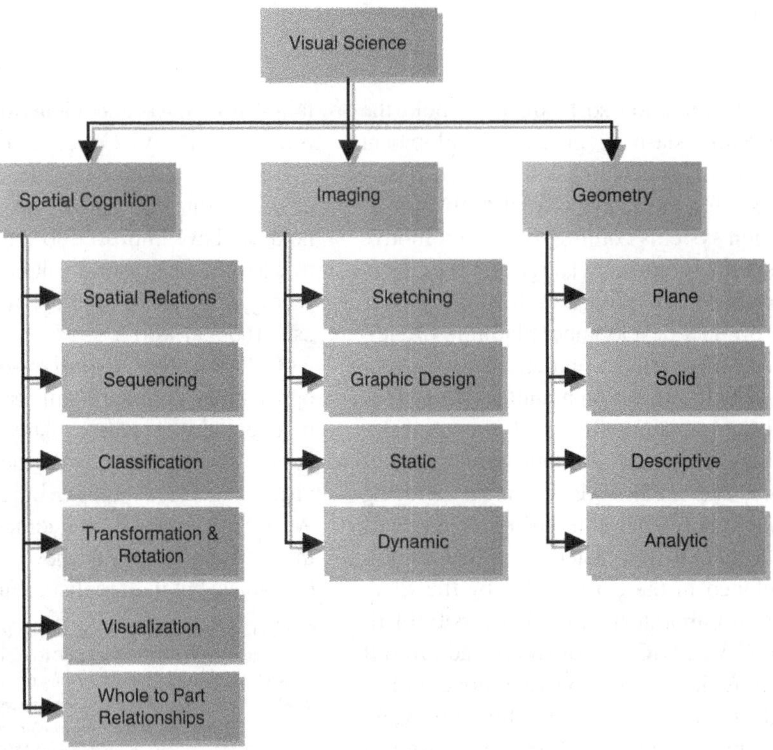

Figure 1.20

Visual science

Visual science includes the study of spatial cognition, imaging, and geometry as applied to artistic and technical processes.

Descriptive geometry is concerned with analyzing and solving space distances and relationships.

Practice Exercise 1.2

1. Look ahead to the engineering drawing shown in Figure 1.25.
2. From the drawing, mentally visualize the 3-D form of the object.
3. Try to sketch your mental image of the 3-D object.

Are you having difficulty making the transition from the 2-D drawing to the 3-D object? Being able to make the mental transition from 2-D to 3-D is part of what you will learn. Visualization is a very important part of technical graphics because engineers and technologists must be able to make the transition quickly from 2-D to 3-D and from 3-D to 2-D.

Artistic applications are concerned with the conscious production or arrangement of color, form, and other elements that affect the sense of beauty (Figure 1.21). **Artistic drawings** are used to express aesthetic, philosophical, and abstract ideas. Of course, this text is primarily concerned with the technical applications of visual science.

Technical graphics or **technical drawing** is a specialized type of graphics used to communicate technical information. Examples of technical graphics include 3-D computer modeling, drafting, and illustrating of a technical device. Technical graphics is a universal language that allows individuals to go beyond the limitations of other communications forms, as described earlier.

1.5.1 Geometry

Geometry is the foundation for technical graphics, just as grammar is for language. Geometry includes the following:

Plane geometry. The geometry of planar figures, such as circles and triangles, and their relationships (Figure 1.22).

Figure 1.21

Artistic application for graphics

Artistic drawings are concerned with colors, forms, and other elements, whereas technical drawings are used to communicate technical information.

(Leonardo da Vinci, *Mona Lisa,* Louvre: Scala/Art Resource, New York.)

Solid geometry. The geometry of three-dimensional objects, such as cylinders, cubes, and spheres, and their relationships (Figure 1.23).

Analytic geometry. The analysis of geometric structures and properties, principally using algebraic operations and position coordinates.

Descriptive geometry. The analysis of space distances and relationships, using graphics.

As a student of technical graphics, you will study plane, solid, and descriptive geometry because they form the foundation or the grammar of technical drawings.

1.5.2 Standards and Conventions

The language of graphics has been used for thousands of years; however, its effectiveness in modern times is due to the establishment of standards. There is no effective communication without an agreed-upon standard of signs or symbols. The letters of the alphabet are the signs used for writing, and grammar forms the science that underlies word language. Standards and conventions are the "alphabet" of technical drawings, and plane, solid, and descriptive geometry are the science that underlies the graphics language.

The English language has many similarities to the graphics language. Following the standard rules of English makes the communication of thoughts between people easier. If the words in a sentence were presented in a random order, it would be very difficult for anyone to understand what was being said.

The graphics language must also follow a set of standards and conventions in order to make communication using technical graphics effective. However, these standards and conventions are not timeless, unchanging

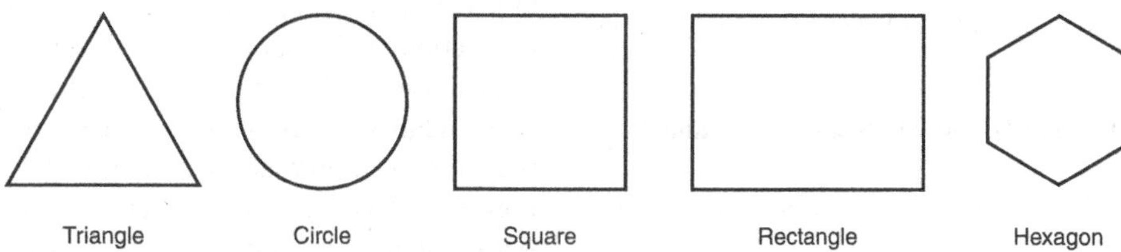

Figure 1.22

Plane geometry

Plane geometry deals with two-dimensional figures and their relationships.

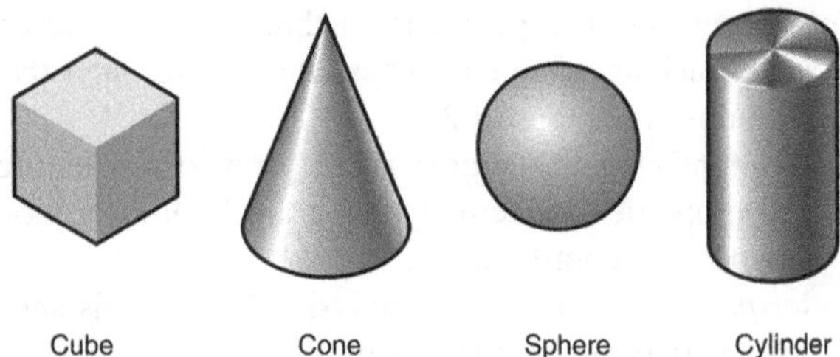

Figure 1.23

Solid geometry

Solid geometry deals with three-dimensional objects and their relationships.

truths. Just as English gradually changes and we no longer speak in the manner of 16th-century Shakespeare, the standards and conventions of the graphics language have evolved over the years and are still changing as new technologies affect how technical drawings are produced.

Conventions are commonly accepted practices, rules, or methods. In technical drawing, an example of a convention is the use of dashed lines on multiview drawings to designate a feature hidden from the current viewpoint (Figure 1.24).

Standards are sets of rules that govern how technical drawings are represented. For example, mechanical drawings are dimensioned using an accepted set of standards, such as placing the dimension text such that it is read from the bottom of the sheet (Figure 1.25). Standards allow for the clear communication of technical ideas. In the United States, the **American National Standards Institute (ANSI)** is the governing body that sets the standards used for engineering and technical drawings. Professional organizations also assist ANSI in developing standards, such as the American Society for Mechanical Engineers (ASME). ANSI standards are periodically revised to reflect the changing needs of industry and technology. The Y series of ANSI standards are the ones most important for technical drawing. Some important ANSI standards used in technical drawings include the following:

ANSI Y14.1–1980(R1987), Drawing Sheet Size and Format (Chapter 6).

ANSI Y14.2M–1979(R1987), Line Conventions and Lettering (Chapter 6).

ANSI Y14.3–1975(R1987), Multiview and Sectional View Drawings (Chapters 10 and 16).

ASME Y14.5M–1994, Dimensioning and Tolerancing (Chapters 17 and 18).

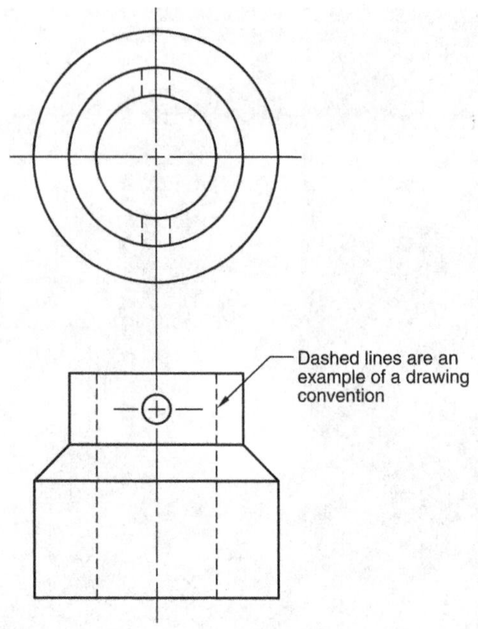

Figure 1.24

Drawing conventions

Dashed lines used to represent hidden features on an engineering drawing are an example of a drawing convention. In this case the drawing convention, dashed lines, is used to represent the location of the drilled hole's diameter, in a view where the hole cannot be seen directly. Following such conventions means that your technical drawing can be accurately interpreted by anyone who reads it.

ANSI Y14.6–1978(R1987), Screw Thread Representation (Chapter 19).

ANSI Y14.6aM–1981(R1987), Screw Thread Representation (Metric Supplement) (Chapter 19).

ANSI Y14.7.1–1971(R1988), Gear Drawing Standards, Part 1 (Chapter 22).

ANSI Y14.7.2–1978(R1989), Gear Drawing Standards, Part 2 (Chapter 22).

Other standards are from the International Standards Organization (ISO), Japanese Standards (JIS), Department of Defense (DOD), and the U.S. Military (MIL).

Standards are used so that drawings convey the same meaning to everyone who reads them. For example, Figure 1.25 is a detail drawing that reflects many of the ASME standards for dimensioning mechanical drawings. It is quite common in American industry to have parts of an assembly produced in many different locations. Having a standard graphics language is the only way this can be accomplished effectively.

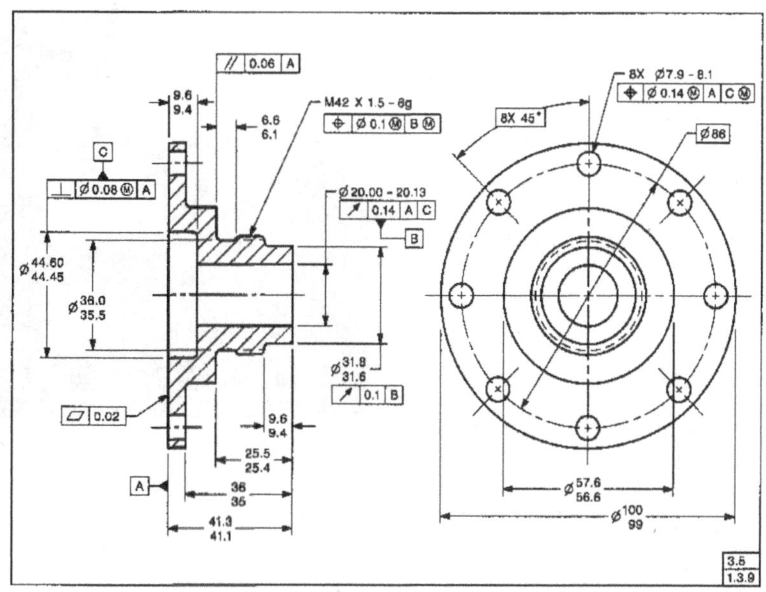

Figure 1.25

Dimensioned mechanical drawing using ASME Y14.5M–1994 standards

The dimension type, placement, size, and other factors are examples of standard drawing conventions. For example, one ANSI standard dimensioning rule states that all diametral dimensions should be preceded by a phi (ϕ) symbol.

Practice Exercise 1.3

Figure 1.25 is a typical technical drawing used in industry to document the design of a product and to aid in manufacturing the product. Carefully read the technical drawing and try to answer the following questions:

1. What do the thin, short-dashed lines represent?
2. What do the areas with closely spaced thin lines drawn at a 45-degree angle represent?
3. What do the numbers and symbols located inside the long, horizontal rectangles represent?
4. What do the thin alternating long- and short-dashed lines represent?

Standards and conventions provide the design detail necessary to manufacture a product to precision. A person with a technical drawing background should be able to easily answer all of the questions listed above. Can you?

1.6 What You Will Learn

In this text, you will learn the six important areas in technical graphics:

Visualization. The ability to mentally control visual information.

Graphics theory. Geometry and projection techniques.

Standards. Sets of rules that govern how parts are made and technical drawings are represented.

Conventions. Commonly accepted practices and methods used for technical drawings.

Tools. Devices used to create engineering drawings and models, including both hand-held and computer tools.

Applications. The various uses for technical graphics in engineering design, such as mechanical, electrical, and architectural.

Each chapter in the text will explain the graphics theory important for a topic, integrate the visualization practices, explain the relevant standards and conventions, demonstrate the tools used to create drawings, and apply the topic to engineering design.

1.7 Specialists and Technical Drawings

Drawings are used throughout the design process to develop and document design solutions. Over the years specialized fields of engineering design have developed to meet the needs of industry. For example, military and civil engineering were the first types of engineering specialties. From these two areas others developed, such as mechanical, electrical, chemical, aerospace, industrial, and many others. Special types of technical drawings such as gears and cams, welding, riveting, electrical components and circuits, piping, structures, mapping and topography also evolved to support the specialized fields of engineering.

1.8 Engineering Technology

The **engineering technologist** assists the engineer and is concerned with the practical aspects of engineering, in both planning and production. Many different fields of engineering technology use special types of technical drawings, such as mechanical, electrical, industrial, manufacturing, and construction.

Along with these specialized fields in technology, based on specific types of engineering, *technical graphics* itself is a specialized field. **Drafters/designers** are specialists that assist the engineer in the design process and create technical drawings that are used to document the design and produce the product. This specialist should be an expert in creating and interpreting technical drawings for many applications and may be called upon to create technical illustrations that enable people with diverse backgrounds to visualize how a product looks or how a device functions (Figure 1.26).

Figure 1.26

Technical graphics

Drafters/designers assist in the design process and produce the technical drawings necessary to document and produce designs.

(Bill Aron, © PhotoEdit, Inc.)

1.9 Summary

When learning to communicate graphically, you will apply the tools used to create engineering drawings and models. Even more important, you will learn the underlying principles and concepts of technical graphics, such as descriptive geometry. You will also learn the standards and conventions that will enable you to create drawings and models that can be read and accurately interpreted by engineers or technologists anywhere.

The ability to draw is a powerful skill. It gives a person's thoughts visible form. Engineering drawings can communicate complex ideas both efficiently and effectively, and it takes special training to be able to produce these complex images. If drawings are "windows to our imaginations," then engineering drawings are specialized windows that give expression to the most complex, technical visions our minds can imagine.

Engineering drawing does more than communicate. Like any language, it can actually influence how we think. Knowing how to draw allows you to think of and deal with many problems that others may not. A knowledge of technical graphics helps you more easily envision technical problems, as well as their solutions. In short, technical graphics is a necessity for every engineer and technologist.

Online Learning Center (OLC) Features

There are a number Online Learning Center features listed below that you can use to supplement your text reading to improve your understanding and retention of the material presented in this chapter at www.mhhe.com/bertoline.

- Learning Objectives
- Chapter Outline
- Questions for Review
- Multiple Choice Quiz
- True or False Questions
- Flashcards
- Website Links
- Animations
- Related Readings
- Solid Modeling
- Stapler Design Problem

Questions for Review

1. What is the difference between artistic and technical drawings?
2. What are the six major components of technical graphics?
3. Define the following terms: drawing, engineering drawing, and technical drawing. What are the distinctions among these terms?
4. What are ideation drawings used for?
5. What is the science that underlies graphics languages?
6. What is the purpose for document drawings?
7. Why are technical drawings an important form of communication for engineers and technologists?
8. How might graphics be used in your area of study or work?
9. Define standards.
10. Define conventions.
11. Define visual science.
12. Name the current standards used for dimensioning and tolerancing.

Further Reading

Booker, P. *The History of Engineering Drawing.* London: Chatto & Windus, 1962.

Ferguson, E. S. "The Mind's Eye: Nonverbal Thought in Technology." *Science* 197, no. 4306 (August 26, 1977), pp. 827–36.

Ferguson, E. S. *Engineering and the Mind's Eye.* Cambridge, MA: MIT Press, 1994.

Higbee, F. G. "The Development of Graphical Representations." In *Proceedings of the Summer School for Drawing Teachers.* Eds. R. P. Hoelscher, J. Rising. New York: McGraw-Hill, 1949, pp. 9–26.

Land, M. H. "Historical Developments of Graphics." *Engineering Design Graphics Journal* 40, no. 2 (Spring 1976), pp. 28–33.

Reynolds, T. S. "Gaspard Monge and the Origins of Descriptive Geometry." *Engineering Design Graphics Journal* 40, no. 2 (Spring 1976), pp. 14–19.

Problems

1.1 Research and report on an important historical figure in engineering design, such as Henry Ford, Thomas Edison, the Wright brothers, or Alexander Graham Bell.

1.2 Identify at least five other individuals who worked as engineers and had an impact on society.

1.3 Research and report on an important historical engineering achievement, such as airplanes, space flight, computers, or television.

1.4 Identify three new products that have appeared on the market in the last five years.

1.5 Research and report on an important historical figure in graphics, such as Gaspard Monge, M. C. Escher, Thomas Alva Edison, Leonardo da Vinci, Albrecht Durer, or Frank Lloyd Wright.

1.6 To demonstrate the effectiveness of graphics communications, write a description of the object shown in Figure 1.27. Test your written description by having someone attempt to make a sketch from your description.

1.7 Make a sketch of a common device, such as a telephone, automobile, computer mouse, or coffee cup.

1.8 Get a clear mental picture of a television, then sketch what you see in your mind. Is this mental image 2-D or 3-D? Try to put words to each feature of the TV you are drawing. In this problem you will experience the difficulty in trying to verbally describe an object with enough detail for it to be manufactured.

1.9 Interview a practicing engineer or technologist and ask how graphics is used in his or her daily work.

1.10 Ask the practicing engineer or technologist what changes are taking place in his or her profession.

1.11 Research and report on an important historical figure in computer graphics, such as Ivan Sutherland, Steve Coons, R. E. Bezier, or George Lucas.

1.12 Briefly describe this professional organization: the American Design Drafting Association (ADDA).

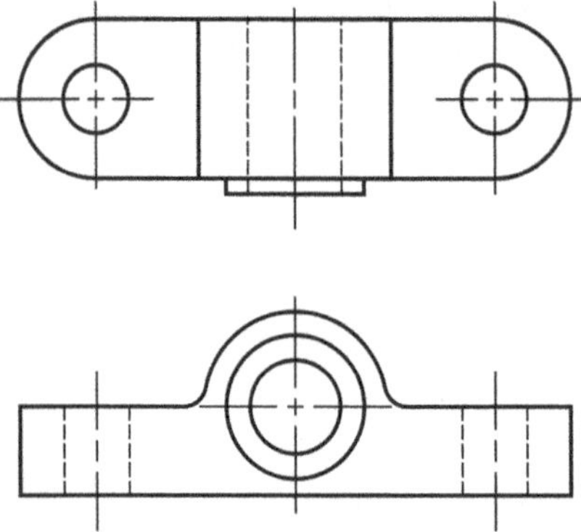

Figure 1.27

Problem 1.6 bearing block to be described verbally

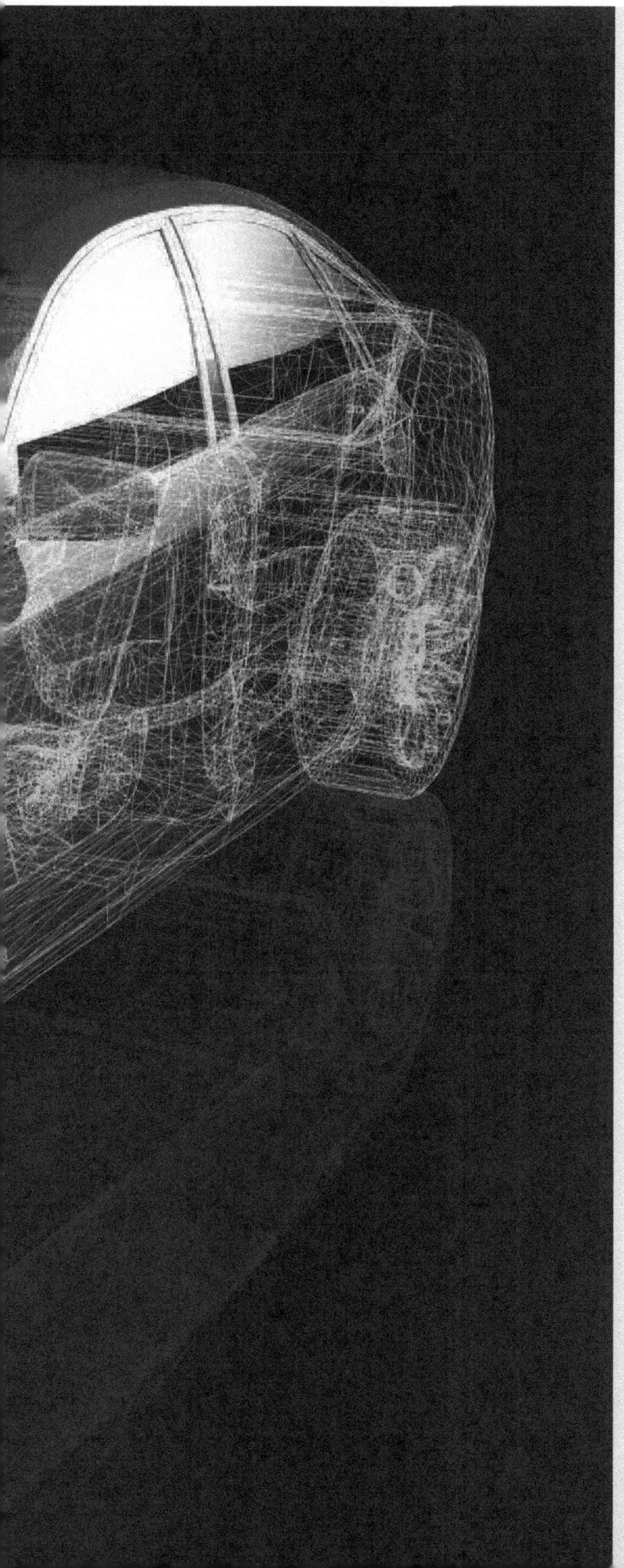

Chapter Two

The Engineering Design Process

A scientist can discover a new star but he cannot make one. He would have to ask an engineer to do it for him.

—Gordon L. Glegg,
***The Design of Design,* 1969**

Objectives and Overview

After completing this chapter, you will be able to:

1. Describe the engineering design process and the role graphics plays.
2. Describe the concurrent engineering design process.
3. Describe design for manufacturability (DFM).
4. List the typical members of a design team.
5. Explain the role 3-D modeling plays in the engineering design process.
6. List and describe the modeling techniques used in design.
7. Describe the important types of graphics used to support the engineering design process.
8. Describe the rapid prototyping process.
9. Describe the ideation process.
10. Describe the implementation process.
11. Describe the role of PDM in drawing control.
12. List and describe the analysis techniques used in design.

Introduction

Technical graphics is an integral part of the engineering design process through which engineers and drafters/designers generate new ideas and solve problems. Traditional engineering design consists of closely related steps that flow both sequentially and back and forth. Many industries in the United States are changing their design methodology from a linear/sequential activity to a team approach in which all parts of the company are working on a project simultaneously. An emerging engineering design approach, based on concurrent engineering principles, is product lifecycle management (PLM).

The engineering design process brings meaning and purpose to engineering graphics. Design is the catalyst for the creation of computer models and drawings. This chapter describes a modern approach to the engineering design process, so that you will have a better understanding of and appreciation for the need and importance of modeling and drawing. The remaining chapters in the text explain technical graphics as it relates to engineering design and production. Knowing the engineering design process and the support provided by graphics will give greater meaning to the remaining chapters in this text.

2.1 Design

Design is the process of conceiving or inventing ideas mentally and communicating those ideas to others in a form that is easily understood. Most often the communications tool is graphics.

Design is used for two primary purposes: personal expression, and product or process development (Figure 2.1). Design for personal expression, usually associated with art, is divided into concrete (realistic) and abstract design and is often a source of beauty and interest (Figure 2.2). When a design serves some useful purpose, such as the shape of a new automobile wheel, it is classified as a design for product or process development (Figure 2.3).

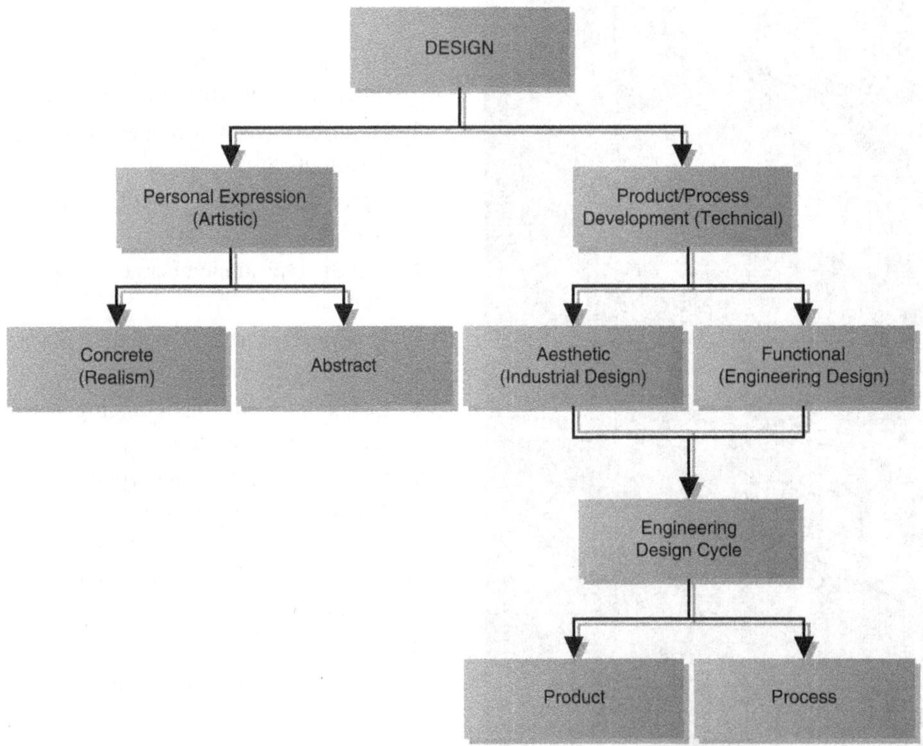

Figure 2.1

Design is grouped as artistic and technical

Artistic design is concerned with personal expression, and technical design is concerned with product and process development. Technical design has elements of both functional and aesthetic design.

Figure 2.2

Abstract design

An abstract design, such as this waveform illustration, is meant to evoke a personal, emotional response in the viewer. Although these waveforms are based on mathematic expressions, the color and texture applied to them is more artistic in nature.

(© Chris Harvey/Crestock.)

Figure 2.4

Functional design

The wind tunnel testing of a new automobile determined how the car would function when moving through the air. This is an example of functional design.

(© Michael Rosenfeld/Stone/Getty Images.)

Figure 2.3

Aesthetic design

Aesthetic design is an important part of the engineering design process. Industrial designers have a major role in the engineering design process for consumer products, such as bicycles, appliances, and consumer electronics.

(© Scott Robertson/www.drawthrough.com.)

Figure 2.5

Aesthetic and functional design

Aesthetic and functional design combine to give this bicycle a look of style and functionality. The bicycle is the result of a product design intended to eliminate the need for training wheels.

(Shift bicycle by Scott Shim, Matt Grossman, Ryan Lightbody.)

Aesthetic design is concerned with the look and feel of a product. *Industrial designers* specialize in the aesthetic qualities of products, as well as other elements related to human-machine functionality.

Functional design is concerned with the function of a product or process. Air flow over an automobile is an example of a functional design element. Most engineers are concerned with functional elements (Figure 2.4).

Many products will have both aesthetic and functional design elements, requiring the engineers and designers to work as a team to produce a product or system that is both functional and aesthetically pleasing (Figure 2.5).

2.1.1 Aesthetic Design

There are certain aesthetic design concepts that are useful for engineers. **Function** means that a product possesses a form related directly to the purpose of that product. For example, a sports car marketed because of its power and speed should have a body design that "radiates" speed (Figure 2.5). The architect Louis Sullivan used the phrase "form follows function," meaning that the form of a design is joined to its function. **Form** is the overall physical appearance of a product and consists of many elements, the arrangement of which is critical to the aesthetics and function of the product. These elements are unity, style, line, space, mass, proportion, balance, contrast, and color.

Unity is the use of similar elements throughout the design or product line. The engineer accomplishes unity by thinking of the product as a whole instead of as individual parts or components.

Style is the addition of decoration to a product and is closely linked to marketing. For example, the basic functional components of an automobile do not change every year, but the style usually does. New styles are created each year to generate consumer interest and increase the product life cycle.

Line is another characteristic of a product. Lines can be thin, thick, straight, or curved and can be used to emphasize the intended function. For example, thin, curved lines on a sports car emphasize the function of speed.

Space is the relationship of a product to its background, as well as to its negative elements (holes, slots, voids).

Mass is the design element that provides a sense of weight or heaviness. The physical space that an object occupies has a bearing on the perceived function of that product. For example, the sports car should appear to have little mass. This can be accomplished by designing the chassis and body so that the car is close to the ground.

Proportion is the relationship of the smaller elements to the whole design. For example, if the sports car had very large wheel wells, they would look disproportionate compared with the rest of the vehicle.

Balance is the design element that gives the product equilibrium. There are two types of balance: symmetrical and asymmetrical. For example, the sports car displays asymmetrical balance between the front and rear halves and symmetrical balance between the left and right sides.

Contrast is the feature used to emphasize or de-emphasize certain elements in a design. For example, the sports car uses a single color and material for the body, eliminating contrast to give the feeling of wholeness. Contrast can be provided by decorations, such as chrome bumpers.

Color is the element used to evoke emotions, give sensations of weight, and enhance a design form. For example, a red-colored sports car tends to evoke feelings of excitement and quickness.

2.1.2 Functional Design

Functional design focuses on the function of the product or process instead of its appearance. Many products are a mix of function and aesthetics, but some are almost exclusively functionally designed. A pair of crutches is designed with little regard for aesthetics, to function as an aid to a person with a leg injury. An automobile radiator used to cool an internal combustion engine is totally designed so that its functional requirements are met with little regard to aesthetics.

2.2 Engineering Design

Engineering design is a problem-solving process that uses knowledge, resources, and existing products to create new goods and processes. Engineering design has both aesthetic and functional elements and can be broken into two broad categories: product design and system or process design (Figure 2.1). The design process, as implemented by industry, varies between companies; some use a linear or step-by-step approach, while others use a more integrated team approach.

2.2.1 Product Design

Product design is the process used to create new products, such as a new automobile model (Figure 2.5), a new appliance, or a new type of wheelchair. Product design is a complex activity that includes market, production, sales, service, function, and profit analyses. The goal of product design is to produce a product that meets the wants and needs of the consumer, is economically produced, is safe for the consumer and the environment, and is profitable to the company.

2.2.2 System Design

System design is the process used to create a new system or process. A *systems engineer* or *industrial engineer* is an engineer who specializes in designing systems. A **system** is an orderly arrangement of parts that are combined to serve one general function. Examples of system designs include the arrangement of the assembly process

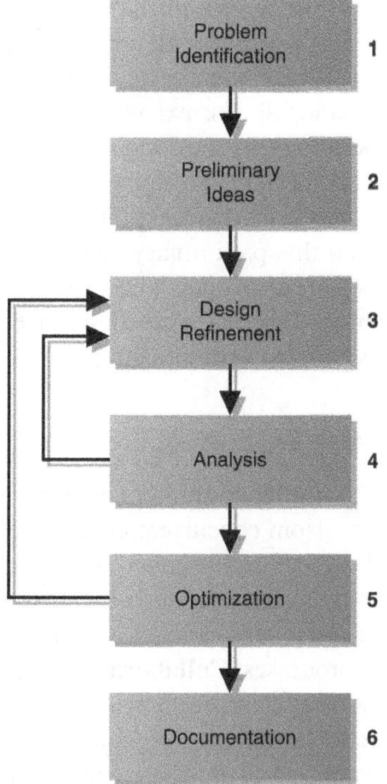

Figure 2.6

Traditional engineering design sequence

The traditional design process is a sequential process that can be grouped into six major activities, beginning with identification of the problem and ending with documentation of the design. Technical graphics is used throughout this process to document design solutions.

in a factory; the heating, ventilation, and air-conditioning (HVAC) system in a structure; and the electrical system in the automobile in Figure 2.5. The objective is to produce a system that serves a specific function economically, is safe for the consumer and the environment, and is profitable for the company.

2.2.3 Traditional Engineering Design

Traditional engineering design is a linear approach divided into a number of steps. For example, a six-step process might be divided into problem identification, preliminary ideas, refinement, analysis, optimization, and documentation (see Figure 2.6). The design process moves through each step in a sequential manner; however, if problems are encountered, the process may return to a previous step. This repetitive action is called **iteration** or looping. Many industries use the traditional engineering design process; however, a new process has developed that combines some features of the traditional process with a team approach that involves all segments of a business.

2.2.4 Concurrent Engineering Design

The production process executes the final results of the design process to produce a product or system. In the past, the creative design process was separated from the production process. With the advent of computer modeling and product data management systems, this separation is no longer necessary, and the modern engineering design approach brings both processes together. See Section 2.3 for a discussion of product data management systems.

Concurrent engineering is a nonlinear team approach to design that brings together the input, processes, and output elements necessary to produce a product. The people and processes are brought together at the very beginning, which is not normally done in the linear approach. The team consists of design and production engineers, technicians, marketing and finance personnel, planners, and managers, who work together to solve a problem and produce a product. Many companies are finding that concurrent engineering practices result in a better, higher-quality product, more satisfied customers, fewer manufacturing problems, and a shorter cycle time between design initiation and final production.

Figures 2.7 and 2.8 represent the concurrent approach to engineering design, based on 3-D modeling. The three

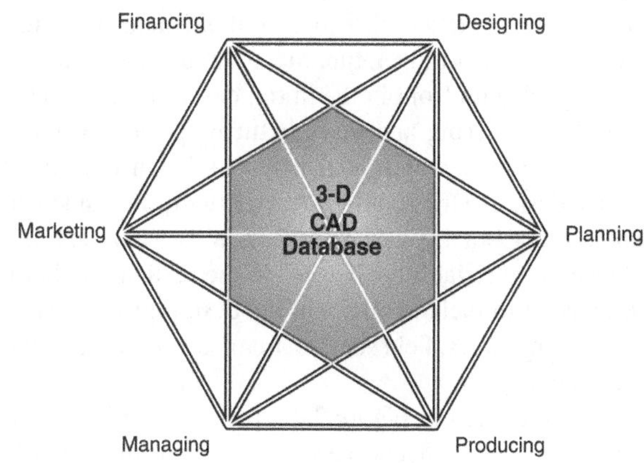

Figure 2.7

Sharing the 3-D CAD database

The concurrent engineering model shows how every area in an enterprise is related, and the 3-D CAD database is the common thread of information between areas.

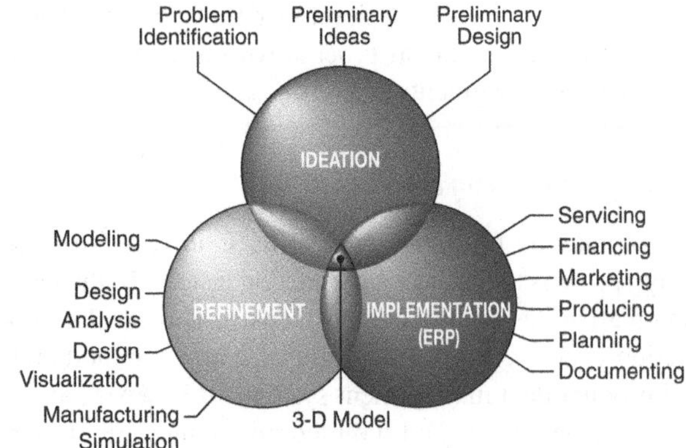

Figure 2.8

Concurrent engineering design

The engineering design process consists of three overlapping areas: ideation, refinement, and implementation, which all share the same 3-D CAD database.

intersecting circles represent the concurrent nature of this design approach. For example, in the ideation phase, design engineers interact with service technicians to ensure that the product will be easily serviceable by the consumer or technician. This type of interaction results in a better product for the consumer. The three intersecting circles also represent the three activities that are a major part of the concurrent engineering design process: ideation, refinement, and implementation. These three activities are further divided into smaller segments, as shown by the items surrounding the three circles.

Design for manufacturability (DFM) and design for assembly (DFA) practices developed out of concurrent engineering as an effort to capture manufacturing and assembly knowledge up front in the initial design process. This allowed engineering and manufacturing professionals to speak a common language that results in an optimized product design. DFM and DFA eventually expanded to include other practices, such as design for serviceability and design for reliability. This led to the realization that it is important to include others in the design process, such as marketing, sales, field service, finance, purchasing, and quality control.

The center area in Figure 2.8 represents the 3-D computer model and reflects the central importance of 3-D modeling and graphics knowledge in engineering design and production. With the use of a standard modeling approach, everyone on the team can have access to the current design through a computer terminal. This data sharing is critically important to the success of the design process.

Through the sharing of information, often in the form of a database, it is possible for all areas of the enterprise to work simultaneously on their particular needs as the product is being developed. For example, a preliminary 3-D model could be created by the design engineers early in the ideation phase. A mechanical engineer could use the same 3-D model to analyze its thermal properties. The information gained from this preliminary analysis could then be given to the design engineers, who could then make any necessary changes early in the ideation phase, minimizing costly changes later in the design process.

2.2.5 Collaborative Engineering

Collaborative engineering has evolved from concurrent engineering into a true enterprisewide integrated product development process. Concurrent engineering sought to establish well-defined organizational and team structures as well as highly structured business processes. **Collaborative engineering** creates the infrastructure and best environment for highly effective team collaboration using computers to store and share information. The development of such tools as e-mail, groupware, video conferencing, and chat rooms was important in the adoption of collaborative engineering in industry. Concurrent engineering is fundamentally process-centric through the creation of well defined, documented, and executed business processes for the development of products. Collaborative engineering is fundamentally a product-centric process that builds onto the concurrent engineering practices a mindset of highly effective collaboration about the product and its manufacturing and support processes. The product becomes the central focus instead of the process.

Collaborative engineering is based on empowered, cross-functional teams and low-level decision making. Figure 2.9 shows the basic structure of collaborative engineering where cross-functional teams share a common goal through the sharing of information using computer networks. Table 2.1 on pages 34–35 is a list of the key functions and some of the information created. This information has some impact on the product as it is being designed and manufactured for eventual distribution to consumers. The need for sharing 2-D and 3-D design data has resulted in a technological migration that places the product database at the center of the design process model. Figure 2.10 on page 36 shows an example of the product database at the center of the design and development process. A contemporary application of collaborative engineering is product lifecycle management, as described in

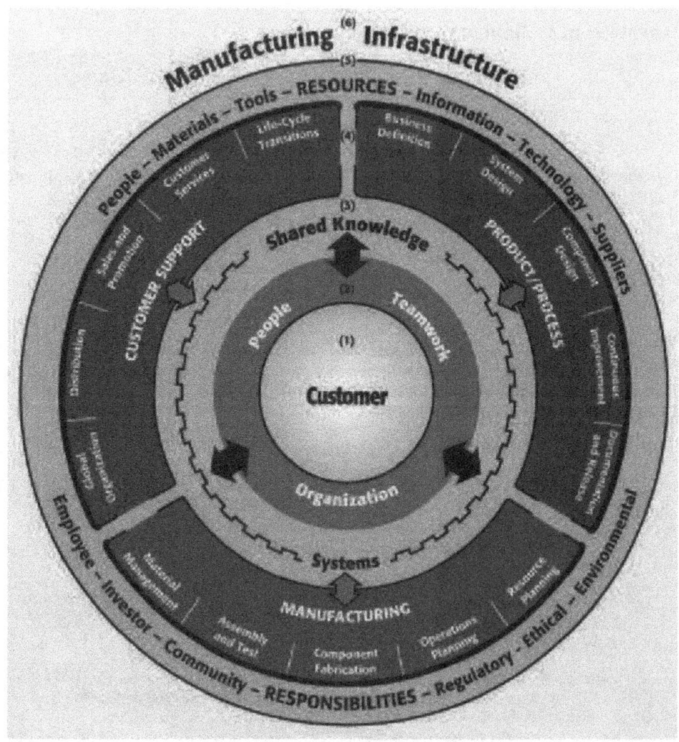

Figure 2.9

Collaborative engineering

This diagram shows the major functions involved in the design, manufacture, and distribution of a product. The information produced by each function is shared through a highly sophisticated network of computers and software tools.

(The CASA/SME CIM Wheel is reprinted with permission of the Society of Manufacturing Engineers, © 1993.)

Section 2.3. It is based on information technology systems, which provide product design and manufacturing personnel with real-time access to product design information.

2.2.6 Virtual Product Representation

Collaborative engineering is highly dependent on computer-based tools. Tools used to support the design process include CAD, CAM, CAE, and office applications. These tools are used to create a virtual representation of a product design through

1. Shaded CAD models.
2. Photorealistic renderings.
3. Large assembly visualizations.
4. Packaging analysis.
5. Tolerance analysis.
6. Structural, thermal, and flow analyses.
7. Dynamic simulations for design and manufacturing.
8. Virtual reality.

2.2.7 Prototyping

One step closer to reality is gained by using physical prototyping through either rapid prototyping to quickly create a physical model of a part or functional prototypes to create a mockup of the part using traditional means, such as machine tools. A rapid prototype is limited, creating geometric and topological representations of a part. A functional prototype includes geometric and topological representations of a part in addition to functional representation of products evaluation in terms of mechanical, structural, thermal, fluid, and electrical behaviors.

Table 2.1 Key Functions Involved in Collaborative Engineering

Strategic Business Planning	Marketing	Sales
• Corporate ideology (mission, vision, values, and so on) • Long-term strategic business plans • Long-term business forecasts and trends analyses • Corporate financial statements and annual reports • Workshop and focus group results	• Short-term market research relating to a particular product concept or market niche • Customer surveys and feedback on current products/conjoint analysis • Lead-user analysis • Competitive intelligence research • Marketing communications literature and publications • Product planning • Product-specific business and market plans • Full product and material specifications/functional requirements • Initial proposals for production volumes, locale, facilities, equipment, and materials • Quality function deployment/Pugh analysis	• Sales proposals • Sales contracts inclusive of product specifications and functional requirements
Human Resources	**Advanced Technical Research and Development**	**Industrial Design**
• Long-term projections of professional personnel requirements to support ongoing product development • Staffing plans for future production levels (short-term and long-term) • Requisite training and development for each group of functional employees • Corporate training plans relating to organizational development initiatives (for example, CE/IPD)	• Highly specialized technical consultations for current development projects • Near-term development of new technologies and plans for matriculation into production • Long-term applied research of next-generation technologies	• Conceptual design feasibility studies • CAD sketches of new product concepts • Representations of new product design proposals • Photorealistic renderings • Physical/rapid prototypes
Forward Engineering	**Project Management**	**Engineering Design**

• Prepackaged leading technology designs (pseudo-detailed design level)
• Design definition and specifications
• CAD models
• Design guidelines and consultations on specific design applications
	• Initial project plans
	  • Budget
	  • Timeline
	  • Work breakdown structure
	• Tracking progress of projects
	• Contingency plans/actions
	• Project milestone reviews (phase/gate reviews)
		• Detailed engineering design information
		• Design requirements, guidelines, and specifications
		• Detailed CAD models and part drawings
		• Geometric dimensioning and tolerancing details
		• Part tooling details
		• Engineering bill of materials (BOM)
		• Functional/rapid part prototypes

Table 2.1 Key Functions Involved in Collaborative Engineering (continued)

Product Engineering	Value Engineering	Quality and Reliability Engineering

• Engineering guidelines, requirements, and specifications (including material specs)
• Engineering BOM
• Detailed CAD models and part drawings
• Product poka-yoke documentation
• Functional CAE analyses (thermal, structural, electrical, hydraulic, packaging, and so on)
• Design for manufacture/assembly/service/analyses (DFX)
• Design verification/product verification plans and results
• Assembly/installation diagrams; service diagrams
• Part tooling designs/assembly fixture designs
• Shipping rack/container designs
• Product release and engineering change notice documentation
• Product financials (material costs, production costs, ER&D expenses)
• APQP documentation (design failure modes and effects analysis ([DFMEA])
• Final engineering sign-off
	• Value analyses
	  • Of current products, materials, and production methods
	  • Of proposed future products, materials, and production methods
	• Proposed product design modifications and material substitutions
	• Proposed production process improvements
		• Warranty analysis (of surrogate products currently or previously in production)
		• Failure mode analysis based on historical surrogate information
		• Proposed product improvements for higher quality and reduced warranty claims
		• APQP documentation [production (quality) control plans]
		• SPC plans (component review team, PIPC, PIST)

Manufacturing Process Design and Planning	**Field Service Engineering**	**Production Planning and Management**
• Manufacturing/assembly process design/specification • Manufacturing/assembly equipment specifications/designs • Production line layouts • Process plans (CAPP)/process flow diagrams • Process poka-yoke documentation • Manufacturing process simulation • CNC programs/verification simulation • Robotic programs/verification simulation • APQP documentation (process failure mode and effects analysis)	• Service part list/BOM • Service manuals/diagrams • Service training materials • Service infrastructure planning	• Production facilities planning • Capital equipment and inventories/procurement plans • Production staffing plans • Production part BOMs • Inventory planning/reorder process documentation • Initial production sequence schedules • Warehousing and distribution plans • EDI/bar coding infrastructure plans
Shop Floor		
• Tool/equipment inventories • Equipment maintenance schedules • Daily production orders/schedules/sequences • Assembly instruction sheets/diagrams • Shipping container/rack inventories and plans		

SOURCE: (Table reprinted with permission of the Computer and Automated Systems Association of the Society of Manufacturing Engineers, © 1999. Please refer to fee table for reproducing copyright material.)

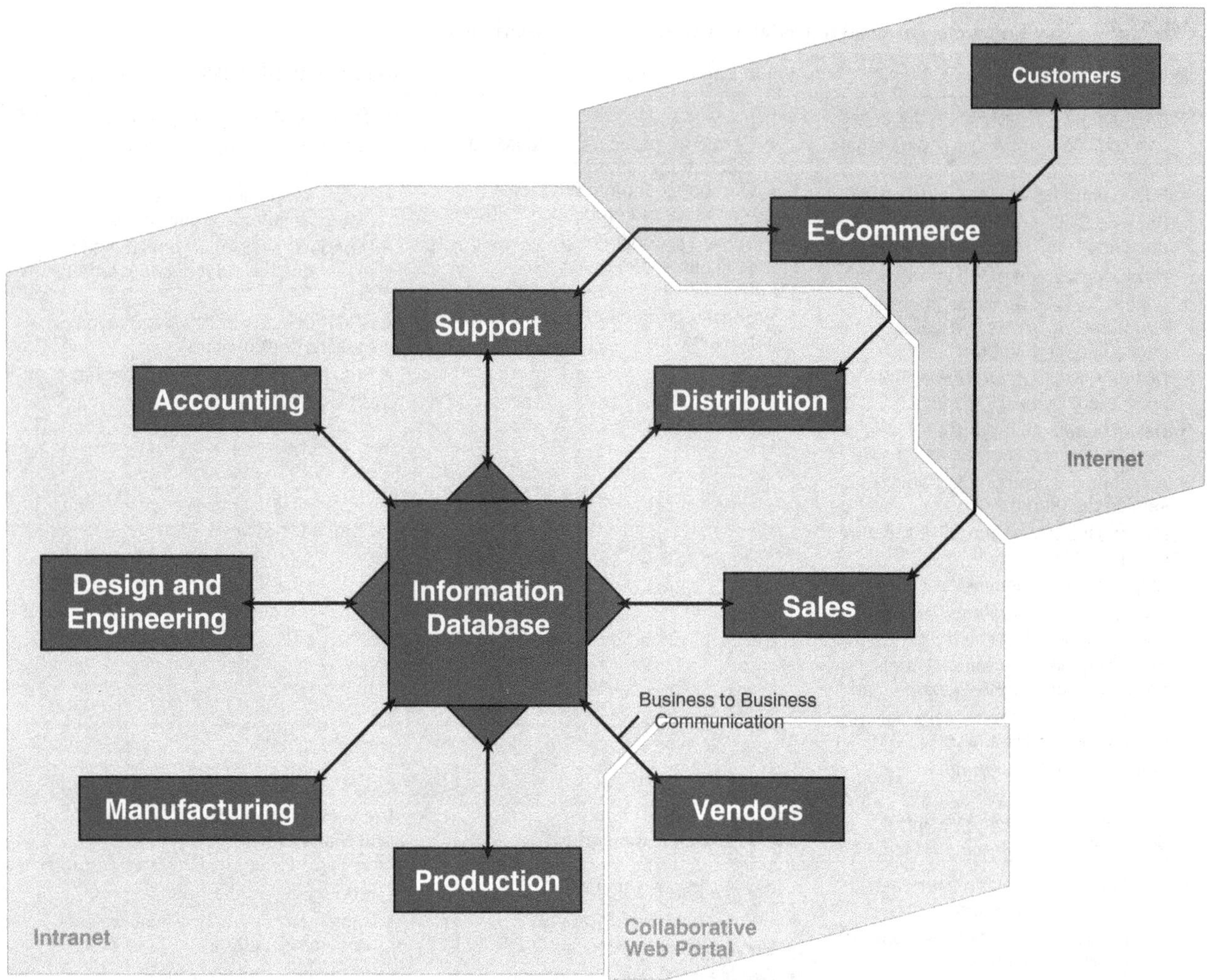

Figure 2.10

The digital enterprise

Diagram representing the relationship of various departments in an organization.

2.2.8 Productivity Tools

There are a number of tools used to enhance overall productivity and sharing of design and manufacturing information. These are used by engineers and technicians on a daily basis to support the overall design process but are not viewed as engineering tools, such as CAD software. Tools to share the output of the design process include e-mail, word processing, spreadsheet, groupware, file transfer, file translation, videoconferencing, and workflow.

2.3 The Digital Enterprise

The manufacture of a new product now calls for the involvement of all the company's departments: engineering, strategy, marketing and sales, planning and production, procurement, finance, and human resources. The digital enterprise is a model that facilitates the simultaneous working of all these departments. It makes it possible to create, manage, simulate, share, and communicate digitally all the information

Historical Highlight
Leonardo da Vinci

Leonardo da Vinci (1452–1519) was a true Renaissance man. He had a strong curiosity about how things worked. Although he is best known as a painter, his interests and talents were far-reaching. He studied everything from botany to mechanics, using his creative mind to innovate and expand almost every field that captured his attention.

Leonardo developed interest in nature and the arts while still quite young and received encouragement from his Uncle Francesco. His interest continued to flourish even after he moved away to Florence with his father. It was there that he was apprenticed to an artist named Verroccho. In Verroccho's workshop, Leonardo learned painting techniques and how to use artists' tools. One such technique was the making of preliminary sketches and drawings, a skill that Leonardo had already been developing and continued to use throughout his life. It is because of Leonardo's drawings that we know of many machines of the time and of many of Leonardo's studies and ideas.

Some Renaissance artists studied human anatomy and botany to help them create more realistic works of art, and Leonardo was no exception. He took his studies further than most artists did, though, because he not only had an artistic interest, but also a scientific one. He knew enough about plants to be a botanist and made important studies and drawings of different muscle groups in the human body, and of the fetus in the mother's womb.

Leonardo also studied various methods of transportation. He was the inventor of the lock (the kind used in canals), and he also studied birds in flight, which led to him designing a flying machine much like the modern hang glider. We even know from his drawings that he anticipated both the parachute and the helicopter.

Yet another one of Leonardo's areas of interest was machines of war. In this area Leonardo was ahead of his time. His designs were too impractical to be built during the Renaissance, but many of them resembled modern machines.

(© Scala/Art Resource, NY.)

For example, he designed a motor that fired explosive shells, a many-barreled machine-gun-like gun, and a vehicle resembling a tank. He even designed a fortress similar to World War II fortifications.

Because Leonardo was motivated by his desire to know how things worked, it is not surprising that he was also knowledgeable about mechanics. As in his other areas of interest, Leonardo made many drawings of mechanical tools. Some of his drawings were from ideas of other people, and some were his own, but they were all very detailed and easy to understand (see picture). They were so well done that it is relatively easy to reproduce the machines that they represent.

We know about many of the machines, tools, and ideas of the Renaissance because of the curiosity of Leonardo da Vinci, and his habit of accurately drawing and writing things down. Leonardo supplemented many of his writings with sketches to better describe his thoughts. Today, sketching still is an important method of communicating our thoughts and designs and is used quite often by engineers and technologists.

related to the company's products, processes, and resources, optimizing its overall performance (Figure 2.10).

In addition to CAD software used to design, specialized software is required to focus on virtual product management, product data management, and tools for sharing product data across the enterprise. It is possible through the use of computer simulation that problems can be discovered early in the product definition when changes are less costly. Companies are using different processes and systems to manage the product data from conceptual design to in-the-field service and they are looking at ways to improve data flow and streamline processes to increase their competitiveness.

A total digital solution is called "the digital enterprise." The overall objective is to provide the capability for companies to design and simulate products "virtually" across an integrated enterprise covering the entire life cycle of a product, all without ever having to build a real prototype. This is achieved through advances in CAD, digital mockup, virtual product modeling, virtual manufacturing simulation, web access, and other key technologies. As a result, companies are dramatically changing the way they do product design and management, including the integration of functions within an enterprise that, to date, have been either "outside" or at the tail end of the product development process.

Manufacturers using CAD systems produce a tremendous amount of digital information and knowledge which remains buried in digital form on hard drives and file servers. The digital enterprise leverages the knowledge found in these digital files by making that information available to the whole organization.

2.3.1 EDM/PDM

Tools to manage the long-term overall design/manufacture process include product data management (PDM) and enterprise data management (EDM) software programs. EDM and PDM are used to track and manage all the electronic documents and data associated with the design and manufacturing of products. Data management has always been important in manufacturing and design, but it was traditionally done using paper-based filing systems. This is being replaced with a digital-based filing system using EDM and PDM software. EDM and PDM software is moving more toward Internet browser interfaces, which is especially important for companies that have operations in multiple locations.

2.3.2 Internet, Intranet, and Extranet

Most software tools described above are used within the context of a computer network to provide the interconnectivity necessary to share information. Recently the **Internet** has become the network most capable of providing the interconnectivity for collaborative engineering. Intranets are used as the backbone of internal corporate information sharing. The **Intranet** is a private internal network that uses web browsers and servers to connect users in an organization to share information. **Extranets** are private and secure networks that allow access to a company's internal Intranet by outside sources, such as supply vendors, through the Internet. Extranets are a part of a rapidly expanding area of *business-to-business* (B-to-B) information technology. See Figure 2.10 for an example of the use of the Intranet, Extranet, and Intranet applied to an organization.

2.3.3 Product Life Cycle Management (PLM)

The manufacture of a new product now calls for the involvement of all the company's departments: engineering, strategy, marketing and sales, planning and production, procurement, finance, and human resources. **PLM** is a model that facilitates the simultaneous working of all these departments. It makes it possible to create, manage, simulate, share, and communicate digitally all the information related to the company's products, processes, and resources, optimizing its overall performance (Figure 2.10).

In addition to CAD software used to design, specialized software is required to focus on virtual product management, product data management, and tools for sharing product data across the enterprise. It is possible through the use of computer simulation that problems can be discovered early in the product definition when changes are less costly. Companies are using different processes and systems to manage the product data from conceptual design to in-the-field service, and they are looking at ways to improve data flow and streamline processes to increase their competitiveness.

A total digital solution is called "PLM." The overall objective is to provide the capability for companies to design and simulate products "virtually" across an integrated enterprise covering the entire life cycle of a product, all without ever having to build a real prototype. This is achieved through advances in CAD, digital mockup, virtual product modeling, virtual manufacturing simulation, web access, and other key technologies. As a result, companies are dramatically changing the way they do product design and management, including the integration of functions within an enterprise that, to date, have been either "outside" or at the tail end of the product development process.

Manufacturers using CAD systems produce a tremendous amount of digital information and knowledge which remains buried in digital form on hard drives and file servers. The PLM leverages the knowledge found in these digital files by making that information available to the whole organization.

PLM is an integrated information technology (IT) environment that allows manufacturers to create, manage, store, and share product data throughout the concept, design, build, and life stages of the product's life cycle. It is a business process that plans for the life cycle of a product from "proposal to disposal" (Figure 2.11).

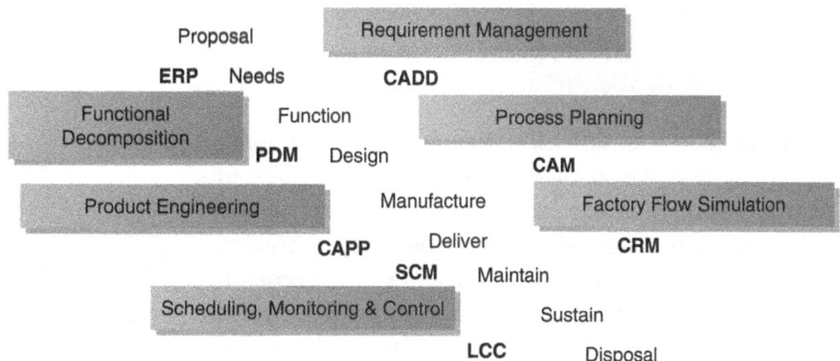

Figure 2.11

Overall view of product lifecycle management

Although many new technologies have emerged in the 1990s, two have had a profound effect on engineering design. The first is Web technology combined with the Internet, which made it possible for product data management (PDM) users to access data from remote locations through the Web. The second is the realization that geometry and other product information (i.e., product definition) can be reused by virtually all business processes downstream of the design process. This reuse ability provides an immense benefit through the elimination of nonvalue-added activities (such as the re-keying of data), enabling concurrent work, as well as avoiding transcription and translation errors.

So fundamental has been the impact of these two developments that they have led to a profound change to the way PDM, CAD/CAM, and other computer-aided technologies are developed and used. The increasing use of the same product definition outside the design office led not only to tight coupling of related technologies, such as CAD, CAM, and CAE, but also to the convergence of these technologies with PDM. The Internet put an end to any site location and geographical constraints. Together, these two developments made it possible, for the first time, to solve the emerging needs of businesses operating in the highly competitive, heavily outsourced global environment.

Business can now:

- Cut costs and time to market through more effective use and reuse of resources
- Be nimble and quick to react to market changes through the ability to focus on core business and increased collaboration with suppliers and partners
- Increase innovation through better visibility of product data to all personnel within both the enterprise and the extended enterprise

With a standard Web browser as the user interface and encryption technology to provide secure access across the Internet, it is possible for multi-disciplined teams to work concurrently on the same product data from anywhere around the world. Another significant development is the emergence of the Web browser as the "standard" user interface. This has provided consistency in the presentation of and interaction with product data, making it easier for team members to communicate. The result is that project teams can include members from a wide range of disciplines, as well as including suppliers, partners, customers, and other interested parties. These *virtual project teams* can be set up and disbanded as the organization business evolves.

PLM is a strategic business approach for the effective management and use of corporate intellectual capital. **Corporate intellectual capital** (CIC) is the sum of retained knowledge that an organization accumulates in the course of delivering its products.

Corporate intellectual capital (CIC) consists of the following:

1. **Product Definition**—all the information relating to what the product (or service) is: its specification and how it is designed, manufactured, delivered, and supported.
2. **Product History**—any information relating to what the organization has done in the past that is of relevance for the delivery of the organization's product, such as audit trails required for legal or regulatory purposes or archives relating to past products.
3. **Best Practice**—this summarizes the experience gathered by the organization in the course of delivery of its products.

Dream **High Tech** Job

Designing Bicyles for Women

This case study provides an example of one career path where the engineering design process is used. In this case, you will find an example of how engineering education is related to the different roles involved in designing a product—bicycles.

The engineering design process is used in many types of jobs from the design of consumer product packaging to the design of land and watercraft recreational vehicles. An understanding of the design process and geometry and geometric modeling along with formal education in a field of engineering can lead to exciting job opportunities, such as the one described here of an engineer who started off by custom designing bicycle frames for women and has turned it into a multimillion-dollar company.

Georgena Terry, after finishing theater and MBA degrees, found that she wasn't satisfied with her life. After taking a vocational test, a counselor recommended that Terry become some kind of engineer. She went back to school and discovered during a design project that she enjoyed brazing and bicycle design. For their project, her group decided to build a hybrid bicycle/car. She learned to braze the bicycle frame from metal tubes, and the rest is history.

Terry wanted to design bicycle frames to reduce riding stress for women. According to Bill Hammack, a chemical engineering professor at the University of Illinois at Urbana-Champaign, "Terry discovered that a woman is not simply a smaller version of a man. For example, a woman's upper body is proportionally longer than a man's upper body. So, a bike that fits a man in the legs and upper body will fit women in only one of those areas. Also, the center of a woman's muscle mass is different than a man's. This means that, when riding a man's bike, a woman's muscles bear more stress. This makes women feel stretched out, giving them neck and shoulder pain. The key to making a woman's bike,

GEORGENA TERRY
Founder and CEO of Terry Bicycles
(© Ron Wu Photography.)

CIC consists of two types of data:

1. **Content**—product definition and all related information.
2. **Meta Data**—data that describe the content, such as creation and last modified dates, author/owner, version/status, how it can be used and by whom, and so forth.

PLM allows everyone—from manufacturing to marketing and from purchasing to field support—to work faster and smarter. This allows the entire network of companies—working together to conceptualize, design, build, and support products—to operate as a single entity. PLM allows companies to share common business processes and a common knowledge of the product throughout all of the stages of its life cycle, from concept to retirement.

Collaboration breeds innovation and product lifecycle management breaks down the technology silos that have limited interaction between the people who design products and the people who build, sell, and use them. Using the collaborative power of the Internet, PLM increases a company's ability to produce innovative product designs, while reducing cycle times, streamlining manufacturing, and cutting production costs.

PLM simultaneously supports and enables three distinct yet deeply interconnected processes:

1. **Supply chain collaboration**—to help access the product expertise and experience within a company and beyond.
2. **Product development**—to help develop better products in a better design environment.

she decided, is getting them into a slightly more upright position. Also, she made the handlebars narrower, because a woman's shoulders are not as wide."

If you do what you love, the money will follow. In 1985, Terry's first year in business, she sold 20 of her custom bikes. The next year she sold 1,300 bikes, and the year after that she sold 5,000. Today, Terry Bicycles is a multimillion-dollar company.

Bicycle Equipment Design Today

Bicycling is a favorite sport among the young and the old. The bicycle is the classic example of a simple machine that attracts almost everyone who wants to go faster than walking or skating, with less energy expended. Bicycles have been around since the late 1600s and, through a process of evolution, the innovative engineers who design them are reaching new heights in aerodynamics, performance, propulsion, weight, and durability. Bikes today might weigh just over nine pounds, and recumbent bikes help riders to win races with rocket-like speeds of 81 mph. All-wheel-drive and electric bicycles have hit the market, along with aquacycles that are being used to cross oceans and Xtracycles, with a long back-end, that can carry surfboards, lumber, or other loads of up to 200 pounds. There are folding bikes, bikes with brains, bikes with flat-free tires, stationary bikes, and full-metal military bikes. These varied designs all provide creative outlets for bike design and the bicycling engineer.

Another example of engineers pushing the envelope to optimize performance is in the materials sector. Optimizing bicycle frame design is a daunting challenge. Different frames are best for different applications and conditions. For example, a mountain bike frame would not be a good choice for a Tour de France bike or a comfort bike. When engineers create frames, they can change the shape or wall thickness of the tubes and use different metals or alloys. Aluminum, titanium, carbon fiber, chromemoly steel, scandium (number 21 on the periodic table—even lighter than titanium), and E5 (a mixture of five other elements in aluminum—also lighter than titanium) are being used to engineer the "perfect" bicycle frame.

Engineers who do this:

- **Manufacturing Engineers**—Determine systems to get bike-related equipment manufactured. Interested in reducing the costs associated with production.
- **Materials Engineers**—Always on the lookout for new materials to have more fun, increase performance, and provide a more comfortable ride. This includes anything that makes up the bike such as the frame, forks, hubs, tires, grips, and seats or bike gear such as clothing, helmets, and shoes.
- **Mechanical Engineers**—May design the frames, derailleur, hubs, forks, handlebars, brakes, spindles, sprockets, and everything in between.

(Courtesy of Terry Bicycles (www.terrybikes.com).)
Portions reprinted with permission, from Baine, C., *High Tech Hot Shots,* 2004, IEEE.

3. **Enterprise process integration**—to help integrate product information with all company business processes.

2.3.4 e-Business

e-Business is the process of buying and selling products over the Internet. However, this revolutionary method of buying and selling can have a profound effect on the design and manufacture of products. e-Business can become the means to exploit the combined power of the Internet and information technology to fundamentally change the design and manufacturing processes. This means using CAD, virtual product representation, PDM, and EDM to conceive, design, build, market, and sell the most innovative, highest-quality, most attractive products to customers.

2.3.5 Design Teams

The membership of a design team will vary according to the complexity and type of design. In small companies, design teams may be only a few individuals, such as a design engineer, a drafter, and a manufacturing engineer. A typical team in a concurrent engineering design process will include individuals from design, manufacturing, quality, materials, vendors, and managers. Team members rotate in and out and involvement levels rise and fall as the design moves from concept to manufacture. Daily meetings are common during critical times in the design

Design in Industry

Desktop Engineering: Fast & Clean

This case describes the design of professional and leisure kayaks using CAD and reverse engineering technologies. In this case you will see an example of how 3-D scanning is used in conjuction with hand-made prototype and 3-D CAD geometry to complete the design of modern kayaks.

Kayaking has two extremes—the slow, leisurely float and the adrenaline-pumping rush of whitewater padding. For these extremes, and everything in between, Watermark Sports has just the right boat. Through its product lines, it offers recreational, fishing, expedition, touring, whitewater, and freestyle kayaks.

Watermark introduces 12 to 18 new boats each year, and year-after-year, the industry honors Watermark's kayaks. Producing a boat requires a combination of skill, experience, and craftsmanship. It also demands the right tools.

Watermark designs their boats using both digital design tools and model-making skills. To bridge the gap between hand-crafted prototypes and CAD data, the company depends on its reverse engineering tools, a laser scanner and 3-D scan data-processing software.

Building a Boat

Design of a new boat begins with CAD, and Watermark applies its years of experience to develop a product that both looks great and performs well. After a designer has done his job at the computer, the design must be refined for peak performance. To do this, Watermark must put a prototype boat in the water.

The prototype, which is called a plug, is milled from high-density foam by a CNC machine. Watermark's design team puts the full-scale model in the water and takes it out for a paddle. The test run provides performances data and highlights needed modifications. The prototype is then sent to the model shop, where it is reshaped by hand. At this point, experienced model-makers take over and adjust the hull's contours with hand rasps, sand-paper, other shaping tools, and body filler.

After repeated testing and reshaping, the design team settles on the perfect boat. The boat, however, exists only as a physical model that is an alteration of its original CAD model. To bridge the gap and get a CAD model from which to manufacture a line of boats, Watermark digitally scans the plug to capture its design modifications.

In the past, Watermark used a touch probe CMM tool mounted on an articulated arm. The problem was that it took as much as a week to gather the data and incorporate the modifications in a new CAD model. And due to time constraints and the manual operation of the touch probe, the input was limited to a few hundred discrete data points. With so little data, the CAD model did not capture all of the subtle contours hand-worked by the model-makers and the finished product often lacked many of the performance-enhancing alterations and some of their cosmetic appeal.

To speed up the process and get more accurate scans, Watermark now uses a laser scanner and point cloud editing software to digitally capture the shape of the boat.

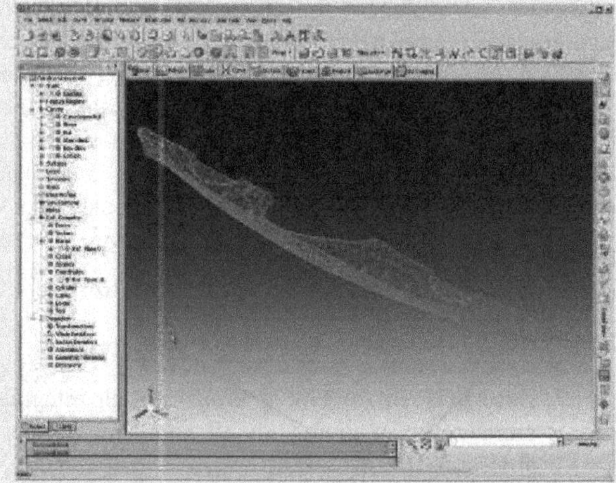

The point cloud for half of the Carolina kayak's hull contains 2.5 million points.

(Courtesy of Todd Grimm/Desktop Engineering Magazine.)

process, although weekly meetings of the design team are more common. Global design teams are possible through the use of the web and other Internet-based tools. It is now possible to share design information, including CAD models, across the web.

The coordination of the design team is critical to the success of the design and in meeting deadlines. Communications becomes a very important element for successful design. The use of computers in the design process can facilitate good communication between members of

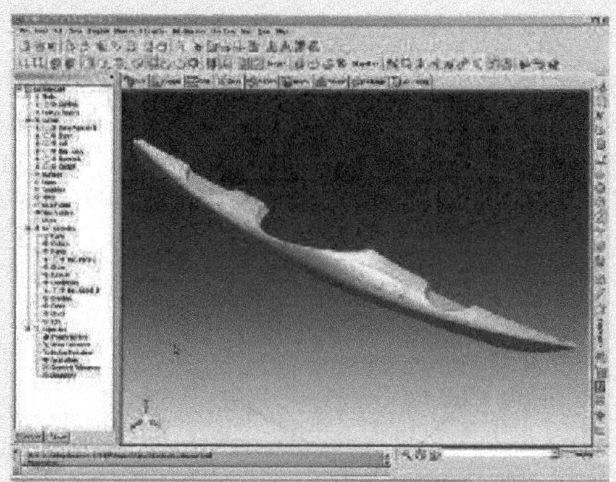

The point cloud is processed to yield a smooth polygonal data file that captures all of the hand-worked detail.
(Courtesy of Todd Grimm/Desktop Engineering Magazine.)

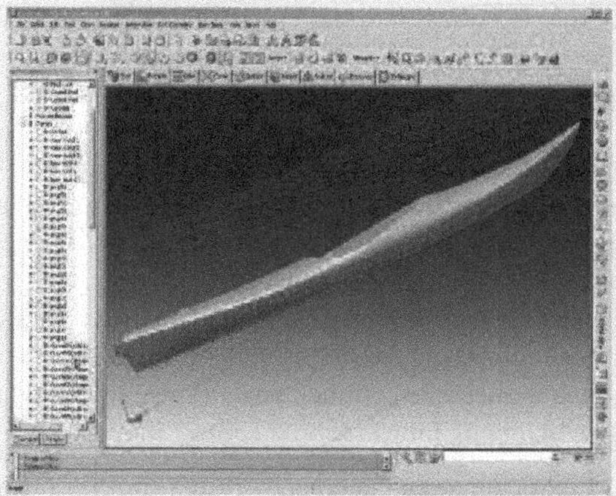

Prior to export, the scanned data is converted into NURBS surfaces. Then desired data is selected and surfaced data is exported in IGES format.
(Courtesy of Todd Grimm/Desktop Engineering Magazine.)

Watermark now captures design changes to its plugs in just three hours, a process that took a week the old way. In addition to the faster processing, the combination of the new hardware and software means increased data accuracy as well as additional control over the scanned data.

The Process

Watermark begins by scanning one-half of the plug, the data from which is later mirrored to create perfect symmetry. Each plug will yield between 20 and 40 scans over the length of the kayak, which ranges from 7 to 19 feet.

After scanning the plug, Watermark imports the point cloud data into the editing software. The scan data is then cleaned up, registered, and aligned. The length of a boat and the soft contours of the hull make this one of the toughest applications for scan alignment.

Once the digital definition is complete, the data is exported to the company's CAD software. In the CAD package, the kayak designer then creates the mirror images of the data to create a complete boat hull with perfect symmetry. From this file he creates his toolpaths and then machines another full-size plug in high-density foam. This new plug becomes the pattern for casting a composite tool used for rotational modeling or vacuum forming a kayak.

"Watermark progresses to the next generation of a boat or to a different size of boat much faster than we have ever been able to do before. With our tight timeframes to get these boats to market, the amount of testing on a specific boat was a compromise. Now, Watermark has more time to get the work done earlier in the design cycle, and they have the time to fully test so that they can deliver the best product.

Reverse engineering also lets Watermark design and test more than just boat hulls. The company has expanded its use of 3-D scanning to include seats, decks, internal components and mounting hardware. With this scanned data, the company mates digital components with the hull and reviews designs for tolerance and fit. Watermark now designs more boats and components, and completes more testing and analysis; all without adding staff.

(Adapted from "Fast & Clean," by Todd Grimm, *Desktop Engineering Magazine*, December 2005, pp. 20–22, 34.

the design team. 3-D model data can be shared by the design team that will allow many of the design processes, such as analysis and manufacturing, to *concurrently* work on and have input into the final design.

If the design is complex, subassemblies are created by the design team within the constraints of the 3-D CAD master model. The shared 3-D CAD database is the way the team can make sure that the design of each subassembly will work through a *concurrent* refinement process. By dividing the design into subassemblies, more members of the design team can work *concurrently* on the design, which can reduce modeling time and product development time that is critical in today's global economy and fierce competitive environment.

2.3.6 Members of Design Teams

The number and type of individuals that comprise a design team is largely determined by the size of the design project. Even though an individual is assigned to a team, all members may not be involved at all times. In a concurrent engineering environment the team members work together to meet the common goal. Typical members of a design team might include:

1. Product design engineer—responsible for the overall product design.
2. Product manager—the person who has the ultimate responsibility for a design and its team.
3. Mechanical engineer—responsible for mechanical and electromechanical product development.
4. Electrical engineer—responsible for electronic components of the design.
5. Manufacturing engineer—responsible for the manufacturing processes used to create the product.
6. Software engineer—responsible for any computer software code needed for a product.
7. Detailer/drafter—assists the engineers with the 3-D modeling and documentation of the product.
8. Materials engineer—responsible for the selection of the material best suited for a product.
9. Quality control engineer—responsible for meeting the quality guidelines for the product and its manufacture.
10. Industrial designer—responsible for the product's appearance, form, and human factors analysis.
11. Vendor representatives—responsible for any outsourcing required by the company making the design.

2.4 Summary

This chapter introduces you to modern design practices. Graphics have been and will continue to be an important part of engineering design. Graphics, in all forms, are the communications medium of choice in the design process. The use of computers to model the design and create a graphics database that can be shared by everyone on the team will even further enhance the role of graphics in the future. The engineer and technologist must know how to use graphics to communicate, visualize, and present technical information efficiently and effectively.

Online Learning Center (OLC) Features

There are a number of Online Learning Center features listed below that you can use to supplement your text reading to improve your understanding and retention of the material presented in this chapter at www.mhhe.com/bertoline.

- Learning Objectives
- Chapter Outline
- Questions for Review
- Multiple Choice Quiz
- True or False Questions
- Flashcards
- Website Links
- Animations
- Related Readings
- Stapler Design Problem

Questions for Review

1. Describe the design process.
2. Describe the engineering design process.
3. Describe functional design.
4. Describe aesthetic design.
5. Define product design.
6. Define system design.
7. Describe collaborative engineering.
8. Describe EDM/PDM.
9. Describe and sketch the concurrent engineering model.
10. Describe and sketch the digital enterprise.
11. Describe e-Business.
12. Describe PLM and its various elements and their relationship to each other.
13. Describe Leonardo da Vinci's influence on the engineering design process.

Further Reading

Burghardt, D. M. *Introduction to Engineering Design & Problem Solving.* New York: McGraw-Hill, 1998.

Eide, A. R. *Introduction to Engineering Problem Solving and Design.* 2nd Ed. New York: McGraw-Hill, 2001.

Grieves, M. *Product Lifecycle Management: Driving the Next Generation of Lean Thinking.* New York: McGraw-Hill, 2005.

Lumsdaine, E., Lumsdaine, M., and Shelnutt, J. W. *Creative Problem Solving and Engineering Design.* New York: McGraw-Hill, 2001.

Rayport, J. F. and Jaworski, B. J. *Introduction to E-commerce.* New York: McGraw-Hill, 2001.

Stark, J. *Product Lifecycle Management.* New York: Springer-Verlag, LLC, 2004.

Ullman, D. G. *The Mechanical Design Process.* New York: McGraw-Hill, 1996.

Ulrich, K. and Eppinger, S. *Product Design and Development.* 2nd Ed. New York: McGraw-Hill, 1999.

Chapter Three

Chapter Three

Design in Industry

A picture is worth a thousand words but only if you can decipher it.

—Stephen M. Kosslyn

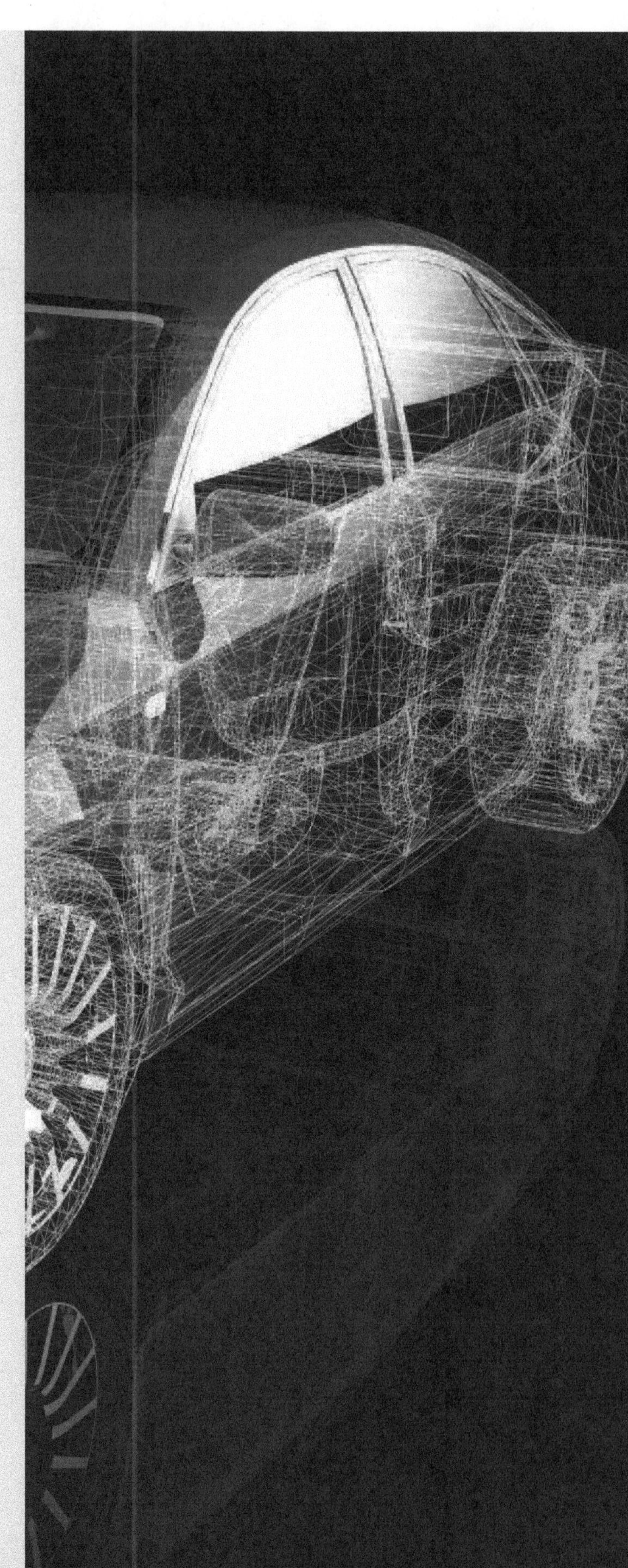

Objectives and Overview

Technical graphics is an integral part of the engineering design process through which engineers and drafters/designers generate new ideas and solve problems. Traditionally, engineering design consisted of closely related steps documented as paper graphics and text that flowed in a linear/sequential manner through an organization. In the face of increased global competition, and with the advent of digital design tools, many industries in the United States have adopted a team-oriented concurrent approach using 3-D CAD model information as a primary means for communication.

This chapter describes a modern approach to the engineering design process as generally found in industry, so that you will have a better understanding of and appreciation for the role of engineering graphics in the design process. Besides describing the design process, advanced technologies such as product data management (PDM) and web collaboration are described. Knowledge of how various information management tools and techniques support the evolving design is important to understanding the modern design process.

After completing this chapter, you will be able to:

1. Describe the engineering design process and the role graphics plays.

2. Describe the concurrent engineering design process.
3. Describe design for manufacturability (DFM).
4. Explain the role 3-D modeling plays in the engineering design process.
5. List and describe the modeling techniques used in design.
6. Describe the important types of graphics used to support the engineering design process.
7. Describe the rapid prototyping process.
8. Describe the ideation process.
9. Describe the implementation process.
10. Describe the role of PDM in drawing control.
11. Describe the role of PDM in the communication of product design information.
12. List and describe the analysis techniques used in design.

3.1 The Engineering Design Process

Engineering design is one of the processes normally associated with the entire business or enterprise, from receipt of the order or product idea, to maintenance of the product, and all stages in between (Figure 3.1). The design process requires input from such areas as customer needs, materials, capital, energy, time requirements, and human knowledge and skills.

Two important societal concerns that an engineer must take into account are legal and environmental issues. Every business must operate within the law that governs their business. When designing, it is important that the engineer understand that legal issues may affect the designed product. Safety laws related to automobiles are an example of how government legislation can affect a design. Government regulations related to the environment may also have a bearing on the final outcome of the design. For example, the emission requirements of an automobile engine have a great effect on the final design.

An example of human knowledge applied to the design process is an engineer's knowledge of graphics, mathematics, and the sciences. Such knowledge is used by the engineer to analyze and solve problems.

An engineering design involves both a process and a product. A *process* is a series of continuous actions ending in a particular result. A *product* is anything created as a result of some process. As the design of a product or process is developed, the design team addresses market specifications, applies engineering principles, follows budgetary constraints, and takes into account legal and

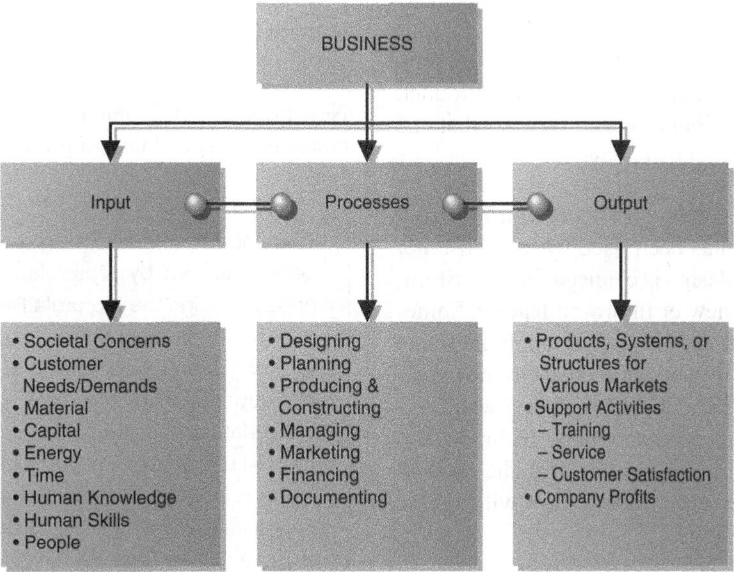

Figure 3.1

The business process

A manufacturing business or enterprise includes all the inputs, processes, and outputs necessary to produce a product or construct a structure. Designing is one of the major processes in such a business.

social issues. For example, when a building is designed, the buyer is consulted regarding intended use and aesthetic elements; engineering principles are used to analyze the structure for loads; determine the structure's cost, based on the materials to be used, the size of the structure, and aesthetic considerations; and create a design that adheres to the local laws.

Graphics is an extremely important part of the engineering design process, which uses graphics as a tool to visualize possible solutions and to document the design for communications purposes. Graphics or geometric modeling using CAD is used to visualize, analyze, document, and create a product or process. In fact, geometric modeling itself could be considered both a process and a product. As a process, geometric modeling is used to create final design solutions, as well as inputs to the production process, in the form of computer databases. As a product, geometric modeling is one output of the engineering design process.

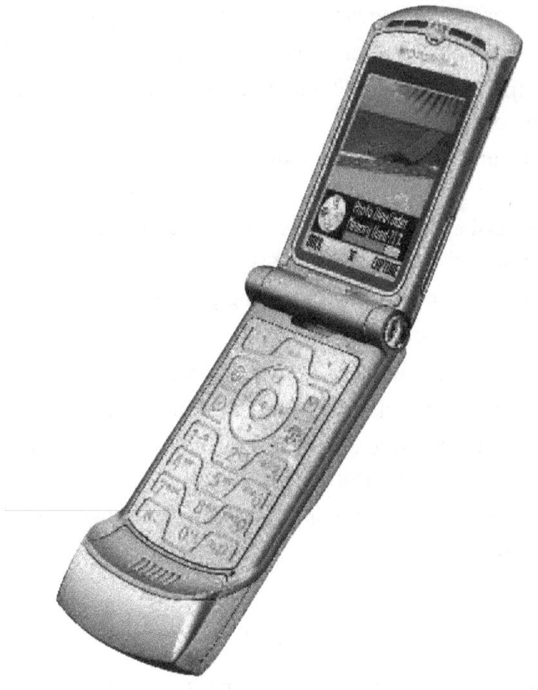

Figure 3.2

Concurrent engineering design case study

The RAZR cellular phone was designed and produced using concurrent engineering and total quality management (TQM) principles.

(© Motorola, Inc.)

3.2 Types of Design Projects

Not all designs are totally new designs of products. In fact most designs have at least some common features with a previous design. For example, the Motorola RAZR phone is a new design, but existing similar designs were used as inspiration for this design. Design projects are grouped as:

Modification of an Existing Design This design will only make very simple design changes to an existing product. For example, the RAZR could be modified so that the clamshell cover shape is slightly changed.

Improvement of an Existing Design This design normally occurs after the product has been used by the consumer for a period of time. The design is changed due to customers who may want some new or improved feature. Sometimes, a vendor will no longer be able to supply the same materials for parts used in the original design, or manufacturing has determined that a design change would result in reduced cost and time for assembly. Technological changes may allow for the improvement of the product or the manufacturing process, which in turn will force a change in the original design.

Development of a New Product The RAZR is an example of the development of a new product (Figure 3.2). This design is based on targeting a specific kind of consumer who could not be reached until the technological development of communication technologies made it possible. New product development is the most complex and time-consuming type of design project.

This chapter will use as an example the design process practiced by Motorola, Inc., Schaumburg, Illinois, to design the Motorola RAZR cell phone (Figure 3.2). Motorola uses a team approach and a concurrent engineering process to develop new products. A group assigned to a project includes mechanical, industrial, and electrical engineers; technicians; industrial designers; and purchasing, planning, marketing, and other support personnel. Each team member brings his or her unique skills, experience, knowledge, and perspectives to the design problem, and everyone participates in the solution process to get the new product to market as quickly as possible. For an in-depth description of the design of the RAZR, see the Case Study in this chapter.

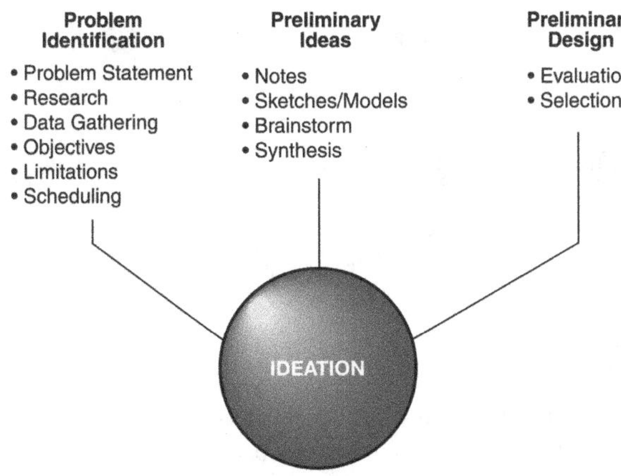

Figure 3.3

Ideation process

The ideation process includes problem identification, preliminary ideas development, and preliminary design. Ideation is the start of the design process.

3.3 Ideation

Ideation is a structured approach to thinking for the purpose of solving a problem. Ideation is that phase of the design process in which the basic design is conceived (conceptual phase). Feasibility studies are often performed to define the problem, identify important factors that limit the scope of the design, evaluate anticipated difficulties, and consider the consequences of the design. The ideation process consists of three important steps: problem identification, preliminary ideas, and preliminary design. Each of these areas can be further subdivided, as shown in Figure 3.3.

3.3.1 Problem Identification

Problem identification is an ideation step in which the parameters of the design project are set before an attempt is made to find a solution to the design. Problem identification includes the following elements:

Problem statement, which summarizes the problem to be solved.

Research, which gathers relevant information useful to the design team.

Data gathering, sometimes called feasibility study, which determines market needs, benchmarking with the competition, and rough physical measurements, such as weight and size.

Objectives, which list the things to be accomplished by the team.

Limitations, which list the factors in the design specifications.

Scheduling, which organizes activities into a sequence.

Engineering design problems must be clearly defined before the design process can begin. The problem definition requires input from customers, marketing, management, and engineering. Data to determine consumer needs are gathered through surveys, such as personal or telephone interviews, mail questionnaires, and focus groups. As an example, Motorola gathered data on the actual and projected numbers of wireless communicator users. Marketing determined the average income, demographics, typical jobs, and other information on cellular phone users, as well as the opinions of the customers regarding the proposed design.

The competition is surveyed to "benchmark" a product line. A benchmark in this context is the study of a product similar to the one being considered for design.

> In our example, wireless communicators marketed by the competition were analyzed for size, weight, material, features, power, price, and many other features. The research and development (R&D) department was also consulted to determine if there were any new developments that would help in the design of a new ultralight cellular phone. For instance, the R&D department may have developed a miniaturized version of the transmission component that could be used in the new design.

Journal and trade magazines are reviewed for reports on developments in related technologies. A patent search may be done, and consultants specializing in areas where the design team is weak may be hired. This process of researching similar products and technologies and applying the results to the new design is called synthesis.

After all the data are gathered, the information is shared with the team before preliminary ideas are developed (Figure 3.4). Presentation graphics are a tool used to display the data in the form of charts and graphs and are thus an important element in the information-sharing process.

After the problem statement is created and the research and data gathering are completed, objectives are developed by the team. Objectives specifically state what is to be accomplished during the design process, and may

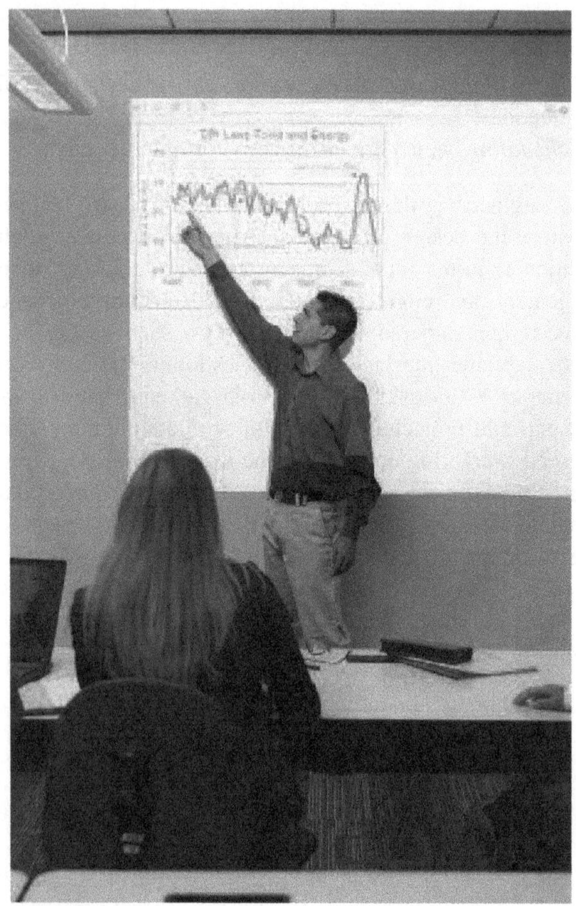

Figure 3.4

Sharing the data gathered

Many times, preliminary data is shared with the team in the form of charts and graphs. The team then uses the data to finalize the goals of the project.

(© Stephen Coburn/BigstockPhoto.)

include factors related to manufacturing, materials, marketing, and other areas. Included in this process are limitations or constraints on the project, such as time, material, size, weight, environmental factors, and cost.

Scheduling of the design activities is one of the last stages in problem identification. To plan and schedule simple projects, a Gantt chart may be used. In a Gantt chart, horizontal bars are used to represent resources or activities, and time is represented by the length of the bars. A method of scheduling large projects is the project evaluation and review technique (PERT), with which activities are scheduled in such a way as to optimize progress toward completion. The critical path method (CPM), used with PERT, defines those activities that must be completed in sequential order while other activities are taking place.

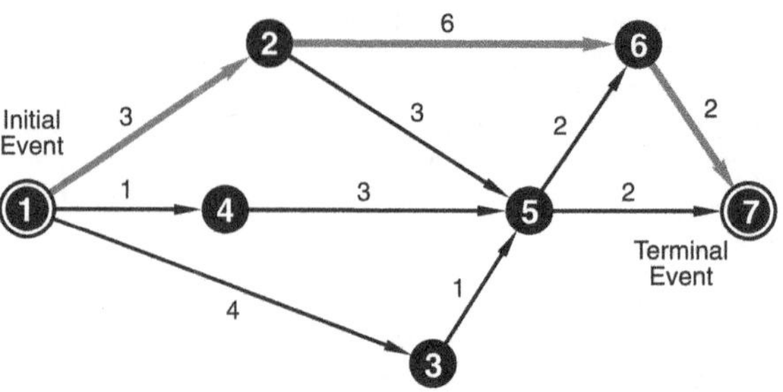

Figure 3.5

CPM chart created for a simple project

The thick line represents the critical path, for those activities that must be completed in sequential order while progressing through the project.

Figure 3.5 is an example of a simple CPM chart. The circles represent events that are the start or completion of a mental or physical task. The lines between the circles represent the actual performance of a task and indicate an increment of time. The numbers along the lines show the amount of time allotted to complete each task. The critical path is the thicker line, which may also be in a different color.

The RAZR phone was developed to distance Motorola's wireless phone from the competition. A team was assembled and project leaders assigned. The team included representatives from manufacturing, mechanical and electrical engineering, industrial design, service, assembly, marketing, finance, and the consumer sector. The team was given the assignment of creating a technological leap forward by drastically reducing the weight and size of the cellular phone. The team was to accomplish this task using concurrent engineering strategies. The problem statement was: Design and produce the world's best wireless communicator that featured a cellphone, two-way radio, text pager, and web browser in a single wearable unit.

A few of the objectives and limitations for RAZR were as follows:

- Integrate total quality management (TQM) into the process.
- Integrate design for manufacturability (DFM) into the process.

- Use outside vendors for the circuit boards and other components not normally produced by Motorola.
- Keep the retail cost of the phone below that of the competition.
- Make the weight with the battery pack at or below 5 ounces.
- Make the product palm-sized, and aesthetically pleasing.
- Make it small enough to fit in a shirt pocket when closed.
- Include an alphanumeric display capable of displaying modified web pages.
- Include battery options for a longer talk time.
- Include call placement features, such as automatic redial, speed dialing, and a memory program.
- Make it sturdy enough to withstand durability testing, including temperature, humidity, shock, dust, vibration, and the 4-foot drop test.
- Produce a product that meets the quality expectations of the consumer.
- Design for compliance with all Federal Communications Commission (FCC) rules and regulations.

Features of the RAZR V3 phone:

- User-customizable Soft key functions, Main Menu and Shortcuts
- Games: 3-D Java-embedded and space for downloads
- Downloadable themes (Ringtones, wallpaper and screen-savers)
- MOTOMIXER™ (Remixable MIDI ringer software)
- Polyphonic ringtones
- Picture phone book
- MP3 ringtones
- Polyphonic speaker: 22 Khz polyphonic speaker, 22 chord support
- Video download
- Video clip playback with sound
- Precision cut metal keypad
- Integrated digital VGA camera with 4× digital zoom and light
- Talk time: Up to 200 to 430 minutes
- Standby time: Up to 180 to 290 hours
- Bands: Quad-band (GSM 850/900/1800/1900)
- Standard battery: 680 mAh Li-ion
- Internal memory: 5 MB
- Weight: 3.35 oz
- External display: 96 × 80 pixel, 4k CSN color, 4 lines of text/line of icons
- Volume: 65 cc
- Dimensions (H × W × D): 3.86 × 2.08 × 0.54 inches
- Finish: Anodized aluminum
- Internal display: 176 × 220 pixel, up to 260 K TFT color, with graphic accelerator, 9 lines of text
- Color: Silver
- Form factor: Clamshell

3.3.2 Preliminary Ideas Statement

After the problem identification is complete, the team begins to develop preliminary ideas for solving the problem. This stage of the process is sometimes referred to as brainstorming. **Brainstorming** is the process of identifying as many solutions to a problem as possible. A brainstorming session normally has a leader or moderator and a recorder. Before a session starts, results of the ideation phase, such as marketing surveys and product research, are shared with the group. This synthesizing process is used as a catalyst to generate as many ideas as possible by giving the group a starting point for the design solution. Ideas are suggested freely, without criticism or discussion of feasibility. The length of the session varies but ends when the free flow of ideas begins to slow down.

Brainstorming results in a list of ideas, along with some preliminary sketches or computer models (Figure 3.6). The computer models would not be dimensionally accurate, but would approximate the preliminary idea. All ideas are sketched or modeled, listed, and shared with the whole team. Eventually, two to six ideas are selected for further analysis. The number of ideas chosen depends on the complexity of the design and the amount of time and resources available.

At Motorola the design team met to begin the brainstorming process. Data gathered in the problem identification stage was brought to the meetings. An agenda was set by each group leader to keep the session on track.

Figure 3.6

Brainstorming

Brainstorming by the team will result in a list of possible solutions, as well as rough sketches or computer models. During brainstorming, members of the design team will generate as many ideas as possible, without criticism or discussion of feasibility.

(© Joseph Pobereskin/Getty Images.)

The various ideas were discussed, using the objectives, limitations, and problem statement as the criteria. The open exchange of ideas generated many possible solutions, which were sketched with detailed notes. The major problems in developing a multifunction phone were discussed, and some team members were assigned the task of determining the feasibility of miniaturizing electronic circuitry to that level.

Every group in the design team had a major role in the development of ideas. Mechanical and electrical engineers concentrated on the design of the case, electronic circuitry, and features, using input from the consumer, as well as data gathered from other sources. Industrial designers interacted with the engineers to create rough sketches and computer models of some of the initial ideas. Industrial engineers and technicians examined the feasibility of assembling some of the proposed designs. Marketing kept the group focused on the wants and needs of the consumer. Finance kept the group focused on cost factors.

The team met several times in smaller groups to discuss the feasibility of some design ideas before four or five were chosen to move on to the refinement stage. Integrated throughout the process was an emphasis on quality, which directed the design team always to keep quality concepts and practices part of its discussions.

3.3.3 Preliminary Design

After brainstorming, the ideas are evaluated, using as the criteria the problem statements, project goals, and limitations. Industrial designers may create preliminary models out of foam or other material, or may use the computer models created in the preliminary ideas phase to control machines that generate physical models.

The choice for the final design may be easy if only one design meets the criteria. However, there is frequently more than one viable design solution. When this happens, an evaluation table may be used to "score" each design idea relative to the goals of the project.

Ideation Graphics and Visualization In the ideation phase, rough sketches and conceptual computer models called ideation drawings or models are produced (Figure 3.7). Ideation drawings communicate new ideas through the use of rough sketches and computer models. These drawings are a synthesis of the information gathered in the preliminary stages of the design process and may combine what was visualized in the mind with what has been put on paper or in the computer. Copying drawings or modifying computer models encourages new ideas to evolve from existing concepts.

At Motorola the wireless communicator ideas were checked for

- Adherence to the specifications of size, weight, appearance, durability, and so forth.
- Manufacturability.
- Quality.
- Cost.
- Limits of the available technology, such as microminiaturization of circuits and components.
- Environmental and safety concerns.
- Comparison against the competition and known solutions to the problem.

The team may have decided that some research was needed because of concerns generated by the preliminary ideas. The evaluation process helped the team determine which designs to continue examining.

Presentation Graphics Presentation graphics are used to present data in more easily understood forms, such as charts or graphs. Preliminary engineering and cost analyses may also be graphed. Presentation graphics is a very

Figure 3.7

Preliminary design sketches of proposed cellular phones, as generated in the brainstorming sessions

These design sketches will be further refined; then one or a combination of two or more will be chosen as the final design.

important part of the design review meeting (Figure 3.8). Ideation requires skills in sketching, visualization, and presentation graphics.

3.3.4 Ideation Resources

Inventive or creative ideas can come from a number of sources. Personal experience is a great source of ideas as is the existing knowledge of an organization. Outside sources for ideas can come from consumer surveys, competition reviews, patent searches, library searches, and searches on the web. Vendors and professional organizations can be helpful when gathering information for new designs. *Thomas Register* is an excellent resource for gathering information about companies and their products. *Thomas Register* and many other vendors maintain web sites, and some vendors have CD ROMs available with their products that can be inserted in CAD drawings and models.

3.3.5 The Designer's Notebook

Designers should get into the habit of taking meticulous notes to ensure that ideas and decisions are kept for future reference. A designer will create many notes and docu-

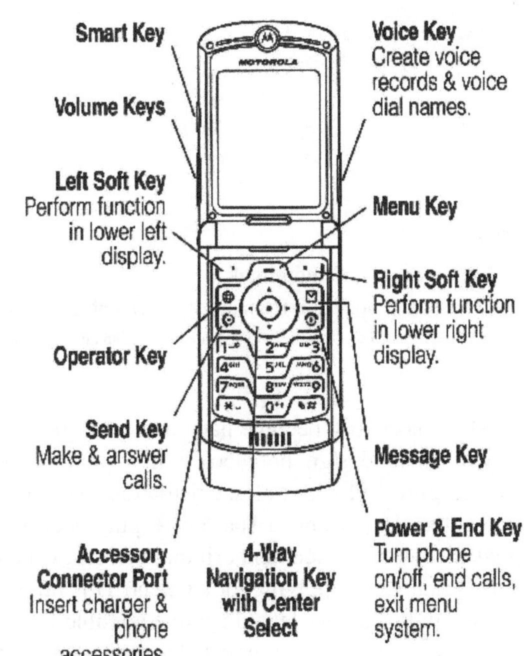

Figure 3.8

Presentation graphic

Sketches, drawings, 3-D models, tables, and graphs are common graphics used to communicate new designs in presentations, such as a design review meeting.

(© Motorola, Inc.)

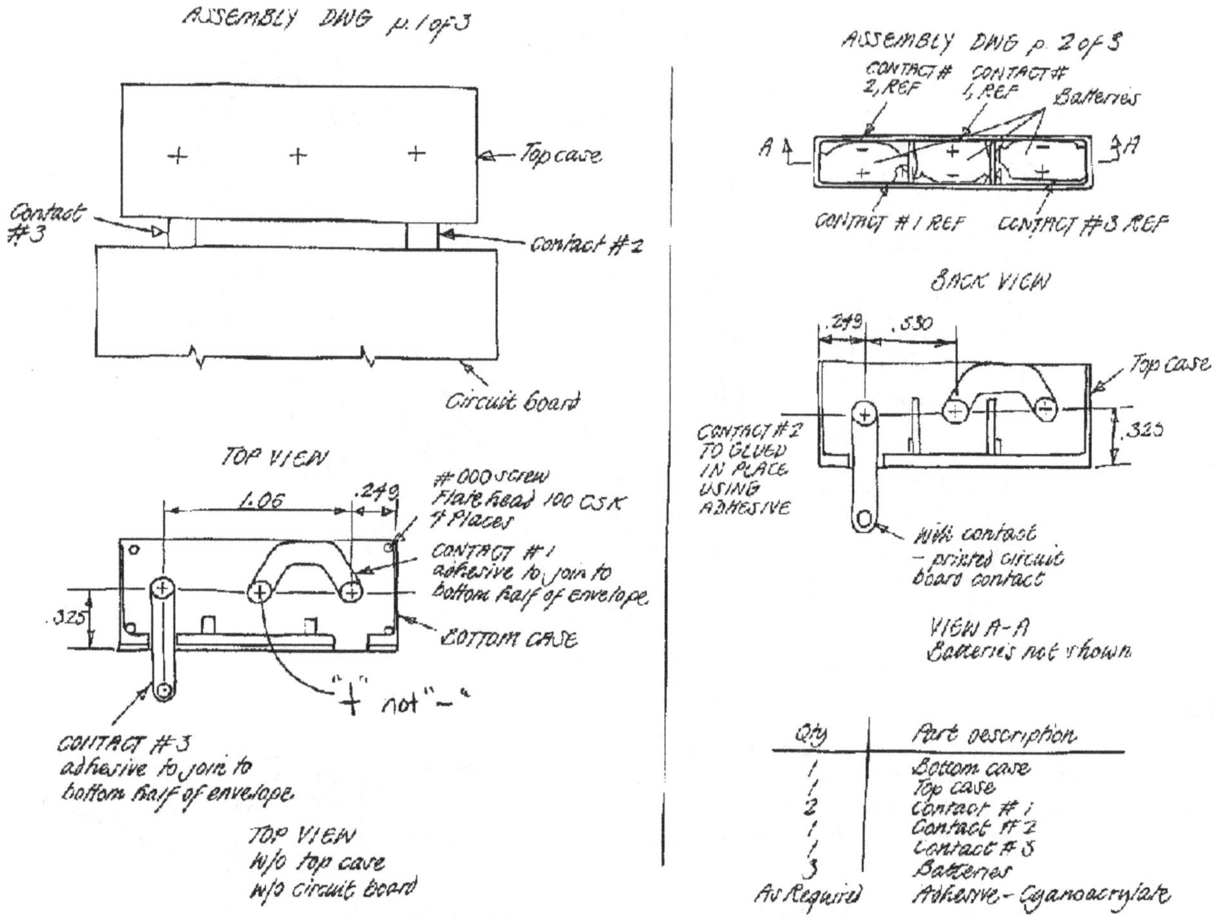

Figure 3.9

Pages from a designer's notebook

These sketches and notes are from an engineer's notebook showing the assembly drawing of a battery case.

(From David G. Ullman, *The Mechanical Design Process,* 2nd edition, The McGraw-Hill Companies, Inc. Reprinted with permission.)

ments which normally become part of the design file. A well-documented design notebook will contain design sketches (Figure 3.9) with notes, calculations, signatures, and dates. One important reason for keeping good notes is to make it easier to document original designs, which is very important when applying for a patent. This information is also important to defend against possible lawsuits arising from the use of the product. The notebook is also a way of creating a history of design for a company (Figure 3.10). This historical record is important so new designers can quickly determine how design has progressed in a company. This historical record also becomes important when modifying existing designs or creating a related product. When this occurs, design decisions and previous design solutions may become a starting point for the modified design. This can save much time and money in the development of the new product.

The notebook is very similar to a diary that records the development of the design solution. It does not have to be neat, but it should be legible and contain all the notes, sketches, and calculations on sequentially numbered pages. A simple bound notebook may be all that is needed for a designer's notebook for a single project.

Today's technology allows collaborative engineering through design across the World Wide Web (WWW), as described in more detail later in this chapter. Keeping a designer's notebook can be accomplished through a computer-based electronic notebook by serving, delivering,

Figure 3.10

Designer's notebook as a historical record

Jack Kilby was the primary design engineer for the first integrated circuit while working at Texas Instruments in 1958. He is pictured holding his design notebook and page from the notebook with his notes describing the basic concept behind the integrated circuit.

(Photo courtesy of Texas Instruments.)

(Graphics courtesy of Texas Instruments.)

and storing the data created by the design team. This allows design documents to be read by a wide variety of people in different departments and even different locations.

3.4 Refinement

Refinement is a repetitive (iterative or cyclical) process used to test the preliminary design, make changes if necessary, and determine if the design meets the goals of the project (Figure 3.11). Refinement is the second major stage in the concurrent engineering design process and consists of three main areas: modeling, design analysis, and design visualization. These areas are further subdivided into activities that ultimately result in the selection of a single design solution.

The refinement stage normally begins with technicians using the rough sketches and computer models to create dimensionally accurate drawings and models (Figure 3.12a). At this point, engineers begin to select materials for component parts, considering such factors as heat, light, noise, vibration, humidity, strength, weight, size,

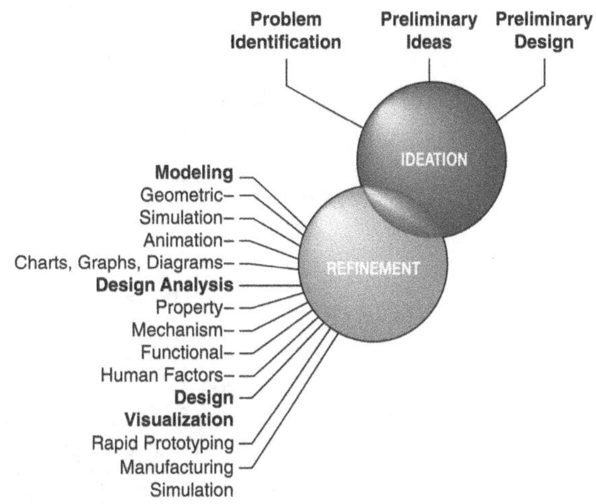

Figure 3.11

Refinement process

The refinement process includes modeling, design analysis, and visualization. These elements are used to determine if the design meets the goals set earlier in the design process. Refinement is an iterative process, which means that changes made to the design may cause elements in the refinement stage to be repeated.

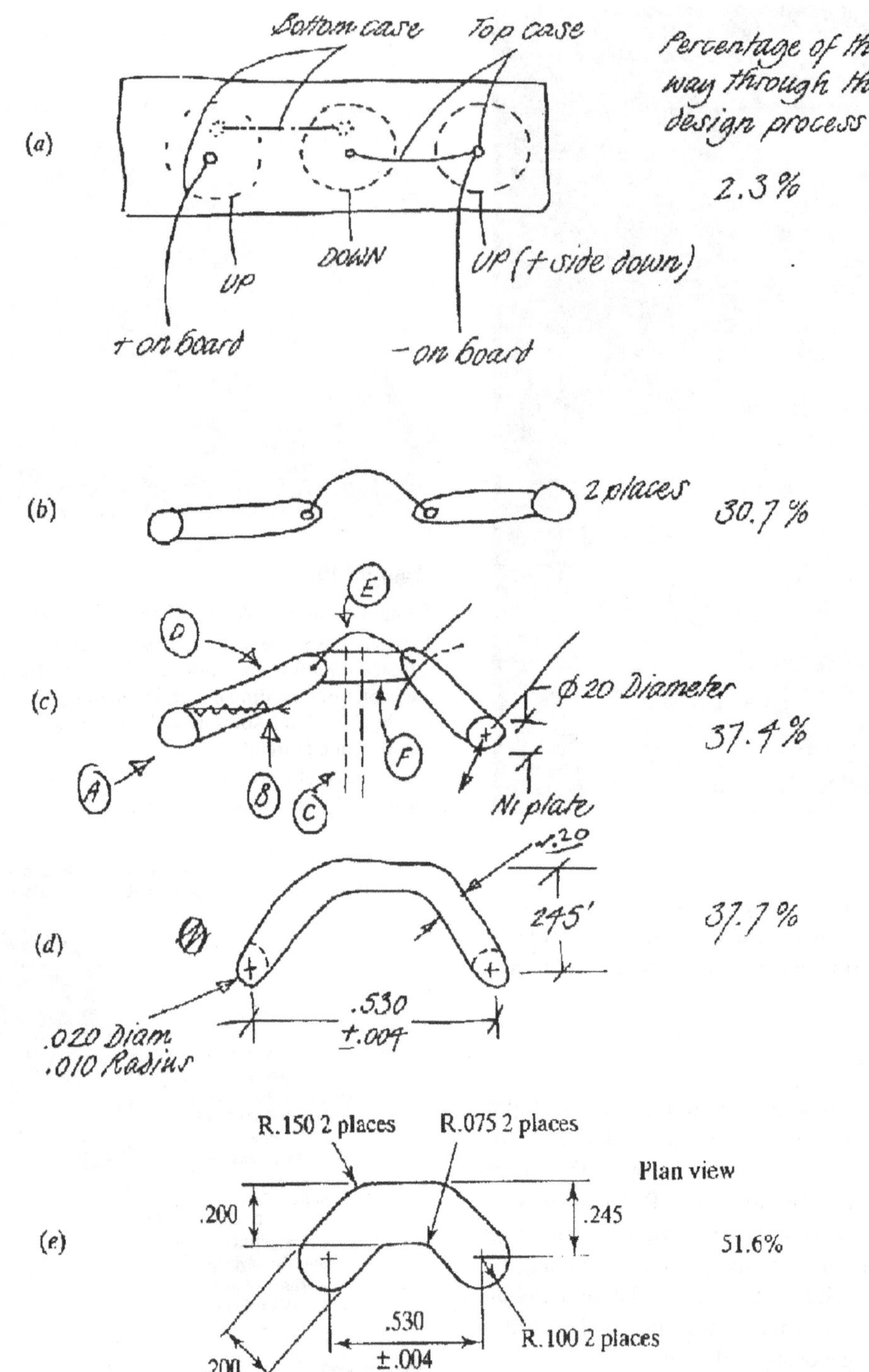

Figure 3.12

Refinement of a battery contact design

Engineering drawings and models that are more dimensionally accurate are produced in the refinement stage.

(From David G. Ullman, *The Mechanical Design Process*, 2d edition, The McGraw-Hill Companies, Inc. Reprinted with permission.)

Figure 3.13

Descriptive model

Cutaway section of a mechanical gearbox.

(Modeled and rendered by Thomas Anagnostou. Courtesy of Robert McNeel and Associates.)

loads, cost, and many others. Engineers work closely with industrial designers so that the materials selected will work well with the proposed form.

The preliminary design is tested physically, using finite element analysis, kinematic tests, animation, and spatial analysis. The design is analyzed relative to the project objectives and problem statement, and manufacturing begins to determine the processes needed to produce the product. The preliminary design is also market tested to a small group. At this stage changes may be recommended in the initial design. The final step in the refinement stage is selection of the final design for the product.

The refinement stage is heavily dependent on graphics to document, visualize, analyze, and communicate the design idea. These drawings and computer models are called refinement drawings or design drawings. Refinement drawings are technical drawings and models used to analyze preliminary design ideas. (See Figure 3.12e.)

3.4.1 Modeling

Modeling is the process of representing abstract ideas, words, and forms, through the orderly use of simplified text and images. Engineers use models for thinking, visualizing, communicating, predicting, controlling, and training. Models are classified as either descriptive or predictive.

A **descriptive model** presents abstract ideas, products, or processes in a recognizable form. An example of a descriptive model is an engineering drawing or 3-D computer model of a mechanical gearbox (Figure 3.13). The drawing or model serves as a means of communication but cannot be used to predict behavior or performance. A *predictive model* is one that can be used to understand and predict the behavior/performance of ideas, products, or processes. An example of a predictive model is a finite element model of a bridge support, which is used to predict mechanical behavior of the bridge under applied loads. (See Section 3.4.3 for a discussion of finite element models.)

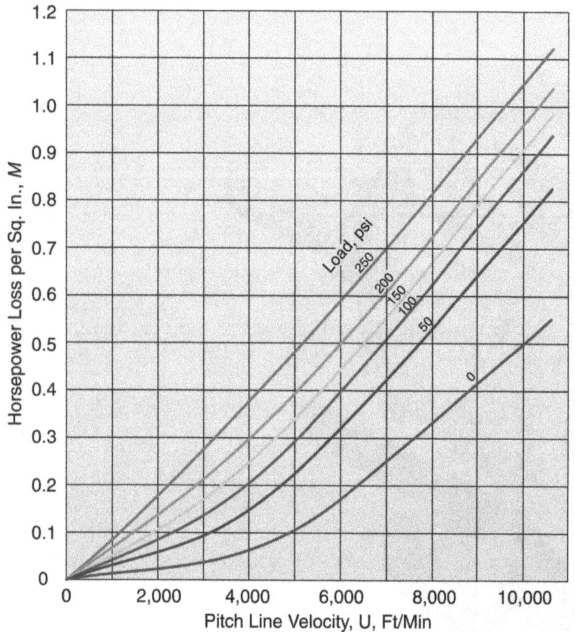

Figure 3.14

Predictive model

A mathematical model is used to predict power loss of a thrust bearing at various speeds.

(From *Machinery's Handbook,* 26e, Jones et al, p. 2222. Copyright © 2000 Industrial Press. Reprinted with permission.)

Figure 3.15

Real model

Real models created from clay are used for spatial, aesthetic, and property analyses.

(Courtesy of the University of Cincinnati.)

During the refinement process, two types of models are useful: mathematical models and scale models.

A **mathematical model** uses mathematical equations to represent system components. This technique is useful for understanding and predicting the performance of large, complex systems. Normally, a large system is broken into its simpler components before being modeled. Figure 3.14 is an example of a mathematical model used to predict the power loss of thrust bearings when velocity is increased. By reading the graph, you can predict how much loss there will be, without having to test the bearing physically at every operating speed. This results in a tremendous savings in time and cost during the refinement stage of the design process.

A *scale model* is a physical model created to represent system components. This is one of the most useful and easily understandable of all the modeling types. The model can be full size or made to scale. Before the advent of 3-D geometric modeling using computers, physical models were made by skilled craftsmen, from clay, wood, foam, or other materials (Figure 3.15). Physical models are extremely useful for conducting spatial, aesthetic, human factors, and property analyses. For example, the cellular phone could be modeled in foam or wood and given to the human factors engineers and the consumers group on the design team to get their feedback on the interaction between the model and the human test subjects. In addition, the circuitry of the cellular phone could be created as a working model using "breadboarding," which is a technique used by electrical engineers and technicians to test new circuits.

For some products, recent advances in computer modeling and rapid prototyping have reduced the need for creating physical models using traditional techniques. **Rapid prototyping** is a broad term used to describe several related processes that create real models directly from a 3-D CAD database (Figure 3.16). This can dramatically reduce the time between modeling and manufacturing.

In some cases, it is not practical to make a prototype because of size or cost. In other cases, the prototype would not respond the way the actual product would. For these situations, as well as others, **virtual reality (VR)** systems offer a viable analysis approach (Figure 3.17). VR systems use the principles of human spatial perception to develop completely immersive environments in which the user can interact with the virtual object through some or all of the senses. In such an environment, the user has the feeling of actually interacting with the virtual model.

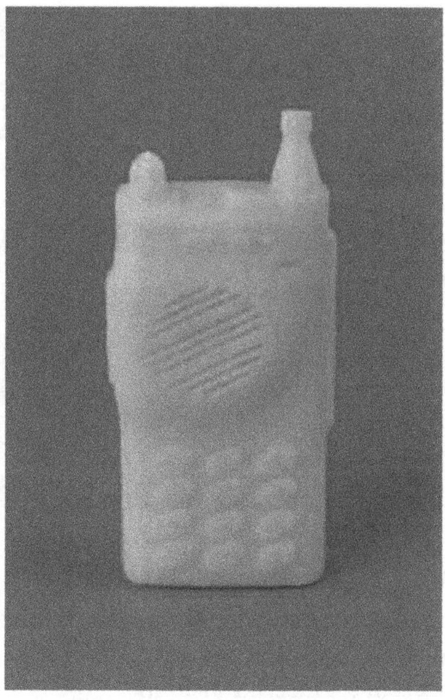

Figure 3.16

Real model of a portable hand-held radio created with a rapid prototyping system

(Courtesy of 3D Systems, Inc.)

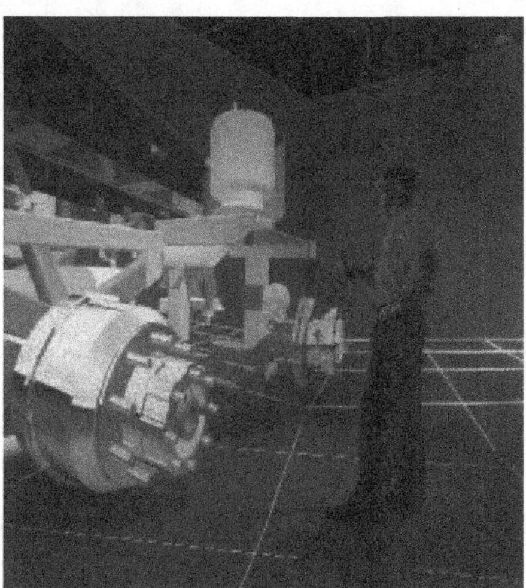

Figure 3.17

Virtual reality technology

This technology allows a more complete use of the senses to explore and evaluate design concepts.

(Courtesy of Fakespace Systems, Inc.)

VR technology requires models that correspond closely to the real object. Also, the system must be able to monitor all actions taken by the user. This includes changing the point of view when the user's head position changes or depicting a virtual hand when the user is reaching out and grasping the virtual object. In addition, the user needs to receive feedback that closely mimics the environment's responses to the user's actions. The visual and auditory fields must be completely controlled by the system, and this is often done with headsets. State-of-the-art technology that would provide kinesthetic feedback is being developed. The virtual model would feel like it has weight when it is being moved around by the user.

Rapid Prototyping The actual process used to create the rapid prototype varies depending on the type of system being used. The actual making of the part can take many hours depending on the size of the part. The basic process consists of creating a 3-D model of the part on a CAD system. The 3-D model is then translated into a file format compatible with a rapid prototyping system, the most popular being an STL file. The rapid prototyping system reads the STL file and breaks the 3-D model into a series of very thin layers.

Rapid prototyping systems are categorized by the process used to create the real model. Stereolithography apparatus (SLA) was one of the first methods developed and uses a process where a focused laser beam hardens a light-sensitive liquid polymer through a series of very thin slices (Figure 3.18). Selective laser sintering (SLS) is a process that uses a focused laser to fuse powdered plastic, metal,

Figure 3.18

Stereolithography system used to create rapid prototypes of parts.

(Courtesy of 3D Systems, Inc.)

or ceramic through a series of very thin slices. Fused deposition modeling (FDM) uses molten plastic deposited in a series of thin layers to create the part. Laminated object manufacturing (LOM) creates real models from sheets of material such as paper or vinyl.

> At Motorola, the RAZR components were modeled on a CAD system early in the design stage. Mechanical engineers and technicians created a 3-D solid model of the phone case from the design sketches, and the industrial designers edited that computer model. Electrical engineers and technicians computer modeled the circuitry and other components. Industrial engineers used the computer models to begin designing the assembly line and to provide feedback to the design team on the phone's manufacturability (DFM). The geometric database was shared by all members of the team in analyzing the final design.

Figure 3.19

Computer model simulating an aircraft in a wind tunnel

The computer model supplements or replaces the need for physical models in engineering analysis.

(Courtesy of Gary Bertoline.)

3.4.2 Computer Simulation and Animation

Computer simulation is the precise modeling of complex situations that involve a time element. The 3-D computer model can be used instead of a physical model for property analyses. Material properties can be assigned to a computer model so that it behaves and looks like the real product. For example, instead of a scale model of a new aircraft being made and tested in a wind tunnel, a computer model can be used to simulate the aircraft in the wind tunnel test (Figure 3.19).

Computer animation is the imprecise modeling of complex situations that involve a time element. The major difference between simulation and animation is the degree of precision. An animation only approximately replicates a real situation; a simulation accurately replicates a real situation. For example, to determine the aerodynamic characteristics of an airplane using computer simulation, the aircraft and the fluid properties of air must be precisely represented, or inaccurate information will be obtained. On the other hand, if all that is needed is a visual representation of the aircraft in flight, then the computer model need not be precise and an animation of the vehicle is sufficient.

> At Motorola, the assembly line used to produce the cellular phone could be either simulated or animated using computer models. The simulation would dynamically show the phone being assembled and would assist the industrial engineers and technicians in determining where bottlenecks or trouble spots might occur during assembly. The information thus obtained would be used to further refine the design to make it more easily manufacturable, following DFM principles.

3.4.3 Design Analysis

Design analysis is the evaluation of a proposed design, based on criteria established in the ideation phase. It is the second major area within the refinement process, and the entire design team is involved. Typical analyses performed on designs include the following:

Property analysis, which evaluates a design based on its physical properties, such as strength, size, volume, center of gravity, weight, and center of rotation, as well as on its thermal, fluid, and mechanical properties.

Mechanism analysis, which determines the motions and loads associated with mechanical systems made of rigid bodies connected by joints.

Functional analysis, which determines if the design does what it is intended to do; in other words, if the design performs the tasks and meets the requirements specified in the ideation phase.

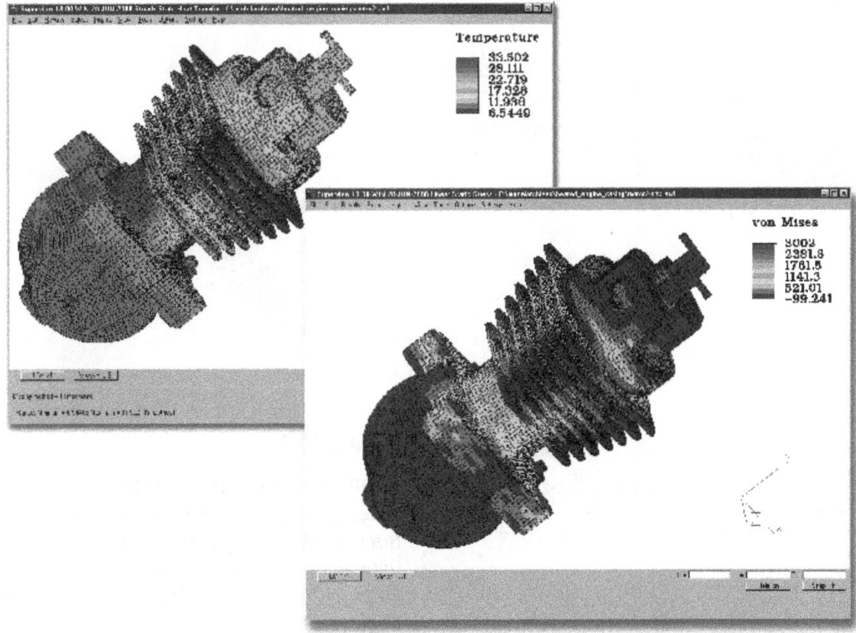

Figure 3.20

Thermal analysis

The use of color assists the user in visually determining the areas of high temperature. Blue is the coolest and red is the hottest area on this part.

(Photo courtesy of ALGOR, Inc.)

Human factors analysis, which evaluates a design to determine if the product serves the physical, emotional, quality, mental, and safety needs of the consumer.

Aesthetic analysis, which evaluates a design based on its aesthetic qualities.

Market analysis, which determines if the design meets the needs of the consumer, based on the results of surveys or focus groups.

Financial analysis, which determines if the price of the proposed design will be in the projected price range set during the ideation phase.

Property Analysis *Property analysis* is normally associated with the engineering profession and includes finite element modeling. Property analysis determines if the product is safe and can stand up to the rigors of everyday use. Models are tested under extraordinary conditions, and the information gained can determine if changes must be made to the design. For example, a component might fail under extreme operating conditions. The design team would then recommend changes in the component itself, or in related parts of the product, to correct the deficiency, and the model would then be reanalyzed. This iterative process is a major part of the design analysis phase.

Finite element modeling (FEM) is an analytical tool used in solid mechanics to determine the static and dynamic responses of components under various conditions, such as different temperatures (Figure 3.20). The fluid mechanics of designs can also be determined using FEM. The interaction of a part with a fluid flow, such as water or air, is simulated through the use of color bands. For example, Figure 3.21 on the next page shows motion analysis of an assembly. The range of motion is shown using a different color.

The FEM process uses the 3-D computer model as input. Through a process called discretization or meshing (Figure 3.22 on the next page), the continuous 3-D solid model is changed into a model comprised of multiple polygonal shapes, such as rectangles and triangles, which are called "elements." Each corner of each element is called a "node." After discretization, the boundary condition is defined. This condition describes how an

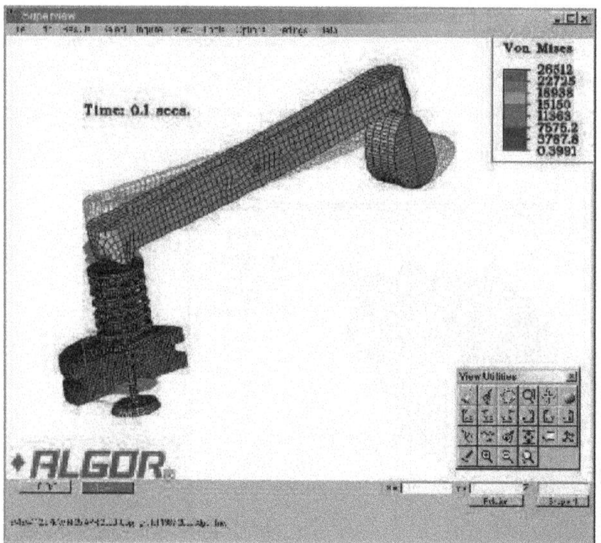

Figure 3.21

Motion analysis

A motion analysis of an assembly is determined using FEM.

(Photo courtesy of ALGOR, Inc.)

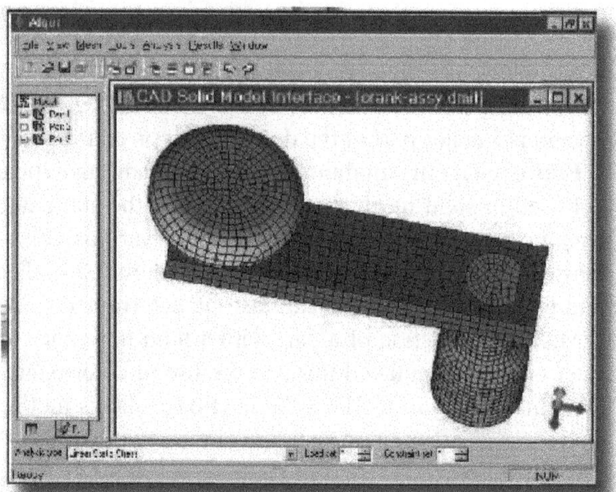

Figure 3.22

Discretization

Before a finite element analysis can be performed, the solid CAD model must be broken into smaller, discrete parts, using a process called discretization. Lines are added to the model after discretization to represent the boundaries of each discrete part of the model.

(Photo courtesy of ALGOR, Inc.)

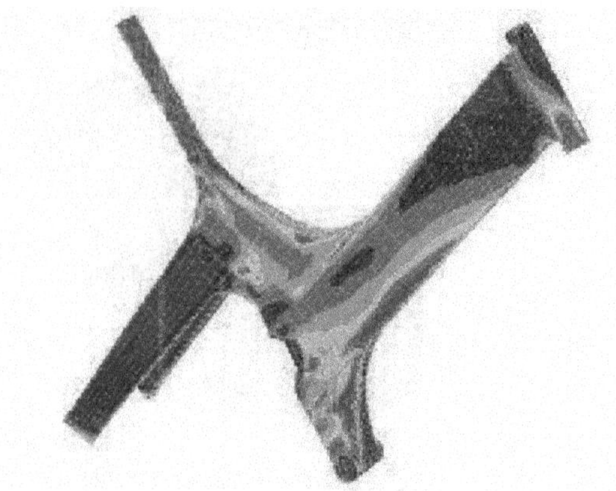

Figure 3.23

Boundary conditions applied

After the finite element model is created, the boundary conditions, such as temperature or load, are defined. The model is then analyzed by the computer. The results are shown using color, or by deforming the model if a load is applied.

(Photo courtesy of ALGOR, Inc.)

object is tied down. For example, an object bolted down to a surface is called fully constrained; in contrast, an object allowed to spin on a shaft is partially constrained. Once the boundary condition is defined, properties, such as material, temperature, and forces, are assigned to the model.

The model is then evaluated under varying conditions. For example, stress forces are applied fully to a constrained model and the results are shown on screen in multiple colors (Figure 3.23). The colors represent various levels of stress. The model might also deform to illustrate the effect of the forces being applied. The model could even be animated to show the deformation taking place and to show the incremental increases in the levels of stress. This process allows the designer to determine if the model will perform safely under extreme operating conditions.

The results of the property analysis are used to recommend changes in the design. This analysis is a critical step in the refinement process.

Mechanism Analysis **Mechanism analysis** is concerned with the calculation of motions and loads in mechanical systems comprised of rigid bodies connected by joints. A clamping device is an example of such a system. Mechanism analysis includes assembly, kinematic, and dynamic analyses.

Assembly analysis is used to define the individual rigid bodies of the mechanism and to assemble them correctly,

Figure 3.24

Assembly analysis

Assembly analysis is performed on the pump to determine proper clearances between mating parts.

(Courtesy of UGS PLM Software, Division of Siemens Automation and Drives.)

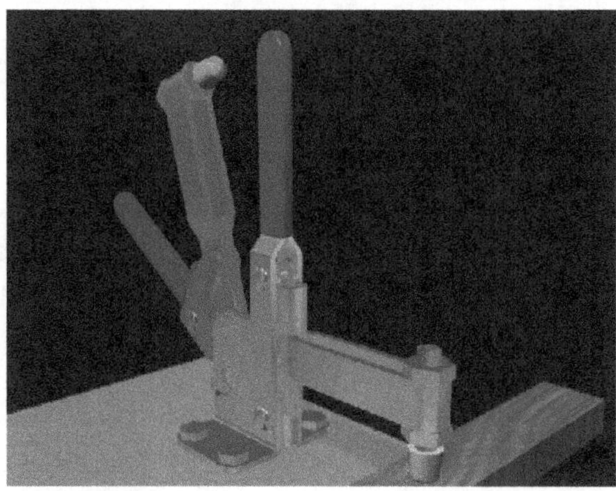

Figure 3.25

Kinematic analysis

The kinematic analysis of a mechanism is used to evaluate the range of motion during operation.

(Courtesy of Gary Bertoline.)

considering both geometry and velocities (Figure 3.24). When the computer model is used to make the assembly and assign the velocities, the computer uses the engineers' input to determine complex geometric and trigonometric relationships.

Kinematic analysis determines the motion of assemblies without regard to the loads. For example, kinematic analysis is used to find the position of any point on the mechanism at any time during movement of the assembly, to determine clearances and range of motion. Computer modeling can be used to trace motion paths in 3-D models (Figure 3.25).

Dynamic analysis determines the loads that drive or create the motion of a mechanism. This type of analysis can be in the form of a computer simulation, as described in the preceding section (Figure 3.26).

Figure 3.26

Dynamic analysis

This dynamic analysis of a clamp evaluates the forces involved with the movement of the mechanism.

(Courtesy of Gary Bertoline.)

Functional Analysis **Functional analysis** is a judgment process in which factors such as cost, appearance, profitability, marketability, and safety are used to determine the worth of a design. Some factors are based on empirical evidence, such as testing to see if the product performs or functions as it was intended. For example, the design of a new computer printer could be tested to determine consistent print quality, frequency of failure, or cost relative to the intended market. The new printer would not be functional if it failed too often or produced poor print quality. The entire project might have to be modified by returning to the ideation phase.

Human Factors Analysis **Human factors analysis** determines how a design interacts with the dimensions, range of motion, senses, and mental capabilities of the population that will use the product. For example, the human dimensions of the hand and the distance from the ear to the mouth are important attributes which must be taken into account in the design of a cellular phone and its dialing

Dream **High Tech** Job

Sloan Career Cornerstone Center

JEFFREY P. MARTIN, P.E.
Product Design Engineer
Ford Motor Company
Dearborn, MI

Profiles of Mechanical Engineers
Education:

MS, Mechanical Engineering, Washington University

BS, Mechanical Engineering, University of Illinois

BA, Physics, Augustana College

Job Description:

Product Design Engineering, developing computer-based design tools used in various Ford vehicle development programs; works in a team of CAD specialists and engineers.

Interview:

Q: OK. Do you want to tell me your name, who you are?

Martin: My name is Jeff Martin. I work for Ford Motor Company. I'm a product-design engineer and I've been here three and a half years.

Q: Could you tell me a little bit about what it's like to be a design engineer at Ford Motor and what does your day consist of?

Martin: Well, I guess you're part of a team and usually your group is like ten, fifteen people. And you work on various projects. You might be part of a vehicle program, which is what I did for the first two years here. I actually worked on a car that's going to go into production around 2000. And right now, I'm working in a group, a core group, where we work with tools, helping the vehicle programs to do their design work.

Q: Do you all work on a whole car, or are you working on a specific part, and then each of you works on a little part of that?

Martin: If you're on a vehicle program, you're generally working on a small part of the car. You have to work with other people to make the whole car. In the area that I'm in, what we're working on are design tools to allow general-vehicle design to be done. We are working on the program to generate what's called a tire envelope. We follow the motion of the tire as it goes into a turn, as it bounces up and down, and as it goes down the road. We're simulating that to be used in design.

Q: When you say simulate, are you doing all this on the computer or do you work with prototypes?

Martin: In the past, it's been done experimentally and what we're trying to do is develop the tools so that we can do it all on the computer. And so it will be a lot quicker when we can do that. We actually have programs in place on this project that can do this right now. What we're trying to do with this project I'm on right now is be able to simulate the movement of the wheel totally on the computer without having to do testing to see whether or not the wheel will actually interfere with the body structure.

keypad. Human dimensions can be found in *The Measure of Man,* by Henry Dreyfuss. There is also computer software that can be used to define a human model, using such criteria as age, gender, build, race, and other factors. The human model thus created is then merged with the computer model of the product, and static and dynamic simulations are conducted.

The design of a product must also match human capabilities, as well as human dimensions. For example, can the controls of the cellular phone keypad be seen in a dimly lit room? Are they confusing to the novice user?

Quite often, the results of this human factors analysis are used to guide the development of graphics and text in the technical and users manuals.

Aesthetic Analysis **Aesthetic analysis** is a process that evaluates a design based on aesthetic qualities. The look and feel of the product are analyzed by industrial designers, marketing personnel, environmental and human factors engineers, and the customer. This is the design process stage that is difficult to measure and quantify. However, it is important because this is where products

Q: Give me your first job after school and kind of the progression. Like a synopsis of your career path thus far.

Martin: OK. Right after I graduated from college, I went directly to McDonnell Douglas and I worked on the drafting board there for three years doing sheet-metal design for airplanes. And I transferred from that job to a job in the testing area of McDonnell Douglas. And what we were doing there was testing airplane parts for ultimate strength to see if they would fail in service, like a landing gear, part of a wing on an airplane, or actually the whole airplane. Then I decided that I wanted to make a change so I quit McDonnell Douglas. Then I went to a place called Svedrup, which does civil-engineering design and I worked there for eleven months and the project that I was on was canceled. So I was laid off from there and I went to another company that does vending machines. I spent a year and a half doing vending-machine design. And then this Ford job came up and so I came up here to Detroit.

Q: What do you think has been the biggest asset to you in terms of versatility?

Martin: Well I guess being able to read a drawing and actually do drawings and use the CAD systems that we use today. That's probably the most basic skill that an engineer has to have. You should be able to read a drawing and to make a drawing also.

Q: OK. How much of your time do you spend on the computer per day?

Martin: I'd say probably about half the time. And it's all split up because, you know, you'll get a phone call and you'll have to talk to somebody about something for fifteen minutes or half an hour. Or you'll have to go to a meeting for an hour. So, probably about half the time I'm sitting here doing things on the computer, checking my mail or working on a project.

Q. What's computer-aided engineering?

Martin: Computer aided engineering is using the computer to, to do engineering. Like this project, that I'm working on right now, what we're doing is suspension-design analysis, vehicle suspension-design analysis on the computer, looking at the motion of the suspension.

Q: What do you think about engineering as a career?

Martin: It can be really an interesting, satisfying job. I've worked in design and I've worked closer to production. And I think it's probably most satisfying to be a little closer to production. That's probably what I'm going to get back into eventually.

"Profiles of Mechanical Engineers" Prepared as part of the Sloan Career Cornerstone Center (www.careercornerstone.org)
Source: "Careers for Mechanical Engineers"

are given the human touch that is so necessary in the design of most products and structures. Aesthetics are more important in some industries than in others. For example, the design of Motorola's RAZR cellular phone used aesthetic analysis to create a "good" look and feel (Figure 3.27). Also, in the design of automobile bodies, extensive aesthetic analyses are done to create a body style that is both pleasing and desirable. Aesthetic qualities are hard to quantify, yet they often make the difference in the product's success or failure in the marketplace.

Market and Financial Analyses A market analysis is performed before a product is sold or even designed. This *market analysis* determines the needs and wants of the customer so that the product produced is the product wanted by the consumer. A market analysis determines the demographic characteristics such as age, gender, education, salary, geographic location, and so forth, of a typical consumer.

Financial analysis determines the capital available for a project, as well as the projected expenses to design, manu-

Figure 3.27

RAZR phone being used to take a photograph

In the design of the RAZR, aesthetic analyses are done to create a good look and feel for the user.

facture, assemble, market, and service a product. Financial analysis also determines the return on investment (ROI) that can be anticipated for a new product. The ROI is the ratio of profit to investment expected from a product.

3.5 Design Review Meetings

A design review is a formal meeting where the design team presents their progress to management. More experienced members of the design team prepare a presentation that might include calculations, charts and graphs, sketches, technical drawings, and 3-D models. It is now possible to have design review meetings across great distances using the web and other Internet-based conferencing technologies. The purpose of the design review meeting is to determine if the design of the product should continue or end. Later in the design phase, design review meetings are occasionally held to report progress and feedback from those outside the actual design team.

For the RAZR, the refinement stage began with the computer modeling of the final design. Dimensions were not critical at this stage but were getting closer to being final. Technicians created a solid model using the design sketches and preliminary models from the ideation phase.

Electrical, manufacturing, and mechanical engineers worked closely together in the design of the circuitry and outside case. The size of the circuitry necessary to create an 8-ounce phone that would fit in the palm of the hand determined the basic size and shape of the outside case. The manufacturing engineers provided input regarding the consequences of using a particular shape and material for the assembly of the phone. The industrial designer began to finalize the aesthetic design of the outside case, given the parameters from the engineers.

This team worked together to produce a refined computer model, which was then shared with the rest of the design team members to gather their input and recommendations. The results of the aesthetic analysis were shared by the whole group, including the consumers, who found that the product did not look appealing: the lines were not thin and the earpiece looked awkward.

The case and circuitry were further refined, then reanalyzed by the engineers. The electrical engineer developed the circuitry to fit in the case, and tested it for power, sound quality, and so forth. The circuitry was first breadboarded, then tested to determine if it worked within the parameters set forth in the design. The mechanical engineer analyzed the strength of the case with respect to dropping, hinge use and misuse, and environmental factors. Much of this testing was accomplished with the computer model.

The stress placed on the case, circuit board, and fasteners from a 4-foot fall was determined using FEM. The 3-D computer model of the design was meshed; then a load was applied to represent the force of impacting the ground after falling 4 feet. The stresses were displayed in varying colors. Areas of the phone that could fail were seen on the model, and design changes were made.

Drawings and models were changed as necessary during the analysis stage. The drawings and models were then further refined. Standard parts were used whenever possible, to save cost and time. For example, the fasteners used to hold the circuit board to the case, as well as many of the resistors, are standard parts in the cellular phone.

A mechanism analysis was conducted to determine the clearances of the circuit board/components/

case assembly. A kinematic analysis was used to determine the ranges of motion for the mouthpiece, from its closed to open positions, and the telescoping antenna.

The manufacturing engineers and related technicians began to design and lay out the factory floor. Sketches and computer models of the assembly line were created. Marketing began to gather information about the product. As the design was further refined, the assembly line computer model was used to begin testing the assembly process. This provided valuable input into DFM strategies. Assembly problems were corrected earlier in the refinement stage. The engineering team viewed the product model as it was being assembled and made changes to the final design to improve the DFM of the cellular phone.

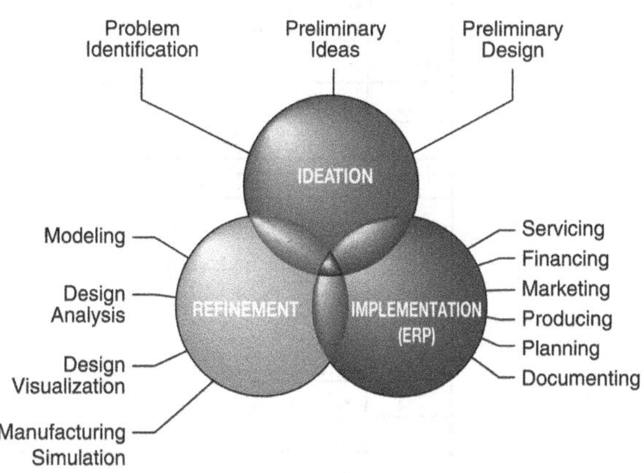

Figure 3.28

Implementation process

The implementation process includes nearly every part of the business. In this phase of the design process, the final design moves from idea to final product.

3.6 Implementation

Implementation is the third and final phase in concurrent engineering design and is the process used to change the final design from an idea into a product, process, or structure. At this point the design is finalized and any changes become very expensive. The implementation process includes nearly every part of the business, such as planning, production, financing, marketing, service, and documentation (Figure 3.28). The goal of this phase is to make the design solution a reality for the enterprise and the consumer.

3.6.1 Planning

The *planning* process determines the most effective method of moving a product through the production cycle. Manufacturing engineers and technologists are the leaders in the planning process, as they schedule the machines and jobs necessary to create the product. Planning requires process sheets, data and material flow diagrams, project modeling and work organization charts, bills of material, and other documents (Figure 3.29). Modern planning techniques include computer-aided process planning (CAPP), material requirements planning (MRP), and just-in-time (JIT) scheduling.

CAPP uses the computer model of the design to determine which machines and processes should be used. MRP calculates the raw materials needed to produce the product and uses solid models to assist in these calculations. For example, the solid model of a part can be analyzed to determine the volumes of various parts, and the results can then be used to calculate the amounts of different materials needed to make the parts.

Just-in-time (JIT) is an operational philosophy that tries to reduce cycle time while eliminating waste. Anything related to the manufacture of a product that does not add value to the product is considered waste. For example, inventory sitting idle in a warehouse does not add value to a product. A JIT system prevents waste by taking deliveries on orders only as they are needed.

3.6.2 Production

Production is the process used to transform raw materials into finished products and structures, using labor, equipment, capital, and facilities. The production process requires engineering drawings, change orders, technical specifications, bills of material, and many other documents. Drawings or 3-D models are used to lay out the factory floor, and computer models can be used to run machine tools that make the parts and simulate the assembly process and the movement of materials in the factory (Figure 3.30).

3.6.3 Marketing

The **marketing** process anticipates customer needs and directs the flow of goods from the producer to the consumer (Figure 3.31). Marketing plays a very important

Material Specs.		Part Name	Plug Housing	Part No.	TA 1274
Purchased Stock Size		Usage	Plug Assembly	Date Issued	
Pcs. Per Pur. Size		Assy. No.	TA 1279	Date Sup'd.	
Weight		Sub. Assy. No.		Issued By	

Oper. No.	Operation Description	Dept.	Machine	Set Up Hr.	Rate Pc/Hr.	Tools
20	Drill 1 hole .32 +.015 -.005	Drill	Mach 513 Deka 4	1.5	254	Drill Fixture L-76, Jig #10393
30	Deburr .312 +.015 -.005 Dia. Hole	Drill	Mach 510 Drill	.1	424	Multi-Tooth burring Tool
40	Chamfer .900/.875, Bore .828/.875 dia. (2 Passes), Bore .7600/.7625 (1 Pass)	Lathe	Mach D109 Lathe	1.0	44	Ramet-1, TPG 221, Chamfer Tool
50	Tap Holes as designated - 1/4 Min. Full Thread	Tap	Mach 514 Drill Tap	2.0	180	Fixture #CR-353, Tap, 4 Flute Sp.
60	Bore Hole 1.133 to 1.138 Dia.	Lathe	H & H E107	3.0	158	L44 Turrent Fixture, Hartford
						Superspacer, pl. #45, Holder #L46,
						FDTW-100, Insar #21, Chk. Fixture
70	Deburr .005 to .010, Both Sides, Hand Feed To Hard Stop	Lathe	E162 Lathe	.5	176	Collect #CR179, 1327 RPM
80	Broach Keyway To Remove Thread Burrs	Drill	Mach. 507 Drill	.4	91	B87 Fixture, L59 Broach, Tap. .875120 G-H6
90	Hone Thread I.D. 822/.828	Grind	Grinder		120	
95	Hone .7600/.7625	Grind	Grinder		120	

Figure 3.29

Process plan

This process plan shows the machining operations, the tools used, setup time, and rate per hour. This level of planning is necessary to estimate cost and to ensure the smooth movement of parts during production.

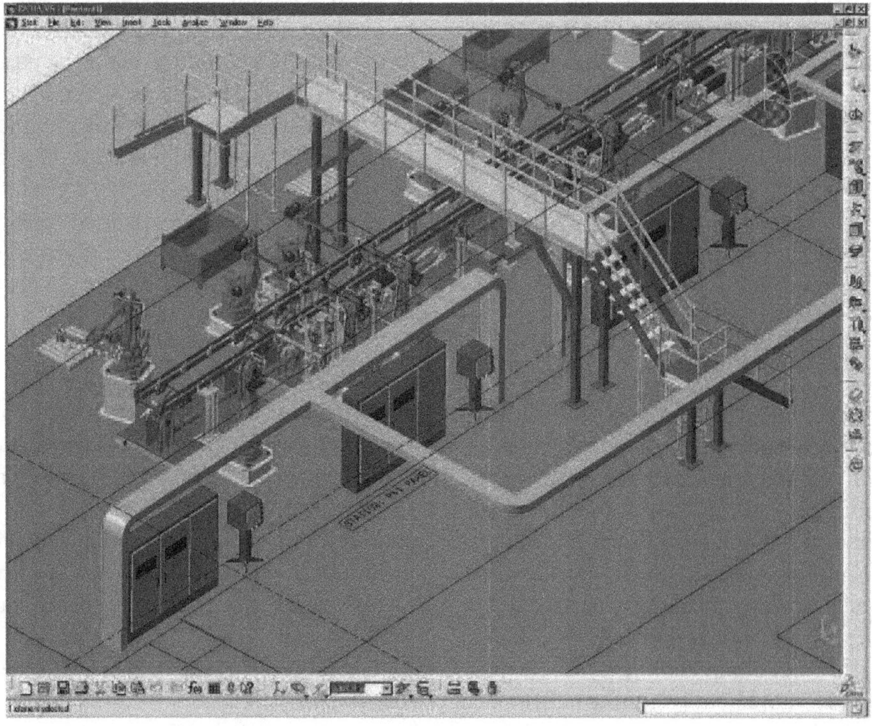

Figure 3.30

Factory floor simulation

The production process is enhanced by using a computer model of the factory floor to simulate activities. This surface model could even be animated to test manufacturing operations, such as the range of motion for the robots.

(Courtesy of Dassault Systemes.)

Figure 3.31

Marketing process

The marketing process is an integral part of the engineering design process. The marketing concept means that an organization aims its efforts at satisfying the customer, but at a profit.

(From *Essentials of Marketing,* 5th ed., by E.J. MacCarthy and W.E. Perreault, Jr., ® 1991 by The McGraw-Hill Companies, Inc. Reprinted with permission.)

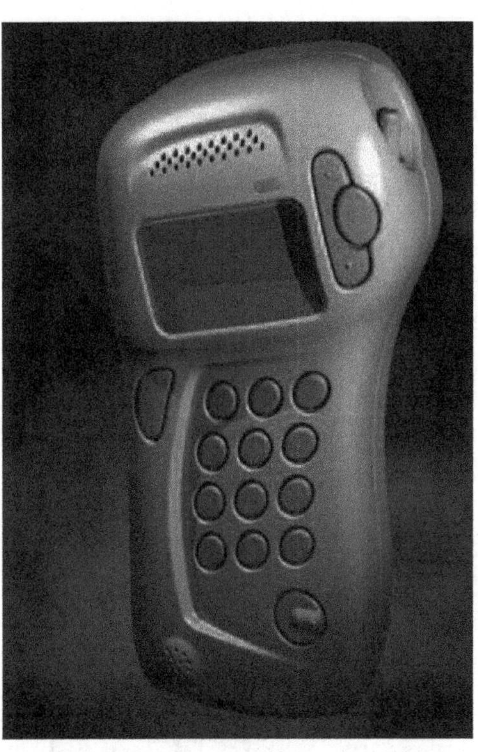

Figure 3.32

A computer-rendered image created by the technical illustrator using the CAD model

The technical illustrator can import the 3-D CAD model into a rendering program, where surface textures and light sources are applied.

(Courtesy of Robert McNeel & Associates.)

role in the ideation, refinement, and implementation stages and is much more than just selling or advertising: Marketing makes sure that the right products are produced and find their way to the consumer. To successfully sell a new product, marketing requires product illustrations and presentation graphics. Computer models and technical drawings can be used as the basis for creating the illustrations needed (Figure 3.32).

The Motorola marketing team

- Analyzed the needs of the people who use cellular phones.
- Predicted what type of cellular phone users would want and decided who the company would try to satisfy.
- Estimated how many people would be using cellular phones in the next few years and who would buy them.
- Determined where these cellular phone users would be and how to get the phone to them.
- Estimated what price they would want to pay for a cellular phone.
- Decided which types of promotions should be used.
- Gathered information about the competition relative to types and prices of cellular phones produced.

3.6.4 Finance

The *finance* process analyzes the feasibility of producing a product, relative to capital requirements and return on investment (ROI). In any enterprise, finance is the management of cash flow such that the means are always available to achieve the firm's objectives as quickly as possible (Figure 3.33). Financial administration includes:

Estimating and planning the flow of cash receipts and expenditures.

Raising from outside sources the needed funds for day-to-day operations.

Controlling the operations to ensure cash flow through the business.

Dividing the earnings between payments to the owners and investment in the future development of the business.

The basic activities in finance, regardless of the type of organization, are financial planning; the actual financing of proposed operations; financial analysis and control; and the disposition of net earnings. Financial planning estimates a firm's dollar volume of sales, which is used by management to determine inventory, labor, and training requirements, as well as facility usage. Budgets are used to estimate and plan the financing necessary for a new design, and the design team must work within budgetary constraints. As the design is finalized, the finance people working on the team determine the expenses, set the price, then project earnings. They use information obtained from other members of the team on such items as sales, pricing, inventory, production, and personnel.

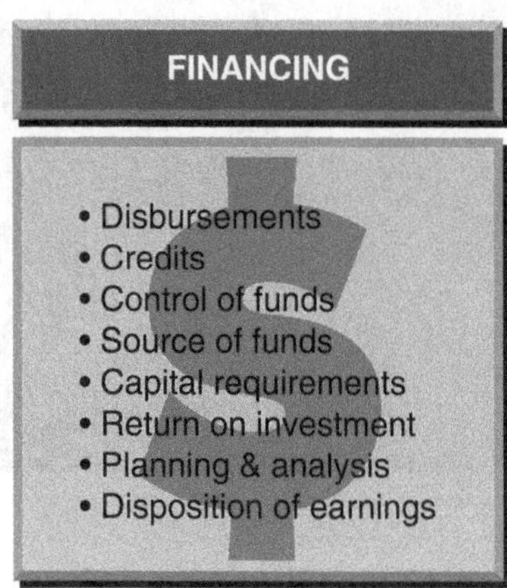

Figure 3.33

Activities involved in financing to analyze the feasibility of producing a product

3.6.5 Management

Management is the logical organization of people, materials, energy, equipment, and procedures into work activities designed to produce a specified end result, such as a product. Managers control or guide the everyday operations of an enterprise. Production managers direct the resources required to produce the goods and services of an organization. Figure 3.34 shows that production managers direct people, plants, parts, and processes, as well as the planning and control systems. Figure 3.35 shows what a plant manager controls in a manufacturing firm. Typically, each group listed under the plant manager has its own manager to run the day-to-day operations. For example, a managing engineer is responsible for engineering support. The managing engineer organizes and executes

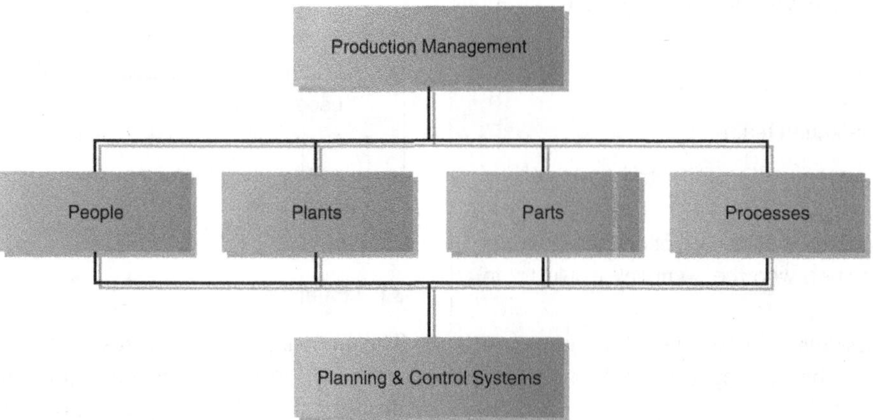

Figure 3.34

Production manager's responsibilities

Production management activities in a manufacturing firm include directing people, plants, parts, and processes.

(From *Production and Operations Management,* 6th ed., by R.B. Chase and N.J. Aquilano, © 1992 by The McGraw-Hill Companies, Inc. Reprinted with permission.)

Historical Highlight
Standards

The need for standards existed as long ago as 4000 B.C. when the ancient Egyptians created the royal cubit as a standard of measurement. However, accurate standards were not needed until the Industrial Revolution. This was because all manufacturing was done by individual craftsmen who were responsible for the production of their products from start to finish. The days of assembly lines and dispersed departments were yet to come. But they did come, and they brought the need for other improved technologies with them, such as much more accurate measurements. This in turn led to the discovery of the existence of variation and the knowledge that it is unavoidable. The concept of tolerance was consequently developed. It logically followed that tolerance should be written on engineering or design drawings. Drawings eventually became the primary means of communication between manufacturing departments.

Since then there has been a slow movement toward creating a national set of standards. In 1935 the first recognized standard for drawings was published by the American Standards Association. A much more comprehensive standard was later published by the British because of the demands brought about by World War II. By the early 1950s three groups emerged in the United States as sources for standards publications: the American Standards Association (ASA), the Society of Automotive Engineers (SAE), and the military. It was in the late 1950s that these groups started working together along with groups from Great Britain and Canada. After several years of deliberation a combined standard was finally published by the American National Standards Institute in 1966, and it has since been updated several times.

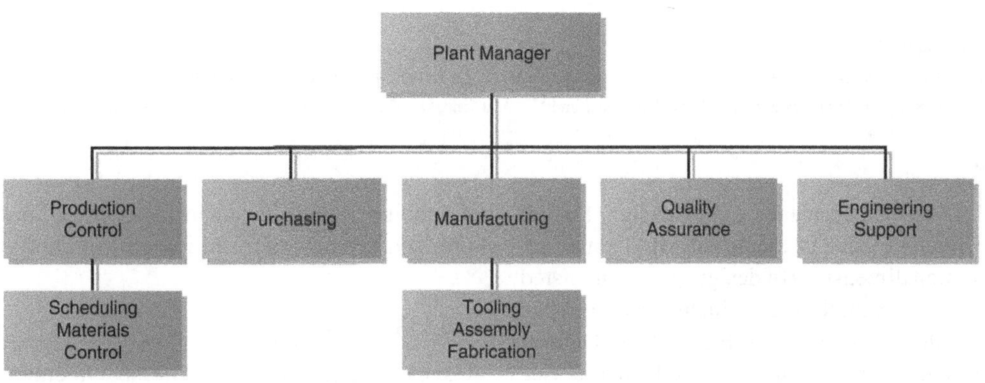

Figure 3.35

Organization of a manufacturing plant

The typical management organization of a manufacturing plant includes production control, purchasing, manufacturing, quality control, and engineering support.

(From *Production and Operations Management,* 6th ed., by R.B. Chase and N.J. Aquilano, © 1992 by The McGraw-Hill Companies, Inc. Reprinted with permission.)

around the priorities of the project and the company, and is guided by the plant engineer.

Global competition has forced industry in the United States to become much more quality conscious. Many industries are using a management process called total quality management (TQM). TQM is the process of managing the organization as a whole such that it excels in all areas of production and service that are important to the customer. The key concepts are as follows: (1) quality is applicable throughout the organization in everything it does, and (2) quality is defined by the customer. To translate customer quality demands into specifications, marketing or product development must accurately determine what the customer wants, and product designers must develop a product or service that consistently achieves that level of quality.

TQM practices require an operational definition of quality, an understanding of its dimensions, and methods for including customer opinions in the specifications. Product quality can be defined as the quality of the product's design

Measures

Dimension	Meaning
Performance	Primary product or service characteristics
Features	Added touches, bells and whistles, secondary characteristics
Reliability	Consistency of performance over time
Durability	Useful life
Serviceability	Resolution of problems and complaints
Response	Characteristics of the human-to-human interface (timeliness, courtesy, professionalism, etc.)
Aesthetics	Sensory characteristics (sound, feel, look, etc.)
Reputation	Past performance and other intangibles

Figure 3.36

Dimensions of design quality

Design quality includes many aspects of a product, such as reliability, durability, features, and others.

(From *Production and Operations Management,* 6th ed., by R.B. Chase and N.J. Aquilano, © 1992 by The McGraw-Hill Companies, Inc. Reprinted with permission.)

and the quality of its conformance to that design. Design quality is the inherent value of the product in the marketplace. The common dimensions of design quality are listed in Figure 3.36. As an example, these dimensions have been adapted to the cellular phone design (Figure 3.37). Conformance quality is the degree to which the product or service design specifications are met. Conformance quality is primarily concerned with the operational functions and the quality of the organizations within a firm.

3.6.6 Service

Service is an activity that supports the installation, training, maintenance, and repair of a product or structure for the consumer. Service uses technical illustrations and reports to support its activities. Technical illustrations are included in installation, maintenance, and repair manuals. The technical illustrations are typically assembly drawings, which show how multiple parts fit together, pictorial drawings, rendered illustrations, and graphics showing the order of assembly, as well as the functionality, of the components of the product. Using a variety of techniques, parts normally hidden from view are shown in their operating positions. Using current CAD technology and internet tools, graphics to support service and maintenance of products are now more easily used and distributed.

3.6.7 Documentation

Once the design is finalized in the refinement process, the design moves into the last phase of development, called documentation. *Documentation* is a process used to formally record and communicate the final design solution. Before concurrent engineering, most graphics documentation was in the form of 2-D engineering drawings and illustrations. With CAD and 3-D modeling, much of the graphics produced in the refinement stage is in the form of 3-D models. These models are used as input to the documentation stage to create engineering drawings, technical illustrations, animations, simulations and visualizations and patent drawings. Documentation thus becomes a concurrent activity throughout the design process, instead of something that occurs only at the end.

Concurrent documentation is a process that creates documents at the same time that the product design is being developed. If concurrent engineering is being employed, it makes sense to use concurrent documentation to facilitate the communication process. Figure 3.38

Measures

Dimension	Meaning (Cellular Phone)
Performance	Strength of signal
Features	Weighs less than 8 ounces
Reliability	Mean time to failure
Durability	Useful life
Serviceability	Ease of repair
Response	Turn-around time for service call
Aesthetics	Look and feel of phone
Reputation	Independent evaluation of product

Figure 3.37

Cellular phone dimensions of design quality

The dimensions of design quality are applied to the cellular telephone.

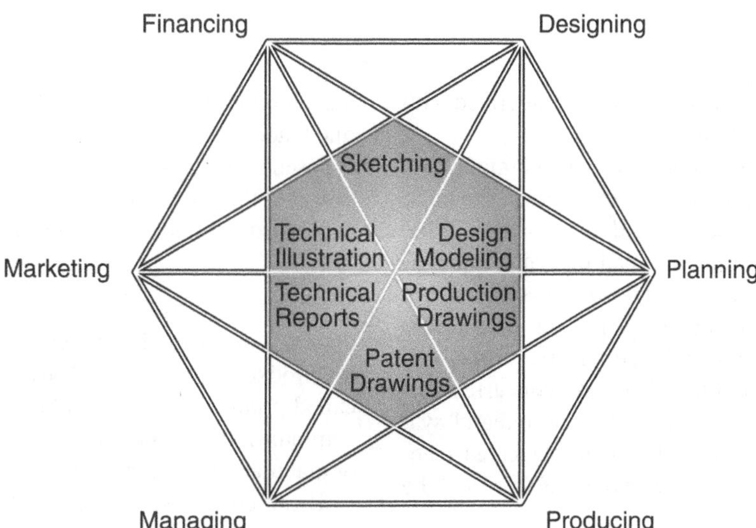

Figure 3.38

Concurrent documentation

The concurrent documentation process integrates all types of graphics to facilitate communications between all areas in a business.

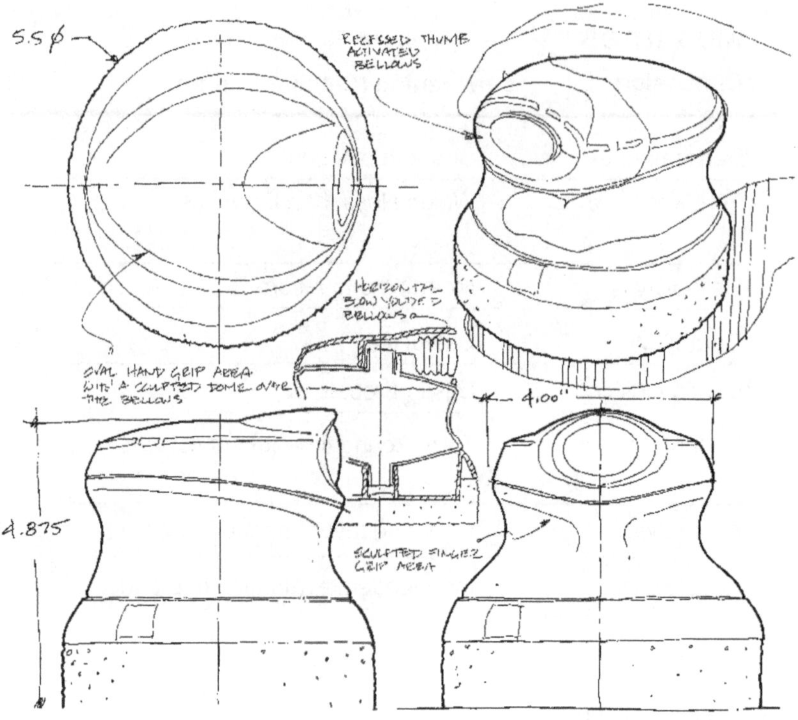

Figure 3.39

A design drawing used in the ideation phase

A new hand waxer shown as an early ideation sketch (top) and as the final rendered model (below).

(Courtesy of Group 4 Design.)

shows the major documentation processes integrated with the concurrent engineering model.

The more effectively a company can communicate information about its products, both internally and to its customers, the more successful the company will be. Documentation is the common thread that runs throughout the entire design process. The documentation becomes the corporate memory for a project. Concurrent documentation practices maximize creative time and minimize documentation time; therefore, concurrent engineering and documentation must be one integral system. All information generated is communicated electronically, using computer hardware and software and the 3-D design model.

Design Drawings and Models *Design drawings* and models are all the sketches, rough design layout drawings, and initial 3-D computer models created during the ideation and refinement phases (Figure 3.39). When concurrent documentation is employed, these drawings and models are refined along with the design. Design drawings and models are used as input to the other documentation processes. For example, the 3-D model created for engineering analysis is used to extract multiview production drawings.

Production Drawings and Models Multiview dimensioned drawings and assembly drawings with a parts list are used for production purposes. These multiview drawings are called *production drawings* because they are used as the communications medium between design and production or manufacturing (Figure 3.40).

If the design is modeled in 3-D CAD software, then multiview drawings can automatically be extracted from the model. Dimensions are added to the drawings by using those dimensions embedded into the model during geometry creation; then assembly drawings with a parts list are produced to create the production drawings. Production drawings contain sufficient detail for the product to be

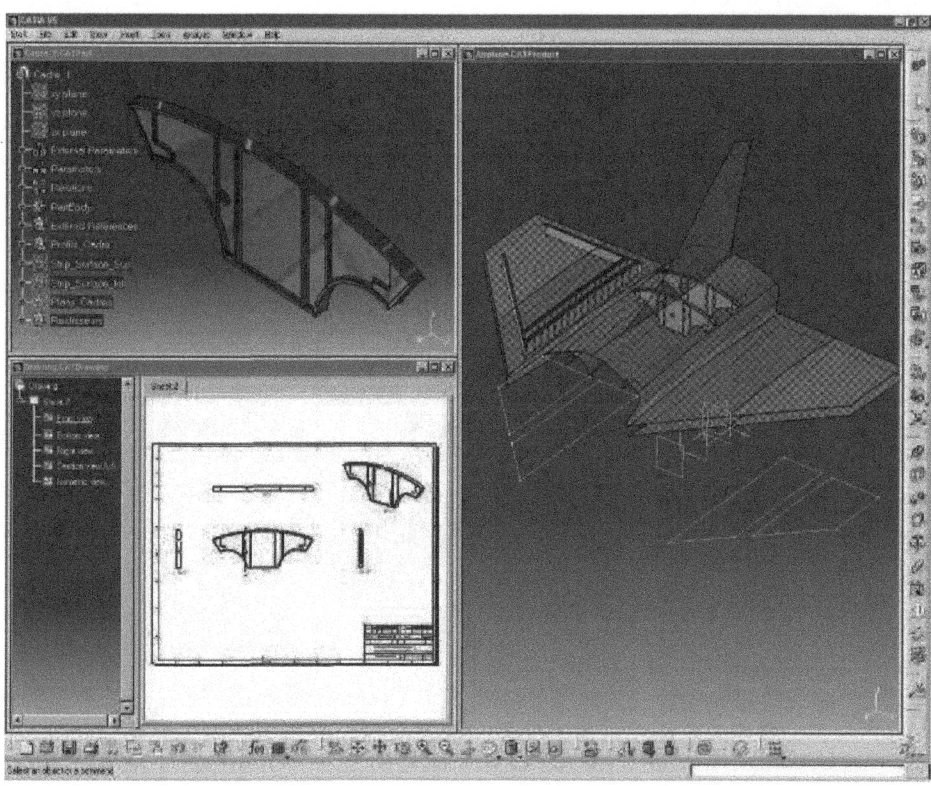

Figure 3.40

Production drawing

A production drawing showing views of a welded body part.

(Courtesy of Dassault Systemes.)

produced. Production drawings are copied, then used by manufacturing engineers and technicians in the fabrication and assembly of the process. Another purpose for engineering drawings is archiving, which is a process used to create a permanent graphics record of the design in the form of drawings saved on vellum, microfiche, computer tape, or some other medium. The archival drawings are placed in a secure environment, such as a vault, to ensure their safety.

It is possible to create a product without the use of paper drawings by linking the entire business to computers. The product would be designed and modeled in CAD. The CAD model would be used as input for computer numerical control (CNC) machines, where the tool path would be created (Figure 3.41). Machinists, engineers, and technicians would use a computer terminal to access a central database, which would contain the engineering drawings and 3-D models. The drawings or 3-D model would be displayed on the computer terminal, serving as the communications medium instead of paper. Although the total elimination of paper in industry may not be possible, some companies are nearly paperless today, with the product and processes controlled by computers.

Technical Illustrations *Technical illustrations* are developed and used throughout the concurrent engineering and documentation cycle, starting with the design database. For example, using computer software, the 3-D model could be viewed from any direction and illustrations could be rendered. Hand- or computer-rendered illustrations are used by industrial designers to convey their ideas to others on the team early in the design process. Rendered illustrations are used by marketing to create advertising and sales information, as well as by service to create technical documents such as installation and maintenance manuals (Figure 3.42).

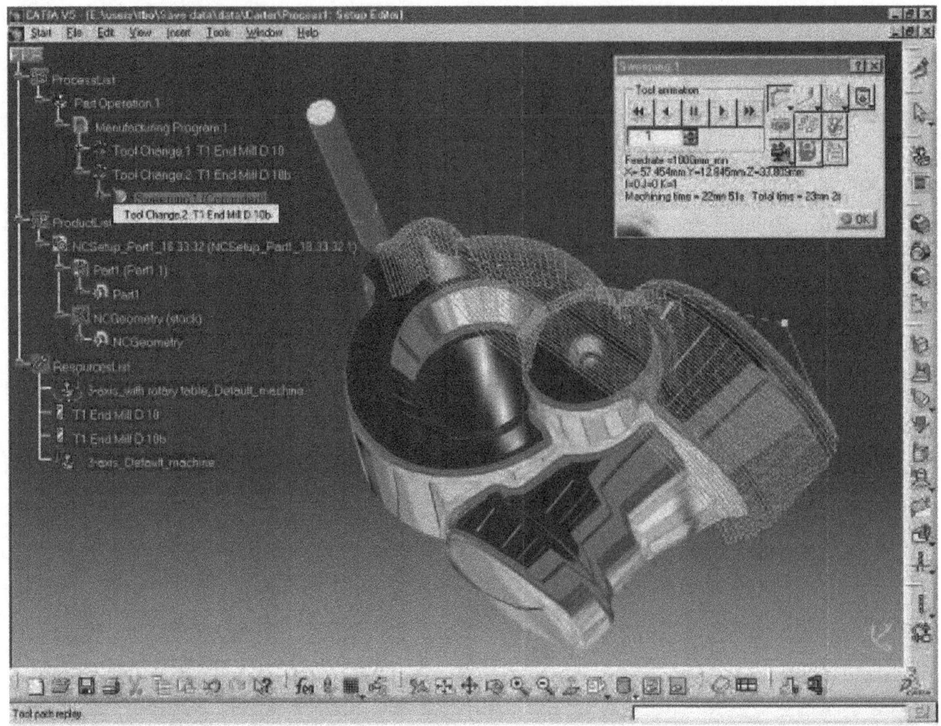

Figure 3.41

Machine tool paths can be generated using the CAD model

(Courtesy of Dassault Systemes.)

Animations **Animations** are used in the documentation phase to support the marketing, training, production, and service activities. In marketing, animations are used to produce advertisements; in service, they are used to create training videos for service technicians; and, in production, they are used to show how the assembly line operates. In the concurrent documentation process, animations are created by the computer animation software, using the design computer model as the input database.

Technical Reports **Technical reports** are in-depth accounts that chronicle the design process. For example, progress reports are created in the early stages of the design process to document the decisions made by the design team. Similar reports are done periodically to review the status of a project.

Final reports, which include both text and graphics, are written at the end of the design cycle and are much more detailed in content. The final report typically contains the following:

- Title page
- Table of contents
- Abstract
- Problem identification
- Procedures
- Problem solution
- Results
- Conclusions
- Bibliography
- Appendixes

A letter of transmittal normally accompanies the final report. This letter briefly describes the contents of the report and the reasons for the project.

The *title page* gives the name of the project, the name(s) of the writers, the members of the design team,

Figure 3.42

Technical illustration

This technical illustration of a building was created by rendering the CAD model created earlier in the design process.

(Courtesy of Bentley Systems, Inc.)

the company name, and the date. The table of contents is a listing of major headings found in the body of the report, along with page numbers. The abstract is a short summary of the entire report and is a separate page preceding the body of the report.

The *problem identification* section begins the body of the report and describes in detail the problem that was to be solved. This part of the report includes technical information, as well as data collected from marketing and finance. The *procedures section* describes in detail the actions taken to solve the problem. This part of the report contains the preliminary ideas and designs considered, the reasons for their selection, and the data supporting the actions taken, presented in the form of graphs, sketches, and drawings.

The *problem solution* section describes in detail the final design decision and the reasoning behind that choice, again using graphics and text. The results section describes the analyses used to determine the feasibility of the design.

Marketing, finance, and physical analysis results are described, using text and graphics.

The *conclusions* section, the final part of the body of the report, summarizes the actions taken to modify the design based on the results of the analyses conducted in the refinement stage. In the conclusion, the final design is detailed, using text and graphics.

The *bibliography* lists the sources consulted in solving the problem. The list contains the titles, authors, sources, and dates of articles in trade magazines, journals, and other sources. Experts interviewed and consultants used might also be listed in the bibliography. The appendixes contain information related to but not directly included in the body of the report. Numerical data, sketches, drawings, and other information might be placed in the appendixes.

Design in Industry [Shaving Seconds from an Olympic Lid]

This case study outlines the use of fluid dynamics software and laser scanning in the development of bicycle racing helmets. The process parallels the refinement stage of the design model presented in this chapter in the areas of design, analysis, and visualization.

Tenths of a second can make the difference between a gold medal and ending up out of the running in Olympic track cycling.

In the months leading up to the 2004 Summer Olympic Games in Athens, Greece, the British Cycling Team had been shaving those precious fractions of a second using CFD (computational fluid dynamics) studies conducted by the Sports Engineering Research Group (SERG) at the University of Sheffield. SERG combined CAD, 3-D scanning, reverse engineering, CFD analyses, and cutting-edge visualization to streamline the overall aerodynamics of the handlebars and front fork/wheel combinations of the team's cycles. Then, just weeks before the games were to begin, cycling's international governing body changed the rules for helmets, sending the team back to the drawing board.

Last-Minute CFD Analysis

The new rule required that only helmets passing a formal safety test in an accredited laboratory could be used in Olympic competition. Since some of the helmets the team planned on using did not fit those specifications because they were designed primarily for speed rather than protection, the team decided to test helmet designs for aerodynamic efficiency from among those that passed the safety regulations.

The team opted for a last-minute CFD analysis. Modeling from scratch with CAD was not an option due to time constraints, and CAD is not well-suited to creating the organic shapes required for accurate modeling and CFD analysis of the helmets and athletes.

Instead, athlete and helmet geometry were captured with laser scanning technology.

"CAD engineers work at different tolerances than those required for CFD analysis," says Dr. John Hart from the University of Sheffield's SERG group. "Even if we had the CAD files for the helmets, we would have had to spend a great deal of time cleaning up the model to make it watertight. Reverse engineering the helmets and surfacing them in Geomagic Studio guaranteed a highly detailed, watertight model in less time."

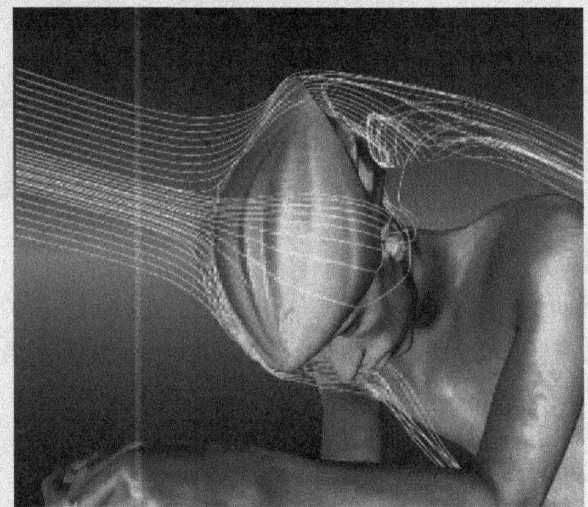

The Sports Engineering Research Group at the University of Sheffield combined 3-D scanning, reverse engineering, CFD, and visualization to study helmet designs for the UK Olympic cycling team. The pathlines here show airflow, and the color maps depict contours of total pressure distribution.

(Courtesy of Erin Hatfield, Desktop Engineering Magazine.)

The text and graphics in the reports are created using computer-based word processing, page layout, spreadsheet, database, and graphics programs. The engineering drawings and models created in the design process are used to illustrate the text. The technical illustrator uses the CAD database to create other types of illustrations, such as exploded assemblies. Spreadsheet and database programs are used to present numerical data in the form of tables, graphs, and charts. The page layout program assembles the text and graphics to create finished documents.

Presentation Graphics **Presentation graphics** are text, illustrations, and other visual aids used when making an oral report to a group (Figure 3.43). Progress and final re-

SERG planned to capture data from the athletes by scanning them in different racing positions: one aerodynamic posture with the cyclist looking ahead and one where the head is down in a sprint to test more fully the effect of the various helmet shapes.

Refining Complex Scan Data

Point-cloud data collected from the scans of the four different helmets was imported into point editing and surfacing software for generating models for accurate CFD analysis and custom manufacturing. The model was cleaned to remove holes and defects, and patches were placed over the polygons, outlining the positions of the NURBS surfaces.

The team applied polygons and NURBS patches to the human model and used the point editing tool to output a STEP file.

"The STEP file format provides a robust geometric file that's not too large," according to the analyst. "We can end up with a model with a large number of NURBS patches in order to capture the detail we need. The accuracy of the CFD study was highly dependent upon the geometrical accuracy of the assembled model."

Visualization that Proves Results

The STEP file containing each helmet design and the human geometry was meshed for CFD analysis, and a flow domain around each model was generated.

The SERG team imported CFD results into a visualization software tool, which produced highly detailed flow visualizations showing the aerodynamic properties of the helmets. SERG chose to concentrate on the drag and lift forces in the simulations, using isosurfaces to show wake structures and particle streamlines to visualize swirling and re-circulating flow paths.

Based on the wake structures and re-circulating flows in the visualizations, SERG was able to quickly identify how different geometric components of the models (i.e., helmet and cyclist) interacted and influenced each other. They were also able to pinpoint large wakes that resulted in high drag forces.

"The flow visualizations and images were vital in presenting the physics-based simulation results in an understandable manner to the cycling team," the team said. "Being able to clearly show a client what is happening is essential to their understanding of the results."

The design team used images and animations to reinforce the hard data results from the simulations and to help the engineers understand the flow physics that create the lift and drag forces. Based on the results, SERG was able to recommend an optimal helmet style that reduces aerodynamic drag and lift.

The optimized bike design and later helmet recommendations from SERG have been credited with helping contribute to the team's best-ever Olympic medal haul. The team won two gold medals, a silver, and a bronze in Athens, but they're not done. SERG is once again working with the team in preparation for the 2008 Beijing Summer Olympics.

Adapted from "Shaving Seconds from an Olympic Lid," by Erin Hatfield, *Desktop Engineering Magazine,* May 2006, pp. 16–18, 36. © 2006 Desktop Engineering. Reprinted with permission.

ports are often presented to managers at various levels in a company. Oral reports are supplemented with visual aids, which help the listener understand the information being presented. Presentation graphics include the following:

- Charts
- Graphs
- Tables
- Flip charts
- Overhead transparencies
- Videos
- Slides
- Photographs
- Real models
- Computer models

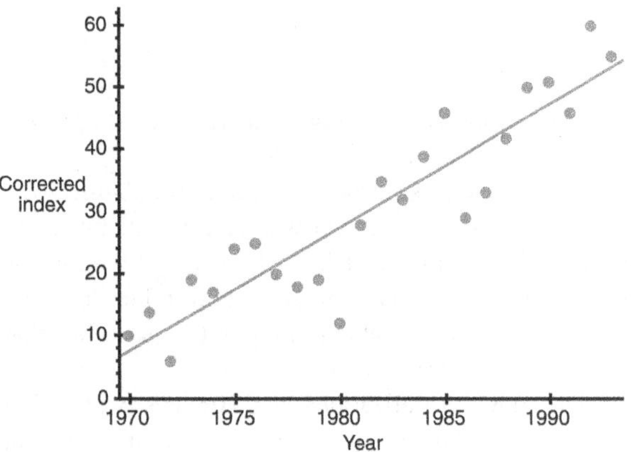

Figure 3.43

Chart used for a presentation

Data from analyses can be summarized in charts and graphs.

The graphics database created in the design process is a source for much of the graphics used in a presentation. The design computer models can be captured on slides and photographs, or as plots. Animations and simulations can be captured on videotape. Multimedia presentations can be created by using authoring software to combine several graphics media into a single, computer-assisted presentation. Multimedia presentations contain text, charts, graphs, scanned slides and drawings, animations, and sound. Authoring software is used to script or organize the various computer-based presentation materials.

> The implementation of the RAZR was a team effort. Marketing developed an advertising strategy that focused on the fact that the phone was the smallest and lightest cellular phone on the market. Graphics documents were created for archiving the final design, communicating the design to production, marketing, and service, and those giving presentations. These graphics documents were in the form of drawings, models, plots, electrical schematics, plant layouts, exploded assemblies, technical illustrations, and sketches.
>
> Concurrent engineering practices and TQM principles were used successfully to create the RAZR in a very short time. The design team members combined their abilities and knowledge to produce a product that has been widely accepted by the consumer. The RAZR was named Best Cellular Phone of the Year by *Mobile Computing* as well as winning a gold award by the Industrial Designers Society of America (IDSA).

Patent Drawings A **patent** is the "right to exclude others from making, using, or selling" and is issued by the federal government. The patenting process was developed to encourage the prompt disclosure of technical advances by granting a limited period of protection for the exclusive use of that advance. A patent is granted for a period of 17 years.

An application consists of three components: the claims, the description, and the drawings. All elements of the patent must be clearly and completely described in the claims, description, and drawings. The claims define those elements that distinguish the invention from known technology of a similar nature; that is, the elements that are "adding to the pool of knowledge." The description should "enable a workman ordinarily skilled in the arts to practice or replicate the invention." The drawings should detail and clarify all elements of the claimed invention.

The patent drawing is a highly regulated piece of graphics. One of the best sources for the applicable regulations is the *Guide for Patent Draftsmen*, from the Patent and Trademark Office. It features selected rules of practice relating to patent drawings and covers such diverse matters as the medium and the style requirements for patent office acceptance.

Patent drawings can be flow block diagrams (Figure 3.44), schematics, or other labeled representations. Standard shapes must be used to illustrate conventional elements. Arrows may be used to show movement of different parts. The views used in a patent drawing may be plan, elevation, section, or pictorial. Exploded views are also permitted, to indicate order of assembly (Figure 3.45).

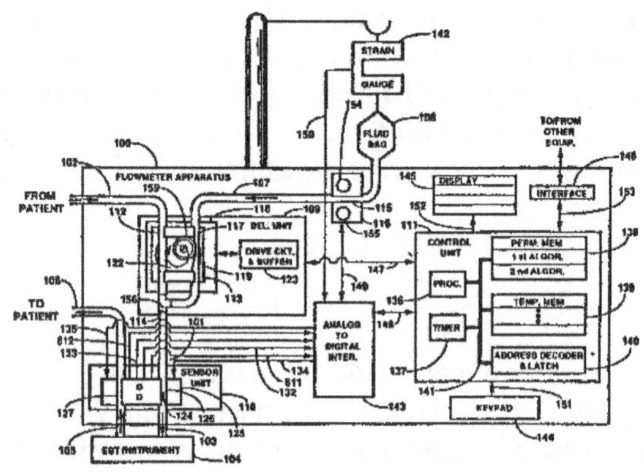

Figure 3.44

Diagram patent drawing

This is a patent drawing of a medical device in the form of a diagram.

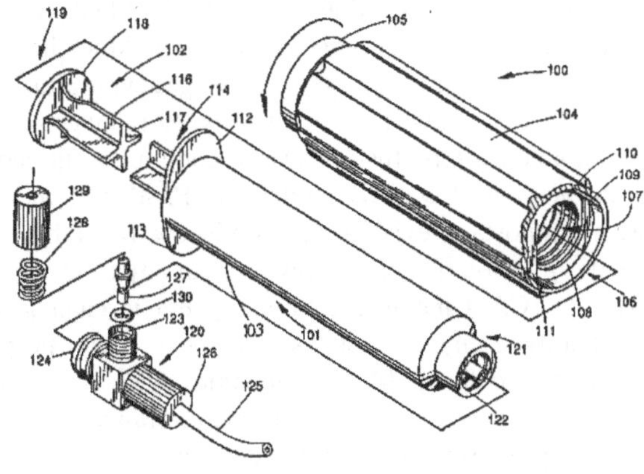

Figure 3.45

Pictorial patent drawing

An exploded patent drawing is used to communicate the assembly.

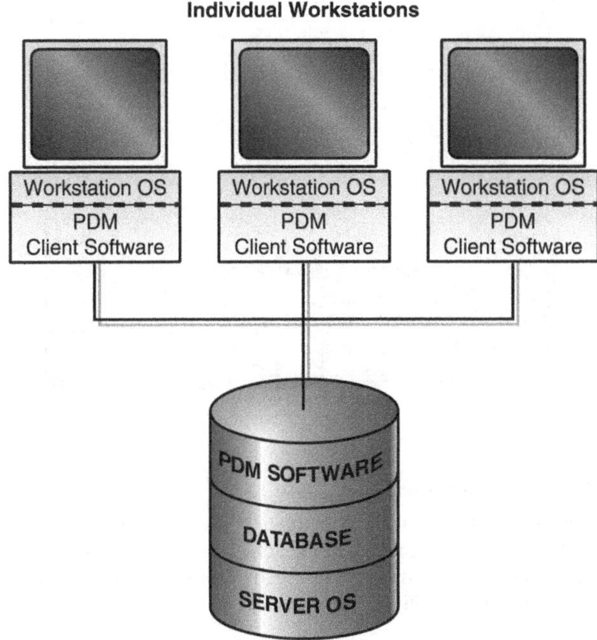

Figure 3.46

PDM in a networked environment

Product data management (PDM) software has two components. The server software manages the product database while the client software provides an interface for the CAD workstation users.

3.7 Drawing Control

3.7.1 Product Data Control

A critical part of the design process is managing all of the information related to the product. All information associated with the design, manufacture, and maintenance of a product is used for both current and future design efforts. EDM/PDM is the name given to the specific computer-based tools and processes used to manage this information. These technologies also form the backbone of PLM implementations discussed in Chapter 2. Concurrent engineering practices have heightened interest in these tools since these practices require close coordination of multiple team members working in parallel in an accelerated design cycle. EDM/PDM is one of the fastest growing segments of the CAD industry. EDM/PDM typically uses some form of a browser interface especially for companies with multiple offices and plants located throughout the world.

Engineering data management (EDM) is a software used to track CAD or office documents with user-defined data fields, such as revisions, authors, date, and so forth. Key information is stored in a database file that may be linked to other business systems in the company.

Product data management (PDM) is a system that focuses around the ordering of material and planning for the materials use in manufacture of a product. PDM systems need a networked computing environment (Figure 3.46). A typical mid- to large-sized engineering group will have CAD workstations, known as clients, networked together and linked to a server. Besides handling electronic data communications such as e-mail, these servers also contain PDM system software. In this type of arrangement, the server contains a central database while the individual workstations (the clients) have software used to access the central database.

The PDM system coordinates all information associated with the design process. Electronic files containing design information are stored and organized within the central database. The system provides tools for users to search and organize the information contained within the database. The database works by associating standardized key pieces of information with each document

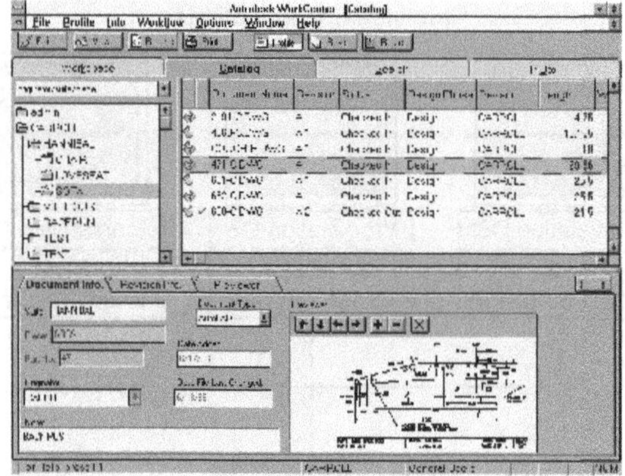

Figure 3.47

PDM client software

Information fields such as Document Type, Piece, Part No., and Date Added are attached to each document in the PDM database. These fields provide a method of searching for and organizing documents in the database.

(Figure 3.47). This information, entered into what are called database fields, might include:

- Part name
- File name
- Drawn by
- Approved by
- Design phase
- Revision number
- Date last revised

Using information entered into these fields, a user can determine how many previous designs may have used a certain fastener or which drafter revised a particular CAD model.

Product data information is normally organized around a single product in a database that has relational capabilities. This type of database is known as a *relational database* because it is possible to link tables of data based on a common field. A relational database allows the searching of any table of data and finding information from all related tables through the common link.

The system also provides administration tools to control access to the database. This security feature means that only authorized individuals can revise or approve engineering documents. These controls also mean that the files can be viewed by a wide variety of people within the organization involved in the design without worry that unauthorized revisions will be made to the drawings.

Using the communications network, the PDM system can also manage engineering change orders. Much like an electronic mail (e-mail) system, messages with attached electronic documents can be sent between managers, engineers, and drafters. Instead of just containing the most current version of a CAD model, the PDM system can store all important revisions of a product so that a history of its design evolution can be reviewed at any time.

Besides CAD models, a PDM system is capable of storing almost any type of document which can be put into electronic form. Many companies have thousands of older (legacy) designs that were hand-drawn and exist only in paper form. These drawings, along with informal sketches, can be scanned into the computer so that electronic records of the drawings exist in the PDM database. In addition to graphic information, spreadsheets, memos, e-mail correspondence, and other text-based electronic documents can also be entered into the database.

Though most PDM systems are built on top of proprietary databases, Internet software tools are also being used to help manage engineering data. Though the most common usage of the Internet is to link remote sites that are geographically far apart, these same communication tools are also being used with local area networks within companies. For example, web browsers such as Netscape or Internet Explorer can be used to display engineering drawings stored on a server (Figure 3.48). One advantage

Figure 3.48

PDM on the Internet

Increasingly, web-based tools are being used to manage engineering information within a company. This PDM browser tool allows you to view product configuration information.

(Courtesy of Dassault Systemes.)

of using WWW browsers and servers to display engineering data is that it can as easily display this information halfway around the world as it can in the next office!

3.7.2 File Management

Even relatively small organizations produce many CAD files in the design and manufacturing process. These files need to be stored, approved, retrieved, archived, and organized for easy access and tracking. The initial process used to manage files is to create an organized directory structure. Most organized directory structures are based on discrete projects. Each project would have its own project-based directory structure. Folders are created by project with subdirectories for subassemblies then part subdirectories. File naming conventions are also created to make retrieval of files easy and logical (Figure 3.49).

3.7.3 ISO 9000

ISO 9000 applies to all types of organizations. It doesn't matter what size they are or what they do. It can help both product- and service-oriented organizations achieve standards of quality that are recognized and respected throughout the world.

ISO is the *International Organization for Standardization*. It is located in Switzerland and was established in 1947 to develop common international standards in many areas. Its members come from the standards bodies in over 90 countries. ISO first published its quality assurance and quality management standards in 1987 and then republished an updated version in 1994. These quality standards are referred to as the "ISO 9000 Standards." ISO's purpose was to facilitate international commerce by providing a single set of standards that people everywhere would recognize and respect.

The value of ISO 9000 certification includes:

- Improve your company's competitiveness.
- Achieve consistency in your firm's products/services and thereby enhance profitability by reducing customer returns.
- Meet and exceed your customer requirements.
- Develop a disciplined business management system for your company.
- Provide your firm with a continuous-improvement tool.
- Establish a venue for regular reviews of your company's management system.

ISO 9000 certification for a company means that it has identified and documented all the processes that affect

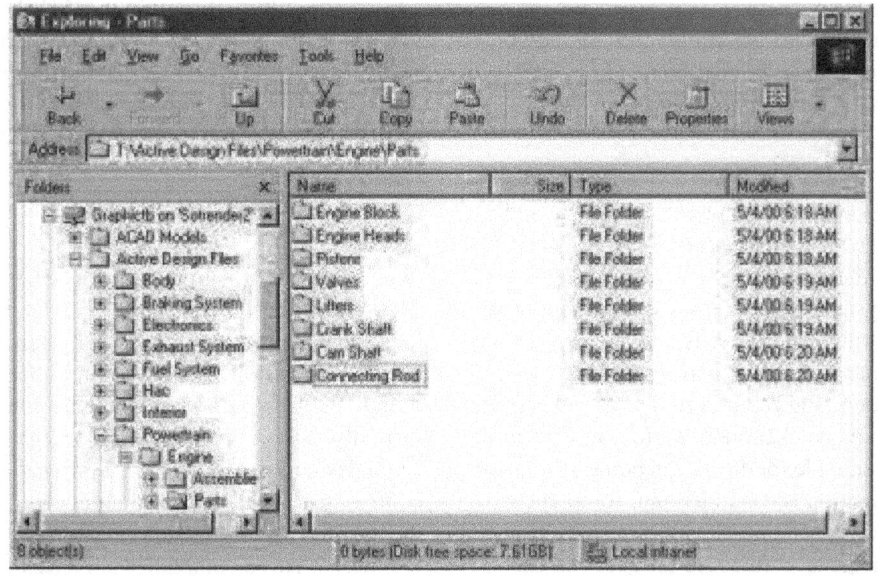

Figure 3.49

File management

File naming conventions used to manage CAD files.

the quality of the service they provide or the product they design.

3.8 Other Engineering Design Methods

Design for Manufacturability (DFM) Design for manufacturability (DFM) is a design technique in which the design is developed by a team and the focus is on simplicity in manufacturing and functionality. This process usually results in a product that is more reliable, has fewer parts, and can be assembled at less cost and in less time.

Using traditional design methods, engineers would create a design, which would then be given to manufacturing engineers, who would have to find a way to make the design work. This could be very expensive. When DFM principles are used, the manufacturability of a design is determined before it is sent to production.

DFM principles are as follows:

1. Minimize the number of parts.
2. Use modular design (breaking a single design into smaller parts).
3. Use gravity in assembly whenever possible.
4. Minimize reorientation and adjustment during the assembly process.
5. Provide easy access.
6. Reduce or eliminate fasteners.
7. Increase part symmetry.
8. Consider ease of part handling.
9. Design parts for ease of alignment.
10. Design parts to maintain location.

Knowledge-Based Engineering (KBE) Knowledge-based engineering (KBE) systems complement CAD by adding the engineering knowledge necessary for a product's design. KBE allows the development of a true virtual prototype. A KBE system is programmed by defining the "rules" or engineering criteria for the design. For example, a rule can relate to the type and strength of the specific material needed, and the programming can require that several materials be examined in order to determine which one is most suitable for the design being developed. The product information is contained in a comprehensive model composed of the engineering design rules specific to that product, the general rules for product design, and standard engineering design practices.

KBE systems can be used to create initial designs for engineering evaluation; compare proposed designs to previous ones; evaluate designs with respect to fundamental physical laws; and produce drawings, bills of material, cost analyses, process plans, MRP inputs, and user-defined reports. KBE systems thus promote concurrent engineering, reduce time to market, and capture the design knowledge of experienced engineers.

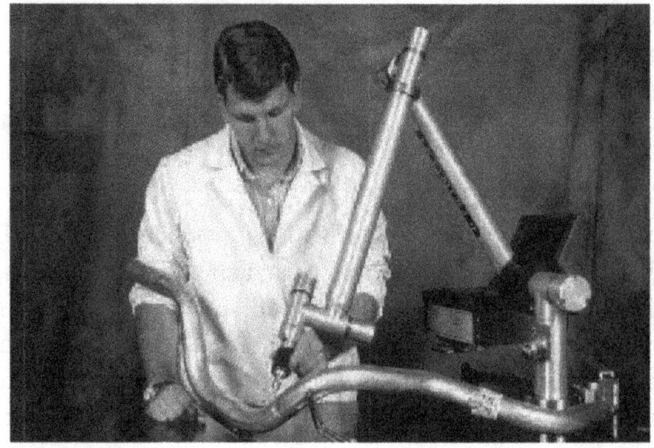

Figure 3.50

Coordinate measuring machine (CMM) used to accurately measure a part for reverse engineering or quality control

Reverse Engineering Reverse engineering is a method of taking an existing product, accurately evaluating it, and putting the information into a CAD database. The measurements of a product are taken using a coordinate measuring machine (CMM). A CMM is an electromechanical device, with a probe on one end, that accurately measures objects and then inputs the 3-D data into a CAD system (Figure 3.50). The 3-D model can then be modified or checked for accuracy.

Web-Based Design Before the Internet became popular, design information was shared through face-to-face meetings, telephone calls, faxes, and mailings of drawings. Geographic distances were a hindrance to the sharing of design information. Now with the Internet available to virtually any civilized location on earth, it is possible to share design information in a new way. Physical presence is no longer necessary for the people doing the design or the documents used to support the design process.

Internet-based companies are developing web sites that allow design teams to establish collaborative web portals that allow the sharing of a wide variety of data almost instantaneously. This allows designers, suppliers, marketing, sales, and others to collaborate electronically through the design process regardless of their locations. Typically, design team members can view CAD drawings and models, sketches, photographs and renderings, specifications, and other documents on a restricted access web site. Different levels of access to the site can be specified so some users can only view drawings while others can red-line the drawings. It is also possible to include direct e-mailing capabilities from the site as well as organization tools for filing documents. Web-based design can speed up the design review process and reduce costs.

Web-based design can also allow access of 2-D and 3-D database libraries. It is estimated that as much as 70 percent of major product design consists of standard components such as fasteners, valves, motors, etc. The use of standard parts is essential for the design and assembly of products. As much as 25 percent of an engineer's time is spent searching for standard parts used in the design of products. Many standard part libraries are available over the web and through business-to-business (B-to-B) web sites.

3.9 Virtual Reality*

Virtual reality (VR) is an emerging technology that is beginning to be more commonly used in engineering design and manufacturing. Although VR was first proposed in 1965 by Ivan Sutherland in a paper he published entitled *The Ultimate Display,* and which he followed with the building of a head-mounted display in 1968, VR has been slow to be adopted and used in industry. Most of the development of VR over the years has been accomplished in government and university research labs. However, in recent years VR has become a technology that is being integrated into the design and manufacturing process through vendors such as FakeSpace©, Panoram©, and Barco©. The automotive, aerospace, and consumer-products companies, such as Boeing, General Motors, and Thomson Electronics, are using VR in various stages of the design process to speed the design and manufacture of products (Figure 3.51).

Since this technology is still relatively new, often the terms are used incorrectly or misunderstood. Figure 3.52 on page 86 shows four closely interrelated terminologies: real-world (natural) interaction, telerobotics, augmented reality, and virtual reality.

*This section was written with contributions from Raj Arangarasan, Research Scientist with the Envision Center for Data Perceptualization at Purdue University.

Figure 3.51

Boeing uses VR in the design of aircraft to better visualize and understand complex engineering problems.

(Courtesy of Panoram Technologies.)

In real-world interaction, the human (or user) interacts with the real-world environment directly. In telerobotics, a telerobot is controlled through a computer interface (such as displays or graphical user interface) to interact with the real-world environment. In augmented reality, the user interacts with the real world directly and interacts with the computer-generated synthetic world through computer controls—at the same time. In virtual reality, the user interacts with the computer-generated, synthetic environment through the computer controls such as displays and graphical user interface.

Virtual Reality—A Definition In general, virtual reality is a three-dimensional (3-D) (in most cases, but not always), computer-generated, simulated environment, rendered in real time with interactive user control of the environment. It presents an illusion of reality by fooling the human senses.

Virtual reality captures the user's multiple senses primarily through computer-generated and other artificial means, to make him or her believe something is real when it is not.

Components of Virtual Reality Figure 3.53 on page 86 shows the primary senses of humans. The primary senses are sight, hearing, touch, smell, and taste. Several artificial methods are used to effectively capture these senses through virtual means. Table 3.1 lists the senses and the media that are used to communicate with each sense, and Figure 3.54 (on page 87) shows the components of VR.

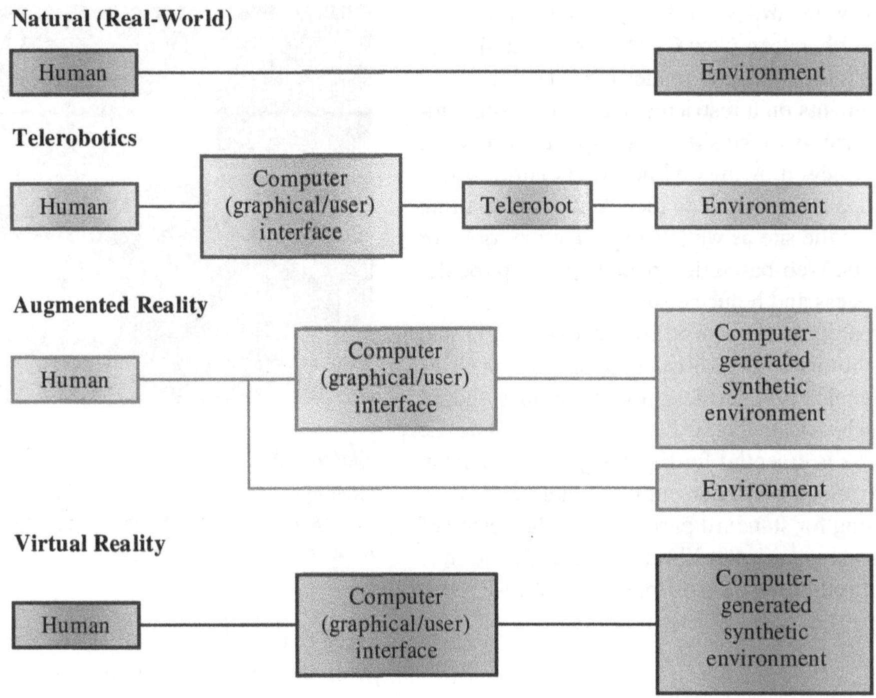

Figure 3.52

Four technologies closely related to VR

Figure 3.53

Primary human senses

(© C Squared Studios/Getty Royalty Free.)

Display Technologies Humans are accustomed to seeing three dimensions. This often is referred to as **stereopsis** or stereoscopic vision, as shown in Figure 3.55 on page 88.

Stereopsis is from the Greek word for "solid sight," and it refers to a perception of 3-D shape from any source of depth information. The basic principle of stereoscopic vision is that we perceive depth because the left and right eye receive two separate images from slightly different perspectives. For simulated images, this is done in several ways. These include

- Wheatstone
- Lenticular (or) AutoStereo
- Cross-Eye
- Anaglyph
- Polarized
- Active stereo

Polarized Stereoscope A common way to display image pairs is to display them on the screen separately with different polarizations. The first image is displayed with vertical polarization and the second with horizontal. When you wear a pair of glasses with different polarizations, each eye

Table 3.1 Sense, Modes of Communication, and Methods of Implementation

Senses	Communication Modes	Body Parts	VR Methods
Sight	Vision	Eyes	Display systems
Hearing	Listen/speak	Ears, mouth	Speakers/microphones
Touch	Feel	Skin (muscle, bones, etc.)	Haptic devices
Smell	Smell	Nose	??
Taste	Taste	Tongue	??
Other senses	Motion/gestures	Fingers, head, hand, other body parts	Gloves, spatial motion trackers, eye trackers

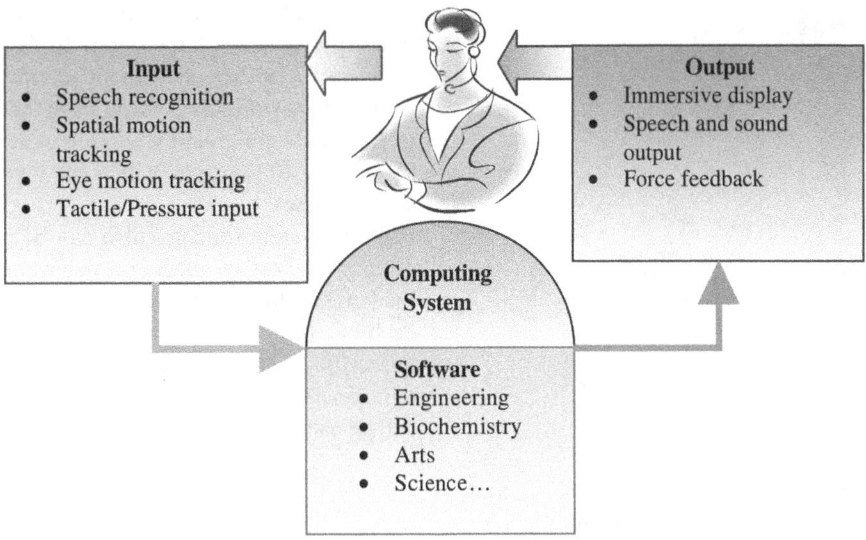

Figure 3.54

Components of virtual reality

only sees the image that matches its polarization. Two types of polarizations can be used: linear and circular. In linear polarization, the light waves are polarized in linear fashion. By using two perpendicular polarization filters, the stereoscopic vision is achieved. In circular polarization, the light waves are polarized in circular fashion. The stereoscopic vision is achieved by combining clockwise and counterclockwise polarization (Figure 3.56 on page 89).

Active Stereo (or Shutter Glasses) An increasingly popular way to view 3-D images on the screen is to use shutter glasses. These glasses have high-speed electronic shutters that open and close in sync with the images on the monitor. Liquid crystals are used for the shutters because an electronic signal can make the crystal turn instantly from transparent to opaque. When the left image is on the screen, the left shutter is open and the right shutter is closed, which allows the image to be viewed by your left eye only. When the right image is on the screen, the right shutter is open and the left shutter is closed. If this sequence occurs fast enough, your brain thinks it is seeing a true stereoscopic image. If this shuttering speed is not fast enough, you still can see a stereoscopic image, but you also may see some flickering. An emitter, sitting on the monitor, broadcasts an infrared signal (shown in dotted lines in Figure 3.57 on page 89). The eyewear receives the signal and synchronizes its shutters to the video field rate.

Head-Mounted Displays The **head-mounted display (HMD)** was the first device that provided its wearer with an immersive experience. Evans and Sutherland demon-

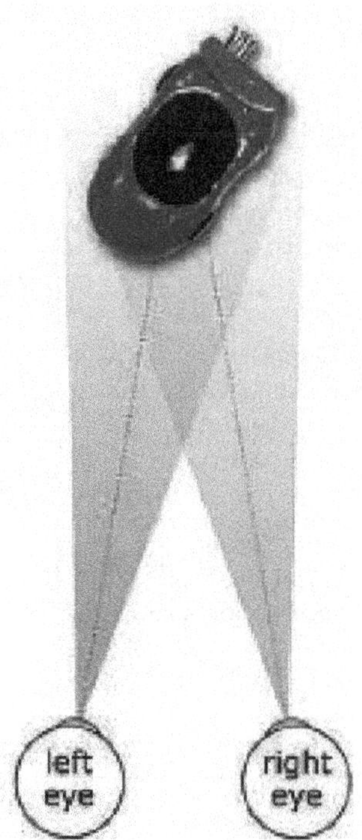

Figure 3.55
Stereoscopic vision

strated a head-mounted stereo display in 1965. It took more than 20 years before VPL Research introduced a commercially available HMD, the famous EyePhone system, in 1989.

The emphasis of the HMD program is on providing information to people where ordinary direct view displays either are inappropriate or are impractical. HMDs have unique applications in virtual environments where total immersion is important, in environments where hands-free operation is desirable or necessary, and in applications involving unique viewing requirements, such as 3-D, mapping graphical images onto real images, and night vision (Figure 3.58 on page 90).

Fishtank Virtual Reality The term **fishtank VR** refers to a system in which a stereo image of a 3-D scene is viewed on a monitor in perspective coupled with the head position and orientation of the user (Figure 3.59 on page 90). The stereo images on the screen are viewed through active stereo glasses. Recent developments in fishtank VR systems allow the user to see 3-D images without the use of glasses. In these systems, the monitor is modified in such a way that a stereo image can be viewed without glasses and still produce a 3-D effect (Figure 3.60 on page 90).

Projection-Based Systems Larger display systems have been developed to display stereo images through the use of computer projection devices. The computer projection devices used to create stereo images can be of three possible types: CRT (cathode ray tube), DLP (digital light processing), and LCD (liquid crystal display), with the LCD and DLP emerging as the most common types in use today. The projectors can project stereo images directly onto a screen (front projection), or they can be mounted behind a screen (rear projection). Rear projection is preferred for large stereo displays so that users can walk up to the screen without interfering with the projected images. Figure 3.61 on page 90 shows a DLP projector capable of creating a stereo image in resolutions up to 1280 by 1024 pixels, which can be viewed with active stereo glasses.

Passive stereo images also can be created from computer projectors by placing a polarizing filter in front of the lenses. This technique requires two projectors, one for each eye (Figure 3.62 on page 91). These filters can polarize the light from the projector in either a linear or a circular pattern. Very inexpensive polarized glasses then can be used to view the stereo images.

Multiple Projector–Based Systems Figure 3.63 on page 91 shows a large rear-projected active stereo system used for engineering design and research. Large screen areas are possible through the use of multiple projectors that can be edge-blended to create a seamless single large image. For example, it is possible to create a very large image 8 feet high and 30 feet long by using three DLP stereo projectors with one-third of the image projected from each projector.

CAVE® Another multiple projection–based VR system is called a CAVE® (computer augmented virtual environment). The original idea for a CAVE was developed in 1992 at the University of Illinois, Chicago. A **CAVE** consists of multiple screens and projectors configured into walls, floor, and ceiling to create a room. Typically, CAVEs are cube-like, with each side approximately 10 feet by 10 feet. The sides of the CAVE are made of rear projection screens with stereo projectors mounted behind each side of the structure. CAVEs commonly are configured as four-sided (three walls and a floor) (Figure 3.64 on page 91). There are a few six-sided CAVEs, but they are very expensive, and a very large area is needed to build

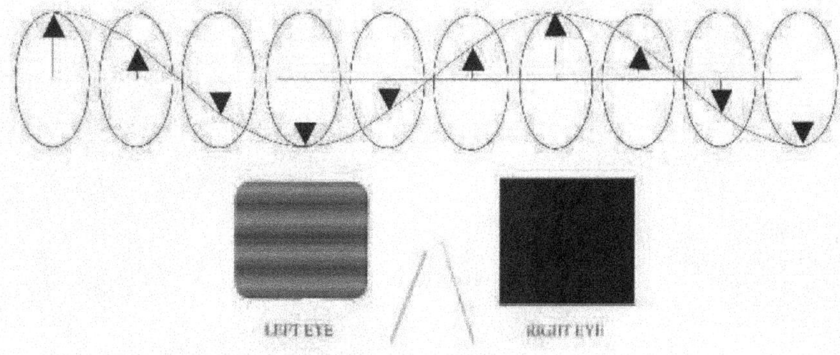

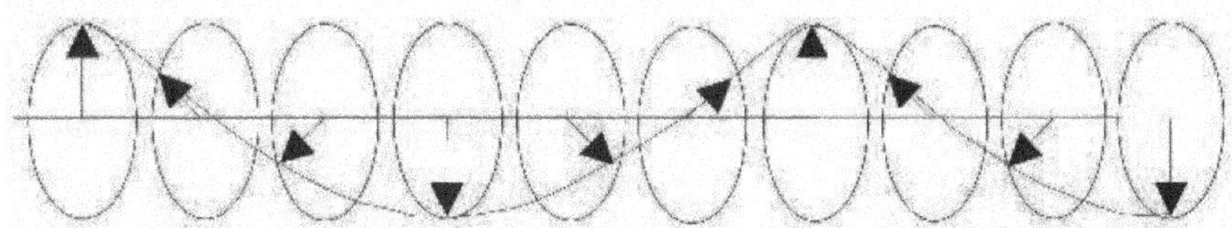

Figure 3.56

Linear and circular polarization used to create a stereo image

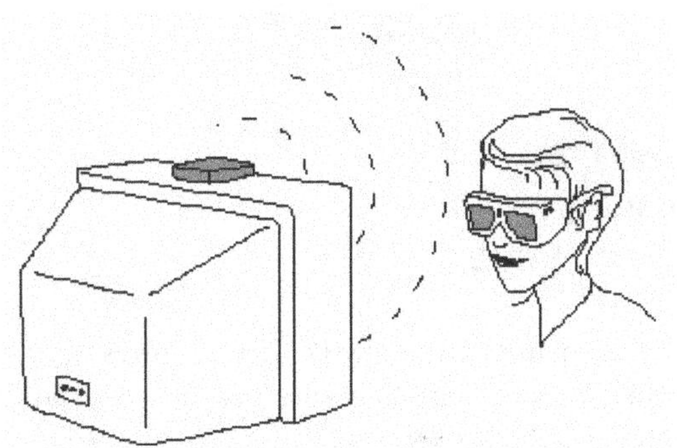

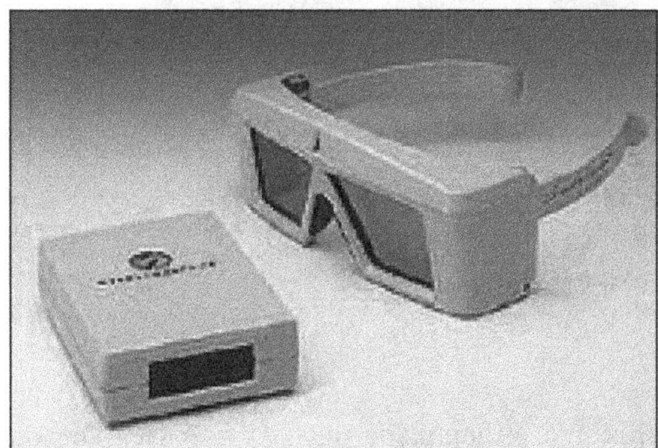

(Courtesy of Stereographics Corporation.)

Figure 3.57

Active stereo graphics using shuttered glasses

(© Lenny Lipton.)

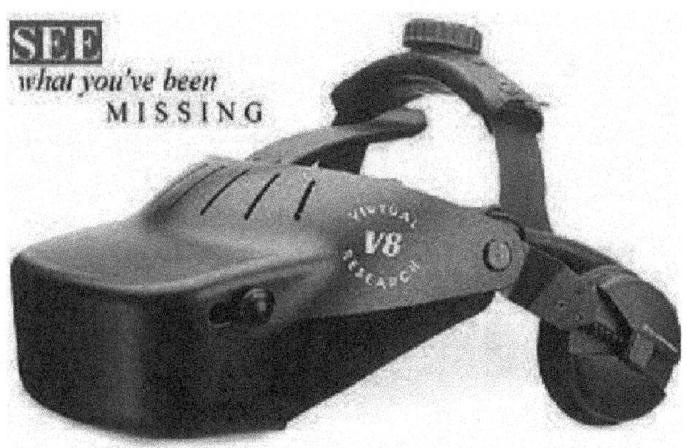

Figure 3.58

Head-mounted display for VR

(Courtesy of Virtual Research Systems, Inc.)

Figure 3.60

VR display

(Courtesy of StereoGraphics Corporation.)

Figure 3.59

Fishtank VR

(Courtesy of StereoGraphics Corporation.)

Figure 3.61

DLP projector

(Courtesy of Christie Digital Systems, Inc.)

one of this size. When using the CAVE, a user's head position is tracked and he or she wears shutter glasses to create a stereoscopic view. The degree of immersion in a CAVE is very high because the person is immersed in computer graphics that are projected for all sides.

Augmented Reality **Augmented reality** is a VR system that combines or overlays computer graphics imagery with a normal view of a scene. A head-mounted display allows the viewer to see the real scene with a transparent computer-generated image overlaid onto the special optical elements in the HMD. This requires very accurate tracking technology to ensure that the real and the computer-generated scenes are accurately aligned.

Tracking Devices In VR, real-time tracking is necessary to monitor the position and orientation of a user's head and hands. Tracking systems are mechanical, optical, ultrasonic, magnetic, or inertial. InterSense's tracking systems use a novel approach of combining inertial with ultrasonic tracking which offer highly stable and realistic interaction with the virtual environment. Most VR systems use an electromagnetic tracking system that has a source that emits an electromagnetic field and a sensor that detects

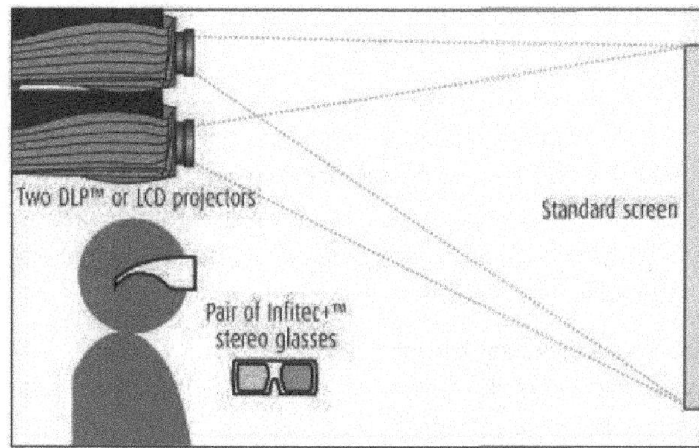

Figure 3.62

Passive stereo system

(Courtesy of Barco.)

Figure 3.63

Large rear-projected stereo display

(Courtesy of Fakespace Systems, Inc.)

Figure 3.64

CAVE®

(Courtesy of Fakespace Systems, Inc.)

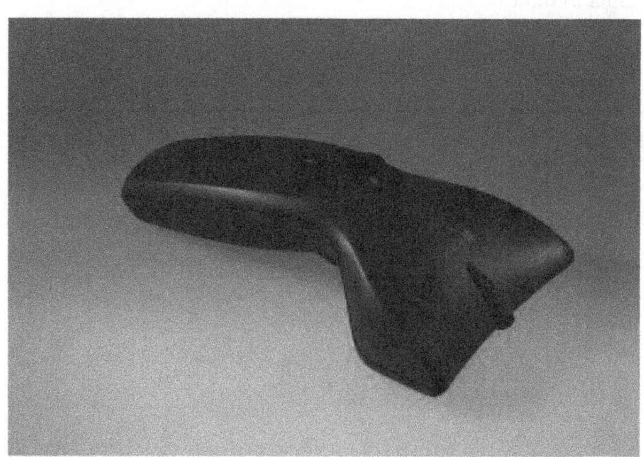

Figure 3.65

Hand tracking device

(Courtesy of InterSense, Inc.)

the radiated field. The source signals can be arrayed as a grid in a space with the sensor attached to a HMD or a 3-D mouse.

Hand and object tracking in VR normally is accomplished using a hand-tracking device (Figure 3.65). Normally these devices provide six degrees of freedom (DOF) for full volume tracking in CAVEs and wall VR systems. These navigation devices will have programmable buttons so they can be used like a mouse to make menu selections and to control 3-D objects in a virtual environment.

Hand tracking also is made possible by using a glove made of lightweight material with strain gauges or fiber optics sewn inside to measure finger joint angles (Figure 3.66 on page 96). Tracking gloves are used to communicate hand gestures such as pointing and grasping virtual objects. Some gloves even can provide tactile feedback through the use of small vibro-tactile stimulators located on each finger and the palm of the glove. When a virtual object is grasped, the tactile stimulators vibrate, causing the sensation of touch. Trackers also are located on the wrists of the gloves to monitor the position and orientation of the hand.

Design Case Study

The Motorola RAZR Mobile Phone

The following case study will provide an example of the design process for a digital communications company. It includes the ideation, refinement, and implementation stages as outlined in this chapter.

The proliferation of wireless communication products has brought with it a desire to integrate various services into one device. Increased efforts to miniaturize and combine capabilities have afforded great opportunities for designers to solve the problems of high function and small format. As wireless products migrate from novelty gadgets for early adopters to mainstream must-haves, designers, engineers, and product planners must concentrate on providing intuitive simplicity and positive product emotion for the end user.

This product, enabled by several breakthroughs in wireless technology, began with three major industrial design goals in mind:

- Generate a universal appeal to attract first time wireless users by restating the traditional "rectangular box" product in a less threatening, more intuitive package. Convey an image of consumer approachability while maintaining the client's heritage of reliable, rugged products.
- Create a desirable physical embodiment for a communication product that reinvents Motorola's long-standing equity in wireless communications by integrating paging, cellular, two-way, and data technologies.
- Develop a design compatible with Motorola's currently accepted manufacturing methods, environmental requirements, and cost goals.

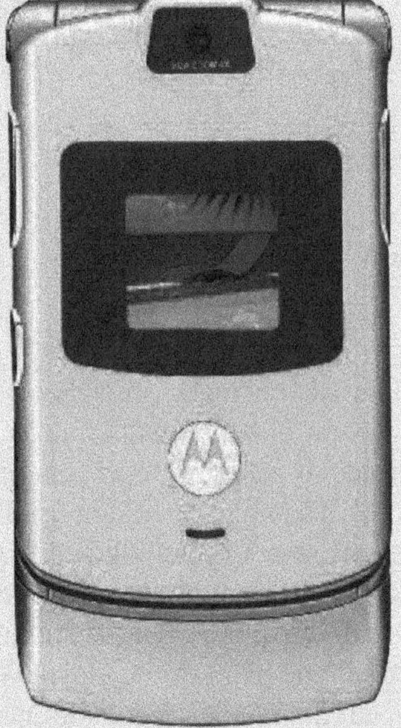

Motorola RAZR V3 phone
(© Motorola, Inc.)

Generate a Universal Appeal

Initial analysis of the "mess" involved multidisciplinary sessions where mindmapping and other creative problem-solving methods were used to identify the problem and create a profile of the user, the product, and the features. Marketing, engineering, human factors, and design team members generated and synthesized results into distinct descriptions of what was to become the RAZR. Early inputs included such diverse "wish list" aspects as the desire to incorporate a hands-free speakerphone, battery life goals, and desired product emotion targets. A clear desire to reach beyond Motorola's traditional commercial user base and connect with white-collar professionals and consumers emerged as a key theme in this early exploration. Establishing a method of capturing and evaluating preresearch data is essential to prevent the loss of early breakthrough ideas.

Effective form factor research in the development of the RAZR was important in light of our desire to generate a universal appeal and enhance the user experience. Three hundred end users in various locations were interviewed and presented with 9 different form factor solutions to gauge preference in such areas as wearability, fit to the face while in use, folding scheme, and general appeal. Forms ranging from crisp to soft and incorporating different folding schemes were generated by industrial designers using solid modeling software and stereolithography tools. This testing yielded data on the form factor direction we should take. The "clamshell," or top-hinged format, emerged as the most preferred in our findings, affording users a high degree of portability while also offering a degree of privacy while in use.

Additional observation during research proved to be a great benefit to us as designers when, in addition to relying on written research reports, we were able to personally observe and participate in one-on-one interviews to discern "unspoken" opinions and comments from users. Research of this type often reveals a lot of peripheral information that is outside the scope of the interviewer's script and doesn't get recorded. Solutions to these unarticulated needs can be those which bring the most satisfaction to the end user.

An observing designer can learn much from the intensity and nuance with which a user discounts a certain feature,

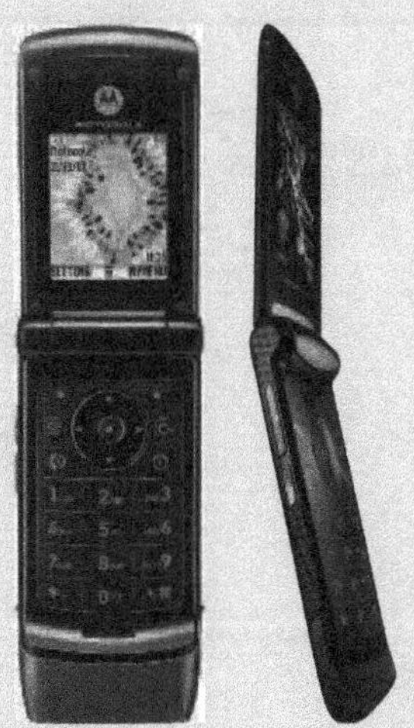

Montage
Several concepts were evaluated as the development of the RAZR progressed.
(© Motorola, Inc.)

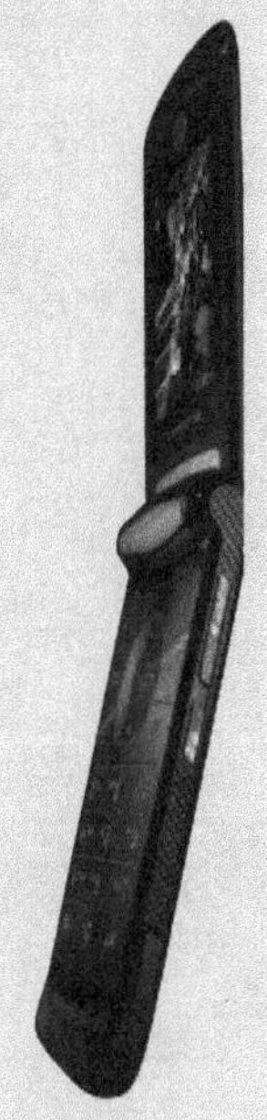

Clamshell design
The final design decision was to create a flip style or clamshell design for the phone.
(© Motorola, Inc.)

embraces another, or casually suggests a third. "Reading between the lines" was especially helpful as many users voiced a need to access certain display information at all times on their communication device. This need conflicted with a high percentage of users who also desired a hinged "clamshell" door to protect and cover the device and provide a face-fitting form when opened. Combining these two seemingly conflicting requirements resulted in the idea of creating a window in the clamshell door which affords protection but also allows the user to access many functions of the product in its closed state. A pair of door-mounted soft keys located at the base of the window actuate various functions by pushing through to corresponding keys on the main body of the phone. The paradox of providing a simplified device with only a few visible keys yet allowing access to the display information was solved by listening to what users really wanted and forming a solution on the fly in the field, not in the isolated confines of the design studio.

Create a Desirable Communication Product

The "clamshell" solution is one we had looked at since 1991 for various telephone only products and it seemed to have good potential to convey the dual personality needed for this application.

It was agreed early on that the form of the RAZR must present a variety of complex technologies in a user-friendly embodiment. A design language combining traditional cellular and two-way radio cues yet introducing a unique character was created to convey the mission of the product to the user. Early design goals called for the shape of this product to invite the user to hold it. A subtle tapering of the form from top to bottom allows the product to fit well in the hand. This borrows from the heritage of Motorola's iconic handheld mobile microphones. The appearance is intended to give the product a character which hints at the underlying features without looking overly complex. The domed feature on the front surface adds visual softness while forming the reverse side of the ear cup.

Meet Motorola's Product Goals

Important in any high-volume product development program are goals regarding cost, time, and manufacturability. Once the initial industrial design solution was agreed upon, a "vision rendering" was archived by Motorola's division general manager and referred to as a master drawing throughout the program to assure we stayed on course.

The hand-held nature of this product demands that it be modeled in 3-D and evaluated as quickly as possible. As industrial designers we generated the external form of the product in its entirety using the same solids modeling software as the engineering development groups. Extensive use of our internal rapid prototyping center enabled the creation of numerous wax deposition and stereolithography models

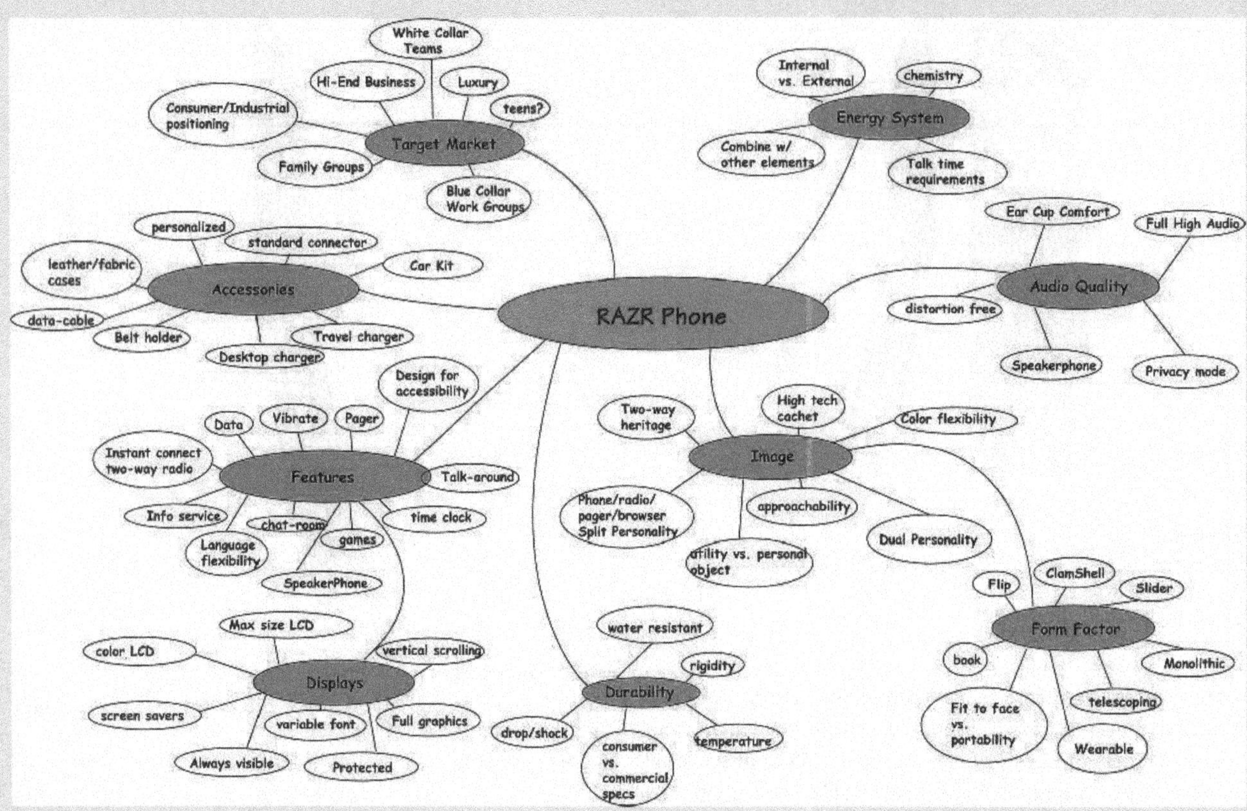

Mind map

Predesign "mind maps" incorporated diverse requirements and "wish list" elements.

to analyze concepts and gain additional user feedback in a greatly reduced time frame.

This common tool platform made for a seamless transfer of data with the design intent remaining intact. It also allowed us to participate in various inevitable last-minute modifications directly on the engineering databases before tooling was initiated. The iterative nature of design is facilitated by the quick results available from common databases and the existence of a common 3-D "language."

Motorola RAZR Final Design Features

Motorola marked an industry first with the unveiling fo the Motorola RAZR V3—an ultra-slim, metal-clad flip phone sporting fantastivally good looks along with full-featured functionality. In a major innovation in design and engineering, the RAZR V3 team has created a phone of firsts. The combination of metals, such as aircraft-grade aluminum, with new advances, such as an internal antenna and a chemically-etched keypad, led to the formation of a device that measures just 13.9 mm thin. Key features include:

Bluetooth® Wireless Technology

Stay connected without wires. Choose from a range of optional Bluetooth® accessories.

- **Anodized Aluminium Case**—the ultra-thin Moto RAZR V3 has the distinctive metallic lustre of anodized aluminum.
- **MPEG4 Video Playback**—download and watch sports action and music clips. They're all beautifully displayed on the large 2.2 color display.
- **Digital Camera**—capture your world in style. Create memorable images with the effective 4× digital zoom and quick exposure controls.
- **Built-in Speakerphone**—keep the conversation flowing when you're busy by going hands-free. Or exchange ideas in a conference call.

Fun Features

User-customizable Soft key functions, Main Menu and Shortcuts

Games: 3-D Java-embedded and space for downloads

Downloadable themes (Ringtones, wallpaper and screen-savers)

MOTOMIXER™ (Remixable MIDI ringer software)

Polyphonic ringtones

Picture phone book

MP3 ringtones

Polyphonic speaker: 22 Khz polyphonic speaker with 22 chord support

Video download

Video clip playback with sound

Precision cut metal keypad

Integrated digital VGA camera with 4× digital zoom and light

Call Management Features

Speech recognition

Integrated speakerphone

Caller group profiling

Time and date stamp

Phone Book: Up to 1000 entries on phone plus up to 250 on SIM card

VibraCall alert

Where to Find Cases

Many engineering case studies, histories, and problems have already been developed and can be used to design your own cases for little or no cost. Here are some sources:

The Center for Case Studies in Engineering
Campus Box 139
Rose-Hulman Institute of Technology
5500 Wabash Avenue
Terre Haute, IN 47803–3999

The catalog of ASEE engineering cases can be accessed free of charge through the Internet; there is a small per-page fee to order copies of the cases.

http://www.cee.carleton.ca/ECL/

National Engineering Education Delivery System (NEEDS)

Supported by the NSF-funded Synthesis coalition—including the University of California at Berkeley, Cornell University, and Tuskegee University—NEEDS makes course materials, including cases, available through World Wide Web and telnet. It can be accessed through:

http://www.synthesis.org

http://ublib.buffalo.edu/libraries/projects/cases/case.html

National Center for Case Study Teaching in Science

http://ethics.tamu.edu/

http://onlineethics.org/cases/index.html

Engineering Ethics Case Studies

Other sources of cases:

H. Scott Fogler, *Strategies for Creative Problem Solving.* Englewood Cliffs, NJ: Prentice-Hall, 1994.

Henry Petroski, *Design Paradigms: Case Histories of Error and Judgment in Engineering.* New York: Cambridge University Press, 1994.

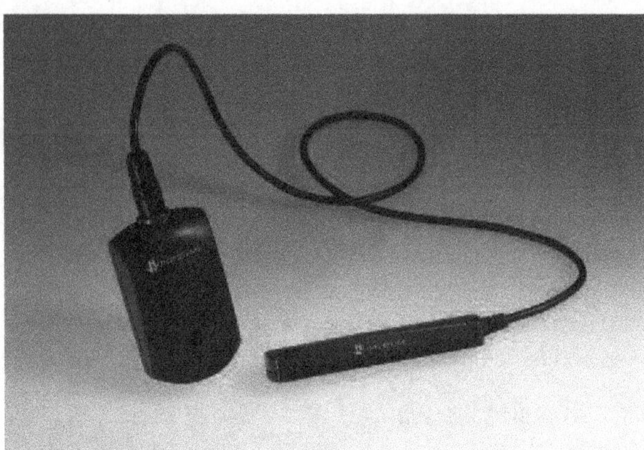

Figure 3.66

Tracking glove

(Courtesy of InterSense, Inc.)

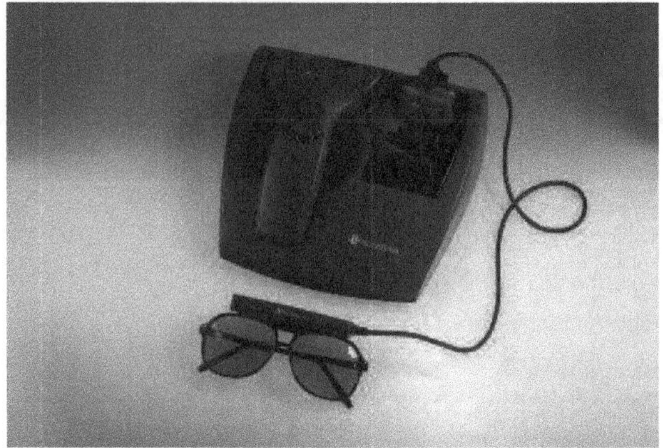

Figure 3.67

Wireless head-tracking device

(Courtesy of InterSense, Inc.)

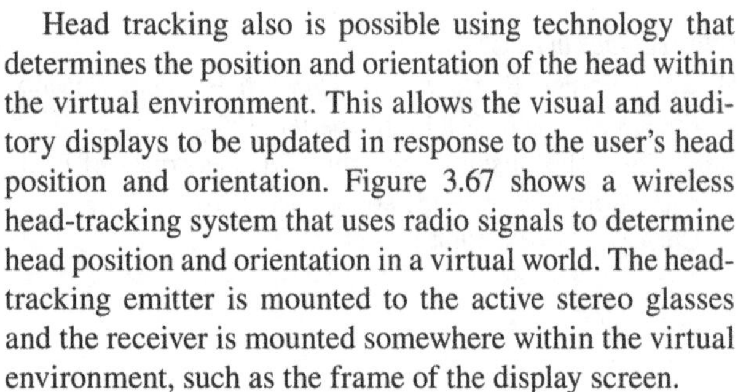

Head tracking also is possible using technology that determines the position and orientation of the head within the virtual environment. This allows the visual and auditory displays to be updated in response to the user's head position and orientation. Figure 3.67 shows a wireless head-tracking system that uses radio signals to determine head position and orientation in a virtual world. The head-tracking emitter is mounted to the active stereo glasses and the receiver is mounted somewhere within the virtual environment, such as the frame of the display screen.

Virtual Reality (Software) Applications There are many applications of virtual reality in business, industry, government, research, and education. The use of virtual reality in industry has shown great promise and is becoming more common for oil and gas exploration, engineering design—especially in the automotive and aerospace industries—and scientific visualization for research in many of the basic sciences. Virtual reality also is beginning to show promise for medical applications, entertainment, architectural design, training, and manufacturing.

3.10 Summary

This chapter introduced you to modern design practices. Graphics have been and will continue to be an important part of engineering design. Graphics, in all forms, are the communications medium of choice in the design process. The use of computers to create 3-D models is a critical part of the modern design process. These models are used to generate a database of information that can be shared with all of the members of the design team and used to develop and analyze the product. In addition to creating 3-D models using CAD software, the design team also makes use of many other types of graphical software to visualize their design problem. Creating visualizations such as charts and graphs requires knowledge of what information you are trying to present and how best to present it to achieve maximum effectiveness. As has always been true, the engineer and technologist must know how to use all types of graphics and integrate them into the design process effectively to be successful in industry.

Online Learning Center (OLC) Features

There are a number of Online Learning Center features listed below that you can use to supplement your text reading to improve your understanding and retention of the material presented in this chapter at www.mhhe.com/bertoline.

- Learning Objectives
- Chapter Outline
- Chapter Overview
- Questions for Review
- Multiple Choice Quiz
- True or False Questions
- Flashcards
- Website Links
- Stapler Design Problem

Questions for Review

1. Describe the design process.
2. Describe the engineering design process.
3. Describe engineering analysis.
4. Describe aesthetic analysis.
5. Define documentation.
6. Define a production drawing.
7. Describe how CAD is used in the design process.
8. Describe the role of graphics in the design process.
9. Describe presentation graphics.
10. Highlight the important ways that graphics are used throughout the design process.
11. Describe and sketch the concurrent engineering model.
12. Describe and sketch the concurrent documentation model.
13. Describe DFM.
14. List and describe the modeling techniques used in design.
15. Describe real or physical modeling.
16. Describe the difference between simulation and animation.
17. Describe the reverse engineering process.
18. Define and describe knowledge-based engineering (KBE).
19. Describe the rapid prototyping process and why it is useful in engineering design.
20. What is a fundamental difference between 2-D and 3-D CAD systems? Is there any overlap between the two types of CAD systems?
21. Explain the advantages and disadvantages of using a virtual model over a real model when designing a product.
22. Describe the areas of technical design in which data visualization is important. How does data visualization differ from traditional engineering graphics?
23. Explain the different roles the network server and client workstations play in product data management (PDM).
24. List and briefly describe three types of design projects.
25. What is the purpose of a designer's notebook?
26. Why are standards important in the design and documentation of a product?

Further Reading

Dreyfuss, H. *The Measure of Man, Human Factors in Design.* New York: Whitney Library of Design, 1967.

Guide for Patent Draftsmen (Selected Rules of Practice Relating to Patent Drawings). Washington, D.C.: U.S. Department of Commerce, Patent and Trademark Office, 1989.

Henderson, K. *On Line and On Paper.* Cambridge, MA: The MIT Press.

LaCourse, D.E., ed. *Handbook of Solid Modeling.* New York: McGraw-Hill, 1995.

Norris, G. et al. *e-business and ERP: Transforming the Enterprise.* New York: Wiley, 2000.

Ullman, D. G. *The Mechanical Design Process,* 2d ed. New York: McGraw-Hill, 1997.

Supplement

Supplement

Design Problems

General Instructions

The following design problems are intended to challenge you to be creative, individually or in a group. Those problems designed specifically for a group are so labeled. The design problems are not meant to teach the design process, as much as how to represent ideas graphically, using primarily computer models and drawings as necessary. Any design problem labeled a concept means that all details of the solution are not necessary.

For each problem, you must create the documentation as necessary to communicate your solution to others. The items to be created are specified with each problem. If not, then the engineering drawings should include the following:

1. Initial design sketches.
2. Multiview drawings, with dimensions. (Concept designs only need critical dimensions and details, where necessary.)
3. Sectioned assembly drawings, with parts list.
4. Pictorial drawings of the final design, with parts list where appropriate.

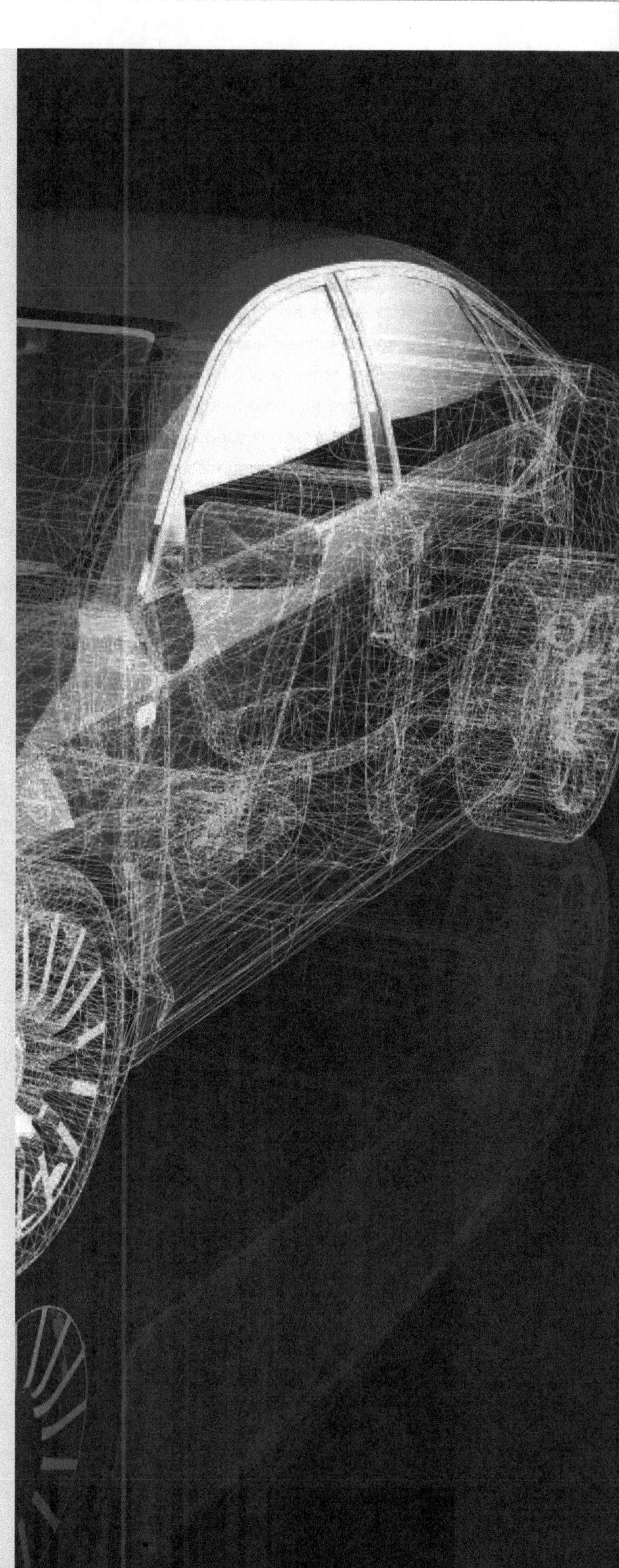

Design Problems

PROBLEM 1:

Desktop Fan Design Project

Project Goals

1. Practice the creation of hybrid geometric models (surface and solid geometry within the same model).
2. Develop techniques for combining surface and solid geometry into one model.
3. Develop basic surface modeling techniques using primitive geometry.
4. Develop basic surface modeling techniques using simple curves.
5. Practice modeling and editing techniques using surface geometry.

STEP 1: Problem Identification

A discount consumer products company has asked you to design a small desktop fan that could be used in an office or apartment setting. The fan will be smaller than current pedestal or box models, and likely will sell for a substantially cheaper price. It will be made of inexpensive (or even recycled) materials. In order to successfully market their product to the intended audience, several criteria have been developed by the corporate marketing and consumer affairs staff. They are:

- The fan will be made of plastic, not to be more than 30% transparent for any given part.
- The design must be consistent with a stylized product—no sharp corners and no square-looking geometry on the housing or stand of the fan.
- You are responsible for modeling the fan housing or shroud, the blades, the motor housing the support stand, and the controls and adjustment mechanisms for the fan. You DO NOT have to model the motor or the power cord.
- Buttons, control knobs, position/angle adjustment mechanisms all should be stylized geometry.
- The fan should have a unique color scheme.
- The fan should have 3 or 4 blades.
- All surfaces and curves should have at least C2 (G2) continuity conditions so that a child will not injure itself.
- Overall size of the fan should be no more than 14″ in its longest dimension.
- Large or major areas of material thickness should be avoided. Typical wall thickness for parts should be 1/6″ to 1/18″.
- The object should weigh no more than 2–3 pounds (remember that this is **EXCLUDING** the motor).

STEP 2: Ideation (Brainstorming)

Make engineering/technical sketches of **at least five** possible design sketches of the fan. Solutions should include appropriate design notations about possible colors and basic dimensional information. To determine appropriate dimensions and to get design ideas, visit local department and hardware stores with sketching paper and tape measure/calipers in hand. Other sources of information may be found on the Internet, television, or in magazines. These sketches should include a combination of orthographic and isometric sketches.

STEP 3: Refine/Analyze

Analyze and critique all of the ideas generated during ***Step 2: Ideation*** with a fellow classmate.

Refine our ideation sketches according to the feedback received from your classmates as well as the instructor. For this step, add more details including color, to the sketches of the design solution. Include in this set of sketches a pictorial view of the object that shows the fan in its completed form. Overall dimensional information also should be included. Some type of assembly would also be relevant here.

STEP 4: Decision

Create a decision matrix and assign a rating for how well each of the five (or more) designs meets the design parameters defined in ***Step 1***. You may add other design parameters that you think are appropriate. Shown here is an example decision matrix for this project. Five is the highest (strongest) value, and one is the lowest (weakest) value. You do not necessarily have to use this numbering scheme, but you must develop a method for weighting your criteria to determine the best design. After the ratings have been assigned for each design, the **highest rated** design will be carried forward to ***Step 5***. Write a one-paragraph rationale for the selection of this particular design.

Example of a Decision Matrix

DESIGN I	DESIGN II	DESIGN III	DESIGN PARAMETERS
5	5	4	Plastic material
5	5	5	Weight
4	5	4	Maximum size
3	4	5	Material thickness
4	4	5	Color
5	3	4	Continuity conditions
26	26	27	**Total**

STEP 5: Documentation

All sketches for the project should be included in the documentation phase of the project. Your decision matrix and rationale also should be included, along with a description of the selection of the final idea from the ideation stage.

STEP 6: Implementation

Create 3-D models of the fan components in the CAD software, taking into account the criteria detailed in the previous steps. **It is expected that surface and solid geometry will be combined within each model file**. An assembly model should be included.

Optional:

- Create a detail drawing of each non-standard part included in your fan.
- Create an assembly drawing of your fan model including a complete bill of materials.

PROBLEM 2:

Wheel Design Project

Project Goals

1. Give a deeper appreciation of the conceptual end of the engineering design process.
2. Develop conceptual 3-D modeling techniques using 3-D curves, surfaces, and solids.
3. Practice manipulation and editing techniques using 3-D geometry.
4. Analyze and adjust boundary conditions to obtain requisite continuity conditions.
5. Practice presentation skills.

STEP 1: Problem Identification

A manufacture of after-market auto parts has contracted with you to design the next generation of custom rims for vehicles. As such, they are looking for something that is similar in functional design requirements to current market offerings, yet is unique in shape and form. The finished wheels will be made out of aluminum or steel, depending on the needs of the customer. In order to successfully market their product and increase its exposure, several criteria have been developed by corporate marketers and outside consultants. They are:

- The wheel should accommodate four or five lugs on the hub of the vehicle.
- The wheel should use three, four or five spokes in its design.
- Sharp edges should be kept to a minimum.
- Excess weight should be kept to a minimum.

- The wheel should be of a standard size, preferably 16,17, or 18 inches in diameter.
- The width of the wheel should be appropriate for the wheel diameter and tire size range selected.
- Given the size requirements in the previous point, the wheel should accommodate a standard tire acceptable for the selected size.
- Surface model must exhibit appropriate continuity conditions.

STEP 2: Ideation (Brainstorming)

Make engineering/technical sketches of **at least five** possible designs that meet the design parameters defined in ***Step 1: Problem Identification***. Solutions should include appropriate design notations about possible colors and basic dimensional information. To determine appropriate dimensions and to get design ideas, visit local auto stores or car dealerships with sketching paper and tape measure/calipers in hand. Other source of information may be found on the Internet, television, or in magazines.

STEP 3: Refine/Analyze

Analyze and critique all of the ideas generated during ***Step 2: Ideation*** with a fellow classmate. Each of you should give verbal and written comments to each other. **Refine your ideation sketches** according to the feedback received from your classmate as well as the instructor. For this step, add more details to the sketches of the design solution, including dimensional information that adheres to the above criteria.

STEP 4: Decision

Create a decision matrix and assign a rating for how well each of the seven designs meets the design parameters defined in ***Step 1.*** Add other design parameters that you think are appropriate. Shown here is an example decision matrix for each criterion. Five is the highest (strongest) value, and one is the lowest (weakest) value. You do not necessarily have to use this numbering scheme, but you must develop a method for weighing your criteria to determine the best design. After the ratings have been assigned for each design, the ***highest rated*** design will be carried forward to ***Step 5***. Write a one-paragraph rationale a justification for the selection of this particular design. Should there be a tie score, include in your rationale a justification for selecting the final wheel design. The following decision matrix should be viewed as an example and **NOT** an all-inclusive list of criteria.

Example of a Decision Matrix

DESIGN I	DESIGN II	DESIGN III	DESIGN PARAMETERS
5	5	4	Number of spokes
5	5	5	Number of lugs
4	5	4	Maximum size
3	4	5	Body contours
4	4	5	Ease of assembly
5	3	4	Weight
26	26	27	**Total**

STEP 5: Planning

Once the final wheel design has been selected for modeling, a modeling procedure should be created to serve as a plan for geometry creation. This will include sketches of the major curves/profiles/contours to be used in the creation of the various features on the object and the surface creation operation to be performed on them. At this stage, you also should consider and label boundary conditions between the major geometric components of the various parts of the wheel for which you are responsible.

STEP 6: Implementation

Create 3-D model of the wheel using your CAD system. Each finished wheel model should include some type of organization scheme for the geometry created specifically in that model. Suggested layers might include (but are not limited to) construction geometry, curves, surfaces, temporary surfaces created as a result of a geometry operation, finished surfaces, solid geometry, etc. Assigning various colors to these layers (stages of the model) may be helpful to keep track of geometry.

Optional:

- Create a detail drawing of your wheel, including cross-section views as necessary to describe the wheel.
- If your wheel is created in multiple parts, include an assembly drawing of the fully assembled wheel, including the bill of materials and identification balloons.

PROBLEM 3:
Infant Toy Design Project

Project Goals

1. Give a deeper understanding of the conceptual end of the engineering design process.
2. Develop basic modeling techniques using primitive geometry and simple curves and surfaces.
3. Develop editing techniques for 3-D geometry.
4. Practice presentation skills.

STEP 1: Problem Identification

A major toy manufacturing company has asked you serve as a contract designer in the development of their new infant toy design. The company is considering a theme that will center on either animals or vehicles, so a set of toys representing something like a car or a giraffe would not be out of the question. An age group of less than two years will be the target range for this new product. In order to successfully market their product and ensure its safety for infants, several criteria have been developed by the corporate marketing and consumer affairs staff. They are:

- The toy will be made of plastic, not to be more than 30% transparent.
- The toy will have a typical wall thickness of 1/16″ inch.
- The design must be consistent with the desired theme: animals or vehicle.
- There should be *very* few, if any, moving parts.
- There should be **NO** removable parts which can be swallowed easily by the child.
- There should be two or three individual toys in the group, and the common elemental geometry *should be obvious to the casual observer.*
- Shape and contour of the object should fit the grasp of an infant within the specified age range.
- Large, bold areas of color should be used in the finished design.
- All surfaces should have smooth edges so that the child will not injure itself.
- Overall size of each individual object should be no more than 6″ in its longest dimension and 2″ in its shortest dimension.
- Each finished object should weigh no more than 6 ounces. Select an appropriate plastic material to meet this criteria.

STEP 2: Ideation (Brainstorming)

Make engineering/technical sketches of **at least four** possible design families that may meet the design parameters defined in ***Step 1: Problem Identification***. Solutions should include appropriate design notations about possible colors and basic dimensional information. To determine appropriate dimensions and to get design ideas, visit local department and toy stores with sketching paper and tape measure/calipers in hand. Check out toys that some of your younger relatives may have played with. Other sources of information may be found on the Internet, television, or in magazines. You can examine existing children's toys for sizes, shapes, and materials, but you should emphasize being different from the competition while still adhering to the criteria. These sketches should include a combination of orthographic and isometric sketches.

STEP 3: Refine/Analyze

Analyze and critique all of the ideas generated during ***Step 2: Ideation*** with a fellow classmate. Refine your ideation sketches according to the feedback received from your classmates as well as the instructor. For this step, add more detail, including color, to the sketches of the design solution. Include in this set of sketches a pictorial view of the object that shows the infant toy in its completed form. Overall dimensional information also should be included.

STEP 4: Decision

Create a decision matrix and assign a rating for how well each of the five (or more) designs meets the design parameters defined in ***Step 1***. You may add other design parameters that you think are appropriate. Shown here is an example decision matrix for each criteria. Five is the highest (strongest) value, and one is the lowest (weakest) value. You do not necessarily have to use this numbering scheme, but you must develop a method for weighting your criteria to determine the best design. After the ratings have been assigned for each design, the ***highest rated*** design will be carried forward to ***Step 5***. Write a one-paragraph rationale for selecting this particular design.

Example of a Decision Matrix

DESIGN I	DESIGN II	DESIGN III	DESIGN PARAMETERS
5	5	4	Plastic material
5	5	5	Weight
4	5	4	Maximum size
3	4	5	Toy theme
4	4	5	Color
5	3	4	Safety issues
26	26	27	**Total**

STEP 5: Documentation

Your finished ideation and refinement sketches also should be included. All project research, engineering/technical sketches for your design, your rationale and decision matrix, and your refined sketches should be compiled in a project packet. An "assembly" sketch also should be included if your group of toys is meant to fit together in some way. Each object should be clearly labeled and given its own color scheme.

STEP 6: Implementation

Create 3-D Models of the infant toy in the CAD system, taking into account the criteria detailed in the previous steps.

Optional:

- Create a detail drawing of the infant you, including cross-section views as necessary to describe the toy.
- If your infant toy was created in multiples parts, include an assembly drawing of the fully assembled toy, including the bill of materials and identification balloons.

PROBLEM 4:

Sports Drink Bottle Design Project

Project Goals:

1. Provide an example of the conceptual end of the engineering design process.
2. Develop basic 3-D modeling techniques using constraint-based techniques.
3. Practice manipulation and editing techniques using constraint-based geometry.
4. Practice presentation skills.

STEP 1: Problem Identification

A major sports drink producer has asked you to develop the new line of packaging for their products, which includes a new primary retail container. This is the same container that consumers will see on the shelf in their local grocery or convenience store, and it also will be sold in vending machines. The company is looking for a fresh, exciting look to their packaging to coincide with today's active lifestyles. In order to successfully market their product and maintain its freshness during shelf life, several criteria have been developed by corporate marketers and food scientists. They are:

- The container will be made of plastic, not to be more than 20% transparent.

- The design must hold one-half (0.5) liter of sports drink. Final model should be +/−0.05 liter. This volume is based on the liquid being 0.5 inches from the top of the bottle.
- To facilitate reuse, the cap to the bottle must be removable, and when reattached, form a liquid-tight seal. This implies that there will be multiple parts to the finished design.
- The container can be no larger than 8″ in its largest dimension.
- The design of the shape of the container must allow for the product to be sold in 12-pack lots using a minimum amount of shelf space. The 12-pack should be no more than 140 square inches.
- The empty container (including cap) must weigh no more than 5 ounces. You will have to select a density ratio for an appropriate plastic to use in the creation of a beverage bottle. Include this selection process in your final documentation.
- The consumer must be able to drink from the bottle.

STEP 2: Ideation (Brainstorming)

Make engineering/technical sketches of **at least seven** possible designs that may meet the design parameters defined in ***Step 1: Problem Identification***. Solutions should include appropriate design notations about possible colors and basic dimensional information. To determine appropriate dimensions and to get design ideas, visit local grocery and convenience stores with sketching paper and tape measure/calipers in hand. Other sources of information may be found on the Internet, television, or in magazines. You can examine existing sports drink container sizes, shapes, mechanisms, and materials, but your design should extend and improve these factors as much as possible. You should emphasize being different from the competition while still adhering to the criteria above.

STEP 3: Refine/Analyze

Analyze and critique all of the ideas generated during ***Step 2: Ideation*** with a fellow classmate. Each of you should give verbal and written comments to each other. Refine your ideation sketches according to the feedback received from your classmates as well as the instructor. For this step, add more detail to the sketches of the design solution, including dimensional information that adheres to the above criteria. Include in this set of sketches an exploded pictorial view of the various bottle designs to describe the assembly and disassembly of each potential container design.

STEP 4: Decision

Create a decision matrix and assign a rating for how well each of the seven design meets the design parameters defined in ***Step 1***. Add other design parameters that you think are appropriate. Shown here is an example decision matrix for each criterion. Five is the highest (strongest) value, and one is the lowest (weakest) value. You do not necessarily have to use this numbering scheme, but you must develop a method for weighting your criteria to determine the best design. After the ratings have been assigned for each design, the ***highest rated*** design will be carried forward ***Step 5***. Write a one-paragraph rationale for the selection of this particular design. Should there be a tie score, include in your rationale a justification for selecting the final container design. The following decision matrix should be viewed as an example and **NOT** and all-inclusive list of criteria. You should have an explicit rationale for how the selected idea meets the final criteria.

Example of a Decision Matrix

DESIGN I	DESIGN II	DESIGN III	DESIGN PARAMETERS
5	5	4	Plastic material
5	5	5	Minimize space
4	5	4	Maximum size
3	4	5	Aesthetic appeal
4	4	5	Ease of assembly
5	3	4	Weight
26	26	27	**Total**

STEP 5: Implementation

Create 3-D models of the various pieces of the sports drink container using your CAD software. Each model should include some kind of organizational scheme for the geometry created specifically in that model. Each part of the container should be given its own unique color and/or material.

Optional:

- Create a detail drawing of your bottle, including cross-section views as necessary to describe the complete bottle.
- Include an assembly drawing of the fully assembled bottle, including the bill of materials and identification balloons.

PROBLEM 5:

Wearable Flashlight Design Project

Project Goals

1. Provide an example of the conceptual end of the engineering design process.
2. Develop basic 3-D modeling techniques using constraint-based techniques.
3. Practice manipulation and editing techniques using constraint-based geometry.
4. Develop a basic understanding of data exchange for modeling purposes.
5. Practice presentation skills.

STEP 1: Problem Identification

A major outdoor and survival outfitter has asked you to develop their new line of wearable flashlights, which are geared towards high-end outdoor and military applications. Since these models will be purchased primarily by civilians, they must accommodate standard batteries and charging devices. The company is looking for a very stylized look to these products, but they must be durable and ergonomic in nature to perform their desired function. You are responsible for the external components of the light, which include any bottoms or switches, the housing, the lens/bulb cover, and the battery compartment and cover. While you are not directly responsible for the mechanisms of the battery compartment or its cover, you need to account for its volume when designing the housing of the flashlight. You will be provided models to use as reference for the battery. It has been determined that the light will operate on the standard batteries. In order to successfully market their product and increase its usability, several criteria have been developed by corporate marketers and outside consultants. They are:

- The major flashlight components will be made of plastic, typically 1/16″ thick.
- Any buttons will be made of some "rubberized" or synthetic material to promote a good grip.
- To facilitate use, the flashlight will operate on four AA batteries or one 9-volt battery.
- The final bulb/reflector combination ideally would have a focal length of around 35 feet. This value should be used as a guideline. Depending on the final geometry of your flashlight housing, your effective lighting distance may vary; however, this specification is similar to those flashlights in the current market. You will need to do some research concerning light/optics and the behavior of light in order to address this requirement. Check out the following sources to get started:

  http://members.misty.com/don/light.html

  http://www.carleylamps.com/reflectors.htm
- The design of the shape of the flashlight housing must address the contours of the human body where it will be located. Particular attention should be given to the head, hands, or upper body, as these make particularly good places to locate a light.
- The design of the light should be careful to avoid unnecessarily hindering the portion of the body to which it is located.

- The empty flashlight (excluding batteries) must weigh no more than 0.5 pounds. Obviously, this will have an effect on the area of the body on which its placed, so something on the head or hand likely will weigh less.
- An appropriate material should be researched and specified relative to the previous point.
- The flashlight must be water tight.
- The body/housing of the light should follow the primary contours of the area of the human body in question. Straps or fabric for attachment purposes should be minimized.
- For packaging and shipping reasons, the flashlight should be no larger than 12″ in its largest dimension.
- The finished flashlight assembly model must contain separate parts for the body, (end) cap, lens, lens housing, bulb, and control switch/button as appropriate.

STEP 2: Ideation (Brainstorming)

Make engineering/technical sketches of **at least five** possible designs that may meet the design parameters defined in ***Step 1: Problem Identification***. To determine appropriate dimensions and to get design ideas, visit local department stores or outdoor/sporting goods stores with sketching paper and tape measure/calipers in hand. Other sources of information may be found on the Internet, television, or in magazines. You can examine existing flashlight sizes, shapes, mechanisms, and materials, but your design should extend and improve these factors as much as possible. You should emphasize being different from the competition while still adhering to the criteria above.

STEP 3: Refine/Analyze

Analyze and critique all of the ideas generated during ***Step 2: Ideation*** with a fellow classmate. Each of you should give verbal and written comments to each other. Refine your ideation sketches according to the feedback received from your classmates as well as the instructor. For this step, add more detail to the sketches of the design solution, including dimensional information that adheres to the above criteria. Include in this set of sketches an exploded pictorial view of the various flashlights to describe the assembly and disassembly of each potential design.

STEP 4: Decision

Create a decision matrix and assign a rating for how well each of the seven designs meets the design parameters defined in ***Step 1***. Add other design parameters that you think are appropriate. Shown here is an example decision matrix for each criterion. Five is the highest (strongest) value, and one is the lowest (weakest) value. You do not necessarily have to use this numbering scheme, but you must develop a method for weighting your criteria to determine the best design. After the ratings have been assigned for each design, the ***highest rated*** design will be carried forward to ***Step 5***. Write a one-paragraph rationale for the selection of this particular design. Should there be a tie score, include in your rationale a justification for selecting the final flashlight design. The following decision matrix should be viewed as an example and **NOT** an all-inclusive list of criteria.

Example of a Decision Matrix

DESIGN I	DESIGN II	DESIGN III	DESIGN PARAMETERS
5	5	4	Location on the human body
5	5	5	Battery accommodation
4	5	4	Maximum size
3	4	5	Geometry contours
4	4	5	Watertight
5	3	4	Weight
26	26	27	**Total**

STEP 5: Implementation

Create 3-D models of the various pieces of the flashlight using your CAD system. As a suggestion, each finished model should have some form of organization scheme to accommodate the various types of construction and final geometry that were created. You also may want to give each part of the flashlight its own unique color for identification purposes.

STEP 7: Presentation

You will be evaluated based on the following criteria:

- Rationale for final design selection including any calculations/figures for determining the shape of the reflector
- Uniqueness of final design
- Quality of project document
- Quality of sketches
- Model quality according to customer criteria

Optional:

- Create a detail drawing of your flashlight components, including cross-section views as necessary to describe the complete part.
- Include an assembly drawing of the fully assembled flashlight, including the bill of materials and identification balloons.

Additional Design Problems

1. **Concept solar-powered vehicle.** (Group) Design a solar-powered concept vehicle, for one passenger, that can travel up to 20 mph.
2. **Concept olympic-sized swimming pool.** (Group) Design an olympic-sized swimming facility that will seat 3500 people.
3. **Ergonomic three-button mouse.** Design an ergonomic computer mouse, with three buttons, that can be used by left- and right-handed people.
4. **Reading lamp.** Design a reading lamp that can be attached to a desk and adjusted to various positions.
5. **Portable stadium seat.** Design a portable stadium seat, with a backrest that can be folded flat and with storage for a rain poncho.
6. **Cordless telephone.** Design a cordless telephone.
7. **Concept mountain bike.** (Group) Design a lightweight frame for a 26-inch mountain bike with a shock-absorbing front fork.
8. **Concept sports car.** (Group) Design a sports car for two passengers.
9. **Workpiece hold-down device.** Design a quick-release hold-down device used for holding down a workpiece in a wood or metal shop. The device must be able to hold material up to 3 inches thick and have at least an 8-inch reach. It should have the ability to release the workpiece quickly, and should be easy to position and move to other work surfaces. The holding strength of the device should also be considered.
10. **Portable light.** Design a battery-powered portable lighting system that leaves the operator's hands free. Define a task for which the operator would need such lighting, and design a light for that situation. Consider the environment in which the operator is working and the amount of light needed for the task.
11. **Cellular telephone mount.** Design a system for mounting cellular telephones in cars. The mount should not be permanent and should be adaptable to most makes and models of cars. The design should not compromise the safety of the vehicle operator by impeding the use of controls.
12. **Human-powered vehicle.** (Group) Design a human-powered boat, aircraft, or submarine. These vehicles should be designed for a single person.

Reverse Engineering Problems

Reverse engineering is a process of taking existing products, evaluating and measuring them, and then creating the CAD database to reproduce them. The following problems can be used as reverse engineering projects. Use a micrometer, scale, and calipers to make measurements. Use manufacturer's catalogs to specify standard parts, such as bearings and fasteners. For each project, the following is required:

1. Disassemble, measure, and sketch each part.
2. Create 3-D models or engineering drawings of each nonstandard part, with dimensions.
3. Specify standard parts, using engineering catalogs.
4. Create an assembly drawing with parts list.
5. Create a written report that summarizes your project, lists the strengths and weaknesses of the product you reverse engineered, comments on the serviceability of the product, and recommends changes to the design, especially as it relates to DFM principles.

The products to be reverse engineered are as follows:

1. 3/8-inch reversible electric hand drill
2. Staple gun
3. Electric kitchen hand mixer
4. Electric can opener
5. Electric hair dryer
6. Electric glue gun
7. Electric hand jigsaw
8. Dustbuster
9. Kant-twist clamp

10. Hold-down clamp
11. Drillpress vise
12. Telephone
13. Computer mouse
14. Paper stapler
15. Paper feeder tray for a laser printer
16. Multiple pen holder for a plotter
17. Computer game joystick
18. Piston and connecting rod for an automobile engine

Problem-Solving Activities

The following problems can be used as individual or group activities. The activities involve the problem-solving process. Some of the activities also involve visualization ability. Most of the problems will require sketches to solve the problem and to communicate the solution.

1. Determine one solid object that will pass completely through the circular, triangular, and square holes (Figure 3.68). The object must pass through each hole one at a time and be tight enough that little or no light passes between it and the sides of the hole. Make an isometric sketch of your solution.
2. Sketch the missing right side view and an isometric view of the two given views in Figure 3.69. The solution cannot have warped surfaces.
3. Create a low-cost lightweight container that will prevent an egg from breaking when dropped from a third-story window onto concrete.

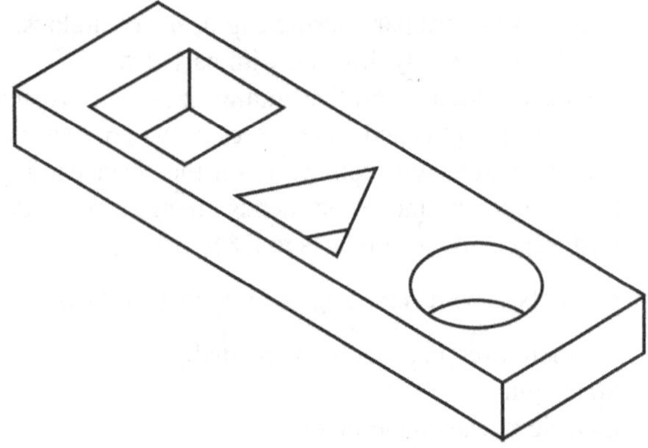

Figure 3.68

Problem solving activity 1

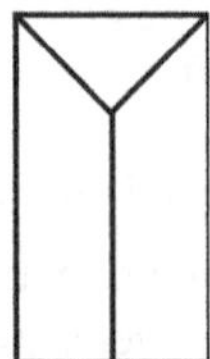

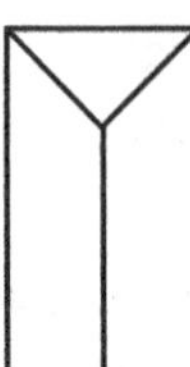

Figure 3.69

Problem solving activity 2

4. Create a method of filling a 2-liter plastic soda bottle resting on the ground, from a third story window.

5.* A mountain climber starting at sunrise takes a well-worn path from the base of a mountain to its top and completes the trip in one day. The mountain climber camps overnight on the mountain top. At sunrise the climber descends the mountain along the same path. Even though the rates of ascent and descent are different, there is one point along the path which the mountain climber passes at the same time of the day. Prove that there is a single point along the path where this occurs, and make a sketch of your solution.

6.* Build the longest cantilevered structure possible using 20 sticks of spaghetti and 24 inches of clear tape. The base of the cantilever must be taped to an 8-inch-square horizontal area. The cantilever must be constructed in 30 minutes or less. When finished, measure the length of the cantilever section from the point on the base nearest to the overhanging cantilever end to the end of the cantilevered section.

*Problems 5 and 6 are adapted from *Experiences in Visual Thinking*, R.H. McKim, 1972.

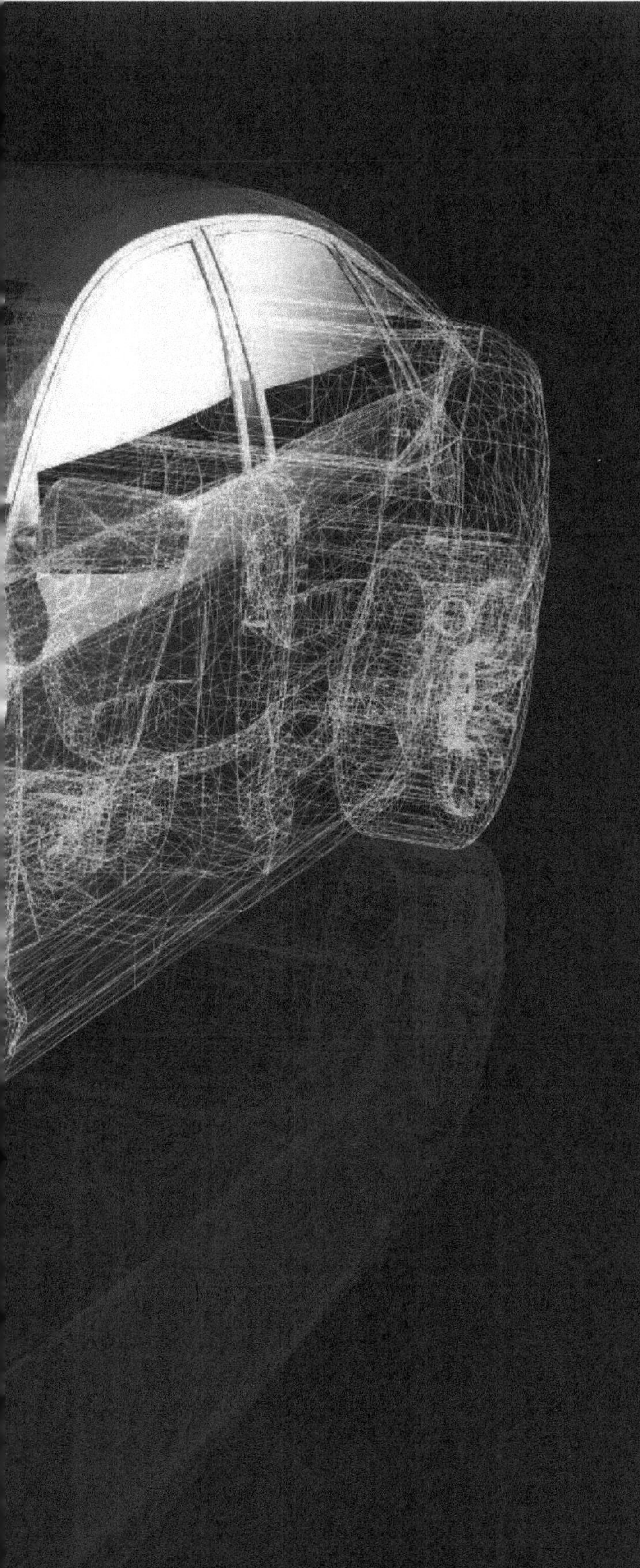

Chapter Four

Chapter Four

The Role of Technical Graphics in Production, Automation, and Manufacturing Processes*

Objectives

After completing this chapter, you will be able to:

1. Describe how advances in technology are impacting manufacturing operations.
2. Describe the role of technical graphics in the integrated manufacturing enterprise.
3. Describe how graphic models drive computer integrated manufacturing.
4. Define the concepts of concurrent engineering, manufacturing planning, production, and total quality management.
5. Define and describe CAPP, MRP2, JIT, and lean production.

Introduction

A manufacturing process transforms raw materials and components into parts, assemblies and products that satisfy a customer. The processes used to complete the transformation require careful attention, control, and planning. Manufacturing enter-

*Contributions by Henry Kraebber, Professor, Purdue University, West Lafayette, IN.

prises must collect and manage a great amount of information from many sources. Design and process information is often communicated to people in manufacturing using 3-D solid models. Solid models are fundamental elements of the modern design, analysis, and production planning effort. Modern manufacturing processes utilizing computers and automation depend on 3-D models of parts, tools, and work areas.

Today, products are being rapidly designed, with fewer parts, at lower cost, with higher quality and greater consideration for efficient production, the environment, and consumer safety. Several emerging trends that have a direct influence on design and production include the following:

- *Global competition*—the production of high-quality, low-cost goods by many nations, marketed throughout the world.
- *Total quality management* (TQM)—in industries throughout the world, companywide efforts to improve the quality of goods produced.
- *Integrated automation and the use of advanced technology*—increased use of computer hardware, software, machine tools, and controls provides the flexibility and ability to change volume, products, and designs quickly and efficiently. The time required to get a product to market is reduced.
- *Worker involvement*—more participation in decision making and problem solving at lower levels in organizations.
- *Environmental issues*—environmentally more acceptable pollution control and waste disposal.

This chapter introduces the issues of integration in manufacturing; manufacturing planning, controlling, and processing; quality; and new philosophies driving manufacturing. Because engineering drawings and graphic models are used to communicate throughout the manufacturing enterprise, it is necessary to have a basic understanding of manufacturing production processes and practices, and their effects on the finished product. A modern manufacturing operation will often emphasize quality and automation along with the new production initiatives to reduce waste and improve the flow of materials and information as it works toward the goal of better serving its customers.

4.1 Integration in Manufacturing

Automation is the use of machinery in place of human labor (Figure 4.1). Automation has been around for a long time, as continuing technological developments and the increased application of computers have had a significant impact on the production process. The modern challenge is the integration of all the various levels of automation, systems, and controls into a planned and cohesive unit that can effectively design and produce products that meet the customer's requirements. Graphic models and 3-D representations of parts, assemblies, tools, and workplaces are the visual tools that are helping people to integrate the complex operations of a manufacturing company.

Figure 4.1

Automation

Robots automate assembly and fabrication process during the production of automobiles.

(© Stockbyte/Getty Images.)

4.1.1 Computer-Integrated Manufacturing

Computer-integrated manufacturing (CIM) involves the systematic linking of the manufacturing operations using an integrated computer system. The Computer and Automated Systems Association (CASA) of the Society of Manufacturing Engineers (SME) developed the concept of CIM, as represented by the wheel shown in Figure 4.2. Notice the strong customer-centered focus of this model of integrated manufacturing.

The production process model is based on the universal systems model, which includes inputs, processes, and outputs (Figure 4.3). Inputs are the tangible and intangible elements required to create a marketable product. Tangible elements include the raw materials and finished materials (standard parts) needed. Raw materials are converted to finished materials using some type of production process. Intangible elements include the human knowledge and skills important to the process, such as knowledge in mathematics, science, design, graphics, communications, and materials.

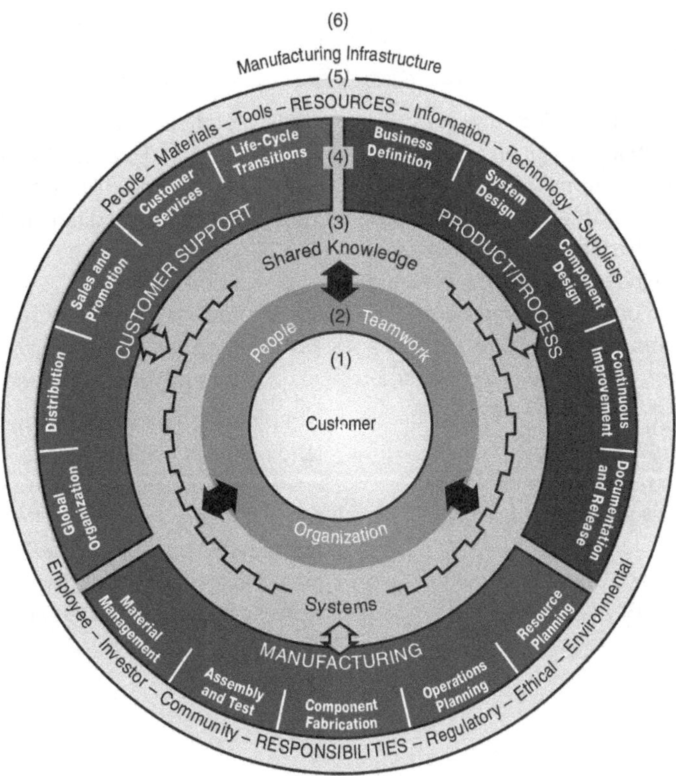

Figure 4.2

Manufacturing Enterprise Wheel

(The CASA/SME CIM Wheel is reprinted with permission of the Society of Manufacturing Engineers, © 1993.)

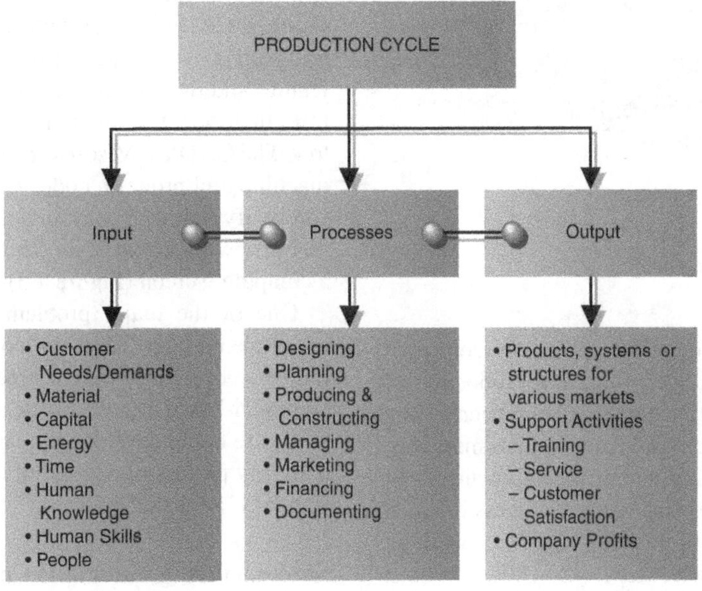

Figure 4.3

Universal systems model

Historical Highlight
Production Management

Industry is influenced by available technology and management trends. Prior to the Industrial Revolution, production relied primarily on physical power from humans and animals. The Industrial Revolution (1800s) emphasized the use of machines to do much of the physical work. Technological changes were relatively slow in the next 150 years, resulting in only gradual improvements in production processes.

Production management was begun in 1776 by Adam Smith, with the division of labor. Other production management concepts followed, including the following:

1790 Interchangeable parts. Eli Whitney.
1911 Scientific management. Frederick W. Taylor.
1911 Motion study and industrial psychology. Frank and Lillian Gilbreth.
1912 Charts for scheduling activities. Henry Gantt.
1913 Moving assembly line. Henry Ford.
1935 Statistical procedures for sampling and quality control. H. F. Dodge, H. G. Romig, W. Stewhart, and L. H. C. Tippett.
1951 Commercial digital computers. Sperry Univac.
1960 Development of quantitative tools. Numerous sources.
1975 Emphasis on manufacturing strategy. W. Skinner.
1980s Emphasis on quality, flexibility, and time-based competition. W. Edwards Deming.

In the 1950s and 1960s, there was significant growth of automation in manufacturing. In the 1970s and 1980s, there were rapid advancements in computer technology and its use in industry. Also during the 1980s, the influence of Japanese manufacturers started a quality revolution, following the principles developed by W. Edwards Deming. Japanese management practices resulted in increased productivity.

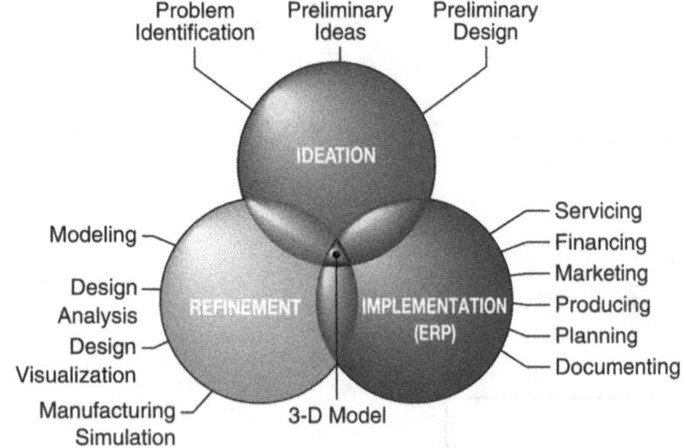

Figure 4.4

Concurrent engineering model

Engineers and technologists are primarily concerned with designing, modeling, planning, and production efforts. In addition, through concurrent engineering and other team efforts, engineers and technologists must work with management, marketing, and finance. Concurrent engineering is a nonlinear product design process in which all the people necessary to produce a product work together as a team (Figure 4.4).

The heart of CIM is a computer-aided design (CAD) system. CAD is truly where CIM began. Computer-aided design has evolved from the original automated drafting systems to become a powerful design and communications tool used to design the part. Computer-aided manufacturing (CAM) systems can be used to generate programs that guide the machine tools from the part geometry that is developed using CAD, in particular a 3-D solid model. Previous to the CAD/CAM systems, the machine tool program would have been manually developed. Using a CAD/CAM system, the operator generates the tool path program interactively by selecting a machinable feature and the tool that will be used to machine that feature, then selecting the part geometry for the tool to follow. The CAD/CAM software automatically generates the machine tool program code. The manufacturing engineer can verify that the program does what it was supposed to do by viewing a simulation of the machining operation on a computer screen (Figure 4.5).

One of the major problems that must be overcome in implementing CIM is communications incompatibility among the different areas of the business and the computer-based systems that each area uses. System standards are being developed to help overcome these incompatibility problems. Several of the most important system standards are listed below.

Manufacturing automation protocol (MAP)—a communications standard for enhancing compatibility between different automated manufacturing systems. The goal of MAP is the total integration of is-

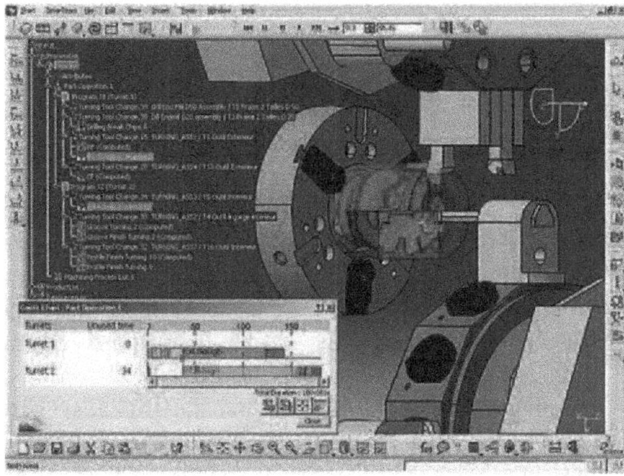

Figure 4.5

Simulation software used to verify machine tool program code

(Courtesy of Dassault Systemes.)

lands of automation in manufacturing, regardless of the type of hardware and software used in each system.

Technical and office protocol (TOP)—a standard for integrating manufacturing and various office environments. The goal of TOP is to allow communications between general business management offices (such as finance, marketing, strategic planning, and human resources) and the islands of automation in manufacturing. TOP will allow file transfer, file management, message handling, standards for document revisions and exchanges, directory services, graphics, and database management.

Initial graphics exchange specifications (IGES)—a protocol used to communicate the graphic (geometric) elements of a design or process between dissimilar CAD, analysis, and production systems. IGES is a translator that converts a CAD file from its native format to the neutral IGES format. The IGES file is then translated into the format required by another CAD system.

Product data exchange standard/Standard for the exchange of product model data (PDES/STEP)—a standard for translating file formats from one system to another, for solid models, nongraphic data management, and electronic design.

Computer-aided design (CAD) not only enhances the capabilities of designers but also provides the essential graphic inputs that *enable* other modern automation technologies and real integrated manufacturing. Computer-aided process planning (CAPP) produces detailed production process information based on the features that make up a part. The use of computer software to evaluate the graphic model has increased the capabilities of production planners and led to more consistent production routings and lower production costs. Computer-aided manufacturing (CAM) software helps engineers generate tool-path programs for computer-controlled machines from the dimensions included in the 3-D model. These systems are discussed in more detail in Section 4.3.

Figure 4.6

Rapid prototyping system

(Courtesy of 3D Systems, Inc.)

4.1.2 Rapid Prototyping

Rapid prototyping is a broad term used to describe several related processes for creating models directly from a CAD database. Stereolithography systems use a special liquid that solidifies when exposed to a laser (Figure 4.6). Others use a process called fused deposition modeling (FDM), which uses filaments of various materials that are melted and then allowed to solidify to form the shape. Rapid prototyping is used to create prototypes for concept modeling, injection molding, and investment casting (Figure 4.7).

Design in Industry — Guitar Maker Sets New Standards with CAD/CAM

Computer-aided design and manufacturing tools are used to design and build many products we use today, especially those used for leisure activities, such as guitars. The following case study outlines the use of sophisticated design tools by a small guitar manufacturer. The choice to use these tools stems from the need to make a quality product within a unique market niche, while still maintaining some creative flexibility.

Guitar companies, like their counterparts in the automotive and aerospace industries, manufacture precision-machined parts at close tolerances, with multiple moving components, and aesthetically pleasing products to attract customers.

From his earliest explorations in guitar design until today, Floyd Rose's breakthroughs continue to amaze and delight the music world. Rose designed his most recent revolutionary new electric guitar, with more than 16 patented advancements, using CATIA V5. Among the new features associated with this guitar are convergent tuning, moving pick-ups, three-axis neck adjustment, and an ingenious integration of the original Floyd Rose tremolo into the guitar, eliminating the need to lock the strings.

Floyd Rose Guitar Company's newest release model is the culmination of more than nine years of guitar innovation, incorporating numerous functional patents that radically improve the playability, sound, performance and ease-of-use for guitar players around the world. Rose digitally designed each of the guitar's hundreds of parts to his precise specifications, assembled them in a 3-D digital mock-up model, and then immediately began production.

In the 1980s, with the development of digital synthesizers and pitch-to-voltage guitar synthesizer controls, musicians looked to squeeze new sounds out of what was by then a 30-year-old guitar technology. Floyd Rose, a young musician at the time, increasingly began to use a whammy bar to create dramatic new sounds. But he grew frustrated by having to constantly keep the guitar in tune when using the device.

Rose turned to CAD tools for solutions. . . .

Rose also uses the numerical control (NC) manufacturing portion of V5, which uses accurate 3-D models for defining the tool paths for production. Now, cycle time from concept sketch to fully defined product takes only a matter of months, thus reducing costs.

4.1.3 Design for Manufacturability and Assembly

The modern concepts of "designing for manufacturing" and "designing for assembly" drive a company to open the discussion of how the manufacturing process relates to the product design. Designing for manufacturing and assembly (DFMA) is an approach that focuses on simplicity of product design for easier, more efficient manufacturability and assembly. Sales/marketing representatives bring knowledge of the customer's requirements and concerns about product reliability and quality. Designers translate the customer's requirements into specific products and features. Engineers address how the product can best be manufactured using current and proposed new processes, equipment, methods, and layouts. Foremen and production operators bring their experience and skills related to manufacturing and the effectiveness of proposed production operations. Purchasing and material management representatives provide critical inputs on material availability, alternative parts, and lead times. DFMA considers the manufacturability of a design before it is sent to production. The benefits are increased quality, reduced cost, and greater product reliability. Open communication between all the functional departments early in the development of the manufacturing process leads to a more effective production process that will meet the customer's and the company's needs. Computer-aided design is an important element of DFMA. It serves as an important communications tool between the various team members. For example, CAD-rendered images and models make it easier for manufacturing engineers to visualize the design and determine the tooling required.

4.1.4 Computer Simulations and Workplace Models

Investments in new production lines and workstations for new product production can be substantial and therefore cannot be left to chance. Software and hardware advances now make graphic simulation of proposed production facilities possible. The graphic models of products, assemblies,

"I was able to make an assembly of the guitar, and rapidly check it for fit and interferences," Rose says.

Traditionally, designers used 2-D CAD systems to pattern a guitar's basic shape. But, because these earlier systems were quite limited in their functionality, only very simple—some say boring—designs were possible. Some critical specifications for a guitar, such as the positioning and alignment of the neck to the body that determines how the strings will be positioned, or the length of the string from the "nut" at the headstock to the tangent point on the string saddles at the bridge, are quite difficult to design with precision.

Once in production, these designs often yielded poorly fitting parts and other errors, requiring extensive time and resources to correct, and then only with a "Band-Aid" fix. In addition to being labor-intensive, repairing these designs manually during the manufacturing phase meant that a repeatable process was almost impossible to achieve. The end product did not maintain the same dimensional shape or fit as intended by the original design. Fixing so many errors during production was consistently an extremely wasteful and costly process.

Now, with CAD, Rose's prototype and production guitar matches the design model. All fittings and functionality for all moving parts are simulated and verified in 3-D digital mock-up. This allows investigation, analysis and optimization of various designs in a much shorter amount of time, thus reducing cycle time and ensuring that the design errors are fixed prior to production.

Making their guitars with the same technology used to build airplanes, automobiles, and the Space Shuttle gives Floyd Rose Guitar Company a competitive edge by allowing creation of better, more innovative designs faster and cheaper.

Figure 1

Guitars are designed and manufactured using computers

(© Spencer Grant/Photo Edit.)

workstations, and production cells prepared for engineering and production are now becoming direct inputs to advanced simulation software packages. The graphics bring true scale geometry into programs that allow engineers to simulate the manufacturing process using the same geometry that was used to define parts, generate machine tool programs, and develop tools and fixtures. Machine tool program steps can be simulated graphically to look for any errors. Production operations at specific workstations can be simulated to determine expected outputs, identify problems related to material flow, timing, and worker ergonomics. The simulation programs allow engineers to prepare and operate virtual systems that help identify potential problems and solutions. The simulation results allow designs and processes to be tested before money and resources are committed. The savings from this approach are substantial. Figure 4.8 shows a sample of a work cell layout for the automated production of an assembly.

3-D solid models are the heart of the modern product design initiative of many companies. Engineers use these models to communicate their design concepts with others. The models provide the critical dimensions and relationships needed for computer-based analysis of design elements. Models of parts, tools, machines, and workstations make it possible for the engineers and others to visualize the design of products and the workstations where they will be produced. With CAD, the material control process is analyzed by modeling the factory floor and then animating the various processes to determine the smooth flow of materials, check for potential collisions of automated vehicles, and check the work envelope of robots (Figure 4.9). The technical graphics specialist will be found in the middle of this exciting area!

4.2 Manufacturing Planning, Controlling, and Processing

Production processes transform raw materials and components into finished products. The critical components of manufacturing's transformation processes are planning, controlling, and processing (Figure 4.10).

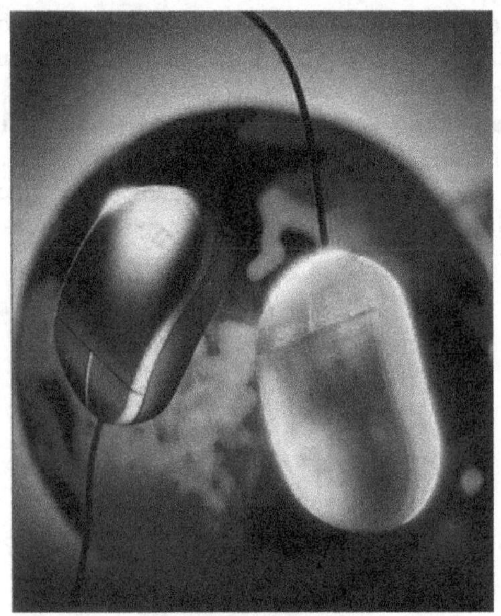

Figure 4.7

A part created with a rapid prototyping system

An ergonomic, two-button computer mouse and its stereolithography (SL) prototype designed, engineered, and built by Logitech, Inc., in only seven days from CAD design to part.

(Courtesy of 3D Systems and Logitech, Inc.)

Figure 4.8

Work cell model prepared using CATIA V5 and Delmia software

(Courtesy of Delmia Corp.)

4.2.1 Planning

Planning determines the most effective approach for moving a product through the manufacturing cycle. Planning involves scheduling the people, jobs, and machines required to produce the product, maintain the tools, receive materials, and ship the product, while reducing the cycle time required. Graphic inputs are a very important part of the documentation that supports the planning process.

The identification and grouping of items with similar design features or manufacturing characteristics is the key concept supporting a planning methodology known as **group technology**. Similar parts are classified into part families (Figure 4.11). Once the part families are identified, a coding system is developed to aid efficient storage and retrieval. Part families can increase productivity and reduce cycle time. A designer can quickly determine if a part already exists or if one with a similar nature can be modified to fit a specific need. Parts that are similar in manufacturing characteristics can also be grouped, and planning can be improved, by matching a new part to one in an existing group. Linking this approach with the CAD and PDM systems can help designers locate similar designs that are already documented and that may become the basis for a new part.

Computer-aided process planning (CAPP) is an intelligent computer system that is used to determine the optimal sequence of operations for manufacturing a part. The part is designed on a CAD/CAM system, and the CAD geometry is transferred to the CAPP system. The CAPP system matches the characteristics of the part to the machines and processes available, and then prints the optimal process and routing sheets for moving the part through the manufacturing process. Once again the product graphics are an essential part of the manufacturing process.

CAPP systems allow the manufacturing engineer to draw upon history and databases of digital assets, such as tools and gauges, to increase effectiveness, consistency, and profits. Detailed plans developed using CAPP provide job times for scheduling, cost information, and sales and marketing, and detailed instructions to the shop floor. CAPP systems build the process plans considering process rules that assure consistency of process and tool selection. Manufacturing engineers can pull information from the database and do not have to recreate each process every time. Part and product characteristics are keys to similar parts. Figure 4.12 shows the relationship of a CAPP system to other systems supporting manufacturing.

Companies that create their process plans by hand or with spreadsheets can greatly improve worker productivity while decreasing costs. A manufacturer of capital equipment who creates over 100 process plans per week might

Figure 4.9

Factory floor modeled in 3-D then animated to verify processes
(Courtesy of Delmia Corp.)

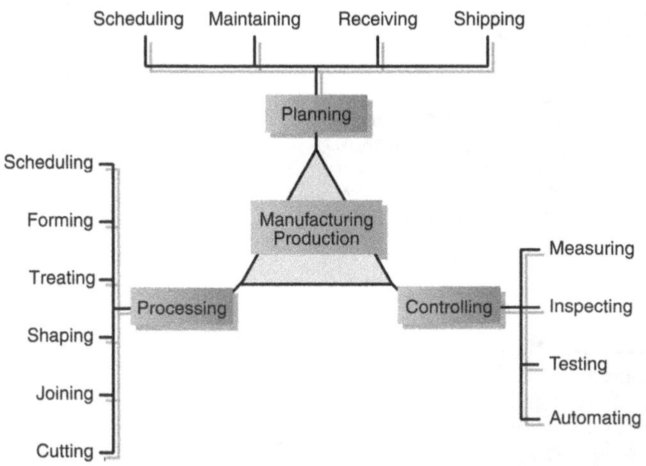

Figure 4.10

Planning, controlling, and processing functions in manufacturing

Figure 4.11

Part families

Part families are grouped by similar design or manufacturing characteristics.
(© 2007 Swagelok Company)

cut the process planning time by an average of 50%, saving hundreds of hours upon implementation of the CAPP system. These documented improvement percentage figures result from:

- Operating more consistent manufacturing processes
- Improved accuracy in calculated standards and cost estimates
- Automatic transfer of information to the company's business system
- Documentation (and retention) of the manufacturing knowledge of senior staff
- Reduced time requirements from manufacturing engineering and process planning

Material requirements planning (MRP) is a computer-enabled process that calculates the time-phased amount of raw materials necessary to manufacture the products

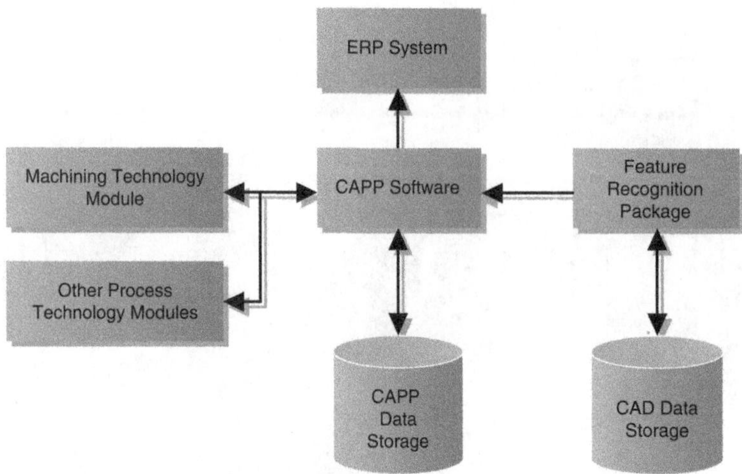

Figure 4.12

CAPP system program and database relationships

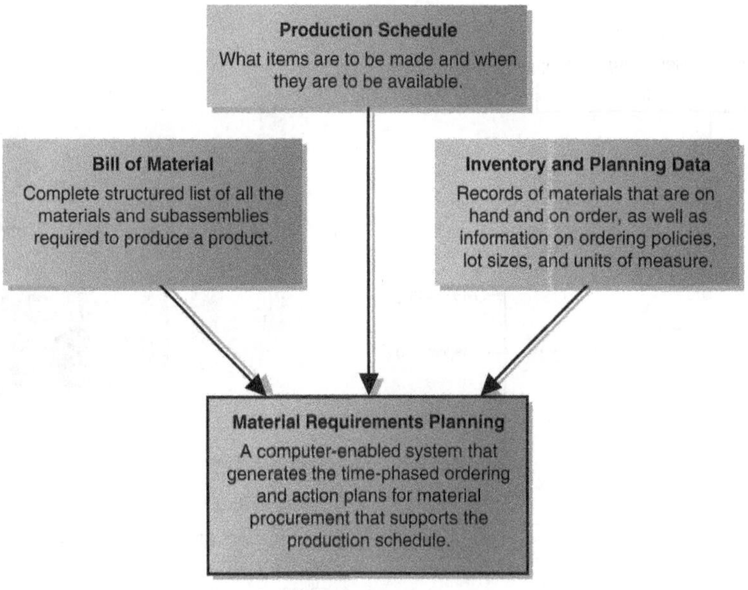

Figure 4.13

The material requirement planning process and its inputs

specified in the production schedule. MRP calculations use the bill of material information from the engineering design information and planning information from the business systems. A concept diagram for material requirements planning is shown in Figure 4.13. The MRP approach to material planning has evolved into a closed-loop system known as manufacturing resource planning (MRP2), which includes higher-level business planning functions that generate a master production schedule (MPS).

Closed-loop MRP—A system built around material requirements planning that includes the additional planning functions of sales and operations planning (production planning), master production scheduling, and capacity requirements planning. Once this planning phase is complete and the plans have been accepted as realistic

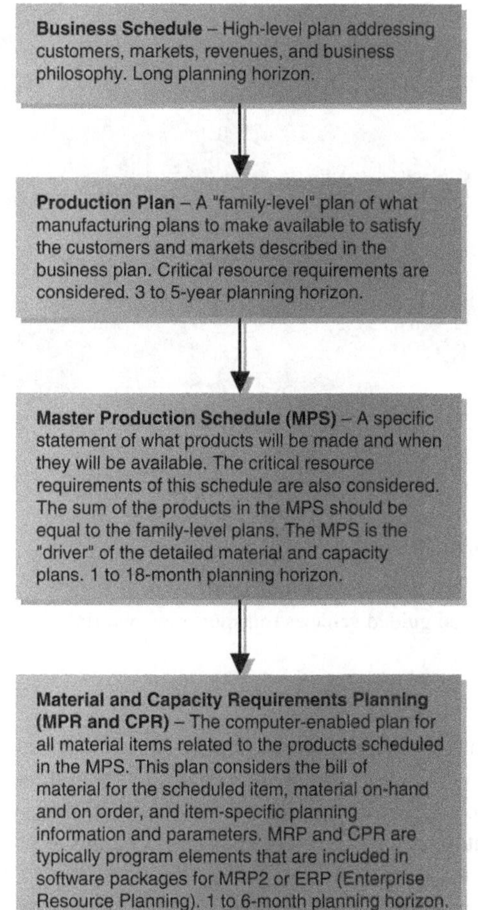

Figure 4.14

Critical elements of manufacturing resource planning (MRP2) systems

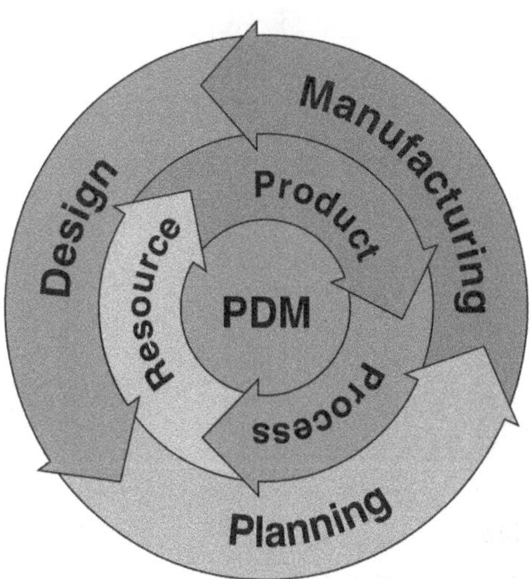

Figure 4.15

Product data management, the hub of modern enterprise systems

(Developed by the Digital Enterprise Center at Purdue University.)

> and attainable, the execution functions come into play. These functions include the manufacturing control functions of input-output (capacity) measurement, detailed scheduling and dispatching, as well as anticipated delay reports from both the plant and suppliers, supplier scheduling, etc. The term *closed loop* implies not only that each of these elements is included in the overall system, but also that feedback is provided by the execution functions so that the planning can be kept valid at all times. (*APICS Dictionary, 9th edition, 1998.*)

The master schedule provides the timeline that drives the company's resource plans. Figure 4.14 shows the steps in the planning process that transform plans at the business and production family levels into the master production schedule and the detailed material and capacity plans for the subassemblies, component parts, and raw materials.

A major obstacle that many companies face when adopting an MRP2 or the next generation of this type of system known as an enterprise resource planning (ERP) system is the monumental task of defining the production processes through routings. CAPP may be of particular value to companies implementing or upgrading their MRP2 or ERP system. A CAPP system can ensure more accurate operation times are available for use in the business system. More accurate time information can lead to improved shop floor scheduling and a reduction of critical errors that can impact the entire planning system in an organization. CAPP is a critical resource that increases routing consistency while improving data integrity.

Product lifecycle management (PLM) is a new term that addresses the management of the key product data from a product's conception through its production life. **Product data management (PDM)** software helps companies complete the integration link between the design and engineering analysis systems, the process design and simulation systems, the production management systems, and the company's business systems. Refer to Chapter 2 for more discussion of PLM. Many changes and advancements are expected in this area as computer-based systems become more developed and product and process data become better managed through the emerging digital enterprise models. Figure 4.15 shows PDM as the hub of the systems of the integrated enterprise.

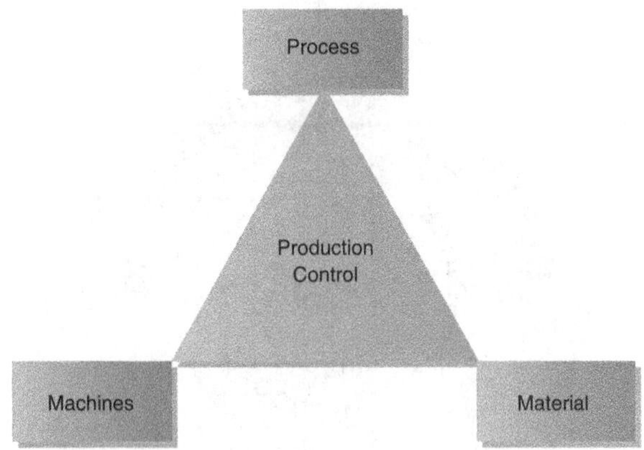

Figure 4.16

Production control model

Processes, machines, and material must be controlled in manufacturing.

Figure 4.17

Automated guided vehicles (AGV)

Automated guided vehicles transport raw materials.

(© Stone)

4.2.2 Controlling and Processing

Process control involves the measurement, analysis, and adjustment of manufacturing processes. The three primary production components that must be controlled are the machines, processes, and materials (Figure 4.16). Controlling procedures encompass automating, sensing, measuring, inspecting, and testing.

Machine control has evolved from human operation to automated operation using numerical control (NC) and, more recently, computer numerical control (CNC). Originally, numerically controlled machines read their instruction programs from punched cards or tape. CNC is the control of a machine tool using a computer as the controller unit. The NC systems sold today are CNC systems where a computer has replaced the punched program and added significantly to the control possibilities. CNC machines have an operator interface that may be used for entering program data and providing feedback to the operator about the machine tool.

Individual CNC controlled machines may be programmed locally or use CNC programs downloaded from a main computer. Direct numerical control (DNC) is a networked version of CNC where the machine tool controllers are directly connected to a main computer. DNC is an important component of flexible manufacturing.

Automated material control may be accomplished with conveyor systems, robots, and automated vehicles. Computer programs often control machine tool operations. Special industrial computers known as programmable logic controllers often control automated manufacturing processes. Material control is a process for recognizing what raw materials are needed and when, using just-in-time (JIT) techniques. Material control systems often include automated machines, robots, conveyor systems, and automated guided vehicle (AGV) systems as shown in Figure 4.17. In some cases automated storage and retrieval systems (AS/RS), as shown in Figure 4.18, have proved to be effective in reducing labor content and improving inventory accuracy.

Automated material handling is becoming more common in production areas. A computer-controlled machine, such as a robot, may be designed to identify and move materials, parts, and tools, using various motions. For example, a robot could be used to transfer a part from one machine tool location to another. Robots may also be used to paint, weld, and perform other repetitive jobs in the production process (Figure 4.19).

A conveyor system may be used to move raw materials through the manufacturing process, principally from one station to another (Figure 4.20). The methods of conveyance might include belts, rollers, air, and water, or a combination of methods. Automated guided vehicles (AGVs) are computer-controlled vehicles used to transport raw materials from storage to workstation or from station to station. AGVs are especially valuable in a hazardous environment. Automated storage and retrieval systems (AS/RS) are computer-controlled warehousing processes used to receive, store, and distribute materials. Robots, conveyors, and AGVs are often elements of an AS/RS system.

Figure 4.18

Automated storage and retrieval

Automated storage and retrieval systems transport raw materials from storage to workstations.

(Courtesy of Paragon Tech.)

Figure 4.19

A robot used to paint an automobile in the manufacturing process

(© Stone.)

Figure 4.20

Conveyor system

(© Digital Vision/Getty Images.)

4.3 Quality in Manufacturing

In the past, poor quality was considered to be just a production problem. Manufacturing companies often used detection/correction systems that relied upon inspection at the end of production. Inspection operations could often catch 90 percent of the defective parts or assemblies produced. However, the products with the remaining 10 percent of the defects were shipped and later found by the consumers. The result of ineffective quality systems is often costly warranty repairs and unhappy customers that may never come back. Defects caught before shipping may be corrected or reworked in the factory, but this has been shown to be very expensive and time-consuming. Modern quality management systems have emerged in response to these problems.

4.3.1 The Rise of Total Quality Management

The "best-in-class" industries are seriously committed to quality with a customer focus. Manufacturing efforts are directed to satisfy the customer's needs and demands, including quality. The customer's opinion is actively sought through focus groups and questionnaires and may even

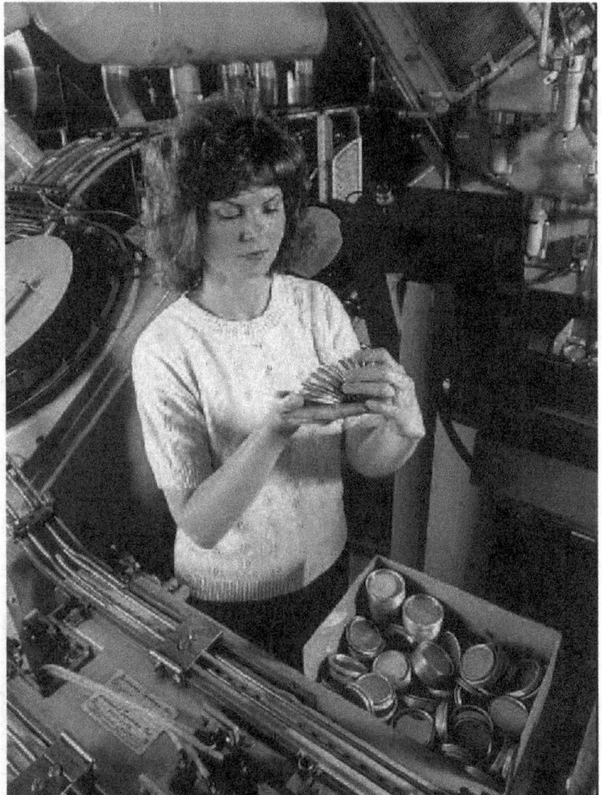

Figure 4.21

Quality: a focal point for industries employing TQM practices

(© David Joel/Stone/Getty Images.)

become part of the concurrent engineering process. The customer determines the priorities and therefore determines the company's goals for a product design and quality requirements. Quality issues relate to the ability of the company to provide a product or service that meets or exceeds the customer's needs and expectations consistently and predictably. Quality is no longer viewed as just a problem for the production departments.

Total quality management (TQM) is a companywide effort to achieve quality in all aspects of the organization. TQM is a quality revolution that has spread to companies throughout the world. With TQM, the customer is the focal point of the company, and customer satisfaction is the driving force (Figure 4.21). Some of the more influential names in the quality revolution include W. Edwards Deming, Joseph Juran, Armand Feigenbaum, Robert Costello, Philip Crosby, Kaoru Ishikawa, Shiego Shingo, and Genichi Taguchi. Figure 4.22 is a TQM model developed by Robert Costello for the U.S. Department of Defense.

TQM is a customer-oriented approach to quality that is built on a new awareness of the quality issues throughout the enterprise. The TQM approach starts a company on a never-ending, continuous process of improvement that uses a team approach and proven problem-solving methods. There must be a strong commitment and participation from the top management of the company to sustain this effort. The management team is responsible for providing the workers with the tools and systems they need to cause quality throughout the enterprise. A new attitude that quality does not cost money but actually saves money must be accepted throughout the organization.

The TQM approach begins with the determination of what the customer wants, using surveys, focus groups, interviews, etc., thus involving the customer in the decision-making process. Products are then designed to meet the customer's needs and that are easy to produce, use, and service. Production facilities and process are developed that will produce the product efficiently and correctly. Quality systems are designed to prevent mistakes, instead of trying to find and correct them. If mistakes do occur, problem-solving procedures are used to determine the cause and eliminate the source of the problem. Accurate records of changes and their results are tracked and used to improve the system. There is a continuous, ongoing effort to improve quality and to extend these concepts to the companies, suppliers, and distributors.

Important concepts of TQM operations include:

- Continual improvement and the persistent effort to improve existing conditions.
- Competitive benchmarking is the evaluation of other organizations that are recognized as the best in their class.
- Empowerment of the employees that provides strong motivation for them to make changes that improve the production processes and systems.
- Implementation of a team approach to problem solving that gets everyone involved in the quality effort.
- A plan for quality system education that provides employees with information on the tools and techniques of quality control and process improvement.

Technology, work, and management practices all play a role in achieving the goals of TQM. Central to any quality endeavor is quality information. Modern technical graphics practices enhance the flow of information throughout the design and production process.

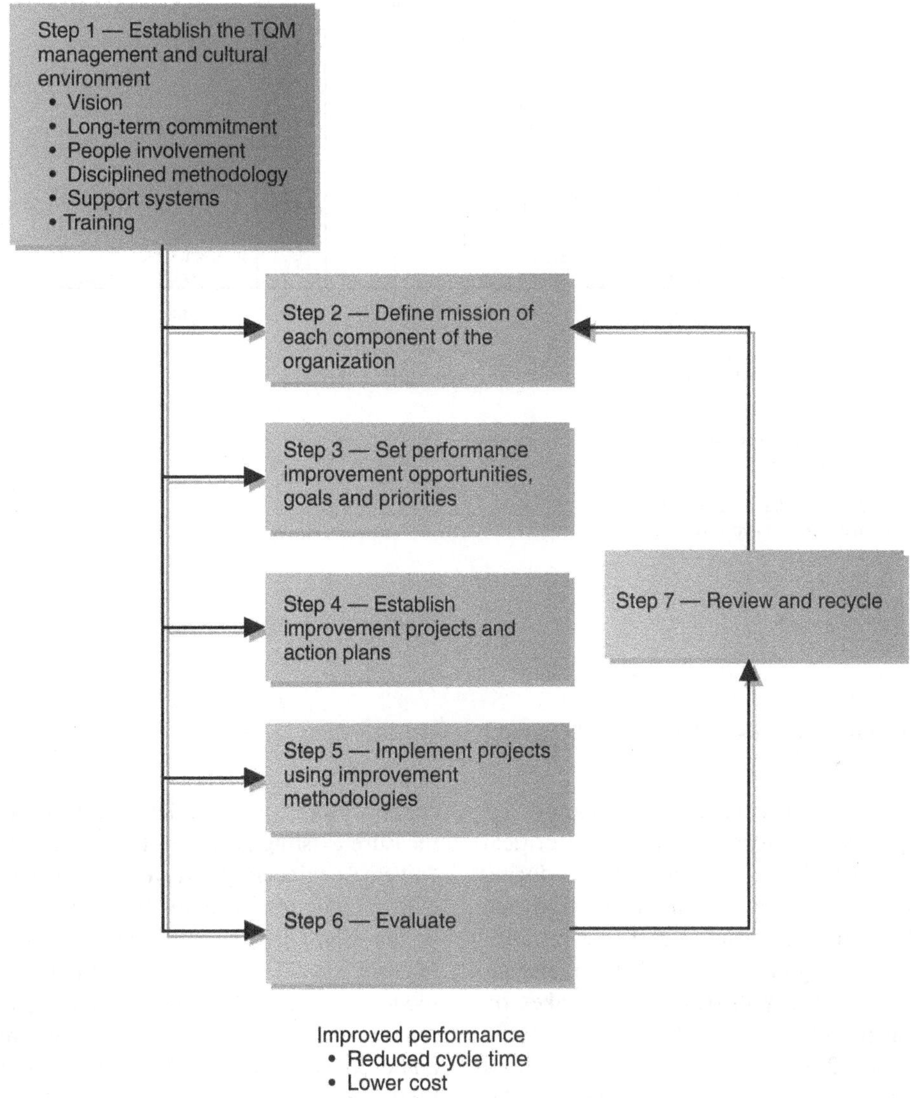

Figure 4.22

TQM model

(U.S. Department of Defense, *Quality and Productivity Self-Assessment Guide for Defense Organizations,* 1990.)

4.3.2 Manufacturing Quality Control

The quality of finished parts is dependent on the design tolerances and the machine tools and process controls used to produce them. It is impossible to make every part exactly the same, but that does not become a problem as long as the parts vary in a controlled way. Controlling the variation of parts is done through measurement of the parts produced and the adjustment, as necessary, of the process parameters. Measurements and other types of inspection techniques may include visual evaluations, manual measurements, automated gaging equipment, and computer-based measurement systems.

Since checking every part made would be extremely time-consuming and costly, random checking is employed, based on statistical techniques. Statistical process control (SPC) is a mathematically based system for

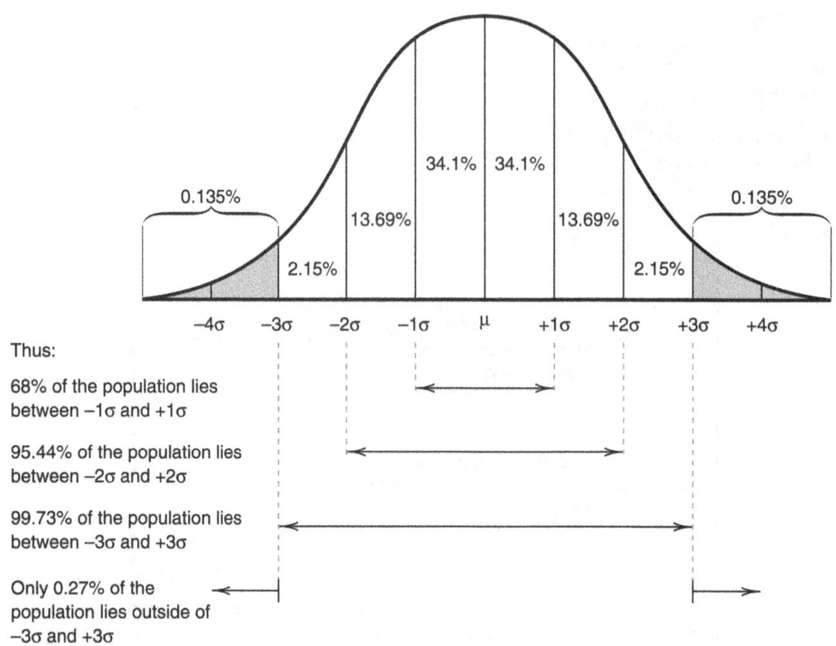

0.135%
2.15%
13.69%
34.1%
34.1%
13.69%
2.15%
0.135%
−4σ
−3σ
−2σ
−1σ
μ
+1σ
+2σ
+3σ
+4σ
Thus:
68% of the population lies between −1σ and +1σ
95.44% of the population lies between −2σ and +2σ
99.73% of the population lies between −3σ and +3σ
Only 0.27% of the population lies outside of −3σ and +3σ

Figure 4.23

The normal distribution, the statistical basis for SPC charts

analyzing measured parts that have been randomly selected from the production process. Measures of critical dimensions are often collected at various times during production. Although the actual dimensions produced can be expected to vary from part to part, the variability in many manufacturing processes tends to be distributed normally. This normally distributed data takes on a characteristic shape often called a bell curve because of its shape (Figure 4.23). Nearly 67% of the measured values can be expected to gather within one standard deviation above or below the mean or "center" of the bell curve. SPC methods involve the calculation of control limits based on the measurements from the process. For example, measurements may be taken on the diameter of a shaft, measured to three decimal places of precision, on samples of parts taken every hour. The sample data collected can be plotted with respect to the calculated control limits (see Figure 4.24). Data points that vary beyond the limits or follow trends that do not follow the normal distribution indicate the process is out of control. Problem solving methods can then be used to determine the cause of the "out of control" problem and get actions started to bring the process back into control.

Coordinate measuring machines (CMM) are modern computer-based measurement tools that are used to support production and design efforts. They are used to measure existing parts for dimensional accuracy, and for "reverse engineering." Reverse engineering involves the collection of design details from an existing (often a competitor's) part or product using the measurement capability of the CMM. Laser scanners or photogrammetric techniques are also used to capture existing part geometry. The dimensional data collected can be interpreted by software and used as the input to the design process using a CAD system.

4.4 The New Philosophies Driving Manufacturing Operations

The quest for more competitive manufacturing operations has been going on for years. The competition between manufacturing companies in Japan and the United States reached a high level in the late 1980s. U.S. companies found themselves losing major market shares, even whole product segments, to foreign competition that did not even exist just a few years earlier. Companies scrambled to figure out what was happening in Japan and to try to replicate the Japanese systems in their plants. Programs in statistical process control (SPC), quality circles, and eventually total

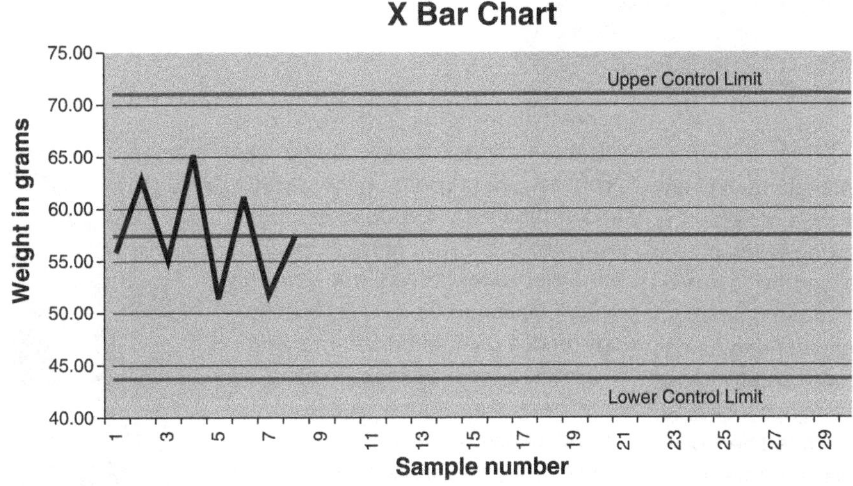

Figure 4.24

Statistical process control (SPC) chart of average sample weights

quality management (TQM) took over in many companies. Quality and a system to cause it to happen is important, but these quality programs alone could not make entire manufacturing enterprises effective. The search for what may be considered a "magic potion" that can transform a traditional manufacturing company into a highly effective and competitive manufacturing enterprise continued.

4.4.1 Just-in-Time Manufacturing

In the mid 1980s the idea of "just-in-time" production was being championed in manufacturing operations across the country. The focus was on reducing material and inventory. Parts were planned to arrive just in time, and in the proper sequence to support the production schedule. The just-in-time approach to manufacturing is much more than just an ordering plan that schedules material deliveries at the time of need. JIT supports the new approach to value added manufacturing.

> **Just-in-Time (JIT)**—A philosophy of manufacturing based on planned elimination of all waste and on continuous improvement of productivity. It encompasses the successful execution of all manufacturing activities required to produce a final product, from design engineering to delivery, and includes all stages of conversion from raw material onward. The primary elements of Just-in-Time are to have only the required inventory when needed; to improve quality to zero defects; to reduce lead times by reducing setup times, queue lengths, and lot sizes; to incrementally revise the operations themselves; and to accomplish these activities at minimum cost. In the broad sense, it applies to all forms of manufacturing—job shop, process, and repetitive—and to many service industries as well. Syn: short-cycle manufacturing, stockless production, zero inventories. *APICS Dictionary, 9th edition, 1998.*

The production approach developed in Japan following the Second World War actually focuses on the elimination of all waste. Robert Hall's 1987 classic book, *Attaining Manufacturing Excellence,* presented many readers with their first summary of the "Seven Wastes" that become the target of elimination in a JIT process. (See Figure 4.25.) JIT takes the manufacturing operations to the extreme level of having *only* the right materials, parts, and products in the right place at the right time. It is a relentless approach where waste at any point in the operation (even management) is not tolerated and operations have only what is needed, nothing more.

Operational savings claims for JIT manufacturing include reduced inventory levels, reduced work-in-progress inventory, shorter manufacturing lead times, and increased responsiveness to customers. Shorter lead times help compress schedules and lead to less work in progress material. Elimination of any non-value-added activity leads to spending less time and money. The streamlined processes work better and faster because the waste has been removed. The challenge facing manufacturing companies has always come in the implementation of JIT. The savings and changes will not work if the management team

Dream **High Tech** Job

Laptops for All

The design and manufacture of any product must always consider the cost of materials and the eventual cost to the consumer based on the characteristics of the intended market. An understanding of engineering fundamentals combined with creativity can make extraordinary things possible, such as the case described here of an engineer working as the chief technology officer for a non-profit organization developing low-cost laptops for children in developing countries.

A little over two years ago, Mary Lou Jepsen flew to Boston to interview for a professorship at MIT Media Lab. A week later, she got a job in Cambridge—not the professorship, but something even better: chief technology officer of the One Laptop per Child (OLPC) project, which is working on an ultracheap but versatile laptop for children in developing countries.

If you're an engineer and a job interview turns into a brainstorming session, that's probably a good sign. It certainly was for Jepsen, who spent 2 hours of her "interview" kicking around ideas for the laptop with Nicholas Negroponte, the Media Lab's cofounder. Negroponte had just launched OLPC, a nonprofit organization independent of MIT, and when he asked Jepsen to be its chief technology officer, she immediately agreed.

Looking for a change of pace, at OLPC she soon found herself at the happy center of a whirlwind. "The whole first year I couldn't sleep past two or three in the morning, I was just so excited to wake up and enjoy what I did again," Jepsen says. "There were no boundaries; we were just running as fast as we could."

Jepsen, now 41, spent her childhood on a family farm in Connecticut. She first dove into technology during the summer after her junior year of college, test-driving nuclear submarines for the U.S. Naval Underwater Systems Center in New London, Conn. She graduated from Brown University, in Providence, R.I., with degrees in art and electrical engineering, and subsequently earned a master's degree from the Media Lab. After brief forays into teaching computer science and creating large-scale holographic art installations, Jepsen returned, somewhat reluctantly, to Brown for a Ph.D. in optics.

At OLPC, Mary Lou Jepsen designs cheap and hardy laptops.
(© Dalsimer Photography.)

Mary Lou Jepsen
IEEE Member
Age: 41
What she does: Dreams up ways to design a high-quality US $100 lap-

only "announces" that the operation is now JIT. It is easy to start the change process to JIT, but more difficult to sustain it over a longer period of time. Soon JIT was considered to be "old news," and the search for something newer and better continued.

The philosophy of JIT is supported by concepts and ideas of how work should be done and operations organized and run that remain rock solid. These really good ideas seem to have been able to withstand the test of time and application in a variety of different environments.

4.4.2 The Toyota Production System

The comprehensive system for manufacturing created at Toyota in Japan by Taiichi Ohno is commonly known today as the "Toyota Production System." When pressed by American executives about the source of this revolutionary system, Ohno is reported to have laughed and said he learned it all from Henry Ford's book (*Today and Tomorrow,* first published in 1926). Take a look at this manufacturing classic and you will see the similarity of the vitop for children in emerging countries; acts as "ambassador" to the laptop's manufacturers in Asia and to the countries that will buy the computers.

For Whom: One Laptop per Child.

Where she does it: Cambridge, Mass., and Taiwan.

Fun factors: Gets to travel the world and meet heads of state.

At age 29, Jepsen found herself suffering form health problems. She was just about to drop out of school until her condition was finally diagnosed and treated. She finished her Ph.D. in the next six months and then cofounded a company that manufactures liquid-crystal-on-silicon chips for high-definition TV displays. She left the company in 2003, citing "creative differences" with its chief executive.

Her health problems weren't quite over, though. Jepsen's body requires a rigid schedule of twice-daily medication to keep her alive. Now that she's a globe-trotting computer executive for the OLPC venture, the regimen can be tough to follow.

The bold technical challenge of designing a US $100 laptop and the chance to work on global problems are what made the project irresistible to her. Her first big assignment was to reinvent the computer's display—by far the most expensive and most battery draining component of a laptop. According to Jepsen, the display her team eventually marshaled into existence requires, depending on the mode, only between 2 percent and 14 percent of a typical laptop display's power consumption. The power needed is low enough to be provided easily by a pull cord or other manual means, charging a nickel-metal-hydride battery pack; 1 minute of charging suffices for 10 minutes of use. To save watts, the display can switch between color with the backlight on, in low light, and black-and-white with the backlight off, in sunlight. OLPC's engineers trimmed battery usage further by, among other things, adding memory to the timing-controller chip, which decides how often a display refreshes. That trick enables the display to update itself continually without using the CPU if nothing changes on the screen.

In June 2005, the OLPC team hadn't even finished its design when it found itself pitching the $100 laptop concept to the Brazilian government. Brazil immediately committed to 2 milion units. "The cacophony it created!" Jepsen marvels. "Every other head of state in Latin America contacted us by the end of the week."

Since then, the pace hasn't slowed a bit. Jepsen still lives one week a month at her home on a peninsula outside Boston, from which she commutes to OLPC's Cambridge offices by ferry. The rest of the month is devoted to shuttling to various places in Asia and meeting with manufacturers. She spends so much time in southern Taiwan, near display maker Chimei Corp., that she now has an apartment there overlooking a canal, where in her few spare hours she likes to explore the bustling city streets by bicycle. "Constantly orbiting the earth is a hard thing to do, but you get a lot done that way," Jepsen says. For those fortunate engineers with boundless enthusiasm, that is indeed so.

—Sandra Upson

Portions reprinted with permission from S. Upson, "Mary Lou Jepsen: Laptops for All," *IEEE Spectrum,* 2007, pp. 28–30. © 2007 IEEE.

sions of Ford and Ohno. This is another example of sound operational ideas that have withstood the test of time. Ford's factories implemented a new system of production and produced quality automobiles at prices that nearly every worker could afford. The Ford system led to fantastic productivity improvements that allowed car prices to be cut in half and worker wages to double.

Ohno explains the motivation for the Toyota system as an attempt to catch up with the automobile industries of the western advanced nations following World War II. Remember in that postwar period the Japanese economy was trying to recover from the ruins left after the war. Resources in Japan were limited at best. He knew that to become a true competitor to the west that his operations had to become more productive and produce quality goods at low cost. His system focused on the ferocious elimination of waste in all manufacturing operations and on the effects demonstrated through actual practice on the shop floor. There was no recipe book showing how to be an effective producer. Toyota learned how to be effective by practicing...making lots of changes and learning along the way. Ohno describes the guiding principles of the Toyota production system in a book published by Productivity Press in 1988. This

Waste of overproduction: Make only what is needed now – reduce set-up time, synchronizing quantities and timing between steps, compacting layout.

Waste of waiting: Synchronize work flow as much as possible. Balance uneven loads by flexible workers and equipment.

Waste of transportation: Establish layouts and locations to make transport and handling unnecessary if possible. Reduce what cannot be eliminated.

Waste of processing itself: Question why this part should be made at all, why is this process necessary?

Waste of stocks: Reduce stocks by reducing set-up times and lead times – reducing other wastes reduces stocks.

Waste of motion: Study motion for economy and consistency. Economy improves productivity. Consistency improves quality. Be careful not to just automate a wasteful operation.

Waste of making defective products: Develop process to prevent defects from being made. Accept no defects and make no defects. Make the process "fail safe."

Figure 4.25

The Seven Wastes from Shigeo Shingo, in Robert W. Hall's *Attaining Manufacturing Excellence,* 1987.

work is long on philosophy, but short on the operational details. It does a great job explaining the foundation principles that guide the manufacturing systems in all Toyota facilities.

On the surface this system appears to be too simple, just an extension of common sense. There is, however, much more to the Toyota system than simple tools and techniques. It is important to look deeper at the Toyota system and consider the impact of the tools and techniques of the system on the people and the organization of the enterprise.

4.4.3 The Emergence of "Lean Production"

A team of educators from MIT completed a major study of the automobile industry and published their findings in a landmark book, *The Machine That Changed the World,* in 1990. This outstanding book provides a look at the history of the auto industry and the tremendous changes that have taken place since 1975. They pull many concepts that have been previously mentioned together under the overarching title of "lean manufacturing."

> **Lean manufacturing**—A philosophy of production that emphasizes the minimization of the amount of all the resources (including time) used in the various activities of the enterprise. It involves identifying and eliminating non-value-adding activities in design, production, supply chain management, and dealing with the customers. Lean producers employ teams of multiskilled workers at all levels of the organization and use highly flexible, increasingly automated machines to produce volumes of products in potentially enormous variety. Syn. lean production.
> *APICS Dictionary, 9th edition, 1998.*

The heart of the concept is the aggressive elimination of waste throughout all parts of the operation and its organization. It is a great testimonial to the power of the Toyota approach and techniques they use.

The book titled *Lean Thinking* has helped to "package" the important concepts about this important approach to manufacturing for busy executives. This book provides readers with case study examples and lays out the five fundamental principles that summarize the lean production concept.

1. Precisely specify the value of a specific product.
2. Identify how the value is actually realized by the customer.
3. Make value flow without interruptions.
4. Allow the customer to pull value from the producer.
5. Pursue perfection . . . continuously improve.

Lean thinking addresses all the areas of waste presented earlier in the discussion of JIT; however, the "lean" approach is more focused. An expert in waste elimination known as a "sensei" is a critical part of the lean approach. The experience of the sensei leads to the identification of problems and the design of solutions in a very short time period. The elimination of waste and the redesign of a work cell, including the relocation of machines, is often done in one day! The benefits of the efficient production cells are immediately visible and often lead to additional changes in other areas. The five principles of lean production sound fairly simple and a lot like commonsense actions that all companies should be doing. Taken together and used as the basis for a plan of action with the help of a skilled sensei, these five steps have helped companies remove amazing amounts of waste from their operations in a very short time. The sensei provides a jump-start to the improvement process. The people involved in the improvement process replace a long learning curve with the insight and knowledge of the sensei. The case examples presented in lean thinking demonstrate how the five principles just stated have been applied in small, medium, and large companies in the United States, Germany, and Japan. The examples build a credible argument for a move toward lean production.

American companies tend to be impatient with process changes. Companies have seen some short-term savings by just applying the tools of lean production. An important key to long-term success is truly understanding the product's value and the related value stream from the customer back to the producing company, and on to the company's suppliers. Weaving the beliefs and concepts of lean thinking into the fabric of the organization leads to ongoing improvements and savings that are not possible any other way.

4.5 Summary

The art of effective communications using graphics is essential to manufacturing. CAD and its associated graphics database enhances automation and is the process at the heart of the new manufacturing revolution. Automation enhances all aspects of manufacturing, including quality control, and the increasing use of computers. Graphics is the principal communications tool used in production processes, of which design and manufacturing are major activities. The CAD graphics database is an extremely important part of CIM and automated manufacturing. Many phases of CIM are controlled by or need access to the CAD database. Therefore, the accuracy of the graphics database is extremely important to the effective implementation of CIM.

Manufacturing and the computer-based systems that provide support are changing rapidly. The Internet can provide additional and timely information about design and manufacturing systems.

Online Learning Center (OLC) Features

There are a number of Online Learning Center features listed below that you can use to supplement your text reading to improve your understanding and retention of the material presented in this chapter at www.mhhe.com/bertoline.

- Learning Objectives
- Chapter Outline
- Chapter Overview
- Questions for Review
- Multiple Choice Quiz
- True or False Questions
- Flashcards
- Website Links

Questions for Review

1. Describe the production process and how it relates to computer-based design systems.
2. Describe rapid prototyping.
3. Compare concurrent engineering and traditional engineering practices.
4. What is TQM?
5. What is DFMA?
6. What is CIM?
7. What is a production process?
8. What are the key planning issues in manufacturing?
9. What are the critical control issues in manufacturing?
10. Describe computer-based systems to plan materials.
11. How does technical graphics support the development of programs used to control machine tools?
12. How are the concepts of TQM and SPC related?
13. Describe the similarities and differences between PLM and more traditional techniques, such as JIT, TQM, and the Toyota Method.
14. How is CAD related to inspection and quality control?

Further Reading

Chase, R. B., N. J. Aquilano, and F. R. Jacobs. *Operations Management for Competitive Advantage,* 9th ed. New York: McGraw-Hill Irwin, 2001.

Cox, J .F., and J. H. Blackstone, Editors. *APICS Dictionary,* 9th ed. Falls Church, VA: APICS—The Educational Society for Resource Management. 1998.

Ford, Henry. *Today and Tomorrow.* Portland, OR: Productivity Press. 1988.

Groover, M. P., and E. W. Zimmers. *CAD/CAM: Computer-Aided Design and Manufacturing,* 2d ed. Englewood Cliffs, NJ: Prentice-Hall, 1991.

Hall, Robert W. *Attaining Manufacturing Excellence.* Chicago: Dow Jones-Irwin. 1987.

Hunt, V. D. *Quality in America: How to Implement a Competitive Quality Program.* Homewood, IL: Business One Irwin, 1992.

Kraebber, H. Process Planning. In J. H. Greene (ed.), *Production and Inventory Control Handbook* (3rd ed., pp. 4.1–4.16). American Production and Inventory Control Society. New York: McGraw-Hill, 1997.

Kraebber, H. "Workforce Education and Development: The Key to Competitive Manufacturing." International Journal of Agile Manufacturing. V3, N2, 2000. 45–52.

Monden, Y. *The Toyota Production System.* Institute of Industrial Engineers. Norcross, GA: Industrial Engineering and Management Press. 1993.

Nahmias, S. *Production and Operations Analysis,* 2d ed. Homewood, IL: Richard D. Irwin, 1993.

Ohno, Taiichi. *Toyota Production System, Beyond Large Scale Production.* Portland, OR: Productivity Press. 1988.

Rehg, J. A., and H. W. Kraebber. *Computer-Integrated Manufacturing,* 2d ed. Upper Saddle River, NJ: Prentice-Hall, 2001.

Rother, M., and J. Shook. *Learning to See.* Brookline, MA: The Lean Enterprise Institute, Inc. 1998.

Stevenson, W. J. *Production/Operations Management,* 4th ed. Homewood, IL: Richard D. Irwin, 1993.

Womack, J. P., and D. T. Jones. *Lean Thinking.* New York: Simon and Schuster. 1996.

Womack, J. P., D. T. Jones, and D. Roos. *The Machine That Changed the World.* New York: HarperPerennial. 1990.

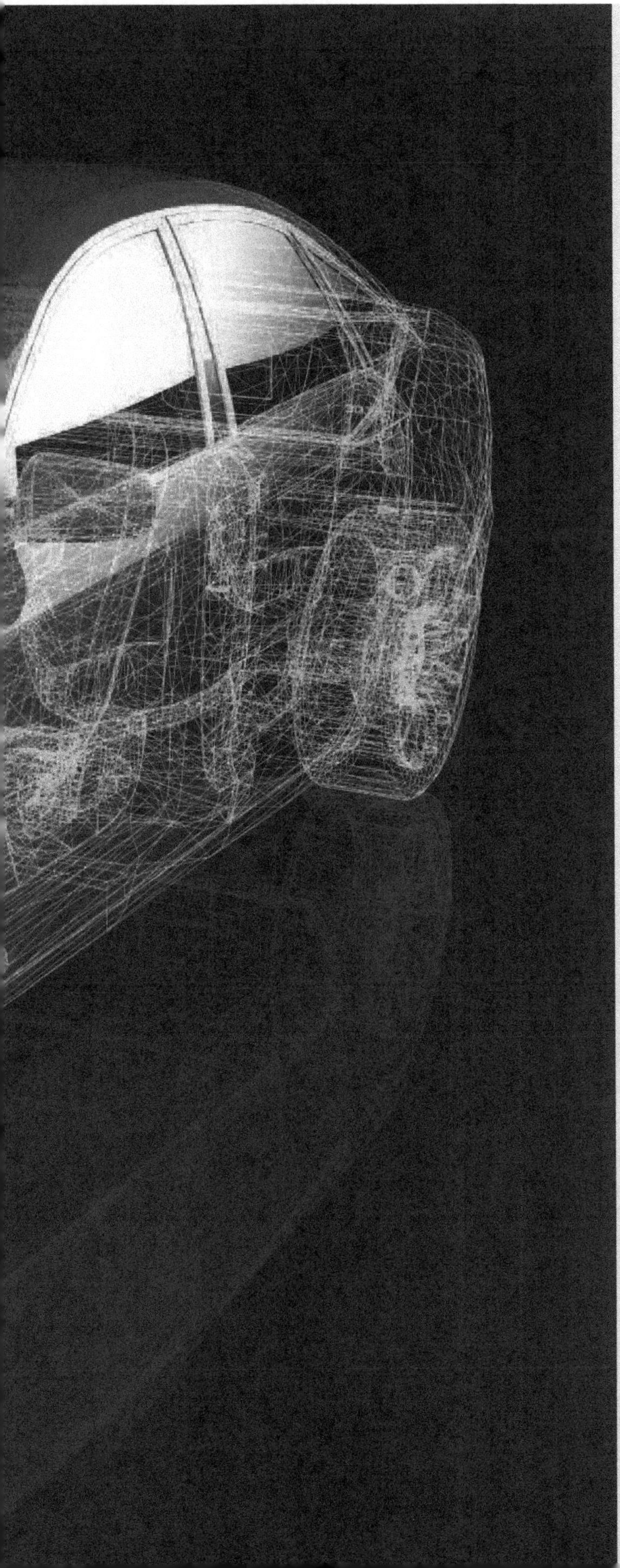

Chapter Five

Design Visualization

I shut my eyes in order to see.

—Paul Gauguin

Objectives

After completing this chapter, you will be able to:

1. Recognize the need for visualization.
2. Use the manipulation of solid primitives as a technique for visualizing 3-D objects.
3. Use the technique of a 3-D object interacting with 2-D surfaces for visualization.
4. Apply the concepts of image planes and projection to visualize 3-D objects.
5. Understand the role of color and rendering in visualizing 3-D objects.
6. Identify the differences between visualizing one object and visualizing a group of objects.
7. Explain how graphing and data visualization can be used in the design process.
8. Understand the role of virtual reality in visualizing 3-D objects.
9. Recognize how visualization can be applied in a number of technical fields.

Introduction

Visualization is the mental understanding of visual information. For students in engineering and technology, visualization skills can be crucial in understanding the fundamental concepts of technical graphics. The ability to visualize also greatly enhances the speed and accuracy with which drawings and models can be made, using 2-D CAD or 3-D modeling tools. Visualization skills can assist you in building and manipulating a 3-D design in the virtual world of the computer.

In this chapter, visualization will be explained primarily through exercises for you to do. You will learn how to better visualize 3-D objects by applying the concepts of solid object features, image planes and projection, and color and rendering. In Chapter 7, a number of sketching techniques will be introduced. These techniques will be the primary vehicle through which you will develop and use visualization skills. Methods using other materials will also be explored.

Figure 5.1

Human vision

Your sight allows you to successfully navigate your environment.

(© Photri, Inc.)

5.1 Visualization Abilities

The brain has an amazing ability to process visual information. Unconsciously, your brain is managing the navigation as you walk through the house or drive down the street (Figure 5.1). Your brain's desire to organize the visual information around you allows you to look at the clouds or the stars and see the shapes of animals, objects, or people. This natural visualization ability can be put to work in more structured ways by engineers, scientists, and technologists to solve problems.

Nikola Tesla, one of the great inventors in electronics, was said to be able to design exclusively with images in his head. Leonardo da Vinci, a great inventor of an earlier generation, used drawings as an integral part of his design process (Figure 5.2). The famous scientist Albert Einstein used visual imagery to solve complex problems in physics. Einstein once said: "The words or the language, as they are written or spoken, do not seem to play any role in my mechanism of thought. The psychical entities which serve as elements of thought are certain signs and more or less clear images which can be voluntarily reproduced and combined."

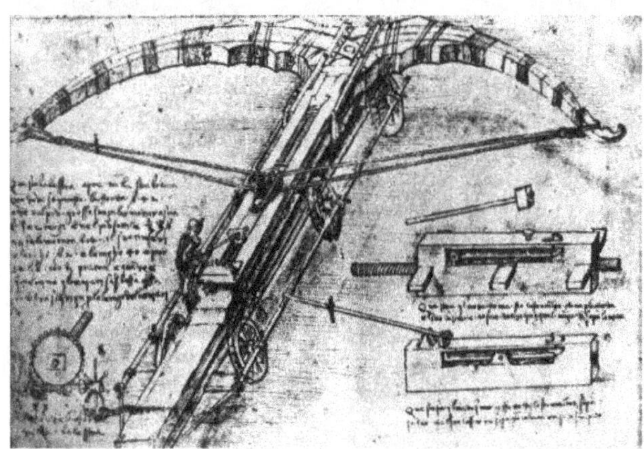

Figure 5.2

Leonardo da Vinci used drawing as a means of visualizing his designs

(© Art Resource, NY.)

We all have the ability to use imagery to solve problems that are spatial in nature. What you may not have is Tesla's ability to do complete designs from beginning to end in your head. You will find, however, that transforming your ideas into tangible graphic images serves both as a permanent record of those ideas and as a means of encouraging further creative thinking.

You do not have to be able to draw as well as Leonardo da Vinci in order for graphics to be of use in the design process. Graphics as part of the visualization process can take many forms. Some are personal visual codes (e.g., sketches, notes, drawings on the back of a napkin, etc.) meant only to be seen and used by the person drawing them. Other graphics are much more formal and are usually meant to communicate ideas to a wider audience.

Vision

Light travels in straight lines, so visual information can be used to determine both the direction and distance of an object. No other human stimulus provides as much detail as the human eye. Vision, the perception of light, is carried out through the eye, which contains receptors that detect photons of light (see the figure). The eye is organized similar to a camera. The receptors are located in the back of the eye and are categorized as either rods, which are receptors for black and white vision, or cones, which are receptors for color. There are three different kinds of cones, cells that absorb either red, green, or blue wavelengths of light to give humans color vision. The field of receptors that line the back of the eye is called the retina. The retina contains approximately 3 million cones and 1 billion rods. Most of the cones are located in the central region of the retina called the fovea. The eyes form a sharp image in the central fovea region of the retina.

The light rays are focused onto the receptors by the lens of the eye. Light first passes through a transparent layer called the cornea, which begins to focus light onto the rear of the eye. Light then passes through the lens, which is a structure that completes the focusing. Muscles are attached to the lens which contract and change the shape of the lens to change the point of focus on the rear of the eye. The amount of light entering the eye is controlled by a shutter, called the iris, which is located between the cornea and the lens. The iris reduces the size of the transparent zone, or pupil, of the eye through which light passes.

The optic nerve transmits visual stimuli more or less directly to the brain in the region called the visual cortex.

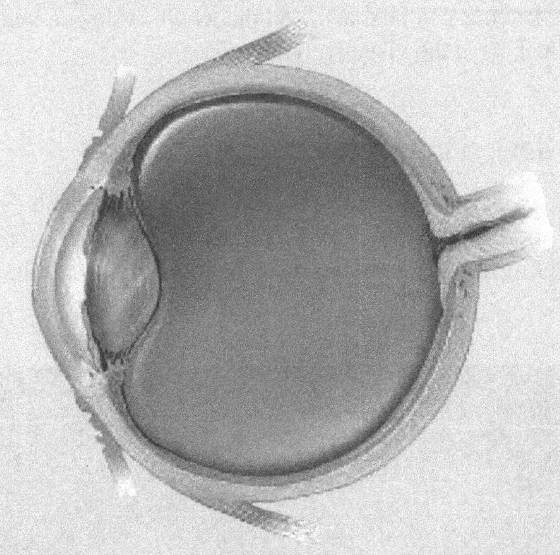

Visual impulses are processed in the brain to determine intensity, color, and point-to-point images.

Having two eyes looking at the same object or scene causes each eye to see slightly different images because they are viewed from slightly different angles. This slight displacement of the images, called parallax, permits very sensitive depth perception. By comparing the differences between the images provided by each eye with the physical distance to specific objects, humans learn to interpret distance, which is stereoscopic vision. We are not born with the ability to perceive distance, but it is a learned trait. Stereoscopic vision develops in babies over a period of months.

Although creating these more formal graphics can involve considerable skill, the current computer graphics hardware and software systems are a great equalizer for those who do not have a natural ability to express their ideas visually (Figure 5.3).

5.2 The Visualization Cycle

To effectively use graphics as a vehicle for visualizing design ideas, you must understand that the two-dimensional graphics you draw—whether on paper or a computer screen—are a *representation* of information existing in another form. In Chapter 7, various sketching techniques were introduced. The exercises in that chapter focused on drawing exactly what you saw, as though there was a direct connection between your hand and the object being drawn (Figure 5.4). In fact, the mind and the information it receives visually play a critical role in guiding what the pencil draws on the paper (Figure 5.5).

The mind *processes* and *interprets* the visual information and *controls* the muscles holding the pencil. Like the 3-D object, the drawings that form on the paper can also be seen, and they serve to organize and focus the images in the mind. A feedback loop thus forms between the mind, hand/pencil, and drawing, and this loop is powerful enough to leave the 3-D object out altogether. In other words, the image can form in the mind without the help of a real object. Now the sketch has an even more important role, because the real object is not in sight (or may not even be in existence!), and the sketch becomes the only record of the object. The eyes and mind, looking at the sketch, can begin to modify and evolve the object, new sketches can be made, and the whole cycle can begin again. This is the visualization cycle.

5.3 Design Visualization

Visualization is important and integral to the design process (Figure 5.6). Using either 2-D CAD or 3-D modeling tools, engineers and technologists must have the ability to document their completed designs, based on well-defined technical graphics standards. They must also have the ability to understand, at a deeper level, the three-dimensional forms they are documenting.

The ability to visualize forms in your mind enhances your ability to understand both existing objects and objects that may not yet have been manufactured. Visualizing three-dimensional forms allows you to play *what-if* games in the early stages of the design process, before there are physical models. The ability to visualize also allows you to spatially analyze more detailed problems later on.

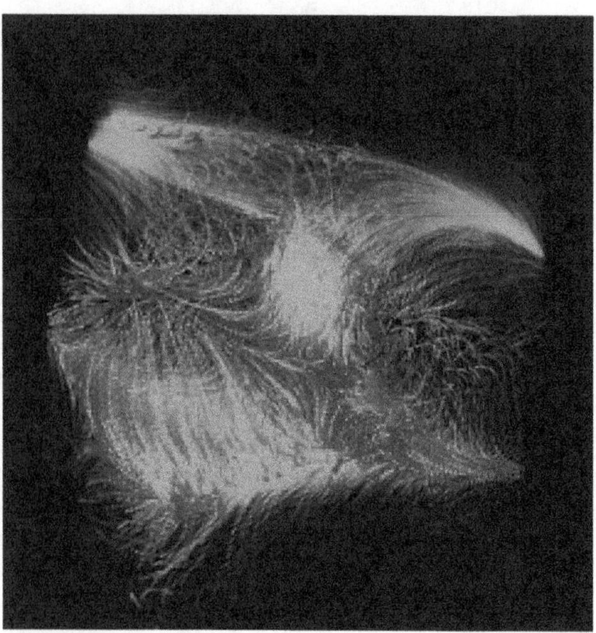

Figure 5.3

Computer-generated scientific visualization

This visualization represents the interactive control of vectors depicting fluid flow or electromagnetic fields.

(Courtesy of Dr. Yinlong Sun.)

5.4 Solid Object Features

The first visualization technique treats objects as you would normally see and feel them. A closer look at a solid object reveals features, or attributes, which help you visualize the object's current form. These attributes are also useful for transforming the object into something new, either on paper or in your mind.

5.4.1 Solid Object Attributes

Figure 5.7 contains two simple, primitive objects, one a *brick* or rectangular prism, and the other a *cylinder.* These two primitives clearly demonstrate several important characteristics, or attributes, of objects.

Practice Exercise 5.1

Put various objects under a strong, directed light. Identify the edges on the object by looking at them, and then feel them with your hand. Does the gradation of light on various parts of the object correspond to the "sharpness" of the corners?

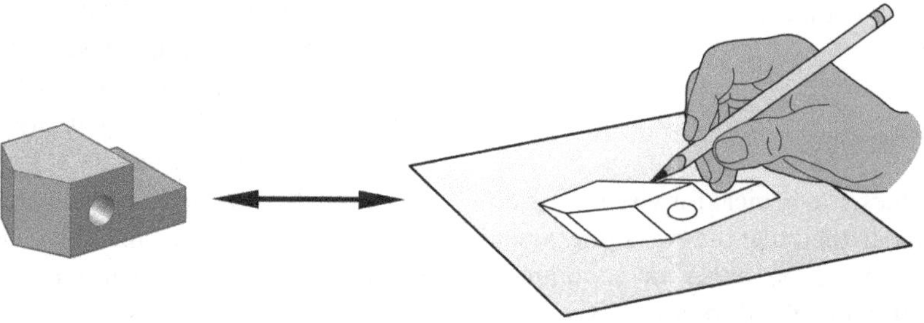

Figure 5.4

Hand/eye connection

The hand/eye connection is important when sketching.

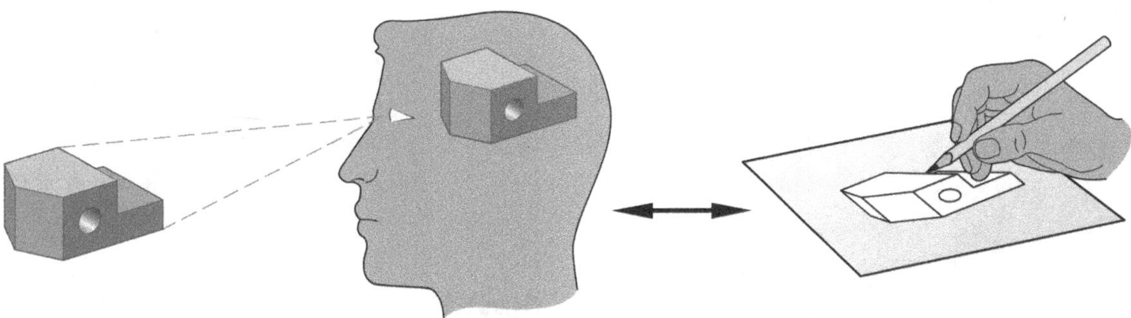

Figure 5.5

Hand/eye/mind connection

The hand/eye/mind connection more accurately describes the processes used to make sketches. The mind forms a mental picture of existing or nonexisting objects, which can then be sketched. The feedback loop between the mind and the hand is so powerful that the object need not exist.

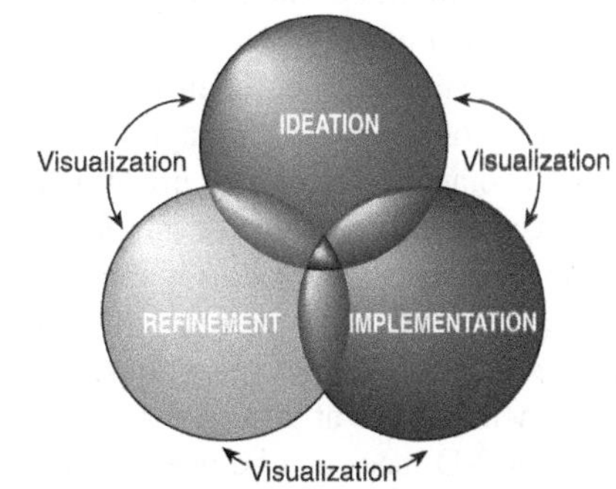

Figure 5.6

Visualization integrated throughout design

Visualization plays an important role in all facets of engineering design and is a process that is used frequently.

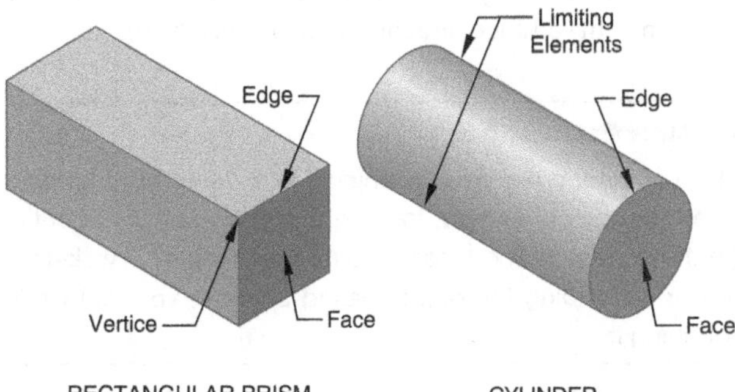

Figure 5.7

Solid object features

These rectangular prism and cylinder primitives show important features: edge, face, vertex, and limiting element.

Edges are the lines that represent the boundary between two faces of an object. On real objects, edges exist at a sharp break in light or dark levels on a surface (see Figure 5.7). **Faces** are areas of uniform or gradually changing lightness and are always bounded by edges. This is an important rule! Both edges and faces can be curved. For instance, as you follow around the curved face of the cylinder, there is gradual change in the lightness of the surface. Only when you go to the front of the cylinder is there an abrupt change in lightness, signaling an edge.

Another important attribute demonstrated by the cylinder is the limiting element. A **limiting element** is a line that represents the farthest outside feature of the curved surface. It is the last visible part of the curved surface as it drops away from your line of sight. Even though it is not a boundary between faces, a line is used to represent the limiting element. The line is tangent to the curved edge at each end of the cylinder. If you examine the cylinder, you will note that, even with an ideal viewing position, a curved face that curves more than approximately 180 degrees will have some of its surface obscured; in other words, you have a face that is only partially visible. For the cylinder in Figure 5.7, its curved face is half hidden, and one of its circular faces is completely hidden.

Another important attribute, found on the brick, is a corner, or **vertex**. If an edge is the place where two faces meet, then a vertex is the place where more than two edges meet. By extension, this means that more than two faces also meet at this point. On the brick primitive seen in Figure 5.7, there are four vertices visible, each with three connecting edges. Can you see three faces connecting at all of these vertices? What about the other places where

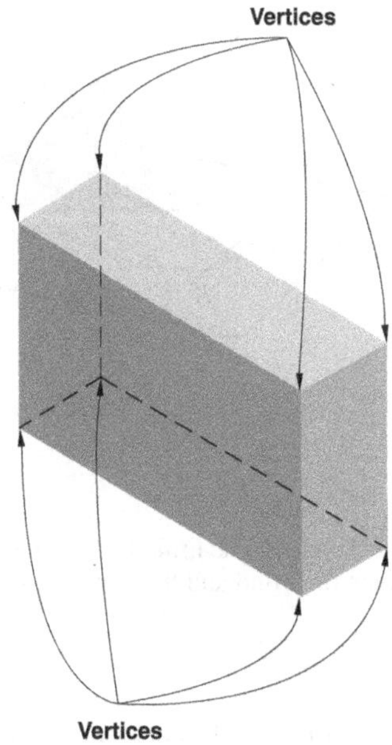

Figure 5.8

Vertices

Vertices are locations where more than two edges meet.

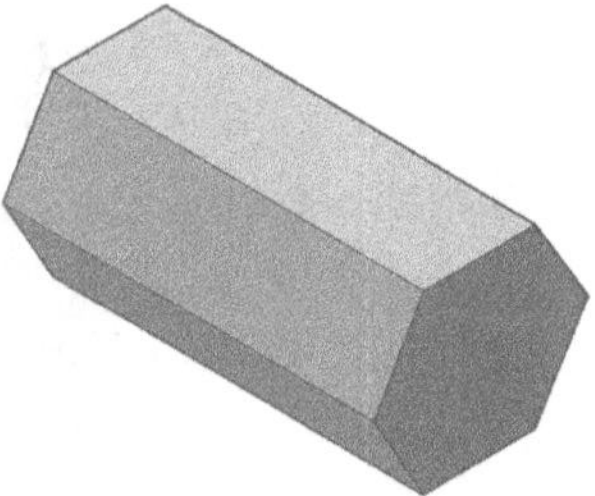

Figure 5.9

Object faces

This hexagonal prism has an end face attached to six other faces.

two edges connect? Are they vertices, too? They are, because of the hidden edges and faces shown in Figure 5.8.

Going back to the cylinder, does it have any vertices? The answer is no, because there is no point at which three edges or three faces come together.

Practice Exercise 5.2

Based on the brick (prism) and cylinder developments found at the end pages of this book, construct the brick and cylinder, using tape or glue to hold the paper forms together. After constructing the two primitive shapes, identify and label:

- The faces, edges, and vertices of the brick (prism).
- The faces and edges of the cylinder.

Hold the cylinder at arm's length and identify the limiting elements on each side of the curved surface. Change the position of the cylinder and notice that (a) the limiting elements change with the cylinder, and (b) you can never view more than 180 degrees of the 360-degree curved surface of the cylinder.

Two other attributes important in defining a solid object are size and the shape of the faces. **Size** describes the physical dimensions of the object. For example, the brick or the cylinder could be 1 inch, or 1 mile, across. The **shape** of the face is described by the number of edges bounding the face and the relative angles of the edges to each other. The relative sizes between edges or faces reveal **proportion**, which also relates to the shape of the faces.

The basic rules of geometry that apply to 2-D shapes also apply to 3-D objects. Since faces are attached to each other at common edges, the shape of one face influences both the number of faces attached to it and the shapes of those other faces. For the brick primitive in Figure 5.7, all of the faces are either rectangles or squares, and the adjacent edges on each face are at 90 degrees to each other.

The shapes of 2-D faces can be used to interpret how a 3-D object is shaped. The square end face on the brick has four edges, which means there are four other faces attached to it. If the end face were a hexagon instead of a square (Figure 5.9), how many faces would be attached to it? What if the end face had one edge instead of four? Since one shape that has a single edge is a circle, the brick would become a cylinder and the end face would have only one curved face attached to it (Figure 5.10).

Practice Exercise 5.3

Have someone put various objects in a paper or cloth bag. Feel the objects without looking at them. Can you identify (a) the edges, (b) the faces, and (c) the objects? Try sketching or describing the object based on what you feel when touching it.

5.5 Visualization Techniques for Technical Drawings

Another technique for combining 2-D planes and 3-D solids is introduced in the following sections. This technique uses image planes and is designed specifically to

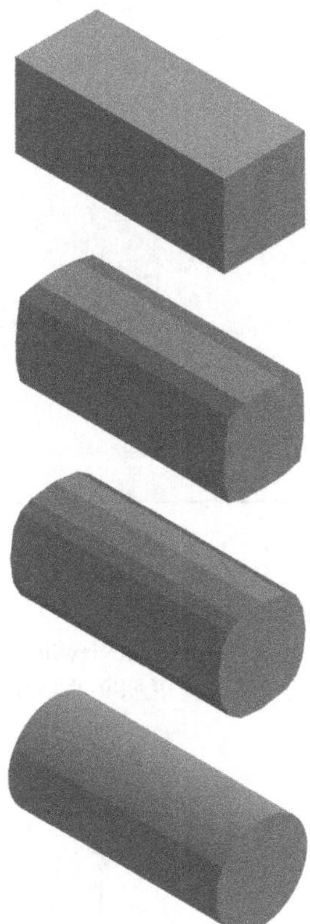

Figure 5.10

As the brick changes into a cylinder, the end face goes from attaching to four surfaces to attaching to just one.

help in the creation of 2-D multiview technical drawings and 3-D computer models.

5.5.1 Image Planes

Imagine placing a 2-D plane between you and the object you wish to visualize (Figure 5.11). The 2-D plane is now called an **image plane** (or picture plane or projection plane): what is imaged by your eyes is also imaged on the plane. Think of the image plane as being transparent, like the viewfinder on a camera. What you see is registered on the film. This analogy will be used in other chapters, such as Chapter 10.

Practice Exercise 5.4

Two ways to demonstrate an image plane are as follows:

1. Using a camera, take pictures of simple objects under good light. (If you use an instant camera, the exercise can be done immediately.) Look at the object from exactly the same viewpoint as that used when the picture was taken. Make sure the lighting is also the same. On the photograph, highlight the contours of the object, using water-based markers. Identify different faces of the object by using different colors. Study the results; then use a damp cloth to wipe the picture clean, to be used again.
2. Alternatively, place a 12″ × 12″ sheet of rigid clear plastic or a cardboard frame with a transparency acetate between you and a well-lit object. Brace the plastic so that you don't have to hold it, and draw the contours of the object, using water-based markers. When done, study the results; then use a damp cloth to wipe the plastic clean.

Using each of these techniques, look at the objects from a number of different viewpoints, either by moving yourself or by rotating the object. From which viewpoints can you see the most number of contours? Which viewpoints afford the fewest number of contours? What happens when you get closer or farther away?

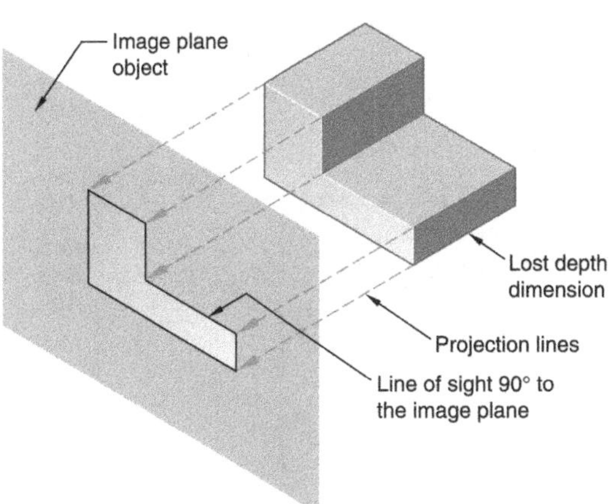

Figure 5.11

Image plane

The image on the plane represents what you would see if you were looking at the object through a semitransparent plane.

The three variables involved in the use of image planes are as follows:

1. The object being viewed.
2. The image plane.
3. The eye of the viewer.

Assume the image plane is always between the viewer and the object. In addition, assume the line of sight of the

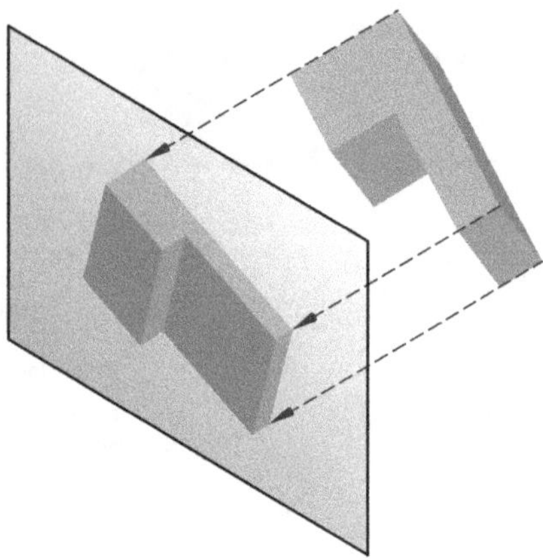

Figure 5.12

Pictorial view

A pictorial view is created by orienting the object such that features in all three dimensions are visible in the image.

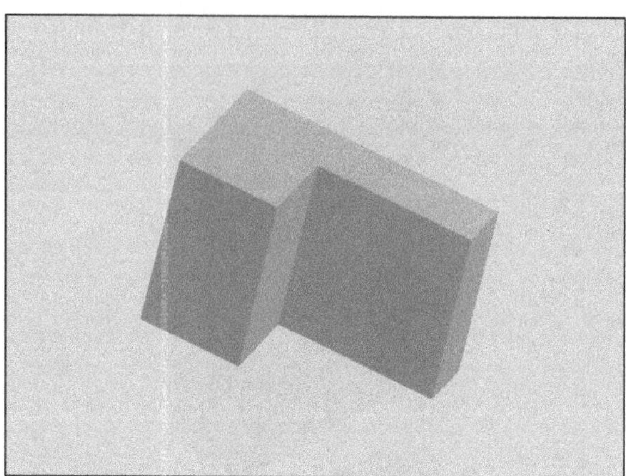

Figure 5.13

Projection on the image plane

This is what you actually see when viewing the object shown in Figure 5.12 when your line of sight is perpendicular to the transparent plane.

viewer is always perpendicular (at 90 degrees) to the image plane (Figure 5.11).

In Practice Exercise 5.4, you drew lines on the image plane wherever you saw edges on the object. Conceptually, you were visualizing *projection lines* from the object to the image plane. The relationships between the eye, image plane, and object determine the angle between projection lines. If the viewer is infinitely far away from the object, all of the projection lines will appear to be parallel to the line of sight and therefore perpendicular to the image plane. This is called *parallel projection* (see Chapter 7) and is the type of projection most commonly used in technical drawings.

Projection onto an image plane transforms a 3-D object into a 2-D representation of that object. The best way to capture all three dimensions of the object in a single 2-D image is to use pictorial projection techniques, as described in Chapter 7 (Figure 5.12).

Practice Exercise 5.5

Use the same setup of object and image plane as you used in the previous exercise. However, instead of drawing directly on the plastic sheet, use it to "frame" your view of the object, and draw what you see on a piece of paper. (If you do not have a sheet of clear plastic, make a cardboard frame.) Instead of drawing the edges in perspective, as you see them, draw them in parallel projection (i.e., all edges that are parallel on the object are parallel in the sketch).

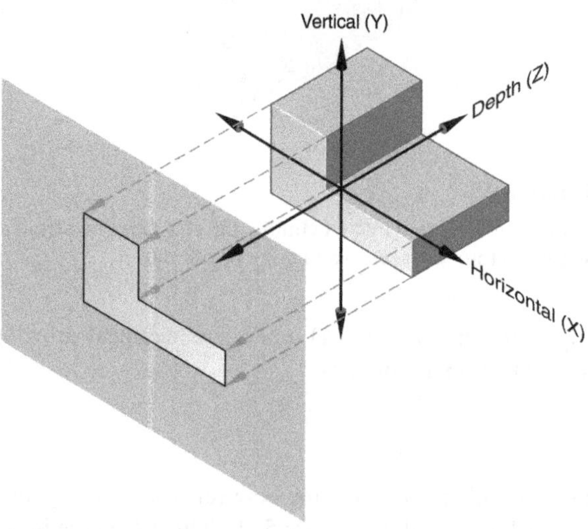

Figure 5.14

Object-image plane orientation

The relationship of the image plane to the standard mutually perpendicular viewing axes.

5.5.2 Object-Image Plane Orientation

What you draw on paper is what you see on the image plane, and what you see is directly related to the orientation of the object with respect to the image plane (Figure 5.13). If the object is rotated relative to the image

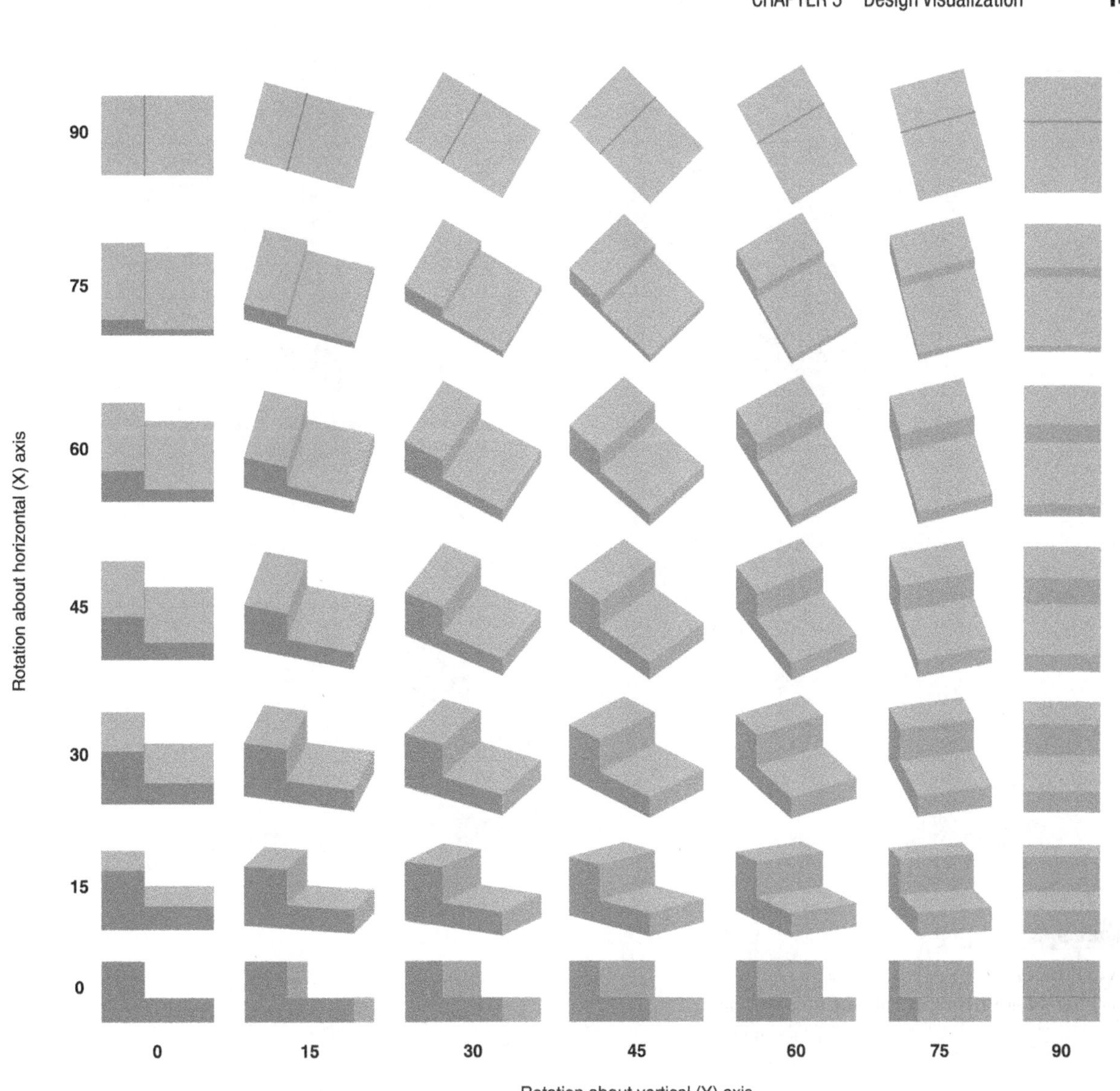

Figure 5.15

Progressive 15-degree rotations of the object about the horizontal and vertical viewing axes

plane, various faces appear and disappear, and an infinite number of projections are created. There are three **primary axes** about which you can rotate the object relative to the image plane. The three axes are *horizontal, vertical,* and *depth* in coordinate space (Figure 5.14).

You need only rotate the object about two of these axes to see all sides of the object. Rotation about the horizontal and vertical axes tends to provide the most information. Figure 5.15 is a matrix of the rotational views, in 15-degree increments between 0 and 90 degrees, for both the horizontal and vertical axes. Notice that only those views near the center of the matrix show all three dimensions. In fact, for those projections along the outer edges of the matrix, one dimension is completely obscured.

The lower left projection in Figure 5.15 is the starting point for the object (rotated 0 degrees in both the horizontal and vertical axes). This projection gives a very clear view of one face of the object, at the expense of the other faces. The projection for the object rotated 45 degrees in both the horizontal and vertical axes gives you a more

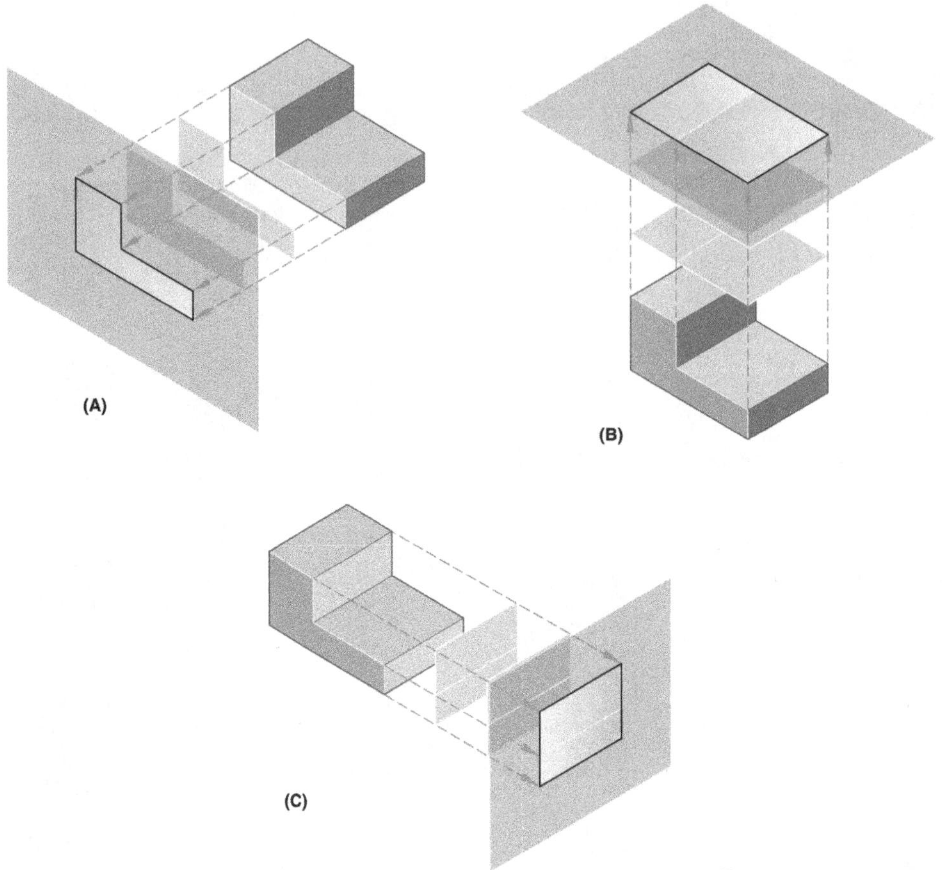

Figure 5.16

Normal faces

Projection of normal faces onto the image plane.

complete understanding of the shape of the object. However, it does not show any of the faces in their true size and shape.

Practice Exercise 5.6

Place a 12″ × 12″ sheet of rigid, clear plastic between you and the object. Replicate the sequence of views from Figure 5.15 by rotating the object about its horizontal and vertical axes.

To determine if a face is shown in its true size and shape, examine the orientation of the face with respect to the image plane. If the face of an object is parallel to the image plane (i.e., is a *normal face*), the face shown on the image plane will not be distorted. Another way of imagining this is to move the object toward the image plane. The normal face will lie perfectly flat on the image plane (Figure 5.16A). This projection is identical to Figure 5.11 and the 0-degree by 0-degree projection in Figure 5.15.

Other faces of this object can also be normal to the image plane. In Figure 5.15, the projections in the upper left and lower right corners are views of the object rotated 90 degrees about the horizontal and vertical axes, respectively. These two views have faces normal to the image plane. In both cases, however, there are two normal faces, not just one, and they are at different depths from the image plane (Figure 5.16B and C). To explain, the 2-D image plane always compresses one of the dimensions of the 3-D object, and that dimension is always the one perpendicular to the image plane; i.e., the depth axis. The result is that two faces sitting at different depths on the

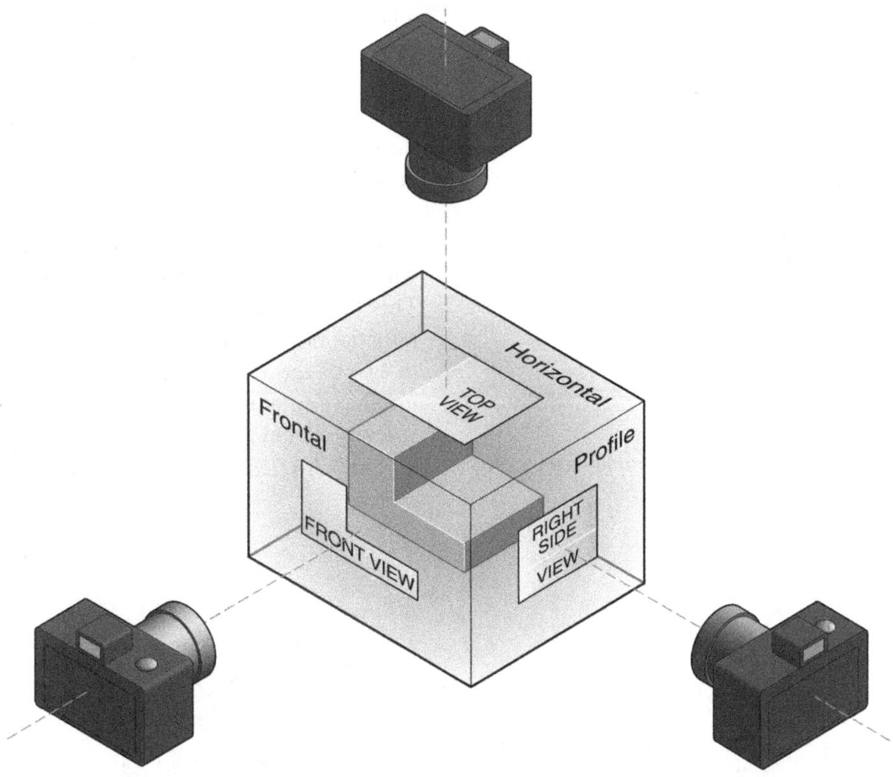

Figure 5.17

Camera metaphor

The metaphor of cameras can be used to describe capturing the three principal views of the object—front, top, and right side—through the three image planes.

object sit side by side on the image plane. One of the challenges of visualization is to reconstruct this third dimension when viewing a projection.

5.5.3 Multiple-Image Planes

A more traditional way of generating multiple views of an object is to hold the object stationary and create a separate image plane for each view. In Figure 5.17, three separate image planes are used to produce the three projections previously shown in Figure 5.16. These three image planes, traditionally named *frontal, horizontal,* and *profile,* generate the three standard views, *front, top,* and *right side,* respectively. Taken together, these three views comprise the standard multiview drawing. (See Chapter 10.)

The three planes are *mutually perpendicular;* that is, each is 90 degrees from the other two. Imagine a face as being completely separate from the rest of the solid object, just a 2-D surface in space (Figure 5.18). This face is parallel to the image plane and perpendicular to the

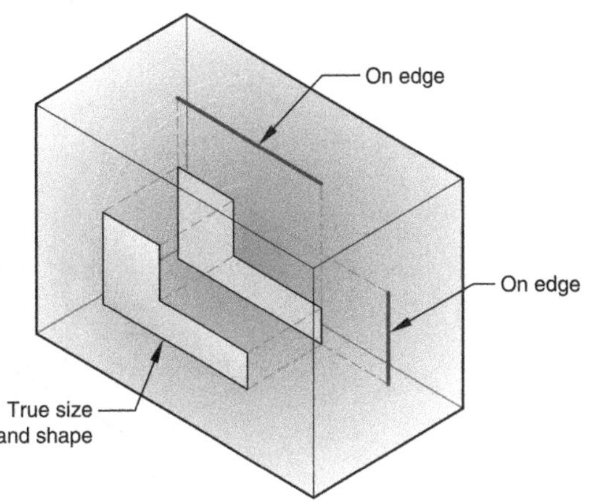

Figure 5.18

Normal face projection

A normal face projects on all three principal image planes. On one image plane, the face appears true size and shape. In the other two, the face appears on edge and is represented as a line.

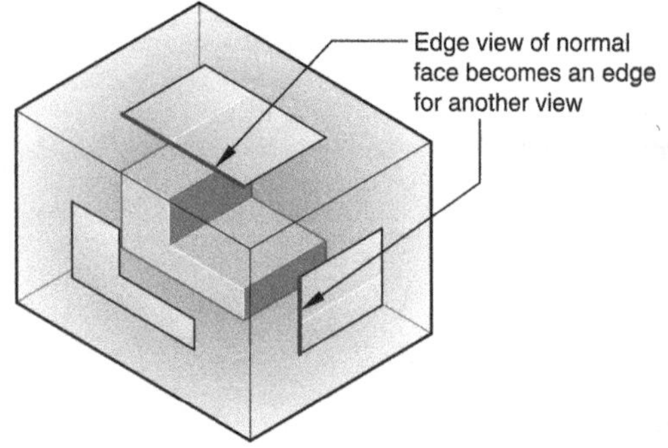

Figure 5.19

Edge views of normal face

In a multiview projection, edge views of a normal face become the outlines of another face.

adjoining planes. The result is that, *if in one plane you are seeing a face in its true size and shape, in the other planes you will see the face as an edge.* Since faces that touch each other share edges, in the multiview projection, the edge views of one face become part of the outlines or contours of faces seen in other views (Figure 5.19).

There are other faces that have a different relationship to the three principal planes. One is an *inclined face,* which is not parallel to any of the principal image planes. This face is rotated about either the vertical or horizontal axis, but not both (Figure 5.20A). The face is visible in two of the views, but *not* in true size and shape. The face has depth in both views, but it is compressed or *foreshortened* onto the image plane (Figure 5.20B and C). In Figure 5.20D, the inclined face is projected as an edge on

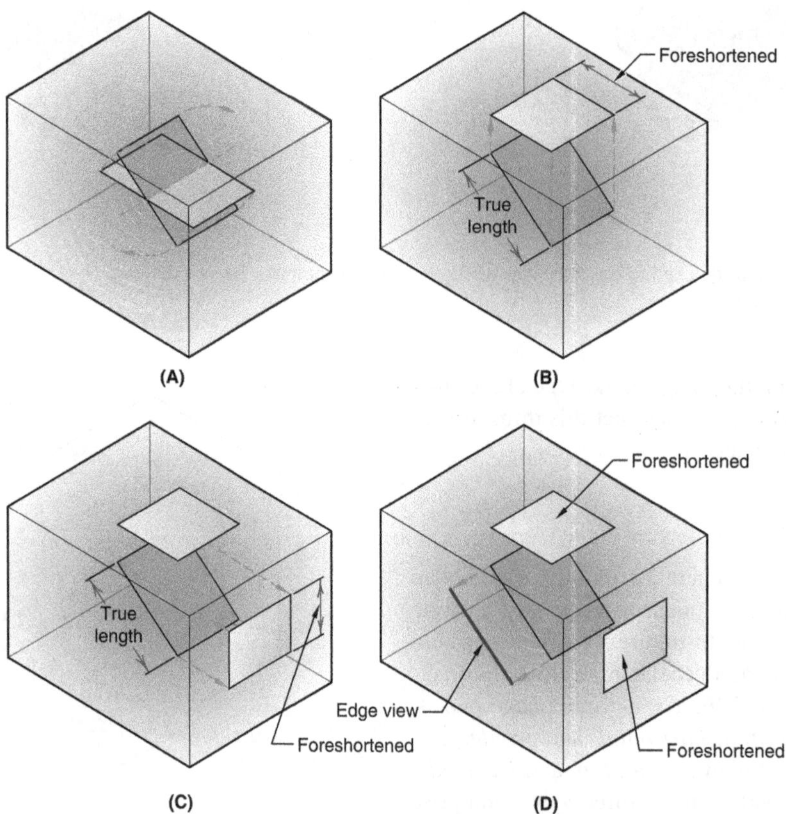

Figure 5.20

Inclined face projection

An inclined face is oriented such that it is not parallel to any of the standard image planes. The inclined face is foreshortened in two views and is an edge in one view.

the perpendicular plane, just as a normal face would be. Inclined faces can, of course, be combined with normal faces in an object (Figure 5.21).

Whereas an inclined face is created by rotating a normal face about either the vertical or horizontal axes, an *oblique face* is created by rotation about *both* axes (Figure 5.22A). An oblique face is seen foreshortened in all three views since it is neither parallel nor perpendicular to any of the standard image planes (Figure 5.22B). Unlike normal and inclined faces, oblique faces are not seen as an edge in any of the standard views. Chapter 13 goes into detail on how image planes that are oriented parallel to inclined and oblique surfaces are used to see those surfaces in true size and shape.

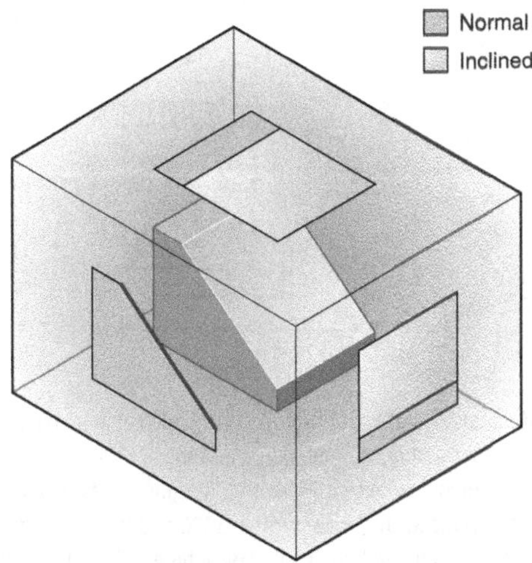

Figure 5.21

Inclined and normal faces

Projection of an object that has both inclined and normal faces onto the three image planes.

Practice Exercise 5.7

Replace the object on the other side of your image plane with a stiff sheet of cardboard representing a single face of an object. Align the cardboard sheet so that it is parallel to the image plane. (Ask a second person to hold the cardboard sheet, if necessary.) Change your viewing direction, but don't move the cardboard sheet, and look at the sheet as an edge view. Do the same by holding the image plane still and rotating the cardboard sheet. Rotate the cardboard less than 90 degrees about either the horizontal or vertical axis, to create an inclined face. Move the image plane around until you can identify the two standard views where the inclined face is visible. Find the view where the face is seen as an edge. How does the amount of rotation affect the size of the projection seen in the image plane? Rotate the cardboard so that it is almost normal to the image plane.

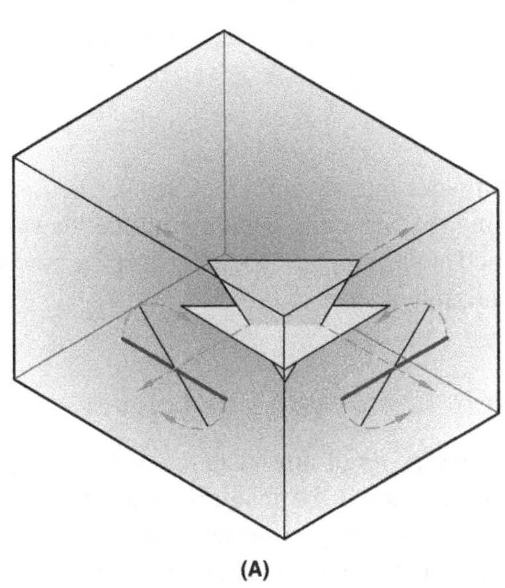

(A)

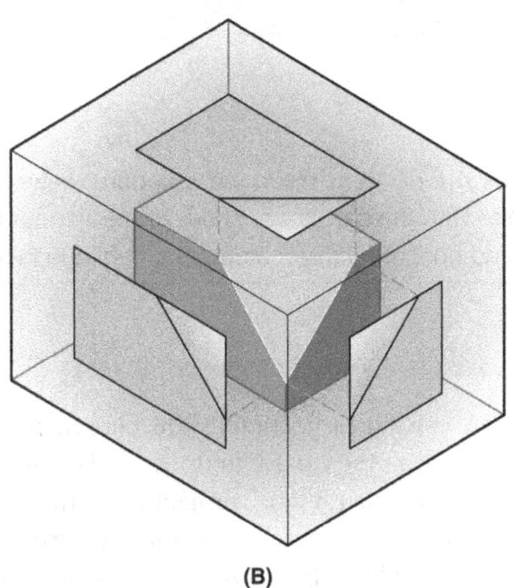

(B)

Figure 5.22

Oblique face projection

The projection of an oblique face is foreshortened in all three standard image planes.

Historical Highlight
Early Technical Drawings

Early technical drawings were often quite crude and very hard to understand due to the lack of drawing standards and projections systems. The drawing shown in the figure is an undershot watermill and was in a book of drawings compiled by the Abbess Herrad of Landsperg about 1160. Some refer to this type of drawing as a one plane projection, but it really uses no formal projection system. The artist tried to represent the geometrical shapes that made up the mill but in doing so really makes it difficult if not impossible to understand. See figure.

The top portion of the drawing represents four columns fixed to a base made of horizontal timbers to support the grindstones. There is a long horizontal shaft running through the structure with a toothed wheel under the grindstone and a water wheel located to the left. There are inconsistencies between the drawing and real object. For example, the main water wheel is shown as two concentric circles when in fact they are circles of the same size with paddles attached. However, if they were drawn the same size, they would coincide and the artist would not have been able to represent the paddles.

The rather crude depiction of devices is quite usual in drawings of this period. Although it may be possible to reconstruct the machines from these drawings, we have to guess the real size of parts. It would have to take development of a formal projection system during the Renaissance period before more accurate drawings could be produced to represent technical objects.

Excerpted from *The History of Engineering Drawing*, by Jeffrey Booker, Chatto & Windus, London, England, 1963.

Drawing of an undershot water mill. The original was in a manuscript on vellum with 636 drawings compiled by the Abbess Herrad of Landsperg about 1160 as an instructive collection for her pupils. The manuscript, called "Hortus-Deliciarum," was burnt in 1870 and the only remains are a few drawings which had been copied by scholars. This drawing is not based upon any conceptions of projection but is a recording of a number of geometric "trusts."

How does it look from the three standard views? Do the same tests with the cardboard sheet rotated about both the vertical and horizontal axes, creating an oblique face.

5.5.4 Choosing a View to Describe an Object

In the past, certain projections were chosen more often because they were the easiest to draw. Today, 3-D modeling systems can generate any projection with equal ease. You can choose the views which most clearly and succinctly show the object being visualized. However, do not produce so many views that you unnecessarily duplicate information and confuse the viewer. Visualize the object, identify the features you need to show, and generate clear, concise images that show them. Use sketches as an aid in visualizing the form and deciding on the views required. The pencil and computer together form a powerful tool for visualizing objects.

5.6 Other Visualization Techniques

The primary goals of any visualization technique are to help you understand the features or attributes of an object and to convey this information to others. In most instances, the information required is geometric in nature. Previous sections of this chapter discussed the use of cutting planes and image planes for visualizing 3-D objects. The following sections expand on those discussions.

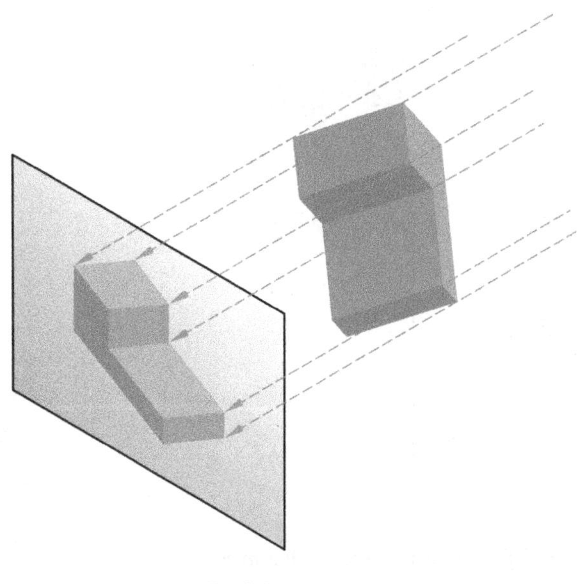

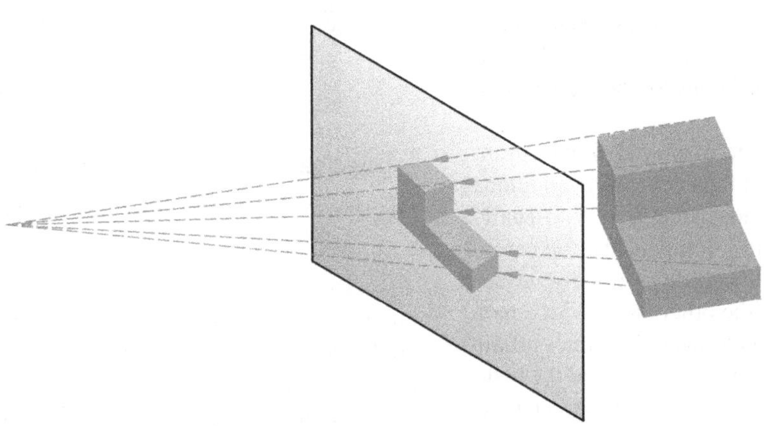

Figure 5.23

Parallel versus perspective projection

In perspective projection, the projection lines are not parallel.

5.6.1 Alternative Projection Techniques

Perspective projections can be used for visualizing an object (Figure 5.23). (See Chapter 12.) Perspective projections are easily generated by a 3-D modeling system. Although perspective projections cannot portray the exact relationships of particular edges and faces, they can provide a sense of the complete object.

All of the projections in the previous sections were generated from one of three standard views, none of which showed the back or the bottom of the object. Also not

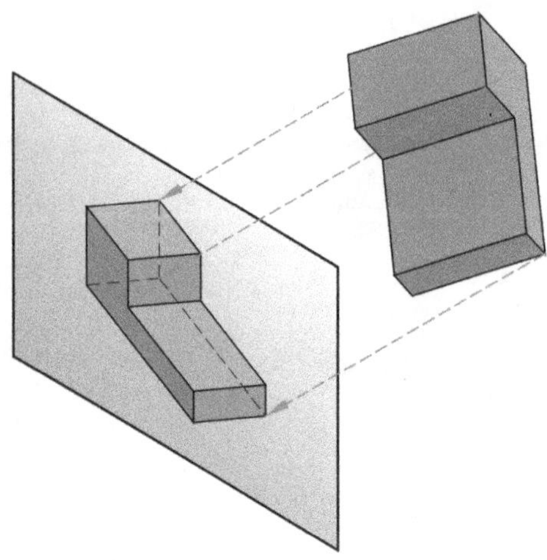

Figure 5.24

Projection using dashed lines to reveal hidden features

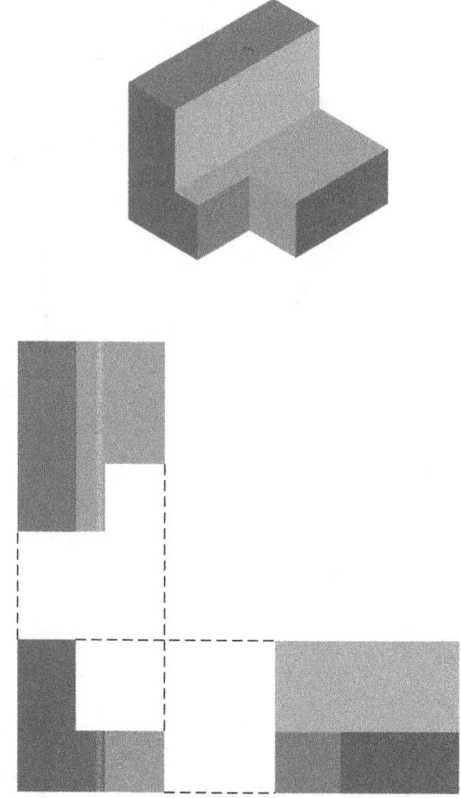

Figure 5.25

Coloring the faces of an object to assist visualization

shown are important features on faces that are partially or completely hidden. One way of showing these hidden features is to use a hierarchy of linetypes, with solid lines for the visible edges and dashed lines for the hidden edges (Figure 5.24).

Hidden features can also be displayed simply by reorienting the image plane and then generating additional views to show the previously hidden features. With smaller or less complicated mechanical components, the careful use of hidden lines and sectional views usually negates the need for extra views. On the other hand, with a more complex structure, such as a building, hidden lines usually confuse rather than clarify, and extra views are the better option. Rendering techniques, such as transparency, and technical drawing techniques, such as sectioning, are also used to reveal hidden features. These are discussed in detail later in this text.

5.6.2 Shading

Most of the drawings in this chapter are **line drawings**; that is, the edges of the objects are represented by dark (usually black) lines. The edges represent the boundaries of faces on the object. On a real object, boundaries are also determined by the orientation of the faces to the light source. The closer the face is to being perpendicular to the direction of the light rays, the lighter the face will be. These gradations of lightness, or **shading**, can be recreated in the image, either in tones of gray or in color. Shading, using gradual or no gradations on a face and strong gradations between faces, is another cue that can aid in the visualization of the object. The discussion on rendering, in Chapter 21, goes into detail on how you can create realistic shading, either by hand or using the computer.

When you are first learning to visualize, often the best way to recreate the effect of an imaginary light source on an object is to code the various features of the object. Individual faces and edges can be color coded on the real object, in a pictorial projection, and in a multiview projection. For example, assume you have a pictorial and a multiview projection of the same object. Faces you can identify in the pictorial projection may also be visible in one or more views of the multiview projection. Assigning the same color to features that appear in both projections can help you identify them in the various views, and can also help you organize the visualization process (Figure 5.25). This coloring technique is as effective on computer generated drawings as it is on hand-drawn sketches.

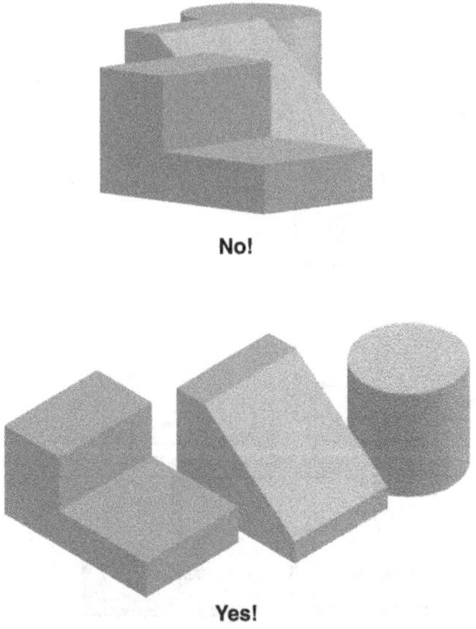

Figure 5.26

Good versus poor viewpoints

A good viewpoint will have some overlap to help place objects in depth but not so much as to obscure features.

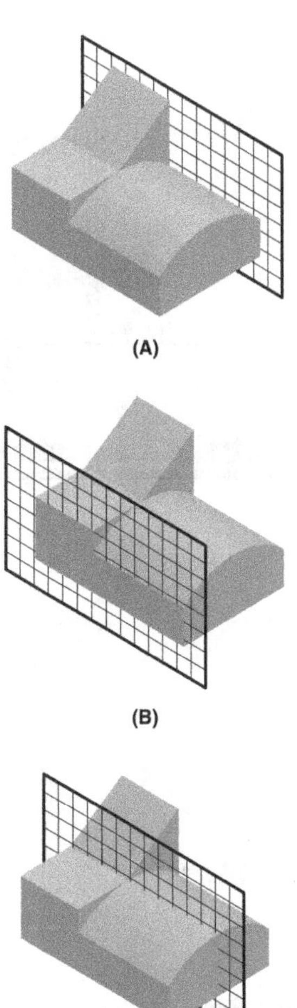

Figure 5.27

Using grid planes

A grid plane can be used to locate and compare features on an object.

Practice Exercise 5.8

Select a number of pictorial and multiview projections from the exercises in the back of this and other chapters. Using colored markers or pencils, color code the object's faces as they are seen in the various views. If you can, make foam, clay, or wood models of the objects and wrap them in paper. Color the corresponding faces of the paper wrapped model. If you unfold the paper, how do the color coded faces compare with the multiview and pictorial projections?

5.6.3 Visualizing Multiple Objects

You can use many of the same visualization techniques on multiple objects that you use on a single object. There are also other techniques available for visualizing multiple objects. When a group of objects, such as the parts of an assembly, moves with respect to the image plane, or vice versa, different objects will assume different positions in the projection. For example, rotating an assembly of objects causes some objects to move in front of others. As the rotation progresses, different features of the back objects are obscured and then revealed again. This effect is known as shearing. The rules of overlay that apply to hidden faces on or in an object also apply to multiple objects. For objects that are either partially or completely hidden by objects in front, the edges can be shown as dashed lines. Showing objects as partially overlapping each other is a powerful visualization technique used to show the relative positions of parts of an assembly. The view position chosen is critical to making this technique work (Figure 5.26).

Not all of the objects shown in an image have to be part of the actual design. An object that is easily visualized, such as a 2-D grid plane, can be used as a reference point in a pictorial image. You can place the reference object in any position relative to the known one. Figure 5.27 shows three different positions of a 2-D grid plane with respect to the object. The risk in adding a reference object is that

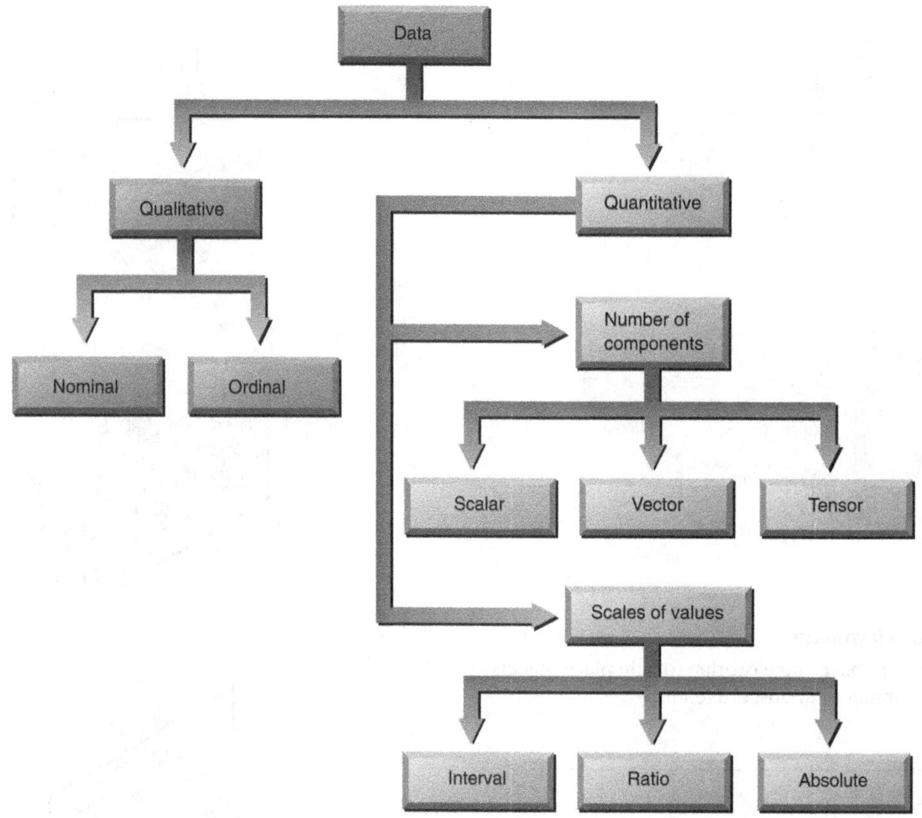

Figure 5.28

Organization of data types

Selecting an appropriate method of analyzing data requires a knowledge of the data's characteristics.

the resulting image can confuse the visualization process more than help, especially if the objects are of equal complexity. Experience will help you decide the conditions under which this technique will be helpful.

5.7 Graphical Analysis of Engineering Data

Graphical analysis is a visualization process used in engineering analysis to display and explore empirical data (that is, data collected in an experiment or test) in the form of graphics. This process breaks the data down so that each key element of the data is coded graphically as surfaces, lines, points, symbols, color, or other graphic representations. For example, computer models of designs can be used to generate data concerning the probable stresses and strains a part will undergo in an actual working assembly. This data can be graphed in a line graph or displayed as color coded data overlaid on the computer model. Besides empirical test data, graphical analysis can also be used with consumer surveys, repair records, costing information, and any other data related to product development and design.

5.7.1 Data Visualization Elements

The analysis data must be evaluated to determine the most appropriate graphical representation format. Depending on the type of analysis performed, there may be considerable differences in the amounts and types of data available before and after the analysis. Common graphical techniques for representing different types of data are discussed in the following sections.

Data Types The data analyzed by engineers and technicians are divided into two basic categories: qualitative and quantitative (Figure 5.28). **Qualitative data** are symbolic, have no inherent magnitude, and are used for la-

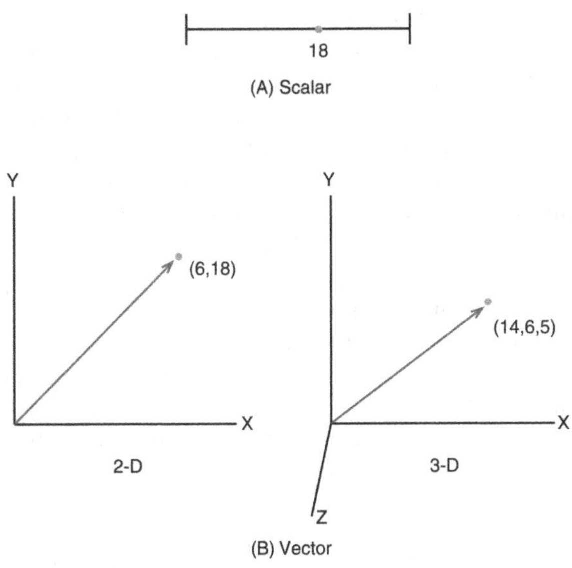

Figure 5.29

Scalar and vector data types

Scalar data have only one component expressed as a magnitude. Vector data can express both magnitude and direction.

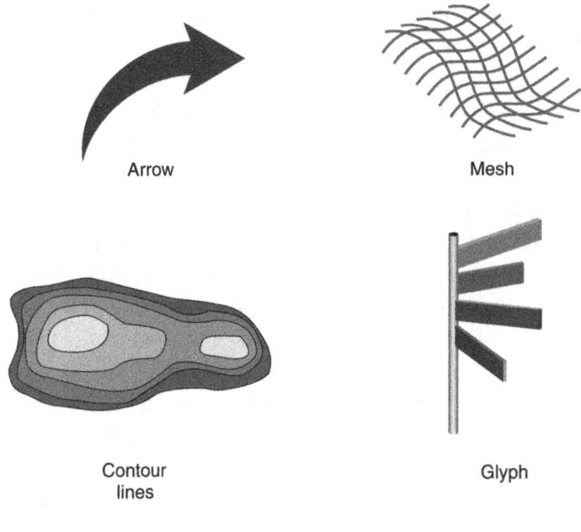

Figure 5.30

Examples of complex marker types

Complex markers are a synthesis of simple marker types and appropriate use of perceptual cues such as color and size.

beling and identifying. Qualitative data with no inherent order (for example, New York, Boston, Houston) are considered **nominal**; qualitative data with an inherent order, such as the months of the year, are called **ordinal**.

The bulk of the data evaluated is **quantitative**, which has an inherent magnitude. Quantitative data are further classified by the number of components and the scales of values. **Scalar** quantitative data have only one component and can only express a magnitude (Figure 5.29A). **Vector** data can express both magnitude and direction (Figure 5.29B). The number of scalar components in the vector depends on the number of dimensions (i.e., dimensionality) of the coordinate system being used. Though in principle any number of dimensions is possible, 2-D and 3-D coordinate systems are the most common and are the ones used in this text.

Marks **Marks** are the fundamental graphic elements used to encode data in a visualization. Marks can be thought of as graphic primitives and are typically classified as either simple or complex. *Simple marks* include points, lines, areas, and volumes, all of which interrelate closely with the dimension of the data type. Points indicate a location in 2-D or 3-D space; lines indicate length and/or connection; areas indicate a region in 2-D space; and volumes do the same in 3-D space.

Complex marks are collections of simple marks, perceptually forming a unit (Figure 5.30). This loose definition covers several possibilities, including arrows, meshes, contour lines, and glyphs. A **glyph** is a compound mark that cannot be defined by other commonly recognized names. Glyphs are usually custom designed to encode multiple data elements into a single mark. The guiding objective for designing glyphs, or any other mark, is to tap into the innate perceptual abilities of the viewers. This is accomplished through careful design.

Data are encoded into an image by varying the qualities of the marks. The qualities manipulated are rooted in human perception. Manipulating such qualities as location, orientation, size, color, and shape reveals differences in data values. Equally important to data visualization are similarities that group marks together. In Figure 5.31, similar colors and symbol shapes result in data grouped together, while changes of location differentiate between individual data points within each group.

An element that does not fit easily into any of the mark categories is *text*. Text should be used to support graphic elements, not as a replacement for them. Text is typically used to label individual qualitative data points, scales, or units of measure. Text is also used for supplementary information. Often a small amount of text can simplify a visualization considerably. However, text should be integrated into the visualization as much as possible, rather than being set apart in a separate legend.

Encoding Data Variables Usually, an analysis is designed to examine data relationships. The functional relationships between variables are described as either independent or dependent. For example, in the earlier discussion of probes applied to a model to create a response, the probes, which are controlled by the experimenter, are *independent* of the model; therefore, they are an **independent variable**. However, the response data are *dependent* on the model's reactions to the probe, so the data are **dependent variables**.

Suppose that heat is the probe, the model is for a reactor vessel, and the response being analyzed is the pressure inside the vessel (Figure 5.32A). The heat is an independent variable because it is controlled by the researcher. As the heat is varied, the pressure inside the vessel is monitored. The researcher knows ahead of time what temperatures to use, but doesn't know what the resulting pressure will be at the different temperatures. The pressure is dependent on the application of the laws of physics to this particular vessel design, and the object of the experiment is to explore this relationship.

The resulting data are encoded, via marks, into a visualization. For every heat value, a corresponding pressure value is recorded. A simple line graph is used to display the data, with the independent variable (temperature) mapped on the horizontal scale and the dependent variable (pressure) shown on the vertical scale (Figure 5.32B).

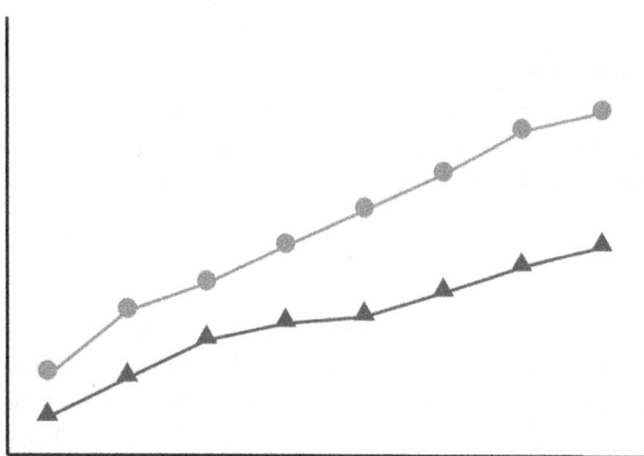

Figure 5.31

Using perceptual cues to encode data

Effective visualizations exploit our natural ability to discriminate between visual elements such as color, size, shape, and orientation.

5.7.2 Visualizations for One Independent Variable

The most common type of visualization is the 2-D graph or plot (Figure 5.33), which is defined by two primary axes (scales). The area within the vertical and horizontal **scale lines** is the region where the data are presented. Text is used to indicate the range and units on the scales. The data are shown with marks in the **data region**, where **reference lines** are used to relate scale values to data marks. Text is used to label marks either directly or indirectly through the use of a key or **legend**. The legend should be isolated from the graph and enclosed by a border. The legend will indicate the variables associated with the point marks or line types on a visualization.

Line Graphs Variations in experimental data mean that points represented on the graph may show a trend, yet may not align perfectly with a straight line. The point

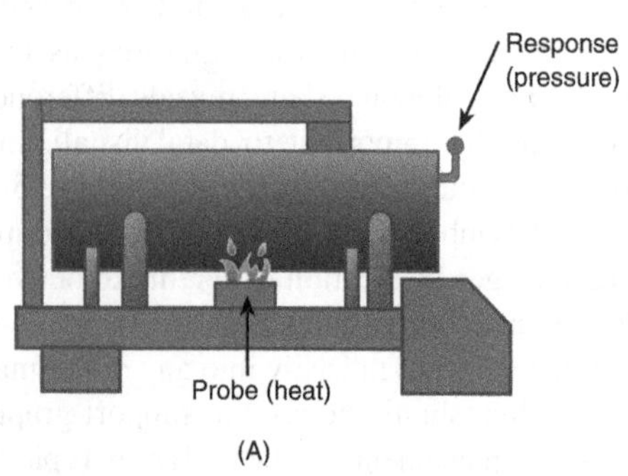

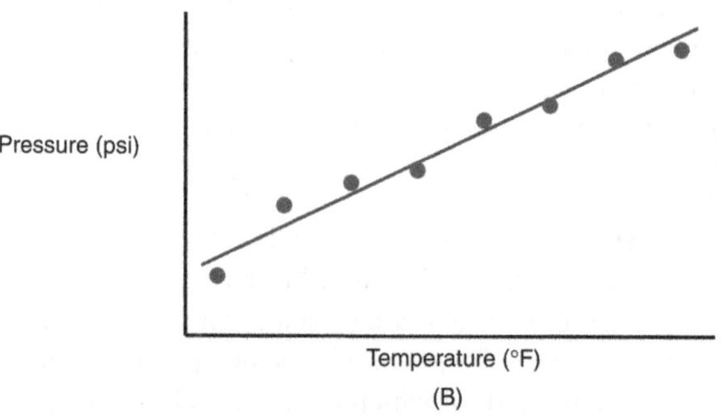

Figure 5.32

Independent and dependent variables

The first task in designing a visualization is identifying the types of variables to be displayed in the visualization.

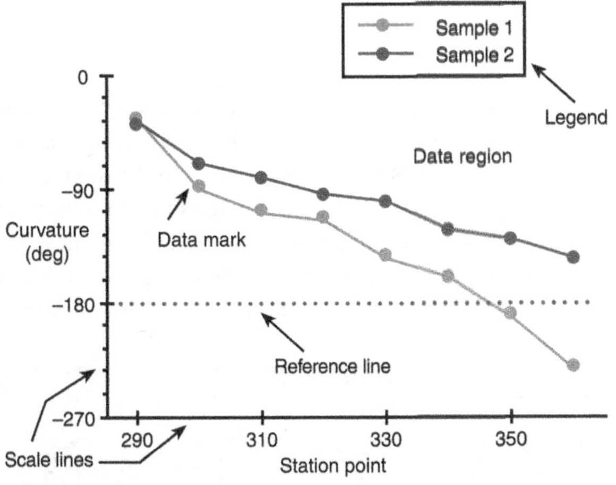

Figure 5.33

Elements of a 2-D graph

These elements include scale lines, data region, reference lines, and legend.

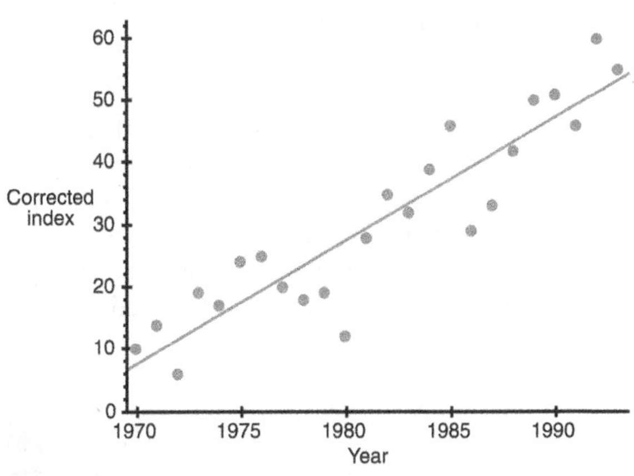

Figure 5.35

Regression line graph

Regression line graphs depict statistical or estimated trends in the data relationship, rather than connecting the individual data points.

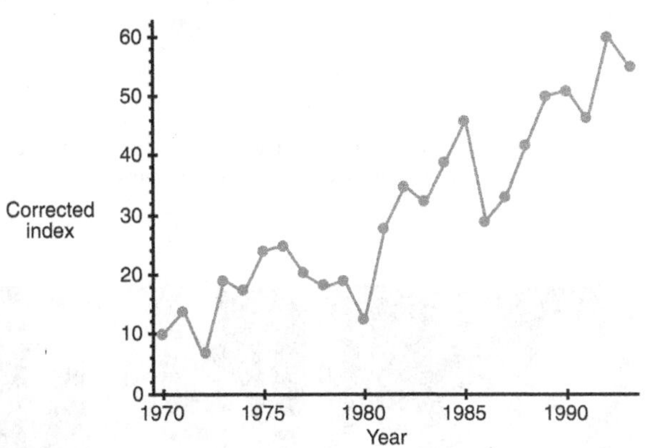

Figure 5.34

Connected line graph

Connected line graphs encode scalar data with line marks. The graph depicts the trend in the data relationship between the independent and dependent variables.

marks can still be connected together to form a **line graph**. The line mark would connect the points by following a progression of independent values, rather than vice versa (Figure 5.34). Using a technique called *regression,* a "best-fit" line, representing the *trend* of the data, is drawn on the graph (Figure 5.35). This **regression line** could be linear, or a second- or third-order curve. Higher order curves are not common, since they are unlikely to represent well-understood phenomena.

Line graphs allow the viewer to perceive *orientation* and *direction.* Absolute values of individual data points are secondary to the trend revealed by the line. The direction of the line reveals information about the relationship between the dependent and independent variables. For example, in Figure 5.35, the line angling up indicates that as time increases, the index value also rises. This depicts a positive relationship between the two variables.

Bar Graphs Another common type of 2-D graph is the **bar graph** (Figure 5.36). A bar graph uses either line or area marks to allow a closer focus on individual data values. However, in a bar graph, the line mark is used to show *length,* rather than orientation. Though area marks are commonly used in bar graphs, one dimension of the bar is held constant, reducing the variability in the mark to the length of the other dimension. Bar graphs are most often used when there are only a few independent variable values, and they are usually qualitative. Also, unlike line graphs, bar graphs sometimes show the independent variable on the vertical axis (Figure 5.37).

Data with a well-defined zero point are best shown by having one end of all of the bars aligned on a common baseline, thus making it easier to compare their absolute values, or to estimate ratios. When the data are depicting

Design in Industry [Scientific Visualization]

Computer graphics use many of the visualization techniques described in this chapter for different applications. The result is a relatively new discipline called scientific visualization, which is the use of computer graphics to supplement or replace traditional design and mathematical modeling techniques in engineering and science.

Computer graphics allow the user to apply sophisticated visualization techniques, such as shading, surface gradients, shadows (A), transparency and translucency (B), aerial perspective, and movement, to computer models. In engineering design visualization, new designs are evaluated early in the design process. Computer models are used to visualize the design, and finite

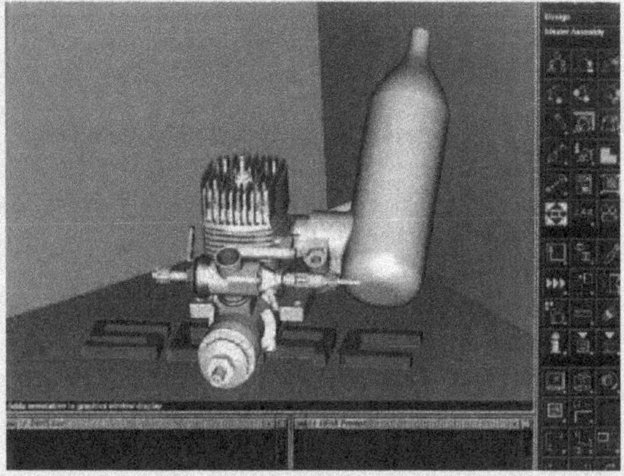

(A)

A mechanical design is modeled on a computer, then given surface properties, and then assigned light positions and intensities before rendering.

(Courtesy of SDRC, Inc. [Structural Dynamics Research Company.])

(B)

A mechanical assembly part is given translucent properties so the designer can visualize the interior properties.

(Courtesy of CADKEY, Inc.)

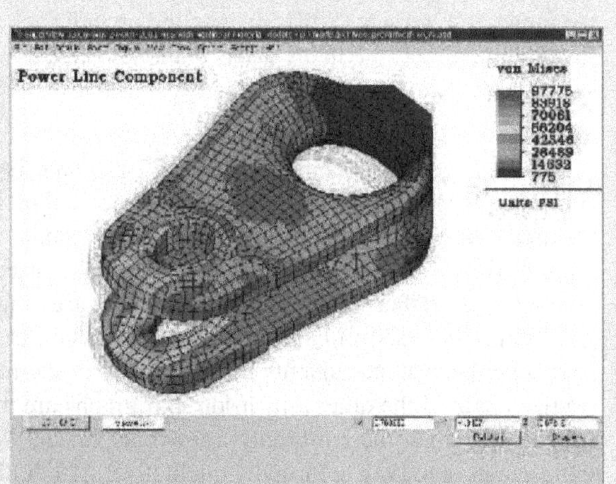

(C)

This is the computer model of a mechanical part that is being analyzed using computer graphics. Through the use of color, it is possible to visually determine areas of high stress.

(Photo courtesy of Algor, Inc.)

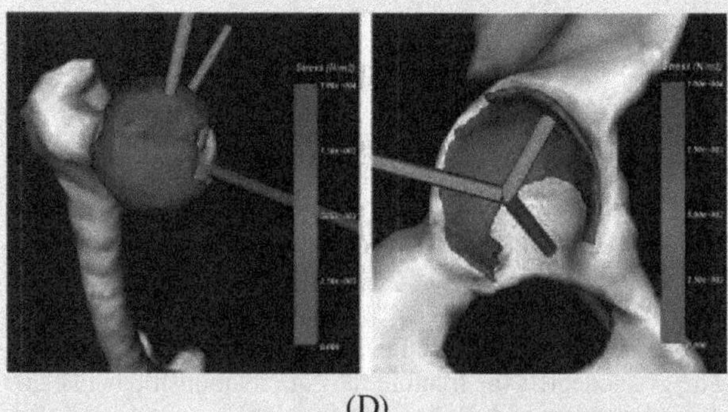

(D)

This computer model shows stress mapping on an artificial hip joint.

(Courtesy of Anderson Maciel and Sofiane Sarni.)

element models are used to visually analyze the effects of loads on a part (C), and the interference between parts. In medicine, computer graphics are used to visualize and analyze complicated surgical procedures, to diagnose illness and injuries, and to aid in rebuilding human joints (D). In building construction, computer graphics can enhance the visualization of new buildings by creating still images and animated walkthroughs (E). Civil engineers and city planners use computer graphics to visualize new roads, before making final design decisions (F). Satellite images of the earth can be merged with computer data to analyze and visualize weather patterns, erosion, environmental impacts, and other effects (G). Scientific visualization is used for many applications to assist scientists, engineers, and laymen in the visualization of complicated structures, environments, and assemblies (H).

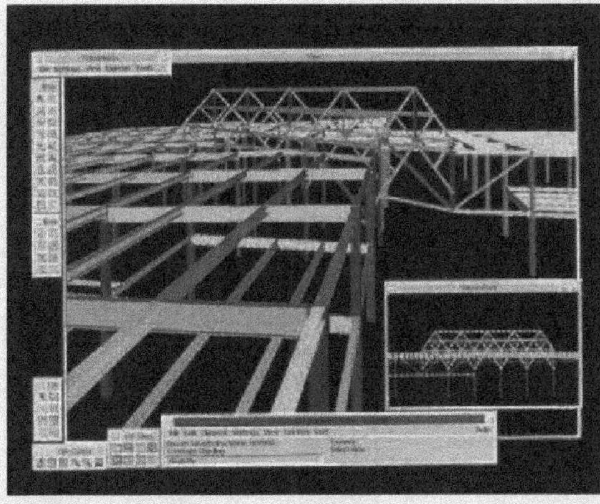

(E)

Animated walkthroughs can be created from the 3-D model to analyze the structure.

(Courtesy of Intergraph Corporation.)

(F)

This computer model shows how a proposed new road would cut a path through the countryside, allowing the planners to visualize the environmental impact of the proposed new road.

(Courtesy of Bentley Systems.)

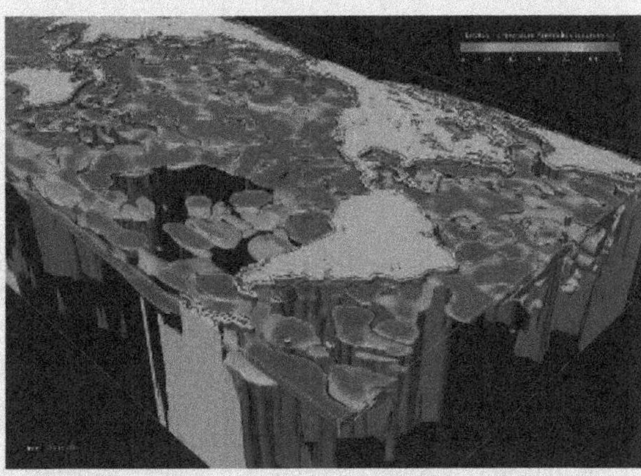

(G)

Large amounts of data can be graphically represented to assist scientists in visualizing information about the earth.

(Courtesy of NOAA/GFDL.)

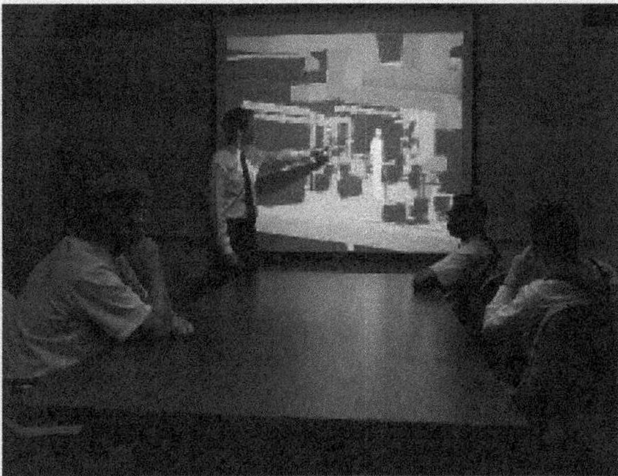

(H)

Computer graphics is a powerful tool used for visualization purposes.

(Courtesy of Newport News Shipbuilding.)

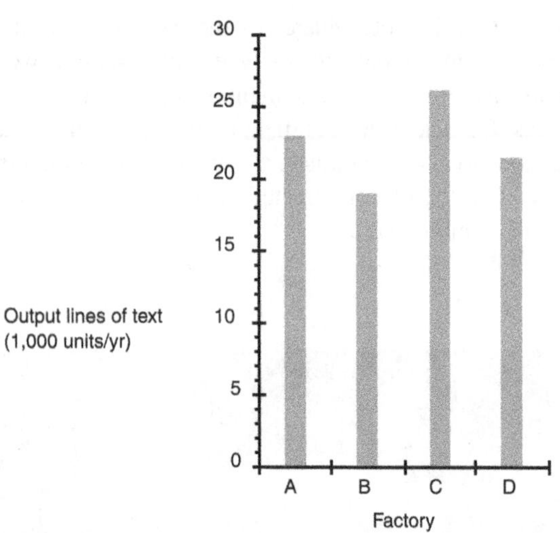

Figure 5.36

Bar graph

Bar graphs are often used when the independent variable is qualitative rather than quantitative. The bar mark represents the distance from some common origin value to the dependent variable value.

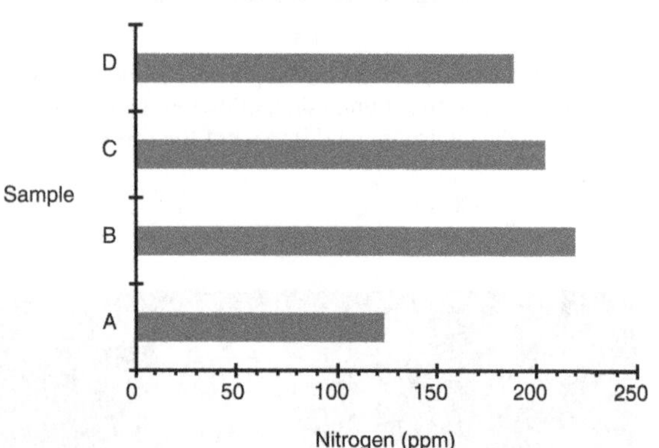

Figure 5.37

Horizontal bar graph

Horizontal bar graphs are sometimes used as an alternative to standard bar graphs. Here, the independent and dependent variable axes are switched.

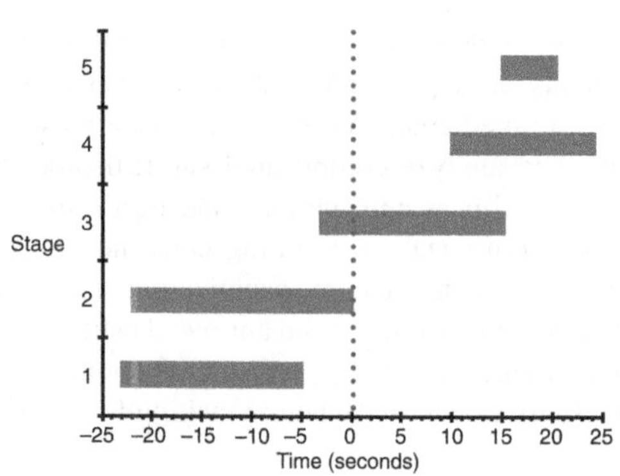

Figure 5.38

Range bar graph

Range bar graphs do not have bars that are anchored at a common origin. These bar markers are used to encode interval (or range) data.

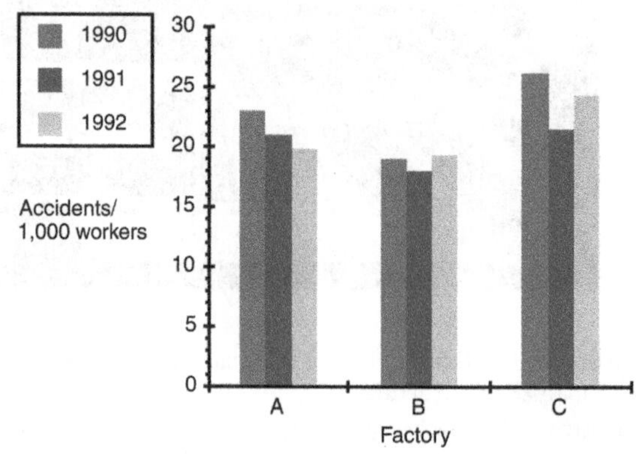

Figure 5.39

Group bar graphs

Group bar graphs can be used to depict subcategories of a data variable.

an interval or range along a scale, with no natural zero point, the bars can float (Figure 5.38). Though more difficult for making comparisons of length, **range bars** are a useful tool for depicting the location of an interval. Mentally or physically drawing a reference line through the range bars at a specific dependent value permits comparisons of the locations of various range bars. For example, using time as the dependent variable, the points at which various independent values turn "on" or "off" can be identified and compared.

A number of techniques are used with bar graphs to group similar data together. If the independent variable has logical subgroups, spacing can be used to depict these groups. In Figure 5.39, separate data points represent each of three years within each category. Three *grouped bars,* each depicting one year, are used with a space between categories. Assuming the categories and subcategories of the independent variable are kept to a minimum, comparisons can be made both between years in a single category and between categories in a single year.

Sometimes, data values are a *composite* of a common group of subvalues. For example, in Figure 5.40, the overall weights of a series of models are divided into metal, plastic, and liquid components. Within a single prototype, comparisons are made of the relative weights of steel, plastic, and aluminum. In addition, comparisons of each of these subcategories are made between models. With this approach, the composite values (i.e., overall weights) of each group are easy to discern, but the lack of a common baseline for the subcategories makes absolute-value judgments difficult.

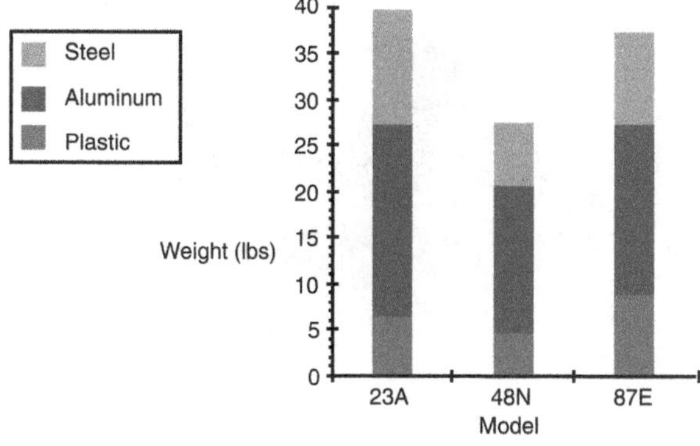

Figure 5.40

Composite bar graphs

Composite bar graphs allow both individual subcategory values and an overall value to be represented by the length of a bar mark.

With both grouped and composite bars, the use of color or pattern coding to distinguish between the subcategories is recommended.

5.7.3 Visualizations for Two Independent Variables

It is common to have two independent variables that must be examined. The same techniques used to display one independent variable can be used to display two, if various encoding marks are employed. Another option is to increase the number of geometric dimensions used to display the data. In both cases, perceptual abilities, such as color discrimination or depth perception, are important for visualizing the second independent variable.

Multiple Line Graphs If the second independent variable has only a few discrete values, a **multiple line graph** can be used. The horizontal and vertical scales of the graph are used the same way as for only one independent variable. Each value of the second independent variable is represented as a separate line on the graph and each line must be coded, typically with either a *color* or a *shape* and a legend to indicate the code-to-value mapping (Figure 5.41A). If there is sufficient room, text labels pointing to the individual lines can be used instead of the legend. The use of color versus shapes to code the second variable depends on how the graph is going to be displayed. Color reduces clutter and is less affected by being reduced or displayed at lower resolution. However, if the graph is to be photocopied in black and white, shape or line style coding is preferable (Figure 5.41B).

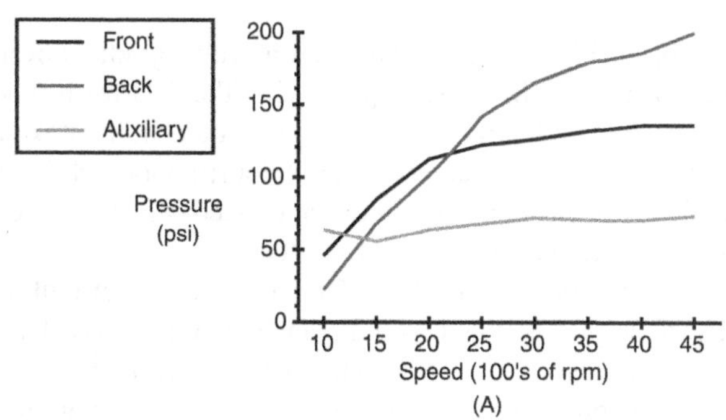

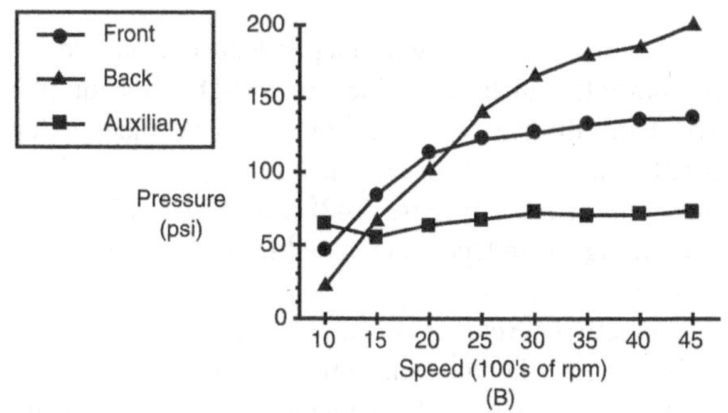

Figure 5.41

Multiple line graphs, with color and shape coding

Multiple line graphs allow more than one independent variable level on a single graph. Each line mark represents a different level (value) of the independent variable.

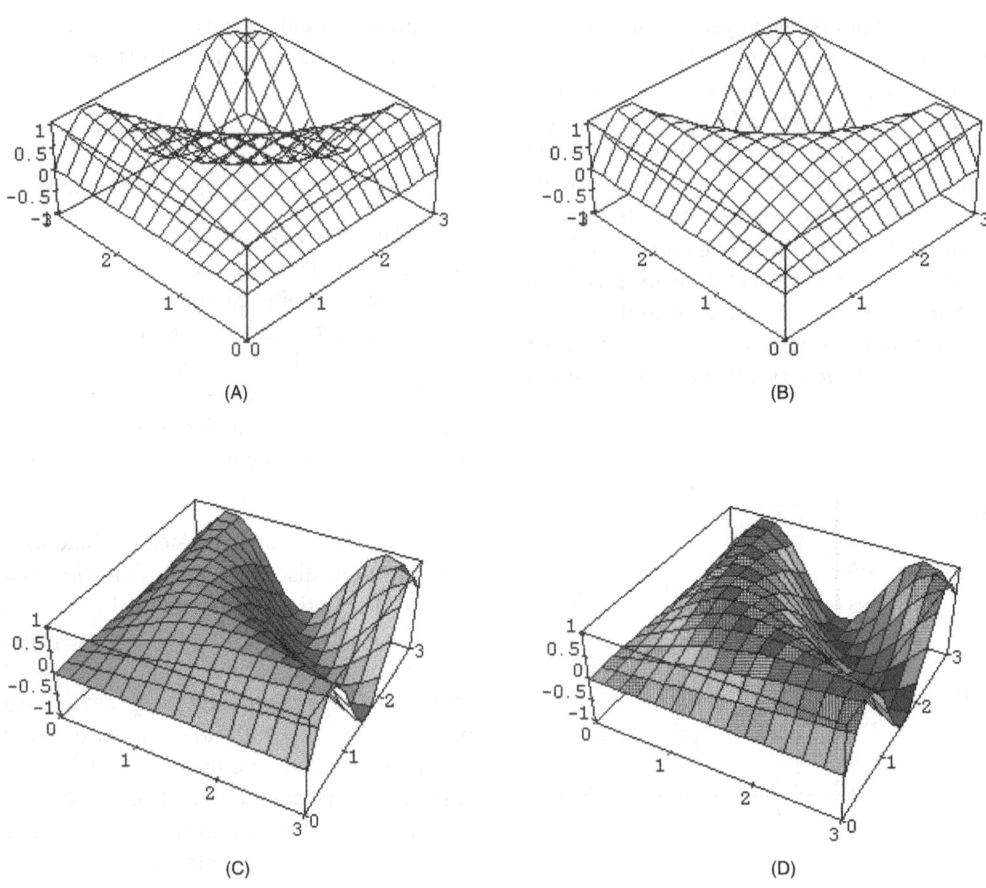

Figure 5.42

Examples of surface plots

Surface plots use a variety of visualization techniques to connect data points in 3-D space with a surface mark.

3-D Graphs and Plots Two independent and one dependent variable can be combined in a 3-D graph or plot. Two of the dimensional axes represent the independent variables, and the third axis (usually Z) represents the dependent variable (Figure 5.42). For every X, Y value representing an independent variable, a Z value maps a dependent variable.

Connecting point marks in a 2-D graph results in a line graph. With a 3-D plot, connecting the points results in a **surface plot**, which can be depicted in a number of ways. The simplest depiction is a mesh covering the surface (Figure 5.42A). Removing hidden lines helps in perceiving the 3-D form, but may hide data points that are occluded (Figure 5.42B). Alternatively, the surface can be shaded. For example, the plot could simulate a light source falling on the object (Figure 5.42C). The shading value gradient over the surface would assist in perceiving the 3-D form, but may cause confusion; shading values could be mistaken for the coding of a data variable. A fourth approach is to shade the surface by varying the color according to the dependent variable value (Figure 5.42D).

A 2-D option for a 3-D surface plot is a **contour plot**. A surface plot is sliced with a plane (Figure 5.43A). This XY plane represents a constant dependent variable value over all possible independent variable combinations. Next, a line is traced at the intersection between the plane and the surface. This **contour line**, or **isoline** (i.e., a line of constant value), represents the independent variable combinations that result in the dependent variable value (Figure 5.43B).

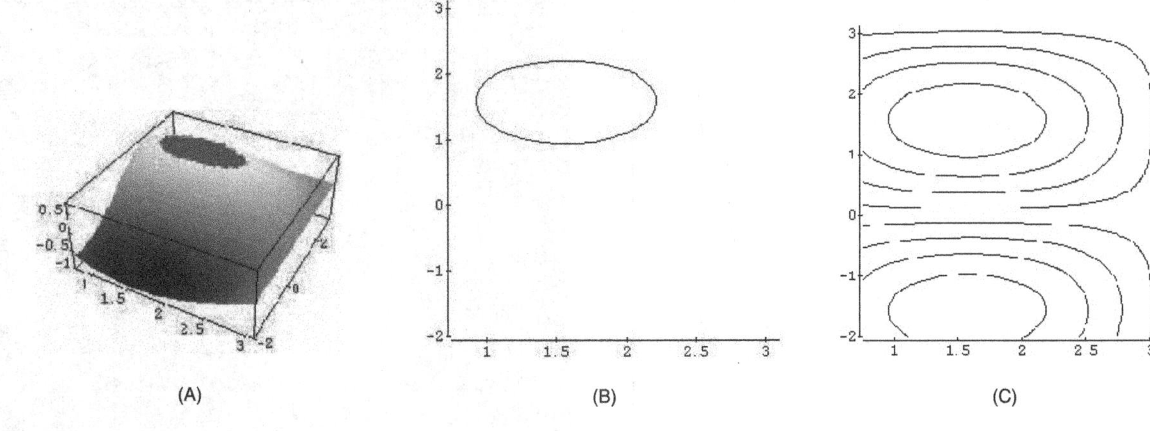

Figure 5.43

Contour plot

Contour plots are a method of visualizing data with two independent variable values in a 2-D plot. Each contour line (isoline) represents combinations of the two independent variables that give rise to a certain dependent variable value.

(© Wolfram Research, Inc. "A New Kind of Science" by Stephen Wolfram, www.wolframscience.com.)

Typically, multiple contour lines are drawn on a contour plot to represent a uniform sampling of dependent variable values (Figure 5.43C). The horizontal and vertical scales represent independent variable values, and the contour lines show the mapping of constant dependent variable values. If the surface is thought of as a piece of terrain, the lines are like elevation contours on a terrain map.

Rarely will collected data points fall exactly on one of the contour lines, since the surface itself is the product of *interpolating* between the data points. The contour line represents an intersection with this interpolated surface, not actual collected data points. The denser and more regular the sampled data, the better will be the interpolation. Both contour and surface plots are most successful when data are sampled at regular intervals of both independent variables.

5.8 Virtual Reality and Visualization

Another way to enhance people's ability to visualize a 3-D object or scene is to make their experience as realistic as possible. If the real object or scene is available to experience, then people are able to put all of their senses to work viewing, touching, hearing, and moving through the space. Many times, though, the real object is not available. Either the object does not yet exist (e.g., a new product design) or is too expensive/dangerous (e.g., a fighter jet). Often when a real object is not available, CAD tools can be used to construct a **virtual model** of the object or scene. The goal is not only to make the model as realistic as possible but also to allow an enhanced interaction with the model that creates a **virtual reality**. This technology strives to create a sense of "being there," as though it were a real experience. Section 3.9 provides a detailed overview of virtual reality techniques and technologies.

5.9 Visualization Uses

Visualization techniques such as the ones described in this chapter can be used in any technology or engineering field to assist in the solution of design problems. The following sections are a few examples of how visualization techniques can be applied in specific professions. The examples show techniques that have been around for a long time, as well as some that are just coming into common use.

5.9.1 Mechanical Design

Many mechanical designs begin as collections of informal ideation sketches created by industrial designers or engineers (Figure 5.44). The sketches are used to visualize larger, more complete designs that meet the design criteria. Once a direction has been chosen, 3-D modeling systems can be used to refine the form of the design. With the projection capabilities of a modeling system, views

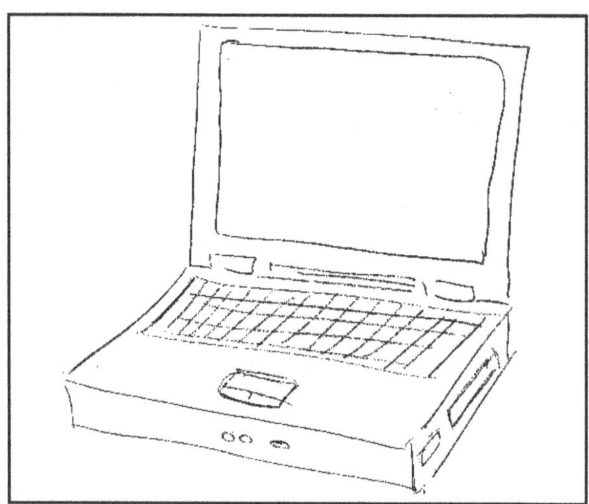

Figure 5.44

Ideation sketches of a laptop computer

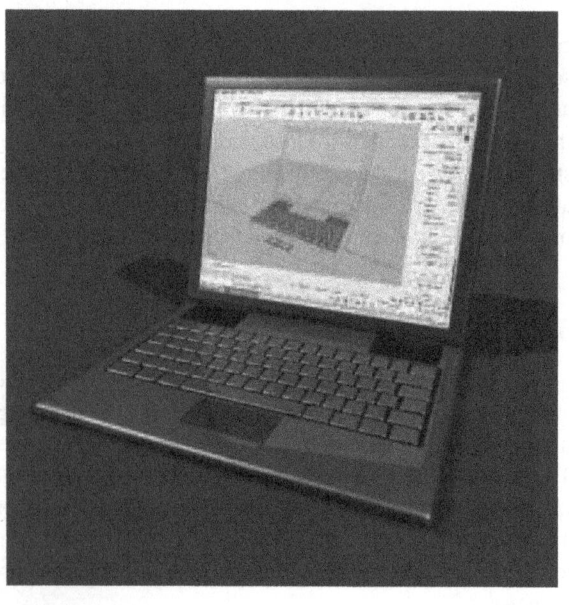

Figure 5.45

Pictorial projection of a laptop computer on a 3-D computer modeling system

(Courtesy of Turbo Squid.)

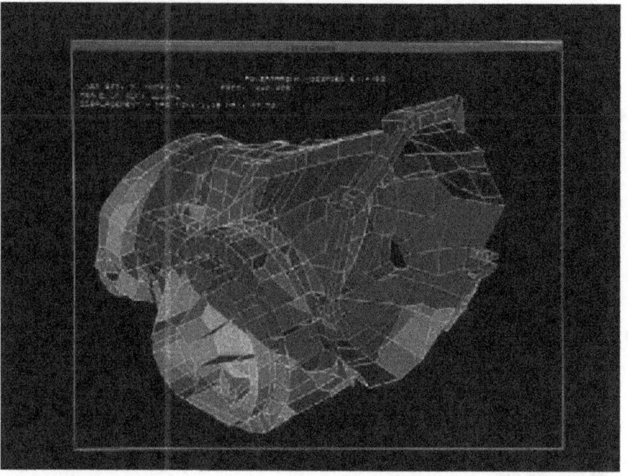

Figure 5.46

Color-coded output from an FEA of a mechanical design

(Photo courtesy of SDRC, Inc. (Structural Dynamics Research Company).)

Figure 5.47

Physical mockups of the mechanical design

(Courtesy of Ford Motor Company.)

that show the design's important features can be generated (Figure 5.45). Many 3-D modeling systems can interact with software that precisely analyzes how a particular design will react under certain stresses (Figure 5.46). Color often plays a role in this analysis. Numeric data detail how a particular location on the design reacts to a load; color can be used to show this reaction visually and quickly.

At some point, physical models are needed for further analysis of the design (Figure 5.47). Sometimes such models are needed for ergonomic evaluations (e.g., the comfort of a car seat) or for troubleshooting to determine how the product is going to be assembled in the manufacturing plant. In the past, constructing physical models was often a laborious process. Now, however, for smaller objects, there are a number of rapid prototyping technologies that

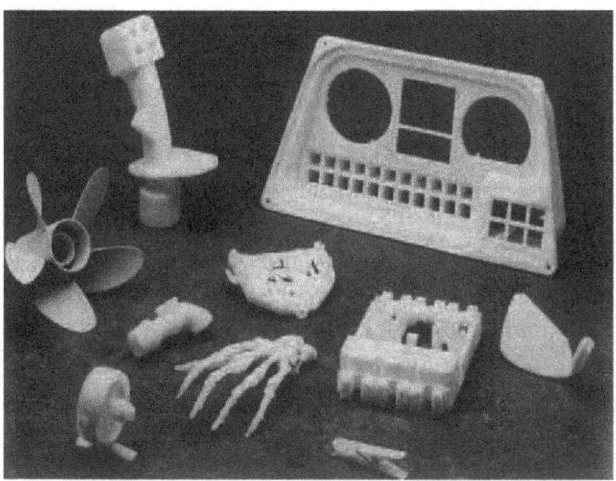

Figure 5.48

Objects made with a rapid prototyping system

take the specifications for a 3-D model directly from the computer modeling system and create a physical model. The ease with which these prototypes can be generated means that a physical model can be made readily available, to hold, turn, and otherwise manipulate, for a better understanding of its form (Figure 5.48). In addition, there are visual cues available in a true 3-D object that are difficult or impossible to represent in a computer model. Section 3.4.1 provides more information on physical and rapid prototyping techniques and technologies.

5.9.2 Civil Projects

Professionals in the architectural/engineering/construction (AEC) industry are often involved with projects that measure in miles, rather than feet or inches. For example, designing a road interchange involves numerous design requirements. The professionals must consider the requirements of the road, as well as the shape of the land. The final interchange must fit within the land boundaries, drain water properly, and have the desired configurations for the entrance and exit ramps.

The traditional method of designing such a project uses 2-D graphics. The *plan view* shows the interchange in a manner similar to that of a road map (Figure 5.49A).

Historically, this was the primary graphic used for such a design project. Training and experience were needed to be able to look at a drawing like this and visualize what the interchange would look like once built.

Communicating such a design to nonprofessionals is difficult since they may not have the visualization skills

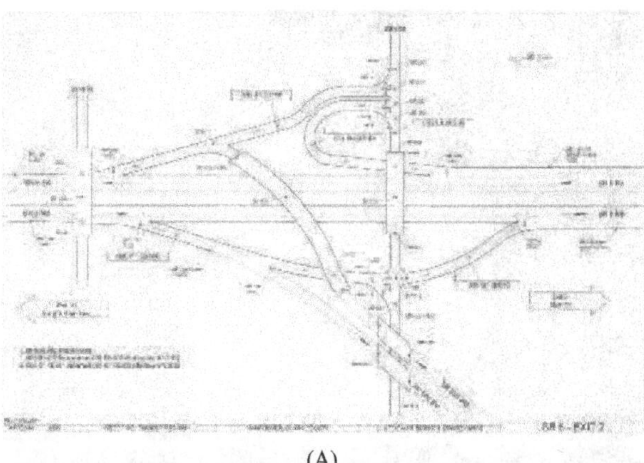

(A)

(B)

Figure 5.49

(A) Highway interchange

(Courtesy of Washington State Department of Transportation.)

(B) 3-D computer model rendering of highway bridge

(Courtesy of 3DLasermapping.com.)

necessary to properly interpret what they are seeing. Although 2-D views are still valuable for making some design decisions, 3-D models reveal additional, essential information that makes the design decision process much more precise (Figure 5.49B). Perspective projections and surface shading to mimic the effect of the sun on the ground tap into basic perceptual abilities, making design visualization easier.

Even more information is obtained by viewing the 3-D model of the interchange as a dynamic sequence of images. By developing a series of views along a predefined path along the road, the modeler can create a *drivethrough* animation. This animation can simulate what it would be

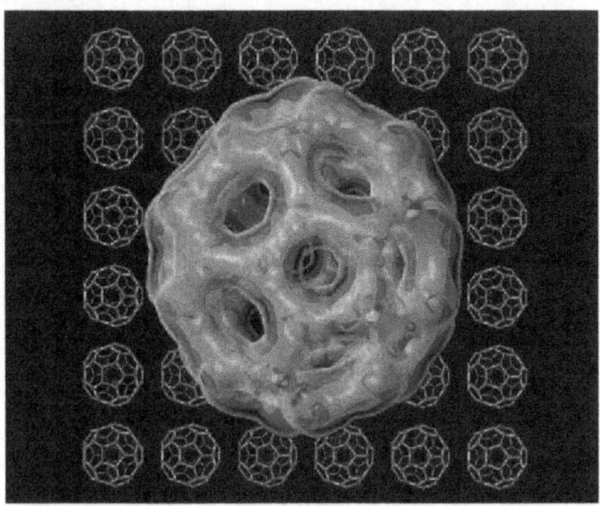

Figure 5.50

Modeling molecules

A representation of a large molecule on a ball and stick computer system provides tactile feedback. The control surfaces represent the dynamic forces between the atoms.

(Tom Palmer and Dave Bock at the North Carolina Supercomputing Center, a division of MCNC.)

like to walk or drive the road. The current generation of computer hardware and software allows drivethroughs to be controlled interactively; designers can explore the design in real time, as though they were driving a car along the road.

5.9.3 Future Directions

The advanced visualization techniques described in the preceding sections are not limited just to the engineering professions. Researchers in the pharmaceutical industry are using sophisticated computer systems to model molecules for new drugs (Figure 5.50). The sheer complexity of potential molecules means that every visualization technique available has been put to work. Visualizing such molecules is hampered by several factors. For instance, they are so small that no one has ever seen a molecule directly. You can only theorize indirectly what one might look like, or how it might react to the forces of other molecules nearby.

Visualizing molecular forces can be enhanced both through additional visual cues and engaging additional perceptual modalities. Visual cues can be enhanced through virtual reality techniques, such as stereoscopic displays, motion tracking, and peripheral view filling. Similarly, haptic interfaces allow you to *feel* the molecular forces. Auditory cues can provide tone changes that map to the relative locations of molecules.

5.10 Summary

The mind uses many tools, working in concert, to interpret the 3-D visual field. The mind engages in constant problem solving in the interpretation process. Part of this problem-solving process is automatic. However, you can develop numerous techniques that will help. With a better understanding of how the mind interprets what it receives, you can use conscious mental power to assist in this process. You can also learn to bring physical processes into play. For example, you may be able to pick up an object and rotate it, to gain a better understanding of the object. More importantly, you may be able to create a sketch which will help you in the visual problem-solving process.

Online Learning Center (OLC) Features

There are a number of Online Learning Center features listed below that you can use to supplement your text reading to improve your understanding and retention of the material presented in this chapter at www.mhhe.com/bertoline.

- Learning Objectives
- Chapter Outline
- Questions for Review
- Multiple Choice Quiz
- True or False Questions
- Flashcards
- Website Links
- Animations
- Related Readings
- Stapler Design Problem

Questions for Review

1. Why is visualization important in engineering and technical graphics? Is it useful in any other fields? Are you born with the ability to visualize, or is it learned?
2. Explain the relationship between seeing real objects, seeing in the mind's eye, and drawing on paper or with the computer.

3. What role do ideation sketches play in the design process? Do they use new or existing graphic information?
4. What is the relationship between faces and edges in the visualization of an object?
5. Do planar and curved surfaces reveal themselves differently on an object?
6. Define an image plane. How is it used in visualization?
7. Describe the process of creating a projection on an image plane. How are the three axes of the image plane defined?
8. How is an object oriented relative to the image plane to create the following:
   - A multiview.
   - An axonometric pictorial.
9. What is the difference between a parallel and a perspective projection?
10. When is a face foreshortened? When is a face seen in its true size and shape? Is a face ever represented as a single edge?
11. Name three industrial applications of visualization. Name the specific techniques used and the perceptual cues they exploit.
12. Give examples of nominal, ordinal, and scalar variables. Are these variables qualitative or quantitative?
13. Look at the results of engineering analyses in journals or textbooks. What are the independent and dependent variables? Can a dependent variable be the independent variable in another experiment, and vice versa?
14. Give examples of at least three different line graphs. What are some of the different ways a second independent variable can be coded in a line graph?
15. Give examples of at least three different bar graphs. What are some of the different ways a second independent variable can be coded in a bar graph? Is this the same in line graphs?

Further Reading

Cleveland, W.S., *The Elements of Graphing Data.* Monterey, CA: Wadsworth, 1985.

Ferguson, E.S. *Engineering and the Mind's Eye.* Cambridge, MA: MIT Press, 1993.

Hanks, K., and L. Belliston. *Draw! A Visual Approach to Thinking, Learning and Communicating.* Los Altos, CA: William Kaufmann, 1977.

Keller, P.R., and M.M. Keller. *Visual Cues.* Pitscataway, NJ: IEEE Press, 1993.

Kosslyn, S.M. *Elements of Graph Design.* San Francisco, CA: W.H. Freeman, 1994.

McKim, R.H. *Experiences in Visual Thinking.* 2d ed. Boston, MA: PWS Engineering, 1981.

Mitchell, W.J., and M. McCullough. *Digital Design Media.* New York: Van Nostrand Reinhold, 1991.

Rodriguez, W. *The Modeling of Design Ideas: Graphics and Visualization Techniques for Engineers.* New York: McGraw-Hill, 1992.

Sorby, S.A., K.J. Manner, and B.J. Baartrams. *3-D Visualization for Engineering Graphics.* Upper Saddle River, NJ: Prentice-Hall, 1998.

Tufte, E.R. *The Visual Display of Quantitative Information.* Cheshire, CT: Graphics Press, 1983.

Wyman, J.D., and S.F. Gordon. *Primer of Perception.* New York: Reinhold, 1967.

Problems

5.1 Gather real examples and/or magazine photographs of both single and multiple objects. The objects should vary in complexity of form. Some should have only simple planar features, while others should have curved, sculpted surfaces. Larger objects or scenes around school or home can simply be identified. These objects, photographs, and scenes will be used in the rest of the problems in this chapter. Some ideas are as follows:

Motor vehicles.
Farm equipment.
Household appliances.
Aircraft and nautical vessels.
Computer equipment.
Audiovisual equipment.
Furniture.
Lighting fixtures.
Sports and exercise equipment.
Hand tools.
Stationary and hand-held power tools.

5.2 Using an image of a single, complex object, create a tracing, showing a single contour line around the object. Then, create another tracing and add two more contours outlining what you consider to be the two most important features on the object. Repeat the process until you have five or six sketches, each time adding two or more contours to the sketch. At what point can you identify the object in the sketch without looking at the photograph?

5.3 Using real scenes and images showing multiple items, or using objects created from the patterns on the end pages at the back of the book, create sketches using contour lines to identify the boundaries between the elements. First, use images and then real-world scenes or objects. Trace the contour lines, and then create more sketches of the same scenes drawing contour lines that divide the scenes into different groupings.

5.4 Make two photocopies of each sketch created in Problem 5.3 and shade in:

- The positive space (the objects in the scene).
- The negative space (the background).

5.5 Repeat Problem 5.3 and Problem 5.4, using CAD or other computer graphics software to draw the contours and fill in the negative and positive spaces.

5.6 Choose an image of a complex scene showing familiar objects and/or people and sketch it without tracing. Now, sketch the same scene with the image upside down. Do not try to identify the objects in the photograph. Concentrate on the individual contours and their relationships to each other.

5.7 Choose either four objects representing basic geometric forms (e.g., a book, a rolling pin, a pencil, etc.), or primitive objects made from the patterns on the end pages at the back of the book. The lighter their color, the better. Place the objects in a strong light coming from behind you, over your shoulder (or equivalent).

a. Sketch the contours of the object.
b. Shade the surfaces of the object to show the darkness as it appears.
c. Move to a new location and sketch them again.
d. Move the light source to a new position.
e. Repeat c and d, but this time imagine the movement in your mind rather than actually moving the object. Create the sketches from what you imagine they would look like.

5.8 Using the objects and setup from Problem 5.7, create the following series of contour and shaded sketches:

a. Systematically move the object in 90-degree increments about all three axes.
b. Systematically move the object in 5-degree increments through 90 degrees.
c. Repeat a and b with a different object, but do the rotations in your mind.
d. Make photocopies of the 5-degree increment sketches. Pick one face of the object and shade it in all of the sketches. How does it change shape?

5.9 Repeat Problem 5.8a through c, with two or three objects in the scene. Rotate the objects around a common imaginary axis. Try setting them on a lazy susan. Make photocopies of the 5-degree increments and darken in the contours that divide one object from another. Do their locations on the background stay the same in the different sketches?

5.10 With the objects and setup from Problem 5.7, create a series of shaded objects using various repeating patterns (textures). Vary the density of the pattern to vary the darkness. Do not show any

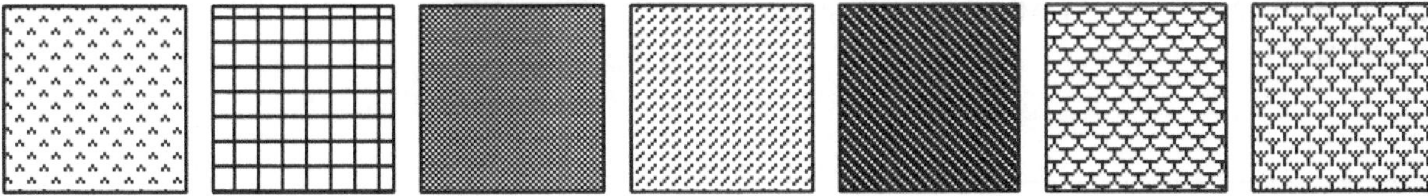

Figure 5.51

Some example patterns to be used in Problem 5.10

contour lines. Some example patterns are shown in Figure 5.51.

5.11 Look at an image of a multicolored object. Squint your eyes or view the photograph under dim light such that the *color* (hue) of the object washes out and only levels of gray are left. Sketch and shade the object in the image.

5.12 Create a traditional flipbook animation. With a note pad bound at the top, draw a series of contour line sketches on the bottom third of each page. Each sketch should vary slightly from the one on the preceding page, and flipping through all the sketches should create apparent movement of the object.

The frames of the animation can also be created on a CAD program. Use a uniformly sized border around each frame of the animation and try to fit four to six frames on each sheet of paper. Starting with simple objects (e.g., a cube), create animations of the object:

a. Translating along one axis.
b. Translating along two axes in sequence.
c. Translating along two axes simultaneously.
d. Rotating about one axis.
e. Rotating about two axes in sequence.
f. Rotating about two axes simultaneously.
g. Rotating and translating in sequence.
h. Rotating and translating simultaneously.

5.13 Create a stereo pair of an object using a 3-D modeling system. Conduct research to determine the difference between what the two eyes see.

5.14 Choose two images showing very different-looking objects. Create contour sketches of both objects by tracing over them. Now create five more sketches that slowly transform one object into the other. Tracing paper may be useful for some parts of the drawing. This process is commonly referred to as *morphing*.

5.15 Figures 5.52 through 5.54. Match objects with target shapes.

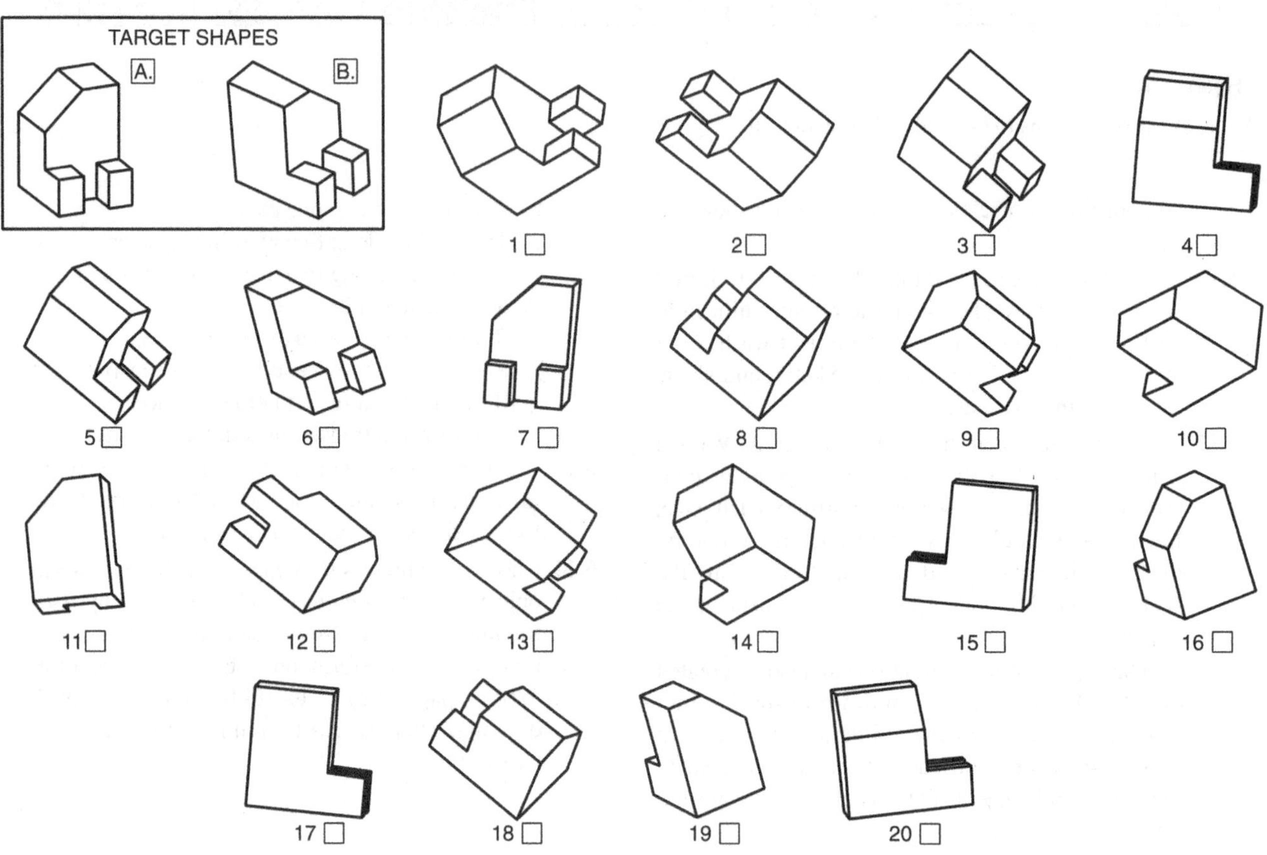

Figure 5.52

Match objects with target shapes

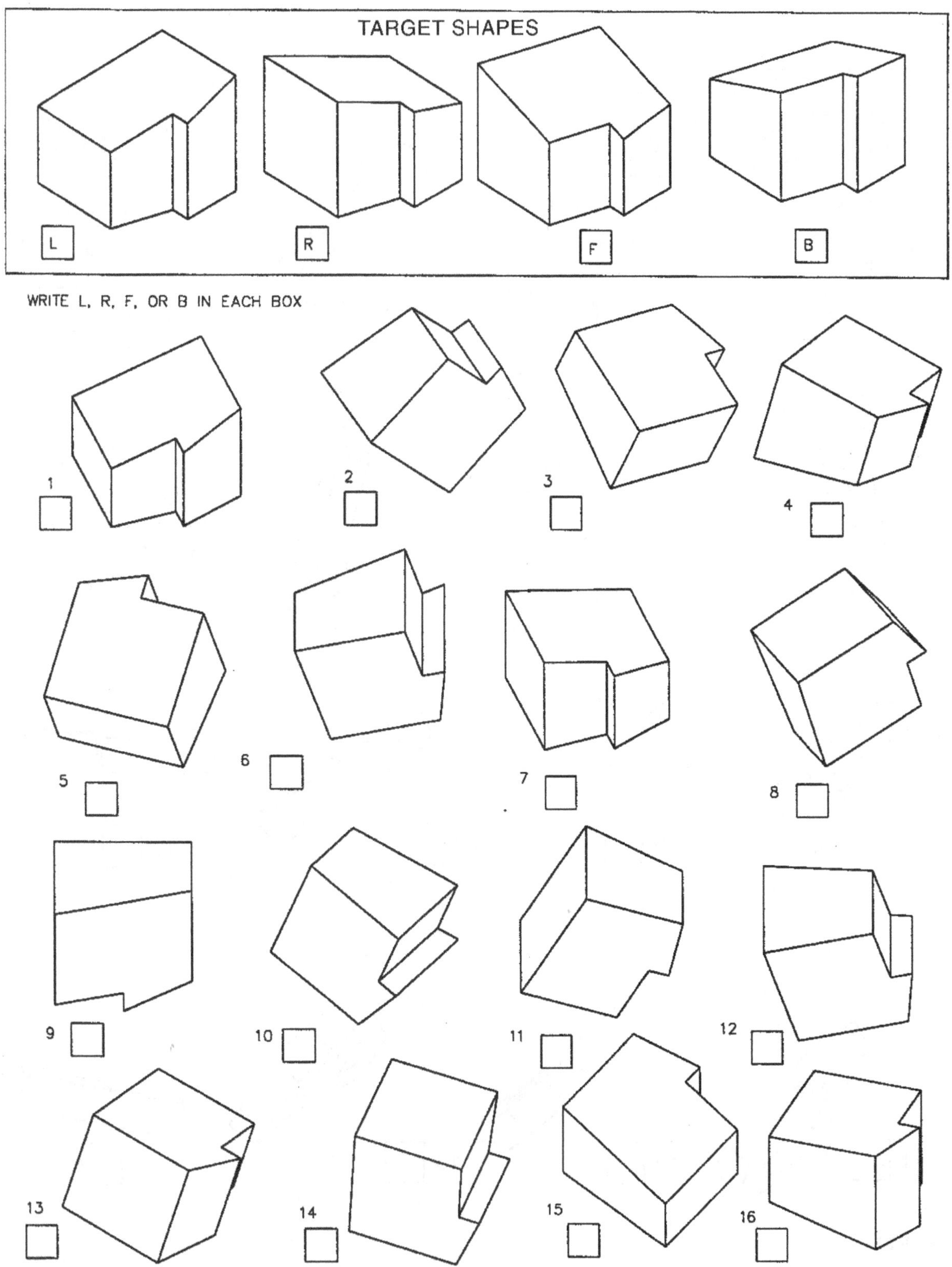

Figure 5.53

Match objects with target shapes

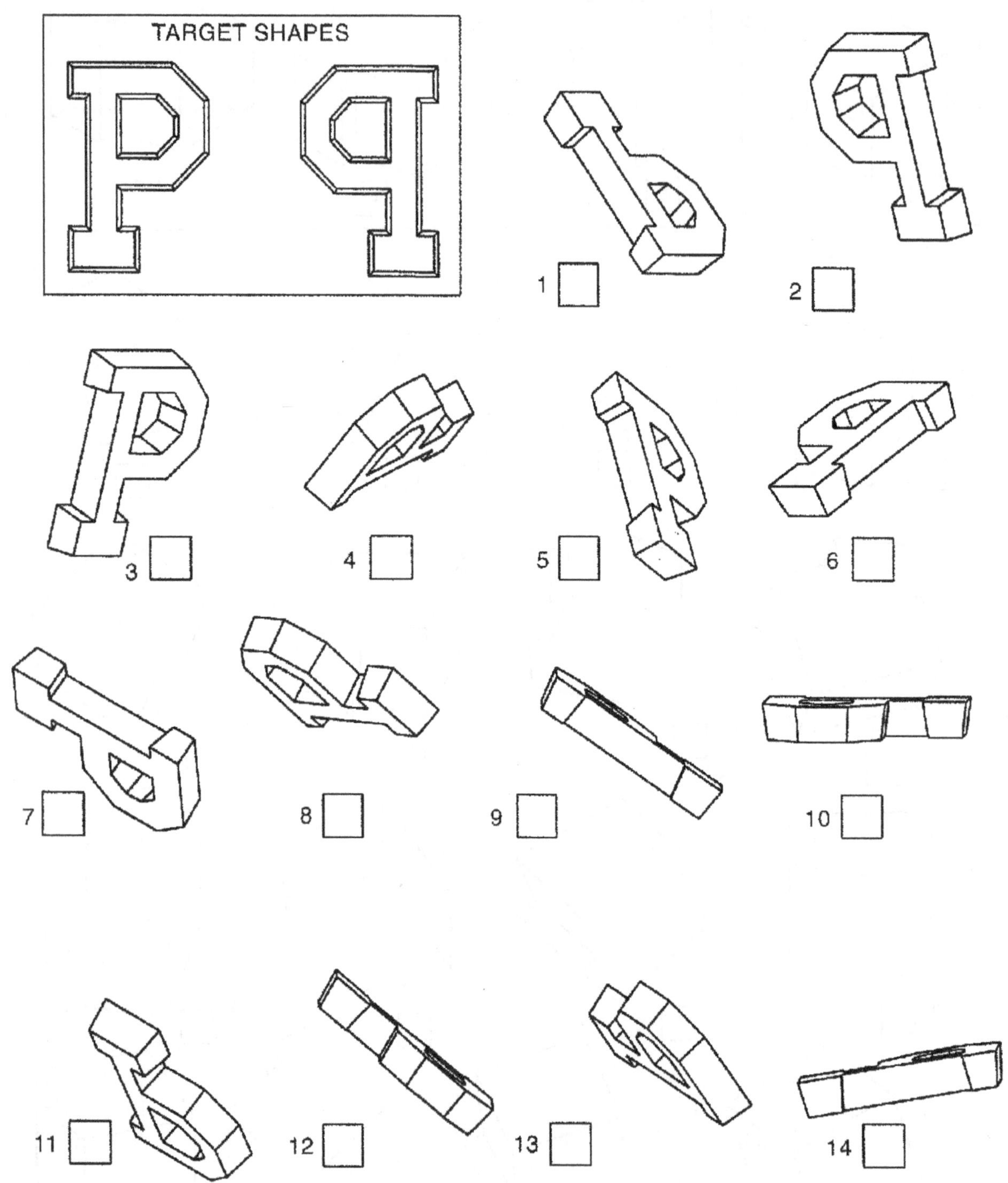

Figure 5.54

Write the letter p or q in the square near the rotated letter

5.16 Figures 5.55 through 5.57. In the table, match the given surface letter from the pictorial drawing with the corresponding surface number from the multiview drawing for each view.

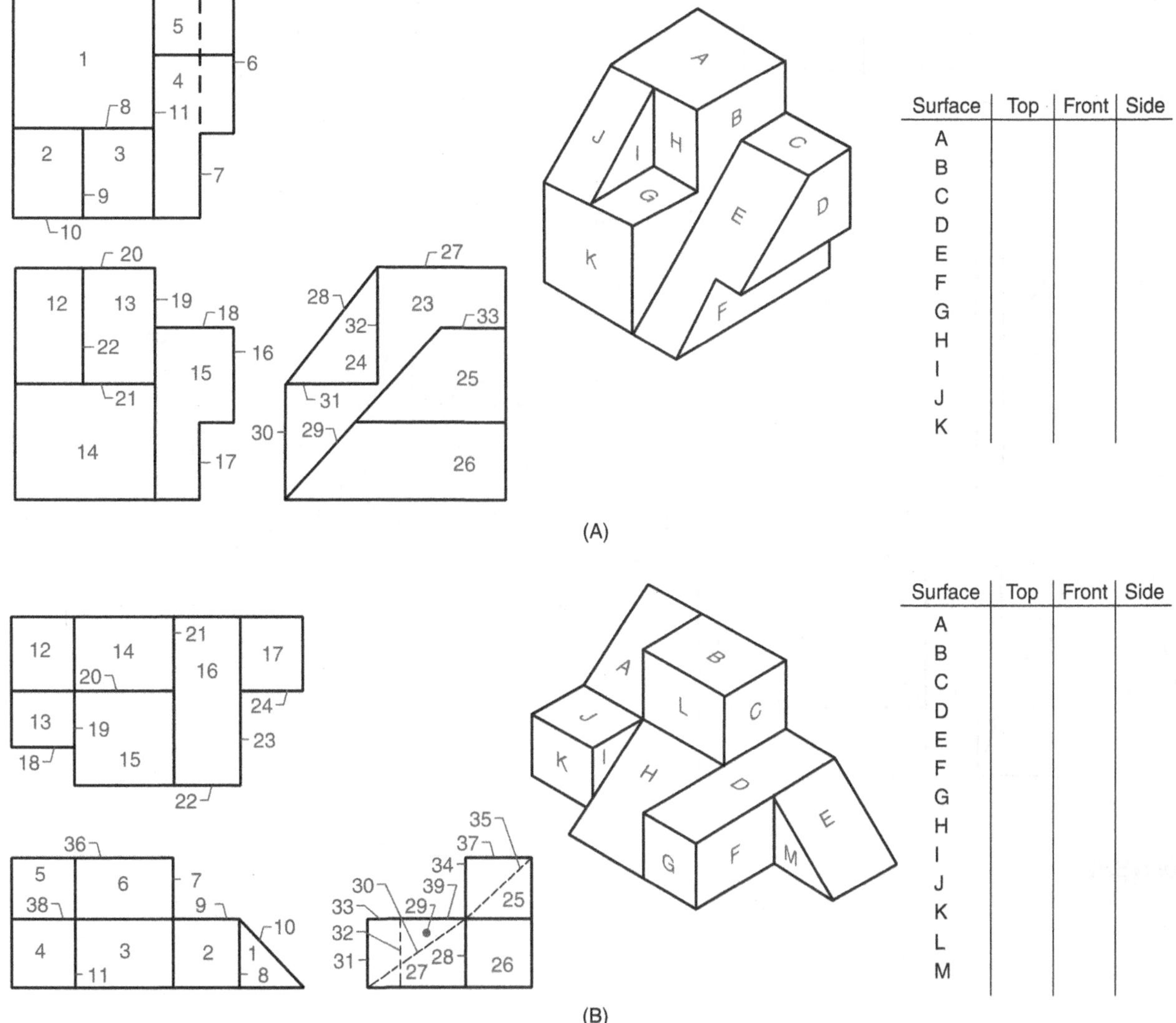

(A)

Surface	Top	Front	Side
A			
B			
C			
D			
E			
F			
G			
H			
I			
J			
K			

(B)

Surface	Top	Front	Side
A			
B			
C			
D			
E			
F			
G			
H			
I			
J			
K			
L			
M			

Figure 5.55

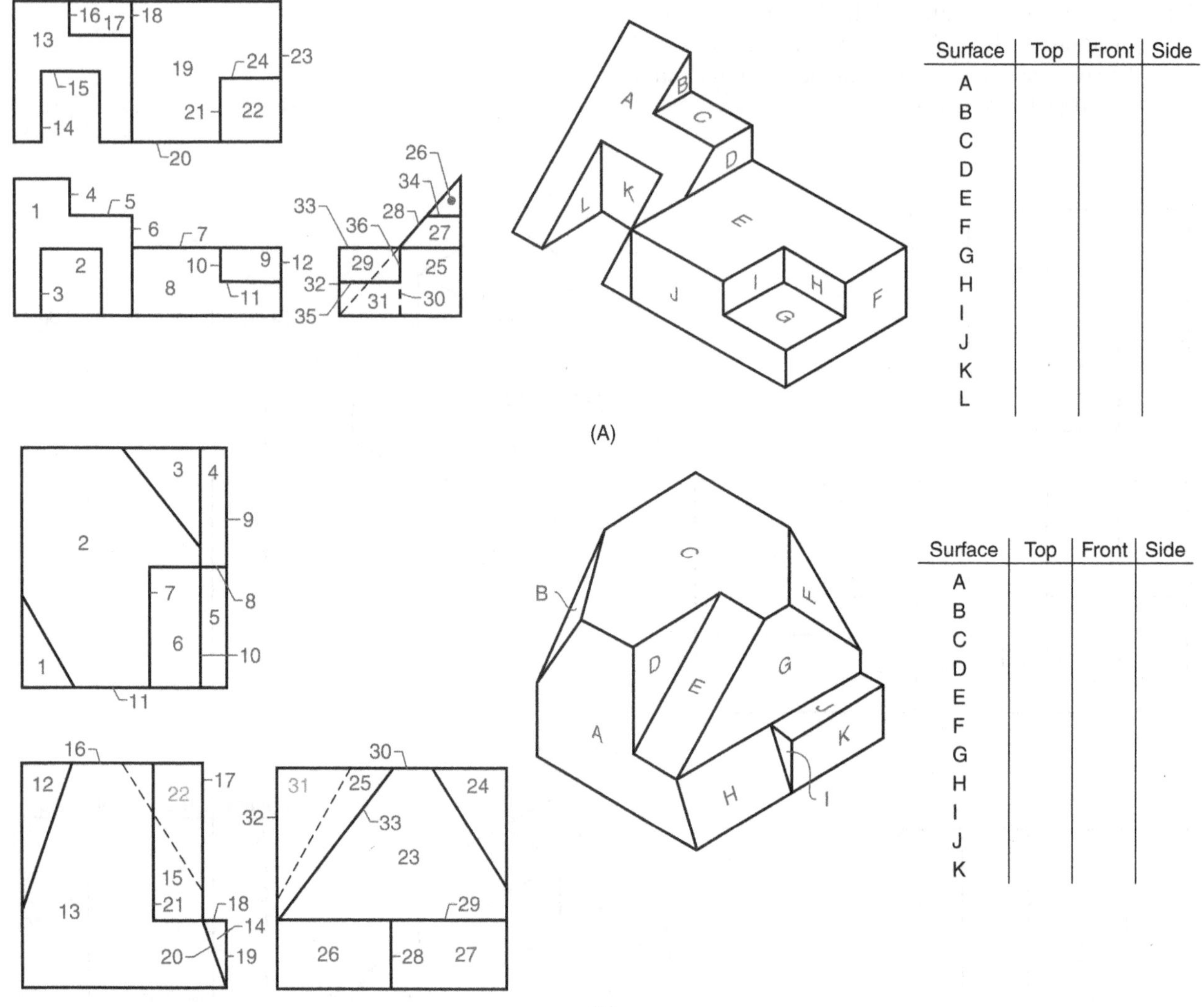

Surface	Top	Front	Side
A			
B			
C			
D			
E			
F			
G			
H			
I			
J			
K			
L			

Surface	Top	Front	Side
A			
B			
C			
D			
E			
F			
G			
H			
I			
J			
K			

Figure 5.56

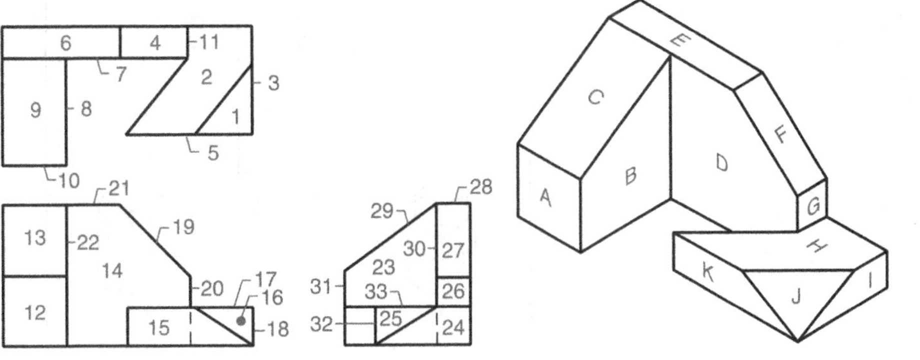

Surface	Top	Front	Side
A			
B			
C			
D			
E			
F			
G			
H			
I			
J			
K			

(A)

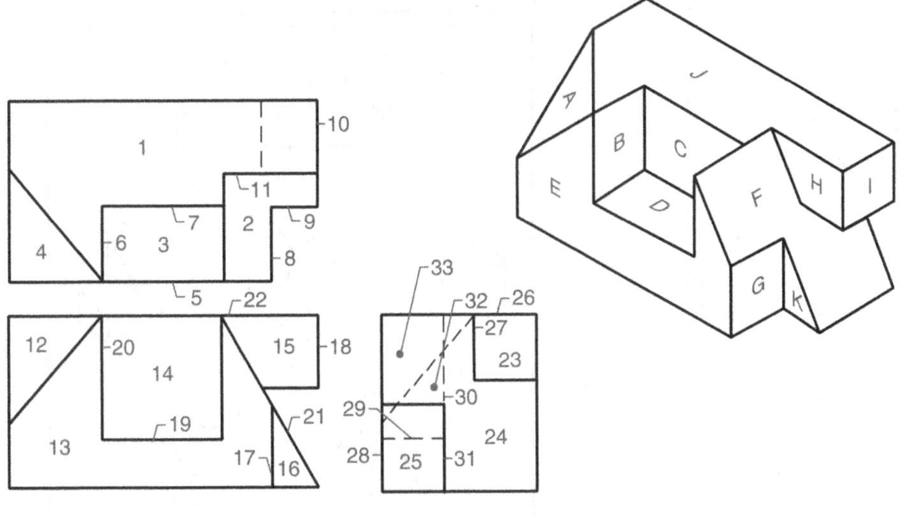

Surface	Top	Front	Side
A			
B			
C			
D			
E			
F			
G			
H			
I			
J			
K			

(B)

Figure 5.57

5.17 Figures 5.58A through E. In this exercise, a development (unfolded) is to be matched to one of five three-dimensional objects. The development shows the inside surfaces of a three-dimensional object with the shaded portion being the bottom surface.

5.18 Figures 5.59A through E. In this exercise, the figure in the top line is rotated into a new position. The figure in the second line will be rotated exactly the same way as the figure in the top line. Match the figure in the bottom line that shows the second figure rotated to the corresponding rotation as the rotation of the figure in line one.

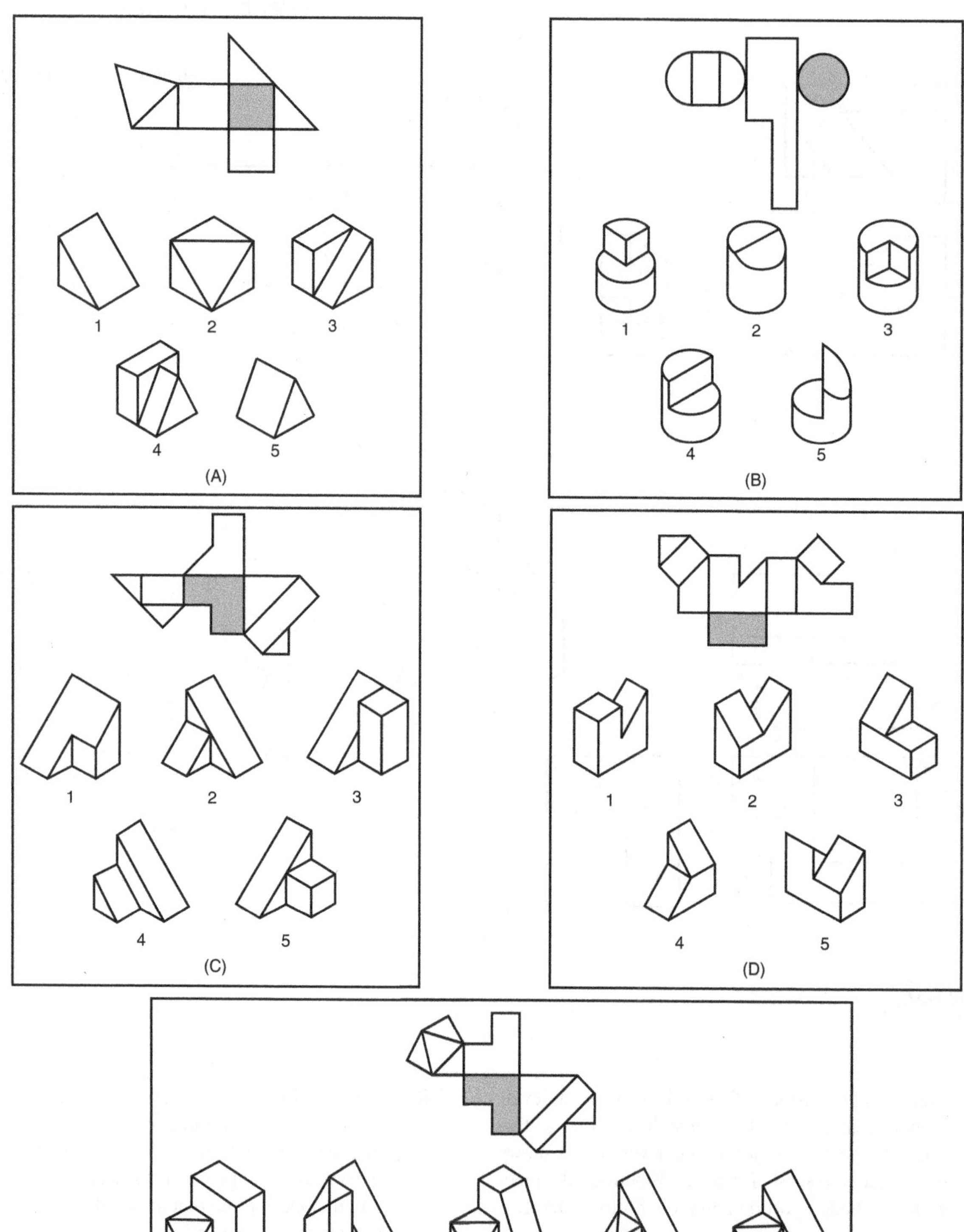

Figure 5.58

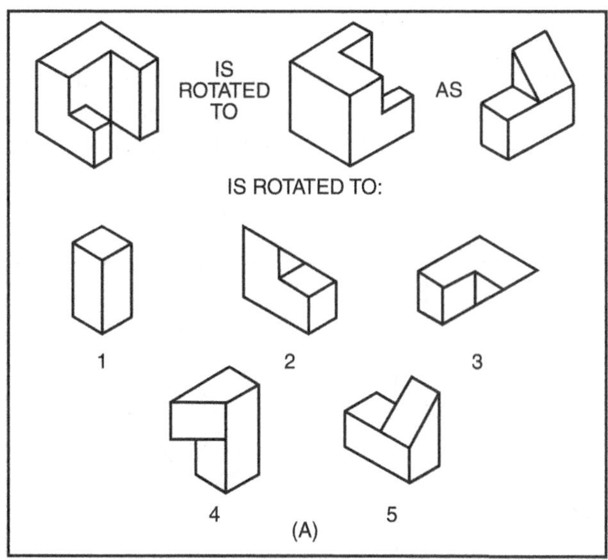
IS
ROTATED
TO
AS
IS ROTATED TO:
1
2
3
4
5
(A)

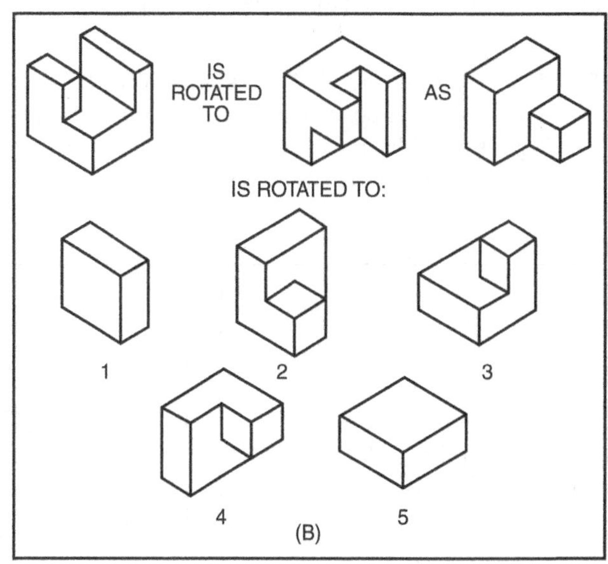
IS
ROTATED
TO
AS
IS ROTATED TO:
1
2
3
4
5
(B)

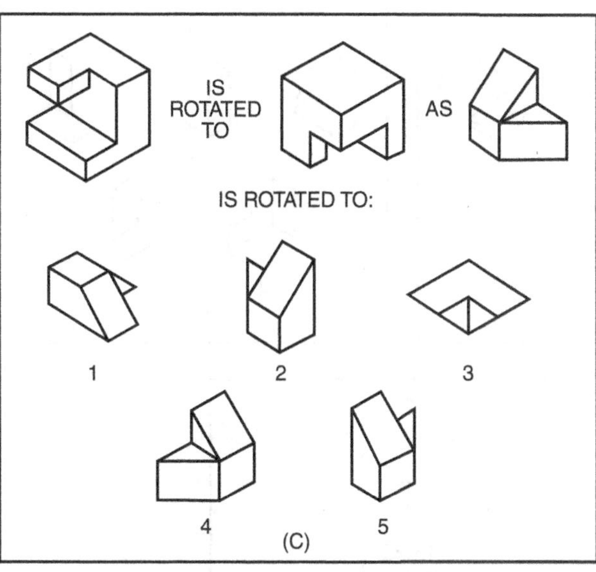
IS
ROTATED
TO
AS
IS ROTATED TO:
1
2
3
4
5
(C)

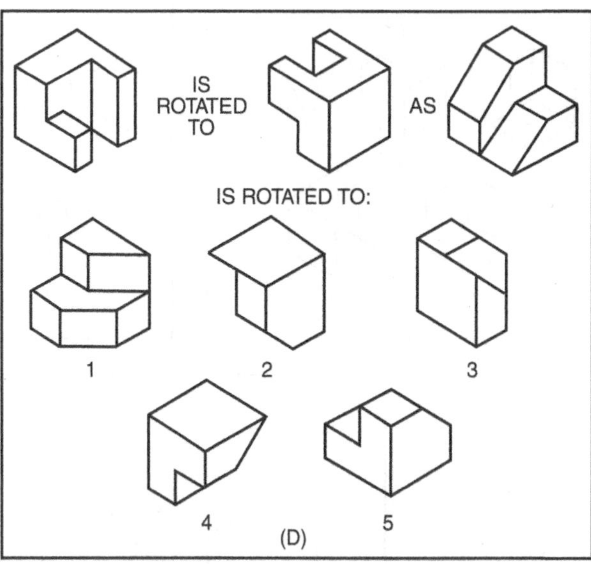
IS
ROTATED
TO
AS
IS ROTATED TO:
1
2
3
4
5
(D)

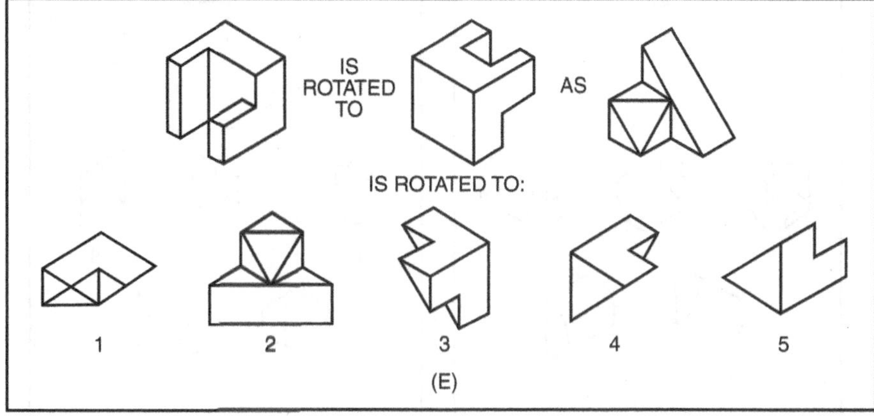
IS
ROTATED
TO
AS
IS ROTATED TO:
1
2
3
4
5
(E)

Figure 5.59

5.19 Figures 5.60A through E. In this exercise, the dot represents your position in relation to the object in a glass box. Match the correct view of the object to one of the alternative views.

5.20 Object feature identification. In Figure 5.61, identify the feature on the object as either an edge (E), face (F), vertex (V), or limiting element (L) in the space provided.

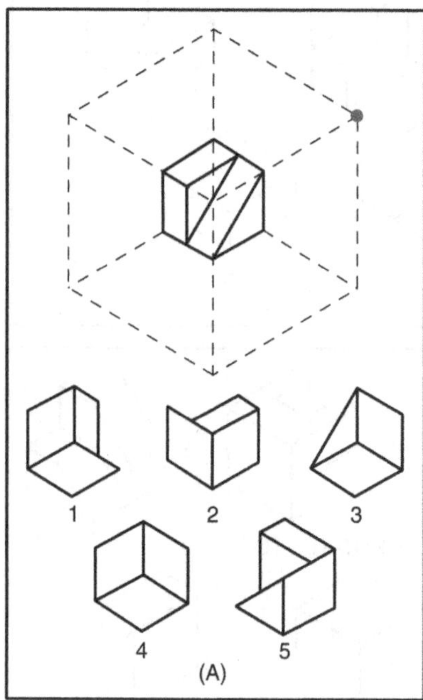

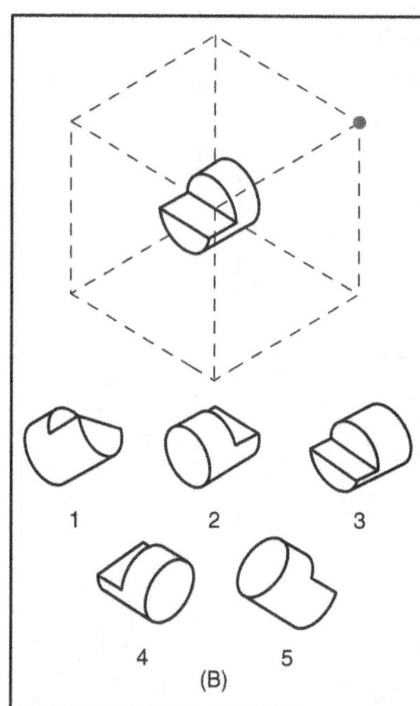

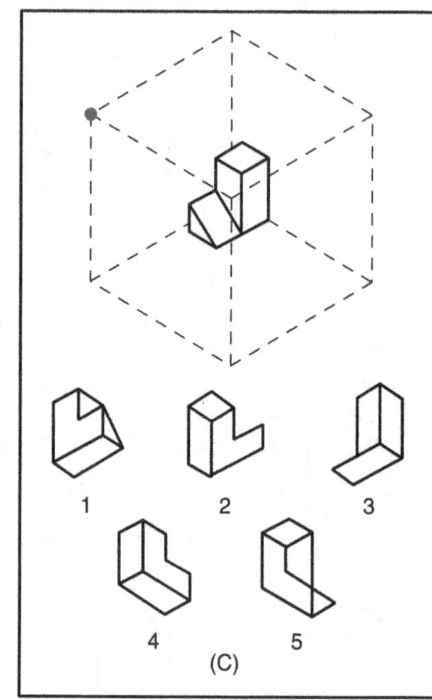

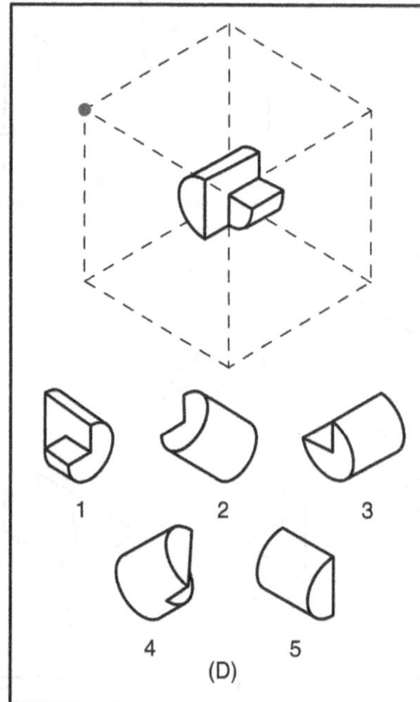

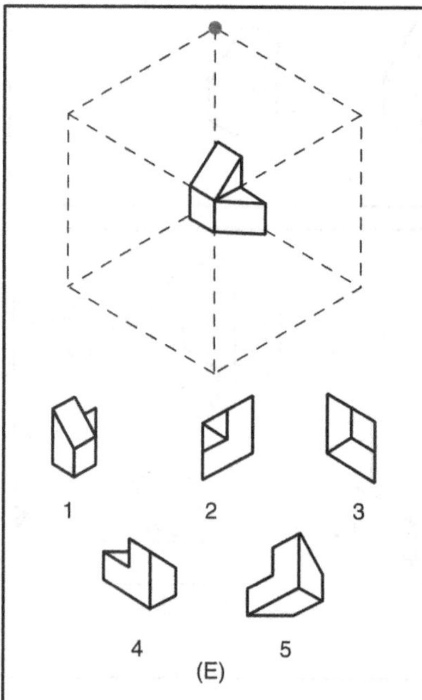

Figure 5.60

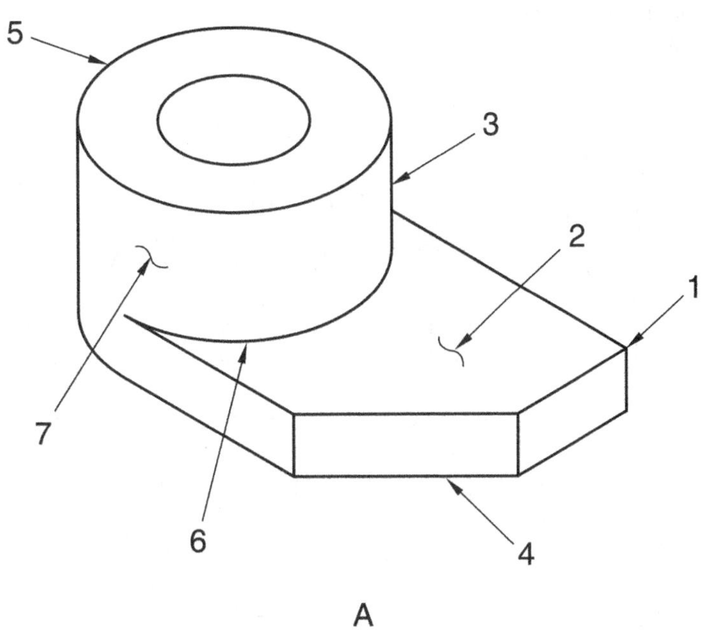

A

1. ______
2. ______
3. ______
4. ______
5. ______
6. ______
7. ______

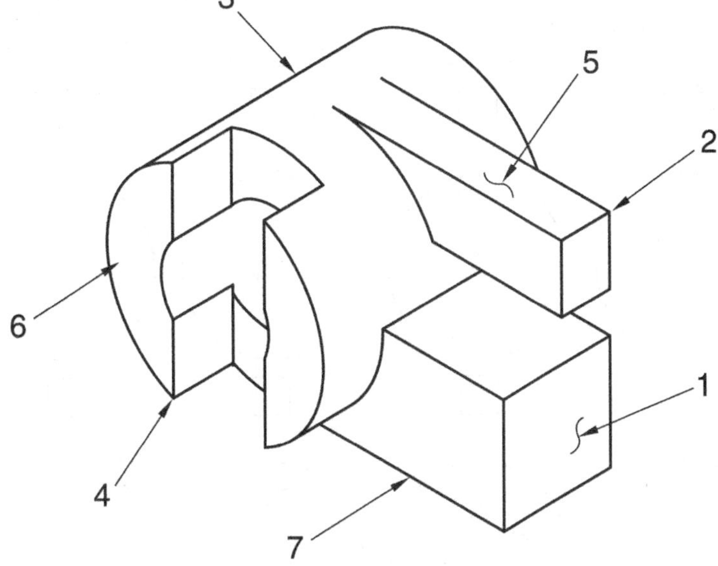

B

1. ______
2. ______
3. ______
4. ______
5. ______
6. ______
7. ______

Figure 5.61

5.21 Figure 5.62. Which two drawings of the four on the right show the same object as the one on the left?

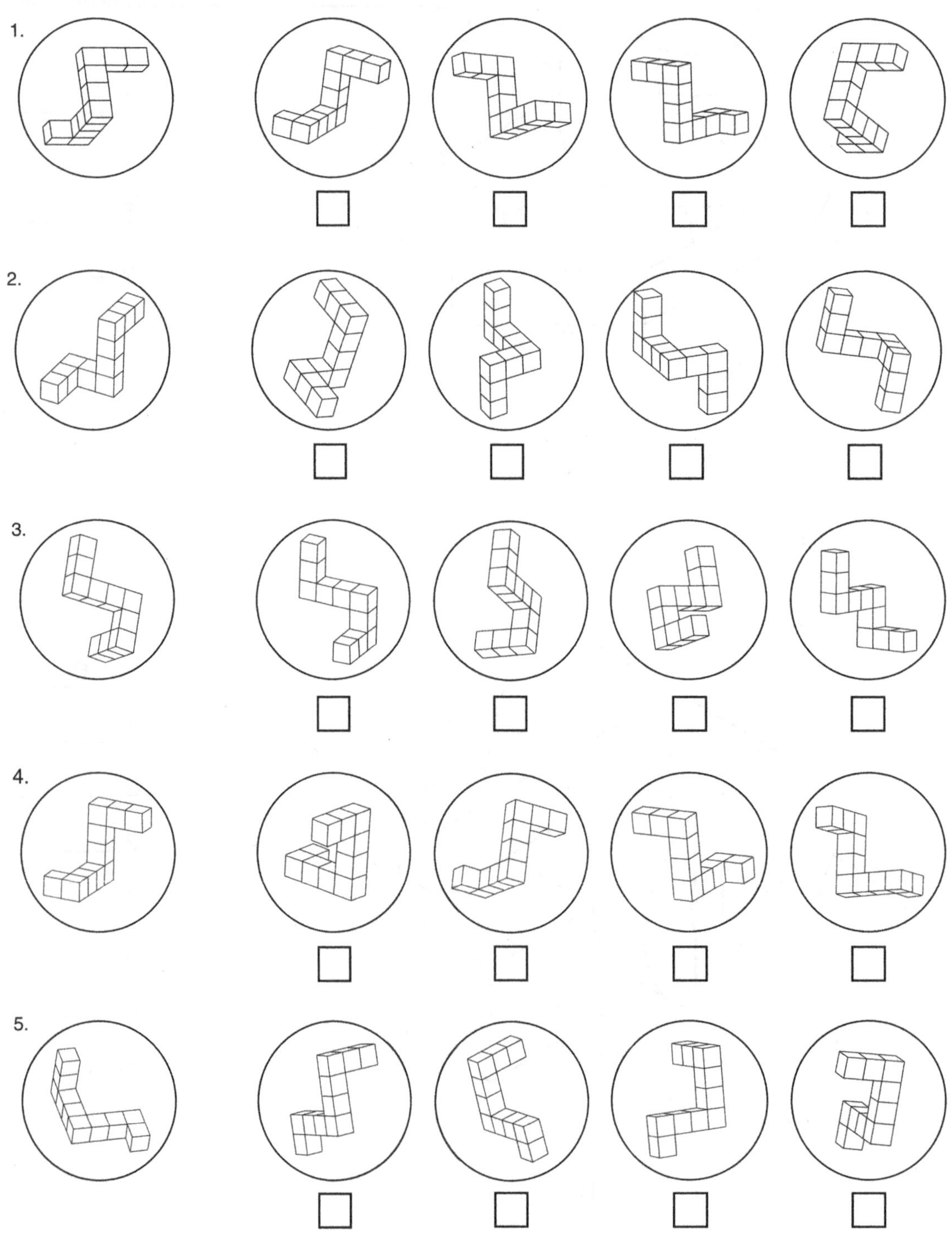

Figure 5.62

5.22 Figure 5.63. Each problem consists of an object that has been cut by a plane. You must visualize then sketch what the shape of the surface would be if cut by the plane.

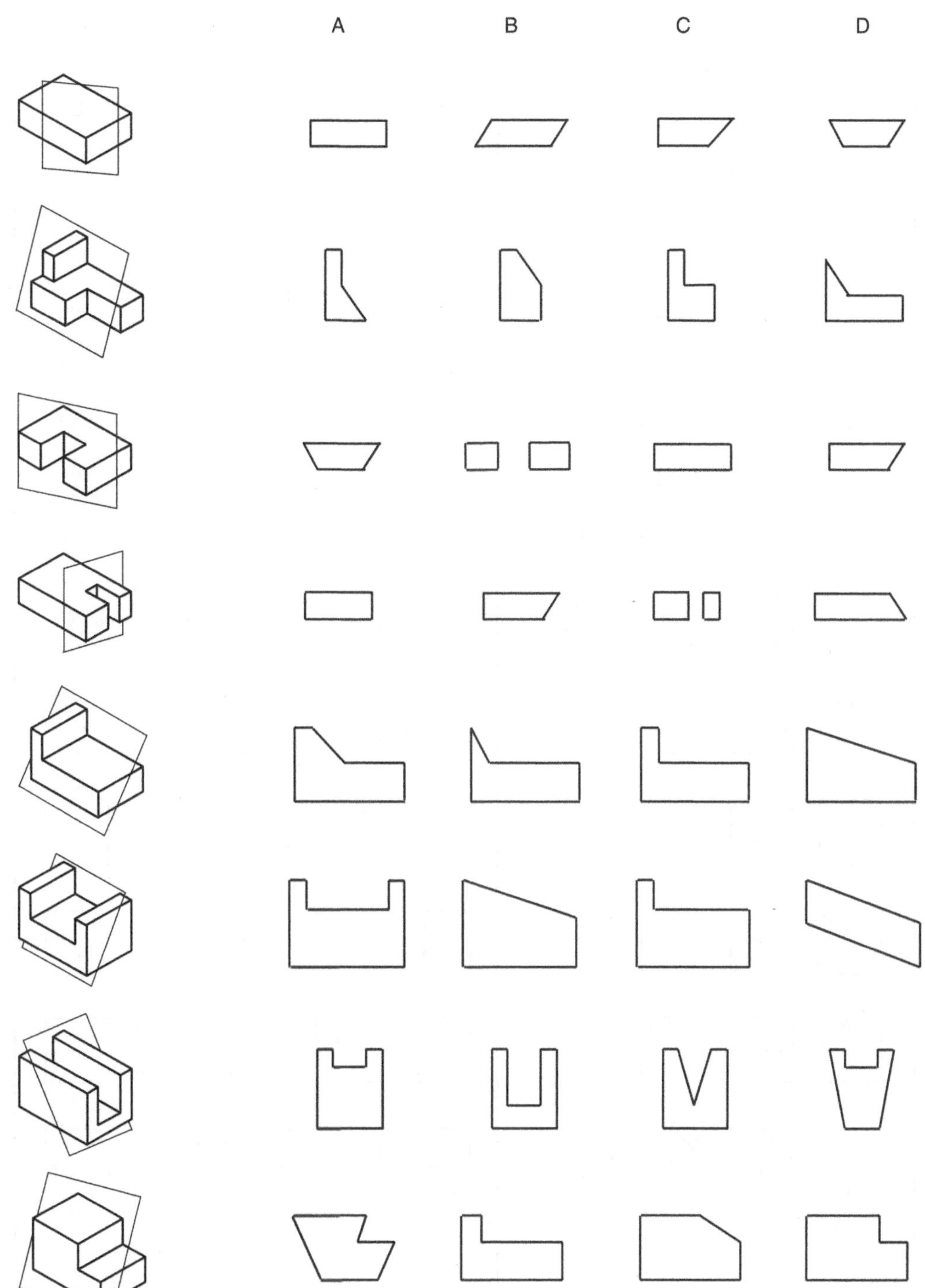

Figure 5.63

5.23 Figure 5.64. Each problem consists of a square piece of paper that is folded a number of times before a hole is drilled through it. You must visualize then sketch the unfolded square piece of paper with the resulting holes.

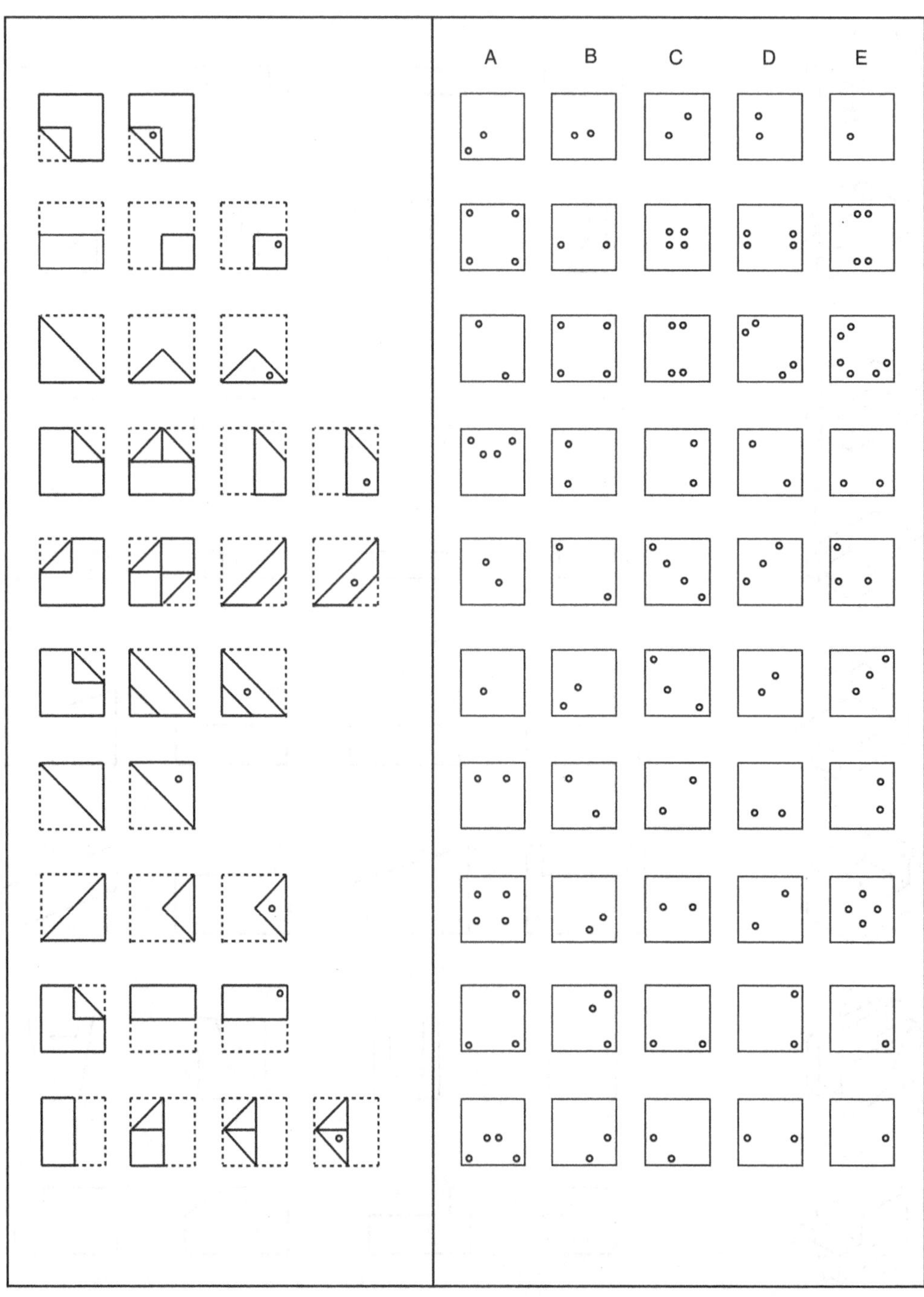

Figure 5.64

5.24 Figure 5.65. If the two pieces on the right were fitted together, what would the resulting figure look like? You must visualize then select from the possible answers on the left what the shape would look like after being fitted together.

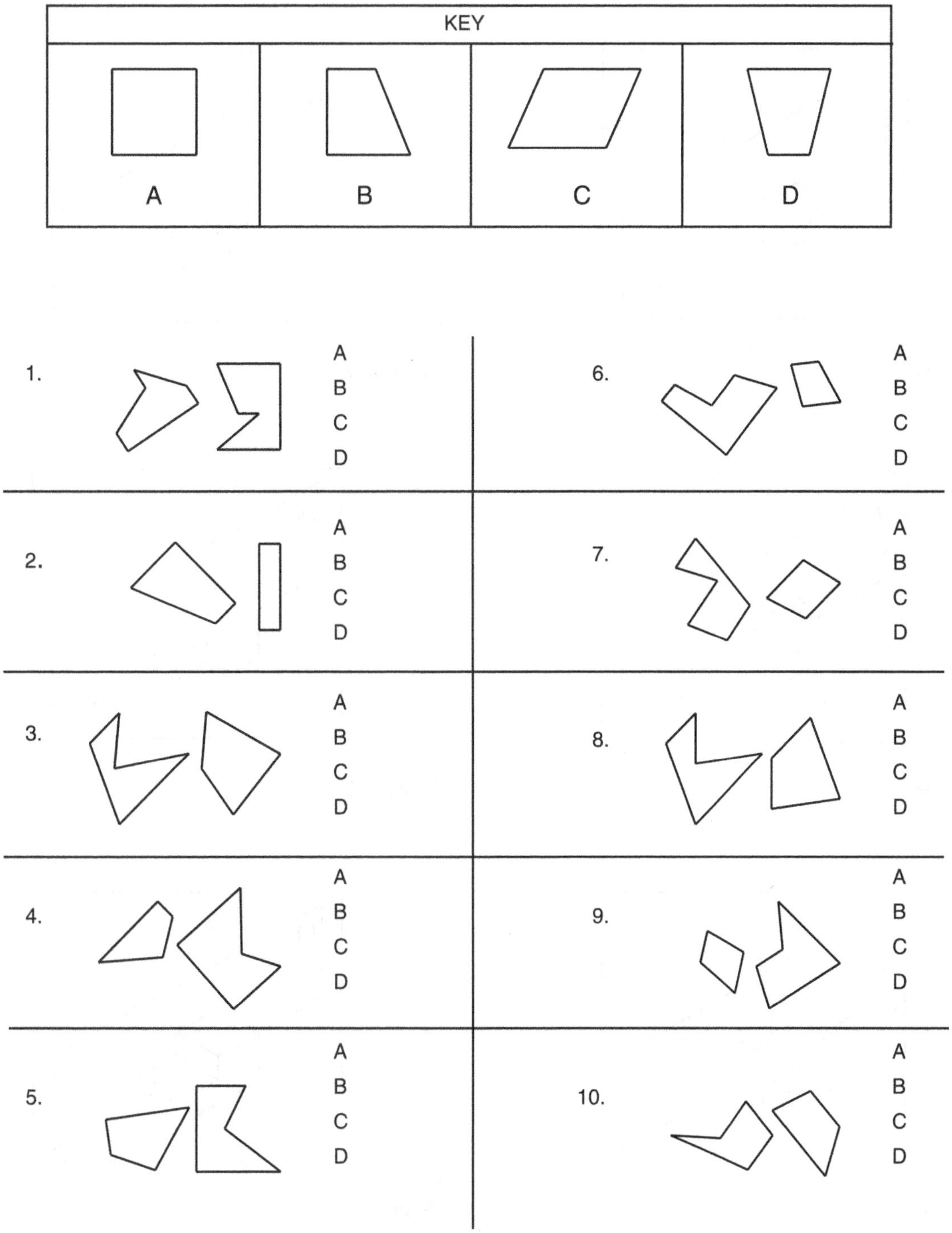

KEY

A B C D

1. A B C D

2. A B C D

3. A B C D

4. A B C D

5. A B C D

6. A B C D

7. A B C D

8. A B C D

9. A B C D

10. A B C D

Figure 5.65

5.25 Sketch a reflection of the object on isometric grid paper as if plane M was a mirror (Figures 5.66 to 5.71).

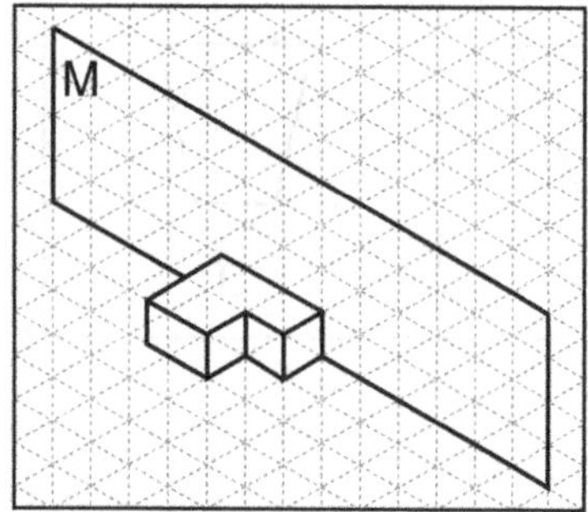

Figure 5.66

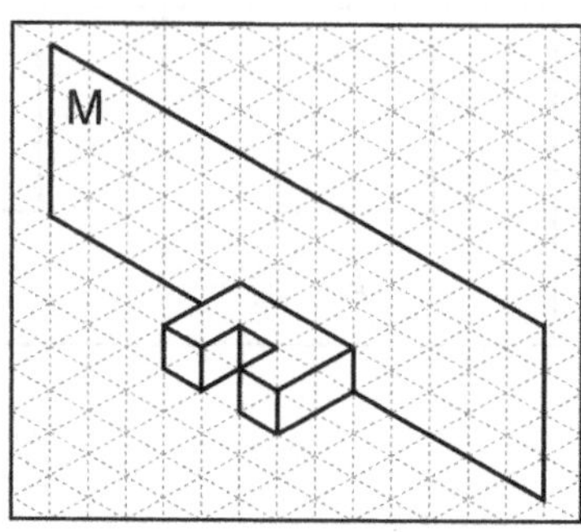

Figure 5.67

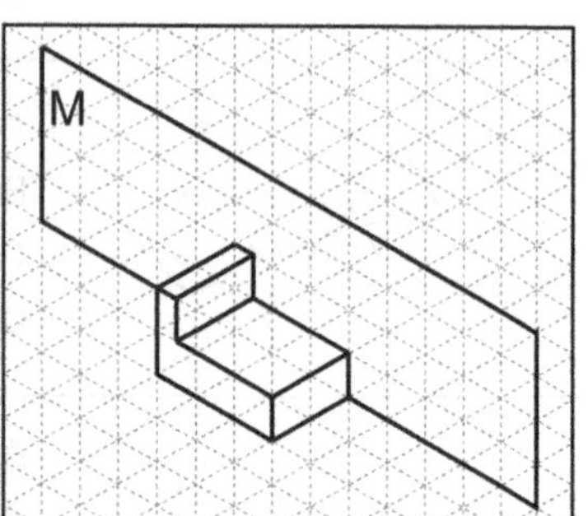

Figure 5.68

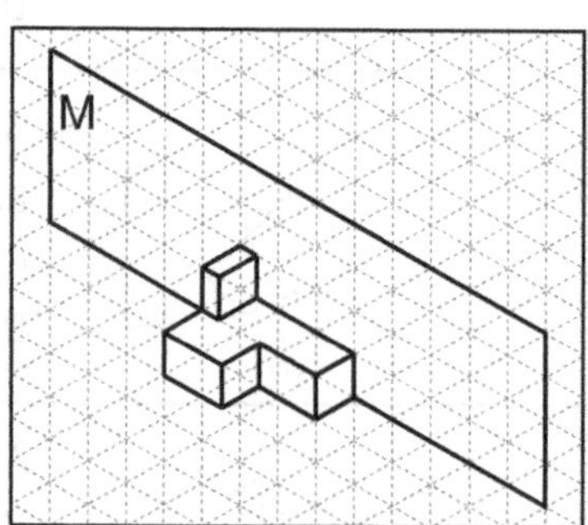

Figure 5.69

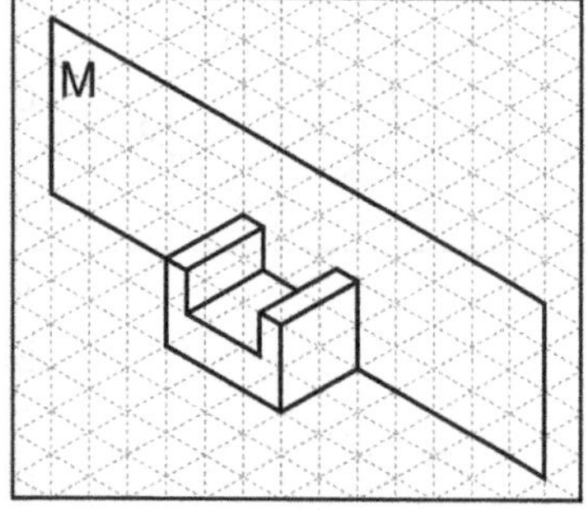

Figure 5.70

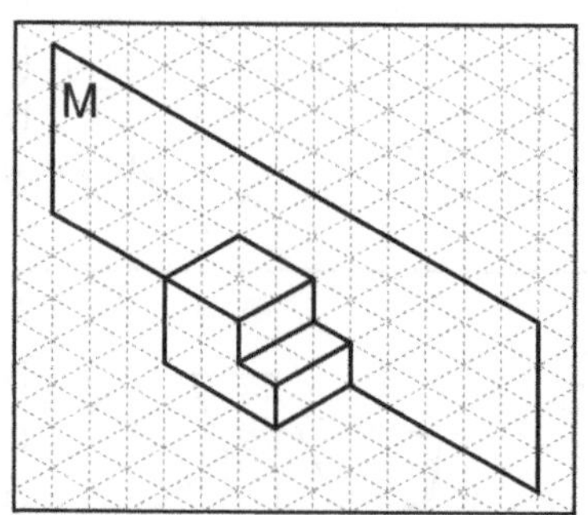

Figure 5.71

General Instructions for Problems 5.26 through 5.42

Using the tables of data, graph or plot the data, using the specified visualization method. In some cases, more than one method may be appropriate. Unless otherwise specified, the first column is an independent variable to be mapped on the horizontal axis, and the other columns are dependent variables to be mapped on the vertical axis. The visualizations may be created by hand, computer, or a combination of the two.

Problems 5.26 through 5.27 Create scatter plots of the data supplied in the tables. For each of the plots, estimate a linear regression line that best describes the trend of the data.

Table for Problem 5.26 Steam Boiler Pressures

Temperature (°F)	Pressure (psi)
290	46
295	58
300	63
305	74
310	80
315	88
320	93
325	94
330	102
335	110
340	127
345	129
350	148
355	156
360	166

Table for Problem 5.27 Steam Boiler Pressure: Four Heating Cycles

Temperature (°F)	Pressure 1 (psi)	Pressure 2 (psi)	Pressure 3 (psi)	Pressure 4 (psi)
290	22	72	35	64
295	43	80	54	73
300	58	84	70	78
305	62	88	85	99
310	74	95	91	92
315	76	110	97	100
320	87	113	99	104
325	88	119	107	100
330	95	112	103	108
335	103	130	117	116
340	143	125	124	128
345	111	146	130	123
350	126	148	136	139
355	134	149	148	145
360	140	157	153	147

Problems 5.28 through 5.30 Create single line graphs of the data supplied in the tables. The data can also be represented as bar graphs.

Table for Problem 5.28 **Copper Wire Resistance**

Size (AWG)	Resistance (Ohms/1000 ft @ 25°C)
18	6.23
16	3.99
14	2.48
12	1.60
10	1.12
8	0.644
6	0.404
5	0.322
4	0.267
3	0.209
2	0.166
1	0.128
0	0.100

Table for Problem 5.29 **Torque Output of a Single Cylinder Engine**

Crank Angle (deg)	Torque (Newton-meters)
0–90	72
90–180	−49
180–270	98
270–360	102
360–450	−80
450–540	48
540–630	−110
630–720	63

Table for Problem 5.30 **Disk Cam Design**

Cam Angle (deg)	Lift (in)
0	0
30	0.11
60	0.39
90	0.78
120	1.17
150	1.45
180	1.53
210	1.48
240	1.40
270	1.28
300	0.88
330	0.33
360	0

Problems 5.31 through 5.33 Create single bar graphs of the data supplied in the tables. The data can also be represented as line graphs.

Table for Problem 5.31 **Pricing of Wireless Access Points**

Brand	Retail Cost (U.S. dollars)
A	210
B	199
C	187
D	340
E	230
F	280

Table for Problem 5.32 **Weight of Materials**

Material	lb/ft^3
Brick	120
Concrete	142
Copper	556
Granite	166
Lead	710
Porcelain	151
Steel	482
Tar	63
Wood, pine	32

Table for Problem 5.33 **Heat of Combustion of Fuel Sources**

Substance	BTU/lb
Acetylene	21390
Alcohol, methyl	9560
Benzine	18140
Charcoal, wood	13440
Coal, bituminous	12780
Gasoline	21350
Kerosene	19930
Hardwood	6980

Problems 5.34 through 5.35 Create multiple line graphs of the data supplied in the tables. Each column in the table represents a separate value of a second independent variable. The data can also be represented as multiple bar graphs.

Table for Problem 5.34 **Calculated Friction Factor of Smooth Cast Iron Pipe**

	Velocity (ft/sec)		
Diameter (in)	0.5	2	6
1	0.0378	0.0318	0.0267
3	0.0345	0.029	0.0244
6	0.0311	0.0266	0.0233
9	0.0299	0.0248	0.0218
12	0.0270	0.0231	0.0206
18	0.0239	0.0210	0.0195

Table for Problem 5.35 **Cost of Production (U.S. Dollars) per Unit for LCD Monitors**

	Plant			
Year	A	B	C	D
2000	120	124	118	130
2001	119	120	115	121
2002	119	118	116	112
2003	117	116	110	108
2004	115	112	105	106
2005	114	109	100	104

Table for Problem 5.36 **Raw Material Costs (German Deutsche Marks) per Unit**

	Material		
Year	Copper	Plastic Resin	Mild Steel
1999	1.30	0.82	1.89
2000	1.25	0.88	1.79
2001	1.21	0.90	1.71
2002	1.24	0.91	1.66
2003	1.28	0.89	1.81

Problems 5.36 through 5.37 Create multiple bar graphs of the data supplied in the tables. Each column in the table represents a separate value of a second independent variable. In a second graph, instead of laying out the bars side-by-side, make composite bars containing all the levels of the second independent variable. The data can also be represented as multiple line graphs.

Problems 5.38 through 5.39 Create time series analyses of the data supplied in the tables. In the layout of the analyses, use range bars in which the time segments are mapped on the horizontal axis and the independent variable is on the vertical axis.

Table for Problem 5.37 **Average Assembly Operation Time (sec) per Unit**

	Operation			
Assembly Line	Install Harness	Attach Clips	Drive Fasteners	Place Cover
Line A	3.2	2.9	5.3	6.8
Line B	3.0	3.1	5.0	7.1
Line C	3.5	4.0	6.3	6.9
Line D	2.9	2.7	5.1	6.0
Line E	4.1	3.6	6.9	8.1

Table for Problem 5.38 **Control Panel Operation Sequence (Decimal Min)**

Operation	Time Begin	Time End
Acknowledge startup horn	0.0	0.2
Monitor low power scale	0.2	5.6
Unlock control rods	0.4	0.6
Lower control rods	0.6	8.0
Switch to high-power scale	5.6	5.8
Monitor high-power scale	4.8	8.4
Lock control rods	8.0	8.2
Set auto control	8.2	8.4

Table for Problem 5.39 Machining Operation Sequence (sec)

Operation	Begin	End	Begin	End	Begin	End
Tool load	0	4.2	45.6	50.1	65.5	68.9
Coolant	4	9.8	10.6	42	49.9	64.5
Trim end	4.2	10.8	—	—	—	—
Rough pass	10.8	21.2	—	—	—	—
Finish pass	21.2	43	—	—	—	—
Chamfer corner	43	45.6	—	—	—	—
End bore	50.1	65.5	—	—	—	—

Problems 5.40 through 5.41 The data supplied in the tables do not plot well on standard linear scales. Decide whether a line or bar graph is more appropriate for the data, and create the following plots:

- Standard linear scale plot
- Semi-log plot
- Log-log plot
- Linear scale plot with scale breaks

What are the problems with the standard linear scale plots? Which alternative plotting method best corrects the problems of the standard layout?

Problem 5.42 Create a histogram using the following instructions. Open a phone book to any page. Look at the *last* two digits of 30 different phone numbers, and count the number of two-digit pairs that fall between 0 and 9, 10 and 19, 20 and 29, etc. Plot the results, with the ranges on the horizontal axis and the count on the vertical axis. Is there a uniform count between ranges? Count 30 more numbers. Is the distribution becoming more or less uniform? Repeat the above process with the *first* two digits of the phone numbers. Is the distribution more or less uniform? Why?

Table for Problem 5.40 Deformation Test of Medium Steel

Unit Stresses (psi)	Unit Elongation (change in length/length)
10,000	0.0003
15,000	0.0013
20,000	0.0022
25,000	0.0034
30,000	0.0045
35,000	0.0158
40,000	0.0203
45,000	0.0381
50,000	0.0508
55,000	0.0792
60,000	0.1284

Table for Problem 5.41 Melting Points

Substance	Melting Point (°C)
Acetylene	−81.3
Aluminum	659.7
Carbon dioxide	−57.0
Magnesium	651.0
Mercury	−38.9
Radon	−110.0
Silver	960.5
Sodium chloride	772.0
Zinc	419.0

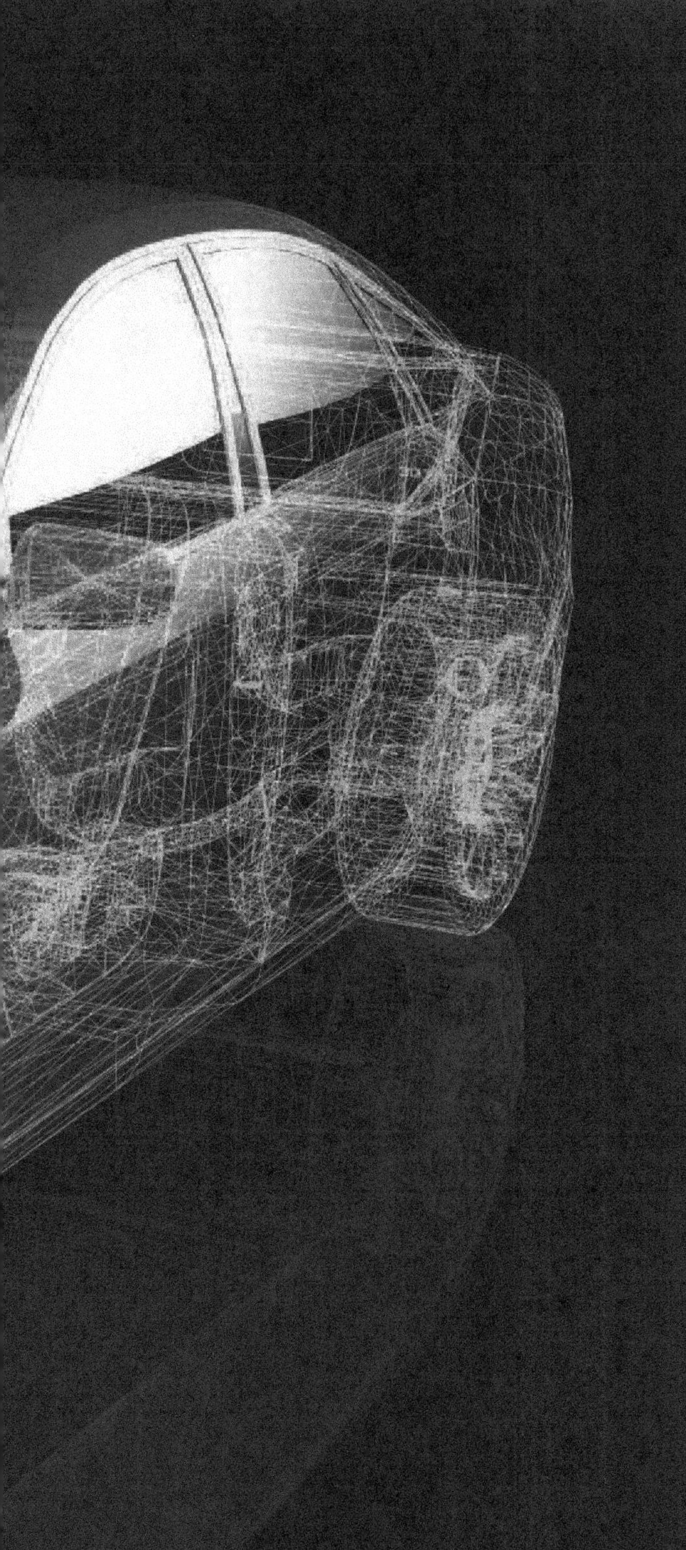

Chapter Six

Technical Drawing Tools

We graphicists choreograph colored dots on a glass bottle so as to fool the eye and mind into seeing desktops, spacecrafts, molecules, and worlds that are not . . .

—Frederick Brooks

Objectives

After completing this chapter, you will be able to:

1. Identify the important parts of a CAD system used to create technical drawings.
2. Define the important terms related to CAD systems.
3. Identify the important traditional tools used to create technical drawings.
4. Define the important terms related to traditional tools.
5. Use traditional tools and CAD to draw lines, circles, arcs, and curves.
6. Use scales, dividers, and CAD to measure and scale drawings.
7. Identify standard metric, U.S., and architectural drawing sheet sizes.
8. Identify standard pencil grades, and identify those most commonly used for technical drawings.
9. Identify the types and thicknesses of the various lines in the alphabet of lines.
10. Use traditional tools and CAD to erase parts of a drawing.

Introduction

Technical drawings are created using a variety of instruments, ranging from traditional tools, such as pencils, compass, and triangles, to the computer. Drawing tools are used to make accurate and legible drawings and models. Traditional drawing instruments are still important, especially for sketching; today, however, the computer can be used for most drawing and modeling requirements. This chapter is an introduction to computer-aided design/drafting (CAD) systems, including the related hardware, software, and peripheral devices, and the traditional equipment normally used by engineers and technologists to create technical drawings and models.

Figure 6.1

CAD workstations

Typical CAD workstations used in industry have large color monitors. The CPU itself is housed in the rectangular box located below or on the side of the monitor, or on the floor.
(Courtesy of Core Microsystems.)

6.1 Technical Drawing Tools

Just as the graphics language has evolved over the years into a sophisticated set of standards and conventions, so have the tools used to graphically communicate technical ideas. Tools are used to produce three basic types of drawings: freehand sketches, instrument drawings, and computer drawings and models. The tools have evolved from pencils, triangles, scales, and compasses to **computer-aided design/drafting (CAD)** systems. **CAD** is computer software and related computer hardware that supplements or replaces traditional hand tools in creating models and technical drawings (Figure 6.1).

6.2 Computer-Aided Drawing Tools

Traditional tools will continue to be useful for sketching and rough layout work; however, CAD software can create virtually any type of technical drawing. Circle commands replace the compass, line commands replace the T-square and triangles, and editing commands replace the dividers and erasing shield.

A CAD system consists of hardware devices used in combination with specific software, as shown schematically in Figure 6.2. The **hardware** for a CAD system consists of the physical devices used to support the CAD software. There are many different hardware manufacturers and types of hardware devices, all of which are used to create, store, or output technical drawings and models.

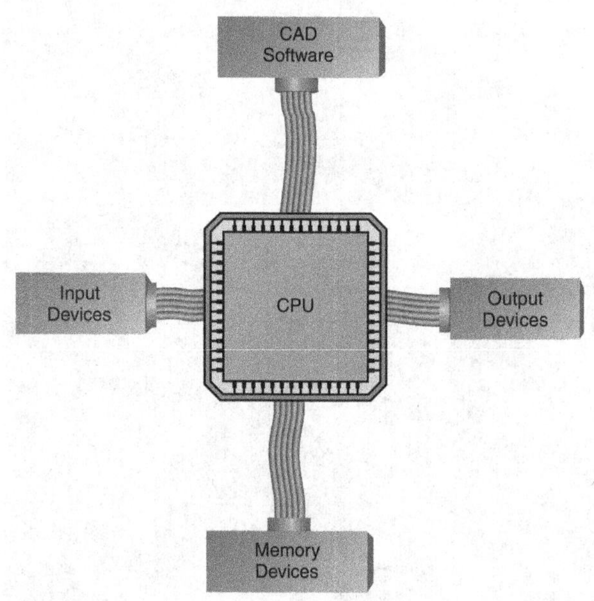

Figure 6.2

Schematic representation of CAD hardware

Components of a CAD system include input, output, and storage devices attached to a CPU, as well as the CAD software.

6.2.1 The Central Processing Unit (CPU)

The **central processing unit (CPU)** is the hardware device that runs the computer programs and controls the various attached input and output devices. Figure 6.3 shows a CPU

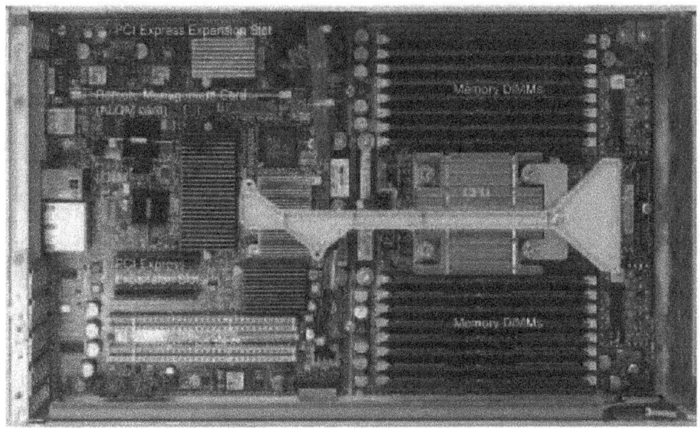

Figure 6.3

Main computer circuit board

The main circuit board, called a motherboard, contains electronic circuits and components, such as the CPU, RAM memory slots, and expansion slots.

(Courtesy of Sun Microsystems Computer Corporation.)

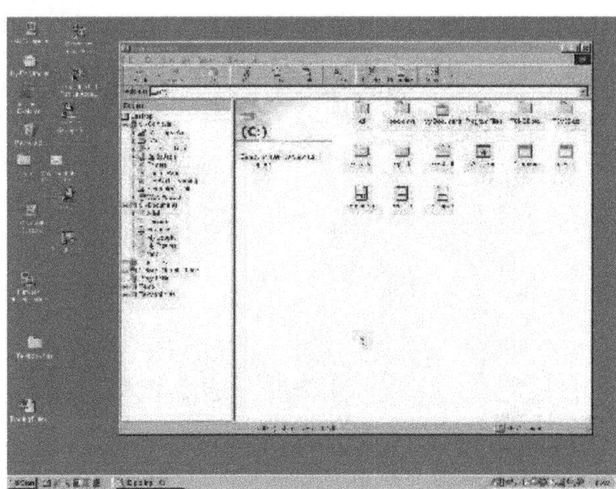

Figure 6.4

The display screen of a computer running the Windows operating system

This type of computer interface is called a graphical user interface (GUI). Notice how icons are used. For example, to delete a file, place it in the "recycle bin" located on the left side of the screen.

circuit board, called a motherboard, which is housed in a rectangular box to protect the circuitry and facilitate connection of the other devices. CPUs are generally classified by the type of microprocessor chip upon which they are based. For example, IBM, Apple, Hewlett-Packard, and Sun are well-known manufacturers of computer systems.

The power of a CPU is based on its clock speed, which is the rate at which it performs functions. The clock speed is expressed in megahertz (MHz); the higher the clock speed, the more capable the CPU. Other measurements used to rate CPUs include millions of instructions per second (MIPS) and system performance evaluation cooperative (SPEC) marks. For graphics workstations, the efficiency of displaying graphics on screen is measured in the number of lines drawn per second and the number of smoothly shaded polygons displayed per second.

6.2.2 Computer Operating System

Every computer uses an **operating system**, which is a software program that controls the internal operations of the computer, such as the memory, storage drives, input and output devices, and data transmission circuitry. **Software** comprises the written and coded instructions that govern the operation of the computer and the functions it performs. Both CAD and the operating system are examples of software.

The operating system is the software interface between the user and the CPU. Many operating systems employ graphics, such as icons, to represent various functions. For example, a trash can might be used to delete files. Common operating systems used with CAD are Microsoft Windows, UNIX, and LINUX. Figure 6.4 is the screen display of a computer using the Windows operating system.

6.2.3 Display Devices

There is a wide range of display devices, or monitors, available for computers. A **display device** is a type of output device, that is, a device through which information flows from the computer "out" to the user.

Display devices are classified by their type, resolution, size, and color capabilities. Monitor sizes range from 9 to 25 inches, measured diagonally. There are two types: vector and raster. A **vector device** locates the endpoints of a line and then draws the line by electronically charging a continuous stream of phosphors on the screen. A **raster device**, which is the most common, creates an image by electronically charging individual points called **pixels**, which are arranged in horizontal rows. The resolution is expressed in terms of the number of pixels horizontally by the number of pixels vertically, such as 1024 × 768, or 1280 × 1024. The more pixels there are on the screen, the higher the resolution, and the higher the resolution,

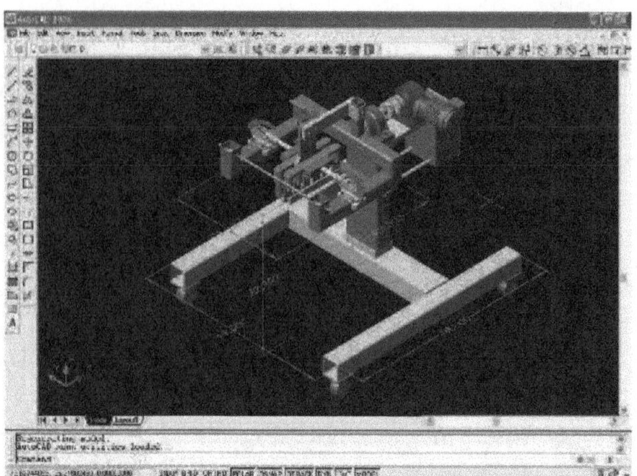

Figure 6.5

CAD display

The screen display of a CAD program has a menu area and an area for drawing.

Figure 6.6

Tablets

Tablets are input devices used to interact with the CAD software.

(Courtesy of Wacom.)

the greater the expense, memory, and processing power required. As for color capabilities, more advanced monitors can display millions of colors.

In a CAD system, the display device can be thought of as the drawing paper or medium upon which technical drawings and models are produced. Figure 6.5 shows a screen from a CAD program. The CAD software commands are located on the left side of the screen. Movement of a screen cursor is controlled by an **input device**, such as a keyboard, tablet, or a mouse, through which information flows from the user "in" to the computer. The cursor is used to select a command by moving the cursor to that command on the screen and highlighting it.

6.2.4 Input Devices

Input devices are used to interact with software programs, including CAD. The computer keyboard is one type of input device and is used to enter alphanumeric data. Other input devices include the mouse, tablet, and scanner. These devices and their application to CAD systems are described in the following sections, as are some very specialized devices developed specifically for CAD use.

Tablets A **tablet** is an input device used to control cursor movement and select menu items (Figure 6.6). For a CAD program, the tablet is covered with a thin plastic overlay that contains the menu options. Attached to the tablet is the cursor control device, which may be a puck or a stylus. A puck has a set of crosshairs, and a menu item is selected by moving the crosshairs over that item and pressing one of the buttons located on the surface of the puck. A stylus is a penlike device that has a button near the tip, and the button is pressed to make a menu selection. Specialized tablets, called **digitizers**, are used to convert a drawing created with traditional tools to a CAD drawing by using the puck or stylus to locate the endpoints of lines, the centers and diameters of circles, and the appropriate elements of other entities.

Scanners A **scanner** is an input device used for converting a paper drawing created with traditional tools to a CAD drawing. The drawing paper is placed on the scanner, which converts the vector image (the drawing) into a raster image (lines made of pixels). Software then changes the geometry and text into a vector computer file that can be edited by the CAD program, to create a CAD drawing. Figure 6.7 describes how a scanner works.

Keyboard The **keyboard** is a device used to input alphanumeric data and to make CAD menu selections. Use of a keyboard for menu selection varies with the type of CAD software, as some programs are more keyboard dependent than others. It is also possible to control cursor movement with the arrow keys on a keyboard, although this is more cumbersome than other methods.

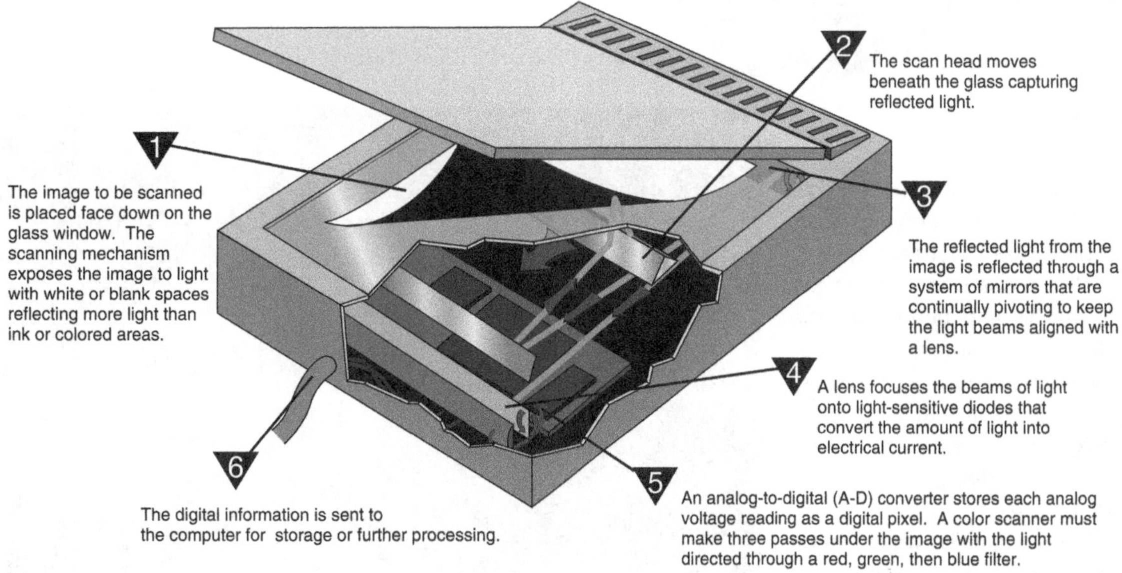

1
The image to be scanned is placed face down on the glass window. The scanning mechanism exposes the image to light with white or blank spaces reflecting more light than ink or colored areas.
2
The scan head moves beneath the glass capturing reflected light.
3
The reflected light from the image is reflected through a system of mirrors that are continually pivoting to keep the light beams aligned with a lens.
4
A lens focuses the beams of light onto light-sensitive diodes that convert the amount of light into electrical current.
5
An analog-to-digital (A-D) converter stores each analog voltage reading as a digital pixel. A color scanner must make three passes under the image with the light directed through a red, green, then blue filter.
6
The digital information is sent to the computer for storage or further processing.

Figure 6.7

How a flatbed scanner works

Mouse The **mouse** is an input device used to control cursor movement and to make menu selections. A mouse can be mechanical, optical, or infrared. A mechanical mouse has a small ball that rolls across a surface. This rolling motion controls small mechanical wheels that convert the motion into electrical signals. An optical mouse uses a tiny source of light emitted from the bottom to locate its position on a reflective surface. An infrared mouse uses an infrared signal, sent to the computer through the air, to track its relative location. This mouse is not physically attached to the computer, as is a mechanical or optical mouse (Figure 6.8).

Figure 6.8

Infrared mouse

An infrared mouse uses an electronic signal to locate its position on the screen.

(Courtesy of Logitech.)

Drawing a Line Using a Mouse

Step 1. To draw a line using a mouse, select the appropriate command, such as LINE, from the on-screen menu by using the mouse to move the screen cursor over the command to highlight it.

Step 2. While the command is highlighted, press the button located on the top left of the mouse to select the LINE command.

Step 3. With the mouse, move the cursor to the starting point on the screen, and then press the same mouse button.

Step 4. With the mouse, move the cursor to the location for the endpoint of the line, and then press the same mouse button.

The mouse can be thought of as the replacement for the pencil when creating technical drawings and models.

Other Input Devices There are many other, less common input devices that are available for CAD, including joysticks, trackballs, mice for 3-D cursor movement

Dream **High Tech** Job

Thrill Builder

© Eurostyle Graphics/Alamy

Slowly the car inches up the improbable incline, defying gravity, and propelled by unseen forces. As the roller coaster car gets to the crest of the hill and peers over the top at the twisted tracks and loop-the-loops that lie just ahead, you try to convince yourself that the person who designed this cruel contraption knows what he is doing.

Relax: he does.

Kent Seko originally wanted to be an architect. He rode roller coasters as a kid, but never thought about designing them until years later, when a friend who worked at Arrow Dynamics, Inc., a roller coaster design firm, talked him into applying for a job. Soon Seko joined Arrow Dynamics at the entry level, in the drafting department.

Seko has worked his way from drafter to conceptual designer over the 12 years he has been with Arrow Dynamics. The primary designer has been a good mentor, working with Seko on his first few design jobs. The two now make up the conceptual design team.

With Seko's help, in 1989 Arrow designed and built the world's first 200-foot tall roller coaster the Magnum XL-200 at Cedar Point. The Magnum was the worlds first "hypercoaster." In 1994, Arrow designed and produced two more hypercoasters—the Pepsi Max Big One at Blackpool Pleasure Beach, and the 80+ mph Desperado at Buffalo Bill's Resort and Casino. Also with Seko's help, in 1998 Arrow entered the Mouse ride market with its debut of the Mad Mouse at Myrtle Beach Pavilion and Amusement Park. He also worked on the Viper at Six Flags Magic Mountain, the tallest looping coaster in the world reaching a lofty 188 feet into the Californian sky.

It takes both design and engineering to develop a thrill ride. Arrow Dynamics, a company of less than 30 people, employs electrical engineers, mechanical engineers, drafting engineers, and structural designers.

There aren't many roller coaster designers (there are about 100 roller coaster design companies in the

(Figure 6.9), programmed function boards, voice recognition devices, dials, and others. Many of these are only used by a particular CAD program to perform some specialized function. A **modem** is an electronic input/output device used to send and receive data via telephone lines.

6.2.5 Output Devices

The **output devices** used to make hard copies of the drawings created on screen are categorized as printers, plotters, or film recorders. These devices can be used to make

U.S.), and there is no special school. But Seko said, "It's a great business to be in. It really gets in your blood."

Designing for the landscape

Roller coasters are usually custom made. A park orders a new ride for the coming year, describing the desired features and the budget. Seko and the design director then develop a proposal for the park covering cost, design features, and environment.

Designers can be creative about all sorts of aspects of the job. A ride can be basic, suspended, looping, or straight; it can be a water log ride; it can be death-defyingly tall or just medium tall. The surrounding landscape, and the available plot, strongly influence the design decisions. There may be a great view, or no view, or hills to work with. The ride could be long or short. The capacity of the ride is another concern: the park views it as how many passengers the ride can handle at a time, while the designer sees it as how many cars to build, and how much weight to account for.

Seko has been asked from time to time to design rides that can snake through the park's existing, surrounding rides.

If the park says yes to the proposal, the engineering designers set to work on the ride, building the track, structure, stations, and controls. The designs then get sent to the fabrications, or manufacturing department, which builds the machine. They then ship it off to the park.

Arrow Dynamics usually likes to have a year to build a ride, but on occasion has completed projects in just eight months. The more complicated the designs, the longer the ride takes to build.

One of the company's most recent innovations is the ArrowBatic, which Seko describes as an "inverted Mouse Ride," meaning an alteration of Arrow Dynamics' Mad Mouse, pictured at www.arrowdynamics.com. The ArrowBatic has loops and corkscrews, as well as a heart-stopping vertical drop. The ride uses a single vehicle, instead of a train, which allows it to maneuver in small areas.

Future ideas are top-secret, but Seko is excited and hopeful about upcoming plans. "Everybody's going higher and taller," he said. "The 310-foot height barrier was recently broken, so there's a little height war going on right now." Arrow Dynamics was responsible for the 200-foot record at Cedar Point with The Magnum in 1988. The Magnum is still rated seventh on rollercoaster.com's top-ten coaster list.

The job that takes you for a ride

Seko said there are a few Arrow Dynamics employees who won't ride the rides they develop, but Seko hops into a roller coaster car whenever possible. As designer, he gets to enjoy a special perk. After finishing a job, Seko sometimes gets invited to meet the people he's worked with from the amusement park. He then gets the honor of "bucking the line" to take his ride for free.

—Leslie Tebbe, Salary.com Contributor

From "Dream Job: Roller Coaster Designer," by Leslie Tebbe. Reprinted with permission from Salary.com.

quick, rough check plots, production plots, presentation plots, or a combination of these.

Printers/Plotters A **printer** is an output device that creates characters, numbers, and graphics on paper. Printers are used with CAD to create check prints. A **check print** is a low-quality hard copy made at high speed. Examples of printers include inkjet, thermal, and laser printers (Figure 6.10).

Inkjet Printers/Plotters **Inkjet printers** use narrow nozzles to spray ink onto the paper (Figure 6.10). The technology uses special paper and ink cartridges to produce color output. Inkjet printers are fast and can be used for

Figure 6.9

3-D cursor control

This type of mouse is used to control 3-D cursor movements.

(Courtesy of 3D Connexion.)

Figure 6.11

Laser printers

Laser printers are small-format output devices used for text and graphics.

(Courtesy of Hewlett-Packard.)

Figure 6.10

Inkjet plotters

D- and E-size inkjet plotters spray ink onto paper, using narrow nozzles, to create colored plots of CAD drawings.

(Copyright 2008 Hewlett-Packard Development Company, L.P. Reproduced with Permission.)

color shading, renderings, and solid filled output. Desktop inkjet printers are measured by the pages per minute (ppm) that can be printed, and the resolution, expressed as dots per inch (dpi). A typical color inkjet printer will print 16 ppm with a resolution of 1200 dpi.

Laser Printers **Laser printers** use a laser beam to record an image in the form of tiny dots on a light sensitive drum. The image is then transferred to paper using a special toner (Figure 6.11). Laser printers are measured by speed in ppm and resolution in dpi. Laser printers today can produce images at the rate of 20 ppm or more, black and white or color, with a resolution of 1200 dpi or more.

6.2.6 Storage Devices and Media

A **storage device** is used to store information on a specific medium and retrieve that information as needed. After a CAD drawing is created, it must be electronically stored on some type of storage medium. Storage media commonly used for CAD drawings are removable disks, hard disks, and streaming tape. Storage devices are combination **input/output (I/O) devices**, and are grouped into five categories:

1. External disk drives and USB flash drives (Figure 6.12).
2. Fixed hard disk drives.
3. Tape drives, which use tape cartridges.

Historical Highlight
Archimedes

Archimedes was a very talented scientist; some say he was the greatest scientist of the ancient world. Not much is known about this great thinker because he did not record much of his work, and even what he did record has been mostly lost. Most knowledge about him is based upon stories and myths that have been passed around for centuries.

It is rather appropriate that Archimedes is probably best known for his famous statement: "Give me a place to stand and I'll move the world." He may not have been able to move the world, but he did move some very large objects, such as boats and huge rocks. This superhuman ability came not from physical strength, but from an unprecedented knowledge of mechanics. Archimedes used this knowledge to design a number of tools and war machines. The best-known ones are the Archimedes screw, a drum with screw-like partitions used to carry water up large distances (see figure), and catapults with adjustable ranges.

Archimedes probably designed many other tools as well, but the knowledge of them has been lost because he probably did not think tool designs were important enough to be drawn out. He chose to record work that was more theoretical in nature, such as his search for an accurate value for pi (which he did find). Chances are that the more practical designs were worked out on trays of sand and never were recorded permanently. Legend has it, in fact, that he was tracing a design in sand when he was killed by a Roman soldier. The practical designs by Archimedes that we do know about are only known through other peoples' stories and drawings.

ARCHIMEDES 287 BC-212 BC

(© SPL/Photo Researchers, Inc.)

SOURCE: Ipsen, D. C. *Archimedes: Greatest Scientist of the Ancient World.* Hillside, NJ: Enslow Publishers, Inc., 1988.

Figure 6.12

Jumpdrive

(Courtesy of Lexar.)

Figure 6.13

Networked attached storage device

This storage device has capacities that range from hundreds of GB to several TB.

(Courtesy of Dell.)

4. Optical storage drives, such as CD and DVD.
5. Network attached storage (NAS) (Figure 6.13).

The 3½-inch removable disks have data storage capacities up to 250 MB. Fixed hard disk drives are peripheral devices that are usually installed in the computer cabinet and have much higher storage capacities than removable disks. Storage in hard disks is measured in gigabytes (GB). A gigabyte is 1000 megabytes (MB). Large removable storage devices have a removable cartridge, which can be changed to add new capacity, or can be transported to another computer. Fixed and removable drives are measured by storage capacity; access speed or seek time, measured in milliseconds (ms); and data transfer rates, measured in millions of bits per second (MBPS). Storage in NAS devices can be in terabytes (TB) which is 1000 GB.

Figure 6.14

CD ROM drive

(Courtesy of Iomega Corporation.)

Figure 6.15

Tape drive

Tape drives are used to back up computer drawings.

(Courtesy of Qualstar.)

Optical storage drives use a high-density medium based on compact disk (CD) technology similar to audio CDs (Figure 6.14). A single 4.7-inch CD can hold up to 660 MB of information. Some CD drives are read-only memory (ROM), which means the information on the CDs can be read, but no information can be written onto them by the users. "Write once, read many" (WORM) is another type of optical technology.

Another optical storage medium is DVD, which can store more than 9 GB of data.

Tape storage is the oldest storage medium (Figure 6.15). Tape drives come in many sizes and are relatively slow, but compared with the other storage media, they are an inexpensive medium for archiving CAD data.

USB flash drives are portable storage devices that are inexpensive, light-weight, and pocket-sized with storage capacities that range from hundreds of MB to a few GB. They are inserted into USB ports on a computer to transfer CAD and other types of files. There are many types of memory cards available that can be used to store images and CAD files. These memory devices commonly are used in digital cameras, but most computers have memory card slots, making them an option for storing CAD-related data.

For large files and sharing large CAD models, many companies rely on network attached storage (NAS) devices. These devices are configured to attach to the companies' intranet, allowing very fast access and storage of files. Typically, NAS devices can store from hundreds of GB to a few TB of data. Most of these devices are scalable, so more storage capacity can be added over a period of time as demand for storage increases.

6.3 Traditional Tools

The traditional tools used to create technical drawings have evolved over time. Many tools were originally used in ancient Greece to study and develop geometry. Although computers may someday replace the need for many traditional tools, they are still useful today for drawing, and more importantly, for sketching. **Traditional tools** are devices used to assist the human hand in making technical drawings. The assistance includes drawing lines straighter, making circles more circular, and increasing the speed with which drawings are made. The tools typically used to create mechanical drawings or sketches (Figure 6.16) consist of the following:

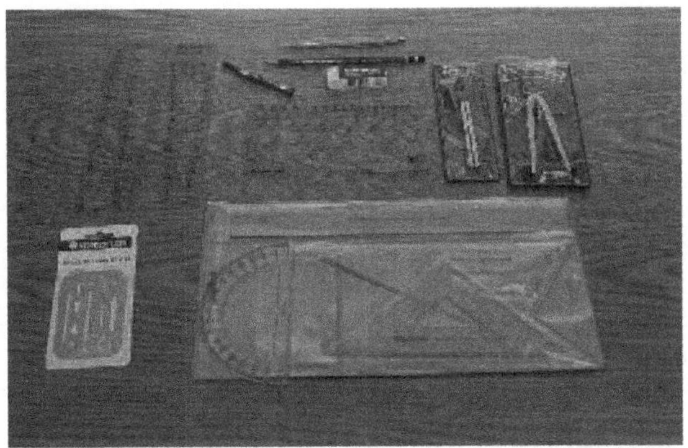

Figure 6.16

Traditional tools

These are some of the many traditional mechanical drawing tools used for engineering drawings.

(Courtesy of Staedtler, Inc.)

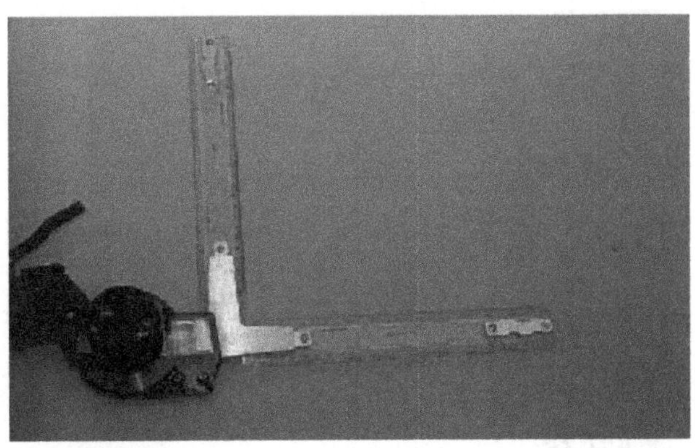

Figure 6.18

Drafting machine

A drafting machine is used to create lines on technical drawings. The head is adjustable to create angled lines.

(Courtesy of Staedtler, Inc.)

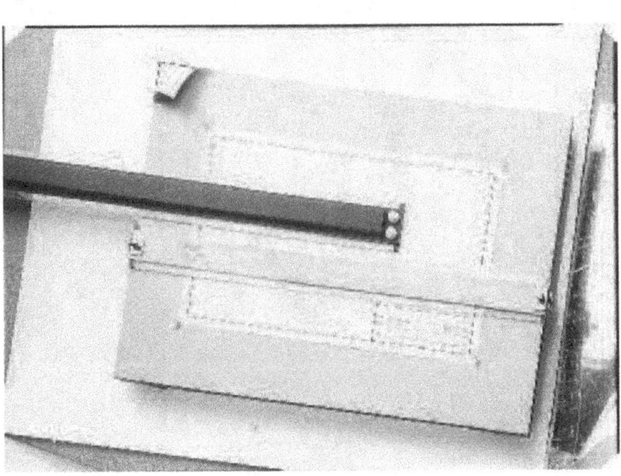

Figure 6.17

Parallel edge

A parallel edge is used as a straightedge for drawing lines.

(Courtesy of Staedtler, Inc.)

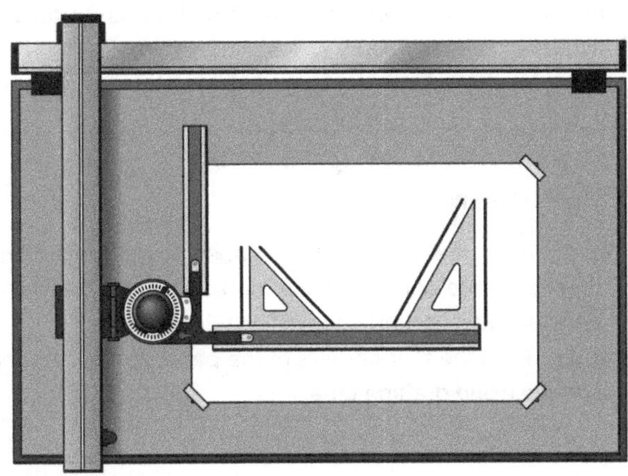

Figure 6.19

Drawing vertical and inclined lines

A drafting machine is used to support triangles for vertical and inclined lines.

1. Wooden and mechanical pencils.
2. Instrument sets, including compass and dividers.
3. 45- and 30/60-degree triangles.
4. Scales.
5. Irregular curves.
6. Protractors.
7. Erasers and erasing shields.
8. Drawing paper.
9. Circle templates.
10. Isometric templates.

6.3.1 Straightedges

Mechanical drawings are started by taping the drawing paper to the working surface. A **straightedge**, such as a T-square, parallel edge (Figure 6.17), or drafting machine (Figure 6.18), is used to draw horizontal lines. They are also used as guides for triangles, which are used to create vertical and inclined lines (Figure 6.19). **Drafting machines** are devices that supplement the T-square, triangles, protractors, and scales. The **parallel edge** is used to replace the T-square on wide drawing surfaces,

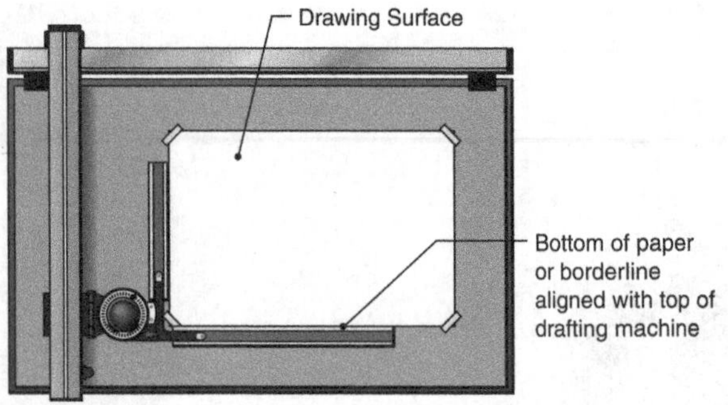

Figure 6.20

Taping paper to the drawing surface

Paper is positioned on the drawing surface by aligning the bottom of the paper to the horizontal blade of the drafting machine, and then taping the paper at the corners.

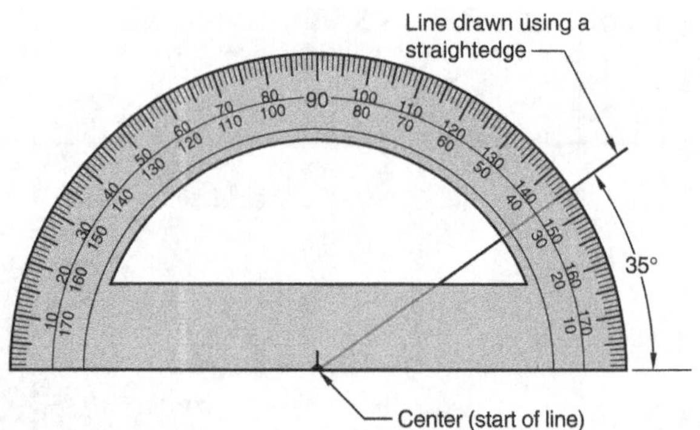

Figure 6.21

Protractor

The protractor is used to measure and mark angles on a technical drawing.

to increase the accuracy and ease of making large-format drawings.

Taping a Drawing Sheet to the Surface

To start a drawing:

Step 1. Align the bottom of the paper or the border line printed on the paper with the top edge of the T-square, parallel edge, or drafting machine (Figure 6.20).

Step 2. Tape the four corners of the paper to the drawing surface using drafting tape.

6.3.2 Protractors

When lines must be drawn at angles different from the 15-degree intervals available using standard triangles, either a protractor, the protractor head of a drafting machine, or an adjustable triangle is required. The **protractor** is a semicircular device whose center is placed at the start point of the line. The angle is then marked (Figure 6.21), and a straightedge is used to create the measured line. The protractor head of a drafting machine serves as a protractor in adjusting the angle for the straightedges (Figure 6.22). The **adjustable triangle** is a special device that can be adjusted to various angles (Figure 6.23).

Using a Protractor to Measure an Angle

Step 1. Place the protractor's center at one end of the line. (See Figure 6.21.)

Figure 6.22

Drafting machine

The protractor head on a drafting machine is used to draw lines at any angle.

(Courtesy of Staedtler, Inc.)

Step 2. Read the angle of the line by viewing where the line passes below a mark on the protractor's semicircular edge.

6.3.3 Pencils

Mechanical pencils are more commonly used in drawing than are wood pencils (Figure 6.24). Mechanical pencils use either drafting leads or thin leads. Drafting leads are thicker and must be sharpened using lead pointers or abrasive paper (Figure 6.25). **Thin-lead pencils** use leads of specific diameters that do not need to be sharpened. These lead diameters closely correspond to ANSI

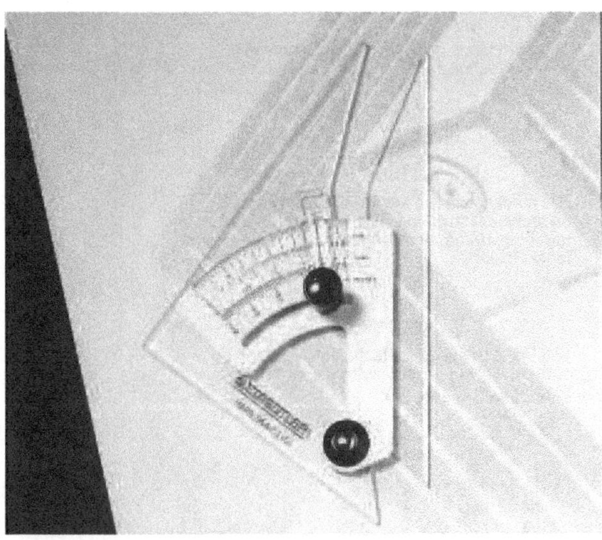

Figure 6.23

Adjustable triangle

The adjustable triangle can be set to a specified angle.

(Courtesy of Staedtler, Inc.)

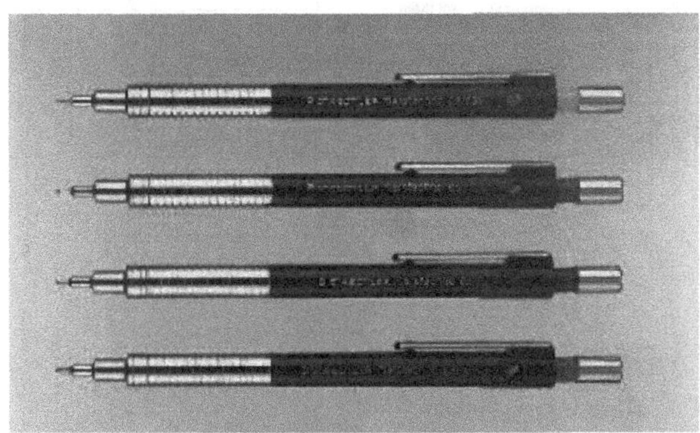

Figure 6.24

Mechanical pencils

Mechanical pencils used for technical drawing come in different lead sizes for drawing the different thicknesses of lines required.

(Courtesy of Staedtler, Inc.)

Figure 6.25

Pencil pointer for mechanical lead pencils

(Courtesy of Staedtler, Inc.)

.3 MM GOOD TECHNIQUE

.3 MM POOR – LINE THICKNESS VARIES

.3 MM POOR – DARKNESS VARIES

.6 MM GOOD TECHNIQUE

Figure 6.26

Line weight

Uniform lines do not vary in thickness or darkness.

standard line thicknesses, such as 0.7 mm or 0.35 mm. A thin-lead pencil can only be used for a single lead diameter; therefore, several thin-lead pencils are required for technical drawings, one for each of the different line thicknesses required.

Wood pencils have to be sharpened, using pencil pointers or abrasive paper, to create the various line thicknesses used in technical drawings. (NOTE: Never sharpen a pencil over a drawing, and always keep the pencil point conical in shape to get good-quality lines.) Hand-drawn lines must be of uniform weight and thickness and must be correctly spaced so they can be legibly reproduced, such as for blueprinting.

Line weight refers to the relative darkness of the line. For example, the line drawn to represent the center of a circle is drawn black using a soft lead. The thickness of the center line is approximately 0.35 mm. Uniform thickness means that the line should not vary (Figure 6.26). Thin-lead pencils are the easiest tool for drawing lines of uniform weight and thickness.

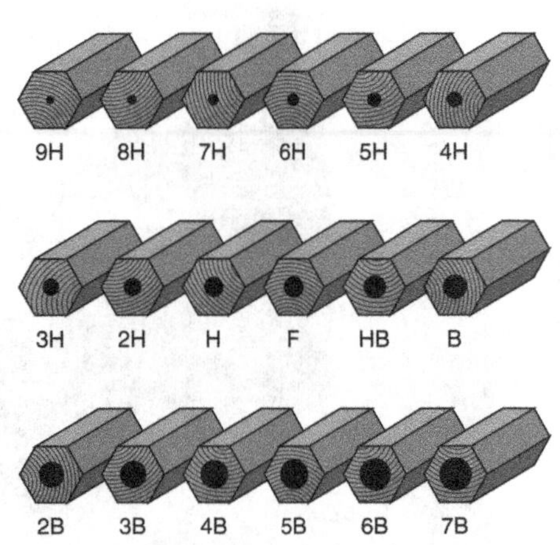

HARD

The hard leads are used for construction lines on technical drawings.

MEDIUM

The medium grades are used for general use on technical drawings. The harder grades are for instrument drawings and the softer for sketching.

SOFT

Soft leads are used for technical sketching and artwork but are too soft for instrument drawings.

Figure 6.27

Pencil grades

Pencils are graded by lead hardness, from 9H to 7B: 9H is the hardest and 7B is the softest.

Mechanical and wood pencil leads are graded to distinguish their hardness (Figure 6.27). Hard grades range from 4H to 9H: the higher the number, the harder the lead. Hard leads are used for construction lines, with 4H being the one used most often. Medium grade leads are 3H, 2H, H, F, HB, and B. These leads are used for general-purpose work, such as visible lines, dimensions, sections, and center lines. The softer grades, such as HB and B, are commonly used for sketching. Soft leads range from 2B to 7B, with the larger number representing a softer grade. This type of lead is not commonly used in engineering or technical drawing but rather for artwork and architectural renderings.

6.3.4 Drawing Paper

Media are the surfaces upon which an engineer or technologist communicates graphical information. The media used for technical drawings are different types or grades of paper, such as tracing paper, vellum, and polyester film. Tracing paper is a thin, translucent paper used for detail drawings. Vellum is a tracing paper chemically treated to improve translucency. Polyester film, or its trade name Mylar, is transparent, waterproof, and difficult to tear. Mylar can be used for lead pencil, plastic-lead pencil, or ink drawings. Mylar is an excellent drawing surface that leaves no trace of erasure.

Special papers have also been developed for CAD plotters. For example, plotter paper used for fiber-tipped pens has a smooth or glossy surface to enhance line definition and minimize skipping. Often, the paper comes with a preprinted border, title block, and parts list (Figure 6.28).

ANSI has established standard sheet sizes and title blocks for the media used for technical drawings. Each paper size is designated by a letter, as shown in Table 6.1, and title block sizes are shown in Figure 6.74 at the end of the chapter.

Custom Printed Engineering & Drafting Decal Appliques

Have the convenience of placing your logo, title blocks, etc., wherever you want them on your drawings or documents. Working from your camera-ready artwork, we can custom print decal appliques that let you position these elements as you see fit. Minimum order: packet of 100 appliques. For information and pricing, please contact the Contract and Bid Department at Alvin & Company headquarters in Connecticut.

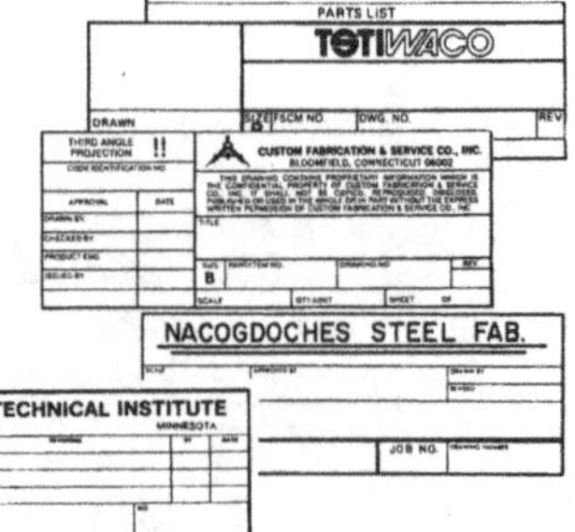

Figure 6.28

Preprinted title blocks

Preprinted standard borders and title blocks on drafting paper are commonly used in industry.

(Courtesy of Alvin & Company, Inc.)

Table 6.1 ANSI Standard Sheet Sizes

Metric (mm)	U.S. Standard	Architectural
A4 210 × 297	A-Size 8.5″ × 11″	9″ × 12″
A3 297 × 420	B-Size 11″ × 17″	12″ × 18″
A2 420 × 594	C-Size 17″ × 22″	18″ × 24″
A1 594 × 841	D-Size 22″ × 34″	24″ × 36″
A0 841 × 1189	E-Size 34″ × 44″	36″ × 48″

Keeping Drawings Clean

Keeping your drawing surface clean is an important part of technical drawing. Drawings become dirty primarily from the graphite from the pencils. To keep a drawing clean, follow these guidelines:

- Never sharpen pencils over your drawing.
- Clean your pencil point with a soft cloth after sharpening.
- Keep your drawing instruments clean.
- Rest your hands on the drawing instruments as much as possible, to avoid smearing the graphite on the drawing.
- When darkening lines, try to work from the top of the drawing to the bottom, and from left to right across the drawing. Work from right to left across the drawing if you are left-handed.
- Use a brush to remove erasure particles. Never use your hands.

6.3.5 Triangles

Vertical and inclined lines are drawn with **triangles** guided by a T-square or a parallel edge. Some triangles are thinner around the perimeter so they can be used for inking. Triangles come standard as 45 degrees and 30 × 60 (30/60) degrees. Triangles come in various sizes, such as 6, 8, and 10 inch, and are made of clear plastic (Figure 6.29). By combining the 30/60-degree triangle and the 45-degree triangle, it is possible to draw angles at 15-degree intervals (Figure 6.30).

6.4 Line Drawing Techniques

Horizontal, vertical, and inclined lines are drawn by hand with traditional tools, such as a straightedge and triangles. If a drafting machine is used, the blades serve as guides for drawing the lines. By adjusting the head of the drafting machine, you can create inclined lines.

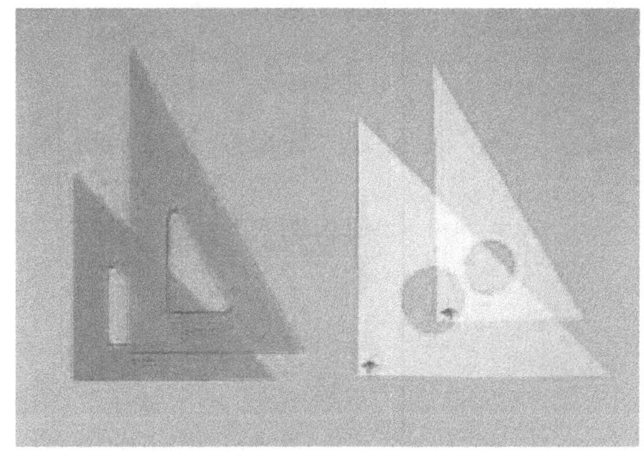

Figure 6.29

Drafting triangles

Drafting triangles are either 30/60- or 45-degree triangles and come in various sizes.

(Courtesy of Alvin & Company, Inc.)

Drawing Horizontal Lines

A horizontal line is drawn using the top edge of the blade of the T-square, drafting machine, or parallel edge.

Step 1. Hold the pencil in your right (or left) hand in a position similar to that used for writing.

Step 2. Hold the straightedge firmly with your left hand as you pull the pencil from left to right across the paper. If you are left-handed, hold the straightedge with your right hand and pull the pencil from right to left.

Step 3. Rest your right (or left) hand lightly on top of the straightedge.

Step 4. Use the top edge of the straightedge as a guide for the pencil, position the pencil at approximately 60 degrees to the paper, and slowly rotate the pencil as the line is being drawn (Figure 6.31).

Horizontal lines are drawn with CAD in a variety of ways. Each endpoint of the line can be defined using X-Y coordinate positions, such as 0,0 for one end and 4,0 for the other, which defines a horizontal line 4 units long. Another method would be to use a rectangular grid and snap to the grid points. (Snapping is a technique used by CAD systems to accurately place endpoints of lines at equally spaced points called a grid.)

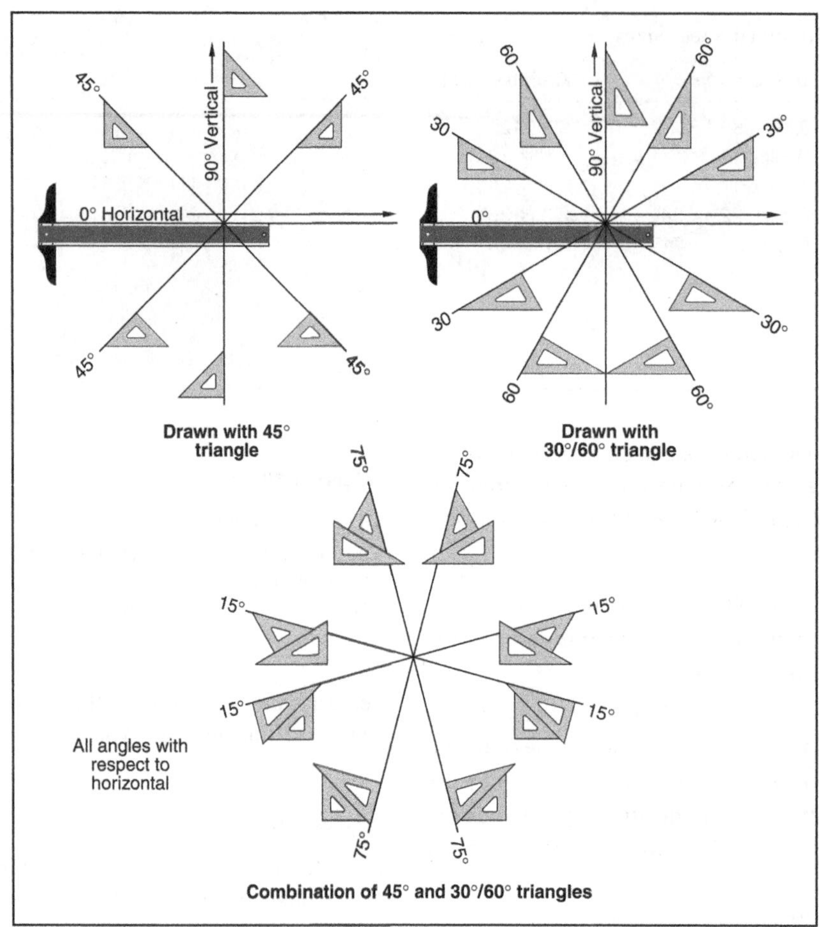

Figure 6.30

By combining the straightedge with the 45- and 30/60-degree triangles, you can draw lines at any 15-degree increment.

Drawing Vertical Lines

Step 1. Draw a vertical line by placing one edge of either the 45- or 30/60-degree triangle on the top edge of the straightedge. The vertical blade of the drafting machine could also be used.

Step 2. Rest the right hand on the bottom of the triangle (Figure 6.32). Hold both the triangle and straightedge in position with the left hand.

Step 3. With the right hand, pull the pencil from the bottom to the top of the paper, holding the pencil at an angle of 60 degrees to the paper and slowly rotating the pencil as you draw. Left-handers hold the triangle with the right hand and draw with the left.

Vertical lines are drawn with CAD using procedures similar to those for drawing horizontal lines. Coordinate endpoints could be specified, such as 0,0 for one end and 0,4 for the other, making a vertical line 4 units long. The rectangular snap and grid could also be used to create vertical lines.

Drawing Inclined Lines

The 45- and 30/60-degree triangles can be combined or used separately, along with a straightedge, to draw lines at 15-degree intervals, as shown in Figure 6.30. Lines at other than 15-degree intervals are drawn using either the protractor head on a drafting machine (Figure 6.33), a hand-held protractor, or an adjustable triangle.

Step 1. Mark the desired angle using the protractor, as described earlier. If the angle to be drawn is at any

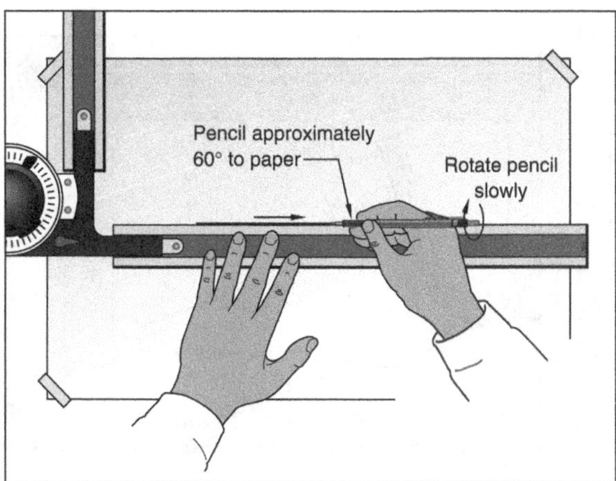

Figure 6.31

Drawing a horizontal line

A horizontal line is drawn by holding the pencil at a 60-degree angle to the paper and rotating the pencil as it is pulled across the paper. The blade of the drafting machine is used as a guide for the pencil point as it is pulled across the paper. By applying even pressure and slowly rotating the pencil, you can produce lines of uniform weight and thickness.

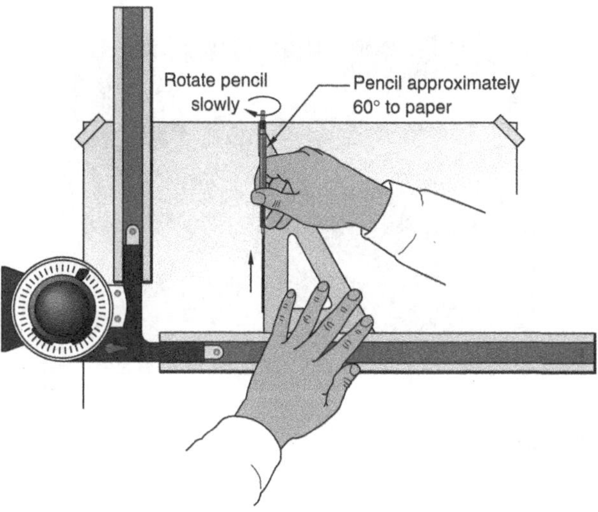

Figure 6.32

Drawing vertical lines

Vertical lines are drawn by pulling the pencil along the edge of a triangle or the vertical blade of the drafting machine, slowly rotating the pencil as it is pulled.

15-degree increment, triangles can be used as the guide, as shown in Figure 6.30.

Step 2. Align the triangle with the marks for the line to be drawn.

Step 3. Use the edge of the triangle as a guide to draw the inclined line.

Inclined lines are created with CAD by using rectangular or polar coordinates. For example, the first endpoint for the line could be located at 0,0, and the second point could be defined by giving the length and the angle relative to the first point, such as 4 units long and 45 degrees. This would result in an inclined line.

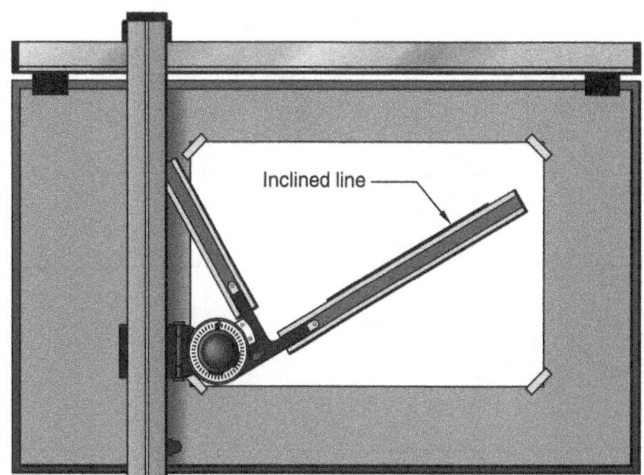

Figure 6.33

Drawing inclined lines

Drawing inclined lines using a drafting machine requires setting the protractor head to the desired angle and locking the head in place. The pencil is then pulled along the blade at a 60-degree angle to the paper and is slowly rotated as it is pulled.

6.4.1 Erasing

Lines are erased using a soft eraser, or the ERASE command when using CAD. To erase in small areas, or protect areas not to be erased, use an erasing shield (Figure 6.34). An **erasing shield** is a thin piece of metal with various sizes and shapes of holes cut in it. The part of the drawing to be erased is exposed through a hole in the erasing shield and the surrounding area is shielded. A CAD system uses a TRIM command, which has a function similar to that of an erasing shield.

6.4.2 Drawing a Line through Two Points

A line is drawn through two points by aligning one side of a straightedge with the two points, then connecting them with a line (Figure 6.35). With CAD, a line is drawn

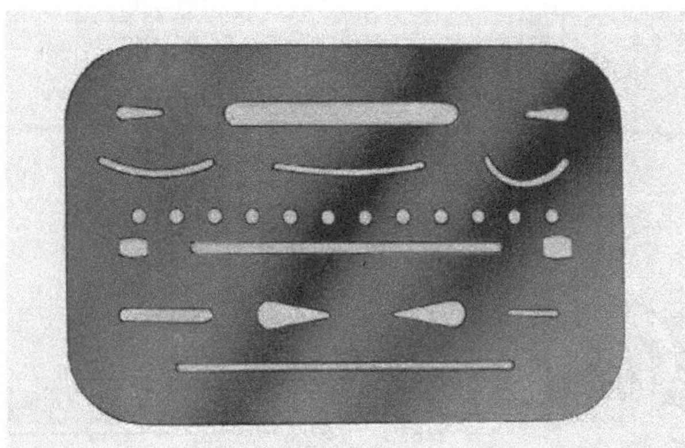

Figure 6.34

Erasing shield

An erasing shield is used to erase parts of a drawing. The part of the drawing to be erased is exposed to an open area in the shield. Areas of the drawing that are not to be erased are protected by the shield.

(Courtesy of Alvin & Company, Inc.)

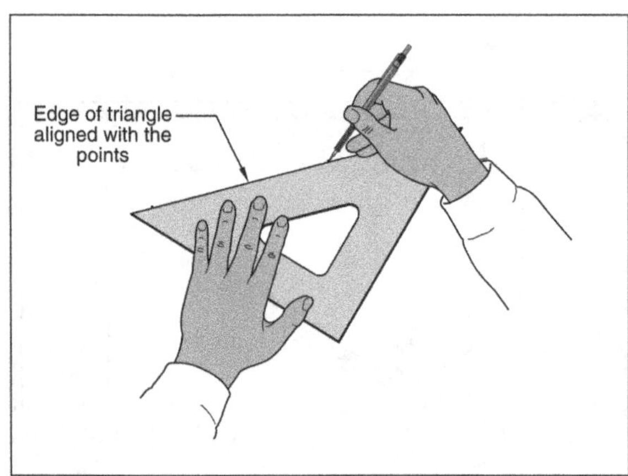

Figure 6.35

Drawing a line through two points

To draw a line through two points, align the edge of a triangle to the two points and then pull the pencil along the edge of the triangle.

through two points by "picking" each endpoint. Normally an existing point is picked using some type of "snap" command. For example, if the two points that must be picked are the endpoints of existing lines, then the SNAP command must be set to "endpoints." The CAD software will then accurately connect the endpoints of the new line.

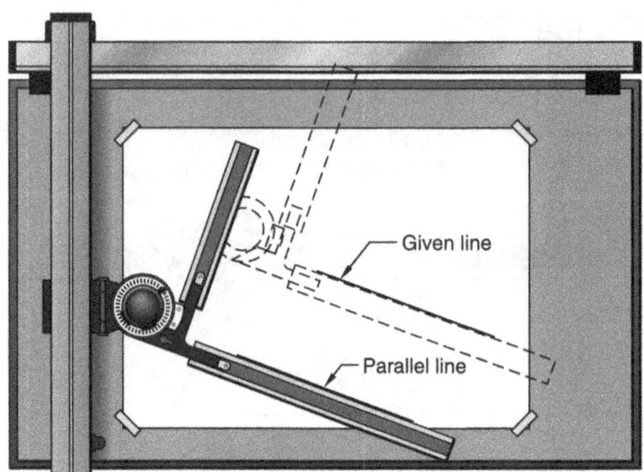

Figure 6.36

Drawing parallel lines

To draw a line parallel to a given line using a drafting machine, align one blade with the given line by adjusting the protractor head and locking it in place. Then move the drafting machine to the new position and draw the line along the parallel blade.

A CAD system provides the user with many options for picking existing entities, such as midpoints, centers, and intersections. Snapping to existing entities is an important CAD technique used to assure the accuracy of drawings and models.

6.4.3 Drawing Parallel Lines

The procedure to follow when drawing a line parallel to a given line varies depending on the tools being used.

Drawing Parallel Lines

Drafting machine

Step 1. If using a drafting machine, adjust the protractor head to align one blade or straightedge with the given line.

Step 2. Lock the protractor head, then move the drafting machine to the new position and draw the parallel line (Figure 6.36).

Two triangles

Step 1. If using two triangles, adjust the two triangles until one edge of one triangle is aligned with the given line, while the other triangle serves as a straightedge and is held stationary.

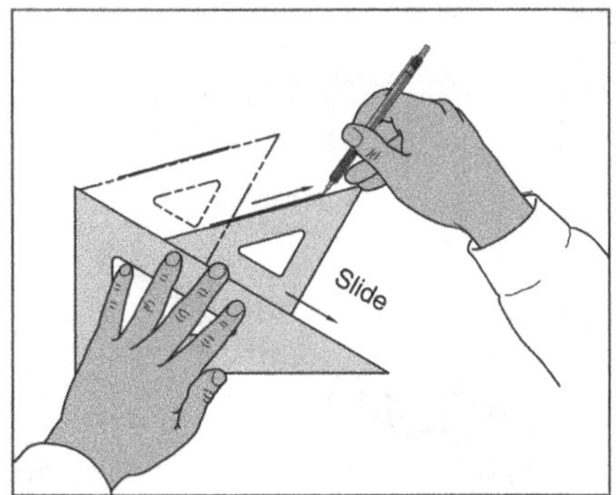

Figure 6.37

Drawing parallel lines using triangles

To use two triangles to draw parallel lines, set up one of the triangles so that one edge aligns along the given line. Use the other triangle as a guide or base for the first triangle. Hold the base triangle stationary and slide the other triangle along the edge of the base triangle to the new position, where the line is drawn.

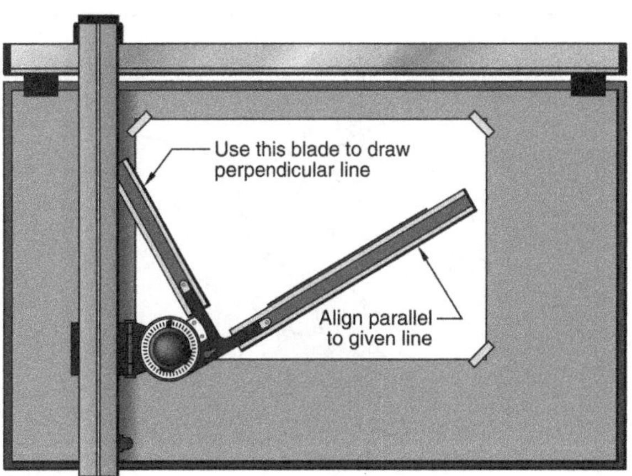

Figure 6.38

Drawing perpendicular lines

To draw a line perpendicular to a given line using a drafting machine, align one blade with the given line by adjusting the protractor head, and then lock the head in place. Move the drafting machine head to the new position and draw the line along the perpendicular blade.

Step 2. Slide the aligned triangle along the edge of the stationary triangle.

Step 3. After the moving triangle is in the new position, draw the line along the same edge that was aligned with the given line (Figure 6.37).

Adjustable triangle

Step 1. Adjust one edge of the triangle to align with the given line.

Step 2. Then move the triangle along the straightedge.

With CAD, there are a number of techniques used to create parallel lines. For example, there may be a PARALLEL command that will automatically draw lines parallel to a given line. The given line is picked, then a point is selected where the parallel line is drawn.

6.4.4 Drawing Perpendicular Lines

A line is drawn perpendicular to another line using two triangles, a triangle and a straightedge, or a drafting machine. The drafting machine is used to draw a line perpendicular to a given line by aligning one blade with the given line, then using the other blade as a guide to draw the perpendicular line. The adjustable protractor head is used to align the first blade (Figure 6.38).

Drawing Perpendicular Lines

Step 1. If two triangles are used, align the edge of one of the triangles with the given line. Do not use the hypotenuse (long edge) of the triangle. Use the other triangle as a straightedge and hold it stationary (Figure 6.39).

Step 2. Slide the aligned triangle along the edge of the stationary triangle.

Step 3. After the moving triangle is in the new position, draw the line, using its perpendicular edge.

With CAD, drawing a line perpendicular to a given line is done using a PERPENDICULAR command or snap option. The endpoint of the new line is picked, then the existing line is selected. The new line is automatically drawn from the picked endpoint perpendicular to the picked line.

6.4.5 Drawing Lines at Angles Relative to a Given Line

A drafting machine, a protractor and straightedge, or triangles are used to draw lines at an angle to a given line. The protractor head of the drafting machine is adjusted to align with the given line, making that position the zero setting (Figure 6.40). The protractor head is then adjusted to the desired angle and the line is drawn.

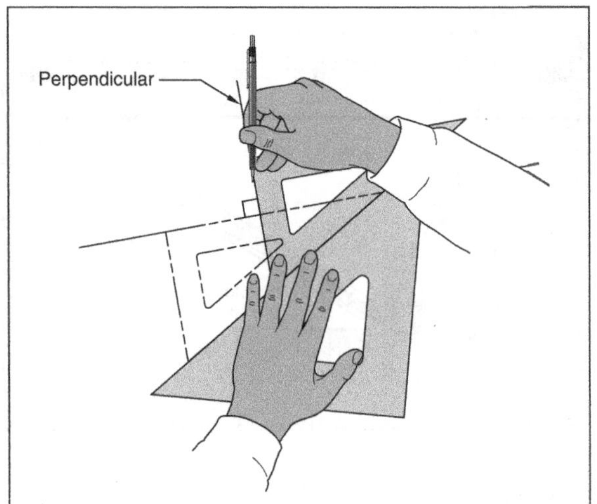

Figure 6.39

Drawing perpendicular lines using two triangles

To use two triangles to draw perpendicular lines, align one of the triangles so that one edge (not the hypotenuse) is parallel to the given line. Use the other triangle as a guide or base. Hold the base triangle stationary and slide the other triangle along the edge of the base triangle to the new position; draw the line using the perpendicular edge of the triangle that was moved.

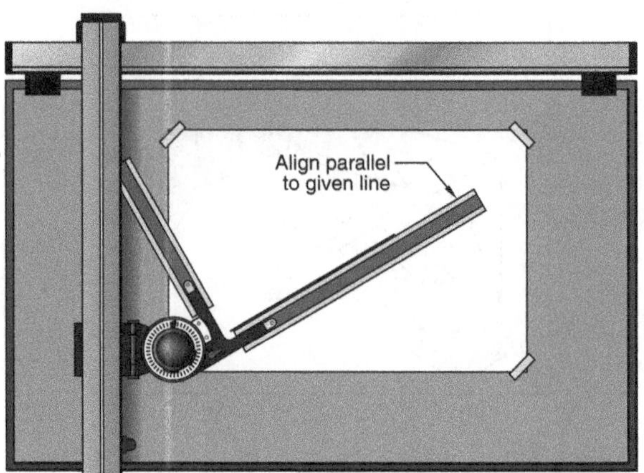

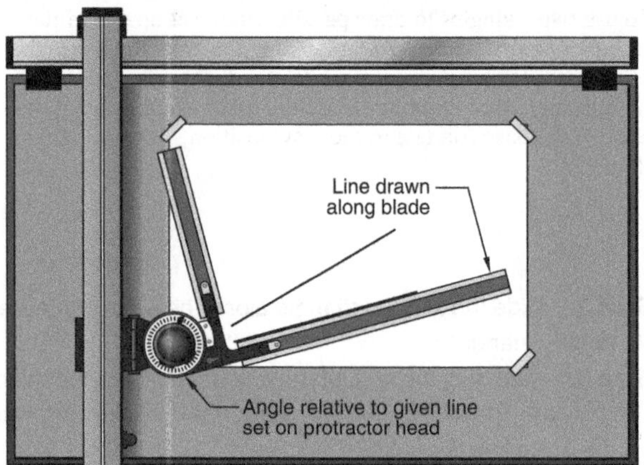

Figure 6.40

Drawing a line at an angle

To draw a line at an angle to a given line using a drafting machine, align one blade with the given line by adjusting the protractor head, and then read its angle. Adjust the drafting machine head to the new angle, lock it in place, and then draw the line along the blade.

Drawing a Line at a Given Angle

Figure 6.41 shows how two triangles, one of which is a 30/60-degree triangle, can be used to create a line at 30 degrees to a given line.

Step 1. Using one triangle as a straightedge, slide the 30/60-degree triangle into position so that the leg adjacent to the 30-degree angle is parallel with the given line.

Step 2. Hold the triangle used as a straightedge stationary, slide the 30/60-degree triangle to the new position, and draw the new line.

With CAD, a line can be drawn at an angle to a given line by using polar coordinate inputs, or rotating the snap and grid to align with the given line.

6.4.6 Drawing Irregular Curves

Irregular or **French curves** are used to draw curves which are not circles or arcs, examples of which are parabolas, hyperbolas, ellipses, and involutes (Figure 6.42). To draw long, irregular curves, a long, flexible device called a **spline** is used (Figure 6.43). A CAD system can draw an irregular curve by using the SPLINE command.

Drawing an Irregular Curve

Step 1. A series of points is used to locate the curve (Figure 6.44).

Step 2. For best results, sketch a curve through the points.

Step 3. Align the irregular curve with only two or three points, then draw the curve only through these points. The curve segment drawn through the last of these points should be aimed in the general direction of the next point.

Step 4. Adjust the irregular curve to go through the next two or three points.

Step 5. Repeat these steps to complete the curve.

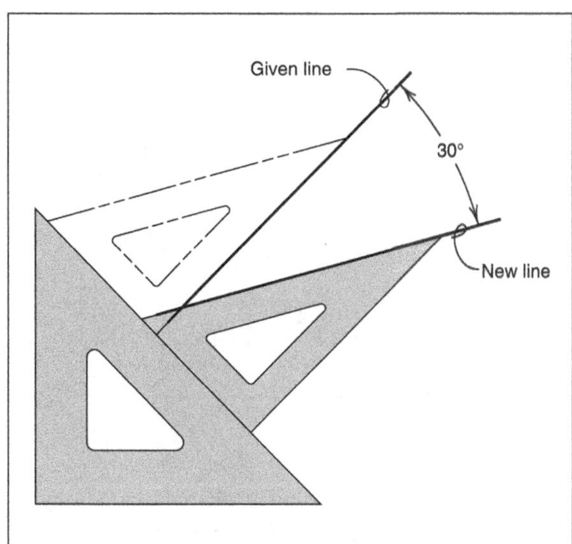

Figure 6.41

Drawing a line at an angle using two triangles

Two triangles can be used to draw a line at an angle to a given line by using one triangle as a guide or base and aligning the other triangle so that one edge is parallel to the given line. Hold the base triangle stationary and slide the other triangle along the edge of the base triangle to the new position, where the line is drawn.

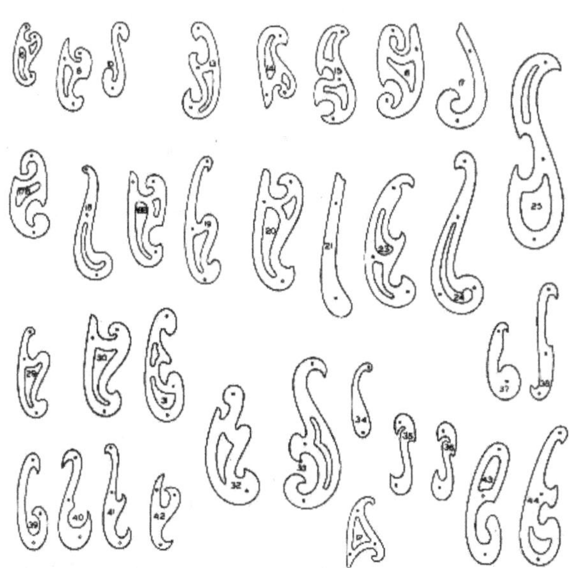

Figure 6.42

Irregular curves

Irregular or French curves come in many shapes and sizes and are used to draw irregular curves.

(Courtesy of Alvin & Company, Inc.)

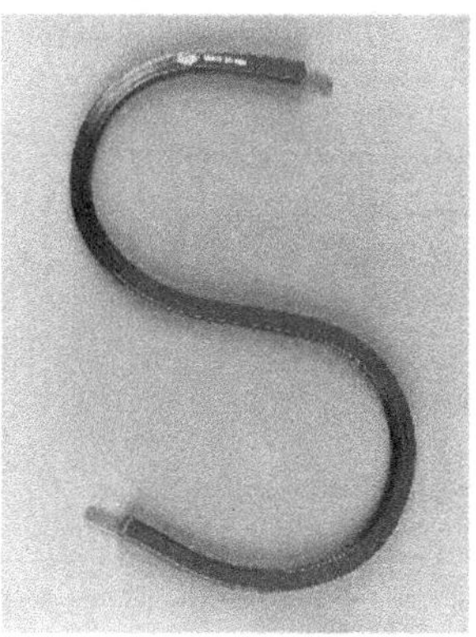

Figure 6.43

Spline

A spline is a flexible device used to draw long, irregular curves through a series of points.

(Courtesy of Alvin & Company, Inc.)

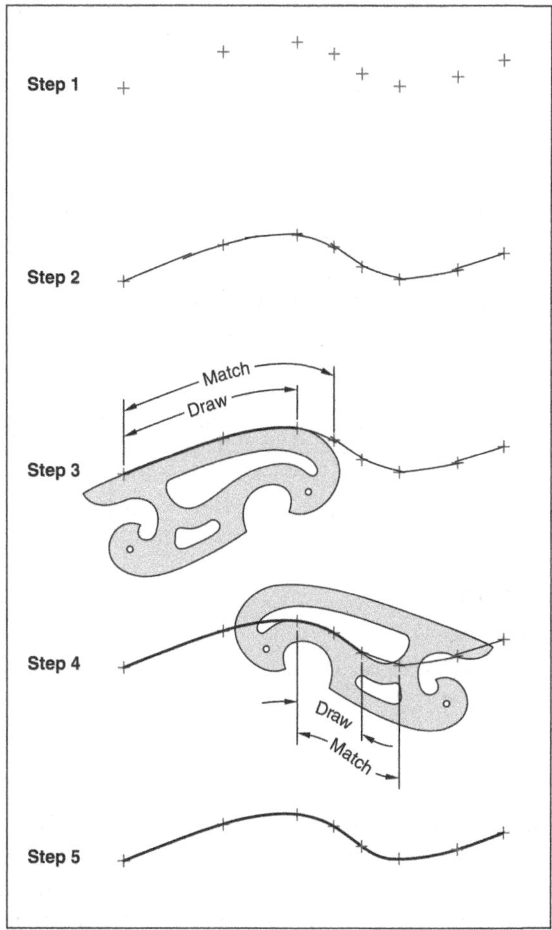

Figure 6.44

Steps in drawing an irregular curve through a series of points

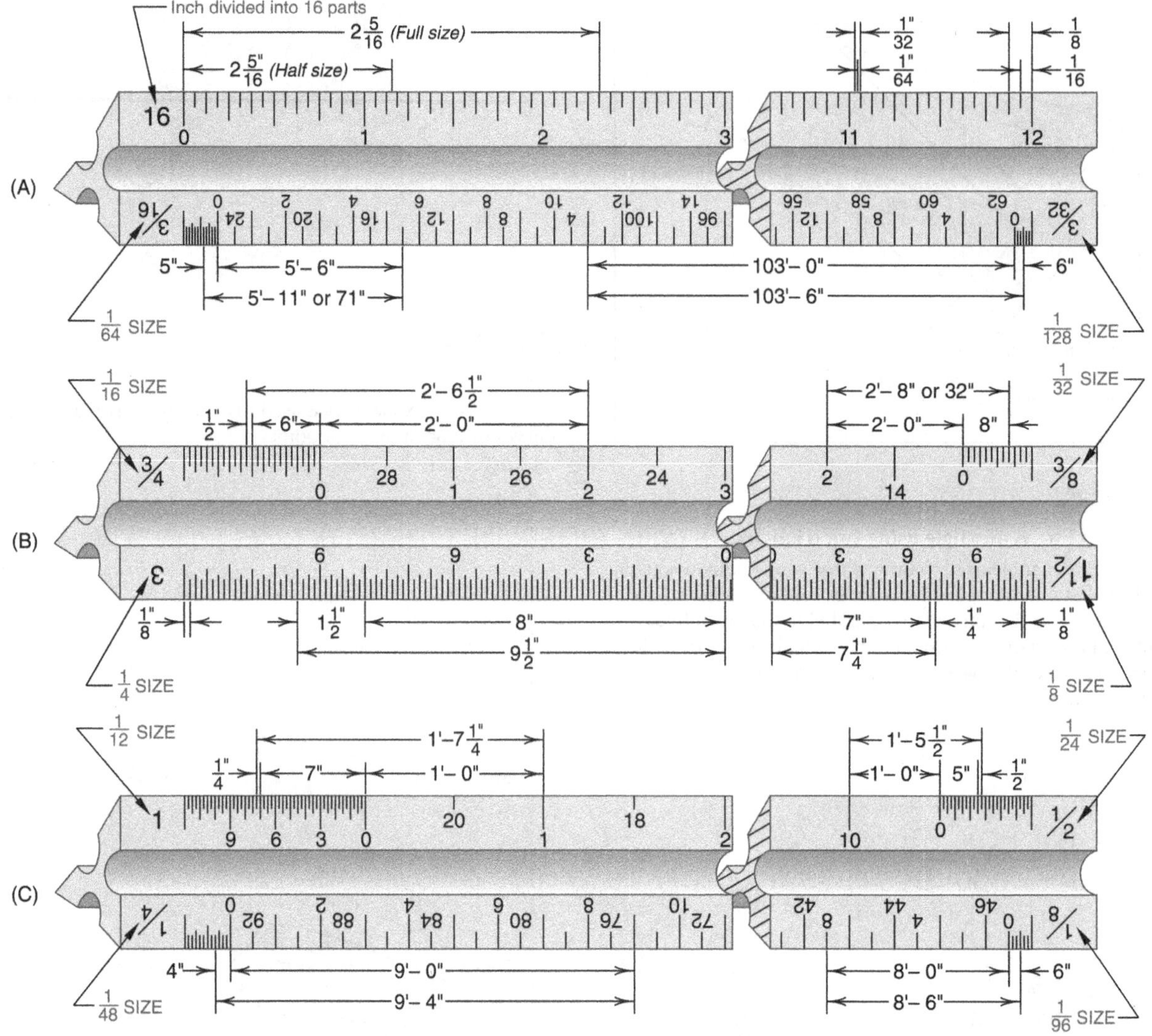

Figure 6.45

Architect's scale

The architect's scale has 11 scales with which to measure distances accurately on architectural drawings.

6.5 Scales

Scales are used to measure distances on technical drawings. Scales are usually 6 or 12 inches long and are made of wood, plastic, or metal. Triangular scales are commonly used in technical drawing because they offer the user a combination of several scales on each side (Figure 6.45). The most common types of scales used in technical drawing are mechanical engineer's, civil engineer's, metric, and architectural scales. A **combination scale** is one that has engineering, metric, and architectural components on a single scale.

The scale chosen to create the drawing must be marked clearly in the title block. For example, a drawing that is done full size is labeled as FULL SIZE, or as a ratio of 1:1. A half-size drawing is marked as HALF SIZE, or 1:2. Other reduced scales are 1:4 (quarter size), 1:8 (eighth size), 1:16 (sixteenth size), and so on. Enlarged scales are 2:1 (double size), 3:1, 4:1, 10:1, 100:1, and so on. When

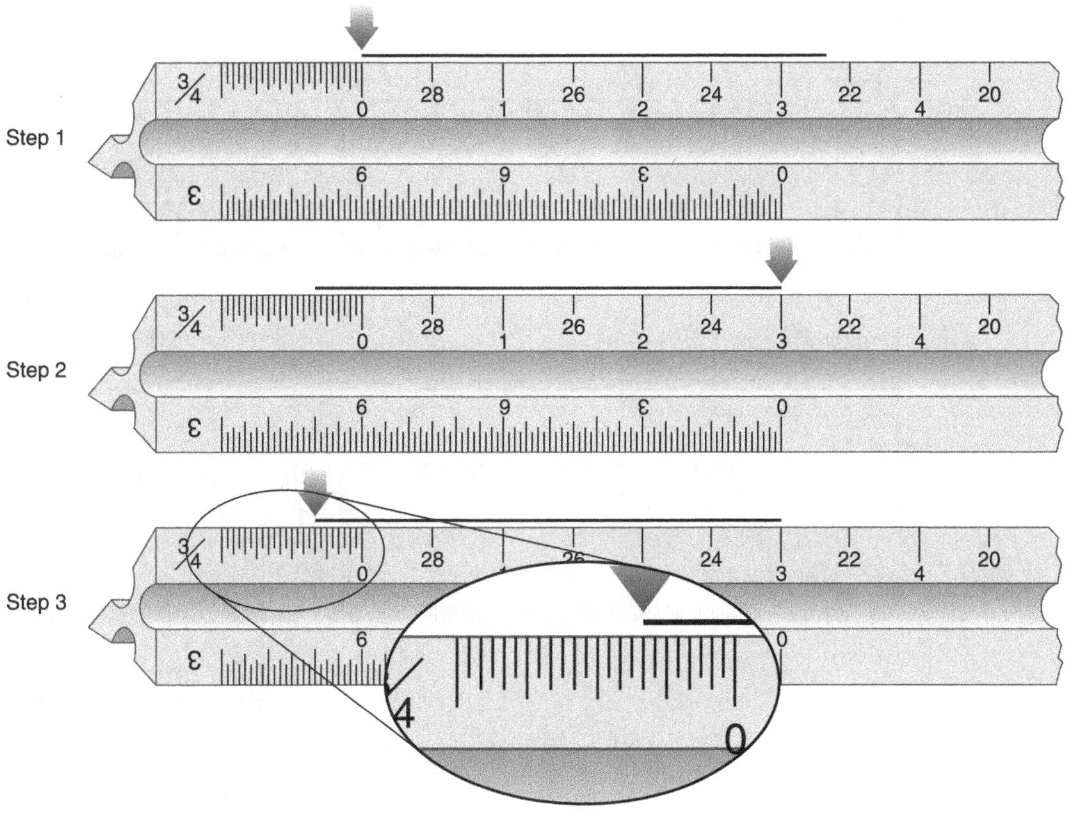

Figure 6.46

Steps in reading an architect's scale

a metric drawing is created, the word METRIC or SI is prominently marked on the drawing.

Normally, CAD drawings are created full size. Only the plotted drawing is scaled to fit the paper. When starting a CAD drawing, set the units desired and draw full size. When ready to choose the paper size, determine the longest horizontal and vertical dimensions on the drawing, then calculate the size paper needed to place the full-size drawing on the sheet. For plots, decide the size of the paper to be used, and then calculate the plotting scale that will make the drawing fit the sheet.

6.5.1 Architect's Scale

An **architect's scale** is used to create drawings of structures, such as a building or a factory floor layout. Because architects work in feet and inches, each scale is divided into a section for feet and a subsection for inches, and it is called an open divided scale. The scale is used by first finding the distance in feet and then adding the number of inches (Figure 6.46). The combination architect's scale has 11 different scales. Some sides have more than one scale superimposed on each other. Notice in Figure 6.45C that the ¼ and ⅛ scales are on the same side; the ¼ scale is read from the left, and the ⅛ scale is read from the right.

Reading an Architect's Scale

For this example, use the ¾″ per foot scale (Figure 6.46). This scale has a ¾ marked at the end. The feet are read to the right of the zero mark. Fractions of a foot are measured to the left of zero. The large numbers (28, 26, 24 . . .) near the left end of the scale represent two things: (1) the number of feet for the 3/8 scale, which starts from the right end, and (2) the 6″ marks for the ¾ scale.

Step 1. Align the zero mark on the scale with the start point of the line to be measured.

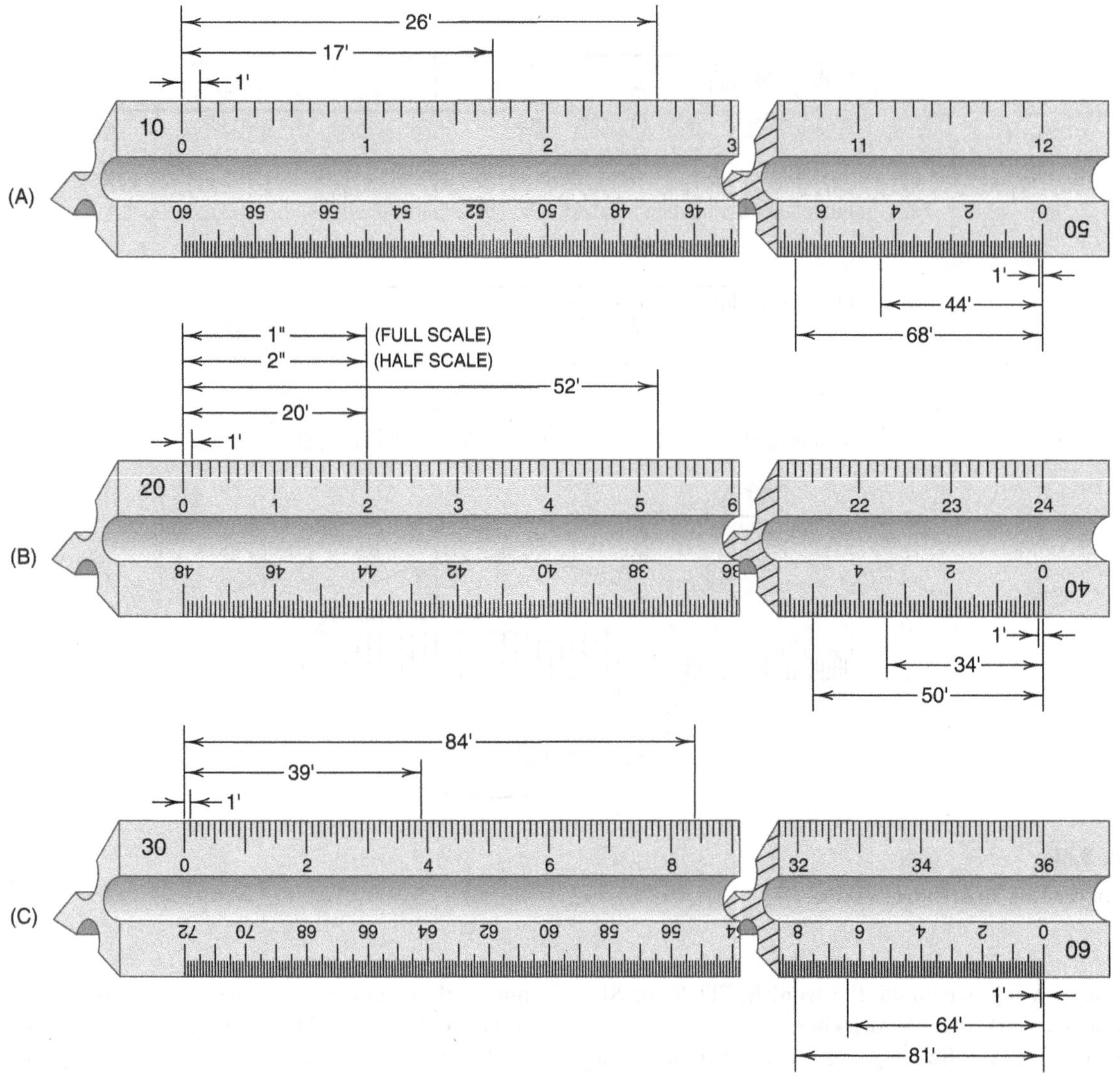

Figure 6.47

The civil engineer's scale

Step 2. Adjust the scale so that the other end of the line is aligned with the smaller of the two foot mark values, which for this example is 3.

Step 3. The fractions of a foot are read to the left of the zero mark. To determine how many parts a foot has been divided into on this scale, count the number of both short and long marks to the left of zero. For this scale, there are 24 marks to the left of zero, meaning that a foot is divided into 24 equal parts, each equal to ½″. The longer marks represent inches. Determine which mark to the left of zero aligns closest to the left end of the line. For this example, the closest mark is the 8, which is read as 4″. So the line is measured as 3′ 4″.

6.5.2 Civil Engineer's Scale

The **civil engineer's scale** is a decimal scale divided into multiple units of 10, and it is called a fully divided scale (Figure 6.47). This scale is commonly used to draw large structures and maps, where one inch on the map or drawing represents some number of feet or miles. Each end of the scale is labeled 10, 20, 30, 40, 50, or 60, which specifies the number of units per inch. For example, the 30 scale has 30 units per inch. Many different scales can be created by simply moving the decimal place, as follows:

10 scale: 1=10′, 1=100′, 1=1000′

The 20, 30, 40, 50, and 60 scales work in a similar manner (Figure 6.48).

The 10 scale is often used in mechanical drafting as a full decimal inch scale where each division equals 1/10″.

Reading a Civil Engineer's Scale

For this example, the 20 scale is used (Figure 6.49). The 20 scale has twenty marks per inch; therefore, each mark equals 1/20 of an inch if the scale is used full size. However, the scale can also be conveniently used for half-size scale and others.

Step 1. Align the zero mark on the 20 scale with the left end of the line to be measured.

Step 2. Determine the closest mark on the 20 scale that corresponds to the right end of the line. For this example, assume a line that ends at the fourth mark past the number 2 on the scale. If this were a full-scale drawing, the length of the line would be 24/20 or 1.2″. On a half-scale drawing, the line would be 2.4″. If the scale were 1 inch equals 20 feet (1″=20′), then the line would be read as 24″.

6.5.3 Mechanical Engineer's Scale

The **mechanical engineer's scale** is used to draw mechanical parts and is either fractionally divided into 1/16 or 1/32, or decimally divided into 0.1 or 0.02

CIVIL ENGINEER'S SCALE

Divisions	Ratio	Scales Used with This Division			
10	1:1	1" = 1"	1" = 1'	1" = 10'	1" = 100'
20	1:2	1" = 2"		1" = 20'	1" = 200'
30	1:3	1" = 3"		1" = 30'	1" = 300'
40	1:4	1" = 4"		1" = 40'	1" = 400'
50	1:5	1" = 5"		1" = 50'	1" = 500'
60	1:6	1" = 6"		1" = 60'	1" = 600'

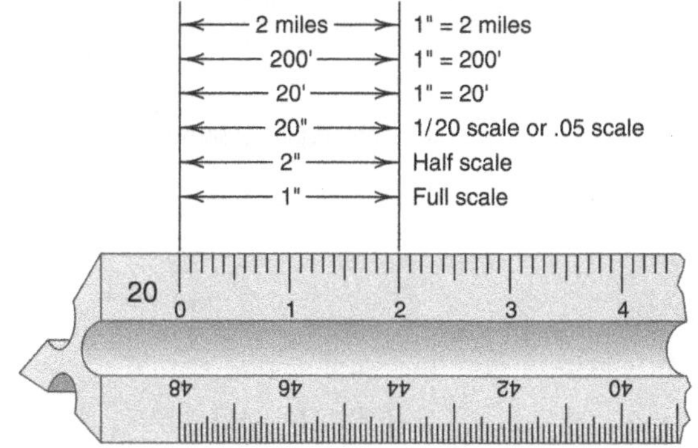

Figure 6.48

How a civil engineer's scale is used

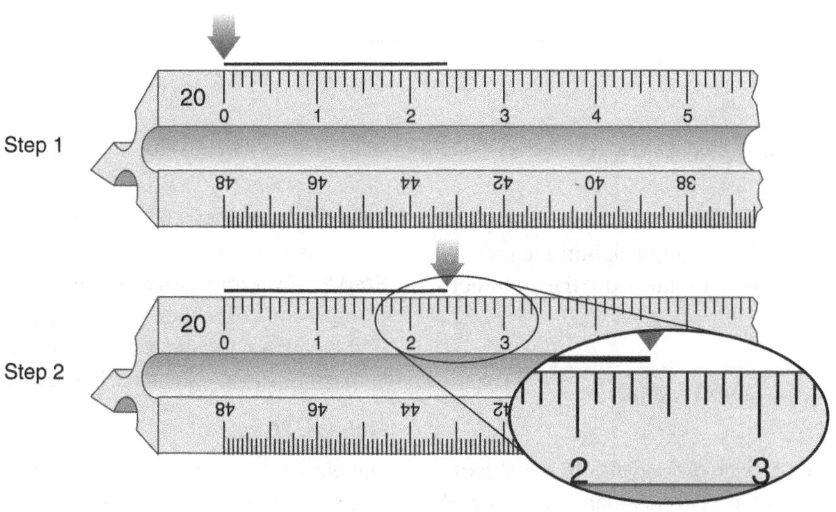

Figure 6.49

Steps in reading a civil engineer's scale

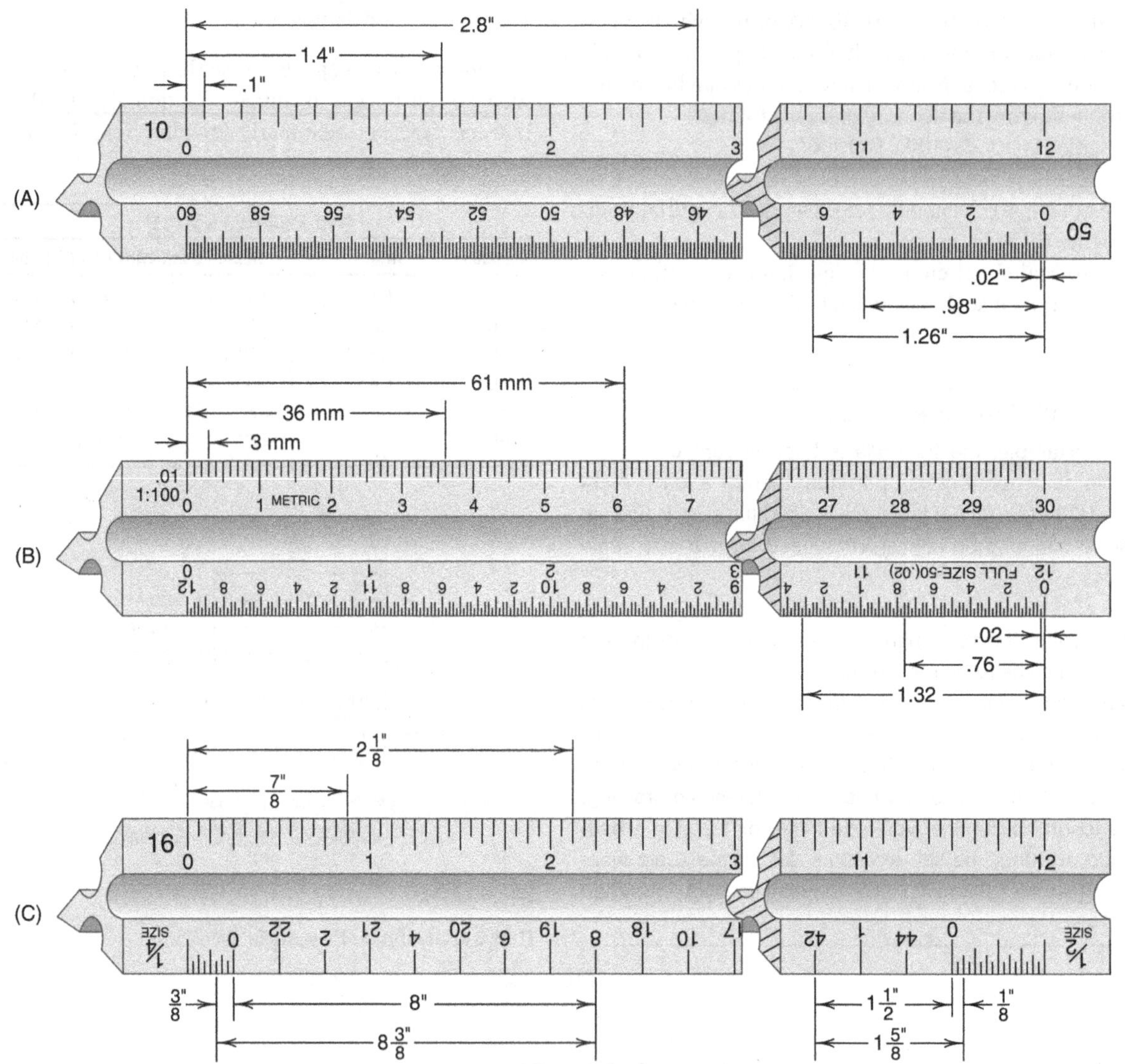

Figure 6.50

The combination mechanical engineer's scale

(Figure 6.50). Typically, the other sides of the scale are half size (½″=1″), quarter size (¼″=1″), and eighth size (⅛″=1″) (Figure 6.50). For scales smaller than ⅛, use the architect's scale.

Reading a Mechanical Engineer's Scale

Full-size 16 scale

The 16 scale represents an inch divided into 16 equal parts; therefore, each mark is 1/16″ every other mark is 2/16″ or ⅛″, every fourth mark is 4/16″ or ¼″, and every eighth mark is 8/16″ or ½″ (Figure 6.51).

Step 1. To measure a line, align the zero mark with the left end of the line.

Step 2. Determine which point on the scale is closest to the right end of the line. For this example, assume a line for which the right end is aligned exactly with the ninth mark past 1″. The length of this line is read as 1–9/16″.

Full-size 50 scale

The 50 scale is commonly used for full-size mechanical engineering drawings because it provides two-decimal-place accuracy (Figure 6.52). The ANSI standard calls for such accuracy on all nontoleranced dimensions, making the

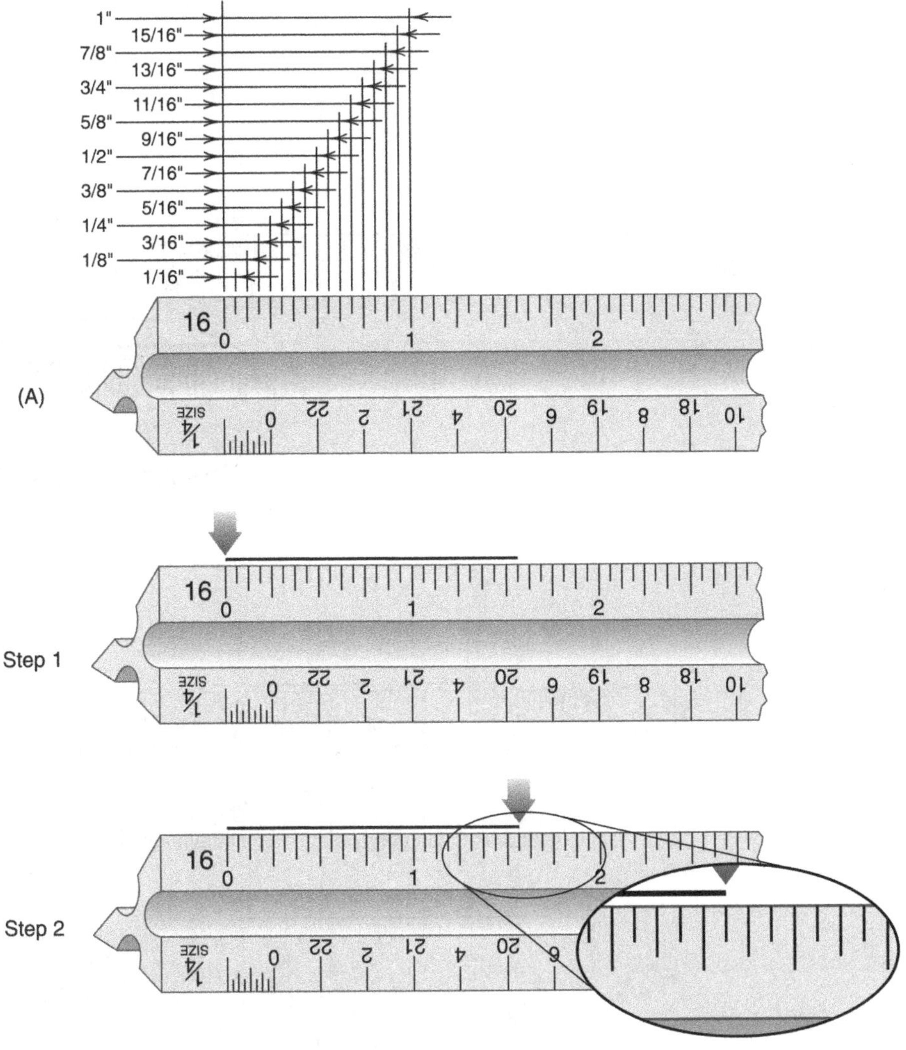

Figure 6.51

Steps in reading the mechanical engineer's scale

50 scale the logical choice. The 50 scale divides an inch into 50 parts, meaning each mark equals 1/50 or 0.02". The numbers between the longest marks on the scale, such as 2, mean 20/50.

Step 1. To measure a line, align the zero mark with the left end of the line.

Step 2. Determine which point on the scale is closest to the right end of the line. For this example, assume a line for which the right end is aligned three marks to the left of the small number 12.

Step 3. The length of the line is read as 2.46".

Half-size scale

The half-size scale is labeled ½ at the end. To the right of zero, each mark represents a full inch; to the left of zero, there is only one inch and it is marked off in fractions (Figure 6.53). There are 16 marks in the inch to the left of zero, which means that each mark represents 1/16". The longer marks represent ⅛", ¼", and ½" increments.

Step 1. To measure a line, position the scale such that the left end of the line is to the left of zero and is within the inch that is marked off. (The exact position is not critical in this step.)

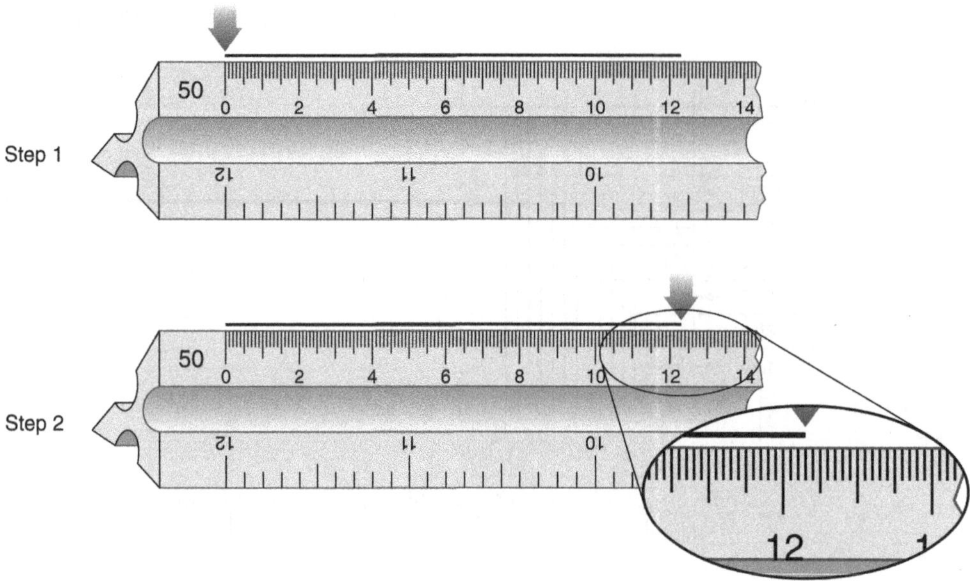

Figure 6.52

Reading a 50 scale

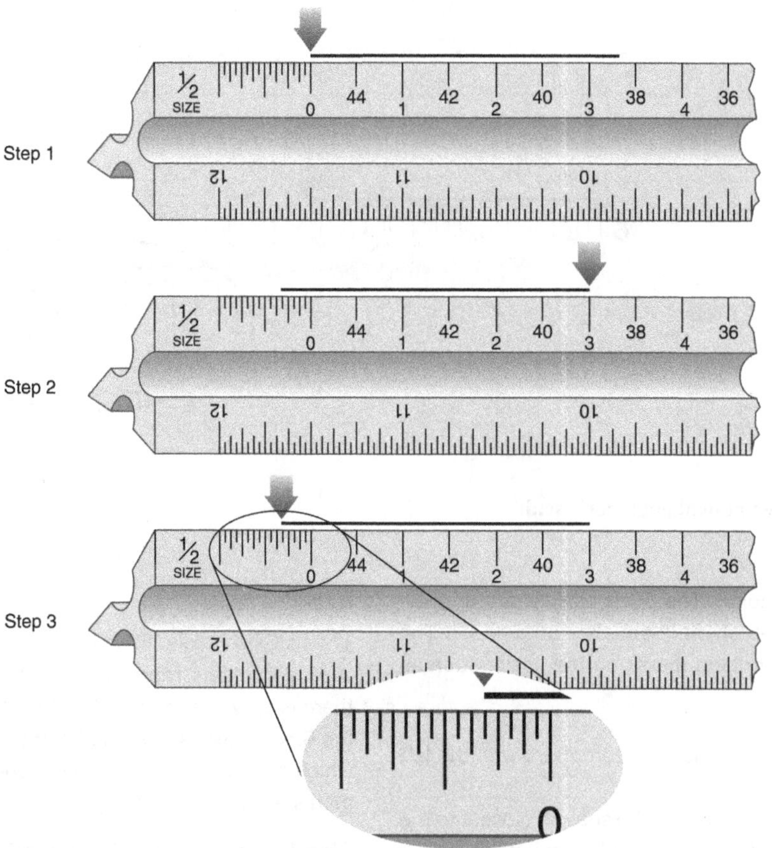

Figure 6.53

Reading a half-size scale

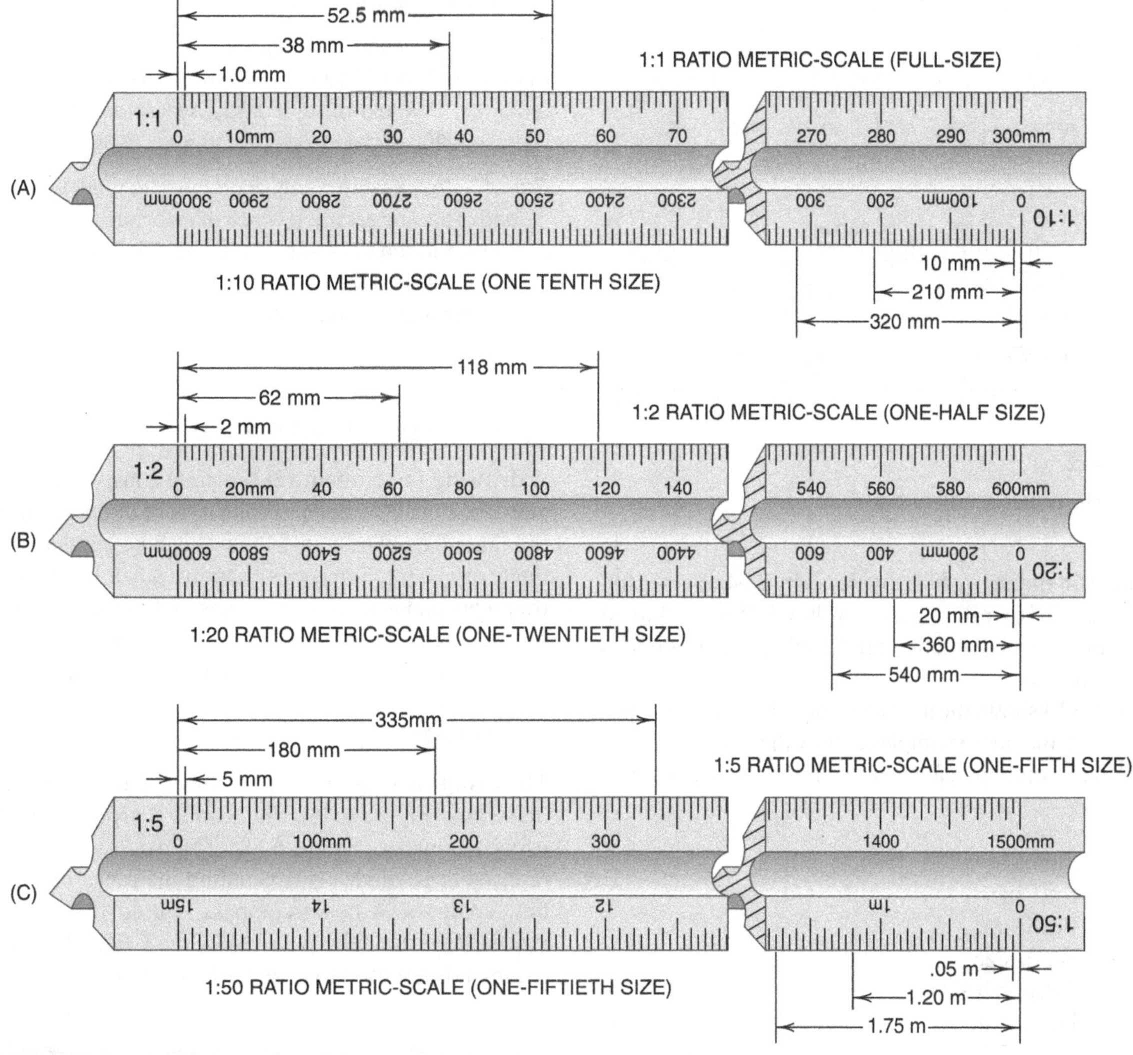

Figure 6.54

The metric scale for using SI units

Step 2. While making sure that the left end of the line stays within the marked-off inch to the left of zero, adjust the scale so that the right end of the line is exactly aligned with the closest full inch mark to the right of zero.

Step 3. Read the full inch mark first; then read the mark to the left of zero that most closely aligns with the left end of the line. As an example, assume a line that is between 3″ and 4″ long. The right end of that line would be at the 3″ mark to the right of zero. The left end of the line would be at one of the marks to the left of zero, such as the fifth mark, which would be 5/16″. The sample line, then, would measure 3–5/16″.

6.5.4 Metric Scale

The international organization that established the metric standard is the **International Standards Organization (ISO)**. The system is called the **International System of Units**, or Systeme Internationale, abbreviated **SI**. The **metric scale** is used to create scaled technical drawings using SI units (Figure 6.54), for which the millimeter (mm), meter (m), and kilometer (km) are the most common units of measure. The meter is the base unit, with the millimeter equal to 1/1000 of a meter and the kilometer equal to 1000 meters. The conversion factor between millimeters and inches is the ratio 1″=25.4 mm. For example,

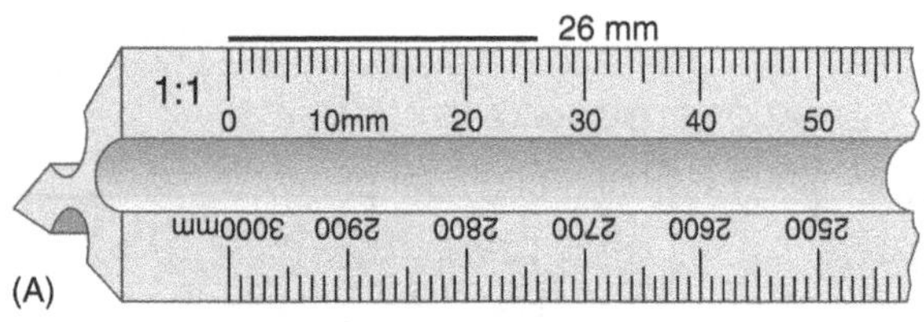

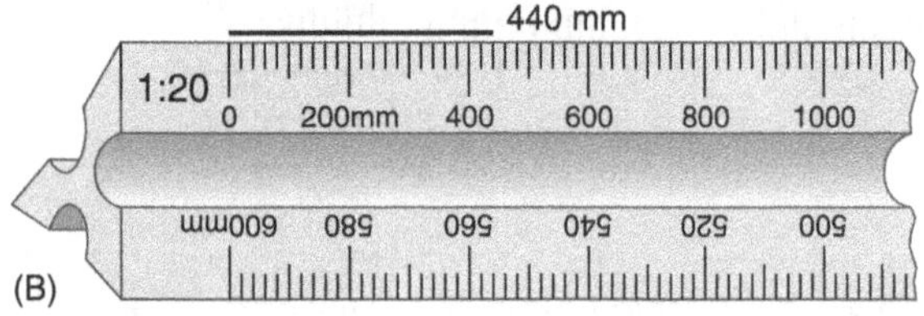

Figure 6.55

Reading the full and 1:20 metric scale

to change 68 mm to inches, divide 68 by 25.4 to get 2.68″. To change 3.75″ to millimeters, multiply 3.75 by 25.4 to get 95.25 mm. Conversion tables are found on the inside back cover of this text.

Figure 6.54 shows the different sides of a triangular metric scale and includes examples of how they are read. Each side of the triangular scale has a different metric scale, as follows:

1:1	Full size
1:2	Half size
1:5	Fifth size
1:10	Tenth size
1:20	Twentieth size
1:50	Fiftieth size

These ratios can be reduced or enlarged by multiplying or dividing by a factor of 10. For example, the 1:20 scale can be reduced to a 1:200 scale by multiplying by 10.

Reading a Metric Scale

Full-size 1:1 ratio

On the 1:1 metric scale, each mark represents 1 mm and every tenth mark represents 10 mm, or 1 cm (Figure 6.55A).

Step 1. To measure a line, align the zero mark with the left end of the line and read the mark on the scale aligned closest to the right end of the line. For this example, assume a line for which the right end is closest to the sixth mark past the number 20. The length of this line would be read as 26 mm, or 2.6 cm.

Twentieth-size 1:20 ratio

For this scale, each mark represents 20 mm and every tenth mark is 200 mm (Figure 6.55B). Multiplying this scale by a factor of 10 would make it 1:200, where each mark would represent 200 mm and every tenth mark 2000 mm.

Step 1. To measure a line, align the zero mark with the left end of the line and read which mark on the scale is aligned closest to the right end of the line. For this example, assume a line for which the right end is closest to the second mark past the number 400. The length of the line is 440 mm.

6.6 Drawing Instrument Set

A **drawing instrument set** typically consists of one large and one small bow compass and a set of dividers, as shown in Figure 6.56. These instruments can be purchased separately or in a set. Some sets contain a small box to hold extra points and lead, and an extension bar for the compass, for making larger circles and arcs. Adapters are available for ink pens or for thin-lead mechanical pencils.

6.6.1 Compass

The **compass** is used to draw circles and arcs of varying diameters (Figure 6.57). The lead is sharpened to a bevel using sandpaper (Figure 6.58). The extension bar is used to draw large circles by extending the range of the large bow compass. A beam compass is used for even larger circles (Figure 6.59). With CAD, the CIRCLE and ARC commands are used to create all sizes of circles and arcs.

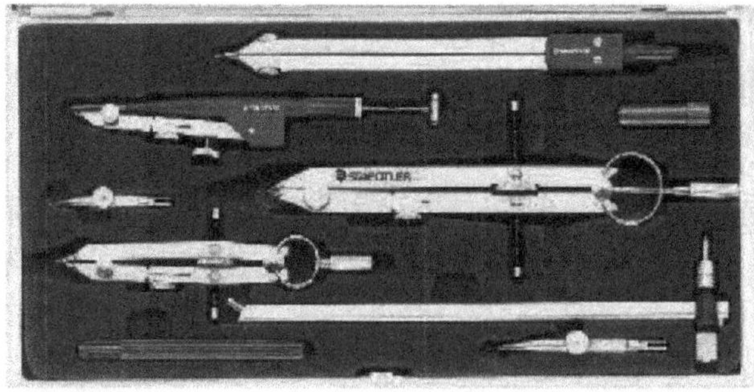

Figure 6.56

Drawing instrument set commonly used for technical drawings

This set contains two compasses, a divider, a beam attachment for large circles and arcs, inking points, and a tube with extra parts.

(Courtesy of Staedtler, Inc.)

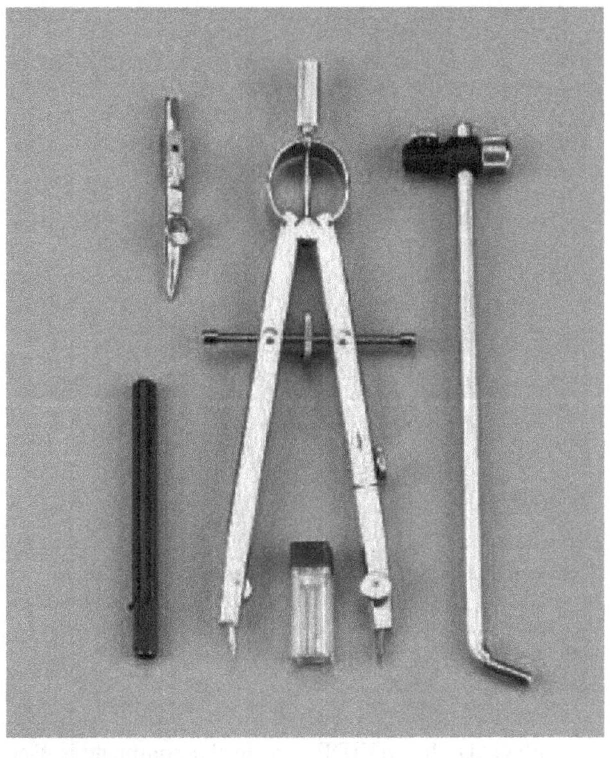

Figure 6.57

A bow compass and extension bar used to draw circles and arcs

(Courtesy of Staedtler, Inc.)

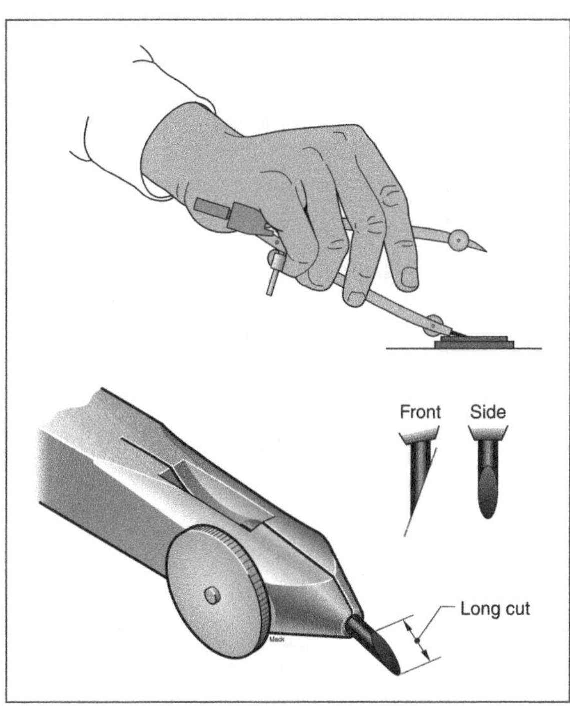

Figure 6.58

Sharpening compass lead

The lead in a compass is sharpened to a bevel using sandpaper.

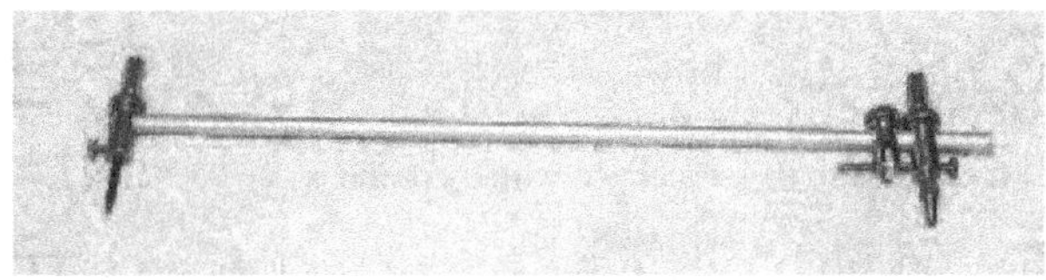

Figure 6.59

Beam compass

A beam is a special attachment to a regular compass and is used to draw large circles and arcs.

Drawing a Circle or Arc

Step 1. Draw two perpendicular lines to mark the center point of the circle or arc, and use the scale to mark the radius along one of these center lines (Figure 6.60).

Step 2. Set the compass point at the intersection of the center lines; then set the compass to the radius by aligning the pencil point of the compass with the mark on the center line.

Step 3. Draw the circle or arc by leaning the compass in the direction that the circle is being drawn, putting most of the pressure on the pencil point. The compass can be moved either clockwise or counterclockwise.

6.6.2 Dividers

A **divider** is similar to a compass except that it has needle points in both ends. There are two types of dividers: center wheel bow and friction (Figure 6.61). The divider is used to transfer measurements on a drawing or divide a line into equal parts by trial and error.

To transfer a measurement, open the dividers to the desired distance; then pick up and move the dividers to the new position, and mark the paper by lightly pushing the points of the dividers into the paper. This will leave two small marks that are the same distance apart as the original measurement.

To divide a line into equal parts, such as three, open the dividers to a distance you believe to be about one-third the length of the line. Then, begin at one end of the line and

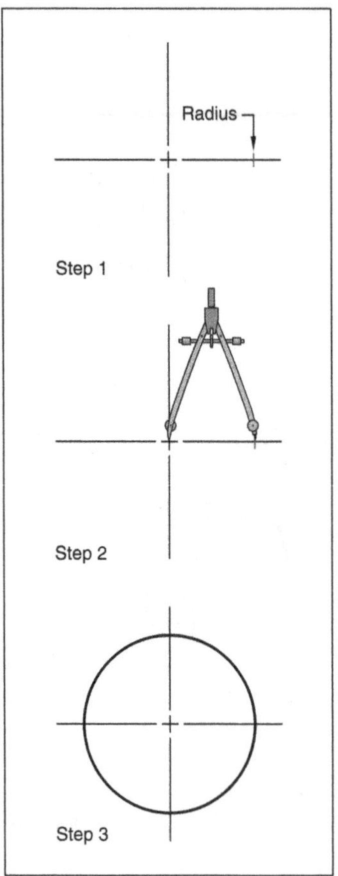

Figure 6.60

Steps used to draw a circle with a compass

Figure 6.61

Friction divider

A friction divider is used to transfer measurements or divide a line into equal parts.

(Courtesy of Staedtler, Inc.)

step off the distance three times. If the last space falls short or goes beyond the other end of the line, reset the divider by a distance equal to one-third of the shortfall or excess, and re-step the line. Repeat these steps, using trial and error, until the line is equally divided.

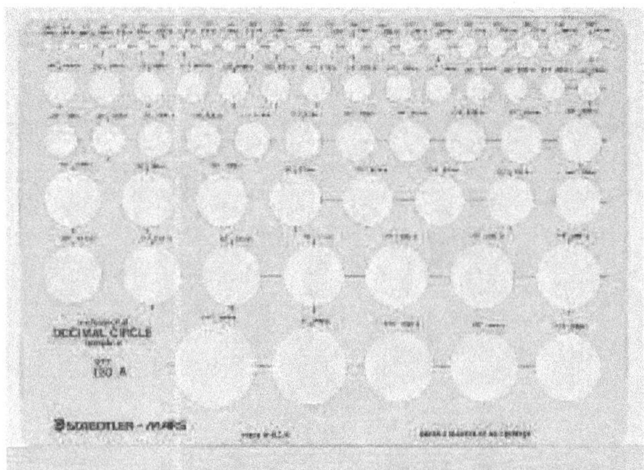

Figure 6.62

Circle template

A circle template is used to draw circles and arcs by aligning marks on the template with center lines on the drawing, then using a pencil to trace the outline of the hole cut in the template.

(Courtesy of Staedtler, Inc.)

With CAD, the DIVIDE or a similar command is used to mark equally spaced points on a line.

6.7 Templates

Templates are devices used to assist in the drawing of repetitive features, such as circles, ellipses, threaded fasteners, and architectural symbols (Figure 6.62). The circle template is used to draw circles, arcs, and fillets and rounds and is quicker than using a compass. The circle template has perpendicular center line marks, which are used to align the template to the perpendicular center lines on the drawing. An ellipse template works in a similar manner to create ellipses. Templates are also available for other common shapes, such as electronic or architectural symbols, and threaded fasteners (Figure 6.63).

CAD software can be used to make templates of virtually anything drawn. Once an electronic template is created for a part, such as a fastener or an electronic or architectural symbol, the template can be scaled, rotated, and placed into an existing drawing. TEMPLATE, SYMBOL, BLOCK, and PATTERN are common CAD commands synonymous with using templates. One advantage of using CAD is that anything drawn has the potential of becoming a template and nothing need be drawn twice. Software products available as add-ons to a CAD program include symbol or template libraries, so the user does not have to draw the symbols from scratch.

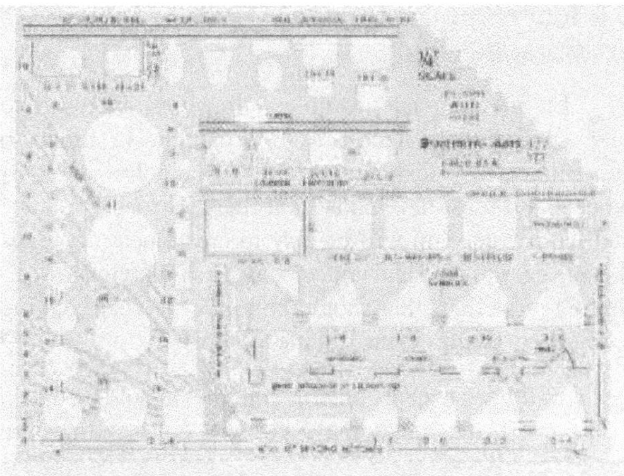

Figure 6.63

Symbol template

This template is used to draw architectural symbols, such as door swings and appliances.

(Courtesy of Staedtler, Inc.)

6.8 Technique for Laying Out a Drawing Sheet

Before an engineering drawing is created, the drawing sheet is laid out. The following steps describe how to lay out an A-size drawing sheet.

Step 1. Position the drawing paper on the drawing board by aligning the long bottom edge of the paper with the top edge of the parallel edge or drafting machine (Figure 6.64). If the paper is prebordered, align the bottom border line with the top edge of the parallel edge or drafting machine. Put a small piece of masking tape at each corner of the paper.

Step 2. If the paper is not prebordered, draw the borders. To do this, measure 0.25″ from each side of the paper and make very light marks with a hard pencil grade. Draw the border lines through these marks, using the straightedge and triangles and a soft-grade pencil to produce thick (0.7 mm) black lines.

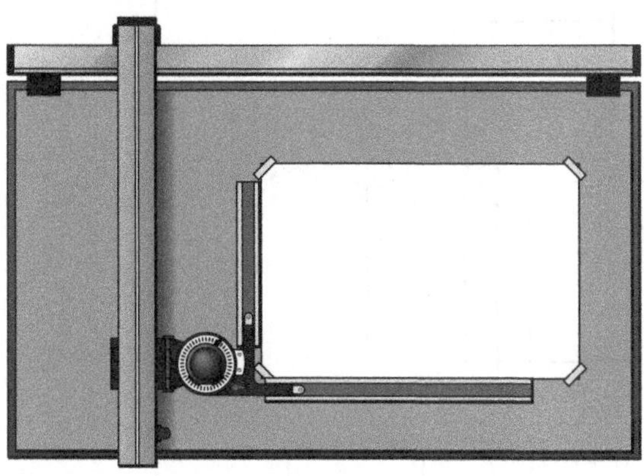

Step 1

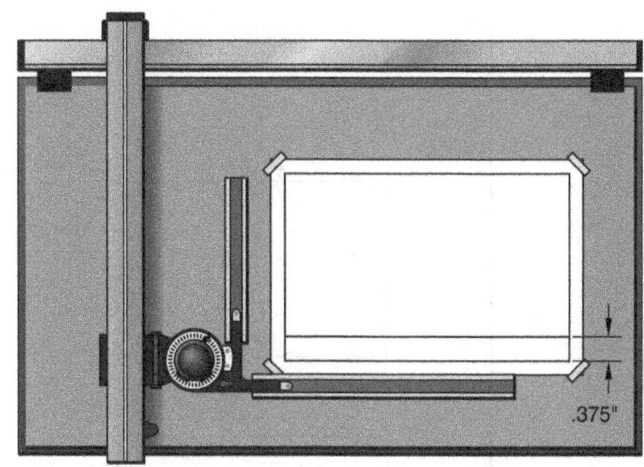

Step 3

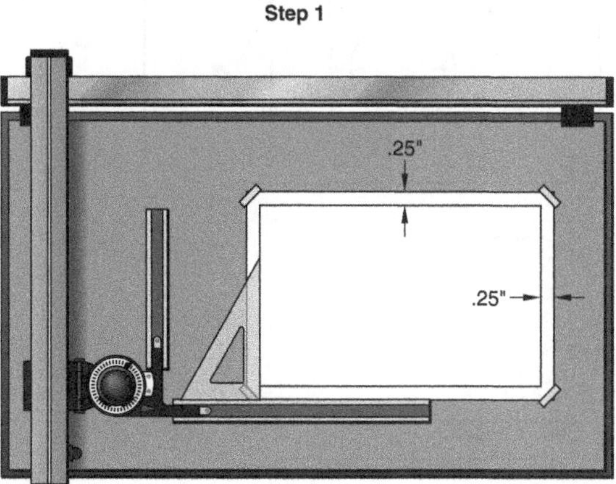

Step 2

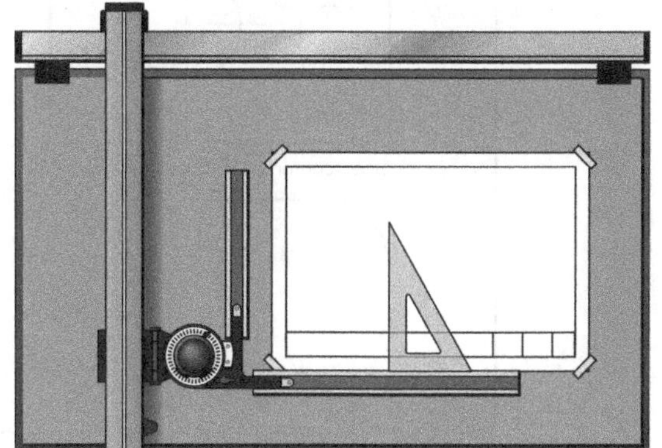

Step 4

Figure 6.64

Steps in laying out a drawing sheet

Step 3. Create a strip title block across the entire bottom of the drawing sheet. To do this, measure 0.375″ above the bottom border line and place a very light pencil mark. Draw the upper title strip line through this mark, using the straightedge and a soft-grade pencil to produce a thick (0.7 mm) black line.

Step 4. Divide the title strip into six parts. To do this, measure the following distances from the left vertical border line: 4.00″, 8.00″, 9.00″, 10.00″, and 10.5″. Place very light pencil marks at each measurement. Draw vertical lines through these marks, using the straightedge and triangle and a soft-grade pencil to produce thick (0.7 mm) black lines.

6.9 Technique for Drawing Using Traditional Tools

Engineering and technical drawings are used to communicate technical information. In order to communicate the technical idea clearly, the drawing must be neat and must have consistent lines. Through practice and hard work, you will be able to create neat drawings that are easy to read and understand. The following are important guidelines that should be followed when making technical drawings using traditional tools:

1. All lines except construction lines should be black, crisp, and consistent (Figure 6.65). Black lines are

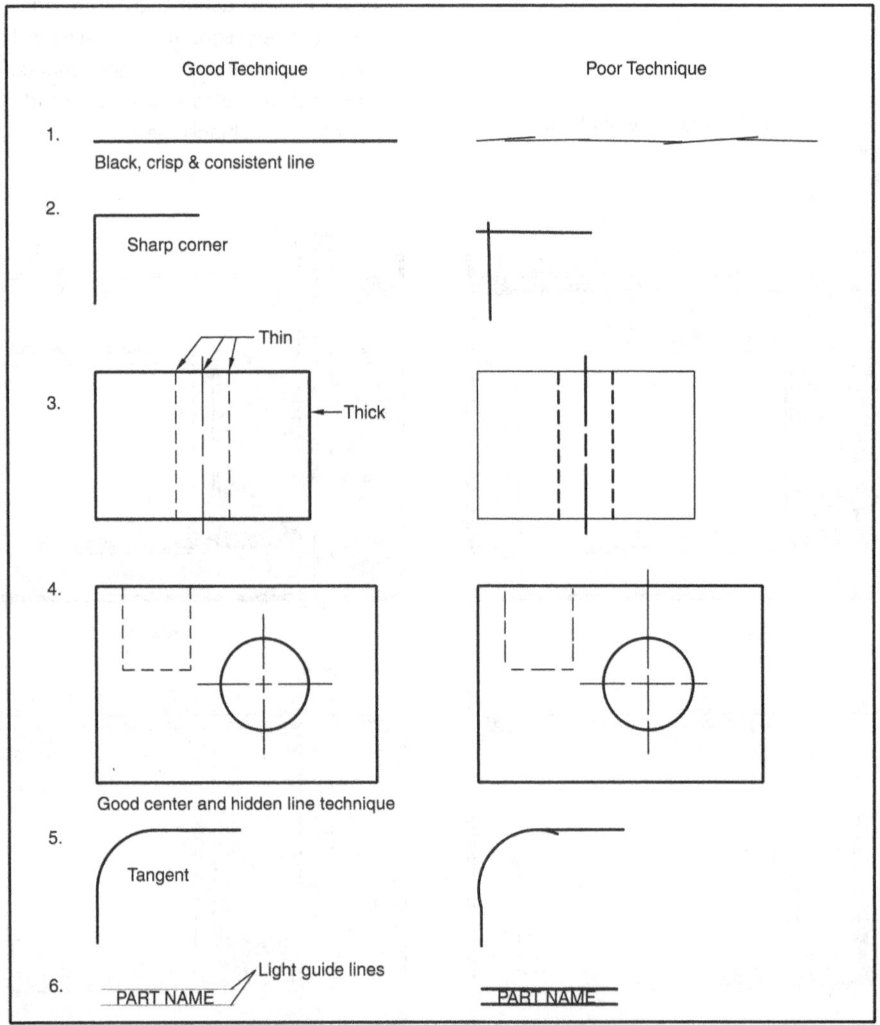

Figure 6.65

Examples of good and poor drawing techniques for lines and arcs, using traditional tools
Lines should be black, crisp, consistent, and the proper thickness.

Design in Industry

3-D Design Pays Off for Bose Corporation

The challenge facing Bose® engineers was to fit an AM/FM tuner and six-disk CD player into an area that previously held only a single-disk CD player. Complicating the effort was that the final product was to be the smallest offering available on the market, yet needed to contain Bose's renowned styling and functionality. Time constraints mandated that the product be brought to market as quickly as possible. Objectives included:

- Engineer the product such that the access door to the CD magazine was on the front of the console. Additionally, the door had to function smoothly and be a high-quality component.
- Fit the CD changer, AM/FM tuner, and all the electronics needed to drive the changer, tuner, and display into an enclosure measuring 15.5 inches long by 8 inches wide by 2.5 inches high.
- Bring the Bose Lifestyle® 20 music system to market in record time.
- Demonstrate the effectiveness of its new 3-D software system to speed the product development cycle.
- The number one criterion for the new software: reducing time to market.
- Maintain the elegant design of Bose audio equipment, with a minimum of buttons and knobs cluttering the design.

The process began when Bose® engineers modeled each of the individual console components. The next step was to pull all the components into a master model of the assembly, so engineers could see how everything fit together. Then, the design team studied the fit of the components and assemblies within the enclosure. Shaded solid models made it easy to visualize the box and its many contents, and in many cases, this was all that was needed to spot problems and optimize the internal configuration. Designing the console door was next using 3-D CAD software to let the team examine the motion of the door directly from the solid model assembly, without creating special mechanism models.

Results

- Bose brought a superior product to market in record time.
- Bose Lifestyle® 20 music system was the smallest multiple-disk CD player on the market.
- The final product contained the sleek, elegant design of all Bose audio equipment offerings.
- The use of 3-D solid models made it much easier for the design team to communicate with electronics designers, manufacturing engineers, and vendors on the project. They conveyed design intent earlier and more accurately than previously possible. This enhanced communications, reduced errors in downstream operations, and also made it possible to perform analysis, get quotes, and make tools sooner because these processes didn't have to wait for drawings.

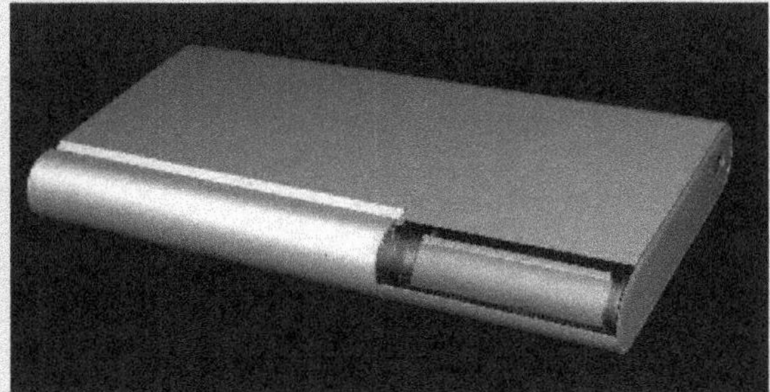

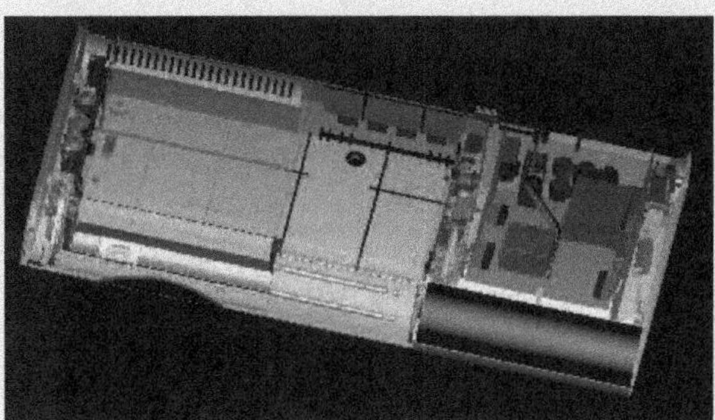

(Courtesy of Bose Corporation.)

created by using a soft lead and putting pressure on the pencil as the line is being drawn. Crisp lines do not have fuzzy edges. A consistent line does not change in thickness from one end to the other.
2. Corners should be sharp and without overlap.
3. Different linetypes vary in thickness, and the drawing should reflect these variances. For example, a visible line is thick (0.6 mm), and a hidden line is thin (0.3 mm). There should be a clear difference between these two lines when drawn.
4. Dashes, such as hidden, center, and phantom linetypes, should have consistent spacing, with definite endpoints.
5. Arcs intersecting lines should have smooth points of tangency.
6. Construction lines should be very light and should be drawn with a hard-grade lead. A good rule of thumb when creating construction lines is that, when the drawing is held at arm's length, the construction lines should be difficult to see.

6.10 Summary

The tools used for technical drawing include traditional ones, such as the triangle and the compass, and CAD. Traditional tools are used to make technical drawings by hand, and it takes practice and repetition to become proficient in their use. Although with CAD there is less emphasis on developing good technique, it still requires practice and repetition to attain proficiency.

Online Learning Center (OLC) Features

There are a number of Online Learning Center features listed below that you can use to supplement your text reading to improve your understanding and retention of the material presented in this chapter at www.mhhe.com/bertoline.

- Learning Objectives
- Chapter Outline
- Questions for Review
- Multiple Choice Quiz
- True or False Questions
- Flashcards
- Website Links
- Animations
- Related Readings

Questions for Review

1. Define CAD.
2. Define traditional drawing.
3. List four different output devices used with CAD.
4. Name the primary parts of a CAD system.
5. List two types of storage media for CAD drawings.
6. List two types of input devices used with CAD systems.
7. What is a CPU?
8. List the typical hand tools used to create a drawing.
9. What are templates used for? Give an example of one.
10. Describe how pencils are graded.
11. List the standard paper sizes used for technical drawings.
12. What is the shape of a sharpened compass lead?
13. What grade pencil is used to create construction lines on technical drawings?
14. List five recommended drawing techniques for creating good technical drawings.
15. How are metric drawings clearly identified on the drawing sheet?

Problems

The problems in this chapter introduce you to the tools of technical drawing. To solve these problems, you must use either traditional tools or a CAD system. By doing the drawing problems, you will learn how traditional tools, such as the straightedge, triangles, compass, dividers, scales, protractors, paper, eraser, and pencils, are used. If solving the problems using CAD, you will learn how to draw and erase lines, circles, arcs, and curves.

To convert the problems to metric, use 25.4 mm per inch and round the value to the nearest whole millimeter. Use capital (caps) letters for all text.

6.1 Using traditional tools or CAD, draw the border for an A-size (8½″ × 11″) sheet, using the dimensions shown in Figure 6.66. Divide the drawing area into six equal parts and label each, beginning with the letter A. Do not include the dimensions. Text is ⅛″ high, all caps, and centered vertically in the space, using light construction guidelines if using traditional tools.

6.2 Using traditional tools or CAD, draw the border for an A4 metric sheet, using the dimensions shown in Figure 6.67. Divide the drawing area into six equal parts and label each, beginning with the letter A. Text is 3 mm high, all caps, and centered vertically in the space, using light construction guidelines, if using traditional tools.

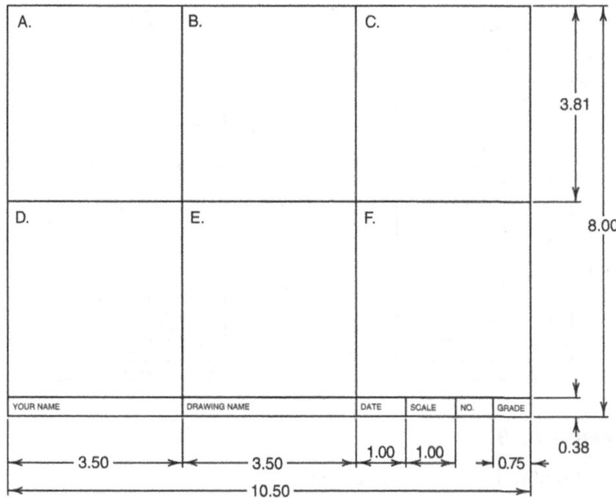

Figure 6.66

Problem 6.1 A-size drawing sheet divided into six equal parts

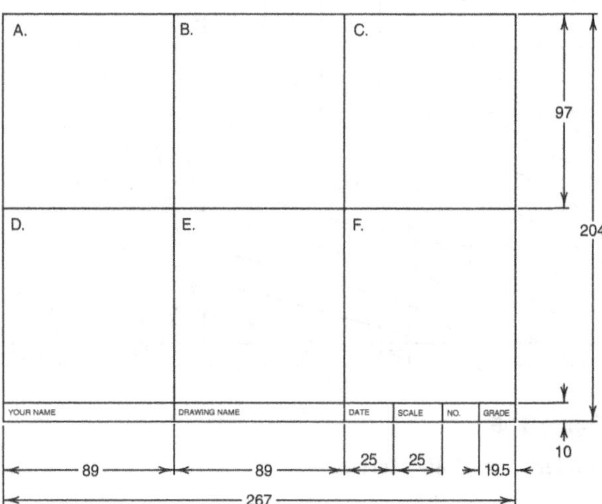

Figure 6.67

Problem 6.2 A4 metric drawing sheet divided into six equal parts

6.3 See Figure 6.68. Using either the A or A4 sheet created in Problems 6.1 and 6.2, do the following in the given space:

a. Draw six equally spaced horizontal lines.
b. Draw six equally spaced vertical lines.
c. Draw eight equally spaced 45-degree lines.
d. Draw eight equally spaced 30-degree lines.
e. Draw eight equally spaced 15-degree lines.
f. Draw eight equally spaced 75-degree lines.

6.4 See Figure 6.69. Draw another A or A4 sheet and divide it into six equal parts. (If using CAD, simply load the drawing sheet created in Problem 6.1 or 6.2.)

a. Create the brick pattern shown, using 1″ (25 mm) as the length and 0.50″ (13 mm) as the height.
b. Create the pattern shown, using 1.60″ (41 mm) as the length and 0.80″ (20 mm) as the width, and using a 45-degree angle.
c. Draw the solid and dashed horizontal lines, using 0.25″ (6 mm) spacing.
d. Draw the pattern shown, using 0.28″ (7 mm) spacing.
e. Draw the 45-degree angled lines, using 0.40″ (10 mm) spacing.
f. Draw the Escher pattern at an angle of 60 degrees. (Estimate distances to approximate the pattern.)

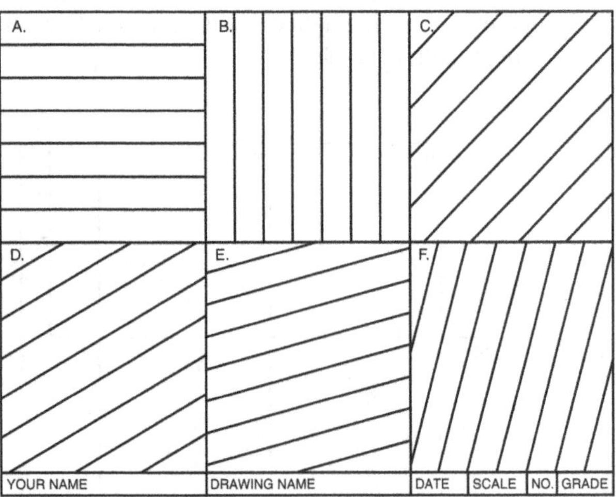

Figure 6.68

Problem 6.3 Line exercise

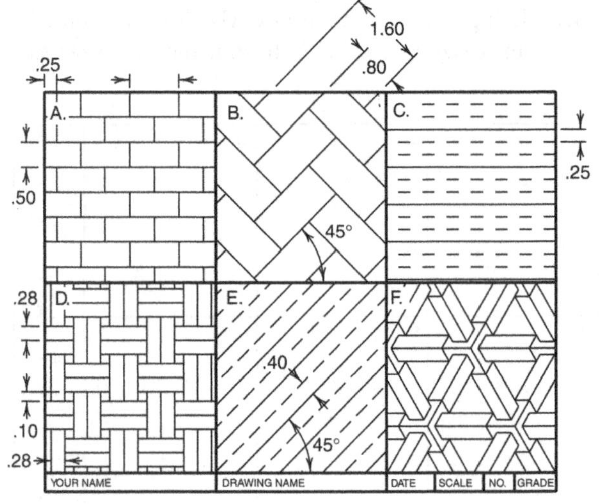

Figure 6.69

Problem 6.4 Pattern exercise

6.5 See Figure 6.70. Determine the measurements shown, on the metric scales.

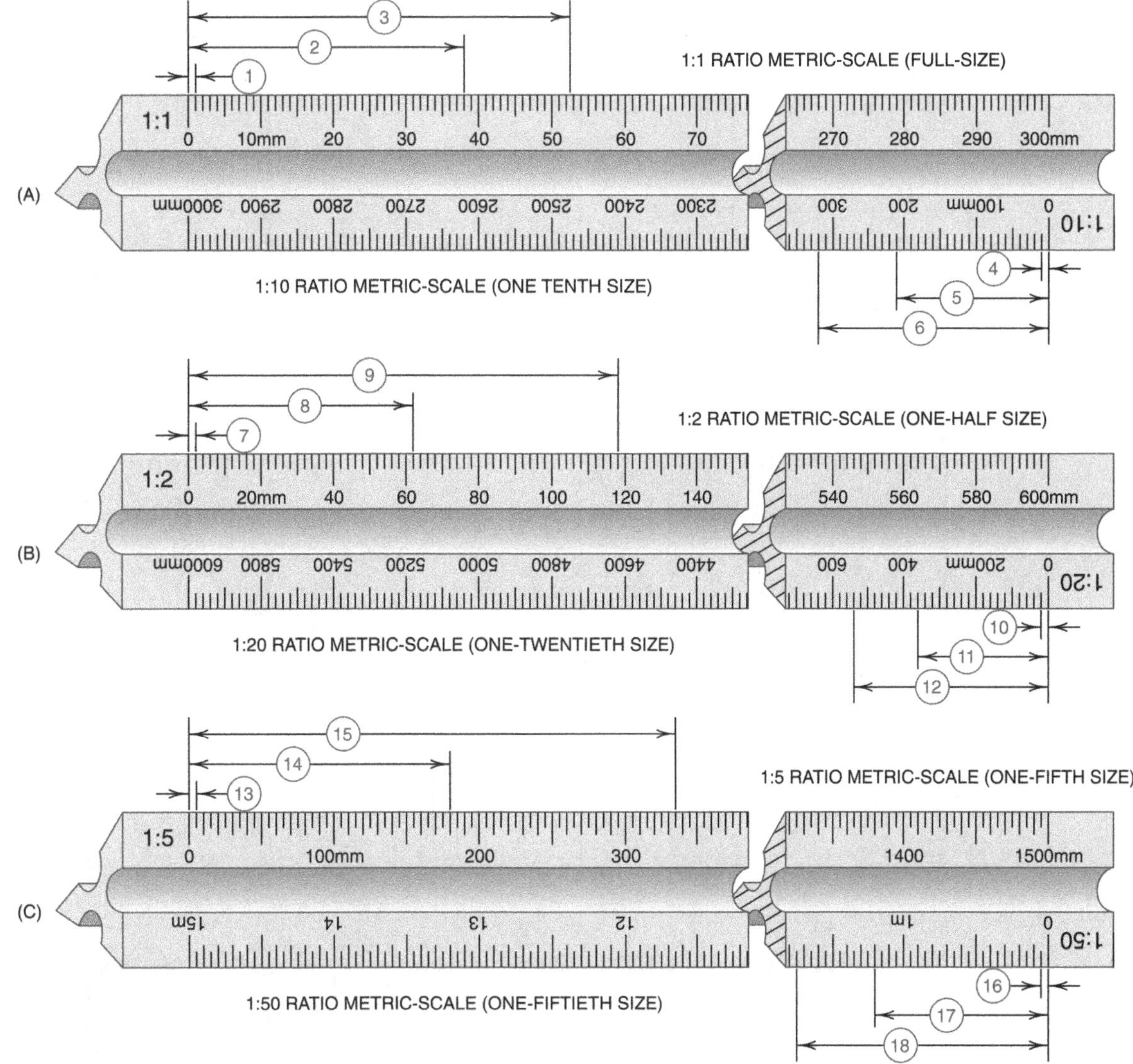

Figure 6.70

Problem 6.5 Reading metric scales

Answers

1. ________	7. ________	13. ________
2. ________	8. ________	14. ________
3. ________	9. ________	15. ________
4. ________	10. ________	16. ________
5. ________	11. ________	17. ________
6. ________	12. ________	18. ________

6.6 See Figure 6.71. Determine the measurements shown, on the civil engineer's scales.

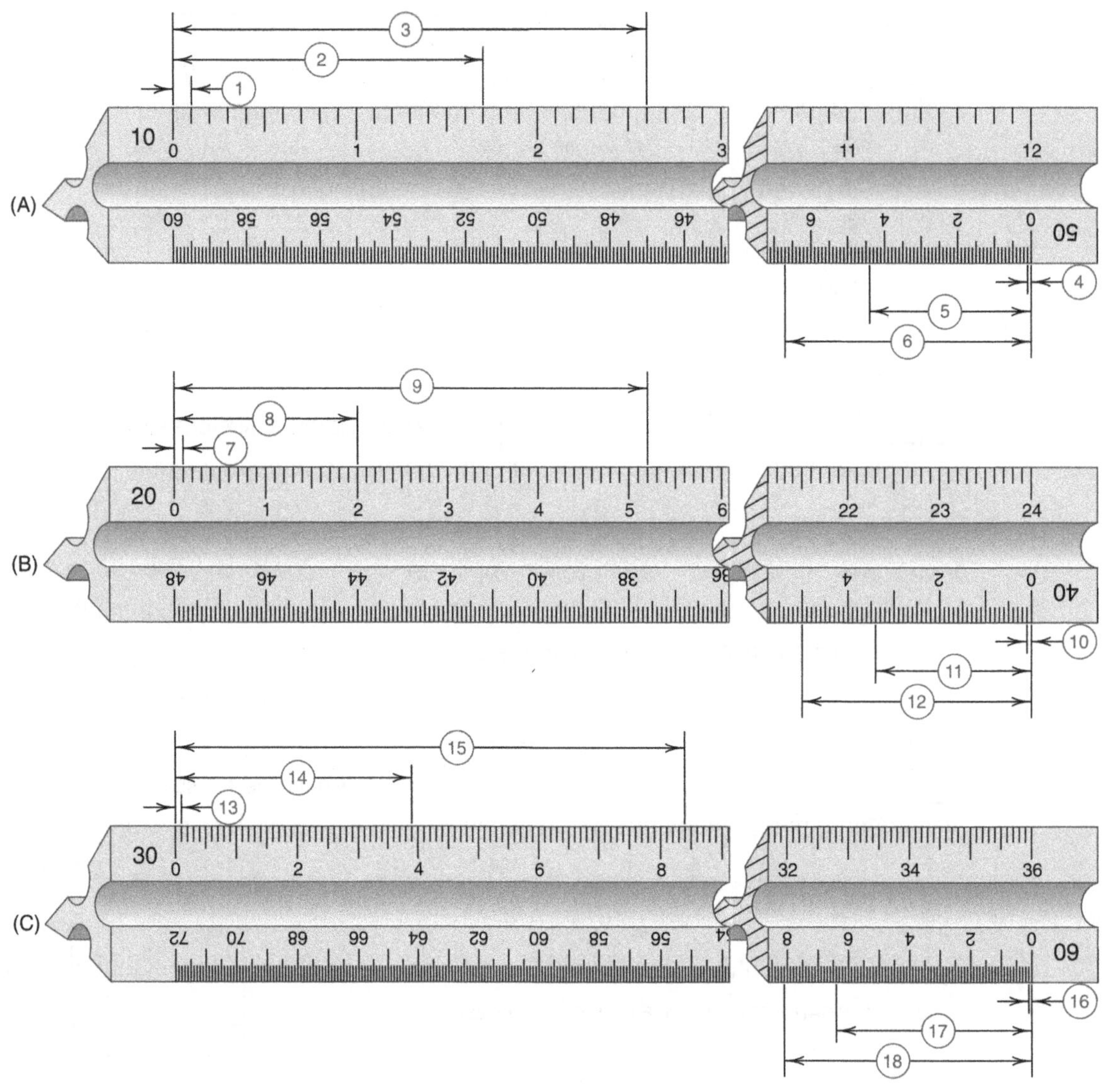

Figure 6.71

Problem 6.6 Reading civil engineer's scales

Answers

1. ________ 7. ________ 13. ________
2. ________ 8. ________ 14. ________
3. ________ 9. ________ 15. ________
4. ________ 10. ________ 16. ________
5. ________ 11. ________ 17. ________
6. ________ 12. ________ 18. ________

6.7 See Figure 6.72. Determine the measurements shown, on the architectural engineer's scales.

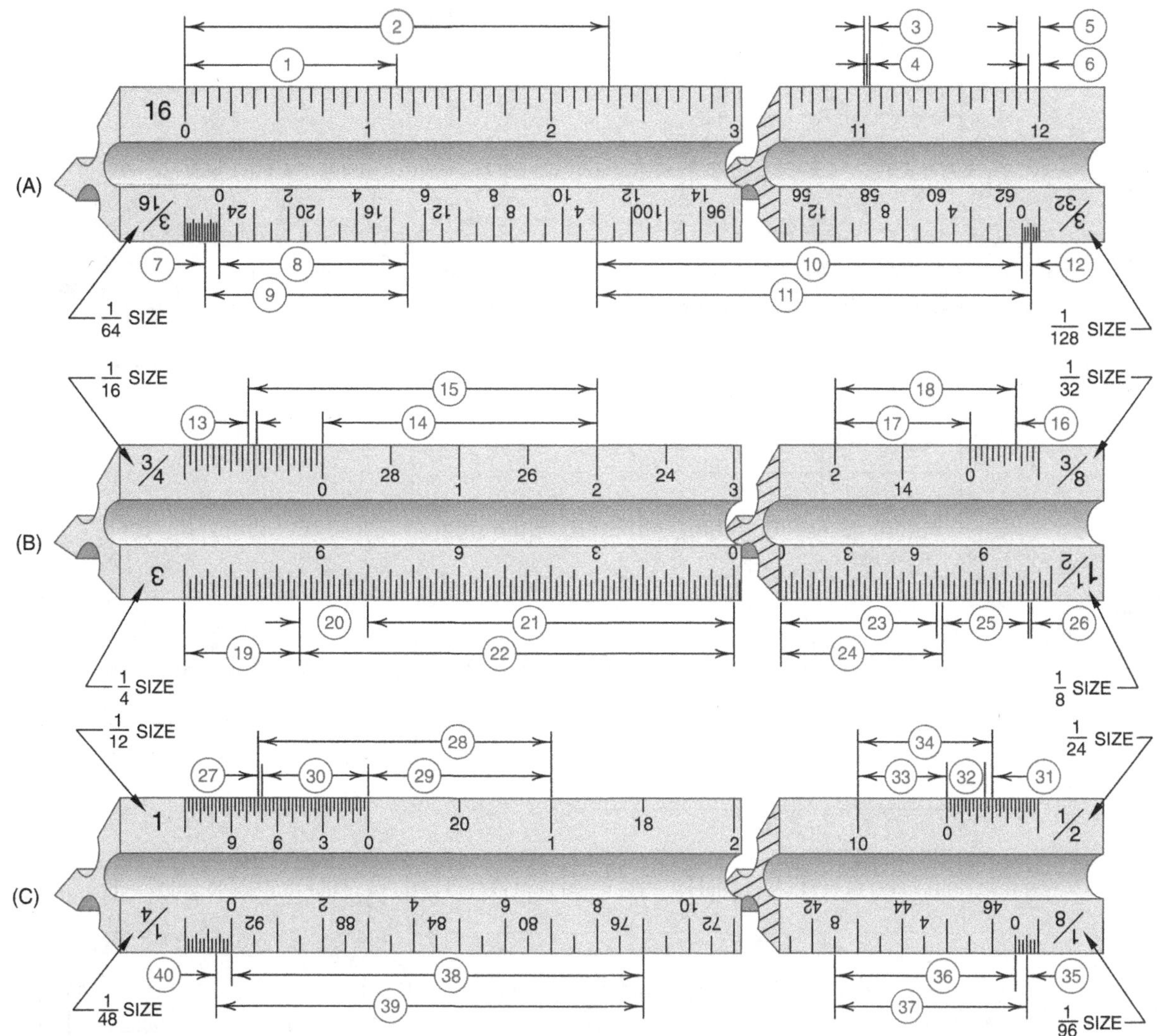

Figure 6.72

Problem 6.7 Reading architectural engineer's scales

Answers

1. ________	8. ________	15. ________	22. ________	29. ________	36. ________
2. ________	9. ________	16. ________	23. ________	30. ________	37. ________
3. ________	10. ________	17. ________	24. ________	31. ________	38. ________
4. ________	11. ________	18. ________	25. ________	32. ________	39. ________
5. ________	12. ________	19. ________	26. ________	33. ________	40. ________
6. ________	13. ________	20. ________	27. ________	34. ________	
7. ________	14. ________	21. ________	28. ________	35. ________	

6.8 See Figure 6.73. Determine the measurements shown, on the combination scales.

6.9 See Figure 6.74. Draw the border lines and title blocks for the ANSI and ISO drawing sheets, using the dimensions shown. Add text as shown, using ⅛″ (3 mm) all caps text.

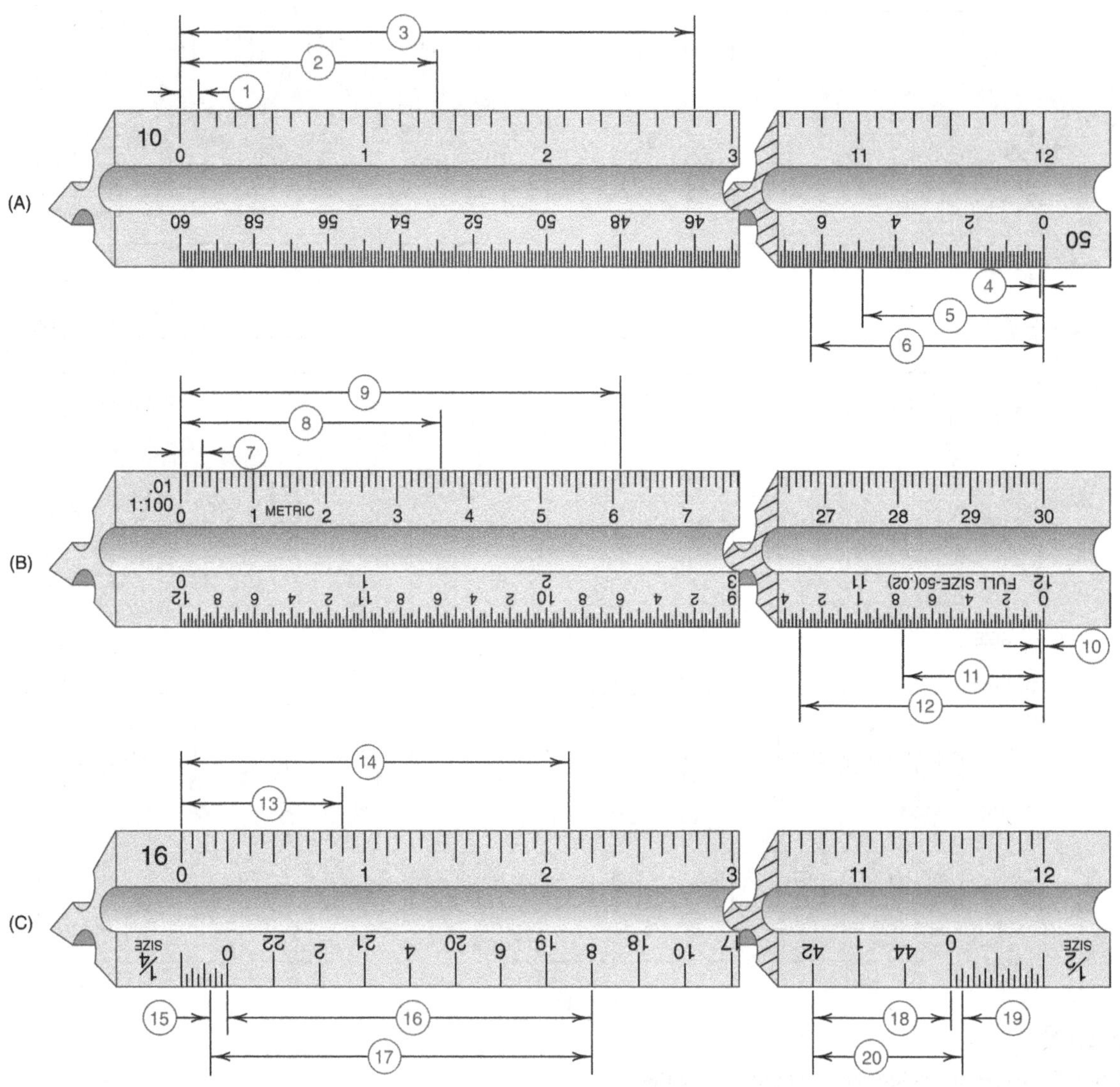

Figure 6.73

Problem 6.8 Reading combination scales

Answers

1. ________
2. ________
3. ________
4. ________
5. ________
6. ________
7. ________
8. ________
9. ________
10. ________
11. ________
12. ________
13. ________
14. ________
15. ________
16. ________
17. ________
18. ________
19. ________
20. ________

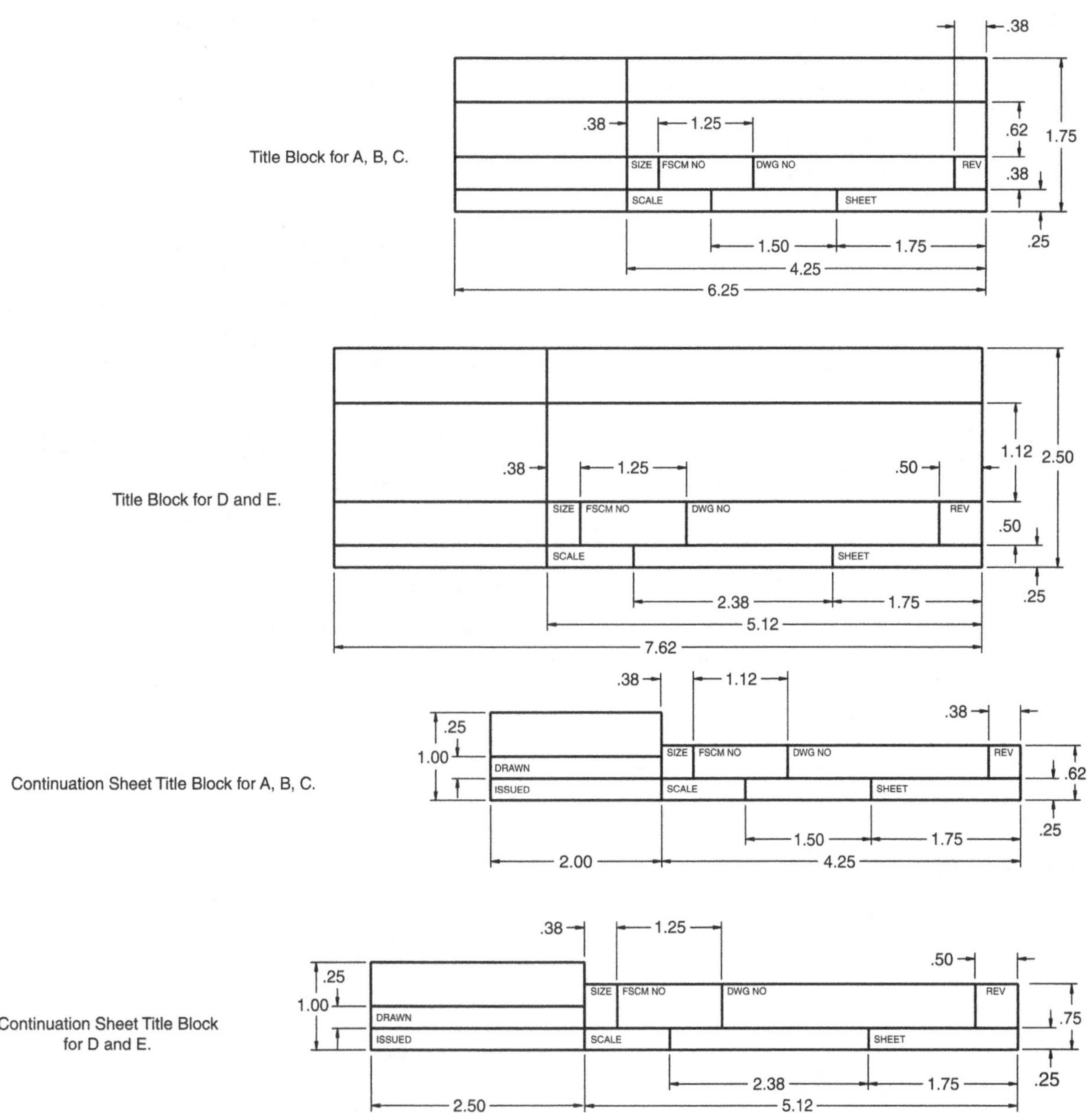

Size Designation	Width (Vertical)	Length (Horizontal)	Margin		International Designation	Width		Length	
			Vertical	Horizontal		mm	In.	mm	In.
A (Horiz)	8.5	11.0	0.38	0.25	A4	210	8.27	297	11.69
A (Vert)	11.0	8.5	0.25	0.38	—	—	—	—	—
B	11.0	17.0	0.38	0.62	A3	297	11.69	420	16.54
C	17.0	22.0	0.75	0.50	A2	420	16.54	594	23.39
D	22.0	34.0	0.50	1.00	A1	594	23.39	841	33.11
E	34.0	44.0	1.00	0.50	A0	841	33.11	1189	46.11

Figure 6.74

Problem 6.9 ANSI standard title blocks and border lines

6.10 See Figure 6.75. Create the grid shown, using the dimensions given. Plot points at the intersections shown; then draw a smooth curve through each point using an irregular curve or the appropriate CAD command. For metric, use a grid of 10 mm in a 120 mm-by-120 mm square.

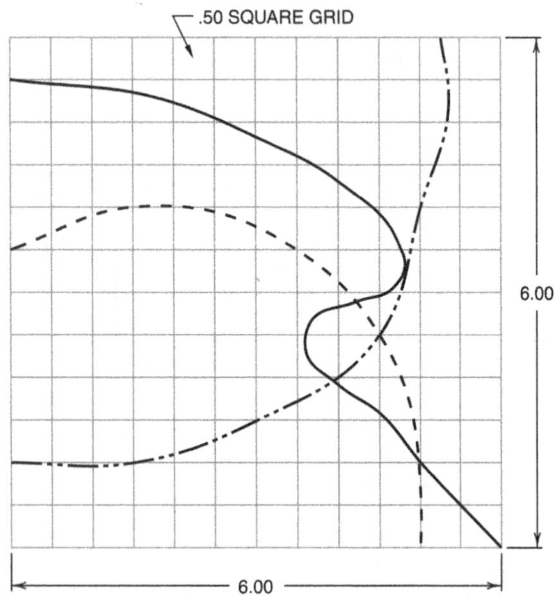

Figure 6.75

Problem 6.10 Irregular curves

6.11 See Figure 6.76. Smooth curves are used in the design of cams to represent harmonic motion. Construct the curve shown in the figure by plotting the points.

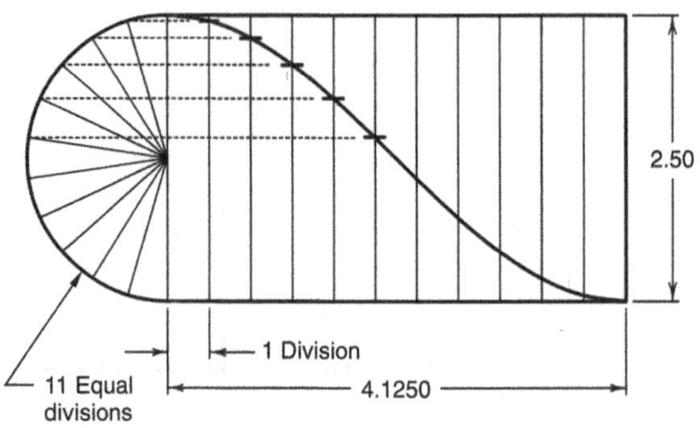

2.50

1 Division

11 Equal divisions

4.1250

Figure 6.76

Problem 6.11 Smooth curve

6.12 See Figure 6.77. Do the problems assigned by your instructor, using the appropriate size drawing sheet. Do not dimension. Whenever you see TYPICAL or TYP on the drawings, it means that similar features are the same size; Ø means diameter of the circle.

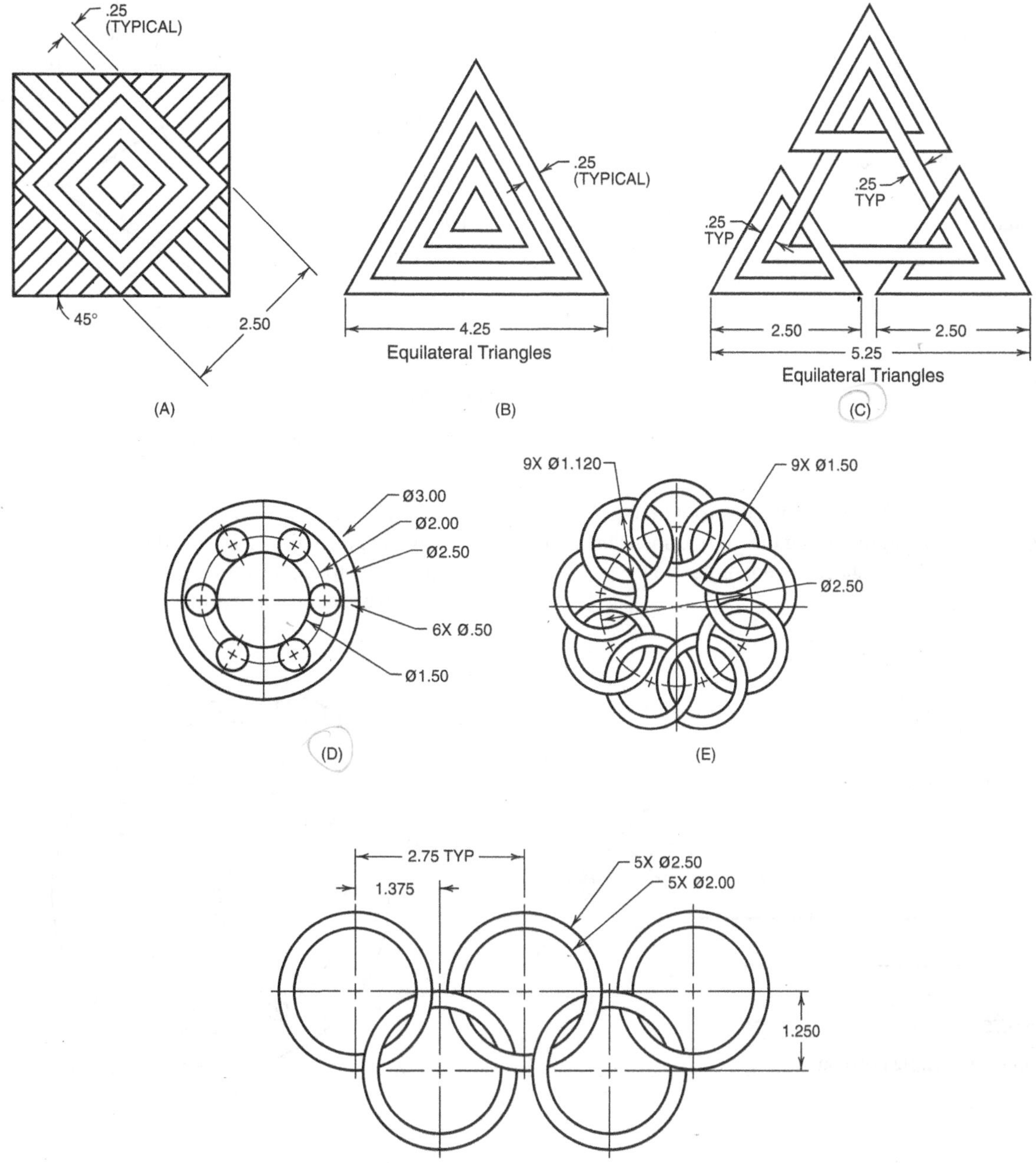

Figure 6.77

Problem 6.12 Shape construction

6.13 See Figure 6.78. Using a scale of ⅛″=1′–0″, draw the truss shown in the figure. The rise (R) is one-fourth the span of the truss.

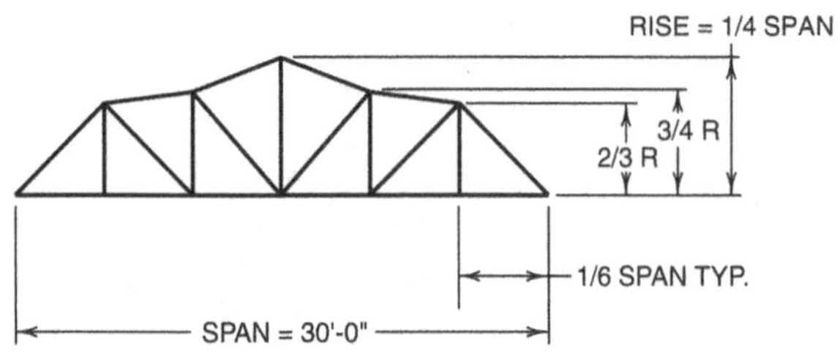

Figure 6.78

Problem 6.13 Truss

6.14 See Figure 6.79. Construct the irregular polygon shown in the figure, using the given dimensions, on an A- or A4-size sheet. Do not dimension.

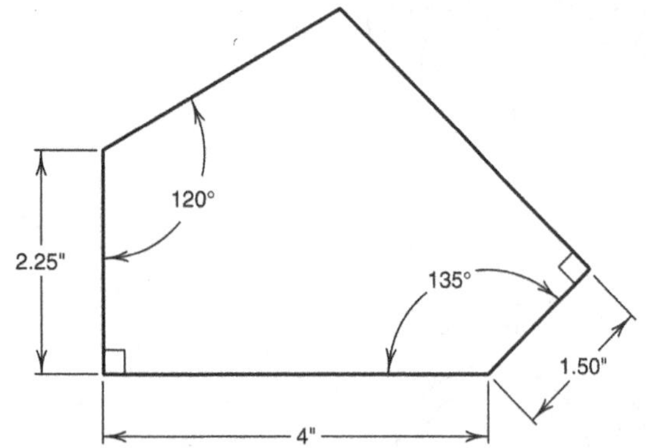

Figure 6.79

Problem 6.14 Angle polygon

6.15 See Figure 6.80. Construct the irregular polygon shown in the figure, using the given dimensions, on an A- or A4-size sheet. Do not dimension.

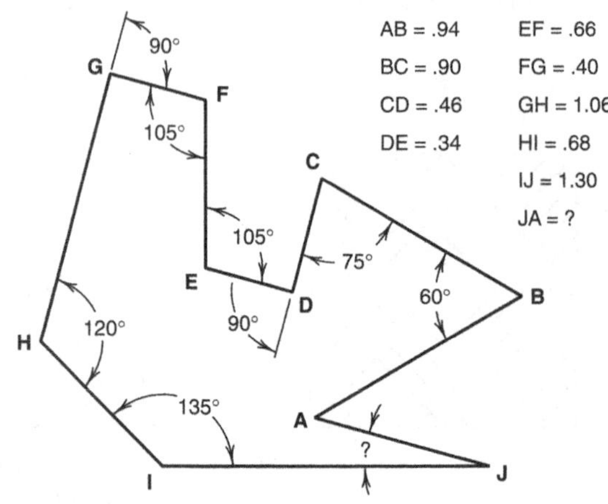

Figure 6.80

Problem 6.15 Irregular polygon

6.16 See Figure 6.81. Construct the centering plate, using the given dimensions. All of the angles are proportional to angle A. Place the drawing on an A- or A4-size sheet. Do not dimension.

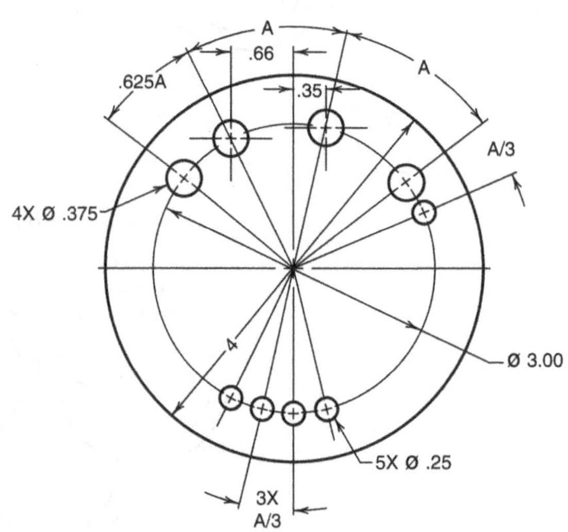

Figure 6.81

Problem 6.16 Centering plate

6.17 See Figure 6.82. A laser beam directed from source A is reflected at a 45-degree angle from mirror B to mirror C, then onto the horizontal machine surface. Draw the mirrors, machine surface, and light path. Determine angle X for mirror C. [*Hint:* Angle Y must equal angle Z (angle of incidence equals angle of reflection).] Use a scale of ¼″ equals 1′–0″ and draw on an A-size sheet.

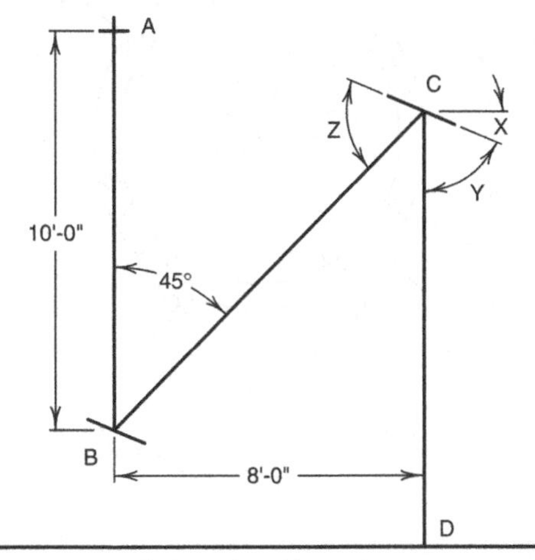

Figure 6.82

Problem 6.17 Reflector

6.18 See Figure 6.83. Construct the retaining ring shown in the figure. Use an A-size sheet and triple the size of the linear dimensions.

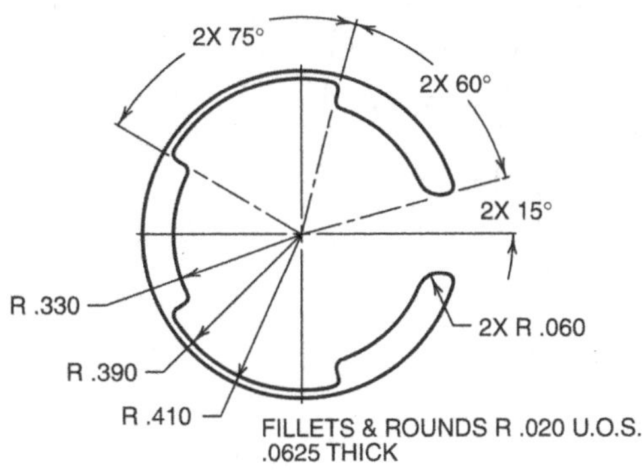

Figure 6.83

Problem 6.18 Retaining ring

6.19 See Figure 6.84. Construct the V-spacer shown in the figure. The letter R in the dimensions means the radius of the arc. Use an A-size sheet.

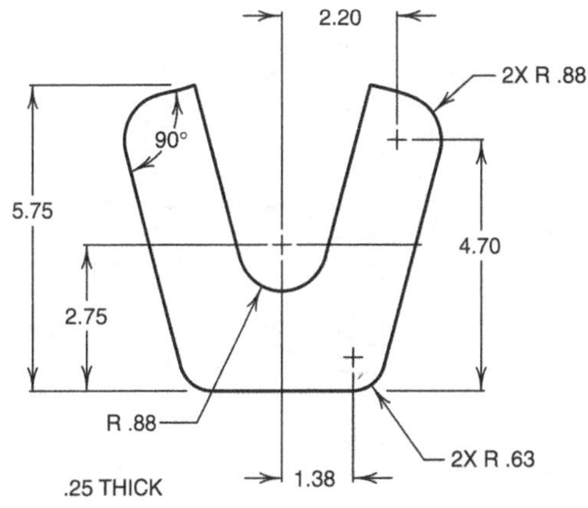

Figure 6.84

Problem 6.19 V-spacer

6.20 See Figure 6.85. Construct the saw shown in the figure. Use an A-size sheet.

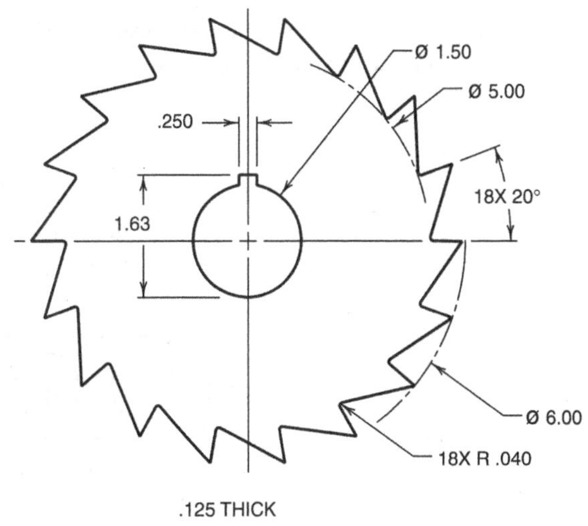

Figure 6.85

Problem 6.20 Saw

6.21 See Figure 6.86. Construct the flow gasket shown in the figure, using a B-size sheet.

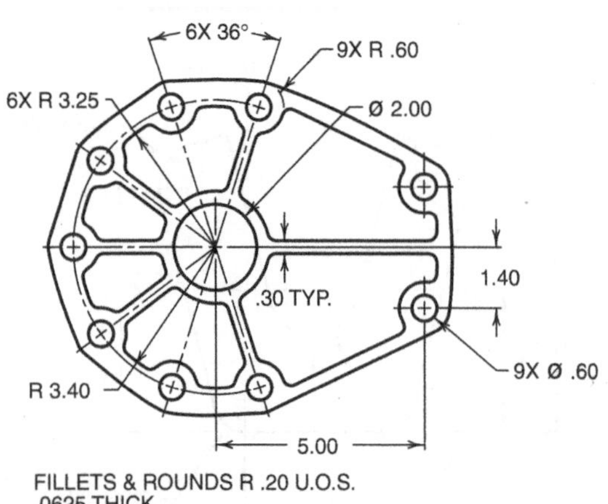

Figure 6.86

Problem 6.21 Flow gasket

6.22 See Figure 6.87. Construct the pump gasket shown in the figure, using a B-size sheet.

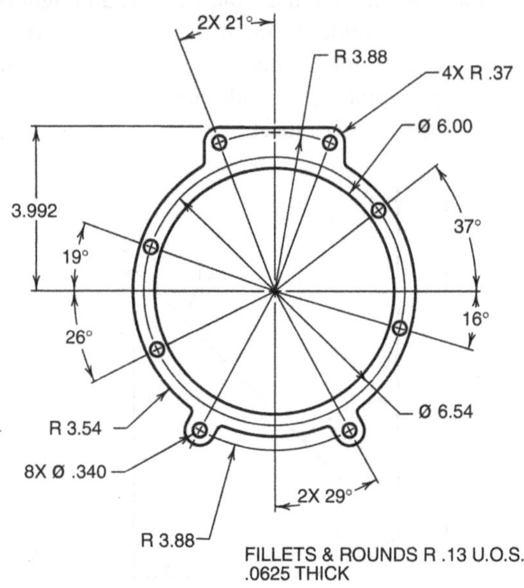

Figure 6.87

Problem 6.22 Pump gasket

6.23 See Figure 6.88. Construct the open support shown in the figure, using an A-size sheet.

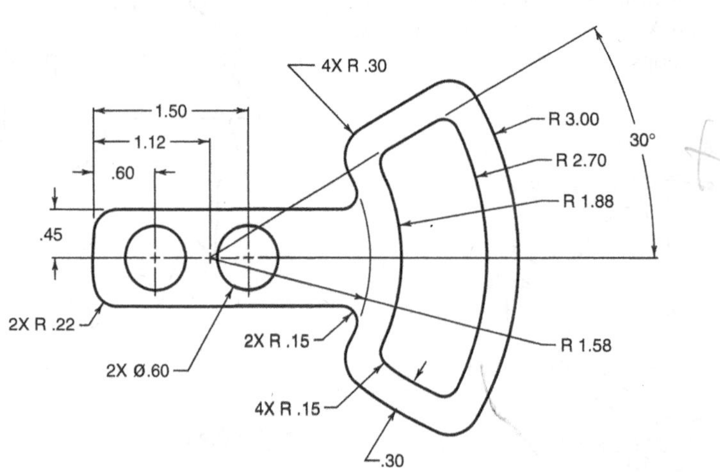

Figure 6.88

Problem 6.23 Open support

6.24 See Figure 6.89. Construct the angle bracket shown in the figure, using a B-size sheet.

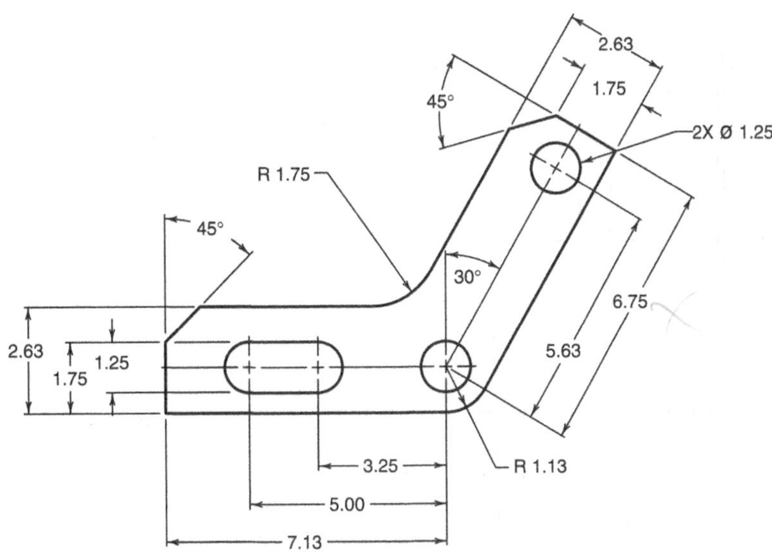

Figure 6.89

Problem 6.24 Angle bracket

6.25 See Figure 6.90. Construct the chamber clip shown in the figure, using a B-size sheet.

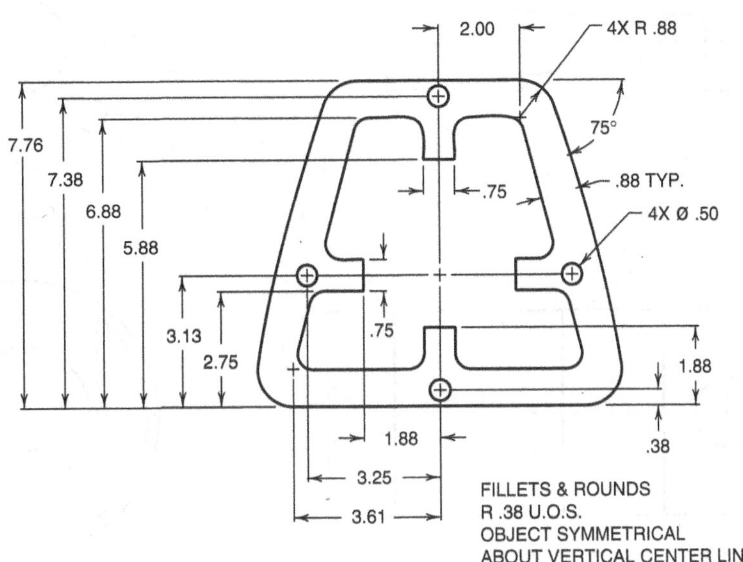

Figure 6.90

Problem 6.25 Chamber clip

6.26 See Figure 6.91 A through I. Using the scale assigned by your instructor, measure and then construct the parts.

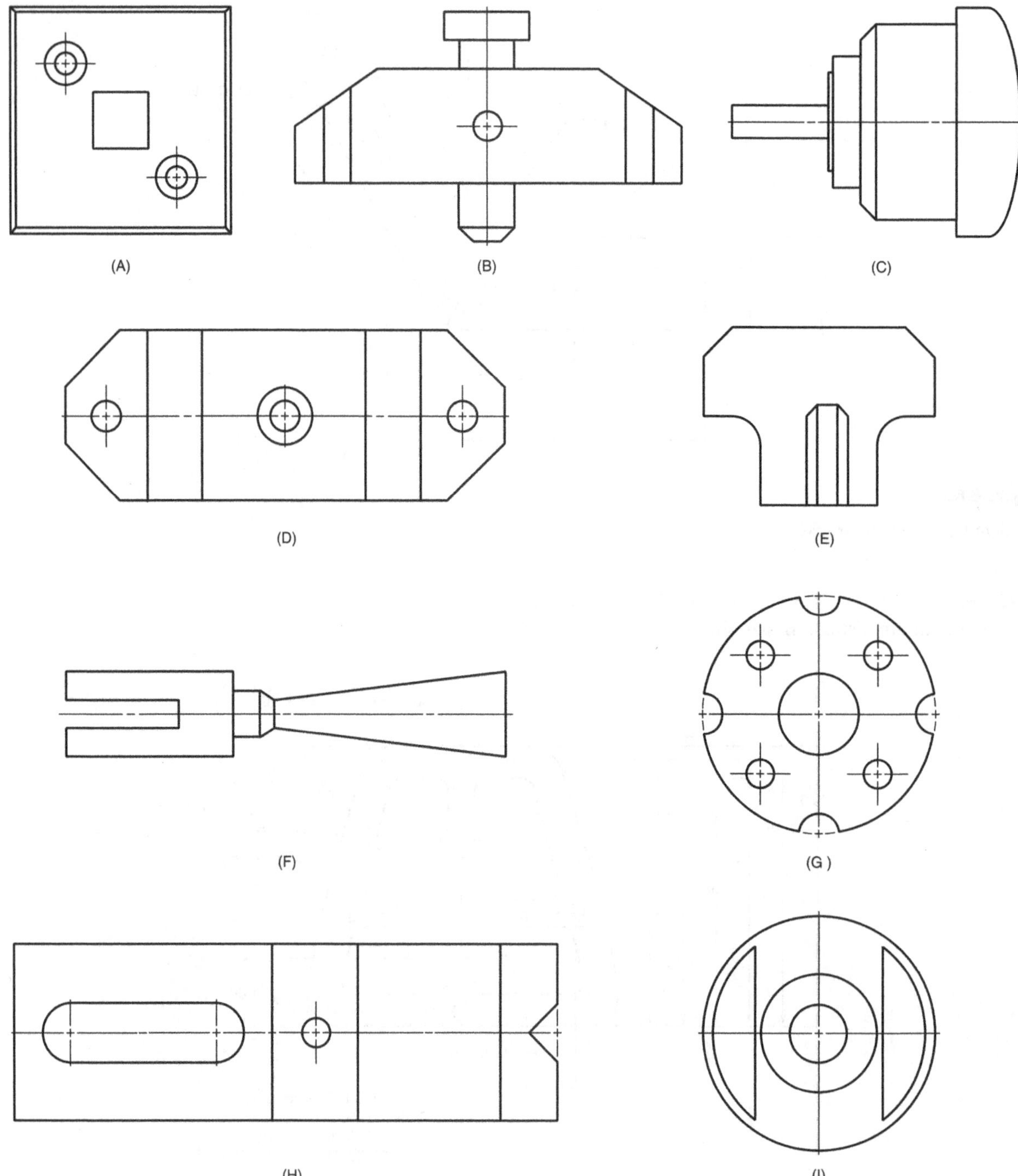

Figure 6.91

Problem 6.26 Scaled drawings

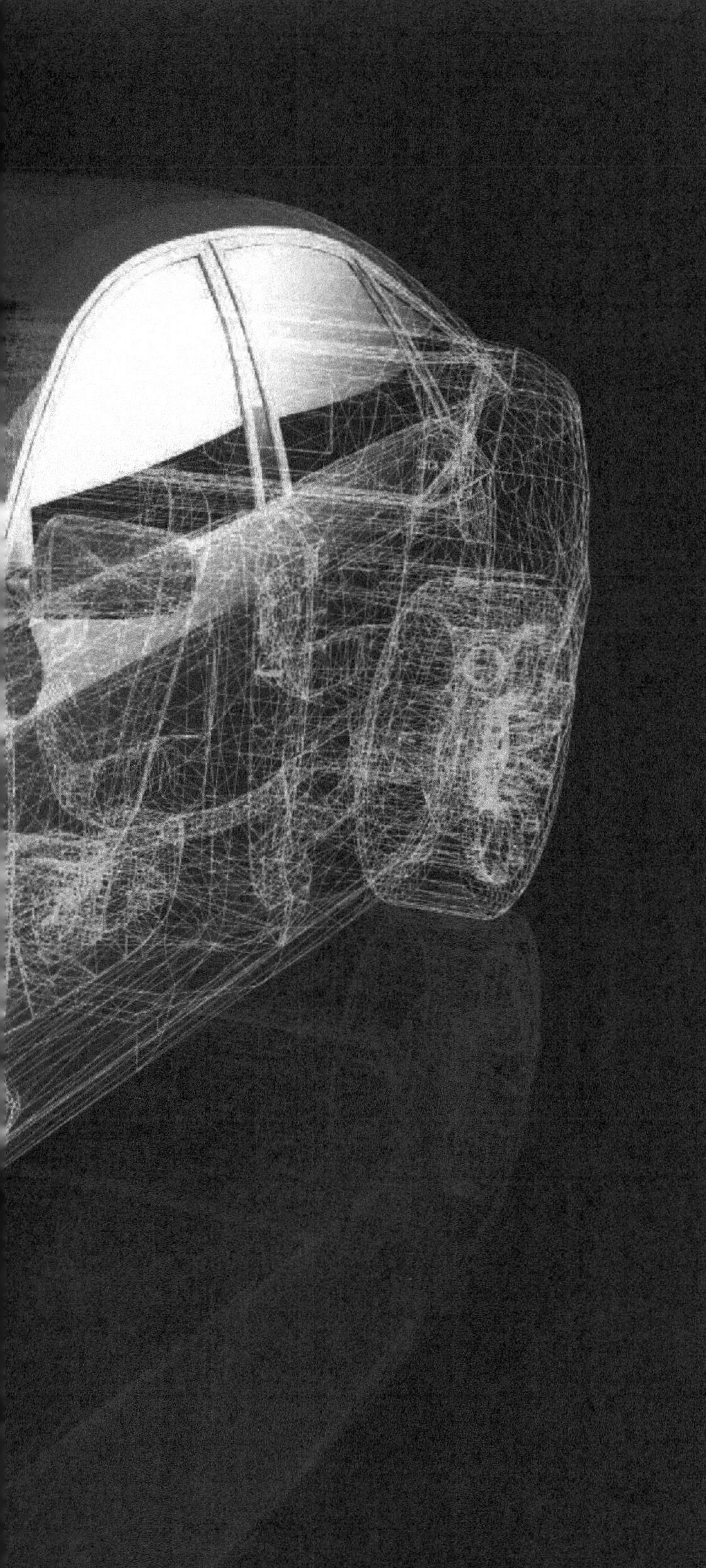

Chapter Seven

Sketching and Text

Chapter Seven

It adds a precious seeing to the eye.

—William Shakespeare

Objectives

After completing this chapter, you will be able to:

1. Define technical sketching.
2. Understand how sketching integrates into the design process.
3. Identify and define two types of sketches.
4. Create a design sketch using pencil or computer.
5. Identify and use sketching tools.
6. Use grid paper to create sketches.
7. Lay out a sketch using proportions.
8. Understand the difference between pictorial and multiview projection.
9. Create a perspective sketch.
10. Create an isometric sketch.
11. Create an oblique sketch.
12. Create a multiview sketch.
13. Identify the types and precedence of lines.
14. Understand how sketching is used in constraint-based modelers.
15. Follow good hand-lettering practice.
16. Identify important practices when using CAD for lettering.

Introduction

Sketching is an important method of quickly communicating design ideas; therefore, learning to sketch is necessary for any person working in a technical field. Sketching is as much a way of thinking as it is a method of recording ideas and communicating to others. Executives, engineers, technicians, and nontechnical people, from children to adults, use sketches to represent new ideas.

Sketching is a form of documentation in the early, ideation phase of engineering design. Most new designs are first recorded using design sketches.

This chapter introduces you to sketching techniques. The next chapter uses these techniques to help you visualize the forms of objects in your mind. Later chapters show you how to take your sketched design ideas and formalize them in models or drawings that can be used in analysis and manufacturing.

Lettering is part of sketching and drawing. Before CAD, lettering had much more emphasis in engineering and technical graphics. Now it is no longer necessary to spend hours working on lettering technique. CAD systems offer the user many different typestyles that can be varied in a number of ways. More and more, hand lettering is used only to add additional information to sketches. Though this lettering will probably not be as refined as the lettering in a mechanical drawing, it should still reflect a standardized style and should be neatly done.

7.1 Technical Sketching

There are three methods of creating technical drawings: freehand, mechanical, and digital, as shown in Figure 7.1. **Technical sketching** is the process of producing a rough, preliminary drawing representing the main features of a product or structure. Such sketches have traditionally been done freehand; today, CAD systems can also be used. A technical sketch is generally less finished, less structured or restricted, and it takes less time than other types of freehand illustrations (Figure 7.2). Also, a technical sketch may communicate only selected details of an object, using lines; whole parts of an object may be ignored, or shown with less emphasis, while other features may be shown in great detail.

Technical sketches can take many different forms, depending on the clarity needed and the purpose of the sketch, both of which depend on the audience for which the sketch is intended. For example, a sketch made quickly to record a fleeting design idea may be very rough (Figure 7.3). This type of sketch is for personal use and is not meant to be understood by anyone but the individual who produced it. A sketch may also use the format of a more formal, multiview drawing intended to be used by someone who understands technical drawings (Figure 7.4). However, this type of sketch would not be appropriate for a nontechnical person. Pictorial sketches would be used to further clarify the design idea and to communicate that idea to nontechnical individuals (Figure 7.5). Shading can be used to further enhance and clarify a technical sketch (Figure 7.6 on page 240).

Technical sketches are used extensively in the first (ideation) stage of the design process and are an informal tool used by everyone involved in the design and manufacture of a product (Figure 7.7 on page 240). For example, an industrial technologist might make several sketches of a layout for a factory floor.

Many designers find that sketching becomes part of their creative thinking process. Through the process of *ideation,* as explained in Chapter 2, sketching can be used to explore and solidify design ideas that form in the *mind's eye,* ideas that are often graphic in nature. Sketching helps capture these mental images in a permanent form. Each sketch is used as a stepping stone to the

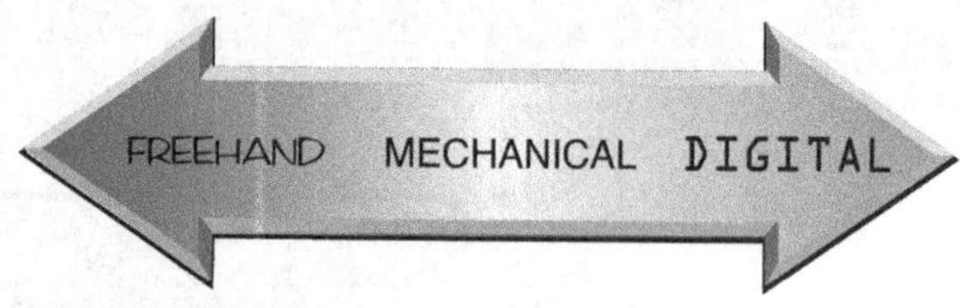

Figure 7.1

Technical drawings are created using freehand, mechanical, or digital means. Freehand drawings are known as sketches and are an important communication tool that engineers use frequently when designing.

Figure 7.2

Freehand drawings are grouped by the level of detail, structure, and restrictions used to create the sketch.

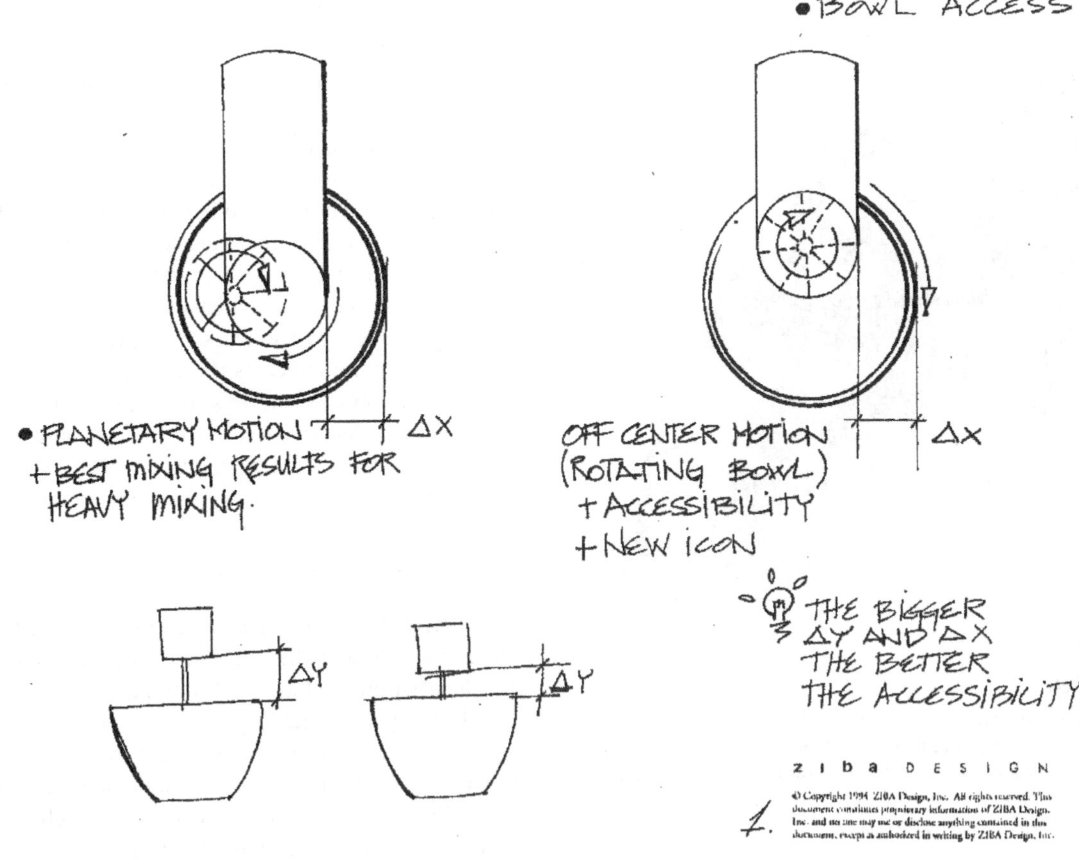

Figure 7.3

Technical sketch

A rough technical sketch can be made to capture a design idea quickly.

(Courtesy of Ziba Design.)

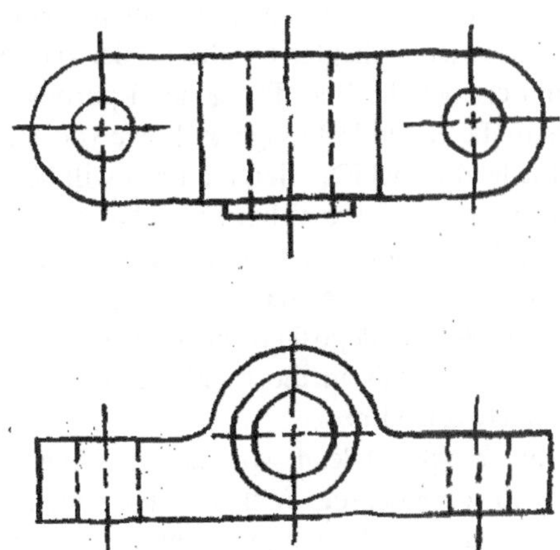

Figure 7.4

Multiview sketch of a mechanical part

Sketches can be used by the engineer to communicate technical information about the design to others.

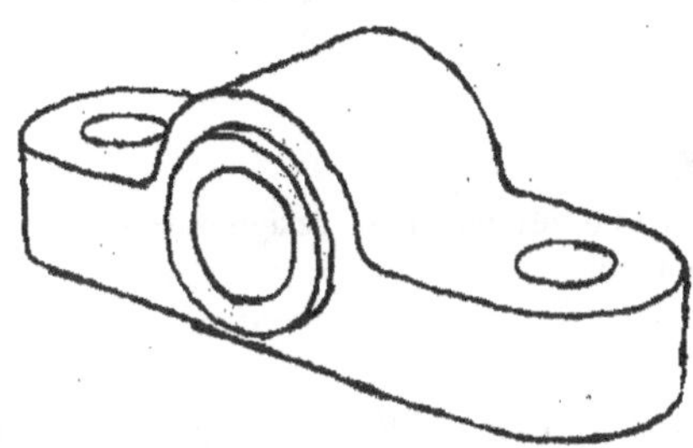

Figure 7.5

Pictorial sketch

Pictorial sketches are used to communicate technical information in a form that is easy to visualize.

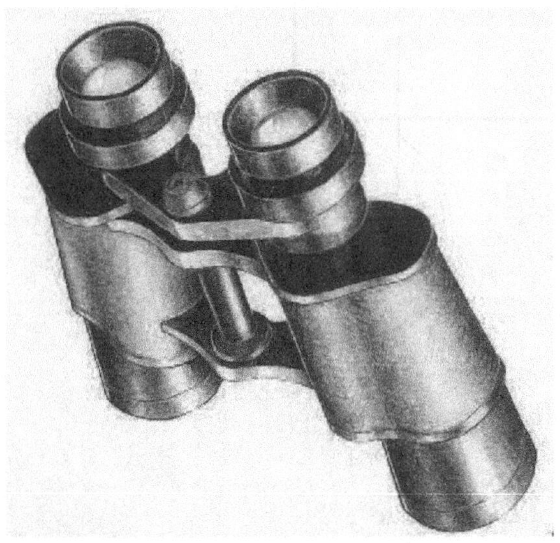

Figure 7.6

Shaded sketch

This rendered sketch is an example of the amount of detail that can be used when creating sketches. This type of sketch is more appropriate for technical illustrations than for design communications.

(Irwin drawing contest winner Tim Brummett, Purdue University.)

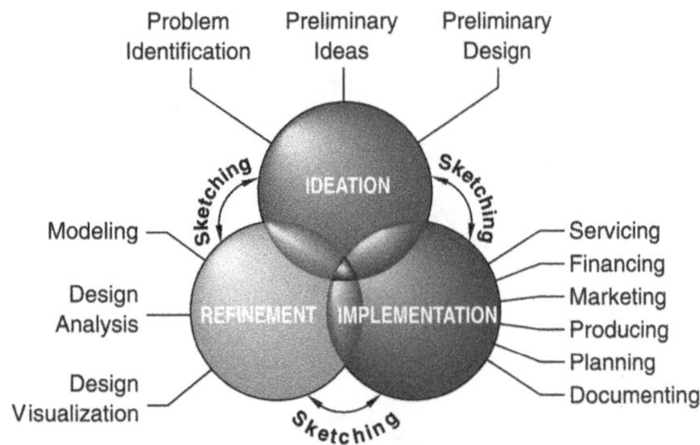

Figure 7.7

Sketching is used throughout the design process to communicate information.

next sketch or drawing, where ideas are refined, detail is added, and new ideas are formed.

On a large project, hundreds of sketches are created, detailing both the successful and the unsuccessful approaches considered for solving the design problem. Since all but the smallest of design projects are a collaborative effort, sketches become an important tool for communicating with other members of the design team.

At the early stages of the design process, highly refined, detailed drawings can actually impede the exploration of alternative ideas. What is needed are informal, nonrestrictive sketches that can communicate both geometric and nongeometric information and can be produced quickly and changed easily. Technical sketching, being fast and less restrictive, can convey ideas at a level of detail that communicates the design intent and, at the same time, allows the viewers to imagine for themselves how different solutions might further the design. Sketches as a communications tool encourage collaborative contributions from other members of the design team.

7.1.1 Freehand Sketching Tools

Normally, tools used for sketching should be readily available and usable anywhere: pencil, paper, and eraser. Although variations on these tools are numerous and sophisticated, the goal of technical sketching is simplification. Just a few pencils, an eraser, and sheets of paper should be all that is needed. Many a great design idea was born on a note pad with a No. 2 wooden pencil! Although there may be a temptation to use straightedges, such as T-squares and triangles, a minimum amount of practice should allow you to draw lines good enough for sketches without these aids. Mechanically drawn lines can slow you down, add a level of accuracy not needed in the early stages of a design, and restrict the types of forms explored.

Pencils The lead used in pencils comes in many different hardnesses (see Chapter 6); the harder the lead, the lighter and crisper the line. For general-purpose sketching, leads in the H and HB range will give you acceptable lines. If the lead is much harder, the lines will be too light and hard to see. In addition, hard lead has a tendency to puncture and tear some of the lighter weight papers used in sketching. On the other hand, if the lead is too soft, too much graphite is deposited on the paper and can be smudged easily. Leads in the middle range allow for a dark, relatively crisp line.

With any weight of lead, you can vary the darkness of the line to some degree. With wooden pencils, lighter lines can be drawn by dulling the point of the lead. With a thin-lead mechanical pencil, the lead is essentially always sharp. Lighter lines can be drawn by easing the pressure on the mechanical pencil as you draw.

Although traditional wooden pencils can be used for sketching, it is more common to use mechanical pencils. If

Historical Highlight
Very Early Attempts at Drawing

Our earliest records of drawings come from caves and from ancient Egyptian tomb drawings. Characteristics of drawings at this time include the human face simply displayed in a profile view. Legs are also shown in profile because bending of the legs will appear in true form. The torso, though, is better drawn from the front because it makes it easier to represent the arms naturally. Most drawings of this period are contrived so that the middle part of the figure is twisted so you see the side view of the head, the front view of the torso, and the side view of the legs. This method to depict humans was also used by the Babylonians from about 2500 B.C.

It is worth noting that most early drawings were of humans or of humans using something. The focus of most drawings seems to be to describe events or stories and not things. Even though the Greeks were quite advanced in geometry, the drawing of things was not important, which may have prevented development of drawing techniques useful for drawing technical devices. The development of drawing techniques suitable for technical drawings would have to wait for the Renaissance.

Excerpted from *The History of Engineering Drawing*, by Jeffrey Booker, Chatto & Windus, London, England, 1963.

E. Strouhal, © Werner Forman/Art Resource, NY.

only a single mechanical pencil is used, one with a 0.5-mm lead size is probably the best. However, if you want to emphasize a group of lines by drawing them thicker, you may want to work with a set of pencils, each with a different lead thickness. The alternative is to draw over the lines a number of times. This is less desirable since it is impossible to draw freehand exactly along the same path twice; each time you draw over a line, you widen or slightly change its path. Also, it is useful to have one pencil with a somewhat harder lead, such as 2H or 4H, to produce a slightly lighter line for preliminary construction lines.

Eraser Erasing should only be used to correct mistakes in a line, not to make changes in a design. Such changes should be recorded on a separate sketch, and the original sketch should be preserved. Still, most people find that a small amount of erasing is helpful. Usually, the eraser on the end of the pencil is sufficient. However, if you are going to do a lot of sketching, you may need a separate eraser, and one of any size or shape will do. You might consider a vinyl eraser, since they leave less residue when used.

Paper There is a wide range of paper choices for sketching (including a napkin you could draw on during lunch). The most accessible and easiest to use is notebook size (8½″ × 11″) paper. Because of the difficulty of drawing long lines freehand, paper much larger than that is normally not useful for a single sketch. On the other hand, larger paper is useful for drawing multiple sketches that should be visually grouped together.

Plain bond paper with no lines offers the highest degree of flexibility; lined paper tends to lock you in visually to drawing along the lines. However, when you want the guidance of existing lines on the paper, it is most useful to have the lines running along both dimensions, forming a grid. Two of the most common **grid papers** used in sketching are square grid (Figure 7.8A on the next page) and **isometric grid** (Figure 7.8B on the next page) for use in certain types of pictorial sketch. Common grid densities run from 4 to 10 lines per inch. A less common type of grid paper is perspective, which is used to create another type of pictorial sketch (Figure 7.8C on the next page).

Often, it would be useful to have grid lines for the sketch, but not for the final drawing. One way this can be achieved is to sketch on thin, plain, translucent tracing paper laid over the grid paper and taped down so that the grid lines show through. When the sketch is done, it is untaped from the grid paper and viewed without the grid lines behind it. This technique is also a money saver because grid paper is more expensive than tracing paper (often called

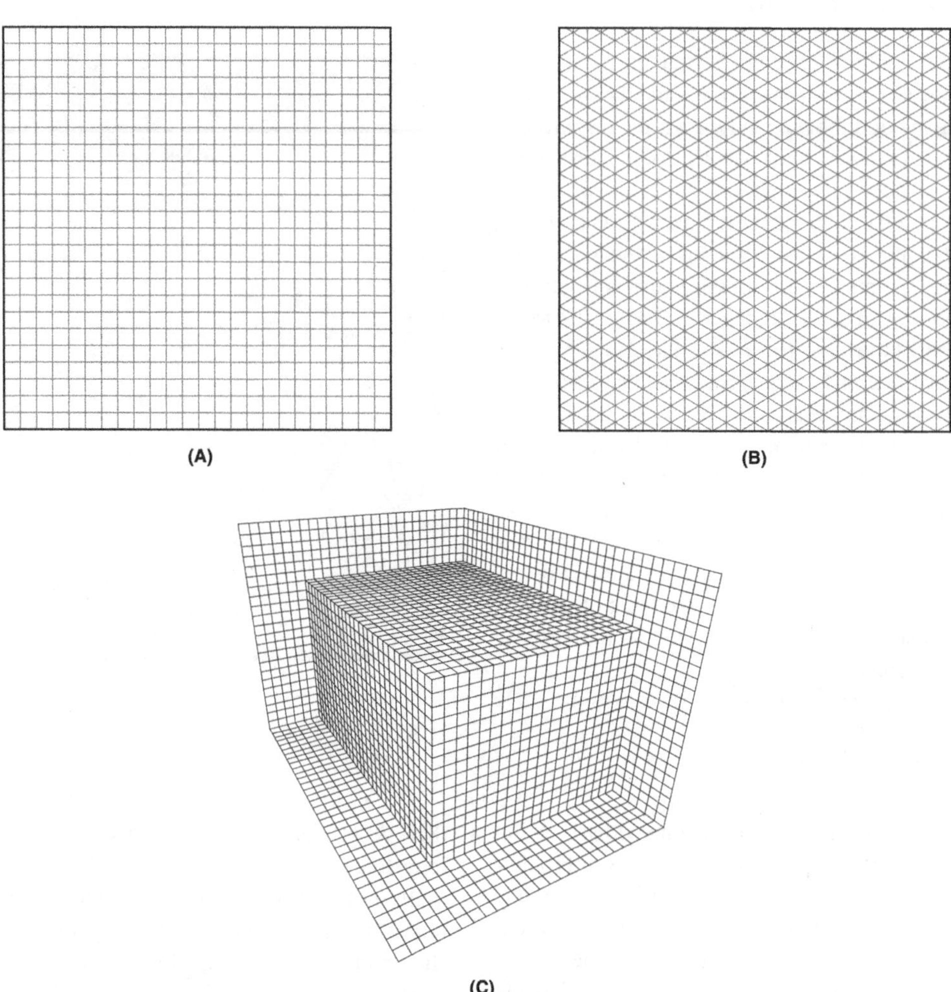

Figure 7.8

Square (A), isometric (B), and perspective (C) grids used for sketching

The grid lines are used as an aid in proportioning the drawing and sketching straight lines freehand.

trash paper), which can be bought in bulk on rolls. The other advantage to tracing paper is that it can be laid over other sketches, photos, or finished technical drawings. A light table can be used to improve the tracing process. Tracing is a fast, accurate method for refining a design idea in progress or for using an existing design as the starting point for a new one.

7.2 Sketching Technique

It takes practice and patience to produce sketches that are both legible and quickly made. The following sections describe common techniques used to produce good sketches quickly. The discussions cover the tools and the techniques for creating straight lines, curves (such as circles and arcs), and proportioned views. With patience and practice, it is possible for you to become good at making quick, clear sketches, regardless of your experience and natural drawing ability.

7.2.1 Straight Lines

All sketches are made up of a series of lines. Lines created for sketches differ from mechanically produced lines in that they are not constrained or guided by instruments, such as a T-square, template, or compass. Instead, the

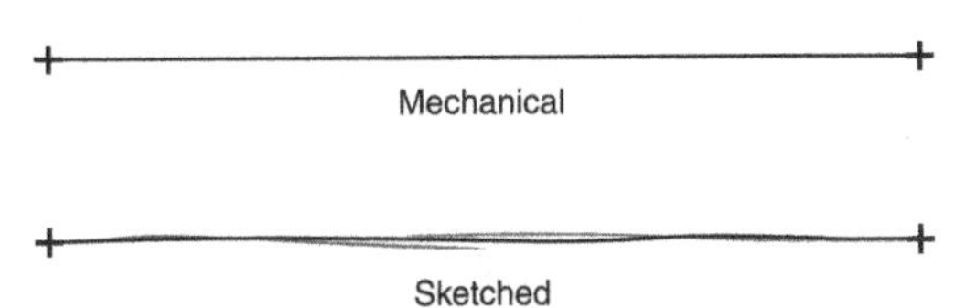

Figure 7.9

A comparison of mechanically drawn and sketched lines

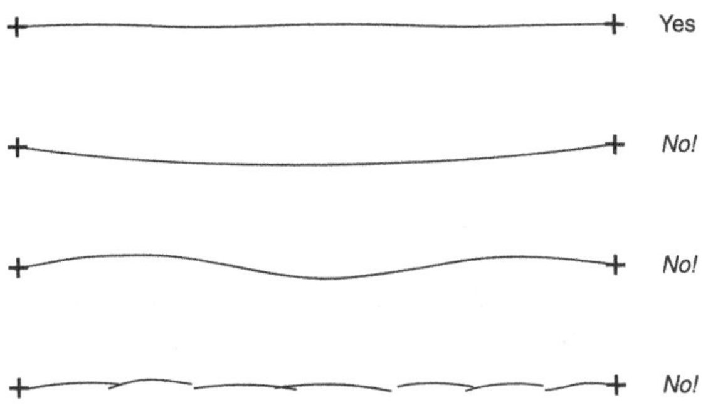

Figure 7.10

Examples of good and bad straight line technique

Sketched lines should be straight and dark and should have a consistent thickness.

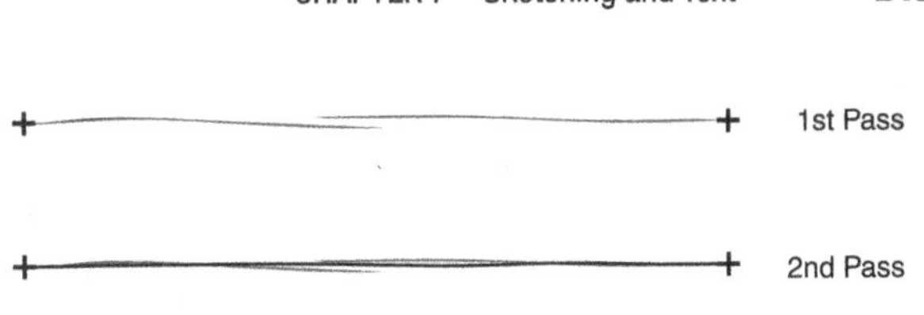

Figure 7.11

Sketching lines

The sequential drawing of a straight line is done by first drawing a very light line, using short strokes. The light line is then drawn over and darkened.

lines are guided strictly by the eye and hand. Such lines have a different aesthetic quality than mechanical lines (Figure 7.9). At a micro level, sketched straight lines are uneven; at a macro level, they should appear to follow a straight path without any interruptions (Figure 7.10).

One of the easiest guides to use for sketched lines is grid paper. Lines drawn right on the grid are the easiest to produce, and even those lines that are offset but parallel to a grid line are fairly easy to produce. The idea is to keep your sketched line a uniform (but not necessarily equal) distance between two existing grid lines.

Curved lines, straight lines not parallel to a grid line, and lines drawn without the aid of a grid are more difficult. In all of these cases, the lines are drawn as interpolations between two or more points. The points are typically marked on an engineering drawing as two intersecting lines, one horizontal and one vertical, and each approximately 3/16″ long. Your eye should take a "global" view of all the points to be connected and should guide your hand as it goes from point to point.

Quite often, the sketched line is built up from a sequence of two or three passes with the pencil (Figure 7.11). The first pass is drawn light, using a hard lead, such as a 4H, sharpened to a point, and may not be as straight as your final line will be; however, it should provide a path on top of which the final, even, darker line is drawn. For particularly long lines, the initial line may be drawn in segments, coming from the two endpoints and meeting in the middle; however, the final line should be drawn in one single pass to avoid choppiness. If necessary, another pass can be used to darken or thicken the line.

Long lines are difficult to control, even for someone with a lot of experience. If you cannot choose a drawing scale that reduces the size of the sketch, use grid paper as a guide, drawing either directly on the grid paper or on tracing paper placed on top of the grid paper. If the line is parallel and relatively close to the edge of the paper, you can rest a finger or a portion of your palm along the edge of the paper to stabilize your drawing hand (Figure 7.12 on the next page). If necessary, you can use a ruler or a scrap of paper to mark a series of points on the sketch, but this will slow you down a bit.

Another technique that helps when drawing lines of any length is changing the orientation of the paper. Sketching paper should not be fixed to your drawing surface. Instead, you should be able to rotate the paper freely, orienting it in the direction that is most comfortable. Practice will determine which orientation is best for you. Many people find that drawing the lines by moving away from or toward the body, rather than from left to right, produces the quickest, straightest lines; others find it most comfortable if the paper is angled slightly away from the body. Again, the longer the line, the more important it is that the paper be positioned comfortably for you.

To sketch quickly, accurately, and without fatigue, your hand and the rest of your body should be relaxed. Paper orientation should allow your whole forearm to be in a comfortable position. Your hand must also be relaxed and comfortable. Students learning to sketch often believe that sketched lines must be as rigid as mechanically drawn

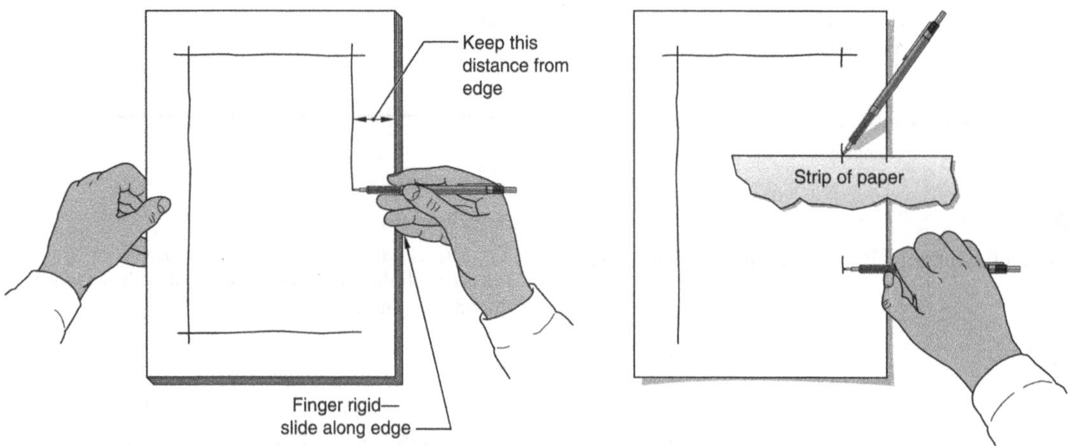

Figure 7.12

Sketching long lines

Very long lines can sometimes be more difficult to draw. One technique is to use the edge of the paper as a guide for your hand. Another technique is to mark equal distances from the edge of the paper using a marked scrap of paper as a guide. The marks are then used as a guide to produce the line.

lines, and they assume that the tighter they grip the pencil, the more control they will have over the line. In fact, the opposite is true. A more relaxed grip (though not relaxed enough to let the pencil slip in your hand) will allow the eye and mind to control the pencil more directly, making almost subconscious corrections to keep it on track.

With experience, although you will be conscious of where you are drawing from and to, the actual drawing of the line will be virtually automatic. The idea is to find the right balance between relaxed, comfortable drawing and sloppy, loose drawing. Although not drawn with instruments, sketched lines should still be crisp, and straight lines should be easily distinguishable from those that are supposed to be curved.

The following summarizes the techniques used to sketch straight lines:

- Orient the paper to a comfortable position. Do not fix the paper to the surface.
- Mark the endpoints of the lines to be sketched.
- Determine the most comfortable method of creating lines, such as drawing from left to right, or drawing either away from or toward your body.
- Relax your hand and the rest of your body.
- Use the edge of the paper as a guide for making straight lines.
- Draw long lines by sketching a series of connected short lines.
- If necessary, draw on grid paper or on tracing paper that is overlaid on grid paper.

Sketching Straight Lines

In this exercise, you are to create a series of 5″ long parallel lines equally spaced at 0.5″. Refer to Figures 7.10 and 7.11.

Step 1. Lightly mark the endpoints of the lines to be sketched on 8½″ × 11″ paper.

Step 2. Orient the paper in a comfortable position for sketching.

Step 3. Comfortably and in a relaxed manner, position your hand so that the pencil is close to one of the marked endpoints of the first line to be sketched. Sketch the top line first, to avoid smearing newly sketched lines with your hand.

Step 4. Quickly scan the two endpoints of the first line to determine the general direction in which you will be sketching.

Step 5. Lightly sketch a short line, approximately 1″ long, by moving your hand and the pencil in the general direction of the other end of the line.

Step 6. Repeat steps 4 and 5 until the other end of the line is reached.

Step 7. Return to the starting point of the line and overdraw the line segments with a slightly longer, heavier stroke, to produce a thick, dark, more continuous straight line.

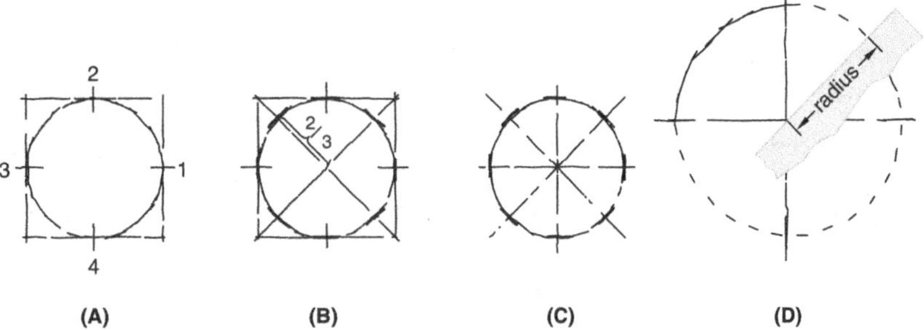

Figure 7.13

Sketching a circle

Sketching a circle is easier using one of the techniques shown. For small circles, use a square or multiple center lines to guide the construction process. For large circles, use a scrap of paper with the radius marked on it as a guide.

Step 8. Repeat steps 3 through 7 to sketch the remaining straight lines.

7.2.2 Curved Lines

Curved lines need multiple guide points. The most common curve is a circle or circular arc. Although very small circles and arcs can be drawn in one or two strokes and with no guide points, larger circles need some preliminary points. The minimum number of points for a circle is four, marked on the perimeter at equal 90-degree intervals. For an arc, use at least one guide point for every 90 degrees and one at each end.

There are a number of ways to lay out the guide points for circular curves quickly. One way is to draw a square box whose sides are equal to the diameter of the circle (Figure 7.13A). The midpoints on each side of the square mark the points where the circle will touch the square. These points are called points of tangency. More guide points can be added by drawing the two diagonals across the square. The center of the circle being sketched is the point where the diagonals cross (Figure 7.13B). Mark the guide points on each diagonal approximately two-thirds the distance from the center of the circle to the corner of the square. This distance is the approximate radius of the circle (Figure 7.13C).

As with longer straight lines, large arcs and circles are harder to draw and may need guide points marked at more frequent intervals. To do this, it is handy to use a scrap of paper with the radius marked on it (Figure 7.13D).

Circular arcs are drawn the same way as circles, adjusting the number of points to suit the degree of curvature (i.e., the length) of the arc. Noncircular arcs, however, can be more difficult. Since these lines are only to be sketched, calculating the points that the curve should pass through is too involved and is not recommended. Simply use the eye to estimate guide points and then gradually draw a curve to pass through those points. (Ellipses and curves in multiview drawings are two special cases treated later in this chapter.)

As with straight lines, positioning the paper and using a relaxed grip are important for helping you create good curves. Unlike straight lines, curves are usually best drawn in a series of arcs of not more than 90 degrees. After each arc is drawn, rotate the paper for the next segment of arc. With practice you may be able to eliminate rotating the paper for smaller arcs, but will probably still have to do so for larger ones.

A common pitfall when drawing circles is not properly estimating the degree of curvature. This leads to arcs that are too flat, too curved, or both (Figure 7.14). Until you get better, more points along the arc will help guide you.

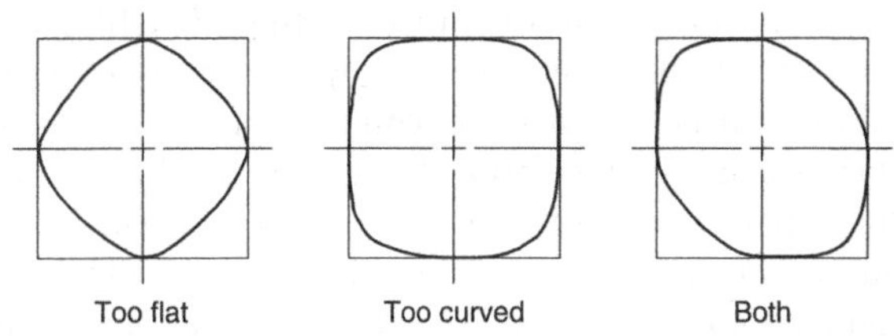

Figure 7.14

Poorly drawn circles will have flat areas and sharp curves

Sketching a Circle or Arc

The following steps demonstrate how to sketch a circle or arc. Refer to Figures 7.13 and 7.14 as a guide.

Step 1. Orient the paper in a comfortable position and relax your grip on the pencil. Lightly mark the corners of a square with sides equal in length to the diameter of the circle or arc to be sketched.

Step 2. Lightly sketch the square, using short strokes to create the straight lines.

Step 3. Mark the midpoints of the four sides of the square. This gives you four marks on the perimeter of the circle.

Step 4. Sketch diagonals across the corners of the square. Where the diagonals cross is the center of the circle.

Step 5. Mark the diagonals at two-thirds the distance from the center of the circle to the corner of the square. This gives you four more marks on the circle's perimeter.

Step 6. Sketch the circle by creating eight short arcs, each between two adjacent marks on the perimeter. Start at any mark and sketch an arc to the next mark (on either side of the first one, whichever is most comfortable for you).

Step 7. Rotate the paper and sketch the next arc from the last mark you touched to the next mark on the perimeter. Repeat this step until all eight arc segments have been sketched. For smoother sketches, rotate the paper in the opposite direction from the one you used to draw the arc.

Step 8. Overdraw the arcs with a thick, black, more continuous line to complete the sketched circle.

7.2.3 Contour Sketching

The most fundamental element to creating sketches is the line or the outline of an object. The lines or outlines of an object are used to represent the edges and contours of objects we see in the world. If we sketch the boundaries, an object slowly takes shape and we begin to recognize it as a familiar object. This technique of sketching the outline of an object is called **contour sketching** and is an important technique used by novice sketchers to gain confidence in their sketching ability. Contours on objects can take the form of edges of an object, lines that separate contrasting light or color, changes in the surface of an object, and overlapping parts. The primary reason for contour sketching is to develop your visual acuity and sensitivity to important object features which are necessary to create accurate sketched representations.

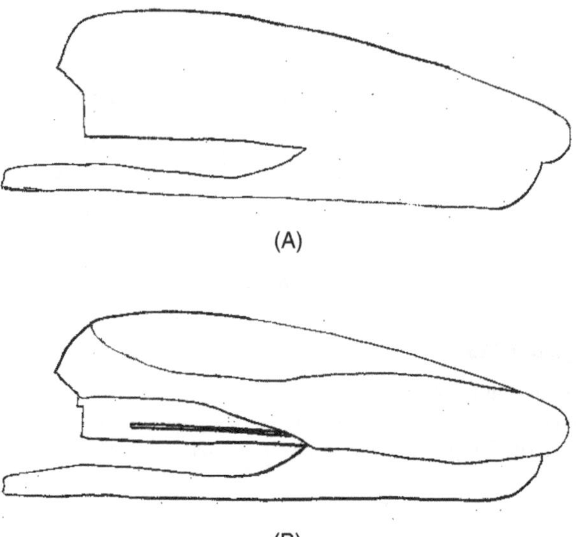

Figure 7.15

Contour sketch

A contour sketch is created by carefully observing the outline of an object while sketching. This technique is used to improve your sketching ability. In (A), the contour sketch was created without looking at the paper. The contour sketch in (B) was created by looking at the object, then looking at the paper as the sketch was produced.

When first learning how to use contour sketching, begin by slowly tracing the outline of an object with your eyes while slowly sketching what you see. At first the sketch may seem crude and out of proportion, but with practice your sketches will be quite good. Figure 7.15A shows an example of a contour sketch created by carefully looking at the outline of the object and sketching what you see without looking at the paper. Figure 7.15B is a sketch created by carefully looking at the outline of the object and looking at the paper as you sketch. Both techniques are useful when learning how to observe and create sketches of what you see.

Making a Contour Sketch

In this exercise, you are to create a sketch of the stapler shown in Figure 7.15 using the contour sketching technique.

Step 1. Using a plain piece of white paper and a soft lead pencil, place your drawing hand with the pencil near the center of the paper.

Step 2. Orient the paper in a comfortable position for sketching.

Step 3. Comfortably and in a relaxed manner, very slowly begin to trace the outline of the object with your eyes.

Step 4. Slowly move your pencil across the paper as your eyes scan the outline of the object. Do not erase or sketch over lines and do not look at your sketch. Sketch very slowly and deliberately.

Step 5. Continue to draw each edge as you view it at a slow and deliberate pace.

Step 6. Look at your sketch after you have completed viewing the contours of the object. Repeat steps to improve technique.

Making a Modified Contour Sketch

In this exercise, you are to create a contour sketch but you will be able to look at your sketch as you are working (Figure 7.15).

Step 1. Using a plain piece of white paper and a soft lead pencil, place your drawing hand with the pencil near the center of the paper.

Step 2. Orient the paper in a comfortable position for sketching.

Step 3. Comfortably and in a relaxed manner, very slowly begin to trace the outline of the object with your eyes.

Step 4. Slowly move your pencil across the paper as your eyes scan the outline of the object. Do not erase or sketch over lines. Sketch very slowly and deliberately.

Step 5. Occasionally look at your sketch to match it with the object being drawn.

Step 6. Continue to draw each edge and interior edges as you view it at a slow and deliberate pace.

7.2.4 Negative Space Sketching

Another useful technique novice sketchers can try to improve their sketching technique is called **negative space sketching.** In this technique you concentrate on the spaces between the objects and not on the object itself. In other words, you concentrate on the geometry of the object, such as lines, curves, angles, tangencies, and not the names of the objects, such as handle, hole, base, cube. An example of a negative space sketch is shown in Figure 7.16. Notice the object itself is not shaded and lacks details, but the space surrounding the object is shaded.

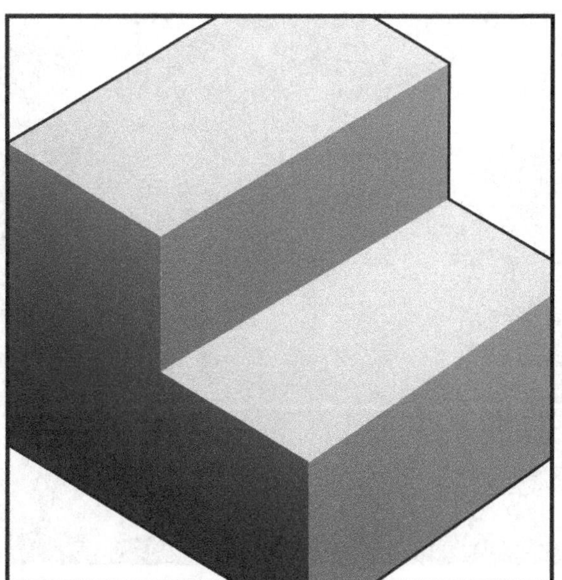

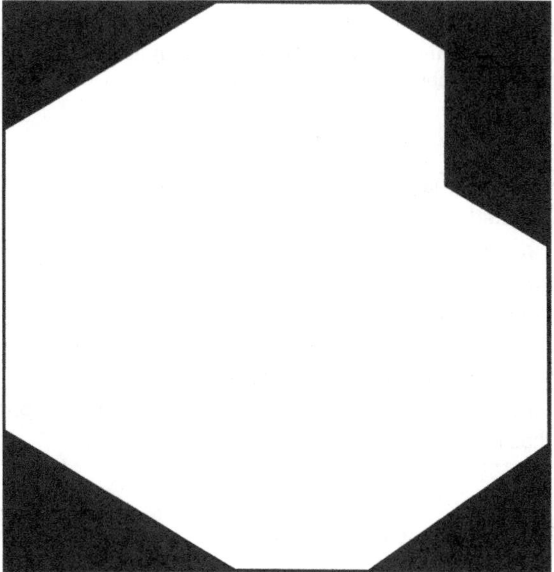

Figure 7.16

Negative space sketching

Negative space sketching produces a sketch having only the spaces between the object and not the object itself.

Making a Negative Space Sketch

For this exercise, you are to create a negative space sketch of the object shown in Figure 7.16.

Step 1. Use a plain sheet of white paper and begin by sketching the box surrounding the object.

Step 2. Sketch over the top of the negative spaces in the figure to reinforce that you are going to be sketching the negative spaces and not the object itself.

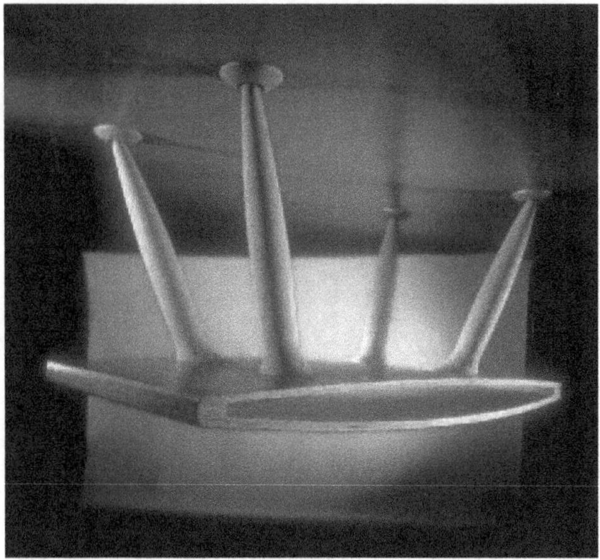

Figure 7.17

Upside-down sketching

Sketch the outline of the object by concentrating on the geometric forms not the names of the parts.

(Courtesy of Lunar Design.)

Step 3. Focus on one of the outlined negative spaces just created in step 2 until you can visualize the negative space.

Step 4. Now begin sketching the negative space form on your sheet of paper. Concentrate on drawing lines and curves by determining the angles, lengths, tangencies, and other geometric characteristics.

Step 5. Repeat steps 3 and 4 until all the negative space has been created.

7.2.5 Upside-Down Sketching

Upside-down sketching is another method that can be used to improve your sketching ability. In this technique you take a photograph of a recognizable object, such as a chair, and turn it upside-down before sketching it. By turning it upside-down you can concentrate on the shape and form of the object, allowing you to create a better sketch. Figure 7.17 is a photograph of a table that is upside-down. Carefully sketch the outline of the object by concentrating on the geometry or form and not the names of the part, such as legs or feet. By doing so you will be able to create a more accurate sketch of the object.

7.3 Proportions and Construction Lines

Frequently, in the sketch of an object, the relative proportions of its primary dimensions—width, height, and depth—are more important than their actual physical sizes. A **proportion** is the ratio between any two dimensions of an object. These proportions are represented in the sketch by a series of preliminary lines, which are drawn light and fast, and which may or may not represent the locations of the final lines in the sketch. Their purpose is to form a backbone, a structure inside which the final linework can be drawn.

The first step in a sketch involves drawing the construction lines, which guide a sketch's overall shape and proportion. **Construction lines** are very light, thin lines used to roughly lay out some of the details of sketches or drawings. Do not try to draw the construction lines to exact lengths since lengths are marked later, by either intersecting lines or short tick marks.

Construction lines have two primary features: the lines themselves and the intersections created where two lines cross. For example, the construction lines become the paths for the final straight lines. Points marked by the intersections of construction lines guide the drawing of circles. Usually, both of these features are used in creating sketches. Since all the dimensions of a sketch are estimated, groups of construction lines forming boxes and other shapes are an important tool for preserving the shape and proportion of the object and its features as the sketch is developed.

Grid paper can be used as a guide in creating construction lines but should not be thought of as a substitute, since the grid does not directly represent the proportions of the object, and there are many more grid lines than there are features on the object. The goal is to draw construction lines on top of the grid to reveal the form of the object. With experience, you may be able to make do with fewer construction lines, but while you are learning how to create properly proportioned sketches, you should use more, rather than fewer, construction lines to guide you.

The level of detail in many objects can be daunting for beginners. The best strategy—even if you are an experienced sketcher—is to draw the object in stages. Before beginning a sketch, look at the object carefully and identify its various features. One feature could be the entire object. Other features may be holes, notches, rounded corners, etc. On more complex objects, groups of features can be combined to form larger features.

Each feature has a proportion that can be represented by a series of construction lines. The following steps de-

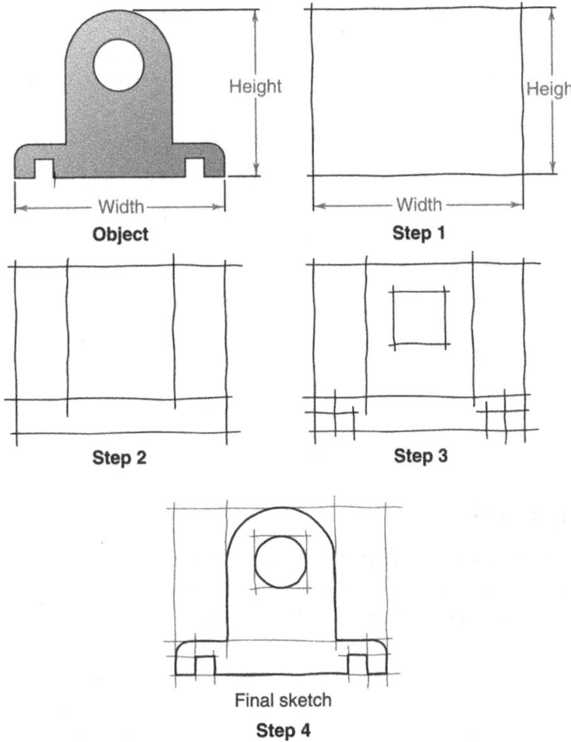

Figure 7.18

Creating a proportioned sketch

To create a well-proportioned sketch, use multiple steps to create lightly sketched boxes that are then used as guides for the final sketch.

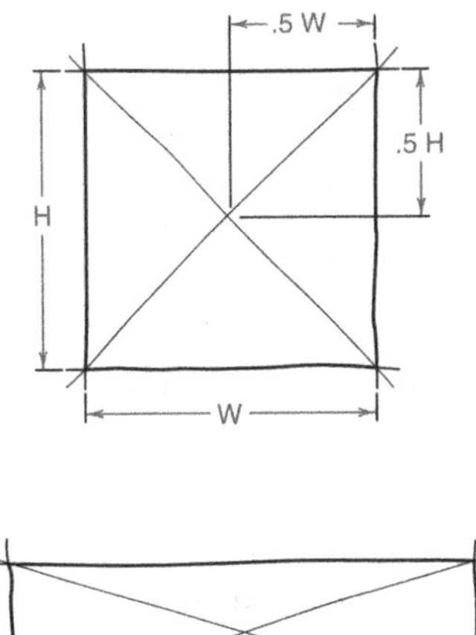

Figure 7.19

Locating the center of squares and rectangles

Construction lines are used to draw diagonals marking the center of a square or rectangle.

scribe how to proportion a drawing by breaking it down into its component features.

Creating a Proportioned Sketch

Step 1. Refer to Figure 7.18. Gage the proportion of the overall size of the object. For the first sketch, use two overall dimensions of the object: width and height. Lightly sketch a box that represents the ratio of these two dimensions (Figure 7.18, Step 1). This box is called a **bounding box** because it represents the outer dimensional limits of the feature being drawn. If the object is rectangular in shape, the final linework will follow the perimeter of the bounding box. In most cases, however, the final linework will only touch on a portion of the box's edges.

Step 2. Inside the first bounding box, draw other boxes to represent the larger features of the object, and within those boxes draw still others to represent the smaller features of the object. Often, a construction line can be used for more than one box. The final boxes each show the proportions of one feature of the object.

Step 3. Continue to draw bounding boxes until the smallest features of the object have been represented. As you gain experience, you may find that some of these smaller features need not be boxed; instead, their final lines can be sketched directly.

Step 4. When all of the features of the object have been boxed, begin sketching the final linework, which is done significantly darker than the construction lines.

The goal is, if you hold the drawing at arm's length, the construction lines are hard to see, and the final linework is clear and sharp. If there is not enough contrast between the construction lines and the final linework, then the construction lines become a distraction. Make the final lines darker, or the construction lines lighter, or both; however, do not erase your construction lines.

Some construction lines are not part of a bounding box. These lines are used to create intersections to mark important points. For example, diagonals inside a bounding box can be used to mark its center (Figure 7.19). This holds true whether the box is square or rectangular. This centerpoint could then mark either the center of the feature to be drawn, or the corner for another, smaller bounding box (Figure 7.20 on the next page).

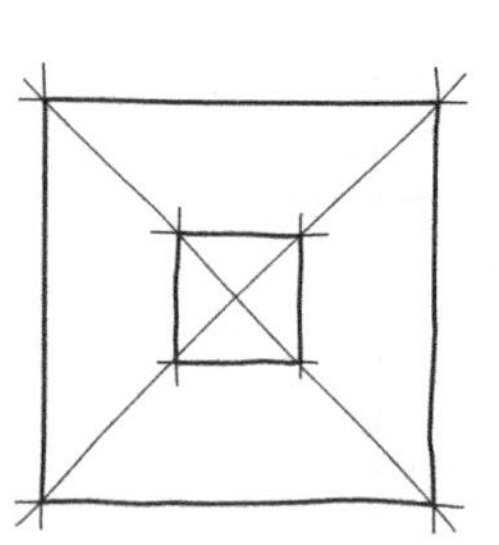

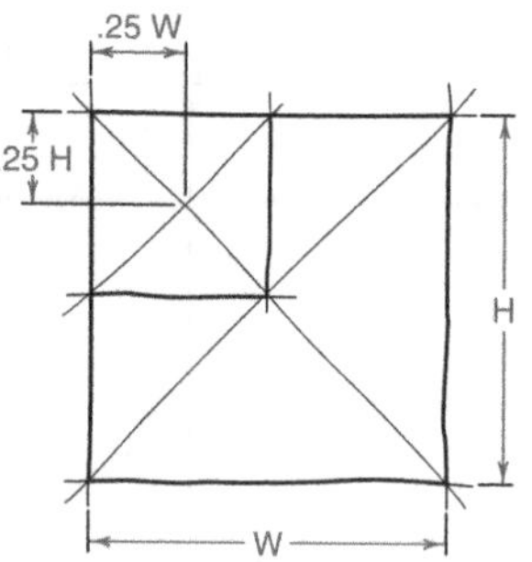

Figure 7.20

Constructing proportioned squares

Construction lines are used to draw diagonals that can be used to construct new squares or rectangles.

Sketching Identically Proportioned Squares

Figure 7.21 demonstrates how to create a series of identically proportioned squares.

Step 1. In the square that you want to duplicate, draw a pair of diagonal lines to locate its center. Through this center point, draw lines to the midpoints of each of its sides (Figure 7.21, Step 1).

Step 2. Extend out to one side the top and bottom horizontal lines of the bounding box. Draw a diagonal line toward one of the horizontal lines, starting from one corner (marked A) and going through the midpoint of the adjacent perpendicular side (marked B).

Step 3. Where the diagonal line crosses the upper horizontal line, mark the corner of the new box. Sketch a vertical line from this point to complete the new square.

The proportioned square method is especially useful when grid paper is not used and you need to create a larger object out of a series of identically proportioned smaller boxes. As shown in Figure 7.21, this method can be adapted to squares of any size.

One of the most difficult sketching techniques to learn is making a sketch look well proportioned. For example, Figure 7.22 shows a well proportioned and a poorly proportioned sketch of a computer monitor. Proportioning skills will improve with practice. A good rule of thumb is, if the drawing does not look or feel right, it probably is not. In the poorly proportioned monitor in Figure 7.22, the ratio of the height to the width is incorrect.

Whether you are copying another drawing or sketching a real object, the temptation is to accurately measure all

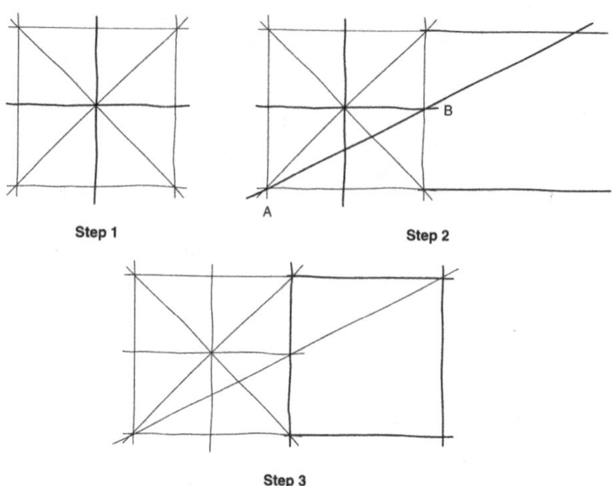

Figure 7.21

Sketching identically proportioned squares

An identically proportioned square is created by extending both top and bottom horizontal lines and constructing diagonals across the existing box.

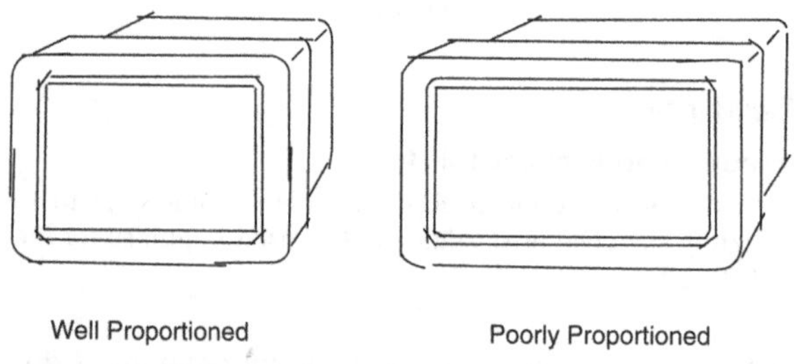

Figure 7.22

Good and poor proportions

One well and one poorly proportioned sketch of a computer monitor. The poorly proportioned monitor looks too wide.

the features. This defeats the purpose of doing a sketch. If you are copying a drawing, the fastest approach is simply to trace over it. If you must enlarge (or reduce) the sketch, use grid paper and multiply (or divide) the number of grids enclosed in a feature, or use a grid of a different size (Figure 7.23). If you are sketching a real object, roughly measure the overall dimensions with a scale, or mark the measurements on any convenient material. If you are going to sketch a larger object, stand at a distance from the object, face it, and hold a pencil at arm's length in front of you (Figure 7.24). Align the end of the pencil with one

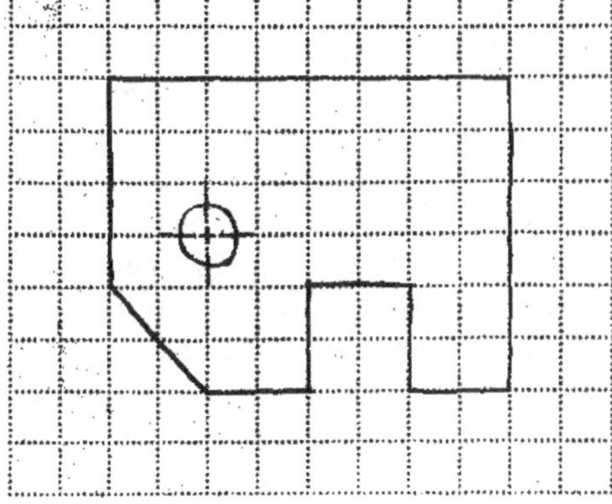

Figure 7.23

Grid paper is used to scale an object

The scale can be changed by enlarging or reducing the values. For example, to double the size of the sketch, multiply 8 and 6 by 2, and sketch the part on a grid using 16 and 12 as the new width and height.

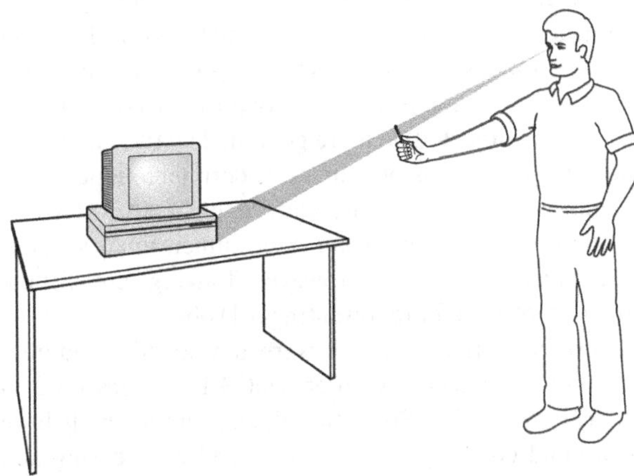

Figure 7.24

Estimating dimensions of larger objects with a pencil held at arm's length

edge of a feature, as sighted along your outstretched arm. Make a mark on the pencil to represent the opposite edge of that feature. Translate this pencil length to the sketch, and repeat the process for other features and their dimensions. Be sure to stand in the same place every time!

In all cases, a progressive refinement of the construction lines from the largest feature to the smallest will allow you to compare your sketch regularly with the object and the proportions being sketched.

Sketching Objects

Step 1. Collect magazine photographs or clippings that show 2-D images or patterns. These can range from pictures of faces, to company logos, to fronts of buildings, etc. Stick with images that look *flat*, that is, images that don't show a depth dimension.

Step 2. Lay tracing paper over the image and tape the paper down.

Step 3. Lightly sketch an overall bounding box of the object. Look at the image contained in the bounding box. Mentally identify as many features on the object as you can. The features may be small and self-contained or a collection of several smaller features.

Step 4. Refine the drawing by sketching a series of progressively smaller bounding boxes. Start with the larger features and work downwards.

Step 5. If desired, you can then darken some of the lines representing the image, to highlight the most important lines of a feature. What are the most important lines of a feature? Experiment with different lines to see which are more critical than others in representing the form of the image.

Hint: Buy a roll of tracing paper from your local blueprint or art supply store. It's cheaper than individual sheets, and you won't run out as often.

7.4 Types of Sketches

Sketching is used to communicate, to yourself and to others, as shown in Figure 7.25. **Ideation sketches** are quickly produced, simplified, annotated,

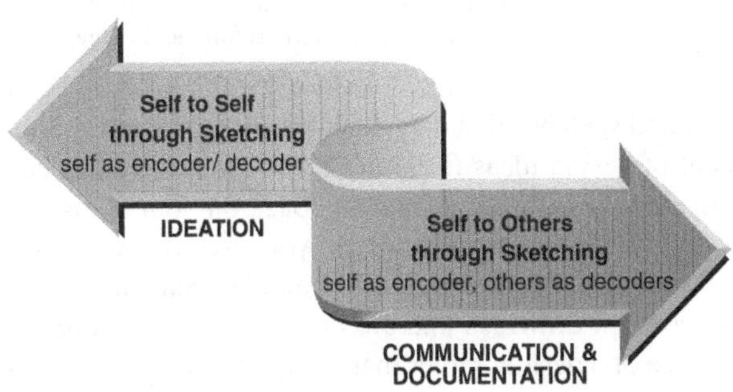

Figure 7.25

Types of sketches

Sketches are used to communicate to oneself or to others. Sketches for oneself are done to record ideas quickly and are usually very rough. Sketches for others are part of a communications process that requires the sketches to be more refined.

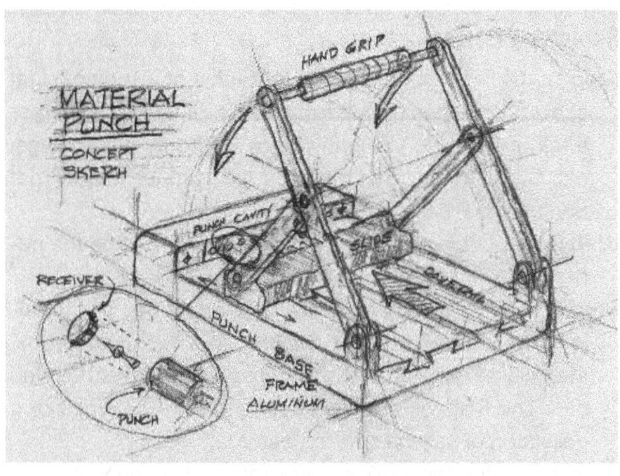

(A)

(B)

Figure 7.26

Ideation sketches

This is an ideation sketch of a material punch (A) and subsequent document sketch (B) for use in the refinement stage.

freehand sketches that document the progressive development of design ideas (Figure 7.26A). These sketches can provide you with immediate feedback on your ideas. By sketching thoughts as they occur, you also create a historical record of the development of an idea. Sketches, then, are concept drawings and are only meant to capture the essence of a design, rather than every last detail. Think of an ideation sketch as a type of graphic shorthand. The sketches may be very rough and may not necessarily be used to communicate to others.

At some point, however, ideas must be shared. Sketches can be used for this purpose. **Document sketches**, though still quickly produced, are more formalized, annotated, freehand sketches that are neater and more refined than ideation sketches (Figure 7.26B). These sketches are used in the refinement stage of engineering design and include many of the standards and conventions appropriate for engineering and technical drawings produced with drawing instruments or CAD.

In many cases, ideation sketches can be traced over and refined to create document sketches. Remember, however, that document sketches are still produced freehand and lack the detail of a final technical drawing. The refinement of the ideation sketch is primarily a transformation of personal graphic notes into a standardized, universally recognized format.

7.5 Introduction to Projections

Both ideation and document sketches can represent the objects being designed in a number of different ways. We live in a three-dimensional (3-D) world, and representing that world for artistic or technical purposes is largely done on two-dimensional (2-D) media. Although a sheet of paper is technically three-dimensional, the thickness of the paper (the third dimension) is useless to us. It should be noted that the computer screen is a form of two-dimensional media, and images projected on it are governed by the same limitations as projections on paper. Modern techniques, such as holograms, stereograms, and virtual reality devices, are attempts to communicate three-dimensional ideas as three-dimensional forms. However, drawings are still the primary tool used for representing 3-D objects.

Most projection methods were developed to address the problem of trying to represent 3-D images on 2-D media (Figure 7.27). Projection theory and methods have taken hundreds of years to evolve, and engineering and technical graphics is heavily dependent on projection theory.

The most common types of projection used in sketching are *multiview*, *isometric* (one type of axonometric), *oblique*, and *perspective*, as shown in Figure 7.28. (See also Figure 10.1 in Chapter 10.) These four types of projection can be placed in two major categories: multiview sketches and pictorial sketches. **Multiview sketches** present the object in a series of projections, each one showing only two of the object's three dimensions. The other three types of projection, grouped as **pictorial sketches**, present the object in a single, pictorial view, with all three dimensions, width, height, and depth, represented. There are always trade-offs when using any type of projection; some are more realistic, some are easier to draw, and some are easier to interpret by nontechnical people.

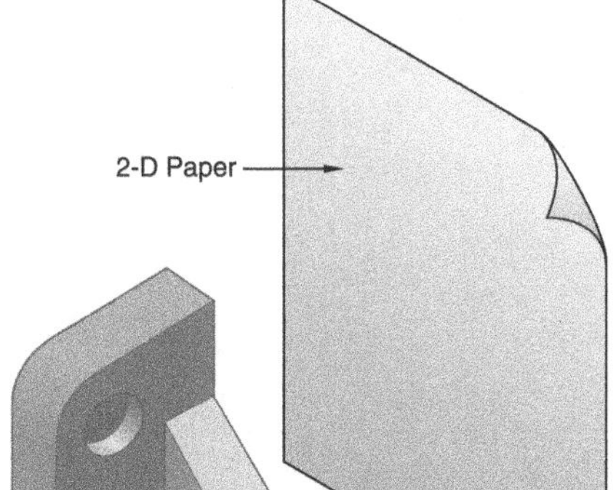

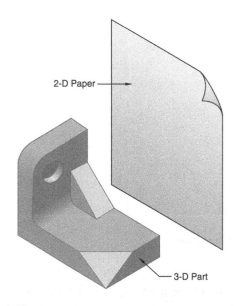

Figure 7.27

3-D object on 2-D medium

For centuries, graphicians have struggled with representing 3-D objects on 2-D paper. Various projection techniques have evolved to solve this problem.

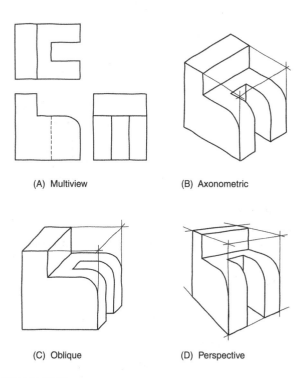

Various 2-D CAD-based tools have eased the process of creating pictorials. Probably the easiest way of creating such views is to use a 3-D CAD package to create a model. This model can easily represent pictorial views and can also generate views for a multiview drawing.

Another way of classifying projections relates to whether they use **parallel projection** or **perspective projection**. Multiview, isometric, and oblique multiview projections use parallel projection, which preserves the true relationships of an object's features and edges. This type of projection is the basis of most engineering and technical graphics. Perspective projection distorts the object so that it more closely matches how you perceive it visually.

Since it is much easier to lay out a sketch in parallel rather than in perspective projection, you will probably find yourself doing a majority of your sketching using parallel projection, even though it is less realistic. Only when the object spans a large distance—such as a house or bridge—will it be useful to represent the distortion your eyes perceive as the object recedes from view. Since parallel projection is the basis for most engineering and technical graphics, Chapters 10 and 11 in this text present the theory and fundamental concepts of this projection technique.

(A) Multiview

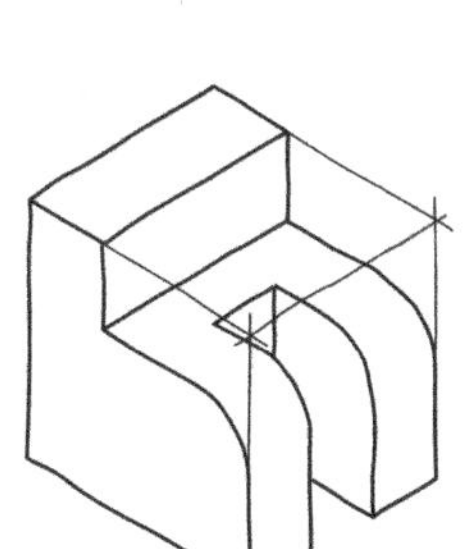

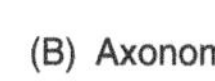

(B) Axonometric

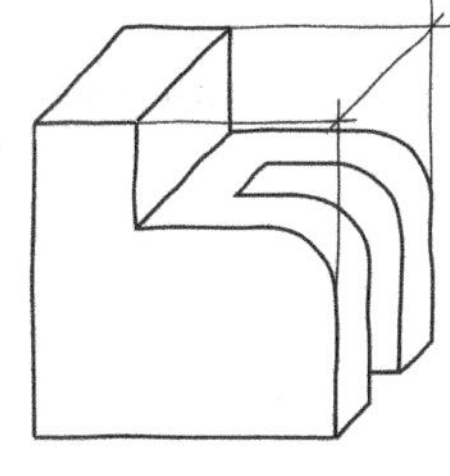

(C) Oblique

(D) Perspective

Figure 7.28

Classification of sketches

Various projection techniques are used to create four basic types of sketches: multiview, axonometric, oblique, and perspective. The sketches shown in B, C, and D are called pictorial because they represent the object as a 3-D form. The multiview sketch uses multiple flat views of the 3-D object to accurately represent its form on 2-D paper.

7.5.1 Isometric Pictorials

An **isometric pictorial** sketch is a type of parallel projection that represents all three dimensions in a single image. Although there are a number of ways of orienting an object to represent all three dimensions, isometric pictorials have a standard orientation that makes them particularly easy to sketch. Start by looking at the two-point perspective in Figure 7.29 on the next page. Then, instead of having the width and depth construction lines converge on vanishing points, have them project parallel to each other at a 30-degree angle above the baseline (Figure 7.30 on the next page). A more complete treatment of constructing isometric pictorials is presented in Chapter 11.

Many CAD systems will automatically produce an isometric view of a 3-D model when the viewing angle is specified. Some CAD systems have predefined views, such as isometric, which are automatically created after selection.

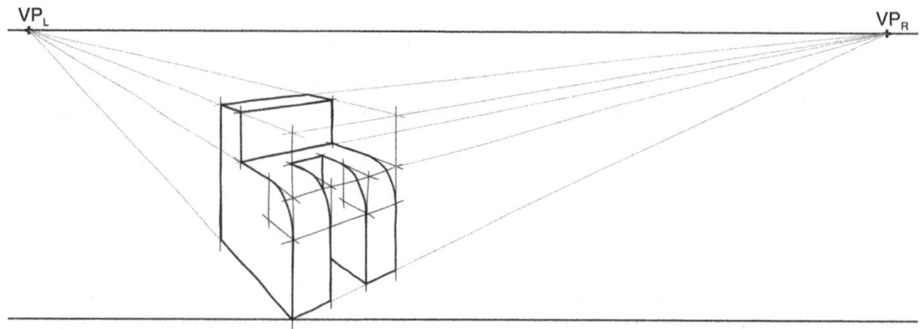

Figure 7.29

Perspective sketch

For perspective projection, the width and depth dimensions converge on vanishing points.

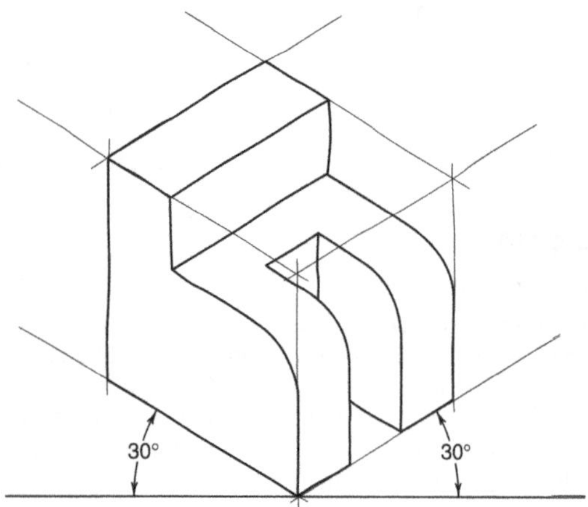

Figure 7.30

Isometric sketch

For this isometric sketch, the width and depth dimensions are sketched 30 degrees above the horizontal.

Making an Isometric Sketch

Make an isometric sketch of the object shown in Figure 7.31.

Sketching the isometric axis

Step 1. Isometric sketches begin with defining an **isometric axis**, which is made of three lines, one vertical and two drawn at 30 degrees from the horizontal. These three lines of the isometric axis represent the three primary dimensions of the object: width, height, and depth. Although they are sketched at an angle of 60 degrees to each other, they represent mutually perpendicular lines in 3-D space.

Step 2. Begin the sketch by extending the isometric axes shown in Step 1, Figure 7.31. Sketch a horizontal construction line through the bottom of the vertical line. Sketch a line from the base of the vertical line to the right, at an approximate angle of 30 degrees above the horizontal construction line. Sketch a line from the base of the vertical line to the left, at an approximate angle of 30 degrees above the horizontal construction line.

The corner of the axis is labeled point 1; the end of the width line is labeled point 2; the end of the depth line is labeled point 4; and the top of the height line is labeled point 3. The lengths of these lines are not important, since they will be treated as construction lines, but they should be more than long enough to represent the overall dimensions of the object. Estimate the overall width, height, and depth of the object using the estimating techniques described earlier in this chapter. Use these dimensions to sketch a block that would completely enclose the object.

Blocking in the object

Step 3. Sketch in the front face of the object by sketching a line parallel to and equal in length to the width dimension, passing the new line through point 3. Sketch a line parallel to and equal in length to the vertical line (1–3), through points 5–2. The front face of the object is complete.

Step 4. From point 3, block in the top face of the object by sketching a line parallel to and equal in length to line 1–4. This line is labeled 3–6. Sketch a line parallel to and equal in length to line 3–5, from point 6. This line is labeled 6–7. Sketch a line from point 5 to point 7. This line should be parallel to and equal in length to line 3–6. Block in the right side face by sketching a line from point 6 to point 4,

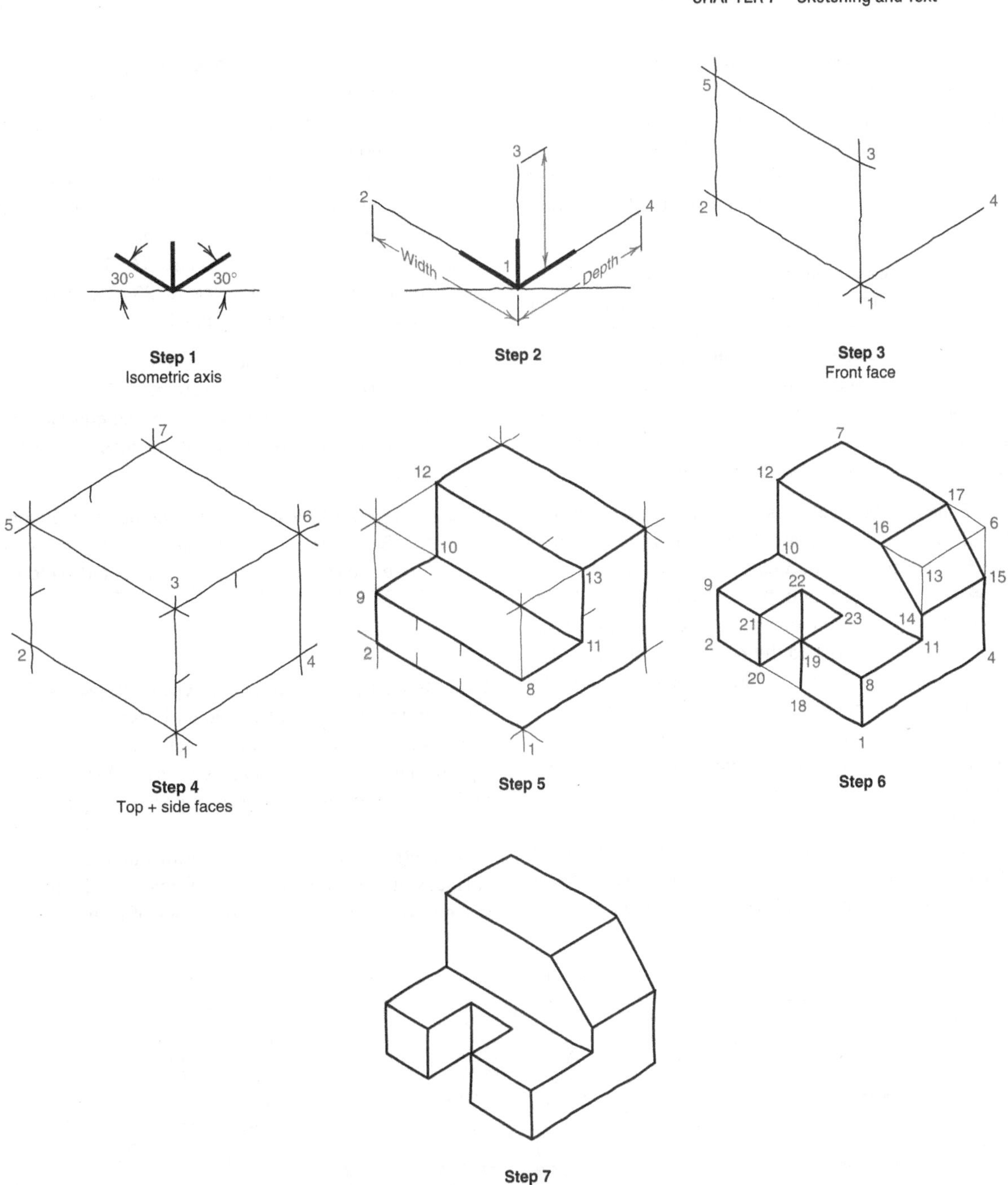

Figure 7.31

The basic steps used to create an isometric sketch of an object

which is parallel to line 1–3. The bounding box of the object, sketched as construction lines, is now finished. The box serves the same purpose as the one drawn in Figure 7.18, but it represents all three dimensions of the object instead of just two.

Adding details to the isometric block

Step 5. Begin by estimating the dimensions to cut out the upper front corner of the block, and mark these points as shown in Step 7. Sketch the height along the front face by creating a line parallel to line 1–2; label it 8–9. Sketch 30-degree lines from points 8 and 9 and label these lines 9–10 and 8–11. Now sketch a line from point 10 to point 11. Sketch vertical lines from points 10 and 11 and label the new lines 10–12 and 11–13. Sketch a line from point 12 to point 13, to complete the front cutout of the block.

With a simple sketch, you can often lay out all of your construction lines before having to darken in your final linework. With more complicated sketches, the sheer number of construction lines can often cause confusion as to which line belongs to which feature. The confusion can be worse in an isometric sketch, where the lines represent three dimensions rather than two. Therefore, after the marks are made for the last two features in Step 5, you can begin darkening in some of the lines representing the final form.

Step 6. Estimate the distances to create the angled surface of the block, and mark these points, as shown in Step 5. From the marked point on line 11–13, sketch a 30-degree line to the rear of the block on line 4–6. Label this new line 14–15. From the marked point on line 12–13, sketch a 30-degree line to the rear of the block on line 6–7. Label this new line 16–17. Sketch a line from point 14 to point 16 and from point 15 to point 17, to complete the sketching of the angled surface. Lines 14–16 and 15–17 are referred to as **nonisometric lines** because they are not parallel to the isometric axis.

Estimate the distances for the notch taken out of the front of the block, and mark these points, as shown in Step 5. Draw vertical lines from the marked points on line 1–2 and line 8–9. Label these lines 18–19 and 20–21, as shown in Step 6. Sketch 30-degree lines from points 19, 20, and 21 to the estimated depth of the notch. Along the top surface of the notch, connect the endpoints of the 30-degree lines, and label this new line 22–23. The 30-degree line extending back from point 20 is stopped when it intersects line 18–19, as shown in Step 6. To complete the back portion of the notch, drop a vertical line from point 22, as shown in Step 6. Stop this new line at the intersection point of line 19–23. The rough isometric sketch of the block is complete.

Note that we have not mentioned hidden features representing details behind the visible surfaces. The drawing convention for isometric sketches calls for disregarding hidden features unless they are absolutely necessary to describe the object.

Step 7. Darken all visible lines to complete the isometric sketch. Since the construction lines are drawn light, there is no need to lighten them in the completed sketch.

7.5.2 Isometric Ellipses

Isometric ellipses are a special type of ellipse used to represent holes and ends of cylinders in isometric drawings. In an isometric drawing, the object is viewed at an angle, which makes circles appear as ellipses. When sketching an isometric ellipse, it is very important to place the major and minor axes in the proper positions. Figure 7.32 is an isometric cube with ellipses drawn on the three visible surfaces: top, profile, and front. Remember Figure 7.32A, because those are the three positions of isometric ellipses

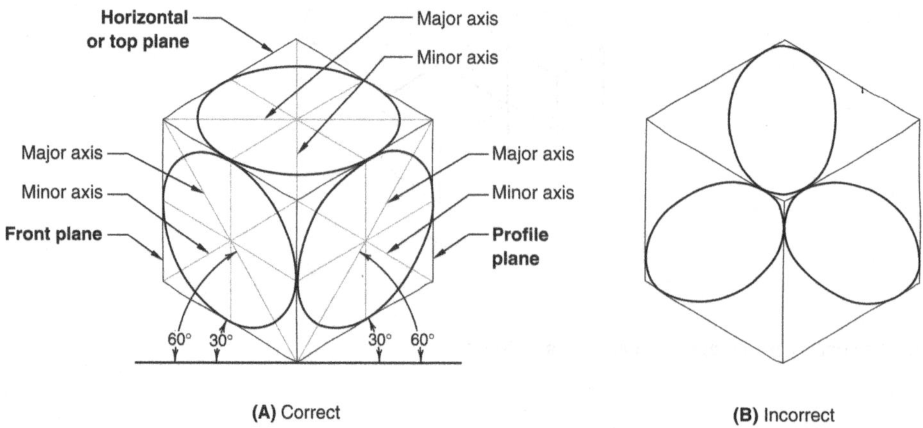

Figure 7.32

Isometric representation of circles

Circular features appear as ellipses in isometric sketches. The orientation of the ellipse is set according to the face on which the circle lies. The correct orientation is shown in (A) and examples of incorrect orientations are shown in (B).

found on most isometric sketches and drawings. The following are the key features of the isometric ellipse on each plane:

- The major and minor axes are always perpendicular to each other.
- On the top plane, the major axis is horizontal, and the minor axis is vertical.
- On the front and profile planes, the major axes are measured 60 degrees to the horizontal.
- The major axis is always perpendicular to the axis running through the center of the hole or cylinder.

Sketching an Isometric Ellipse

Figure 7.33 shows the steps for creating an isometric ellipse. Notice that the steps are almost identical to those for sketching a circle as explained earlier in this chapter. The difference is in the orientation and proportion of the primary axes.

Step 1. This isometric ellipse will be drawn on the front plane. Begin by sketching an isometric square whose sides are equal to the diameter of the circle.

Step 2. Add construction lines across the diagonals of the square. The long diagonal is the **major axis**, and the short diagonal is the **minor axis** of the ellipse. The two diagonals intersect at the center of the square, which is also the center of the isometric ellipse.

Step 3. Sketch construction lines from the midpoints of the sides of the square through the center point. These lines represent the center lines for the isometric ellipse. The midpoints of the sides of the isometric square will be tangent points for the ellipse and are labeled points A, B, C, and D.

Step 4. Sketch short, elliptical arcs between points B and C and points D and A.

Step 5. Finish the sketch by drawing the elliptical arcs between points C and D and points A and B, completing the ellipse.

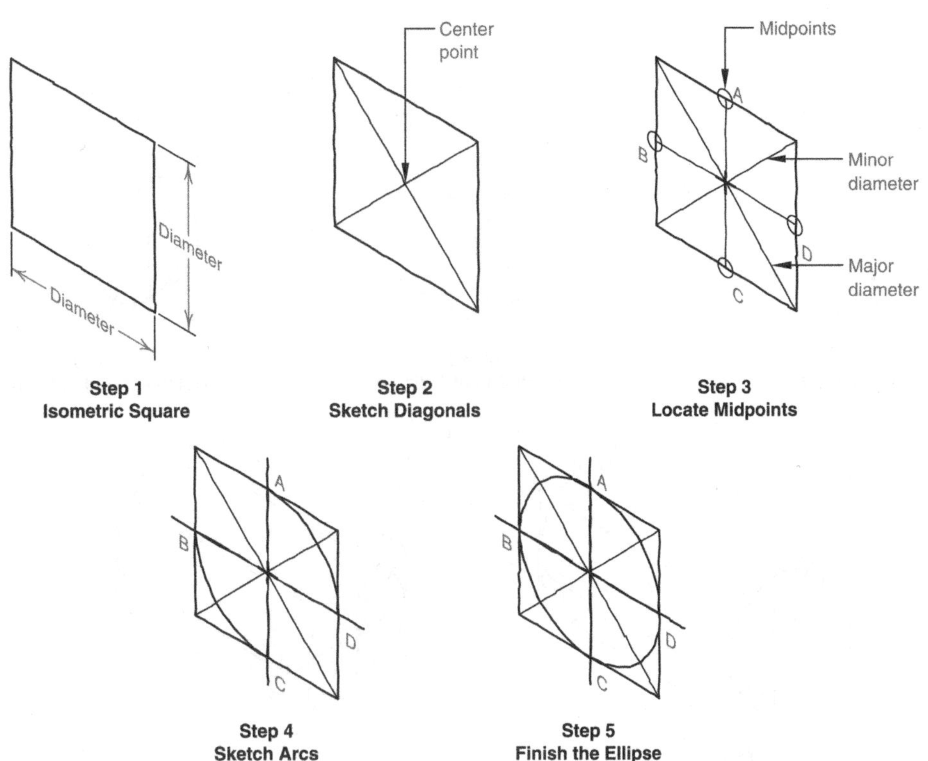

Figure 7.33

Sketching an isometric ellipse

The steps used to create a sketch of an isometric ellipse begin with constructing an isometric box whose sides are equal to the diameter of the circle. The center of the box and the midpoints of the sides are found, and arcs are then drawn to create the ellipse.

Sketching an Isometric Cylinder

Figure 7.34 shows the steps for creating an isometric view of a cylinder.

Step 1. Sketch the isometric axis. To sketch the bounding box for the cylinder, begin on one 30-degree axis line and sketch an isometric square with sides equal to the diameter of the cylinder. This square will become the end of the cylinder. Next, mark the length of the cylinder on the other 30-degree axis line, and sketch the profile and top rectangles of the bounding box. For the profile rectangle, the length represents the length of the cylinder, and the height represents the diameter of the cylinder. For the top rectangle, again the length represents the length of the cylinder, but the width represents the diameter of the cylinder. Note that only three long edges of the bounding box are drawn (the hidden one is not), and only two lines for the back end of the bounding box are drawn (the two hidden ones are not).

Step 2. Draw diagonals and center lines on the isometric square, and sketch in the ellipse, to create the end of the cylinder, as described in "Sketching an Isometric Ellipse."

Step 3. Where the center lines intersect with the top and front sides of the isometric square, mark points A and B. Sketch construction lines from points A and B to the back end of the bounding box and mark points C and D. Sketch an arc between points C and D.

Step 4. On the isometric square, locate the two points where the long diagonal intersects with the ellipse. From those two points, sketch two 30-degree lines to the back of the bounding box. (These 30-degree lines are tangent to the ellipse on the front of the cylinder.) Then, sketch short elliptical arcs from points C and D to the tangent lines, as shown in the figure. The cylinder should now be visible in the bounding box.

Step 5. Darken all visible lines to complete the cylinder. Note that the major axis of the ellipse is perpendicular to the axis running through the center of the cylinder, and the minor axis is coincident to it.

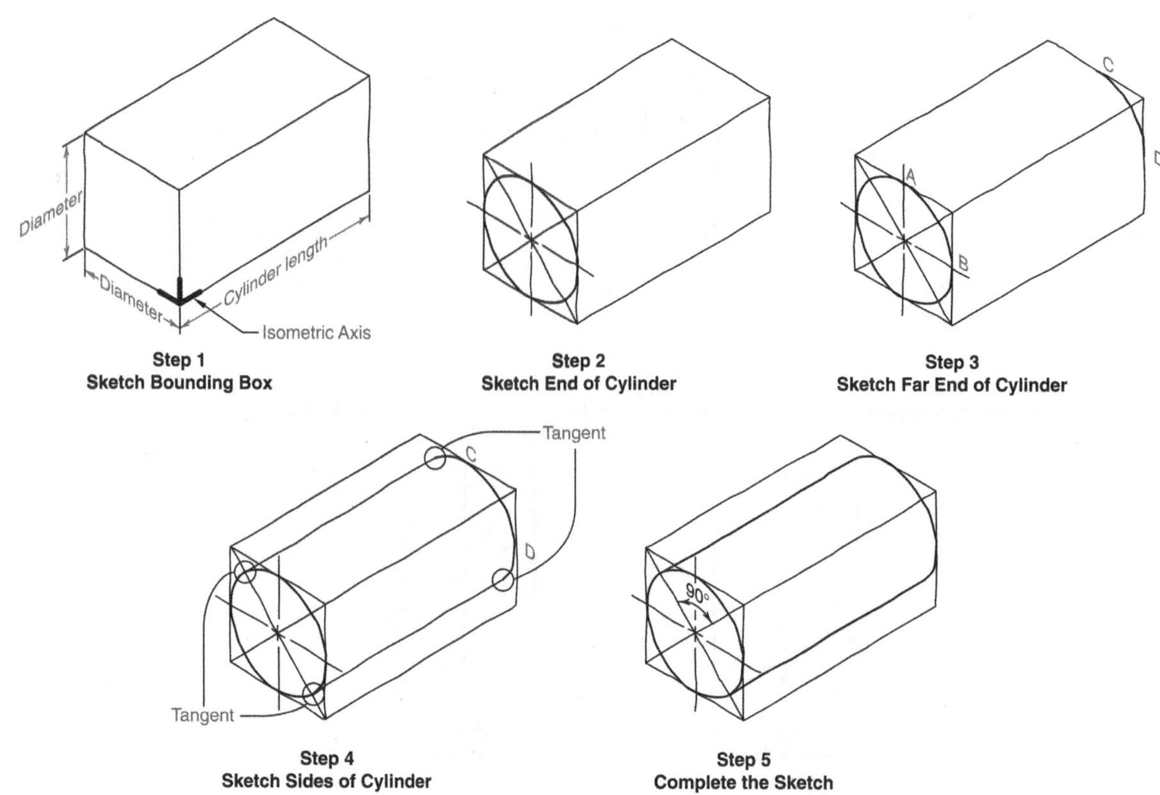

Figure 7.34

Steps used to construct a sketch of an isometric cylinder

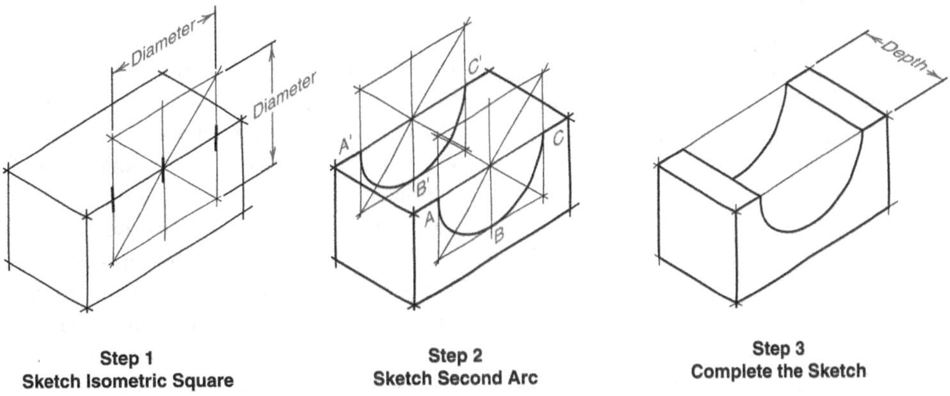

Figure 7.35

Steps used to construct a sketch of a semi-ellipse

Sketching Semi-Ellipses

Figure 7.35 shows how to sketch a semi-ellipse.

Step 1. This isometric ellipse will be drawn on the profile plane. Begin by sketching an isometric square whose sides are equal to the diameter of the arc. Add construction lines across the diagonals of the square. The two diagonals intersect at the center of the square, which is also the center of the isometric ellipse. Sketch construction lines from the midpoints of the sides of the square through the center point. These lines represent the center lines for the isometric ellipse.

Step 2. The midpoints of the sides of the isometric square will be tangent points for the ellipse and are labeled points A, B, and C. The long diagonal is the major axis, and the short diagonal is the minor axis. Sketch short, elliptical arcs between points B and C and points B and A, which create the elliptical arc on the near side of the object. The back part of the semi-ellipse can be sketched by constructing 30-degree parallel lines that are equal in length to the depth of the part, from points A, B, and C. This locates points A', B', and C' on the back side of the object. Add the back ellipse by sketching an arc between points B' and C' and points B' and A'.

Step 3. Finish by darkening the final lines and lightening the construction lines.

7.5.3 Isometric Grid Paper

The use of isometric grid paper can improve your technique and decrease the time necessary to create an isometric sketch. Isometric grid paper is made of vertical and 30-degree grid lines, as shown in Figure 7.8B. There are two primary advantages to using isometric grid paper. First, there is the advantage obtained by using any kind of grid paper. Proportions of the object's features can be translated into certain numbers of blocks on the grid. This can be especially useful when transferring the dimensions of a feature from one end of the object to the other. Unlike square grid paper, each intersection on an isometric grid has three lines passing through it, one for each of the primary axis lines. This can create some confusion when counting out grid blocks for proportions. Just remember which axis line you are using and count every intersection as a grid block.

The second advantage of the isometric grid is the assistance it provides in drawing along the primary axis lines. Although estimating a vertical line is not difficult, estimating a 30-degree line and keeping it consistent throughout the sketch is more challenging. Remember that the only dimensions that can be transferred directly to an isometric sketch are the three primary dimensions. These dimensions will follow the lines of the grid paper. When blocking in an isometric sketch, lay out the dimensions on construction lines that run parallel to the grid lines. Angled surfaces are created using construction lines that are nonisometric; that is, they do not run parallel to any of the grid lines and are drawn indirectly by connecting points marked on isometric construction lines.

If there is a disadvantage to using isometric grid paper, it is the distraction of having the grid in the finished drawing. As with square grid paper, this problem can be solved in a number of ways. You could use tracing paper over the grid paper, allowing the grid paper to be used over and over. You could work out a rough sketch on grid paper and then trace over it. You could also use grid paper with grid lines printed in a special color that does not reproduce in photocopies. Grid paper with a very dark grid can be flipped over and the sketch can be made on the back side. You can see the grid through the paper, but it won't reproduce on the photocopier.

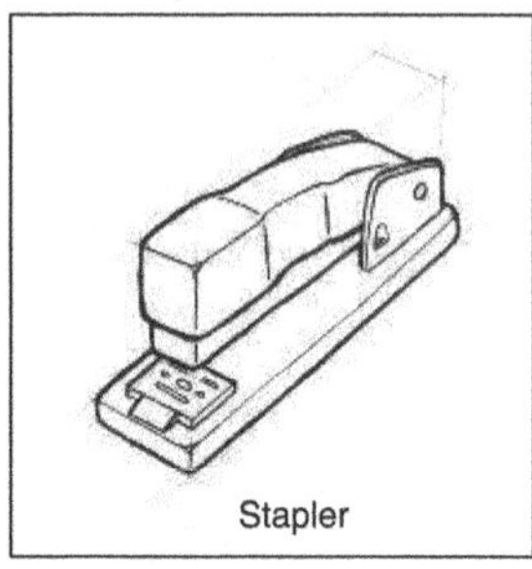

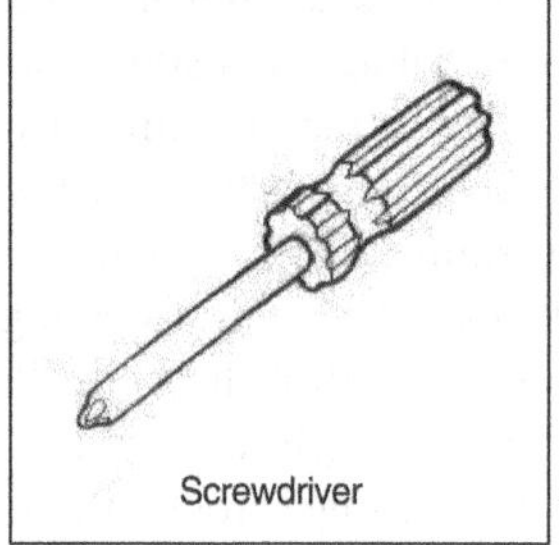

Figure 7.36

Isometric sketches of common objects

Practice Exercise 7.1

Using isometric grid paper, sketch common, everyday objects. Some examples are given in Figure 7.36. Sketch objects with a variety of features. Some should require sketching isometric ellipses, while others should have angled surfaces that require nonisometric lines. Start with simpler forms that only contain isometric lines and work toward more complex forms. Another approach is simply to leave out some of the details. You can capture the essence of the form by representing just its primary features. This is a common approach in creating ideation sketches.

The cost and availability of isometric grid paper can be a discouraging factor in using it to create lots of sketches. You can minimize the expense by using roll tracing paper over a sheet of grid paper. The two sheets can be held together with low-tack tape or put in a clipboard. With practice, you will find that grid paper is not needed and you can create sketches on the tracing paper alone.

7.5.4 Oblique Pictorials

Oblique pictorials are another method of creating a pictorial sketch of an object. Oblique sketching attempts to combine the ease of sketching in two dimensions with the need to represent the third dimension. In an oblique sketch, the front face is seen in its true shape and is square with the paper, and only the depth axis is drawn at an angle (Figure 7.37). As with an isometric pictorial, the lines of projection are parallel to each other.

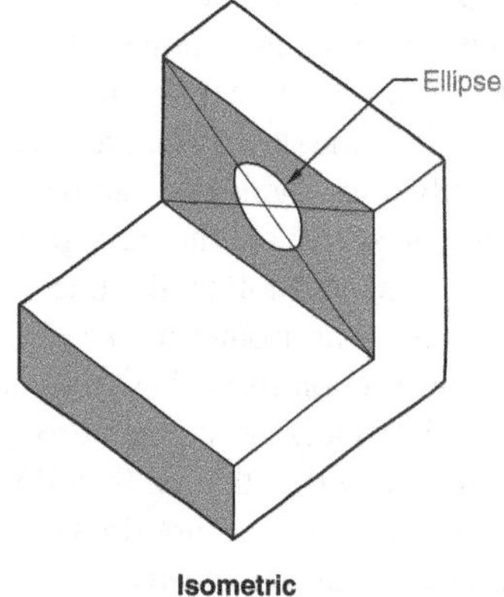

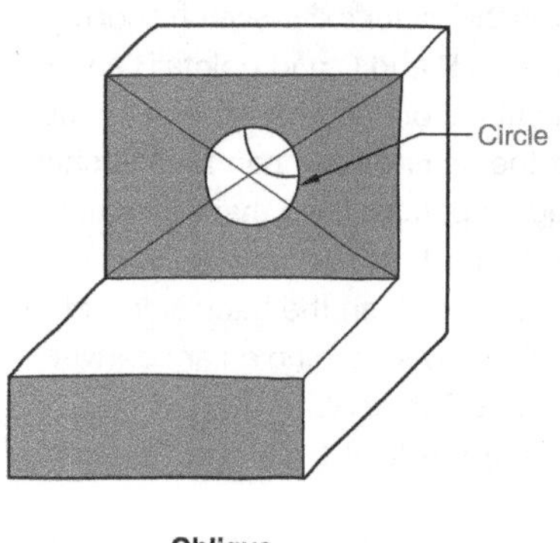

Figure 7.37

Isometric versus oblique sketches

In oblique sketching, the front face of the object (showing the height and width dimensions) is squared with the paper, and the depth dimension is drawn at an angle to the horizontal. This is different from an isometric sketch, where no faces are squared with the paper.

Because of the ease with which the front face is drawn, oblique sketching is useful when the majority of the features are on the front face of the object. Many types of furniture are conveniently drawn in oblique, especially cabinets with a lot of detailing on the front. On the other hand, oblique sketching should not be used if the object has many features (especially, circular ones) on faces other than the front.

As with isometric sketches, hidden features are not shown on most oblique sketches, unless absolutely necessary to describe the object. Because of the difference in how the depth dimension is drawn, scaling the depth to half or two-thirds its actual size helps the visual proportions of the sketch.

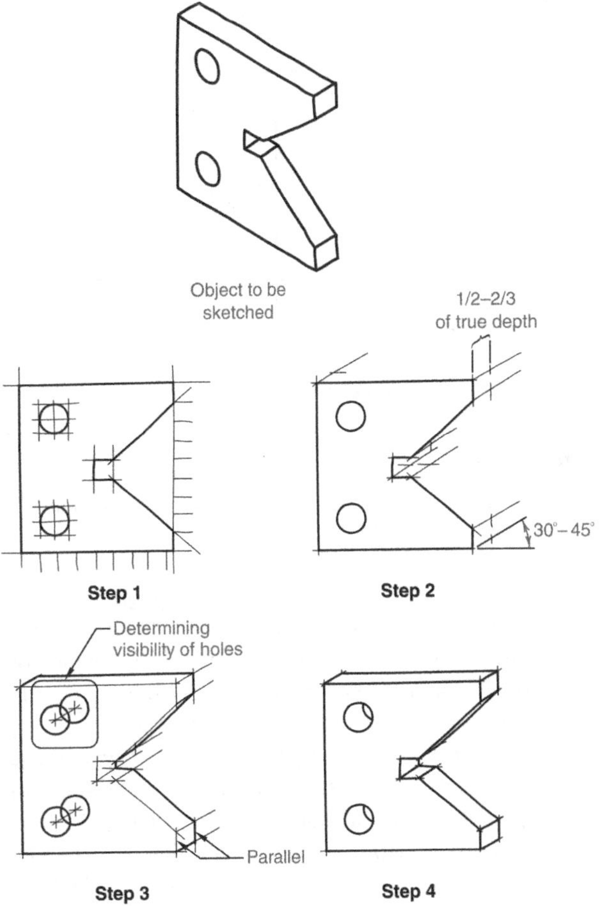

Figure 7.38

The construction of an oblique sketch is a multistep process that begins by boxing in the front view, adding details, and then boxing in the depth dimension.

Creating an Oblique Sketch

Figure 7.38 shows the steps used to create an oblique sketch. The object is oriented so that most of the details are represented in the front view.

Step 1. Begin the sketch by boxing in the front face of the object as if you were creating a front view. Estimate distances and box in features to create a proportional sketch.

Step 2. To view the object from the right and above, sketch depth construction lines at an angle of 30 to 45 degrees above the horizontal and to the right of the front face (Figure 7.38, Step 2). To view the object from below, sketch the depth lines below the horizontal. To view the object from the left side, sketch the depth lines to the left of the front face. Sketch only corners that will be visible.

Estimate the distance for the depth along the sketched lines. Full-length depth lines may make the object look out of proportion. Two-thirds or one-half size depth lines will create a better proportioned sketch. If full-size depth dimensions are used, the sketch is called a **cavalier oblique.** If the depth is one-half size, the sketch is called a **cabinet oblique**. For the example in Figure 7.38, one-half size depth is marked along each depth line.

Step 3. Draw a line between each depth mark to create the back edge of the object. These lines are parallel to the edges of the front view. The next step is to determine if any part of the hole on the rear of the object can be seen from the front. This is done by marking the locations of the centers of the holes on the front and sketching depth lines from those center points. The depth is marked on the depth lines, the marks are used as centers for the back holes, and circles equal in diameter to the front circles are sketched.

Step 4. If any part of a back circle is inside a front circle, that part will be visible in the oblique drawing and is darkened along with the other visible lines.

Using Grid Paper to Create an Oblique Sketch

Figure 7.39 on the next page shows how square grid paper can be used as an aid in creating an oblique sketch. Use tracing paper over the grid to avoid grid lines in the final sketch. The front face can be sketched much like a 2-D drawing. The depth axis is sketched along a 45-degree line that is a diagonal of the square grid boxes.

Step 1. Count the number of squares to determine the dimensions of the object. For the example in the figure, the

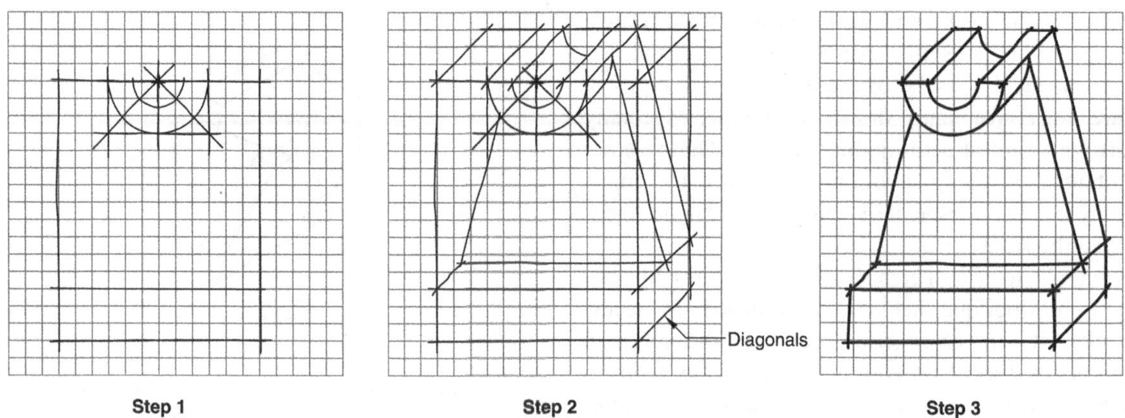

Figure 7.39

Square grid paper can be used to assist in the construction of an oblique sketch.

width of the object is 12 and the total height is 15. Use these measurements to begin boxing in the features on the front face of the object. Sketch the details of the front face by locating the center of the concentric arcs, then sketching the arcs and the corners of surfaces.

Step 2. Sketch the depth of the object by drawing diagonals of the square grids, which are 45 degrees above the horizontal. Make this sketch a cabinet oblique by using half the actual depth. As with an isometric sketch, many of the features on the front face have to be projected to the back face. Be careful when determining which edges or portions of edges will be hidden.

Step 3. Darken all visible lines.

7.5.5 Multiview Projections

Multiview drawings are based on parallel projection techniques and are used when there is a need to represent the features of an object more accurately than is possible with a single (pictorial) view. A multiview drawing is a collection of *flat* 2-D drawings that work together to give you an accurate representation of the overall object. With a pictorial drawing, all three dimensions of the object are represented in a single view. The disadvantage of this approach is that not all the features in all three dimensions can be shown with optimal clarity. In a multiview projection, however, each view concentrates on only two dimensions of the object, so particular features can be shown with a minimum of distortion (Figure 7.40). Enough views are generated to capture all the important features of the object.

Given their advantages, why are multiview drawings not always used? For one thing, there are the multiple views, rather than a single view, to be drawn. These views must be coordinated with one another to represent the object properly. You have to carefully visualize the views as you sketch them, and so does the person viewing them. Without training and experience, you might find it hard to interpret multiview drawings. The choice between multiviews and pictorials is often one of exact representation of features versus ease of sketching and viewing.

Orienting and Selecting the Front View When creating a multiview drawing of a design, the selection and orientation of the front view is an important first step. The front view is chosen as the most descriptive of the object; for example, what would normally be thought of as the side of the car is chosen as the front view because it is the most descriptive (Figure 7.41A). In addition, the object must be properly oriented in the view. The orientation of the object is based on its function. For example, for an automobile, the normal or operating position is on its wheels, rather than on its roof or bumpers (Figure 7.41B).

Choosing the Views for a Multiview Drawing Another way to understand the views of an object is to pick it up and turn it around. This may be hard to imagine with something like a car, but many of the objects you will be sketching are considerably smaller and can be held in the hand. Imagine picking up the object shown in Figure 7.42 on page 266 and holding it so that you are looking at the front. Now, rotate the object so that you are looking at its top. Rotate it back to where you started and then rotate

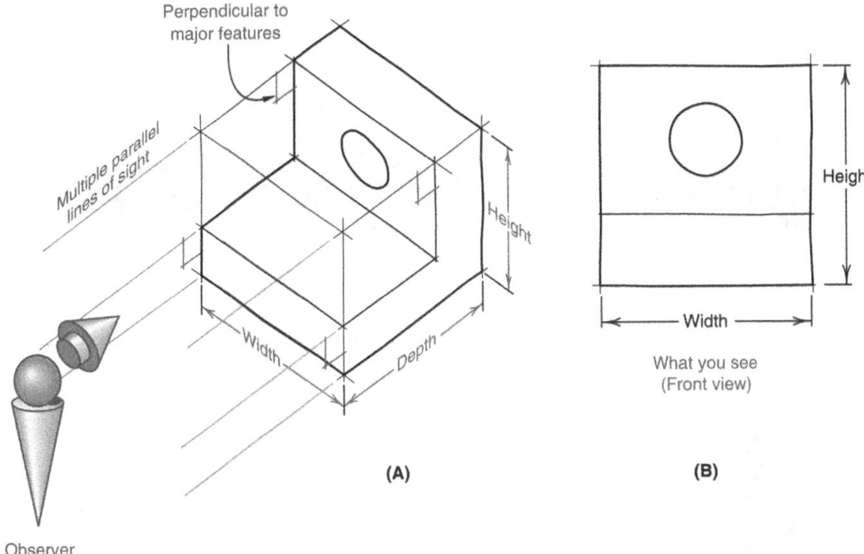

Figure 7.40

Multiview drawings

Multiview drawings are classified as a parallel projection, because the lines of sight used to view the object are parallel. This method of viewing an object results in a single view, with only two of the three dimensions represented. Therefore, it takes multiple views to show all three dimensions.

it so you are looking at its right side. There are an infinite number of intermediate views of the object between the points of rotation at which you stopped; for right now, however, consider only those views that are rotated 90 degrees from each other. These are considered *regular* or *principal views*, and each represents two primary dimensions of the object. If you continue rotating the object in 90-degree increments, you will see as many as six regular views (Figure 7.43 on page 267).

A multiview drawing should have the minimum number of views necessary to describe an object completely. Normally, three views are all that are needed; however, the three views chosen must be the most descriptive ones. The most descriptive views are those that reveal the most information about the design, with the fewest features hidden from view.

For example, Figure 7.43 shows one isometric view and six orthographic views of a simple object. Of the six orthographic views, which are the most descriptive? Although all the views given reveal much about the size and shape of the object, some are more descriptive than others. The choice of views is determined as follows:

1. Identify the most descriptive or important features of the object.
2. Determine the views that best represent those features.
3. The normal or usual orientation of the object as it is encountered.

After deciding the most descriptive features of the part, choose the views which show these features. Part of this selection will involve determining which views do the best job of neither obscuring nor hiding other features. For example, the object in Figure 7.43 has four important features: the hole, the rounded top, the L-shaped profile, and the slot cut out of the base in front. There are only two views that show the hole and rounded top: the front and rear. Although both views show these features equally well, the front view is chosen over the rear view because it does not hide the slot cut in the base. The L-shaped profile is shown equally well in both the right and left side views, and they have an equal number of hidden features. Although either view can be used, convention favors choosing the right side view. The slot in the base is shown in both the top and bottom views. However, the top view has fewer hidden lines, so it is preferred over the bottom view for the sketch. For this object then, the preferred views are the front, top, and right side views.

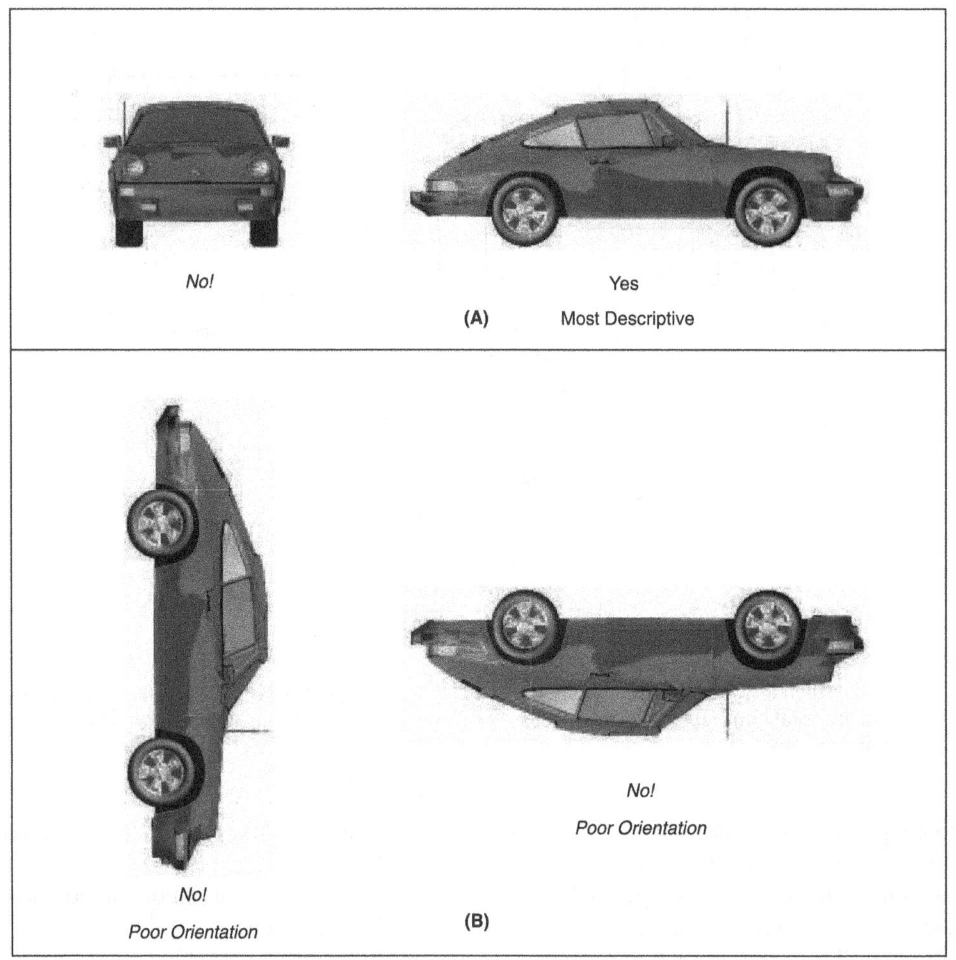

Figure 7.41

Most descriptive view

Proper orientation and the most descriptive features of an object are important when establishing the front view for a multiview sketch. Objects should be positioned in their natural orientation; for this car, that position is on its wheels.

Practice Exercise 7.2

Find a number of small objects that can be picked up in your hand and rotated. Look at them carefully and identify their important features. Orient each object so that the most important features are seen. Make this view the front view. Before rotating them, try to imagine what the top and right side views will look like. Now rotate them and see if that is how they look. Do all of the important features show up in these three views? If not, what other front view can you select that would result in seeing all of the important features in the three views?

Next, look at some larger items you cannot pick up. For each object, move around it and look at it from different viewpoints. Try to imagine picking it up and rotating it. Is there any difference in how the object looks if you pick it up and rotate it rather than walk around it?

Figure 7.44 on page 268 shows some common objects represented in multiview drawings.

7.6 Multiview Sketching Technique

As with other types of drawings, there is a certain technique, or standard set of methods, followed when creating multiview sketches. The technique includes line conventions, proportioning, and methods for creating circles, arcs, and ellipses. A knowledge of the proper and effec-

Design in Industry

Concept to Victory in 7 Months

This case study describes the design of a special bike frame designed for Lance Armstrong using 3-D modeling and CAD. In this case study, you will see examples of how the design process is used and the importance of 3-D modeling to shorten the design time from 12 months to seven months.

Designing a Winning Tour de France Bike

The courageous story of recovering cancer victim Lance Armstrong centered the world's attention on the US Postal Service team in the 2000 Tour de France® bicycle road race. Could Armstrong repeat his win and wear the yellow jersey again? Not only did he emerge victorious from the Tour de France, but just a month later he captured a bronze medal at the Sydney, Australia, Summer Olympics™.

You might think the bicycle a champion like Armstrong rides would take a long time to develop, with a team of engineers puzzling over the design, tweaking and re-tweaking time after time. The USPS Team Time Trial carbon fiber bike, made by world class bicycle manufacturer, Trek® Bicycle, moved from initial concept to finished product in just seven months. "That's a first," said Michael Sagan, Industrial Designer of Trek's Advanced Concept Group. "Normally it takes 12 to 14 months to complete a project like this."

A Single Prototype

Sagan believes Trek was able to achieve the dramatically fast turnaround in large part because the company had the right people and the right computer tools. Trek has been using Alias|Wavefront™ Studio™ for the past five years and for this project the company moved to an NT system and paired it with the latest release of Studio.

Sagan used the new integrated paint function in Studio to sketch out different 3-D views of the bike's frame over Pro-E centerlines created by Trek Lead Engineer Doug Cusack. After concepts were reviewed and a direction decided, a complete 3-D digital frame was created. Advanced Concept Group modelmakers used the digital information to cut a phenolic resin prototype using SurfCAM. Then the prototype was taken to Texas A&M University for wind tunnel testing.

The test was conducted by aeronautical engineer, John Cobb and Cusack, with Armstrong riding the experimental model in the tunnel. Variations were tried by adding clay to the model, but the original prototype delivered the best performance. "We nailed it right off the bat," said Sagan. "We did make more changes later to improve the lateral stiffness, but we had such a high confidence level in our digital model that we didn't feel the need to make another prototype and could proceed directly to tooling. It really was a *concept to victory*."

About the Bike

The USPS Time Trial bike frame is made of Optimum Compaction Low Void carbon, a compressed super light fiber. OCLV minimizes air pockets and maximizes strength. The only thing close to it is a fighter aircraft wing. The frame features an aerodynamic downtube, a steeper seat tube and flared chain stays for a power-generating and wind-splitting riding position. The complete design results in a bike that is not only fast, light and strong, but also more comfortable for the rider.

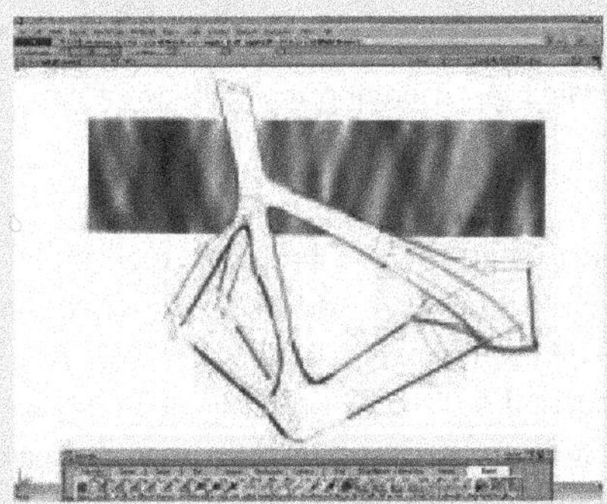

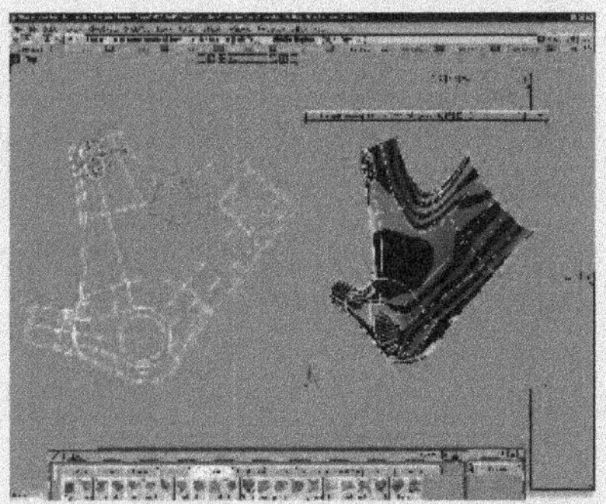

(Courtesy of Michael Sagan, Industrial Designer, Trek Bicycle Corp.)

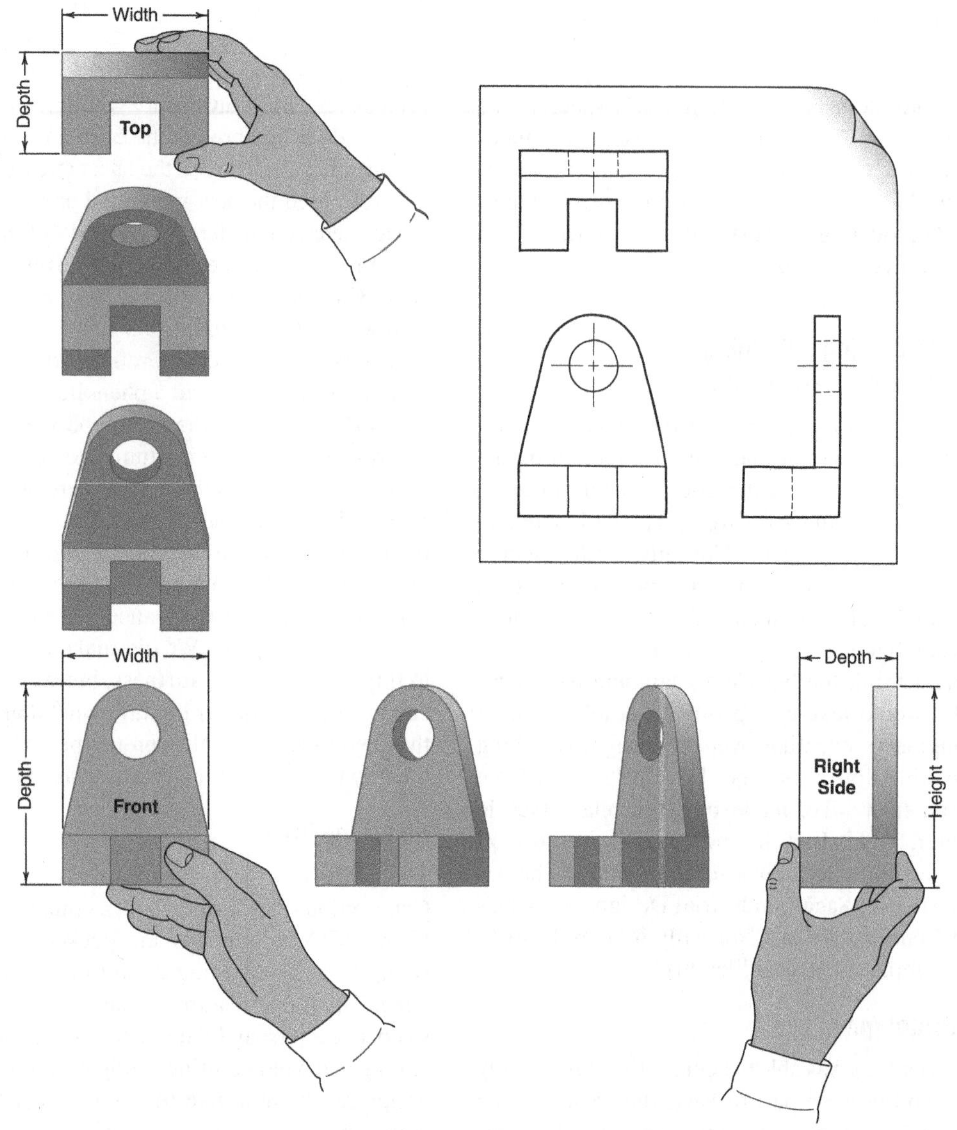

Figure 7.42

Visualizing a multiview drawing

By rotating a real object in your hand, you can simulate how a multiview drawing is created. A different principal view of the object is produced for every 90 degrees of rotation.

tive technique will assist the beginner in creating legible multiview sketches.

7.6.1 Line Conventions

As in all engineering and technical drawings, multiview drawings and sketches require adherence to the proper use of the alphabet of lines. Figure 7.45 on page 268 shows the alphabet of lines, sketched rather than drawn with drawing instruments, and includes the recommended pencil thicknesses. Figure 7.46 shows the application of each linetype on an engineering sketch.

In engineering and technical drawing, it is important that hidden features be represented, so that the reader of the drawing can clearly understand the object. Many conventions related to hidden lines have been established over the years. Figure 7.47 on page 270 shows the **hidden line conventions** that must be followed when creating

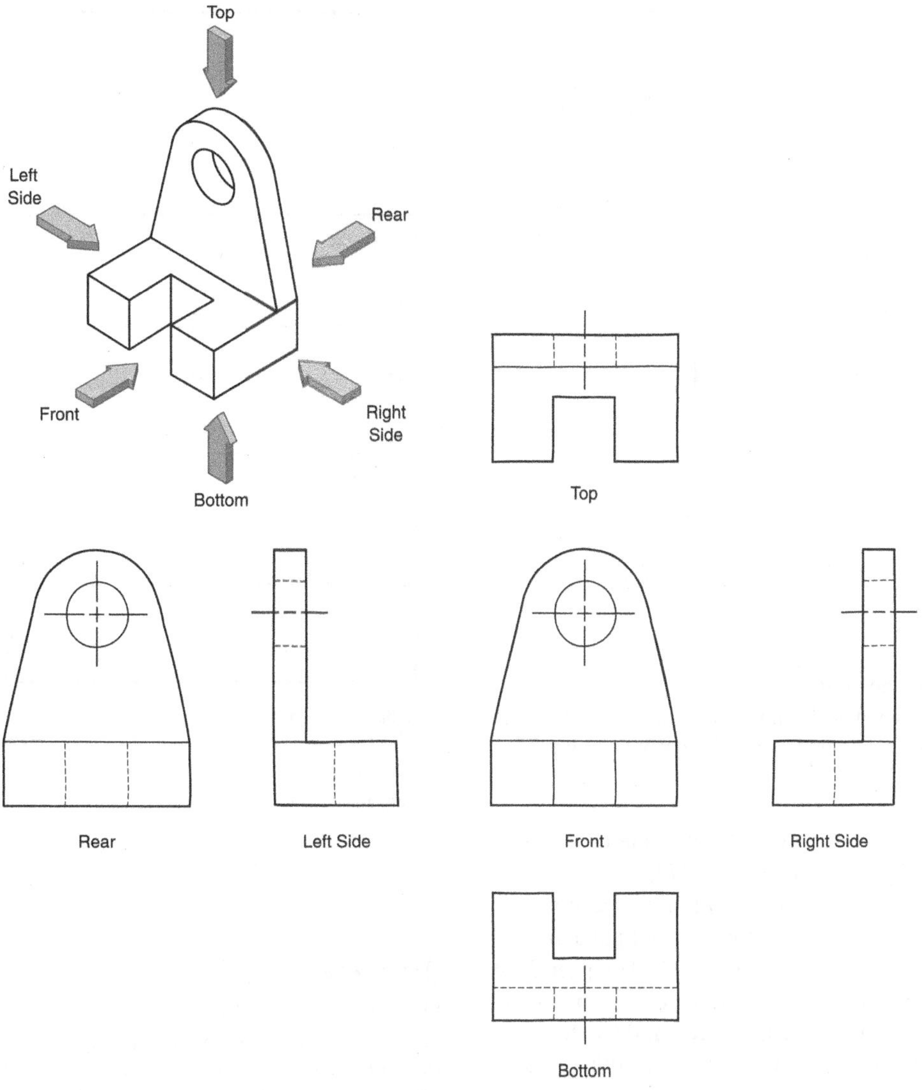

Figure 7.43

Six principal views

A multiview drawing of an object will produce six views, called regular or principal views. The object is viewed from six mutually perpendicular viewpoints. The six views are called front, top, bottom, rear, right side, and left side.

technical sketches or instrument drawings unless a CAD system has limitations that make it difficult to comply with these requirements. These conventions are as follows:

- There should be no gap when a hidden line intersects a visible line when the feature terminates (Figure 7.47A on page 270).
- Corners on hidden lines should be joined (Figure 7.47B on page 270).
- There should be a gap when a hidden line intersects either a visible corner or visible arc (Figure 7.47C on page 270).
- Three (hidden) intersecting corners, found in holes that are drilled and that end inside the object (i.e., do not go all the way through the object), should be joined as shown in Figure 7.47D on page 270.
- At the bottom of the drilled hole, the lines indicating the tip (created by the drill, which has a pointed tip) are joined (Figure 7.47E on page 270).

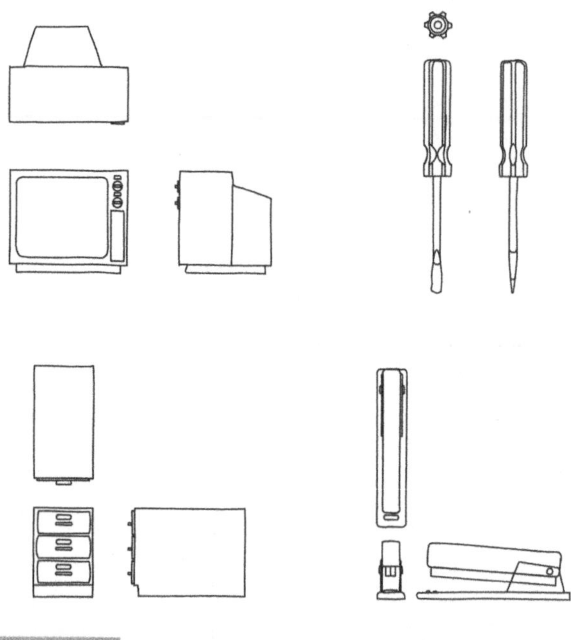

Figure 7.44

Multiviews of common objects

These multiview drawings of common objects show the front, top, and right side views. Hidden lines have been omitted for clarity.

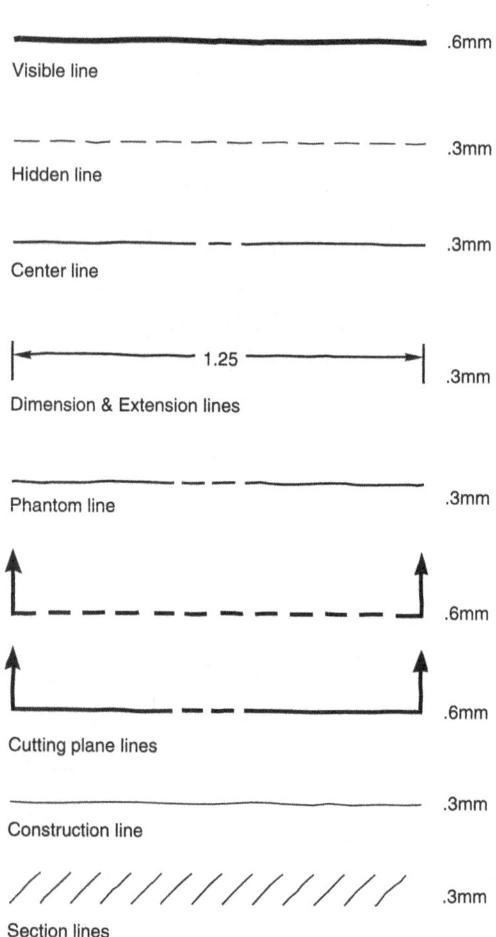

Figure 7.45

Sketched alphabet of lines

Standard engineering drawing practice requires the use of standard linetypes, which are called the alphabet of lines. The sizes show the recommended line thicknesses.

- Hidden arcs are started on the center line or the point of tangency (Figure 7.47F on page 270).
- When a hidden line passes behind a visible line (i.e., does not intersect the visible line), do not put a hidden-line dash on the visible line (Figure 7.47G on page 270).
- At the point where one hidden line crosses in front of another hidden line (indicating two hidden features, one closer to the visible view than the other), use a dash for the hidden line in front; that is, if the front hidden line is horizontal, use a horizontal dash at the point of crossing (Figure 7.47H on page 270).

7.6.2 Precedence of Lines

It is fairly common in technical drawings to have two lines in a view coincide. When this happens, the conventional practice called the **precedence of lines** dictates the linetype to draw when two or more lines in a view overlap (Figure 7.48 on page 270).

For example, in Figure 7.49A on page 271 a visible line in the top view coincides with the hidden lines for the hole. The precedence of lines requires that the visible lines be drawn and the hidden lines not be shown in the top view. Figure 7.49B on page 271 shows an example of a hidden line that has precedence over a center line. Figure 7.49C on page 271 is an example of a visible line having precedence over a center line. Notice that whenever a hidden or visible line has precedence over a center line, the center line is still drawn in the view by leaving a space and then extending it beyond the edge (Figure 7.49D on page 271).

7.6.3 Conventional Practices for Circles and Arcs

Circles are used to represent holes and the bases of cones and cylinders. Arcs are used to represent portions of these elements, as well as rounded corners on objects. Whenever representing a hole, cylinder, or cone on a technical drawing, the conventional practice is to draw center lines,

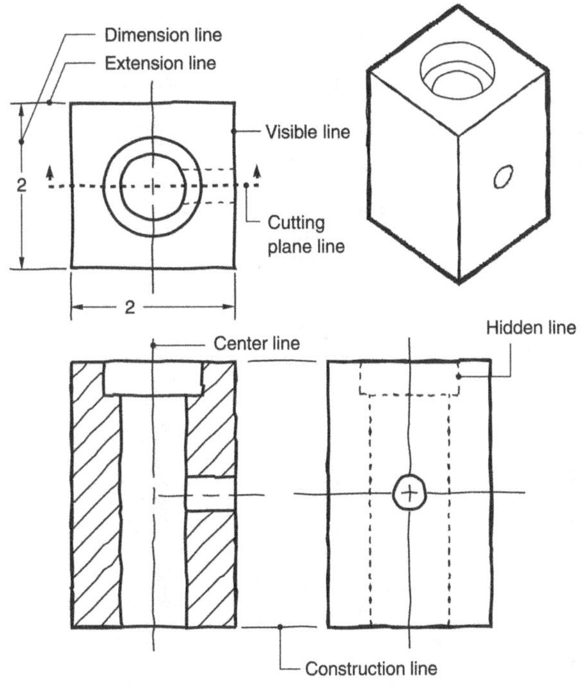

Figure 7.46

This engineering sketch has labels to identify some of the alphabet of lines.

which are used to (1) locate the centers of circles and arcs; (2) represent the axis of cylinders, cones, and other curved surfaces; and (3) represent lines of symmetry.

Figure 7.50 on page 271 is a multiview drawing of a cylinder. In the top view, horizontal and vertical center lines are drawn to locate the center of the circle. In the front view, a very thin center line is drawn to show the location of the cylinder's axis. The small dashes that cross at the center of the circle extend approximately 8 mm or 3/8″ from the edges of the object. The short segment of the center line is approximately 3 mm or 1/8″ long. The long segment can be from 20 mm to 40 mm, or 3/4″ to 1 1/2″ long. For very long cylinders, the center line is drawn as a series of long and short segments.

Figure 7.51 on page 272 shows some applications and the associated conventions for placing center lines. Notice that center lines are used in both the circular and horizontal views of a hole. When adding center lines to the circular view of a very small hole, a solid center line may be used rather than a dashed line, as shown in Part C. Part D shows how center lines are used to locate the centers of holes around a bolt circle. Part E shows how center lines, along with phantom lines, are used to show a path of motion.

Sketching Ellipses for Multiview Drawings

Lines, arcs, circles, and ellipses are common features sketched in multiview drawings. Sketching lines, arcs, and circles was explained earlier in this chapter. Occasionally it is necessary to sketch an ellipse on a multiview drawing. Smaller ellipses can be sketched inside a rectangular bounding box whose dimensions equal the major and minor axes of the ellipse (Figure 7.52A on page 273).

For larger ellipses, the trammel method, explained below, may be needed (Figure 7.52B on page 273).

Step 1. Mark half the length of the major axis of the ellipse on a piece of scrap paper, and label the endpoints A and C, as shown in Figure 7.52B, Step 1. The scrap paper is the trammel.

Step 2. Mark half the length of the minor axis of the ellipse on the piece of scrap paper, starting from point A, and label the endpoint as B.

Step 3. Sketch the major and minor axes, and use the trammel to mark points along the ellipse. This is done by placing point C anywhere on the minor axis and point B on the major axis and then placing a mark at point A. Repeat the process by moving the trammel, until you have a series of points marked.

Step 4. Connect the points to complete the ellipse.

7.7 Multiview Sketches

Multiview drawings can have from one to three or more views of an object. However, multiview sketches rarely have more than three views.

Multiview sketches are important in that they provide more accurate geometric information than a pictorial sketch, without requiring the time that a formal multiview drawing would take. If dimensions are provided, they are usually only for a particular feature(s) and are often only approximations, since these sketches are used early in the design process before final specifications have been made.

As is the goal with all sketches, multiview sketches should be done quickly and clearly. Straightedges, such as triangles and T-squares, should be avoided since they will only slow you down and will compel you toward a level of finish that is inappropriate in sketches. In addition, you should draw only as many views as are necessary to show the features accurately. An initial analysis of the features should tell you if one, two, or three views are needed to clearly show the elements of interest.

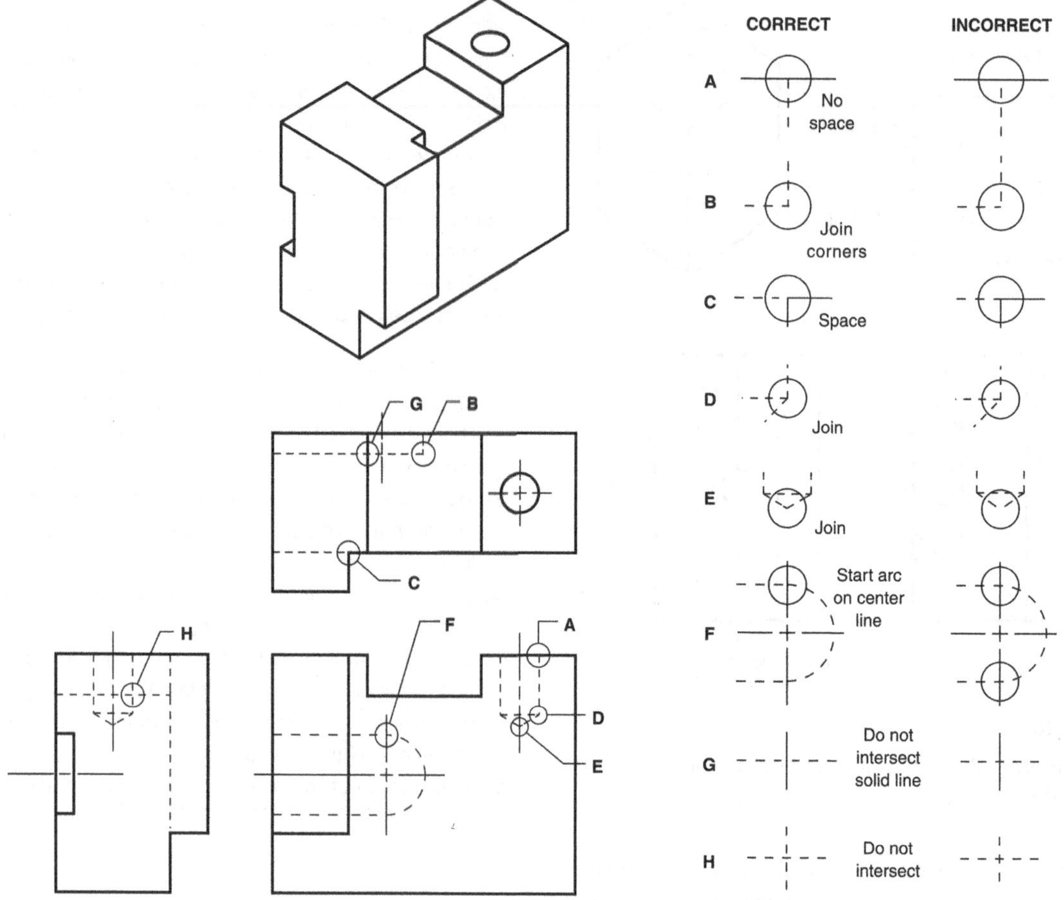

Figure 7.47

Drawing conventions for hidden lines

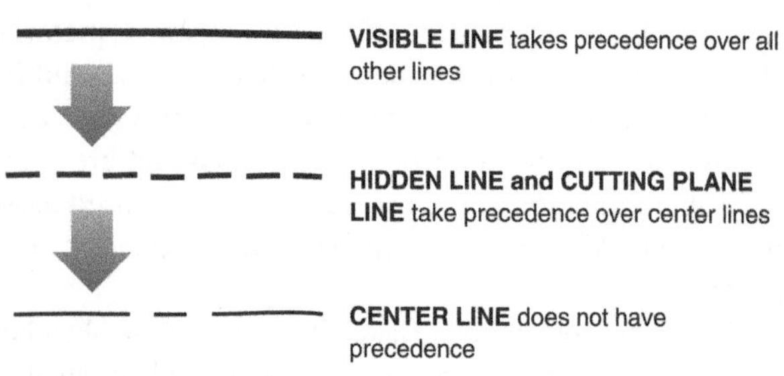

Figure 7.48

Precedence of lines

The precedence of lines governs which lines are drawn when more than one line occupies the same position on a drawing. For example, a visible line has precedence over all other types of lines, and a hidden line and a cutting plane line have precedence over a center line.

7.7.1 One-View Sketches

The simplest multiview sketch represents just the front view of an object. Though not truly a *multiview*, it is still meant to represent only two dimensions of the object, which is the basic concept of multiview drawings. This sketch can be produced using the techniques shown in Figure 7.18 on page 249.

7.7.2 Two-View Sketches

Occasionally, an object can be completely described using only two views. As an example, Figure 7.53 on page 274 shows a symmetrical part that can be described using two views. If the front view is as shown in the pictorial, the top and side views would be the same. Nothing would be gained by drawing both the top and side views, so only one of these views is sketched.

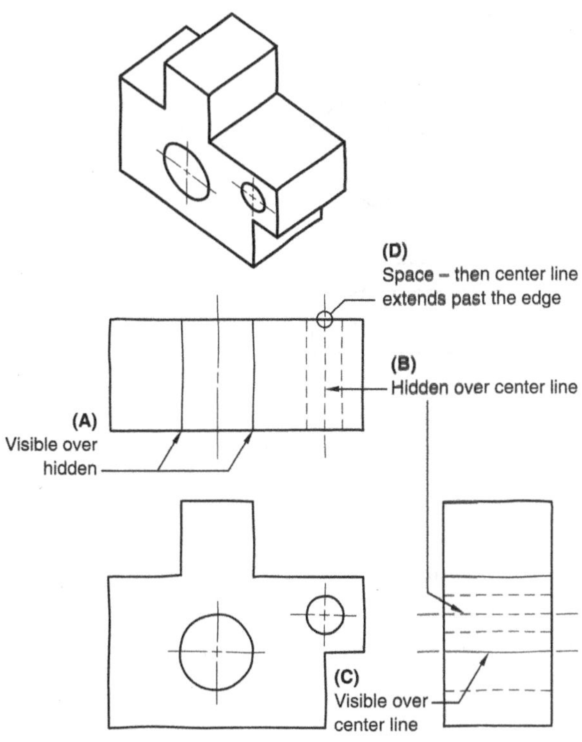

Figure 7.49

An engineering drawing showing how the precedence of lines is applied

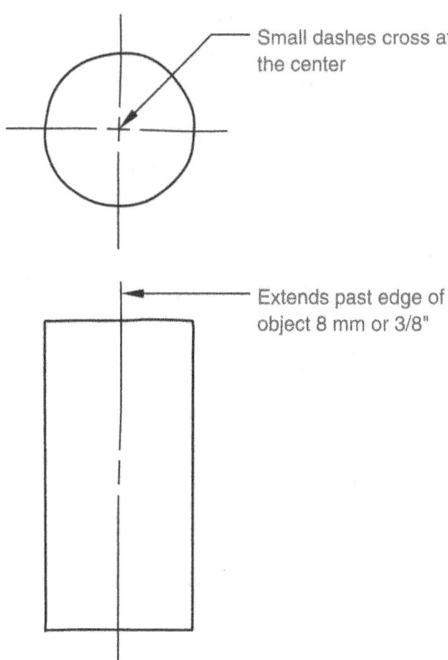

Figure 7.50

An engineering drawing of a cylinder, showing the application of center lines

Creating a Two-View Sketch

Figure 7.53 on page 274 and the following steps describe how to create a two-view sketch.

Step 1. In the front view, block in the squares with sides equal to the diameters of the circles. Since both the front and right side views show the height dimension, construction lines can be used to project the height of the squares onto the right side view. Block in the rectangles representing the details for the side view.

Step 2. Using the squares and center lines as guides, sketch the circles for each hole and the cylinder, in the front view. Using the construction lines as guides, sketch the hidden lines for the holes, in the side view.

Step 3. Darken all visible, center, and hidden lines.

Scale and locate the views on the drawing so that there is approximately equal spacing between the two views and between each view and the edge of the paper (Figure 7.54 on page 274). Normally, if the front and right side views are used, the paper is oriented so that the long dimension runs horizontally; if the front and top views are used, the long dimension of the paper runs vertically. There are exceptions to this if the object has particularly extreme proportions. Remember that the top view is *always* aligned with and placed above the front view, and the right side view is *always* aligned with and placed to the right of the front view. *Do not* rearrange the views just to fit them on the paper.

7.7.3 Three-View Sketches

When an object is more complex, three views are needed. The object used in Figure 7.55 on page 275 was chosen because it has many of the most common features you will be sketching, such as holes, arcs, lines, and planes.

Creating a Three-View Sketch

Figure 7.55 on page 275 and the following steps show how to create a three-view sketch.

Step 1. Begin by blocking in the front, top, and right side views of the object, using the overall width, height, and depth. Sketch the front view first, then use construction lines to project the width dimension from the front view to the top view. Also, use construction lines to project

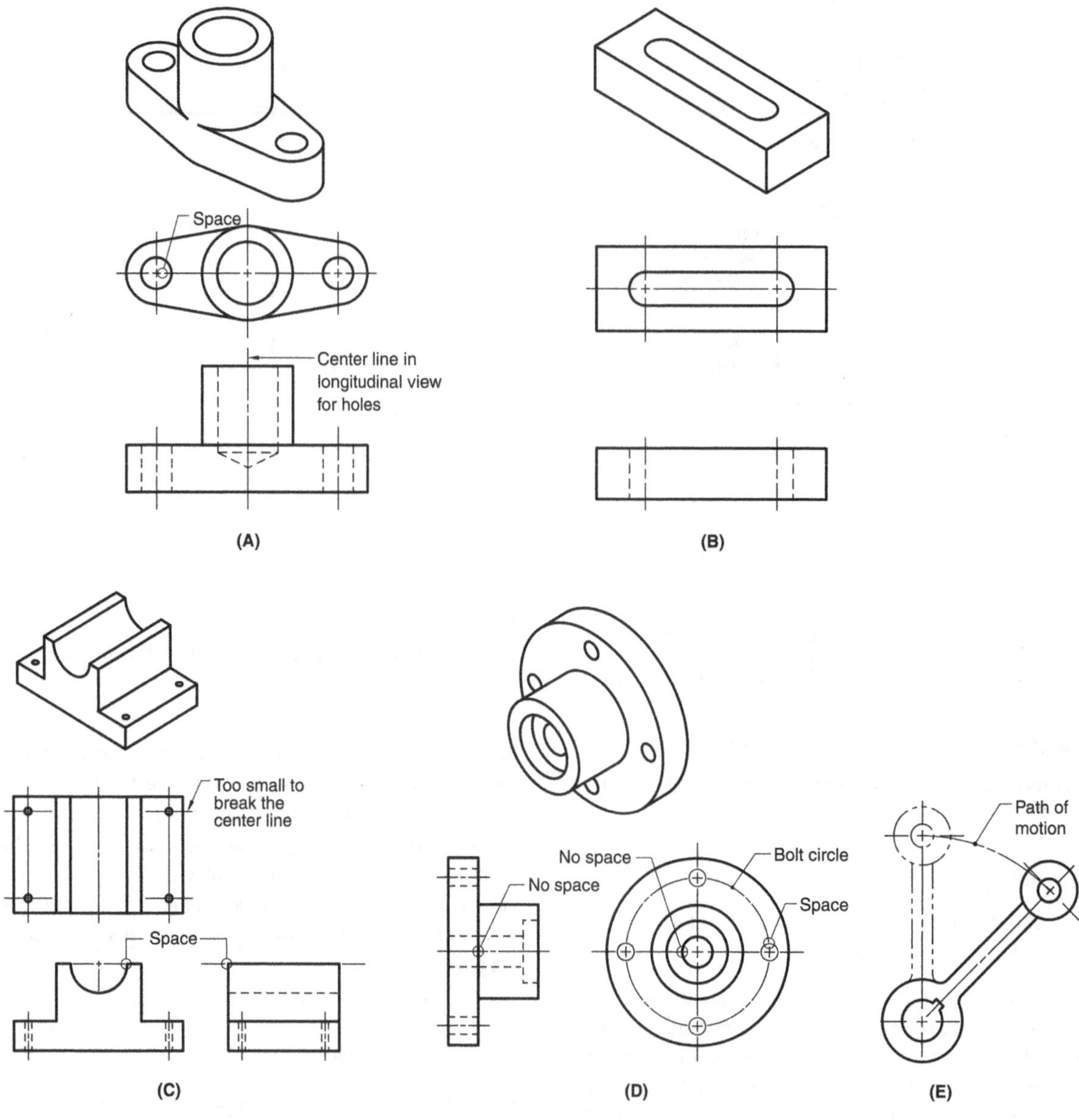

Figure 7.51

Center line conventions

These engineering drawings show various applications for center lines. Study each example to learn how center lines are used.

the height dimension from the front view to the right side view. Leave room between the views so the sketch does not look crowded and there is room to add text for notes and dimensions. The spaces between each view should be approximately the same. Make sure the depth dimension is equal in the top and side views by measuring the distance using a scale or dividers.

Step 2. Lightly block in the major features seen in each view. For example, the drilled holes are blocked in on the views where they look round. The angled edge and the rounded corner are most clearly seen in the top view. Begin darkening these major features.

Step 3. Quite often, features will appear in two and sometimes all three of the views, and construction lines can

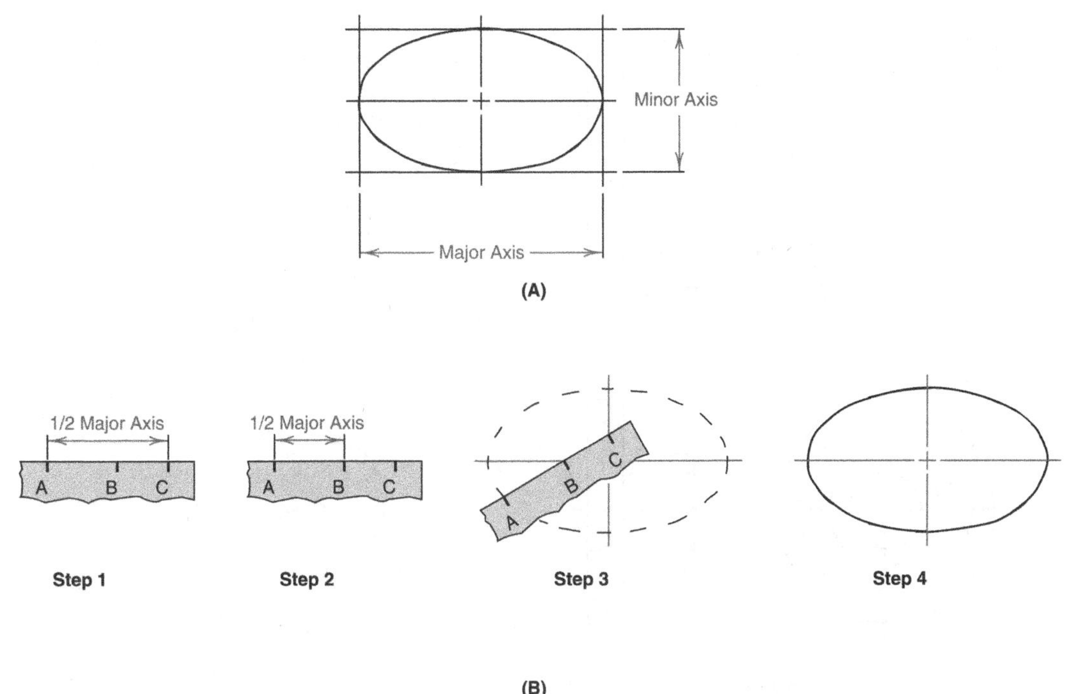

Figure 7.52

Sketching ellipses

An ellipse is created by sketching the major and minor axes, then sketching a rectangle whose sides are equal to the axes. A scrap of paper can be used to create an ellipse, using the trammel method.

be used to project the location or size of a feature from one view to another. Remember that each view always shares one dimension with an adjoining view. The depth dimension can be shared between the top and right side view with a special construction line called a **miter line**. The miter line is drawn at a 45-degree angle and is used as a point of intersection for lines coming to and from the right side and top views. For example, the width of a hole in the top view can be projected down to the front view. Then the location of the hole can be passed across the miter line to the right side view.

Step 4. Finish adding the rest of the final lines. Be careful to do all hidden lines and center lines for the holes. Darken all final lines.

As with the two-view drawing, there are conventional practices that must be followed when arranging the three views on the paper (Figure 7.56 on page 276). Make sure that all three views stay aligned with their neighboring views (Figure 7.56B on page 276). If they do not, they will not be able to share dimensions via projection lines. As with the two-view drawing, there is a strict organization for the views: the top view goes directly above and is aligned with the front view, and the right side view goes directly to the right of and is aligned with the front view. Do not rearrange the top, front, or right side views, or substitute other regular views in their places.

7.8 Perspective Projection

Perspective projection is the projection method that represents three-dimensional objects on two-dimensional media in a manner closest to how we perceive the objects with our eyes. If you were to take a photograph, lay tracing paper over it, and sketch the objects in it, the result would look like a perspective projection (Figure 7.57 on page 276). Like the other pictorial sketches, all three dimensions of the object are presented in a single image.

If you were to stand in the middle of a straight, flat road and look toward the horizon (Figure 7.58 on page 276), the road would appear to narrow to a single point, called

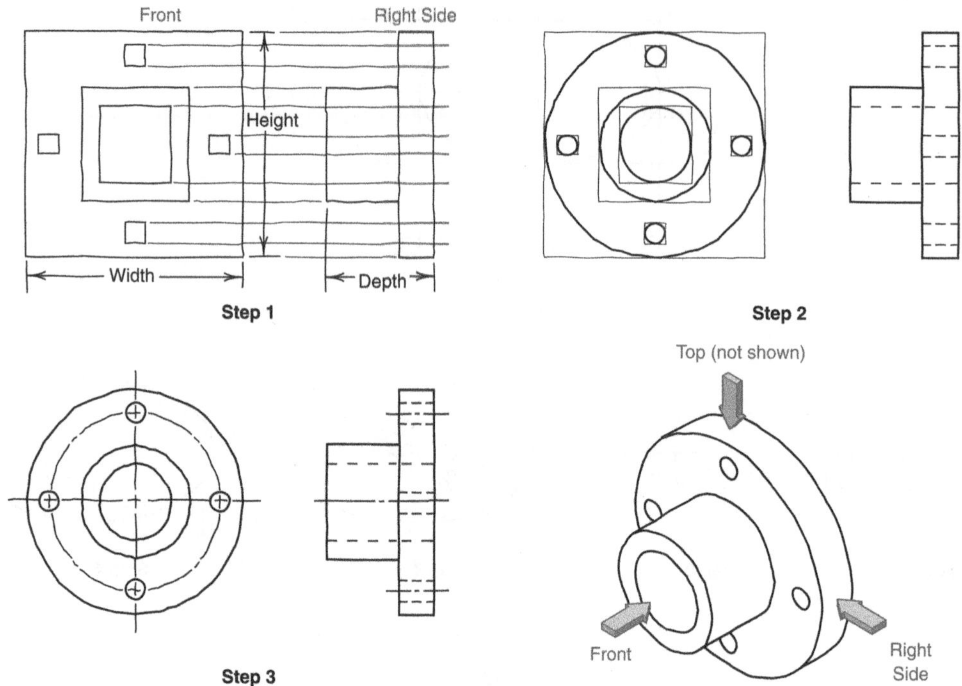

Figure 7.53

Creating a two-view sketch

A two-view sketch is created by blocking in the details, then adding center lines, circles, arcs, and hidden lines.

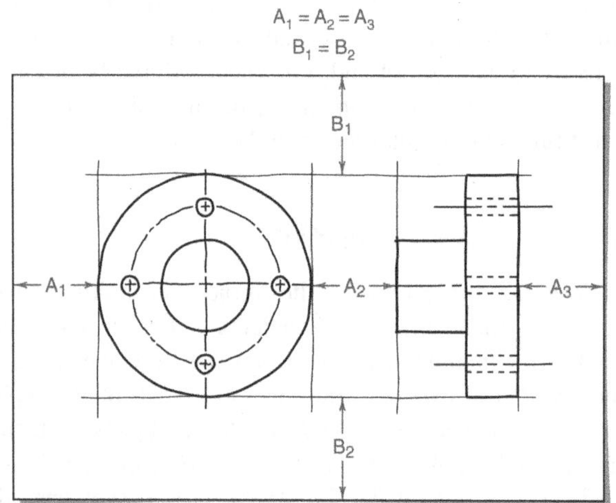

Figure 7.54

Centering a two-view sketch

A two-view sketch is centered on a sheet of paper by equally dividing the areas between and around the views.

the vanishing point. Even though the road appears to go to a point, in reality it does not. You know that the edges of the road are parallel to each other and, as you travel down the road, the portion of the road that looked so small before will be full size. Objects, whether they are portions of a road, cars, or billboards, look smaller as they get farther away. Also, parallel lines—such as the two edges of the road—will appear to *converge* (come together) as they recede from you. Through the use of construction lines in your perspective sketch, you can control the convergence of the parallel edges of an object, as well as the proportional sizes of objects as they recede in the distance (Figure 7.59 on page 276). For more information on how the human mind perceives and interprets what the eyes see, refer to Chapter 5.

Figure 7.59 on page 276 shows the labels for the important elements of a perspective sketch. Most important is the **horizon line (HL)**, which is an imaginary line in the distance, where objects are infinitely small and parallel lines converge. The point on the horizon line where parallel lines converge is called the **vanishing point (VP)**. Where the portion of the object closest to the observer

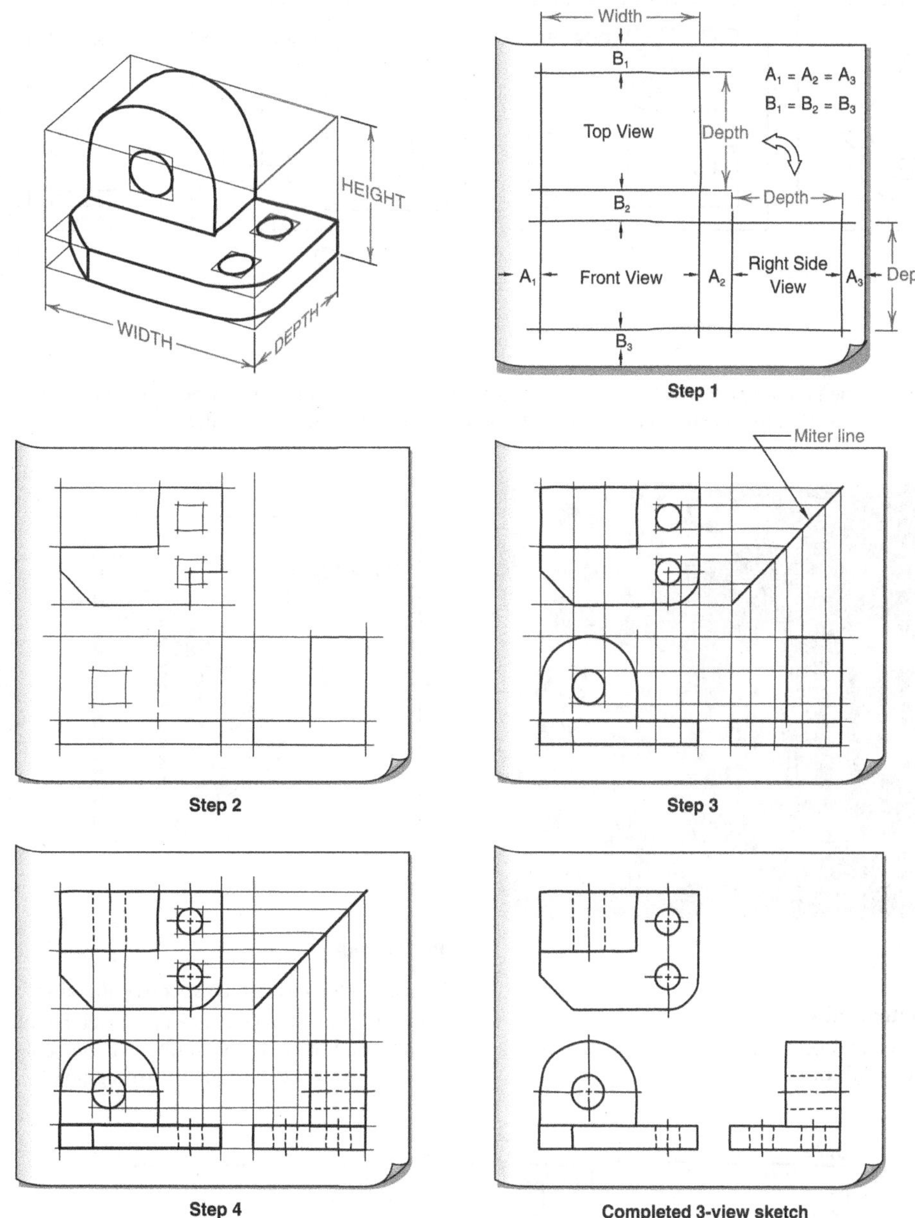

Figure 7.55

Creating a three-view sketch

A three-view sketch is created by blocking in the overall width, height, and depth dimensions for each view, then blocking in the details, using a miter line to transfer depth dimensions between the top and side views, and then adding the final details, such as circles, arcs, center lines, and hidden lines.

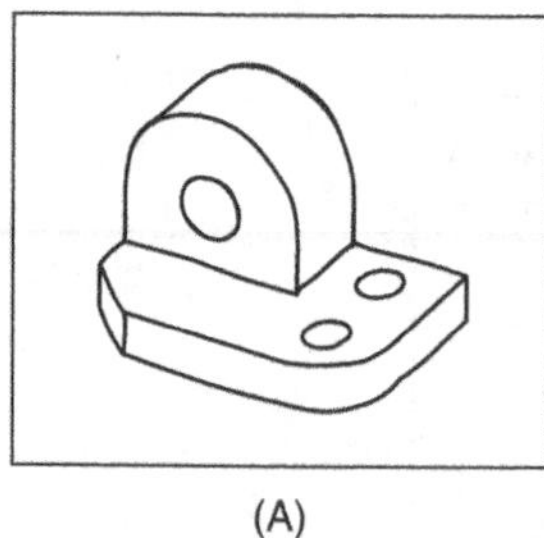

(A)

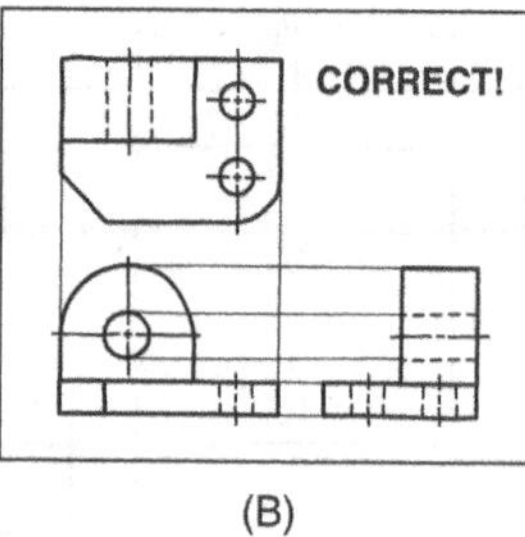

(B)

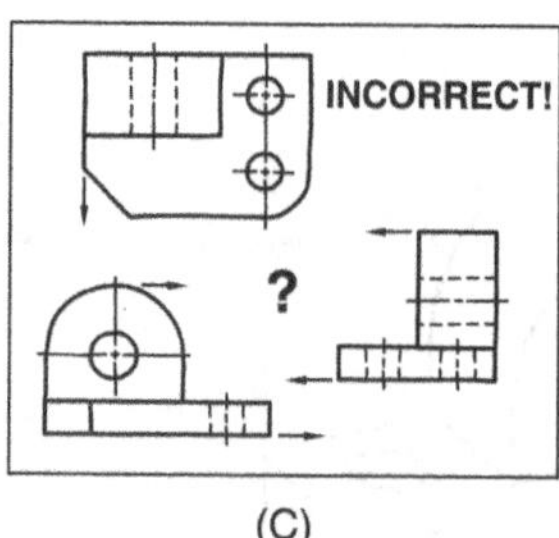

(C)

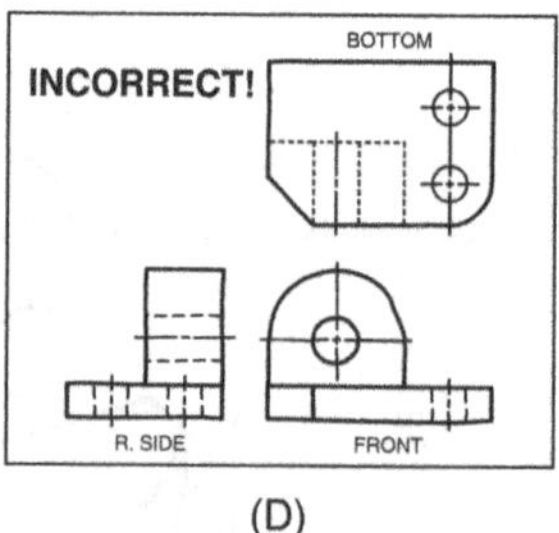

(D)

Figure 7.56

View alignment

A three-view sketch must be laid out properly, following standard practices. The width dimensions on the front and top views are aligned vertically, and the height dimensions on the front and side views are aligned horizontally.

Figure 7.57

Convergence in photographs

This photograph shows an object in perspective, with major lines of convergence overdrawn.

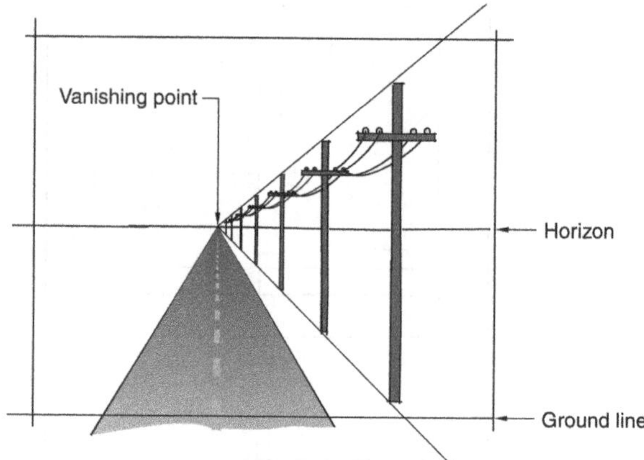

Figure 7.59

Principal elements in perspective sketches

Principal elements of a perspective sketch include the horizon, vanishing point, and ground line. All elements in a perspective sketch are drawn to a single vanishing point.

Figure 7.58

Humans view their environment in perspective, where lines appear to converge to a single point. Even though it looks as though the edges of a road converge on the horizon, we know they don't.

(By permission of John L. Hart FLP and Creators Syndicate, Inc.)

rests on the ground plane is called the **ground line (GL)**, as shown in Figures 7.59 and 7.60.

The horizon line shown in Figures 7.59 and 7.60 also represents the observer's eye level. The relationship of the ground line to the horizon line reflects the height of the observer relative to the object. Figure 7.61 on page 278 shows the different types of views created by raising or lowering the ground line, and each view type has a specific use, as shown in Table 7.1.

The human's eye view is the most commonly used for sketching everyday objects. The ground's eye is useful for one- to three-story buildings, and the worm's eye view is used for taller structures (Figure 7.62 on page 279).

Figures 7.58 through 7.61 show perspective projections with only one vanishing point. In Figures 7.60 and 7.61, the parallel edges of only one of the object's three dimensions converge to the vanishing point. If you want more of the dimensions to converge, more vanishing points are needed. Perspective views are classified according to the number of vanishing points used to create the drawing.

Figure 7.63 on page 279 shows one-, two-, and three-point perspective sketches. Although three-point perspective is the most *realistic*, one- and two-point perspectives are usually adequate and are simpler to sketch. By varying the number and positions of the vanishing points, and the position of the ground line relative to the horizon line, it is possible to create virtually any perspective view of an object. Chapter 12 goes into more detail on perspective projection and perspective drawings.

Creating a rough perspective sketch is quick and does not require artistic skill. However, mechanically creating a very accurate perspective drawing can be involved and time consuming. 3-D modeling systems usually offer perspective projection as an option, making the generation of perspective pictorials almost automatic.

7.8.1 One-Point Perspective Sketch

One-point perspective sketches are used to quickly create a pictorial representation of an object or structure.

Creating a One-Point Perspective Sketch

The following steps describe how to create a one-point perspective sketch of the guide block shown in Figure 7.64 on page 280.

Step 1. For a one-point perspective sketch, begin by determining the type of view you want (human's eye, ground's eye, etc.); then place the corresponding horizon and ground lines on the paper.

Step 2. Establish the relationship of the vanishing point to the object, such as to the right of the object. With the vanishing point marked, box in a front view of the object with construction lines, marking the height and width dimensions of the features of the object.

Step 3. From three corners of the bounding box (points 1, 2, and 3), draw converging lines to the vanishing point. The fourth corner would be hidden, so it is not drawn. Based on the depth of the object, determine where the back of the object would be on the converging lines, and

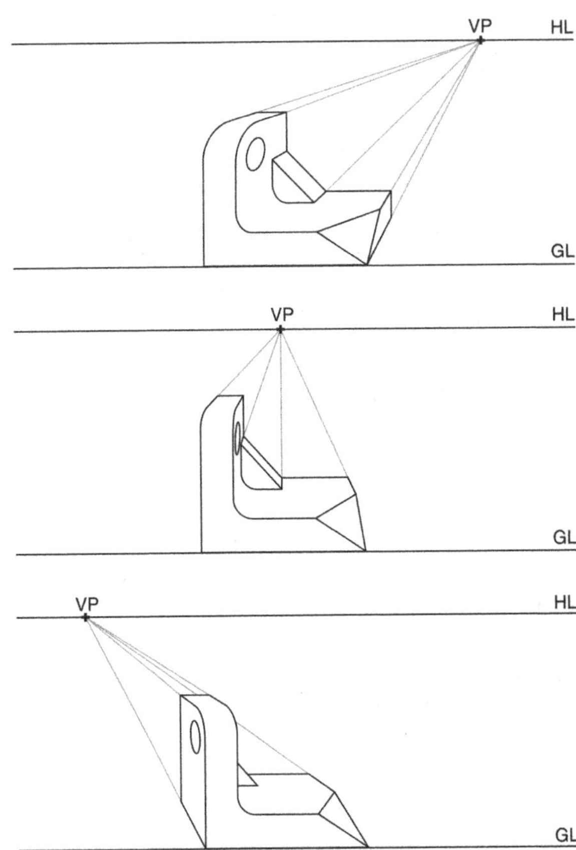

Figure 7.60

Moving the vanishing point right to left

The view of the object can be dramatically changed by moving the vanishing point along the horizon line. Points to the right of center will reveal details about the right side of the object; points to the left of center will reveal details about the left side of the object.

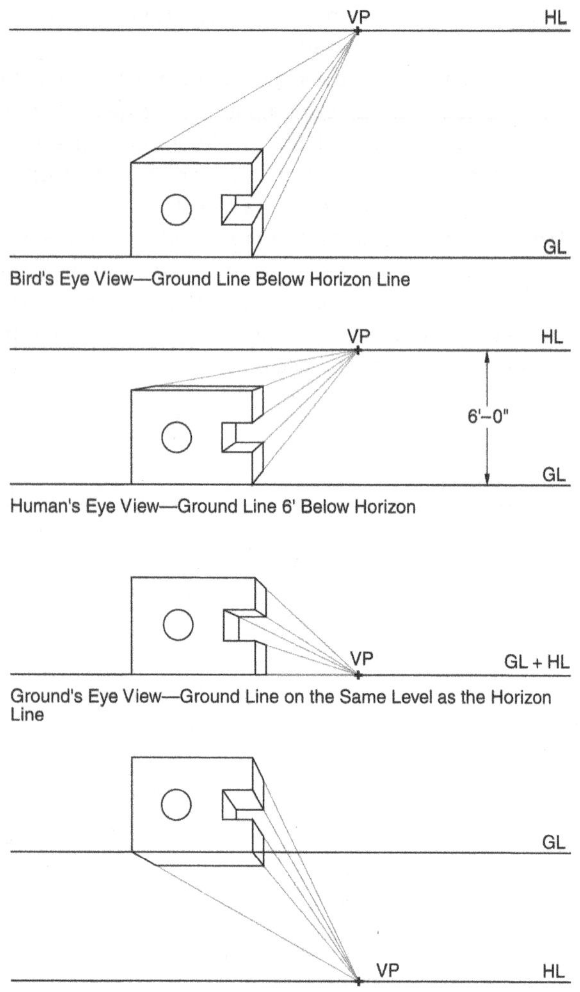

Figure 7.61

Ground line position

Changing the ground line relative to the horizon line changes the perspective view created.

draw a horizontal and a vertical line to mark the back of the object.

Step 4. A bounding box in all three dimensions is now established for the object. Continue refining the object by sketching more bounding boxes representing other features. Remember that bounding boxes drawn on the front and back faces of the object will be square, while those placed on the top and sides will not. On the right side, the vertical edges will all be parallel, while on the top the horizontal edges will be parallel. Those edges going back in depth on either face will converge at the vanishing point.

Step 5. Finally, sketch the dark lines representing the object, paying close attention to those edges that converge.

Figure 7.65 on page 281 shows another one-point perspective view that has other features of interest. In Step 3, the depth dimension is only half of what it would normally be. This improves the visual proportion to the width and height dimensions. In addition, the back circle and arc are drawn slightly smaller than in the front plane. Also, some of the features on the left side are not projected back to the vanishing point because they are completely hidden by the front. However, there are other features that need to be projected back. One is a line drawn tangent to the front and back arcs (Figure 7.65, Step 4). Leaving this line out would give the object a hollow appearance, as shown in Figure 7.66 on page 281. Remember to include part of the hole in the back plane if it can be seen, as shown in Figure 7.65, Step 7. All visible object lines are darkened to complete the sketch.

7.8.2 Two-Point Perspective Sketch

A two-point perspective sketch is used when more realism is needed in a pictorial representation. With two-point perspective, instead of having just one vanishing point, there are two. Now, instead of the parallel edges in only the depth dimension converging, the parallel edges

Table 7.1 **Relationship between the Ground Line and Horizon Line**

View Name	Relationship	Effect
Bird's eye view	Ground line well below the horizon line.	Observer is much taller than the object.
Human's eye view	Ground line six feet below the horizon line.	Observer is somewhat taller than the object.
Ground's eye view	Ground line at the same level as the horizon line.	Observer is the same height as the object.
Worm's eye view	Ground line well above the horizon line.	Observer is much shorter than the object.

Figure 7.62

A worm's eye perspective view of a building, created with CAD

This view simulates what the building would look like when viewed looking up from the ground.

(Courtesy of Michael Sechman and Associates, Oakland, California.)

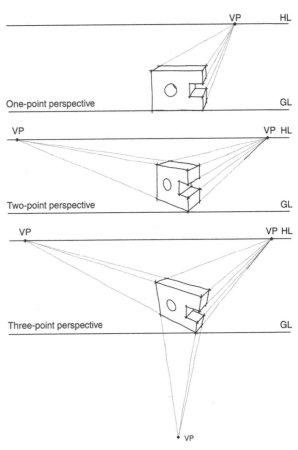

VP HL
One-point perspective GL
VP VP HL
Two-point perspective GL
VP VP HL
Three-point perspective GL
VP

Figure 7.63

One-, two-, and three-point perspective sketches of the same object

in the width dimension also converge. Only the vertical edges—those in the height dimension—remain parallel.

Creating a Two-Point Perspective Sketch

The following steps describe how to create a two-point perspective sketch of a seating block. Refer to Figure 7.67.

Step 1. A two-point perspective sketch starts the same as a one-point sketch: Establish a ground line and a horizon line, then place two vanishing points near the right and left ends of the horizon line, respectively.

Step 2. In one-point perspective, you were able to draw the entire front face in its "true size," that is, without any converging lines to distort it. With two-point perspective, only vertical lines are in true size. Draw a single vertical line at a location between one-quarter and one-third the distance from the left vanishing point. This line will represent the closest edge of the object. Mark the height of the object on the vertical line, measuring upward from the ground line, and draw converging lines from the top and bottom of the vertical line to both vanishing points.

Step 3. Continue by creating the bounding box and roughing in the features. Remember that only the vertical lines will not converge.

Step 4. Finish the sketch by darkening in all of the final lines.

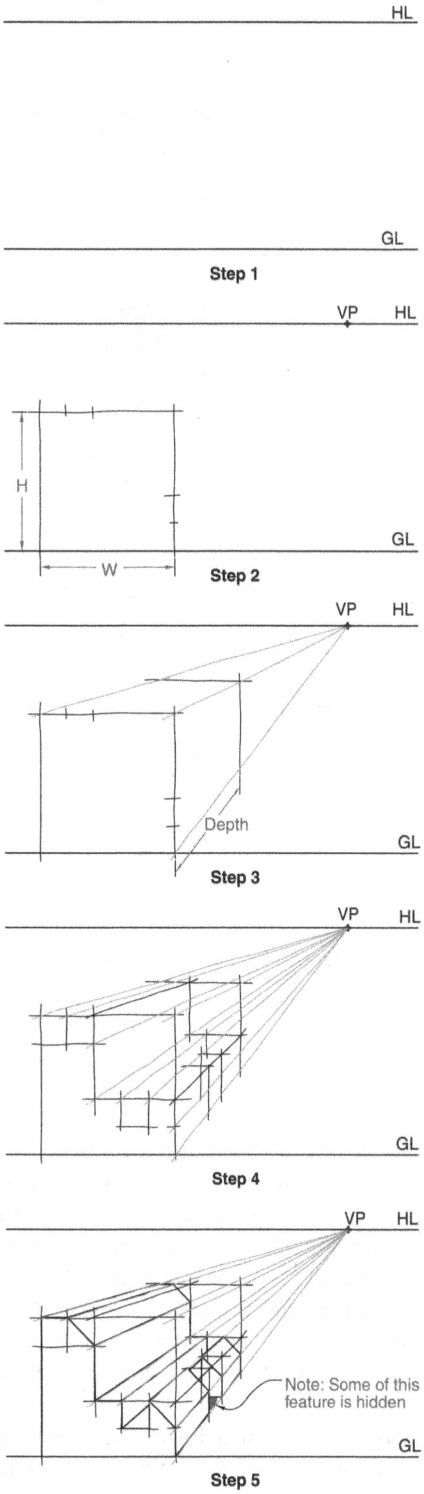

HL

GL

Step 1

VP HL

H

GL

W

Step 2

VP HL

Depth

GL

Step 3

VP HL

GL

Step 4

VP HL

Note: Some of this feature is hidden

GL

Step 5

Figure 7.64

Constructing a one-point perspective sketch, using five steps

7.8.3 Perspective Circles

Both Figures 7.65 and 7.67 have complete or partial circles as a feature. In Figure 7.65, the circle is in the front view, which is not distorted by the converging depth dimension. In Figure 7.67 on page 282, the arc has a converging dimension, but it is small enough not to require calculating its convergence. When you have an arc or circle that is much larger, the following technique should be used to estimate how it will be distorted by convergence.

Before sketching a circle in perspective, determine the dimensions of the circle when viewed full size. Refer back to page 245 and Figure 7.13 to see how a full-size circle is sketched using diagonals. The circle drawn inside the square in Figure 7.13 touches the square at points 1, 2, 3, and 4. The circle crosses the diagonals of the square at two-thirds the distance from the center. Knowing this will be helpful when making a perspective sketch of a circle.

Sketching Perspective Circles

Figure 7.68 and the following steps show how to draw a circle in perspective.

Step 1. Draw the ground line and the horizon line. From the ground line, sketch a vertical line equal in length to the diameter of the circle. Locate the left vanishing point on the horizon line. Project the base and top of the vertical line to the left vanishing point. Estimate the depth and mark it along the depth lines.

Step 2. Sketch the diagonals of the square to locate the center of the circle, and then sketch the center lines.

Step 3. Locate points 1, 2, 3, and 4, and then mark the two-thirds distances along the diagonals. The perspective circle is then sketched using each mark.

Practice Exercise 7.3

Using the same idea as in an earlier demonstration, clip images from magazines, or take photographs, showing objects that are clearly 3-D in nature. Place tracing paper over each image and begin laying out construction lines. How large does the object have to be before you can clearly see edges converging? Does it make a difference how close or far you are from the object? Try to define a horizon line and project lines back to vanishing points. The vanishing points may be of the image itself, so start with a large piece of tracing paper. Where is the horizon line relative to the object? What type of view is it (i.e., ground's eye, bird's eye, etc.)?

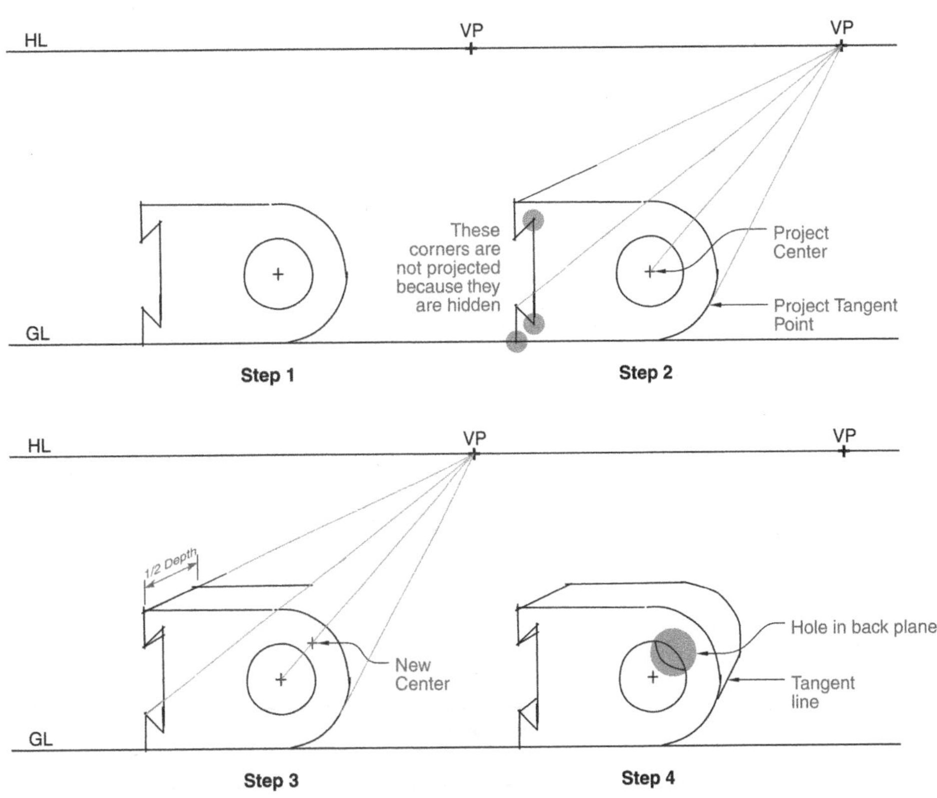

Figure 7.65

Sketching a one-point perspective of an object with circles and arcs

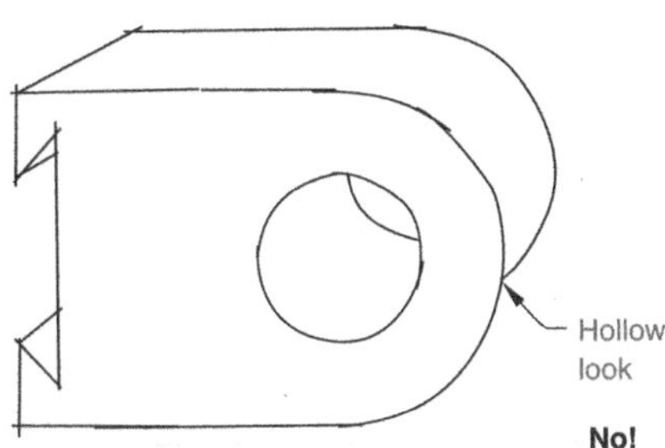

Figure 7.66

Line tangent to arcs

A line tangent to the arcs must be constructed to represent the object accurately. Leaving out the tangent line between the front and back arcs leaves the sketch with a hollow look.

7.9 Sketching Using a Constraint-Based Modeling Software Program

A fundamental technique within most constraint-based modeling programs is to sketch 2-D features then use a 3-D construction operation, such as extrude, revolve, or sweep, to create a 3-D model. Most constraint-based modeling CAD software programs provide a number of tools to fully define a sketch and capture design intent. When sketching, it is important to make sure that the intent of the design is met through the definition of the feature. Feature tools used to capture design intent include:

- *Dimensions*—the primary tool for capturing the intent of a design through the description of the size and location of entities.
- *Constraints*—used to define the relationship of sketched entities to other entities, such as defining two lines as being parallel to each other or two lines of equal length.

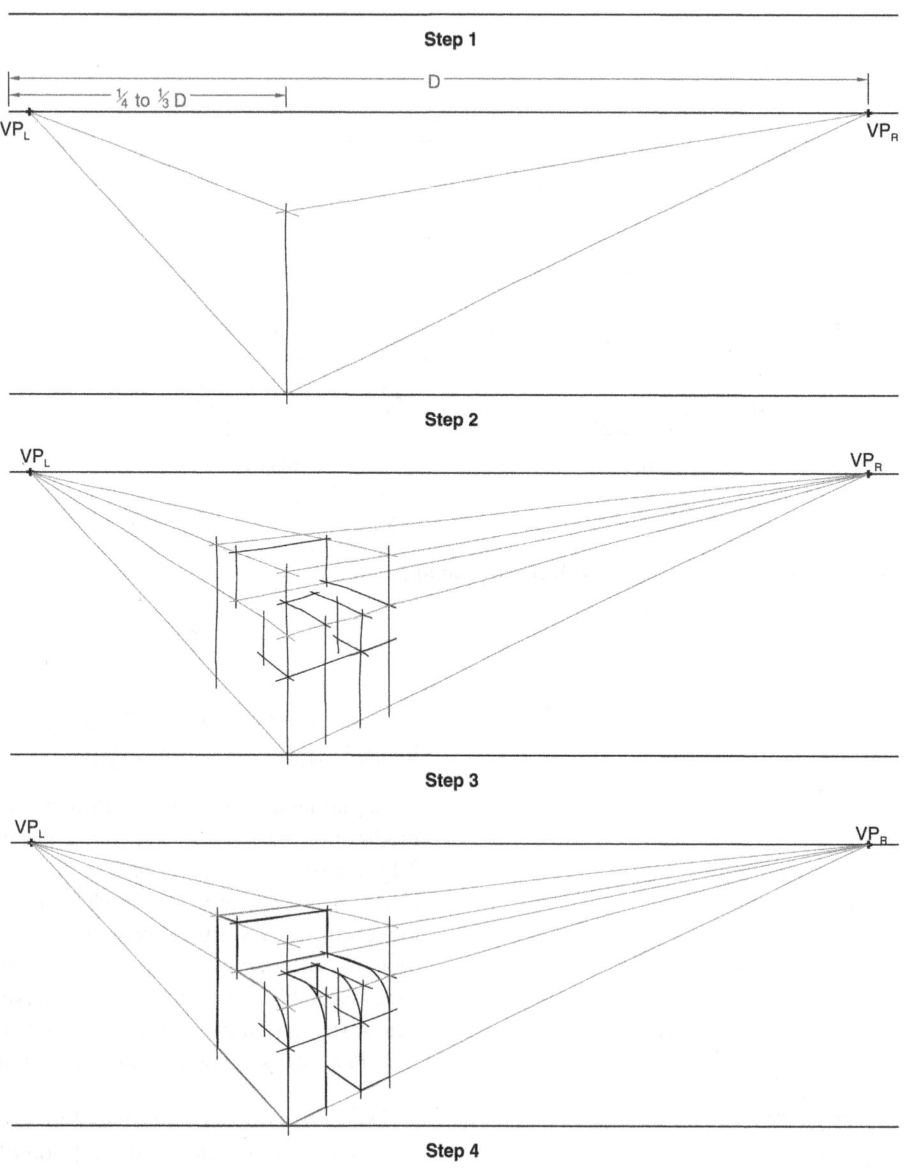

Figure 7.67

Constructing a two-point perspective sketch

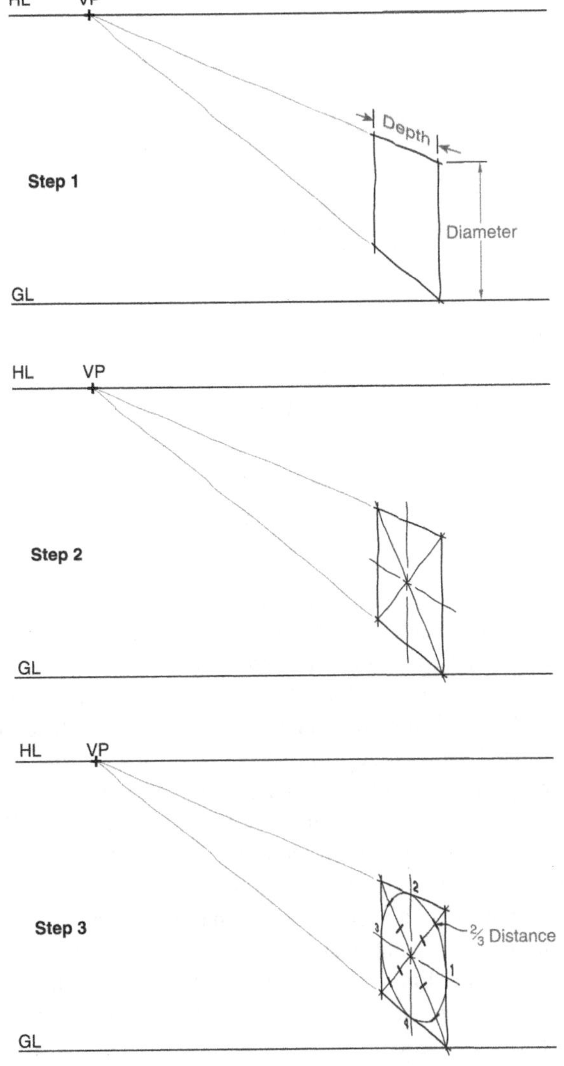

Figure 7.68

Constructing a perspective sketch of a circle

- *References*—when constructing a feature, a sketch entity can reference existing features of a part or assembly, such as datums, edges, or axes.
- *Relations*—relationships can be established between two dimensions, such as using algebraic or trigonometric equations to create mathematical relationships between entities.

When using 2-D CAD programs, it is common to enter precise values for geometric elements. For example, if you are drawing a line that is one inch long, it must be drawn precisely one inch. Most constraint-based modeling programs do not require precise sketches of geometric entities. Instead of creating geometry with precise dimensions, geometry is sketched much like you would if you were creating a pencil sketch. The following guidelines are important when making a sketch with a parametric modeling program:

- The shape and proportions of the sketch are important, not the size.
- The dimensions used to describe the features should match the design intent.
- Geometric constraints of the features should match the design intent.

Some constraint-based software programs have an automatic constraint feature that will assign constraints to entities as they are being sketched. For example, if you are sketching a square, as you sketch the opposite sides of the square, the software will automatically assume that opposite sides are parallel.

See Chapter 9, Three-Dimensional Modeling, for a more complete discussion of sketching features.

7.10 Lettering

All engineering and technical drawings, including sketches, contain some notes or dimensions. All text on a drawing must be neat and legible, so it can be easily read on both the original drawing and a reproduction, such as a blueprint or photocopy. Although precise lettering is not required, legibility is very important.

Until the invention of printing by Johann Gutenberg in the 15th century, all text was hand lettered, using a very personalized style. With the invention of printing, text styles became more standardized. Although some early technical drawings were embellished with personalized text, current ANSI standards suggest the use of single-stroke Gothic characters, for maximum readability (Figure 7.69 on the next page).

The tools used to add text to engineering and technical drawings have evolved over the years from quill pens to the computer. Pencils are still a common tool, but their use is declining as more drawings are being produced with CAD software. Mechanical lettering guides, such as the lettering template in Figure 7.70 on the next page, the lettering machine, and press-on type, were developed in the years before CAD.

In a modern engineering or technical graphics office, it is more important to have good typing skills than it is to

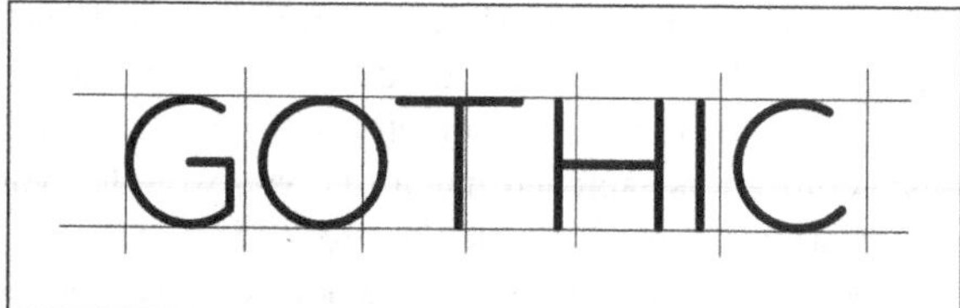

Figure 7.69

An example of hand-lettered gothic text style commonly used in engineering drawing

Figure 7.70

A mechanical lettering template used to assist in the drawing of text on engineering drawings

(Courtesy of Chartpak, Inc.)

have or practice hand-lettering skills. The keyboard has all but eliminated the need to do hand lettering on final drawings. One of the greatest productivity advantages of CAD over traditional tools is the speed with which text can be added to a drawing. The use of computers to create engineering and technical drawings has resulted in the choice of many different text styles and placement options for engineering and technical drawings.

7.10.1 Lettering Standards

ANSI has developed a set of standard practices for adding text to a drawing. In this book, other techniques have been added to those standards to help you create legible text using hand lettering or computer tools. These standards and techniques include the following:

- Use a Gothic text style, either inclined or vertical.
- Use all capital letters.
- Use ⅛″ (3 mm) for most text height.
- Use ¼″ (6 mm) for the height of fractions.
- Determine the minimum space between lines of text by taking the text height and dividing it by 2.

Figure 7.71 shows examples of these standards.

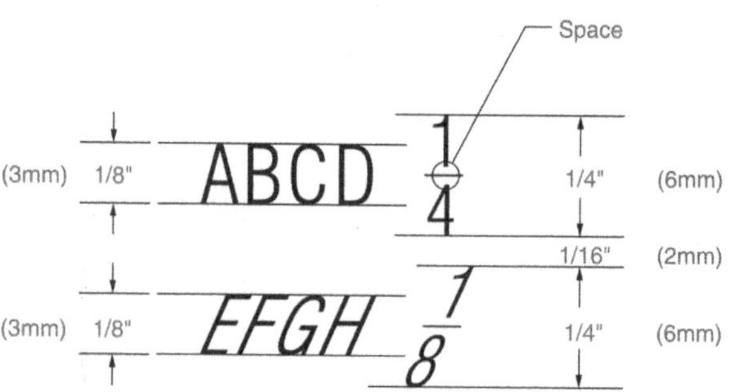

Figure 7.71

Recommended text heights

The recommended heights for text on technical drawings are ⅛″ or 3 mm high for letters and ¼″ or 6 mm for fractions.

7.10.2 Hand Lettering

Though hand lettering is used less and less, you must still be able to produce clear, legible, hand-lettered words and numbers that conform to a standard style.

Whenever lettering by hand, you should use guide lines. **Guide lines** are very thin, very light construction lines used as a guide to create uniform letters on engineering and technical drawings. Guide lines are constructed using a very sharp, hard pencil, such as a 4H, 5H, or 6H. One method of creating guide lines is to measure the distances between them using a scale, or a piece of scrap paper with the distances marked on the edge. In addition to horizontal guide lines, beginners often find vertical guide lines to be useful. Vertical guide lines are placed every fourth or fifth letter to help keep the letters vertical and aligned.

Lettering guides can also be used to make guide lines, as shown in Figure 7.72. The lettering guides are a convenient method for laying out various distances for text, as well as the angle used to create inclined text. These lettering guides are used against a straight edge, such as a T-square, and a pencil is inserted into a hole and used to drag the guide across the paper. As the guide is dragged across the paper, a line is drawn. More lines are added by placing the pencil in different holes and dragging the guide across the paper again. Lettering guides can be used to create horizontal, vertical, or inclined guide lines.

Within these guide lines, the individual letters are drawn. There is a particular style to each letter. Figure 7.73 shows examples of each letter in its vertical format. Notice that all of the letters are in capitals. In general, lowercase letters are never used. In Figure 7.73, a recommended

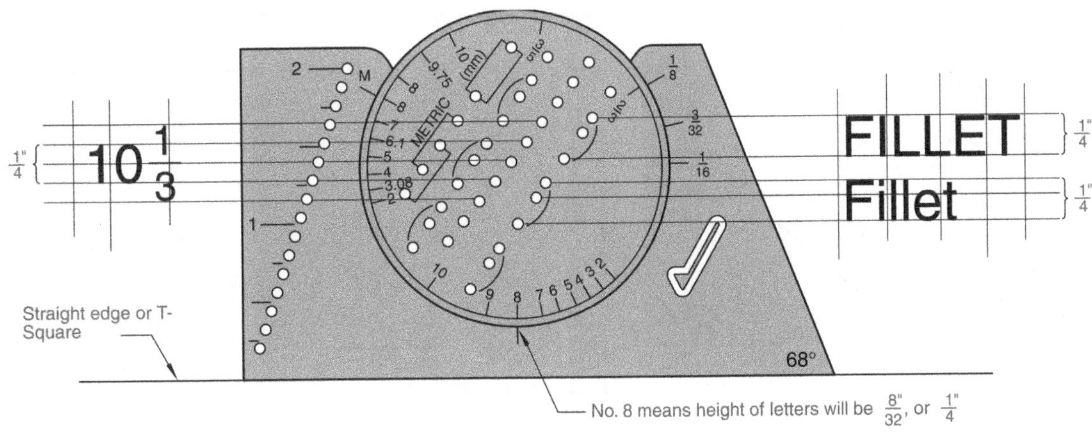

Figure 7.72

An adjustable lettering guide used for hand lettering on drawings

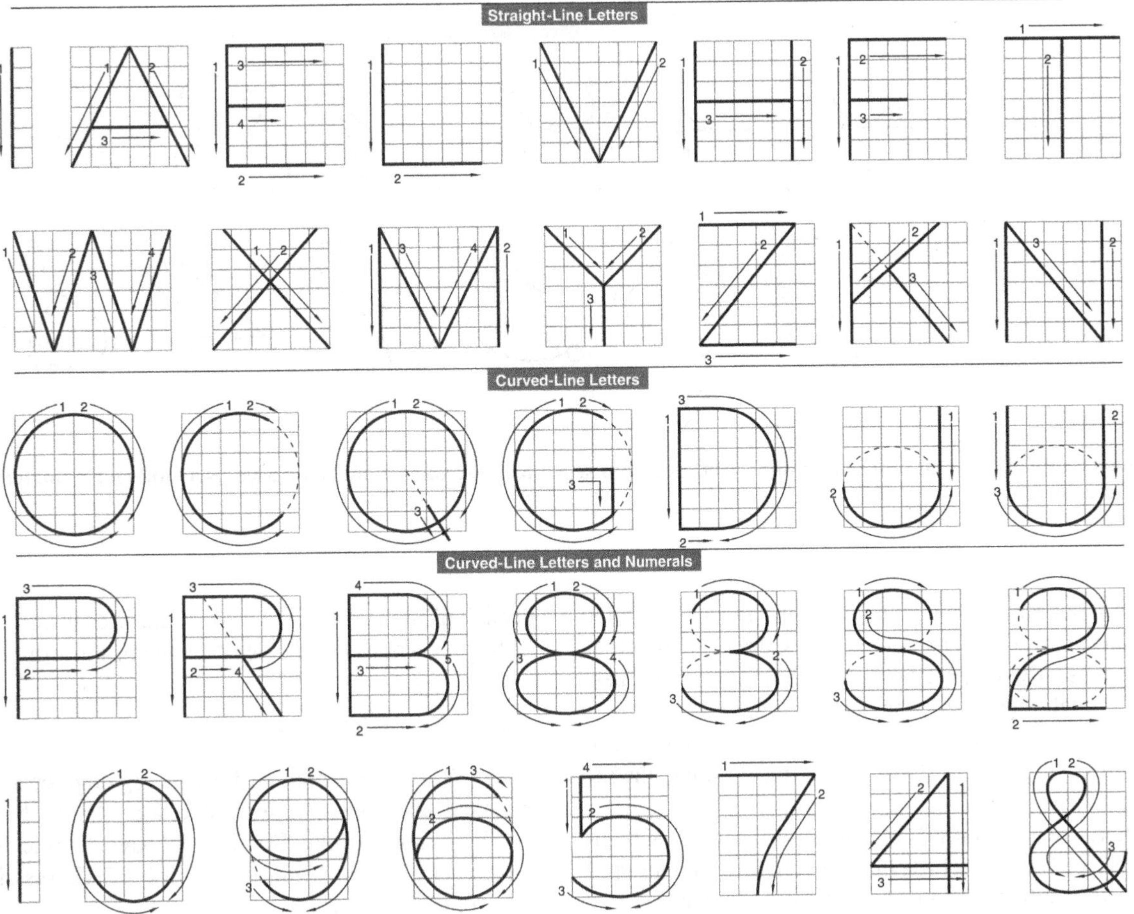

Figure 7.73

Vertical Gothic letter and numeral design, with suggested sequence of strokes that can be used as a guide for hand lettering a technical drawing

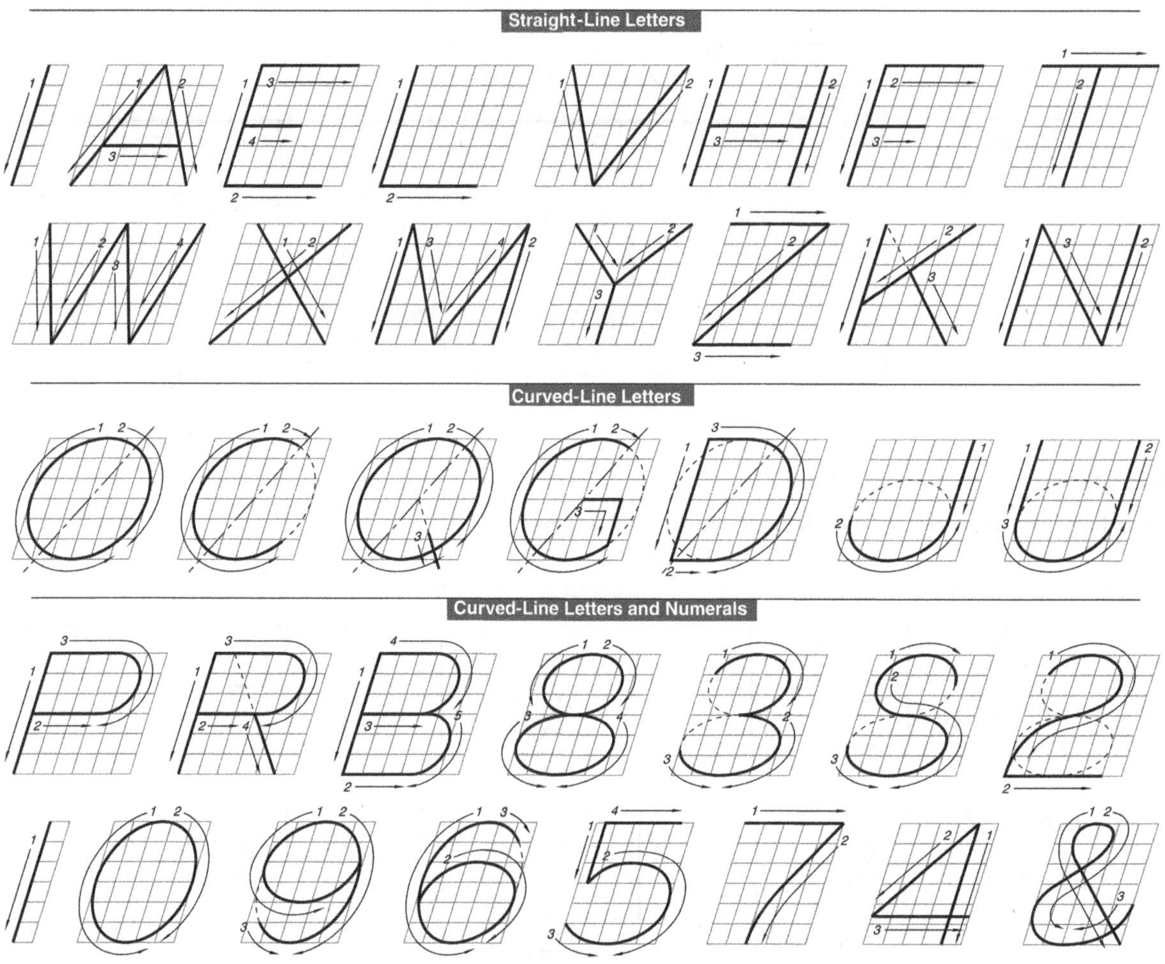

Figure 7.74

Inclined Gothic letter and numeral design, with suggested sequence of strokes that can be used as a guide for hand lettering a technical drawing

stroke sequence is given. Each straight segment of a letter is drawn as a separate single stroke. Curved strokes that are particularly long are broken up into multiple strokes. Even though there is the temptation to draw an "O" in a single stroke, you will create a better shape if you do it in two halves. Figure 7.74 shows the Gothic design in the inclined format.

There are many pitfalls in hand lettering. Most of them are correctable with a little bit of practice and attention to your work. Whenever lettering a drawing by hand, follow the format illustrated in the top line in Figure 7.75. Take particular note of the uniformity of spacing between letters. Do not have equal spacing between each letter. Instead, look at the volume of background area in and around each letter. This volume is what should be uniform.

7.10.3 Alternate Text Styles

Until CAD became popular for creating engineering and technical drawings, the text style was standardized by ANSI as single-stroke Gothic. Although Gothic is still the standard set by ANSI, the user of a CAD system has many other choices.

CAD text is classified and grouped by its characteristics. The size and style of a type define its **font**. Most CAD systems can make use of the same fonts available in word processing systems. However, it is usually best to use as few different fonts as possible. Use fonts that are standard to the industry generating the drawings.

Text can also be varied by using bold or italic versions. Boldface is a heavyweight version of a typeface. An italic typeface is slanted and is generally lighter in weight.

Figure 7.76 is a guide to type characteristics. Type size is measured in **points**, and there are 72 points per vertical inch. So 36-point type is about ½ inch high, where

ESTIMATE

EsTiMaTE — Letters not uniform in style.

ESTIMATE
ESTIMATE — Letters not uniform in height.

ESTIMATE
ESTIMATE — Letters not uniformly vertical or inclined.

ESTIMATE
ESTIMATE — Letters not uniform in thickness of stroke.

ES T IM AT E — Areas between letters not uniform.

ABILITY WILL NEVER CATCH UP
WITH THE DEMAND FOR IT — Areas between words not uniform.

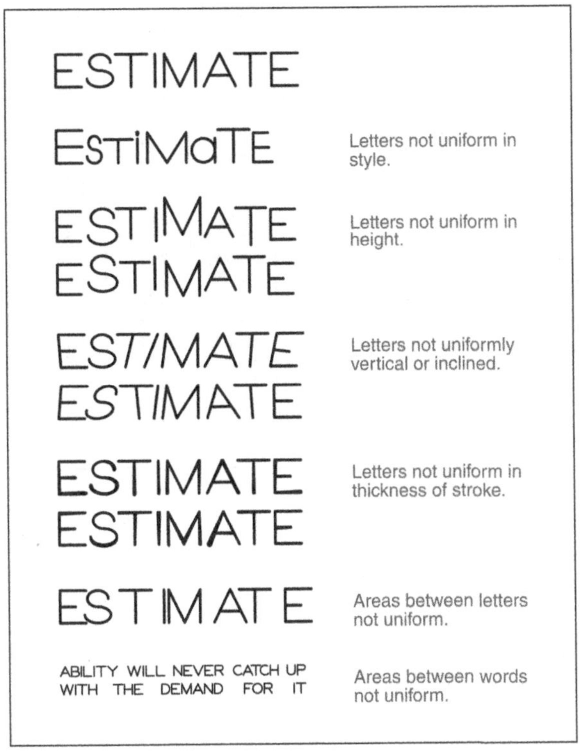

Figure 7.75

Examples of poor hand-lettering technique

the height is measured from the top of the letter to a fixed depth below the letter. The ascender is the portion of a lowercase character that extends above the letter height. The descender is the portion of a lowercase letter that extends below the baseline. A serif is a small finishing stroke perpendicular to the main character stroke. A sans serif typeface is one without serifs. Gothic is a sans serif typeface.

7.10.4 Computer Lettering Technique

Text is added to a CAD drawing by selecting the appropriate command, entering the letters and numerals with the keyboard, and then picking a point on the drawing where the text is to be placed. Before adding text to a drawing, many variables must be set. Some of the more common computer text variables are height, font, alignment, aspect ratio, slant, and rotation. Although some CAD software makes it easy to use different fonts, technical drawings that adhere to ANSI standards should always use the block Gothic style for maximum clarity when reproducing technical drawings.

Text Height The height of the text is controlled by entering a numerical value. Think of this as setting your guide lines for the text. The advantage of CAD is that it is easy to create virtually any size text for a drawing. One important consideration is the scale to be used for the drawing itself. For example, suppose you were a drafter/designer and had to create a drawing of a new section of interstate highway. The section of the road you are to draw is approximately 1000 feet long and the text height is set at ⅛″. Obviously you cannot plot the drawing full scale, so a scale of 1″ = 25′-0″ is chosen to fit the drawing on a D-size sheet. This will plot the drawing at 1/300 scale. If the ⅛″ text is also plotted at 1/300 scale, it would be reduced to a series of dots, at best. Figure 7.77 on the next page provides text heights for some common plot scales.

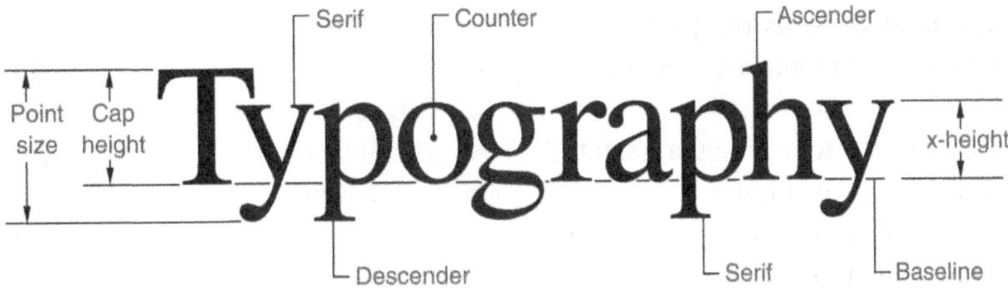

Figure 7.76

Important terms associated with text

This information is useful when using CAD for lettering.

Scale	1/8" Text Height
1/32" = 1'	48
1/16" = 1'	24
1/8" = 1'	12
1/4" = 1'	6
1/2" = 1'	3
1/4 size	.5
1/2 size	.25
Full size	.125
2/1	.0625
3/1	.0416
4/1	.0312
5/1	.0250
10/1	.0125
100/1	.00125
1000/1	.000125
1" = 1000'	1500
1" = 500'	750
1" = 100'	150
1" = 10'	15

Text Size and Plot Scale Reference Table

Desired Text Size (On paper)		Plotted Drawing Scale								
		1:128 $^3/_{32}$" = 1'	1:96 $^1/_8$" = 1'	1:48 $^1/_4$" = 1'	1:32 $^3/_8$" = 1'	1:24 $^1/_2$" = 1'	1:16 $^3/_4$" = 1'	1:12 1" = 1'	1:4 3" = 1'	1:2 6" = 1'
1/32"	0.03125"	4	3	1.5	1	0.75	0.5	0.375	0.125	0.0625
1/16"	0.0625"	8	6	3	2	1.5	1	0.75	0.25	0.125
3/32"	0.09375"	12	9	4.5	3	2.25	1.5	1.125	0.375	0.1875
1/8"	0.125"	16	12	6	4	3	2	1.5	0.5	0.25
5/32"	0.15625	20	15	7.5	5	3.75	2.5	1.875	0.625	0.3125
3/16"	0.1875"	24	18	9	6	4.5	3	2.25	0.75	0.375
7/32"	0.21875"	28	21	10.5	7	5.25	3.5	2.625	0.875	0.4375
1/4"	0.25"	32	24	12	8	6	4	3	1	0.5
9/32"	0.28125"	36	27	13.5	9	6.75	4.5	3.375	1.125	0.5625
5/16"	0.3125"	40	30	15	10	7.5	5	3.75	1.25	0.625
11/32"	0.34375"	44	33	16.5	11	8.25	5.5	4.125	1.375	0.6875
3/8"	0.375"	48	36	18	12	9	6	4.5	1.5	0.75
13/32"	0.40625"	52	39	19.5	13	9.75	6.5	4.875	1.625	0.8125
7/16"	0.4375"	56	42	21	14	10.5	7	5.25	1.75	0.875
15/32"	0.46875"	60	45	22.5	15	11.25	7.5	5.625	1.875	0.9375
1/2"	0.5"	64	48	24	16	12	8	6	2	1
17/32"	0.53125"	68	51	25.5	17	12.75	8.5	6.375	2.125	1.0625
9/16"	0.5625"	72	54	27	18	13.5	9	6.75	2.25	1.125
19/32"	0.59375"	76	57	28.5	19	14.25	9.5	7.125	2.375	1.1875
5/8"	0.625"	80	60	30	20	15	10	7.5	2.5	1.25
21/32"	0.65625"	84	63	31.5	21	15.75	10.5	7.875	2.625	1.3125
11/16"	0.6875"	88	66	33	22	16.5	11	8.25	2.75	1.375
23/32"	0.71875"	92	69	34.5	23	17.25	11.5	8.625	2.875	1.4375
3/4"	0.75"	96	72	36	24	18	12	9	3	1.5
25/32"	0.78125"	100	75	37.5	25	18.75	12.5	9.375	3.125	1.5625
13/16"	0.8125"	104	78	39	26	19.5	13	9.75	3.25	1.625
27/32"	0.84375"	108	81	40.5	27	20.25	13.5	10.125	3.375	1.6875
7/8"	0.875"	112	84	42	28	21	14	10.5	3.5	1.75
29/32"	0.90625"	116	87	43.5	29	21.75	14.5	10.875	3.625	1.8125
15/16"	0.9375"	120	90	45	30	22.5	15	11.25	3.75	1.875
31/32"	0.96875"	124	93	46.5	31	23.25	15.5	11.625	3.875	1.9375
1"	1"	128	96	48	32	24	16	12	4	2

Instructions:

1) Find the plotted text size you want in the column on the left of the large table.
2) Read across until you reach the correct plotting scale column.
3) The value shown is the size of text (in inches) you create in your CAD drawing.

Example:

Desired text size is 9/16", and drawing is plotted at 3/8" = 1' - 0". Make text 18" high in CAD.

Calculated as: $^9/_{16} \times \left[\frac{12}{^3/_8}\right] = 18$

Figure 7.77

Recommended text height and plot scale settings for CAD drawings

Text Alignment **Text alignment** controls the justification of a line of CAD text. Typical alignments are: center, left, and right.

Center justification centers the text about a selected point, which is indicated by the X in Figure 7.78A. Left justification places the text flush left with a margin and results in a ragged right margin (Figure 7.78B). Right justification places the text flush right with a margin and results in a ragged left margin (Figure 7.78C). Some CAD systems provide even more precision in placing text, using the following:

- Top center
- Top left
- Top right
- Middle center
- Middle left
- Middle right
- Bottom center
- Bottom left
- Bottom right

Other CAD Text Variables Depending on the type of CAD system, there are many other text variables that can be controlled. Text slant is used to create individual text characters at an angle away from vertical (Figure 7.79). Text rotation is the angle, measured from horizontal, used

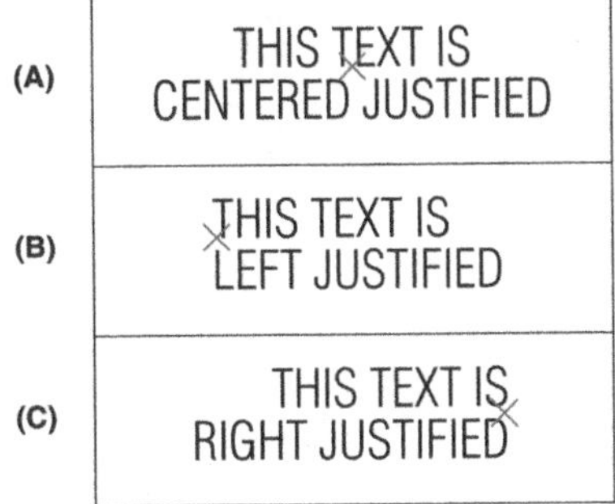

Figure 7.78

Justifying text

Most CAD systems allow text to be justified about a given point.

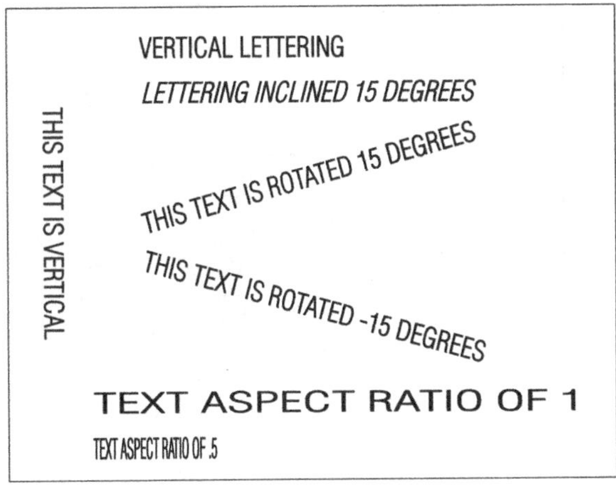

Figure 7.79

Examples of CAD text slant, incline, and aspect ratios

to create entire lines of text at an angle. Text aspect ratio is the numerical ratio of the width versus the height of individual characters. Text aspect ratio can be controlled to create letters that range from narrow to wide. For example, a text ratio of 1 produces characters that are equally wide and high. A text ratio of 0.5 produces characters that are twice as high as they are wide. Ratios greater than one create extended letters; ratios less than one create compressed letters. Some CAD systems even allow text to be drawn upside down, backwards, and vertically.

Occasionally, special text characters not found on a standard computer keyboard must be added to technical drawings. Examples are the degree, plus–minus, and diameter symbols. By entering a special string of text (a code), it is possible to create such symbols. Using one particular CAD software product, entering %%D results in the degree symbol being created on the drawing. Another CAD software may have a different code for creating the degree symbol.

7.11 Text on Drawings

Without text it would be nearly impossible to describe engineering designs completely. Text on engineering and technical drawings is used:

- To communicate nongraphic information.
- As a substitute for graphic information in those instances where text can communicate the needed information more clearly and quickly. (Examples: the name of a part or assembly, the number of parts needed, the dimensions of a part.)

The use of text on drawings should be kept to a minimum, and the text should be short and concise.

Although text can be placed anywhere on a drawing, there are a few areas where text is more commonly found. These areas are described in the following paragraphs (Figure 7.80 on the next page).

Title Block Text is used in **title blocks** to identify the drawing name and its relationship to other drawings. Other important information also found in a title block includes the scale, date drawn, company, name of the person who made the drawing, name of the person who checked the drawing, etc.

Revision Block A **revision block** is located adjacent to the title block and lists the revisions made to a drawing.

Bill of Materials Text is used in a **bill of materials** to identify part numbers and names, part materials, quantities needed for the assembly, dimensional sizes, and other information.

General Notes Text can be used to provide general information that cannot otherwise be effectively or quickly communicated. Part names and numbers are sometimes placed near the orthographic views when more than one part of an assembly is drawn on a single sheet. Special manufacturing information may also be noted.

Dimensions Text is used on dimensions to identify the measurements necessary to make the product or structure. Most dimension text is numerals ⅛″ or 3 mm high.

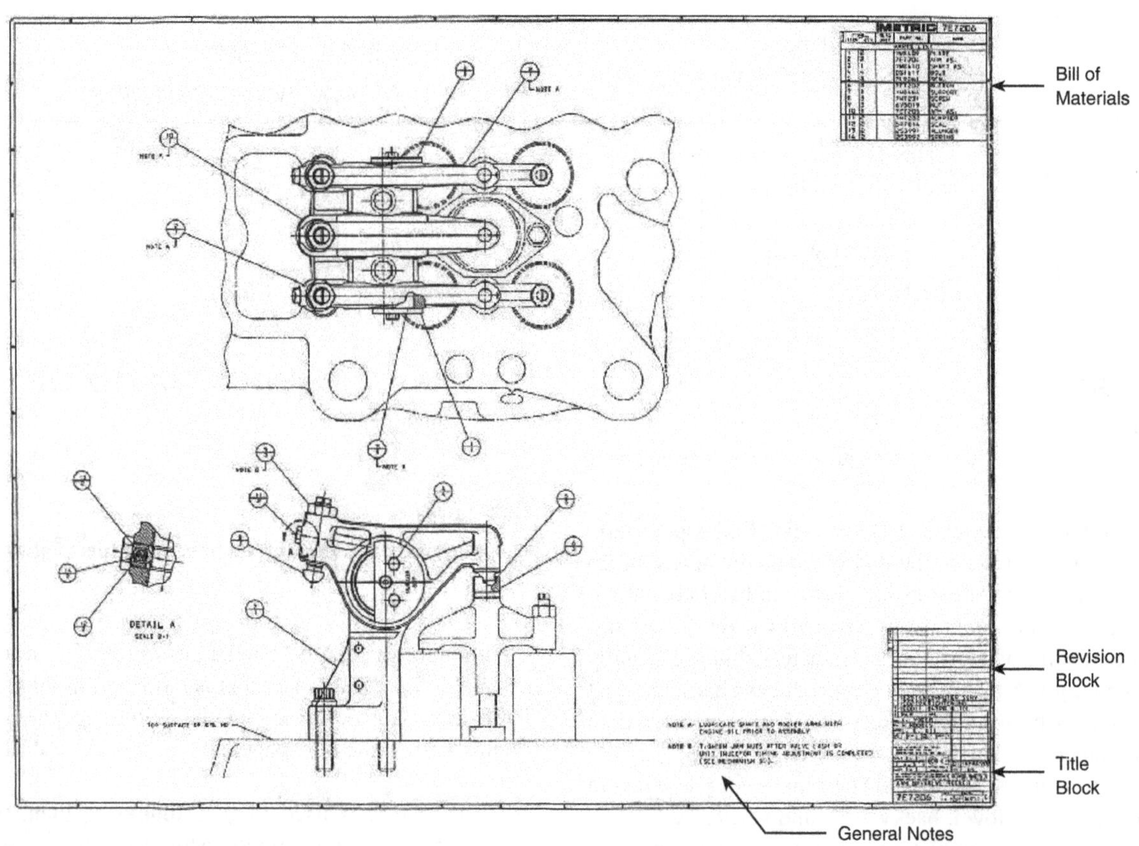

Figure 7.80

Examples of a title block, general notes, a revision block, and bill of materials on a technical drawing

7.12 Summary

Sketching is an important tool for quickly and efficiently communicating design ideas. It is a particularly useful tool early in the design process, when several ideas are being explored. One of the appealing characteristics of sketches is the minimal amount of equipment needed for their creation. A pencil, eraser, and paper are the only tools really necessary for creating a sketch. Increasingly, software being developed to run on low-cost computer systems has many of the same attributes as hand sketching. This new software has the potential of allowing a more direct translation of sketched designs into final, refined models that can be used in manufacturing and construction.

Whether a sketch is created by hand or on the computer, there is a basic set of techniques that should be used. Sketches are meant to be quickly created approximations of geometric forms. Therefore, exact measurements are usually not used in sketching. Instead, construction line techniques are used to preserve the proportions of different features of the object.

The process of transferring the features of a 3-D object onto a 2-D sheet of paper is called projection. One way of defining the projection relates to whether the lines projecting the features of the object are all parallel to each other. The types of projection include isometric pictorial, oblique pictorial, and multiview. These projections constitute the most popular methods used in engineering and technical graphics. Another type of projection, perspective, more closely matches how you perceive objects in the real world. This type of projection is less commonly used, in part because of the difficulty in laying out the sketch, and also because of the distortions it creates in the features of the object drawn.

The graphical methods used in creating a sketch communicate considerable information. At times, however, words are more effective for providing information on a drawing. The use of a standard method of lettering ensures that text in a drawing will be clear and legible. Computers are used extensively for generating text. This is due in part to the flexibility with which text can be generated and modified to meet specialized needs. Later chapters in this book will go into more detail as to the proper use and placement of text in engineering and technical graphics.

Online Learning Center (OLC) Features

There are a number of Online Learning Center features listed below that you can use to supplement your text reading to improve your understanding and retention of the material presented in this chapter at www.mhhe.com/bertoline.

- Learning Objectives
- Chapter Outline
- Questions for Review
- Multiple Choice Quiz
- True or False Questions
- Flashcards
- Website Links
- Animations
- Related Readings
- Stapler Design Problem

Questions for Review

1. Define and describe the uses for technical sketching.
2. Define an ideation sketch, and explain how it differs from a document sketch.
3. List the four types of sketches, grouped by projection methods. Sketch an example of each type.
4. Describe the major differences between parallel and perspective projection.
5. Define multiview drawing, and make a sketch of one.
6. Define principal view.
7. Describe the precedence of lines.
8. Describe how sketching is used in constraint-based modelers.
9. List the two important uses for text on a drawing.
10. Define font.
11. Define text alignment, and sketch an example.
12. Define text aspect ratio, and give examples.

Hints for Isometric Sketching

- Identify the major features and overall dimensions of the object.
- Use clean, crisp strokes.
- Do not use straightedges or scales when sketching.
- Start by drawing a bounding box, using construction lines.
- Only measure dimensions along the primary axes.
- Do not directly transfer angles from a multiview to a pictorial.
- Use light construction lines to locate vertices and edges.
- Sketch faces roughly in this order:
  1. Normal faces on the perimeter of the bounding box.
  2. Normal faces in the interior of the bounding box.
  3. Inclined faces.
  4. Oblique faces.
- Darken all object lines.

Hints for Multiview Sketching

- Identify the major features and overall dimensions of the object.
- Use clean, crisp strokes.
- Do not use straightedges or scales when sketching.
- Start by drawing bounding boxes and a miter line, using construction lines.
- Align the views.
- Use light construction lines to locate vertices and edges.
- Only measure dimensions along the primary axes.
- Map inclined and oblique faces between all three views.
- Follow the precedence of lines.
- Doublecheck to make sure there are no missing hidden or center lines.
- Darken all visible, hidden, and center lines.

Further Reading

Duff, J. M., and W. A. Ross. *Freehand Sketching for Engineering Design.* Boston, MA: PWS-Kent, 1995.

Edwards, B. *The New Drawing on the Right Side of the Brain.* New York: St. Martin's Press, 1999.

Hanks, K., and L. Belliston. *Draw!* Los Altos, CA: William Kaufmann, 1977.

Hanks, K., L. Belliston, and D. Edwards. *Design Yourself!* Los Altos, CA: William Kaufmann, 1978.

Knowlton, K. W. *Technical Freehand Drawing and Sketching.* New York: McGraw-Hill, 1977.

Problems

7.1 Using visible, center, and hidden line styles, practice sketching the following types of lines/features using size A or A4 plain or grid paper:

- Straight lines
- 90- and 180-degree arcs
- Circles
- Ellipses

7.2 Refer to Figures 7.81A–G, multiview sketching problems. Sketch (freehand) the necessary views, using size A or A4 plain or grid paper. Divide the long dimension of the paper with a thick dark line. A multiview drawing can fit on either half of the paper. Add a border line and title block like that shown in Figure 3.78.

7.3 Refer to Figures 7.82A–C, pictorial sketching problems. Sketch (freehand) pictorials, using size A or A4 plain or grid paper. Pictorials can be perspective, isometric, or oblique. Divide the long dimension of the paper with a thick dark line. A pictorial drawing can fit on either half of the paper. Add a border line and title block like that shown in Figure 6.67.

7.4 Draw a pictorial sketch of one of the multiviews in Problem 7.3. Pass the pictorial sketch to another student in the class, but do not specify which multiview you used. Have that student draw a multiview from your sketch. Compare that with the original multiview. Do they look the same? Reverse the process by starting with one of the objects in Problem 7.2.

7.5 Create 2-D CAD drawings or 3-D CAD models from the sketches drawn in Problems 7.2 and 7.3. Compare the time taken and the strategy used with that of sketching.

7.6 Using one object from either Problem 7.2 or 7.3, sketch and compare the following pictorials on size A or A4 plain or grid paper:

a. One-, two-, and three-point perspective.
b. One-point perspective and oblique.
c. Two-point perspective and isometric.

7.7 Using one object from either Problem 7.2 or 7.3, sketch isometric pictorials from three different viewpoints, on size A or A4 plain or grid paper.

7.8 Using one object from Problem 7.2, sketch different multiviews using three different front views as a starting point, on size A or A4 plain or grid paper.

7.9 Using one object from Problem 7.2, sketch all six standard views (front, top, right side, left side, bottom, back), on size A or A4 plain or grid paper. Which views are identical?

7.10 Using one object from either Problem 7.2 or 7.3, sketch four one-point perspective pictorials on size A or A4 plain or grid paper. Use different combinations of vanishing point and horizon line, as follows:

Vanishing Point	Horizon Line
To the Right of the Object	Bird's Eye View
Behind the Object	Human's Eye View
To the Left of the Object	Ground's Eye View
To the Right of the Object	Worm's Eye View

7.11 Using sketches made from either Problem 7.2 or 7.3, identify the following features, with color pencils or markers: edges, faces, and voids (negative space).

7.12 Gather real examples, computer images, or magazine pictures of common objects. Have the objects vary in complexity of form. Some should have only simple, planar features, while others should be curved, sculpted surfaces. Some ideas are motor vehicles, farm equipment, household appliances, aircraft and nautical vessels, computer equipment, audio/visual equipment, furniture, lighting fixtures, sports and exercise equipment, hand tools, and stationary and hand-held power tools.

7.13 Choosing one of the objects from Problem 7.12, sketch isometric pictorials or multiview drawings, using either plain or grid paper. Identify the major features of the object and choose the best viewpoint to begin the sketch.

7.14 Choosing from one of the larger objects identified in Problem 7.12, sketch a multiview of it on grid paper using the "finger-on-pencil" method of judging proportions (see Section 7.3). Then create a pictorial sketch of the object on grid paper, but at twice the scale. Use the grid blocks to adjust the scale of the drawing.

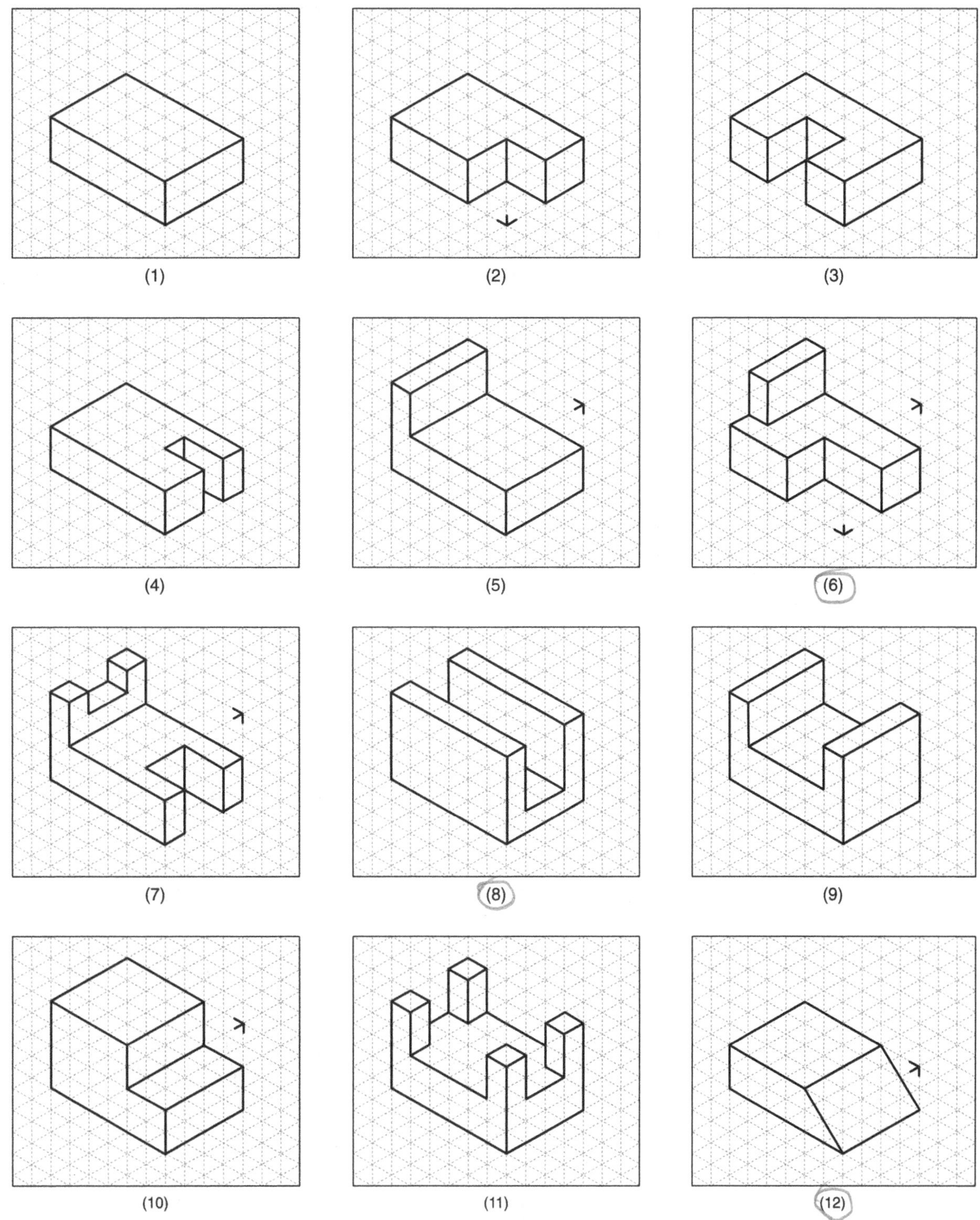

Figure 7.81A

Problem 7.2 Multiview sketching problems

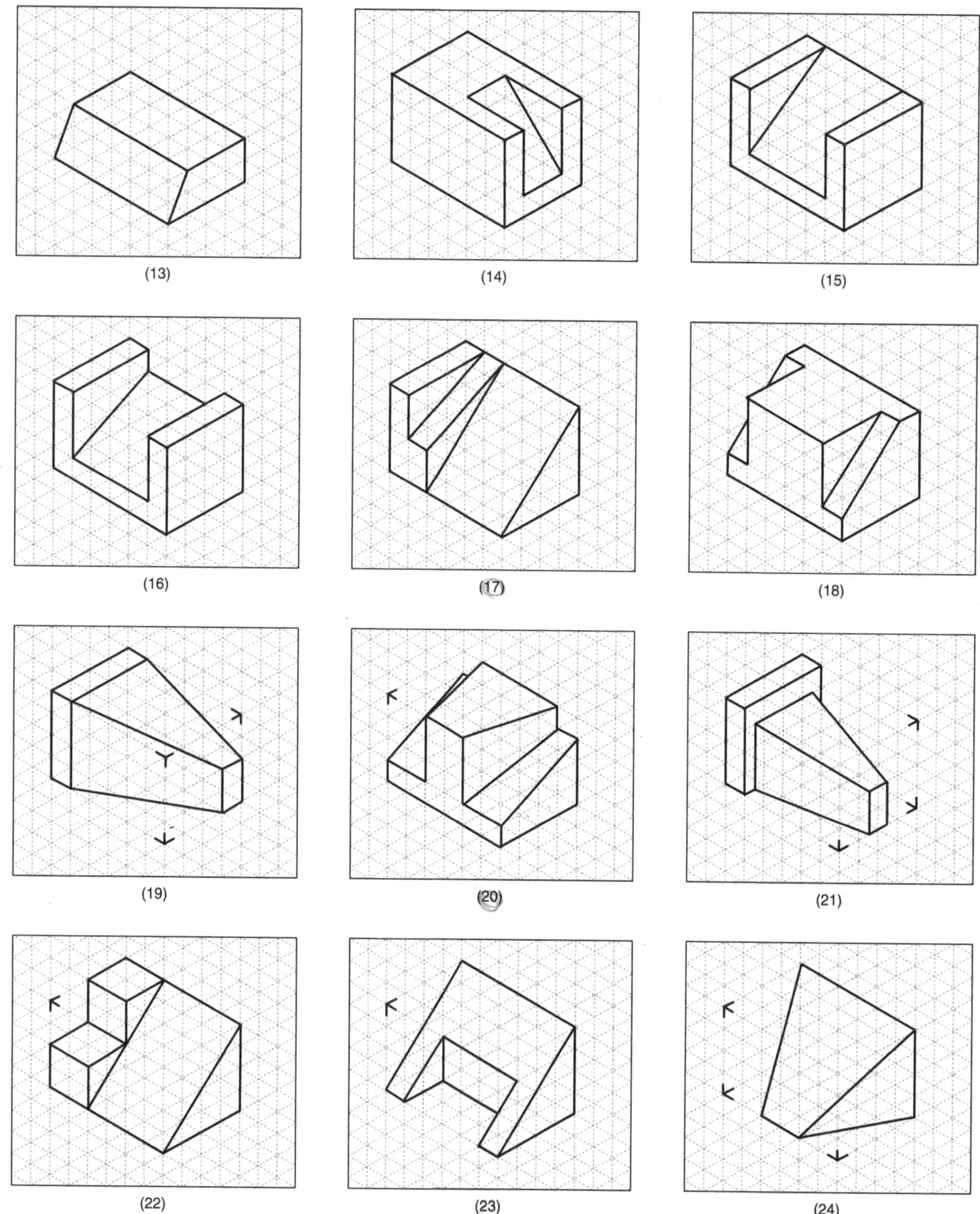

Figure 7.81B

Problem 7.2 Multiview sketching problems

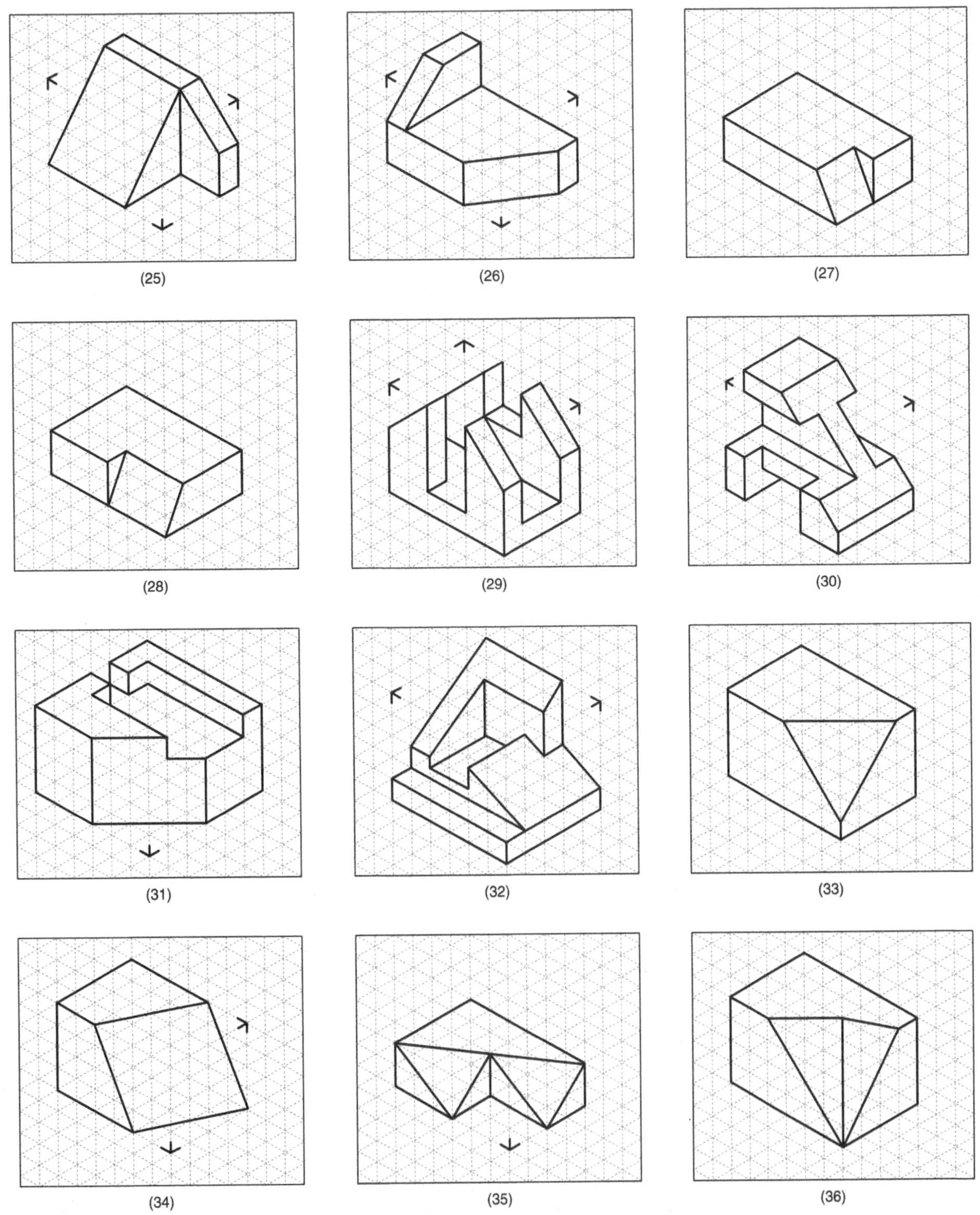

Figure 7.81C

Problem 7.2 Multiview sketching problems

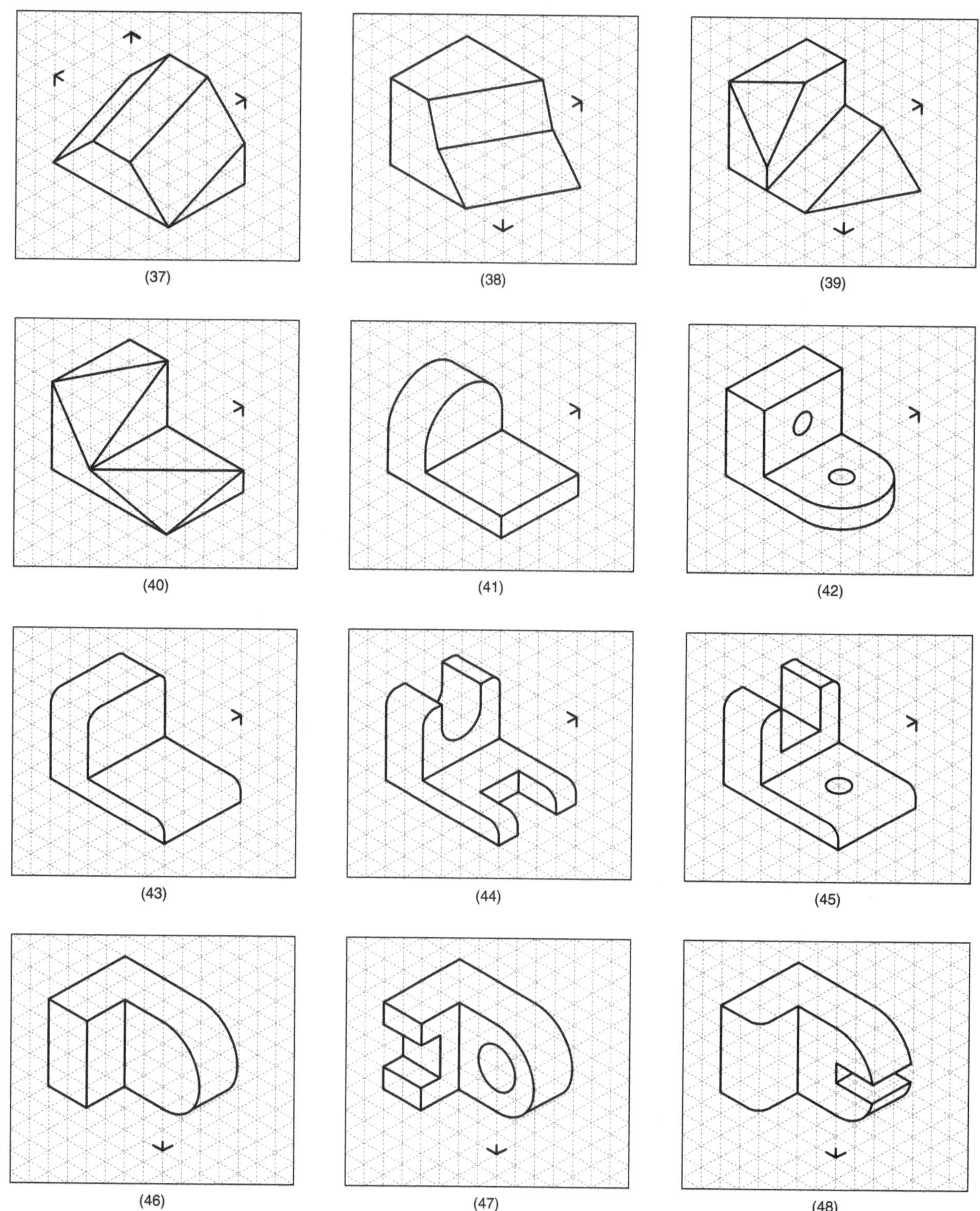

Figure 7.81D

Problem 7.2 Multiview sketching problems

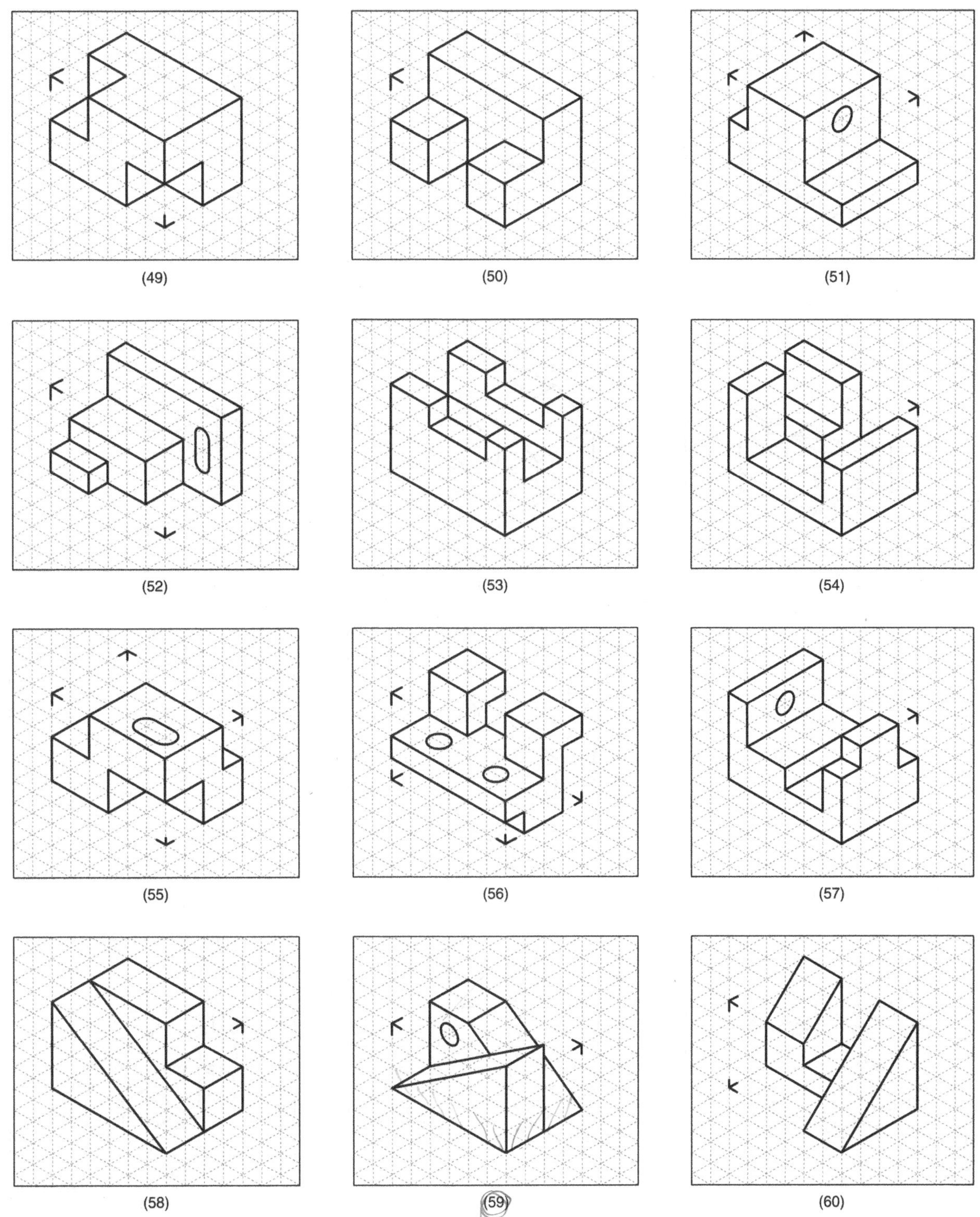

Figure 7.81E

Problem 7.2 Multiview sketching problems

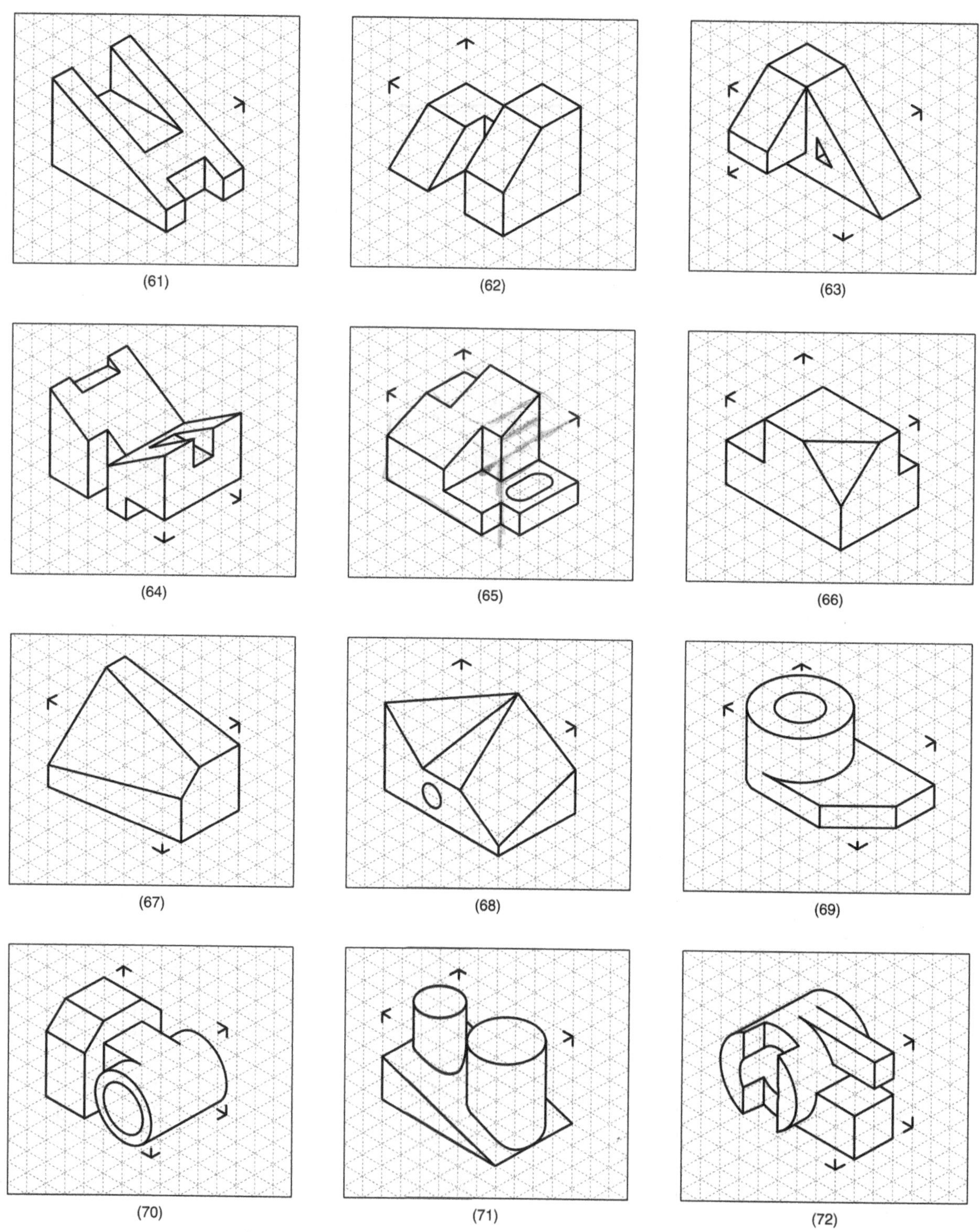

Figure 7.81F

Problem 7.2 Multiview sketching problems

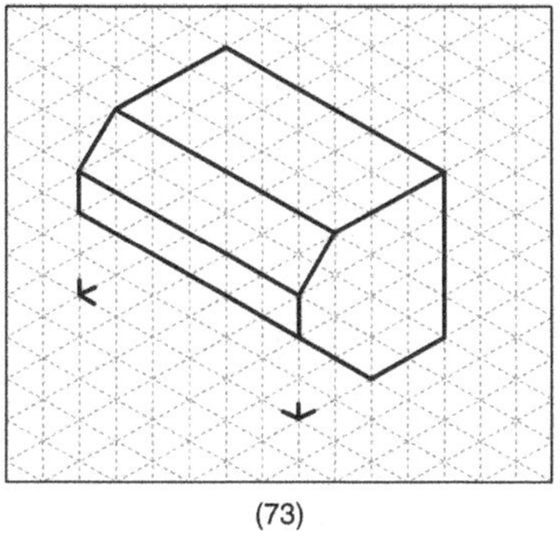
(73)

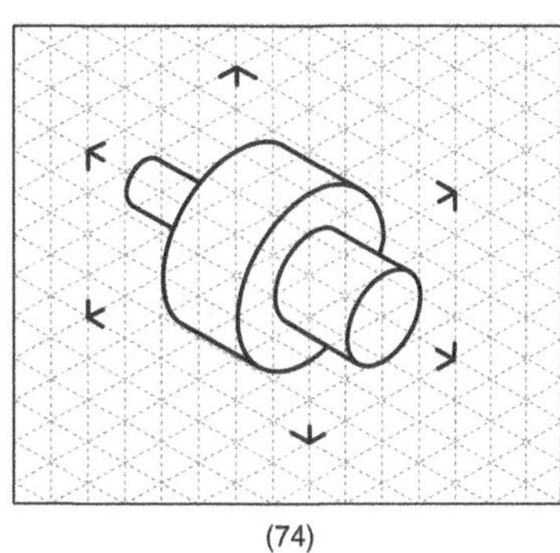
(74)

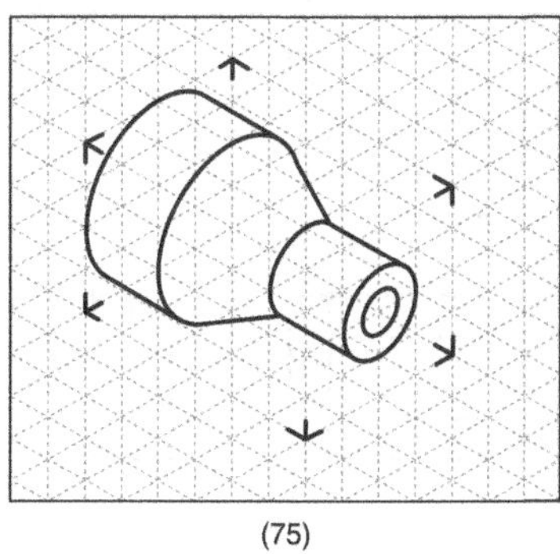
(75)

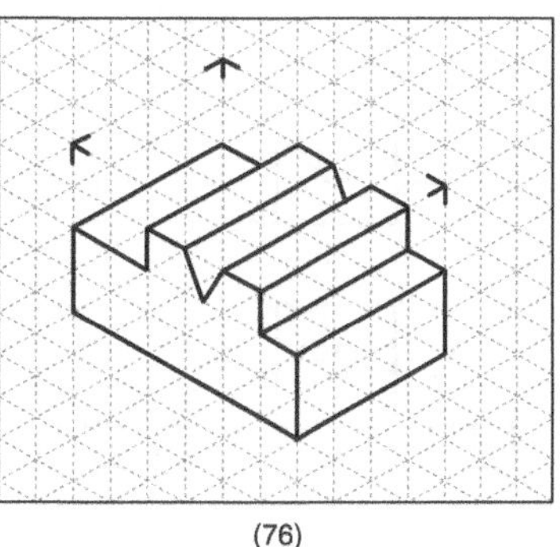
(76)

Figure 7.81G

Problem 7.2 Multiview sketching problems

7.15 Using one photograph from those gathered in Problem 7.12, create 10 alternate designs of the object with tracing paper. With each sketch, trace most of the features as they are in the image, but change some to create a new design.

7.16 Create 10 designs as you did in Problem 7.15, but instead of developing each new design from the original image, evolve the design from one sketch to the next.

7.17 Evolve a design through three stages of refinement. First, generate 10 rough, ideation sketches, showing different design ideas. Use techniques outlined in Problems 7.15 and 7.16, and sketch on plain or grid paper. Spend about three minutes on each ideation sketch. Pick the three best designs and refine them, spending about 10 minutes on each sketch. Finally, pick the best design and spend about 30 minutes creating a detailed pictorial sketch. The final sketch may combine ideas from all three of the previously sketched designs.

7.18 Sketch one of the objects or photographs gathered in Problem 7.12, in two different ways: (a) as a pictorial and (b) as a functional diagram. The functional diagram depicts the functions and actions of the object, and how they interrelate.

7.19 Draw each letter of the alphabet and all nine numerals four times, using guide lines, the proper style, and the proper stroke sequence (see Figures 7.73 and 7.74). Do both vertical and inclined style lettering.

7.20 Letter the name of the linetype under three examples of each type in Problem 7.1.

7.21 Letter the names of each of the standard views in the sketch done in Problem 7.9.

7.22 Label each of the views sketched in Problem 7.10 by lettering the locations of the vanishing point and horizon line used.

7.23 Letter the names of the major components of the final design in Problem 7.17.

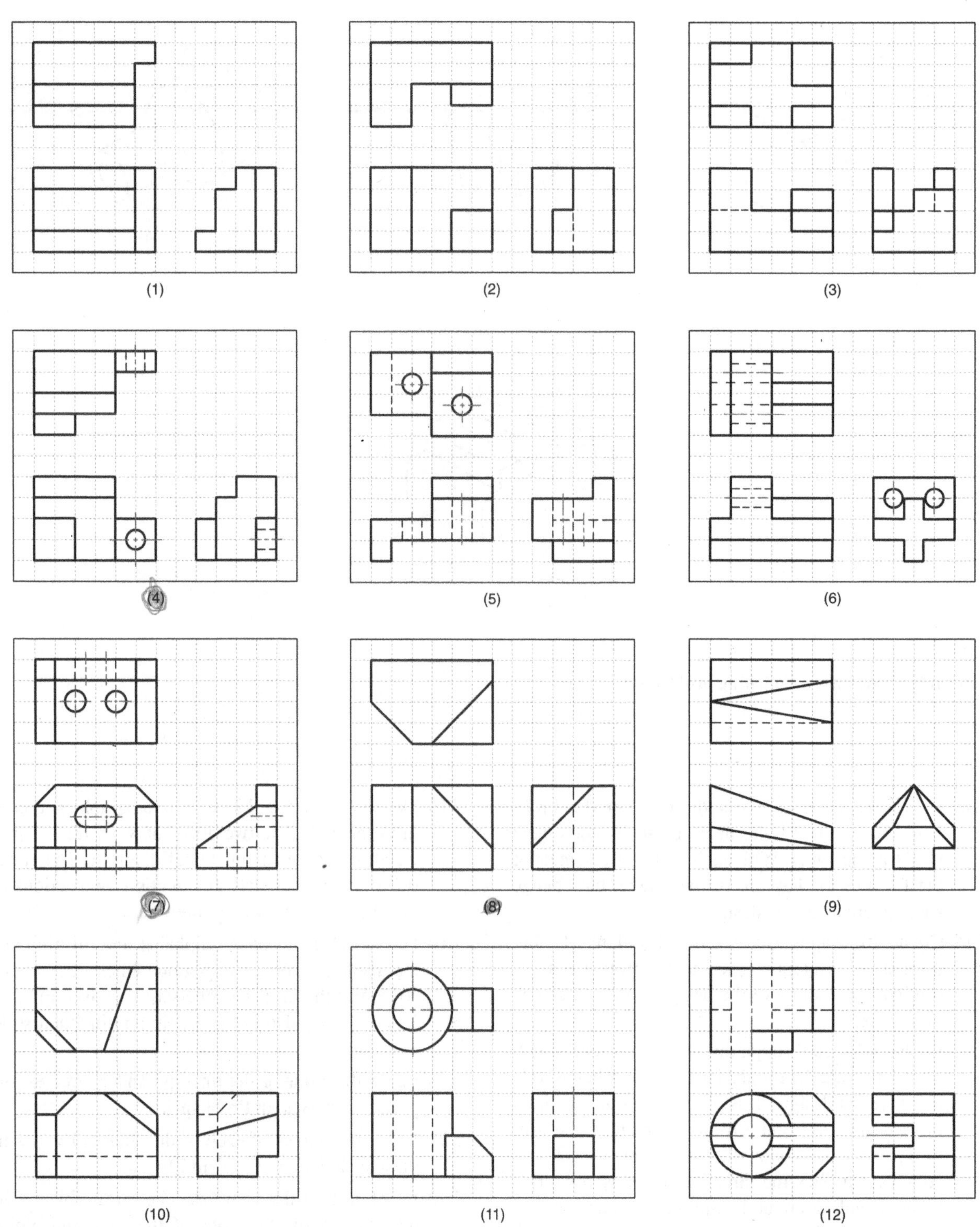

Figure 7.82A

Problem 7.3 Pictorial sketching problems

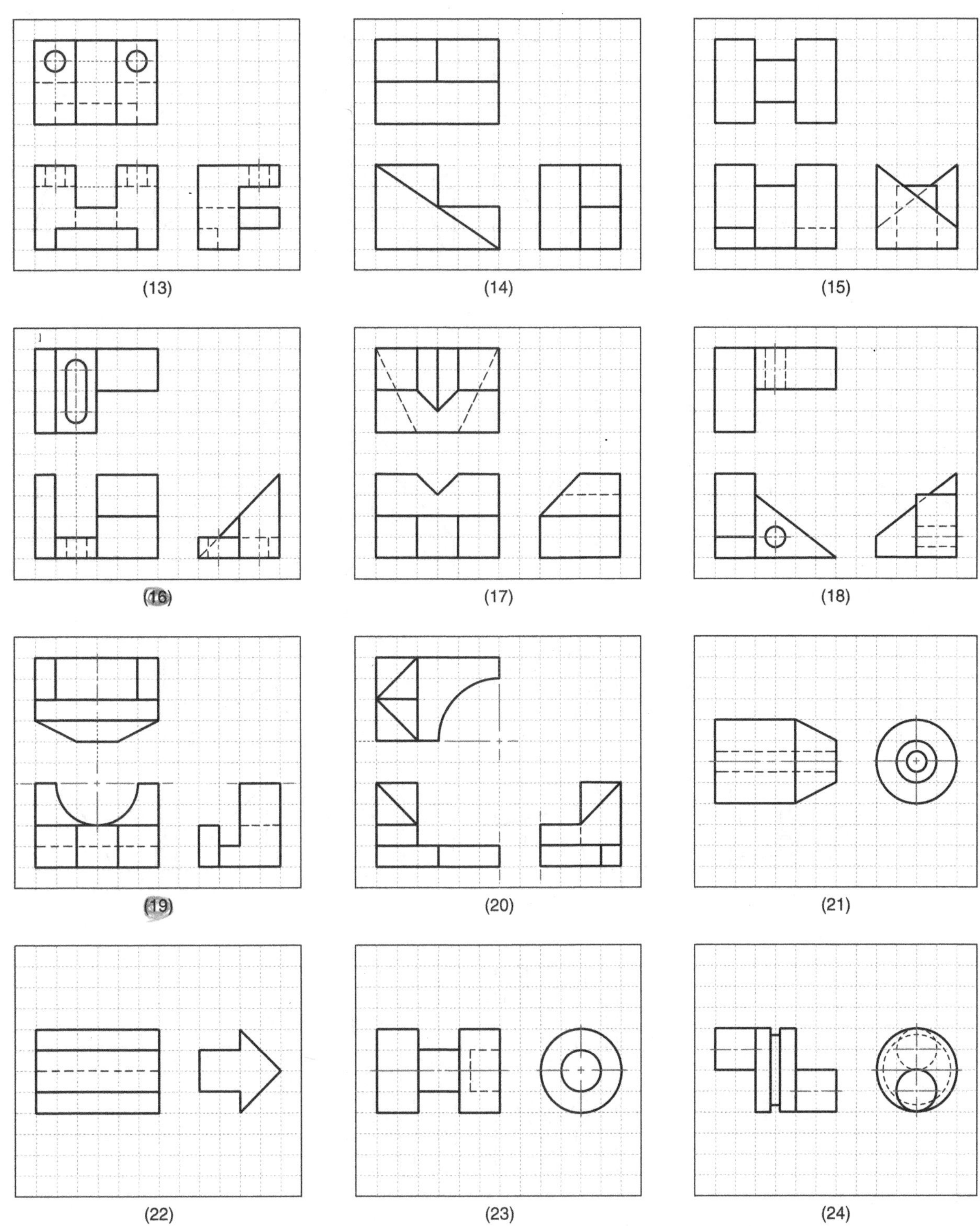

Figure 7.82B

Problem 7.3 Pictorial sketching problems

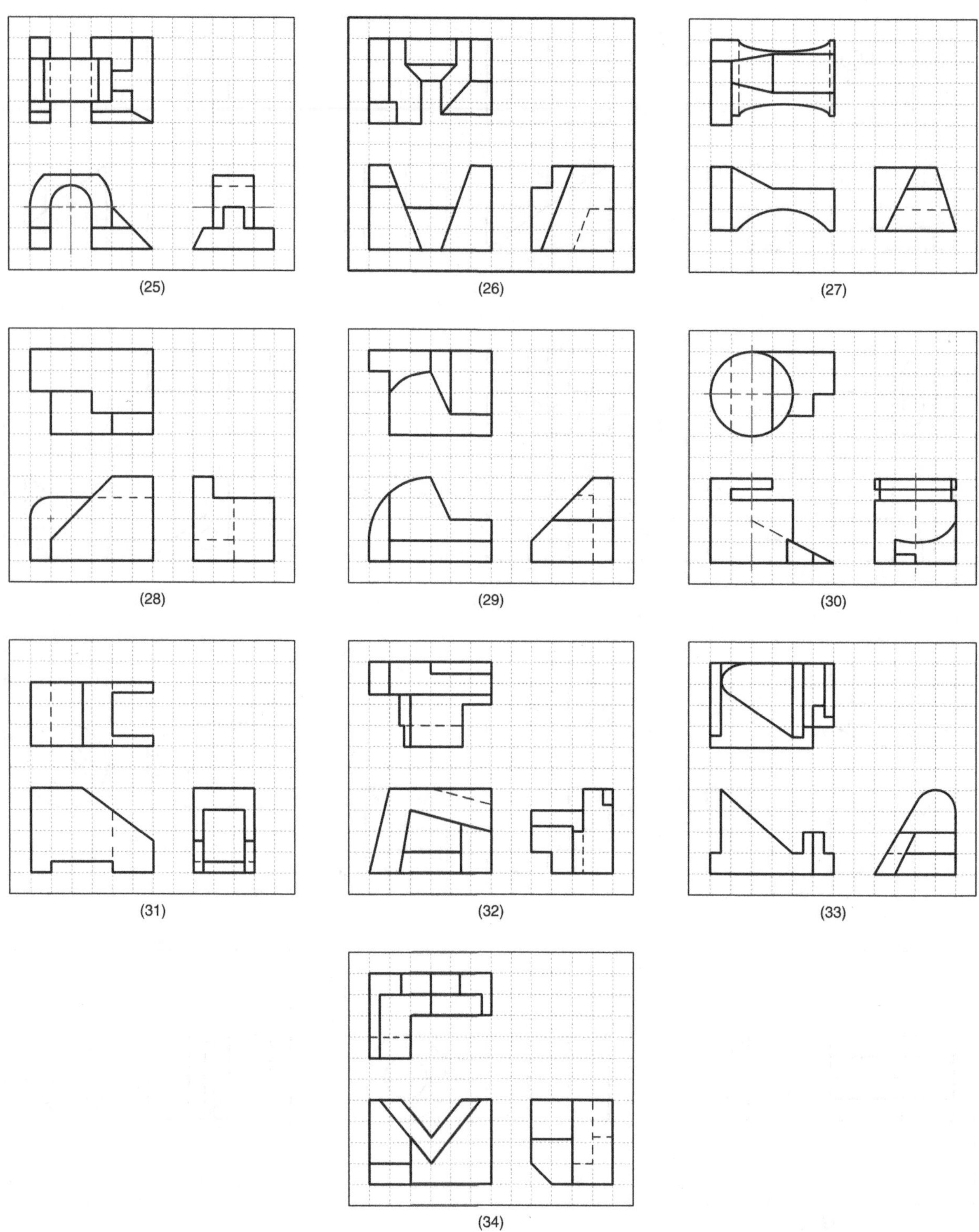

Figure 7.82C

Problem 7.3 Pictorial sketching problems

7.24 Sketch and letter title blocks for any of the exercises in this chapter. See Problems 6.1 and 6.9 in Chapter 6 for examples of typical title blocks.

7.25 Using a CAD system, create example sentences of text, using a mix of the following variables:

- Height
- Font
- Alignment
- Aspect ratio
- Slant
- Rotation

Some example sentences:

ALL LETTERS SHOULD BE UPPERCASE.
SINGLE-STROKE GOTHIC IS THE ANSI STANDARD.
AVOID RAMBLING SENTENCES.
USE ANSI STANDARD ABBREVIATIONS.
EXPLAIN IN A NOTE WHAT CANNOT BE DRAWN.
USE PROPER SPACING BETWEEN LINES.

7.26 Use upside-down sketching to create the word sketch as shown in Figure 7.83.

7.27 Use upside-down sketching to create the table shown in Figure 7.84.

7.28 Use upside-down sketching to create the chair shown in Figure 7.85.

7.29 Use contour sketching to create the series of cubes and cylinders shown in Figure 7.86.

Figure 7.83

Problem 7.26 Upside-down sketch of the word SKETCH

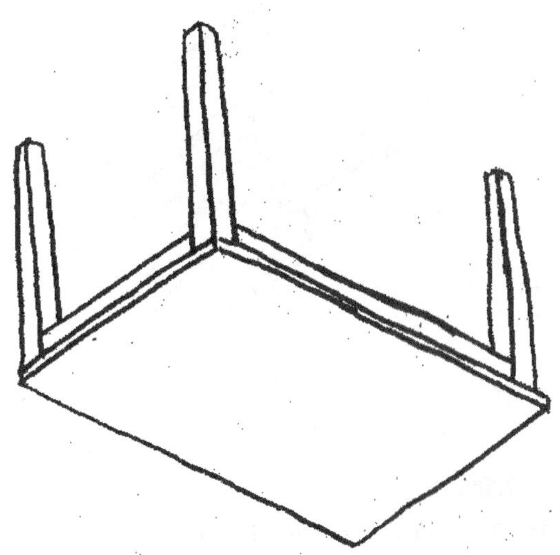

Figure 7.84

Problem 7.27 Upside-down sketch of a table

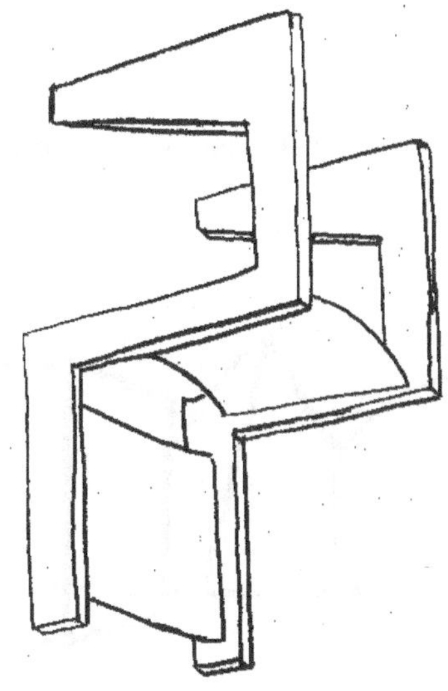

Figure 7.85

Problem 7.28 Upside-down sketch of a chair

7.30 Use contour sketching to create the overlapping shapes shown in Figure 7.87.

7.31 Use contour sketching to create the optical illusions shown in Figure 7.88.

7.32 Create a negative space sketch of the paper clips shown in Figure 7.89.

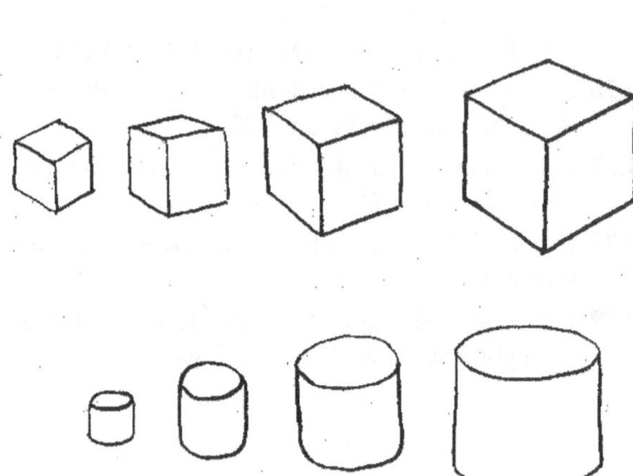

Figure 7.86

Problem 7.29 Contour sketching of cubes and cylinders

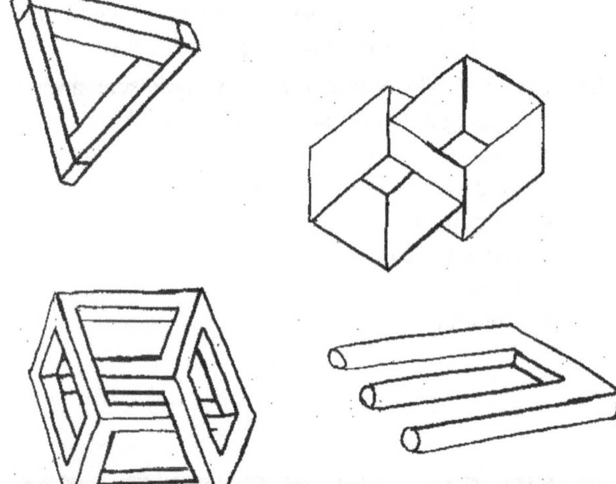

Figure 7.88

Problem 7.31 Contour sketching of optical illusions

Figure 7.87

Problem 7.30 Contour sketch of overlapping shapes

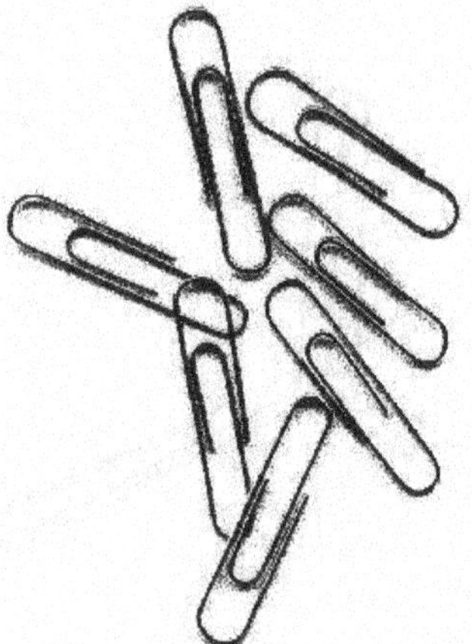

Figure 7.89

Problem 7.32 Negative space sketching

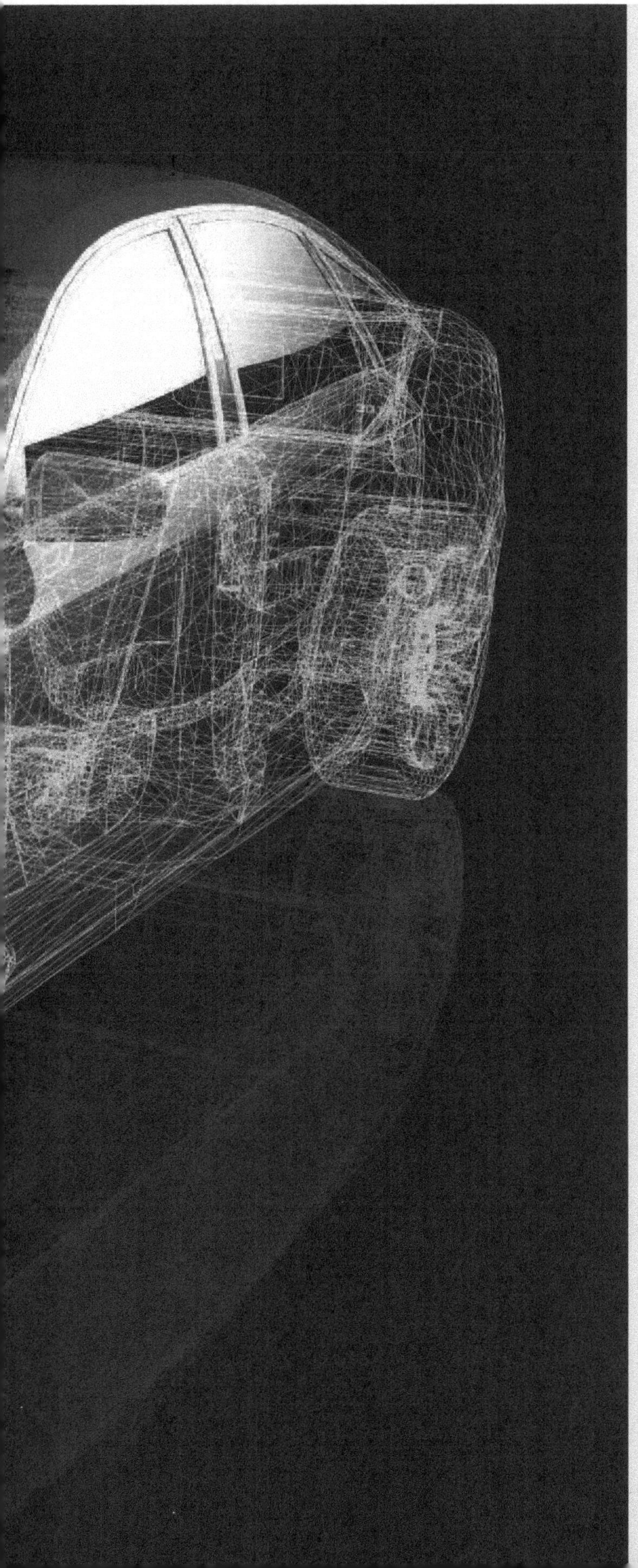

Chapter Nine

Three-Dimensional Modeling

Any sufficiently advanced technology is indistinguishable from magic.

—Arthur C. Clarke

Objectives

After completing this chapter, you will be able to:

1. Place 3-D modeling in a historical perspective.
2. Understand the terminology used in 3-D modeling.
3. Define the most common types of 3-D modeling systems.
4. Apply Boolean operations to 3-D objects.
5. Understand how constraint-based and feature-based modeling affects 3-D modeling strategy.
6. Apply common construction techniques used in building models.
7. Apply generalized sweeps to the creation of model features.
8. Apply construction geometry in the support of feature creation.
9. Understand how feature order affects feature editing and final model geometry.
10. Apply feature duplication and geometric transformations to build part and assembly models.

11. Understand the role that projection theory plays in displaying 3-D models on the computer screen.
12. Define the ways that 3-D modeling integrates into the design process.
13. Compare 2-D CAD with 3-D CAD.
14. Develop assembly models using part models and existing assembly models.
15. Define the different types of analysis that can be performed on a 3-D model.
16. Generate 2-D documentation from a 3-D model.
17. Define different data exchange standards.

Introduction

Three-dimensional modeling has emerged as the modern method of CAD use in product design and manufacturing, revolutionizing the way industry integrates computers into the design process. Commercial 3-D modeling packages, available since the mid 1980s, have become commonplace in a wide range of industries.

Two-dimensional CAD has, in many ways, matured to the point where simply using a more powerful computer will not have much of an impact on how well a 2-D CAD program functions. Like traditional drafting methods, 2-D CAD programs attempt to represent objects in two dimensions; in fact, the packages were developed to be *computer drafting tools,* with the end product being a drawing on paper. In contrast, a 3-D computer model is more like a real object, not just a drawing of the object; 3-D CAD is considered a *computer modeling tool.*

This chapter introduces the possibilities for, and the limitations of, integrating 3-D CAD operations into the design process. While 3-D modeling software has enhanced such integration, current computer models fall short of being a complete replacement for physical objects, because of the mathematical and computational limitations of existing computer software.

The chapter outlines the most common approaches for generating 3-D computer models, in addition to how these models are viewed and modified on the computer. The chapter concludes with examples of 3-D computer modeling applications in the design process.

9.1 Wireframe Modeling

The simplest 3-D modeler is a **wireframe modeler**. In this type of modeler, which is a natural outgrowth of 2-D CAD, two types of elements must be defined in the database: *edges* and *vertices* (Figure 9.1). For the tetrahedron in the figure, the vertex list contains the geometric information on the model. Each vertex is defined by an (X, Y, Z) coordinate, which anchors the model in space. The topology of the model is represented by the edge list. The edge list does not contain coordinate information. The location, orientation, and length of an edge must be derived indirectly, through calculations of the vertices at either end of the edge. For example, edge E_1 consists of vertices V_1 and V_2. The coordinate locations of V_1 (0,0,0) and V_2 (1,0,0) indicate that E_1 has a length of 1 and is oriented along the X axis.

A wireframe model can also contain information about *faces,* including size, location, and orientation (Figure 9.2). Just as edges are defined as a pair of vertices, faces are defined as three or more edges. However, there is no information about the surfaces of the object because a wireframe model is only a collection of edges. There is no "skin" defining the area between the edges.

Most wireframe modelers support curved edges, as well as straight edges. Because of the added mathematical complexity, the curved edges are usually only circular curves. An example is a cylinder, as shown in Figure 9.3. The use of curved edges in a wireframe model reveals one of the deficiencies of a wireframe model as a representation of a 3-D object. Take the cylinder as an example. The

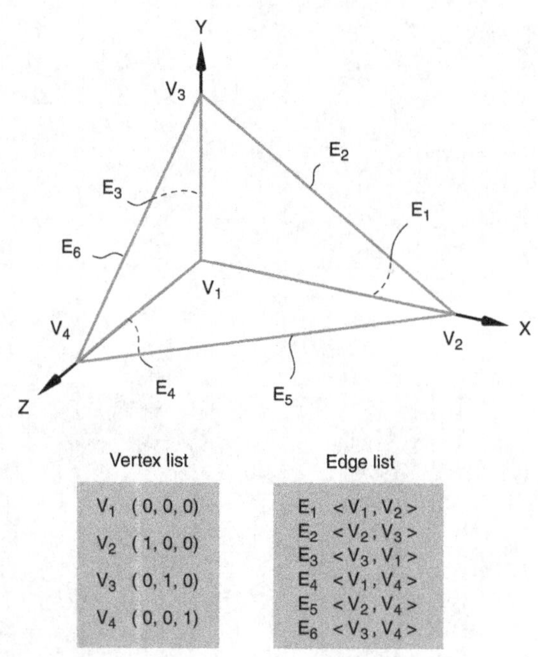

Figure 9.1

The vertex and edge list of a wireframe model

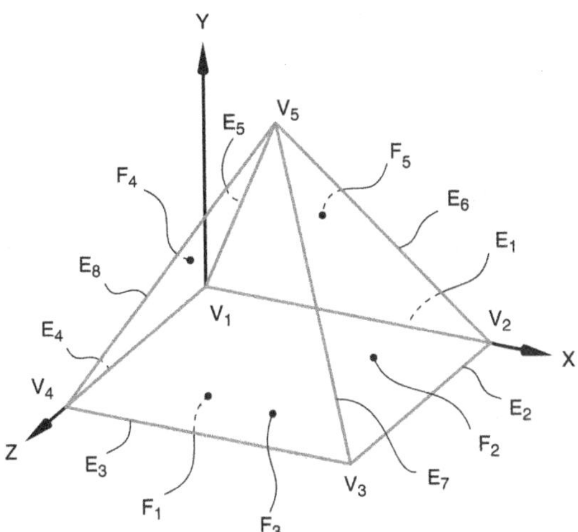

Vertex List	Edge List	Face List
V_1 (0, 0, 0)	E_1 <V_1, V_2>	F_1 <E_1, E_2, E_3, E_4>
V_2 (1, 0, 0)	E_2 <V_2, V_3>	F_2 <E_2, E_7, E_6>
V_3 (1, 0, 1)	E_3 <V_3, V_4>	F_3 <E_3, E_8, E_7>
V_4 (0, 0, 1)	E_4 <V_4, V_1>	F_4 <E_4, E_5, E_8>
V_5 (.5, 1, .5)	E_5 <V_1, V_5>	F_5 <E_1, E_5, E_6>
	E_6 <V_2, V_5>	
	E_7 <V_3, V_5>	
	E_8 <V_4, V_5>	

Figure 9.2

A wireframe model represented with a vertex, edge, and face list

Though faces are listed in the database, they do not describe true surfaces.

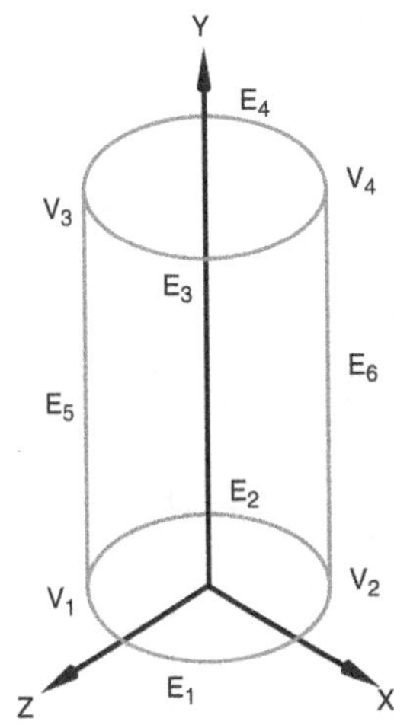

Vertex List	Edge List	Type
V_1 (−1, 0, 1)	E_1 <V_1, V_2>	Circular
V_2 (1, 0, −1)	E_2 <V_2, V_1>	Circular
V_3 (−1, 5, 1)	E_3 <V_3, V_4>	Circular
V_4 (1, 5, −1)	E_4 <V_4, V_3>	Circular
	E_5 <V_1, V_3>	Linear
	E_6 <V_2, V_4>	Linear

Figure 9.3

A wireframe model using circular and linear edges

Full circles are broken into two arcs to allow them to connect to other edges.

end faces of the cylinder are represented by single, continuous, circular edges. But a cylinder has no side edges, making it difficult with a wireframe modeler to connect the top and bottom faces of the cylinder. The two linear edges (E_5, E_6) shown in the figure are artifacts of the wireframe model and are necessary for maintaining integrity of the database and for visualizing the model.

To maintain the integrity of the database for a wireframe modeler, a number of trade-offs must be considered. As more flexibility for building the model is provided, greater risks for *invalid* models are introduced. An invalid model is one that represents an object that cannot exist in real life.

Integrity rules for models containing only straight edges could be defined, as follows:

- Each vertex must have a unique coordinate location.
- Each vertex must be associated with at least three edges.
- Each edge can have only two vertices.
- Each face must contain at least three edges that form a **closed loop**.

This list demonstrates how the software must check each operation performed by the user, to make sure a *valid* model is being created. The requirement that each face be a closed loop is an outgrowth of the previous rules; it basically says there cannot be any dangling edges. However, in the intermediate phases of building a wireframe model, there may be exceptions to this rule, and this situation must also be considered by the software (Figure 9.4 on the next page).

Introducing circular edges increases the domain of the modeler but complicates some of the rules just defined. Distinctions must be made between the minimum number of straight edges and curved edges needed to define a face.

Wireframe models also have problems with *uniqueness*. Figure 9.5 on the next page shows a wireframe model and some of the possible objects it could represent. In the model, the lack of information about surfaces gives

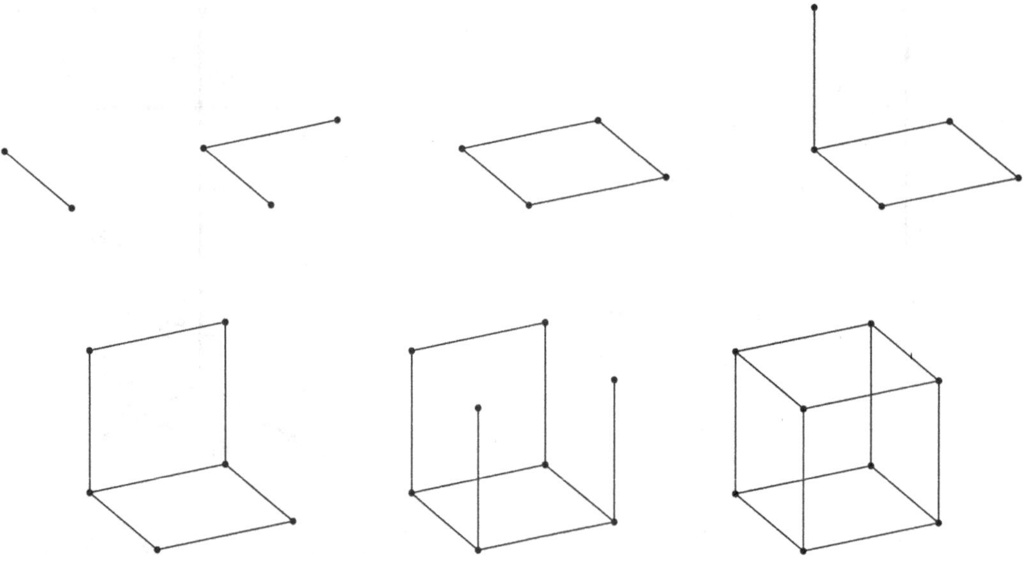

Figure 9.4

The stages in building a valid wireframe model

During the construction of the model, there will be intermediate stages when there is an invalid model.

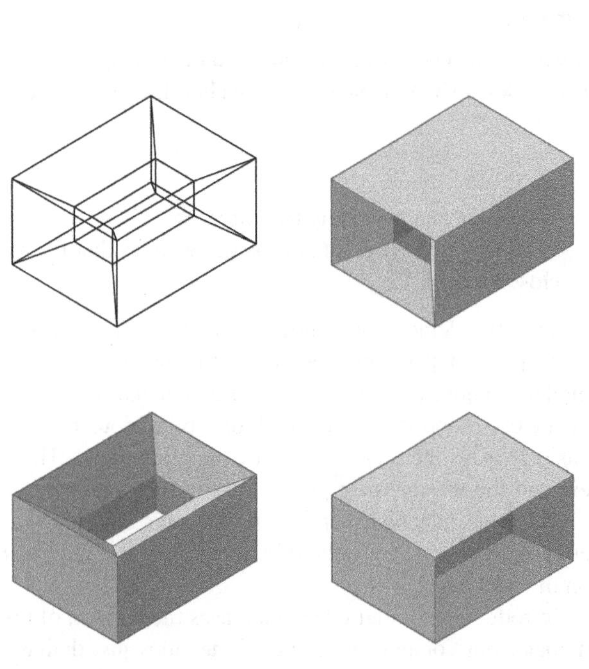

Figure 9.5

Example of a wireframe model lacking uniqueness

The same edge and vertex list can describe different objects, depending on how the faces are interpreted.

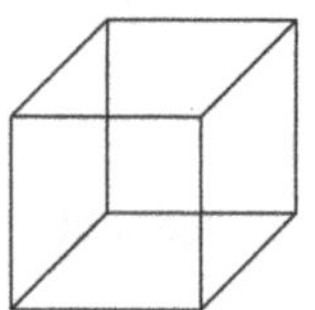 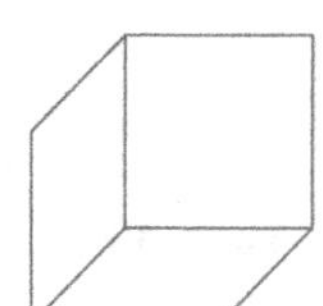 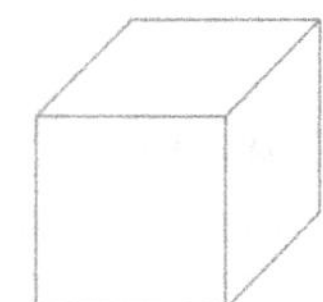

Figure 9.6

A wireframe model with an ambiguous orientation: the necker cube

Which face is in front and which is in back?

rise to *ambiguities* concerning the orientation of the object. The Necker cube is a classic example (Figure 9.6). Because surface information is not available, edges that would normally be hidden are not, and the orientation is unclear. Some wireframe modelers have implemented computational routines to calculate and remove hidden edges. Since this involves calculating surface information that is not inherent in a true wireframe modeler, the process is often slow and cumbersome.

An advantage of a wireframe modeler is that it is easy to implement. Because a basic wireframe modeler only contains vertex and edge information, similar to what a 2-D CAD program contains, expanding a 2-D CAD database to a 3-D wireframe model database is fairly easy.

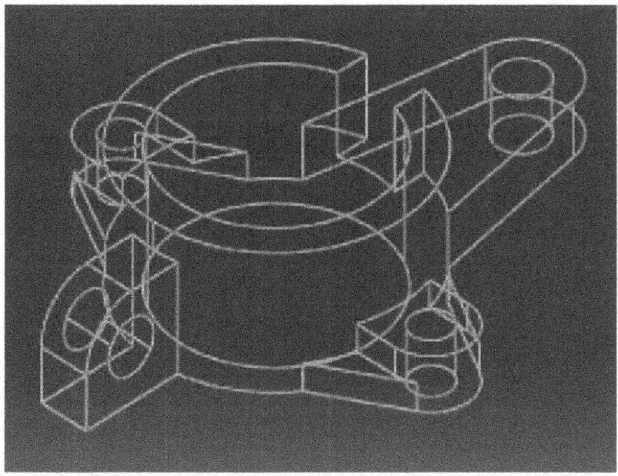

Figure 9.7

Wireframe representation of a collar part

(© Nathan Hartman.)

Rules guaranteeing a valid model may be put into code or can be left up to the operator. Wireframe modeling is also computationally efficient. On older computer systems, where computing power is at a premium, wireframe is the only viable 3-D modeling option.

While this section provides an overview of how wireframe geometry is theoretically derived and computed, the approach to using wireframe geometry in modern CAD systems has changed. Due to high-powered desktop PCs and improved software and graphics computing capabilities, engineers and designers typically do not create geometry in a wireframe mode. Geometry most often is created as either a solid or surface representation or a combination of both types. Wireframe geometry typically is used only as a display option (Figure 9.7) generated by the execution of a simple command in the CAD system, since both solid and surface geometry definitions include wireframe by default. As described in the following sections, surface and solid geometry creations have become the methods of choice for current engineers and designers.

Practice Exercise 9.1

Using thin, stiff wire (electrical wire, pipe cleaners, etc.), build wire models of common objects. Count the number of edges and vertices on the models that you build. Using the rules for a valid wireframe model listed in this section, try building invalid models. Which rules are broken by your invalid models?

9.2 Surface Modeling

The pressures of wartime production of ships and aircraft during World War II and the expanding consumer market after the war led to the development of systems using the mathematical descriptions of curved surfaces. *Parametric techniques* popularized by Steven A. Coons were adopted as a way of precisely describing the curvature of a surface in all three dimensions. **Surface models** define the surface features, as well as the edges, of objects.

Surfaces can be created using a number of different techniques. The technique used is determined both by the shape to be created and by the tools available in the surface modeler. Among the most popular methods for creating surfaces are sweeping, revolving, lofting and creating patches with curve boundaries or sets of points (point clouds).

Sweeping is a modeling technique that allows you to define surfaces by moving a directrix along a generatrix (Figure 9.8 on the next page). The directrix is typically a 2-D curve, while the generatrix can be a line, planar curve, or 3-D curve. Figure 9.8 shows an oblique cylinder being created by moving a circle directrix along a straight-line generatrix. Figure 9.8 also shows increasingly complex directrix curves being swept out with straight-line generatrixes to created ruled surfaces. Using curved generatrixes allows for even more complex surface generation. Figure 9.9A on the next page shows a directrix curve being swept out along a curve generatrix to create a surface model (Figure 9.9B). Notice that a closed-curve directrix creates a tubelike, hollow surface model.

An alternative to defining a generatrix directly is to revolve the directrix about an axis. In this case, the axis of revolution acts as the generatrix. Figure 8.99C shows a classic **revolved** surface; a half circle revolved 360 degrees to form a sphere. More complex forms can be created by using techniques such as placing the axis of revolution so it does not touch the directrix, using a complex curve as a directrix, and revolving less than 360 degrees (Figure 9.10 on the next page). Depending on the software being used, the generatrix axis may have to lie in the same plane as the directrix curve.

Using a series of directrix curves to define multiple intermediate points along the generatrix path can create more complex surfaces. This technique, **lofting**, allows you to define critical changes in the directrix shape over the surface. These directrix curves can be placed parallel or skew to each other at set distances. Figure 9.11A shows three directrix curves defining the loft. The resulting surface in Figure 9.11B shows the resulting interpolation between the three curves. In this case, the generatrix

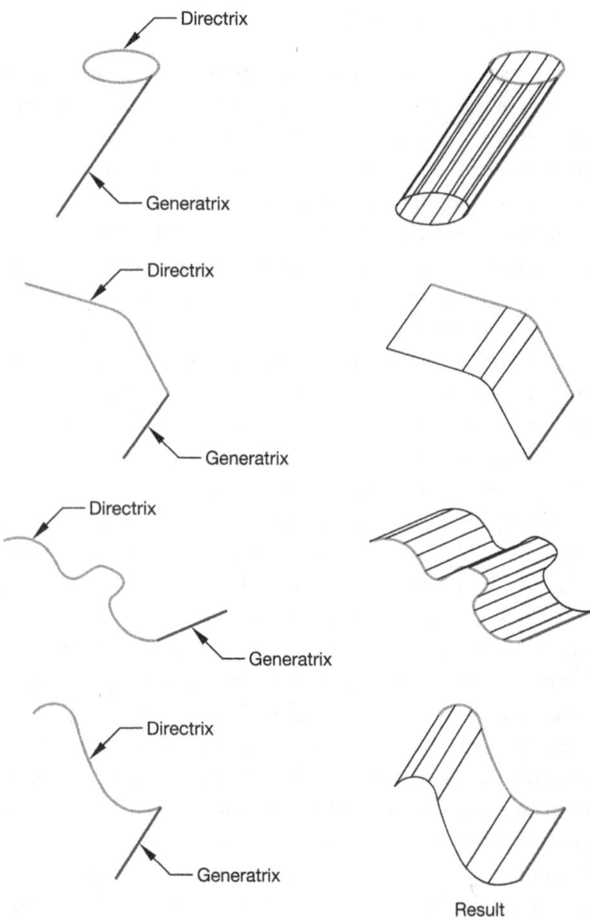

Figure 9.8

Swept surfaces

Generating swept surfaces by sweeping generator entities along director entities.

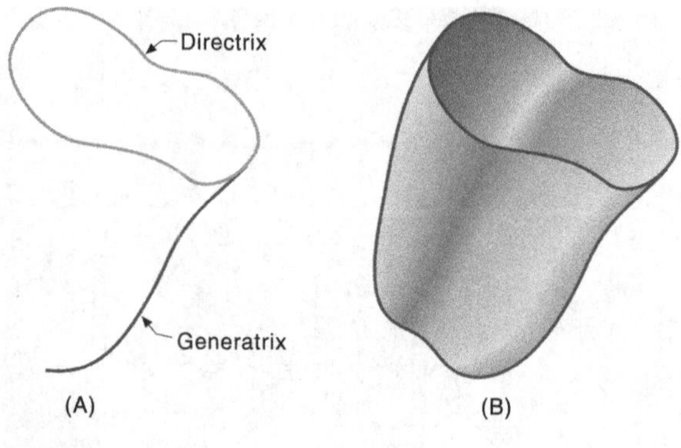

Figure 9.9

Complex surface

A more complex surface can be created by sweeping the directrix along a curved generatrix.

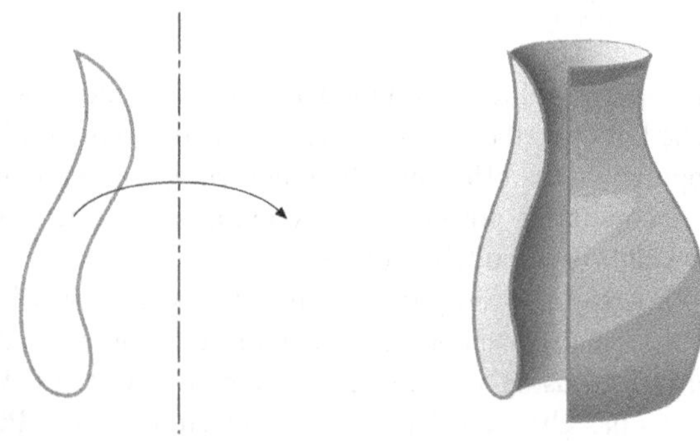

Figure 9.10

Revolved surface

A directrix can be rotated about an axis between 1 and 360 degrees.

is implied, not directly defined. By explicitly drawing a generatrix curve, we can exercise more control over the path taken by the surface between the directrix curves (Figure 9.11C and D).

For swept, revolved, and lofted surfaces, the directrix and generatrix can be made from a combination of different linetypes. In addition to straight lines and circular curves, freeform curves such as B-splines and Bezier curves can be used to generate all or part of the curve. Freeform curves usually provide controls that allow you to both define the curve prior to surface generation and edit the resulting curve by redefining the original curves used to generate the surface.

Freeform curves are regularly used to create surface **patches** from boundary curves. With this technique, all sides of the surface are initially defined by a set of curves. If all of the curves lie in the same plane, then the resulting surface will also be planar. More commonly, one or more of the boundary curves moves out of the plane, creating more complex surface patches. Figure 9.12 (on the next page) shows a surface patch made from four Bezier curves. To form a surface, the boundary curves should form a closed path. Just as with creating polygons, there need to be at least three boundary curves, but the surface can contain more than four. The upper limit is typically a practical matter of managing the surface.

Boundary curves create a surface patch by interpolating between each of the curves. Just as with lofting, the interior of the surface will be a transition between each

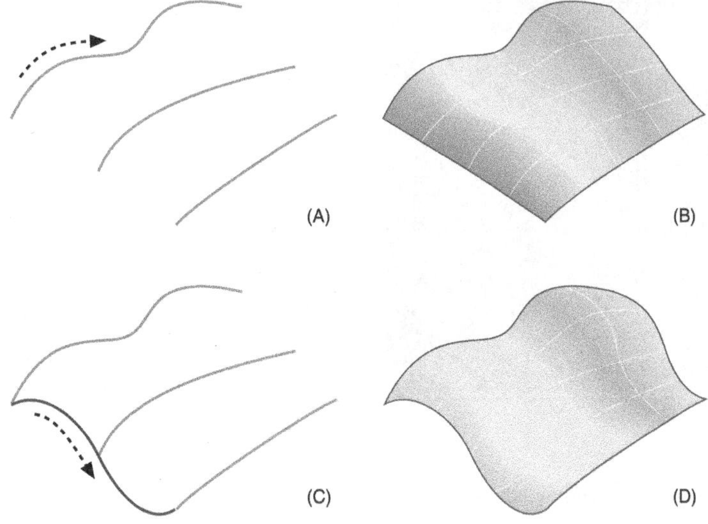

Figure 9.11

Lofting to define a surface

Lofting uses two or more directrix curves to define a surface.

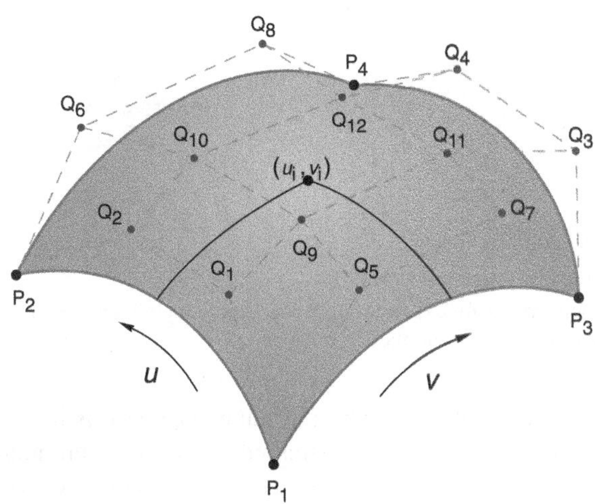

Figure 9.12

A Bezier bicubic surface patch

The patch consists of four connected Bezier curves and 12 control points.

of these curves. The closer you get to one of the boundary curves, the more the surface takes on the shape of the curve. When you use boundary curves, the surface is guaranteed to end at the surface boundaries but not to pass through any specific point between the curves. Defining points or curves on the interior of the surface can give you more control over the surface. Groups of points—often called point clouds—can be created that the surface must pass through. In fact, point clouds without boundary curves can be used to define the entire surface. This technique is popular for reverse engineering (creating a model from an existing physical object) since actual points on the surface of the object can be fed into the surface modeling system.

A very popular curve type used to create surfaces using all types of techniques is NURBS. NURBS stands for Non-Uniform Rational B-Splines. Rational B-splines can define a wide variety of curves including linear, circular, and conic curves. This means that NURBS can define the complete set of curves used in a surface model and rapidly deform, changing curve type on the fly as needed (Figure 9.13 on the next page).

Rarely are surface models made from a single surface. Instead, several surfaces are integrated using a variety of procedures. In addition, surfaces often have to be cut, or **trimmed**, to integrate properly in the overall model. Figure 9.14 on the next page shows an example of a curved surface patch being created by trimming a sphere with a circle. The trimming is typically defined by projecting a curve onto the surface to be trimmed or by the intersection of two surfaces.

Merging two or more surfaces requires decisions as to how one surface will transition into the other. Creating a

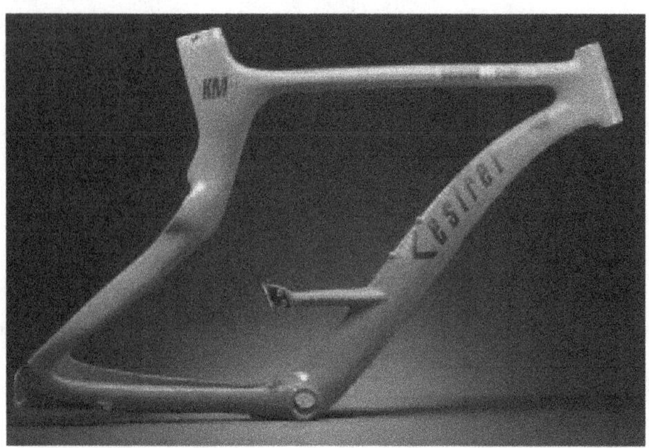

Figure 9.13

A bicycle frame defined with complex surface patches.
(Courtesy of IDE Incorporated.)

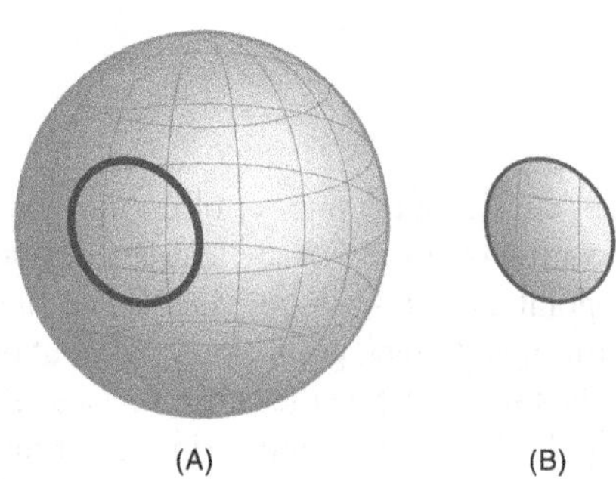

Figure 9.14

Trimmed surface

Existing surfaces can be trimmed with curves or other surfaces.

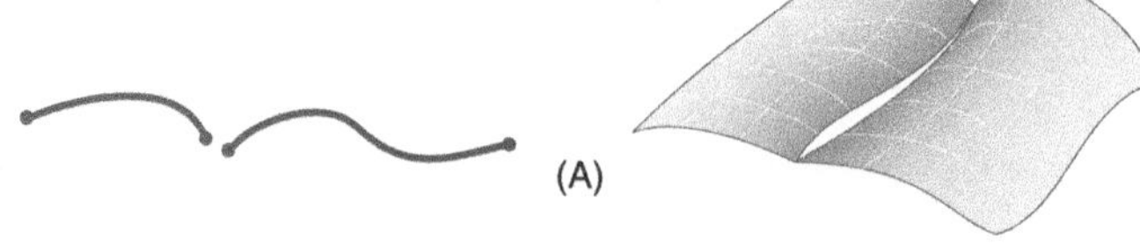

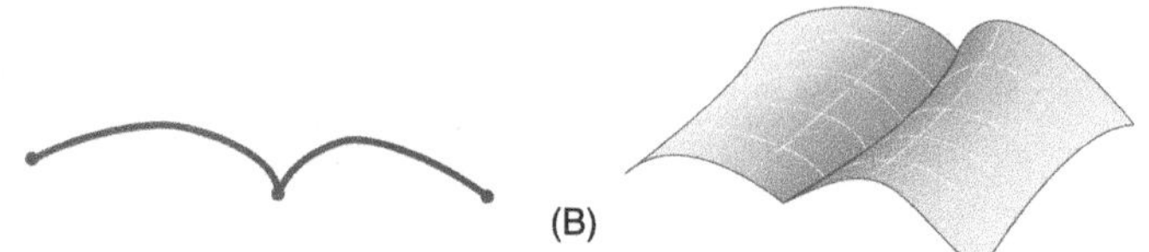

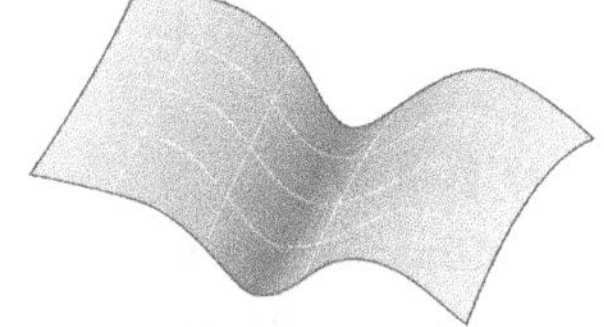

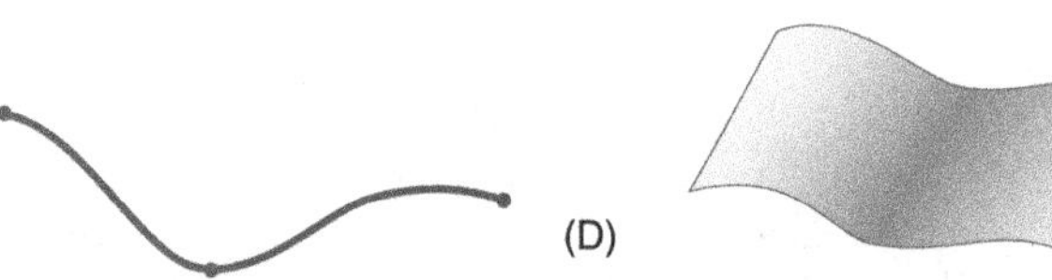

Figure 9.15

Continuity between surfaces

When two surfaces are brought together, varying degrees of continuity can be defined.

quality surface model that will be usable in later design analysis and manufacturing requires careful attention to the way in which surfaces connect to each other. To control this, surfaces are defined as having varying degrees of **continuity** with each other. If surface boundaries change or are edited such that the surfaces do not touch along their length, or that there are holes or gaps in the model, the surfaces are said to be discontinuous (Figure 9.15A). If discontinuity conditions occur in a finished CAD model, it is possible that the model may be of no use in supporting later design and manufacturing operations.

Positional continuity means that the edges of the two surfaces touch along their length—that is, they share an adjacent boundary edge (Figure 9.15B). Positional continuity means surfaces share the boundary edge, but the two surfaces do not share the same slope at this boundary, leaving a "crease" at this edge. Tangent continuity means that there is a smooth, tangent transition between the two surfaces (Figure 9.15C). However, with a tangent transition, the two curves can have different curvatures coming into the tangency. To merge two surfaces without a noticeable transition, a continuous curvature between the surfaces is needed (Figure 9.15D).

Defining the merger between surfaces is often a multistep process. For example, a cylindrical surface may be merged with a freeform surface (Figure 9.16A) and then trimmed back (Figure 9.16B). While there initially may be only positional continuity between the surfaces, tangent continuity between surfaces can be created with the addition of a fillet (Figure 9.16C).

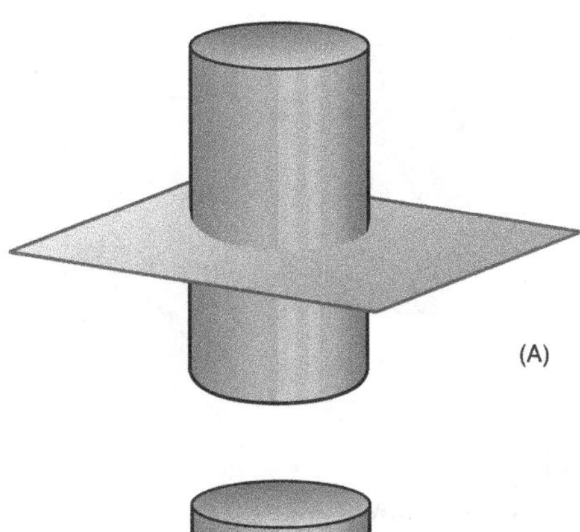

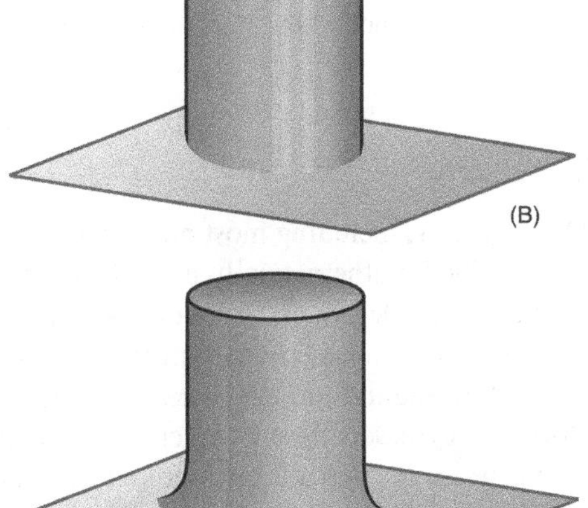

(C)

Figure 9.16

Merging two surfaces

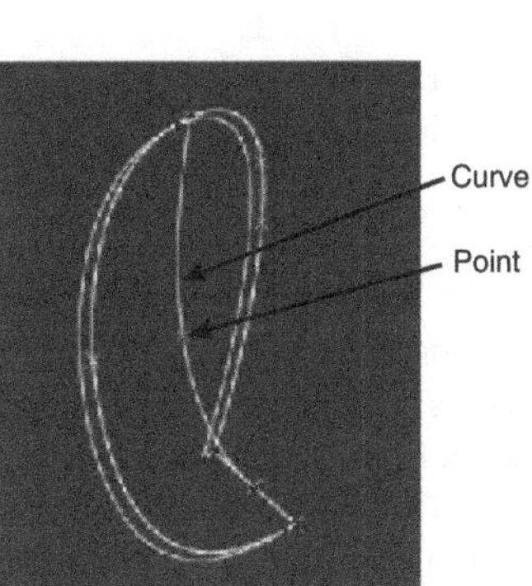

Figure 9.17

Points and curves used to define surface geometry

(© Nathan Hartman.)

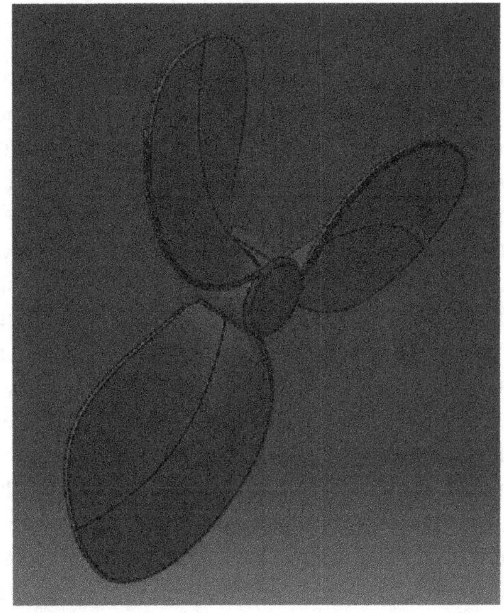

Figure 9.18

Finished surface geometry of a fan blade based on points and curves

(© Nathan Hartman.)

Finished surface models commonly are used with objects that are cast, molded, or stamped. The shape flexibility of a surface model makes it ideal for representing complex, organic forms often seen on the outer shell of consumer products such as cars, audiovisual equipment, or computers. The decision whether to use surface modeling depends on the designer's skill and the tools at their disposal. In many cases, surface models can be integrated into solid models to capture the advantages of both types of modeling tools. Solid modeling is covered in depth in the following section.

There are several different methods for creating surface geometry in modern 3-D modeling tools, although the method that fits most closely with the scope of this text includes the creation of wireframe geometry. Wireframe geometry typically is created as a series of points and curves that define critical locations and boundaries (Figure 9.17).

These geometric reference entities then are used to build surface geometry to define an object. While the exact nature of the commands will vary between software systems, the general concept is the same. First, the engineer or designer would build points, curves, and planes to define the reference geometry. After that process was finished, surface geometry would be created to define the final contours and boundaries of the object (Figure 9.18). Finally, it is possible that the surface model would be made into solid geometry, depending on the eventual use of the data. Solid modeling is discussed in the following section.

Practice Exercise 9.2

Glue or tape four lengths of stiff wire to the edges of a sheet of paper. The wires represent the curves defining the edges of a surface patch. Even with the wires representing straight edges, there is still quite a variety of curves that can be represented. Try moving the edges into different positions relative to each other. Then, bend two opposing wires but leave the other two straight. What kinds of surfaces can you create? Can you bend all four wires and still use a sheet of paper to describe the patch?

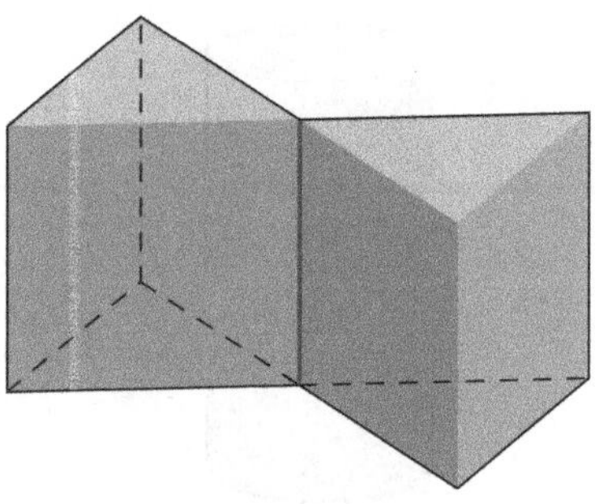

Figure 9.19

Example of a nonmanifold object

Most modelers do not support the creation of these types of objects.

9.3 Solid Modeling

Through the use of parametric description, surface modelers can accurately describe the surface of an object. Often, however, information about the inside of an object, that is, its solidity, is also required. **Solid models** include volumetric information, that is, what is on the inside of the 3-D model, as well as information about the surface of an object. In this case, the surface of the model represents the boundary between the inside and outside of the object.

Most solid modelers define only what is termed a **manifold model**. A manifold boundary unambiguously separates a region of space into the inside and the outside of the model. A lengthy theoretical discussion of manifolds is not appropriate here and is also not necessary because the idea of manifold models is fairly intuitive. It is easy to imagine solid objects as dividing space into what is part of the object and what is not. Manifold objects may contain no voids within the solid, like bubbles trapped in an ice cube. Also, objects such as the one shown in Figure 9.19 are not allowed. The highlighted edge belongs to four faces of the object, when only two faces are allowed; in real life, you would not have an infinitely thin edge holding two halves of an object together. Just as wireframe and surface geometry are both mathematically defined, so is solid geometry. Currently, two options are used to define 3-D solid geometry—constructive solid geometry and boundary representation. These geometry definitions manifest themselves in modern CAD systems through various database and display combinations to define an object. A more recent method for defining geometry within a CAD system is hybrid modeling. It combines both constructive solid geometry and boundary representation, as well as surface and solid geometry, in the same file in order to define an object.

9.3.1 Constructive Solid Geometry

Many objects, including most mechanical parts, can be described mathematically using basic geometric forms. Modelers are designed to support a set of *geometric primitives,* such as cubes, right rectilinear prisms (i.e., blocks), right triangular prisms (i.e., wedges), spheres, cones, tori, and cylinders (See Chapter 8). Although most geometric primitives have unique topologies, some differ only in their geometry, like the cube and the right rectilinear prism.

Modeling with primitives uses only a limited set of geometric primitives; therefore, only certain topologies can be created. This is called primitive instancing. However, there is generally no limit to the quantity of instances of an allowed primitive in a single model. The geometry of an individual instance is defined with parameters, but modelers designed for more specific purposes can use a more specialized set of primitives. For example, a modeler used for designing hardware could represent bolts through the special parameters of head type, head diameter, shaft diameter, and shaft length.

Many modelers also allow primitives to be joined together to create more complex objects. The user mentally decomposes the object into a collection of geometric primitives and then constructs the model from these elements (Figure 9.20).

Once the numerical values for the geometric parameters of an instance are defined, the model must have values for its location and orientation. For example, Figure 9.20A shows the location and orientation of each individual primitive that will go into the final object, a camera. Figure 9.20B shows the camera assembled. To manipulate the camera as a whole, the modeling system must then be able to act on a group of objects all at one time (Figure 9.20B).

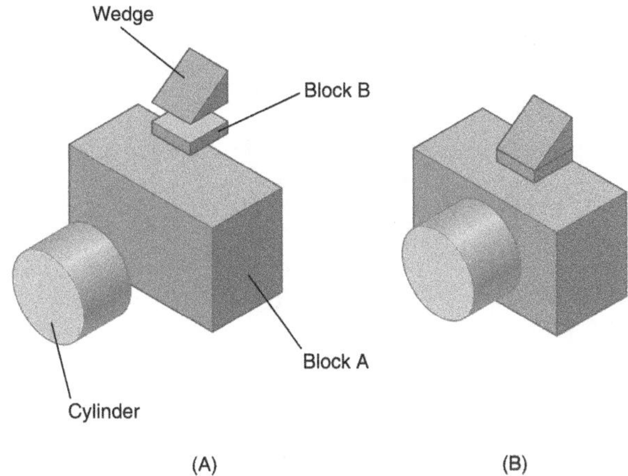

Figure 9.20

A camera described with geometric primitives

Additive modeling with geometric primitives allows a variety of objects to be represented.

There are a number of positive aspects to using a limited set of primitives. First, limiting the allowed topologies reduces the risk of an *invalid* model. Typically, the only safeguards needed are limits or rules on parameter input. For example, the diameter of a cylinder could not be specified as zero. Second, the limited number of allowable shapes means a very concise and efficient database. Third, the limited range of primitives means a model that is unique and is easy to validate.

On the other hand, a limited set of primitives limits the ultimate flexibility in the models that can be represented. Even if you have the ability to glue primitives together, this building block style of construction is purely *additive*. There is no way to represent a hole in an object. This *limited domain* means that the correspondence between a model and an actual object can be lacking. Modeling with primitives in a CAD system typically is accomplished through a means known as constructive solid geometry.

Constructive solid geometry (CSG) modeling is a powerful technique that allows flexibility in both the way primitives are defined and the way they are combined. The relationships between the primitives are defined with **Boolean operations**. There are three types of Boolean operations: **union** (∪), **difference** (–), and **intersection** (∩). Figure 9.21 shows how each of these operations can be used to create different forms. The critical area is the place where two objects overlap. This is where the differences between the Boolean operations are evident. The union operation is essentially additive, with the two primitives being combined. However, in the final form, the volume where the two primitives overlap is only represented once. Otherwise there would be twice as much material in the area of overlap, which is not possible in a real object. With a difference operation, the area of overlap is not represented at all. The final form resembles one of the original primitives with the area of overlap removed. With the intersection operation, *only* the area of overlap remains; the rest of the primitive volumes is removed.

In Figure 9.21 on the next page, Boolean operations are shown in their mathematical form. The union (∪) operation, like the mathematical operation of addition, is not sensitive to the order of the primitive operands (i.e., $11 + 4$ and $4 + 11$ both equal 15). On the other hand, the difference (–) operation *is* sensitive to order. To extend the analogy, $11 - 4$ equals 7, but $4 - 11$ equals -7. For a Boolean difference operation, the shape of the resulting geometry depends on which primitive (A or B) is first in the equation (Figure 9.22 on page 411). The result of the difference operation is that the overlapping volume is removed from the primitive listed *first* in the operation.

With Boolean operations, it is possible to have a form that has no volume (a null object, Ø). If the second primitive of the difference operation completely encompasses the first primitive, the result will be a null object since negative geometry cannot be represented in the model.

Primitives that adjoin but do not overlap are also a special case (Figure 9.23 on page 411). Performing a union operation on such primitives will simply fuse them together. A difference operation will leave the first primitive operand unchanged. An intersection operation will result in a null object since such an operation only shows the volume of overlap, and there is no overlap for the adjoining primitives.

The final form of a model can be developed in several ways. As with pure primitive instancing, you can begin by defining a number of primitive forms. The primitives can then be located in space such that they are overlapping or adjoining. Boolean operations can then be applied to create the resulting form. The original primitives may be retained in addition to the new form, or they may be replaced by the new form. More primitives can be created and used to modify the form, until the final desired shape is reached. Figure 9.24 on page 412 shows how the union and difference operations result in a much more realistic camera than the one depicted in Figure 9.20.

As with pure primitive instancing, the person doing the modeling must have a clear idea of what the final form will look like and must develop a strategy for the sequence of operations needed to create that form. The use of *sweeping operations* to create primitives can lend even

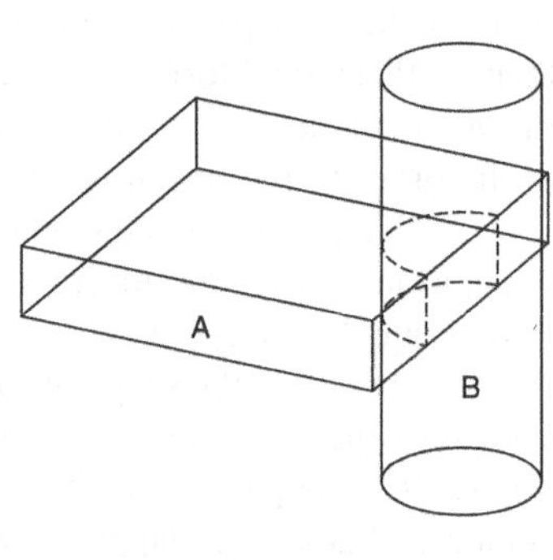

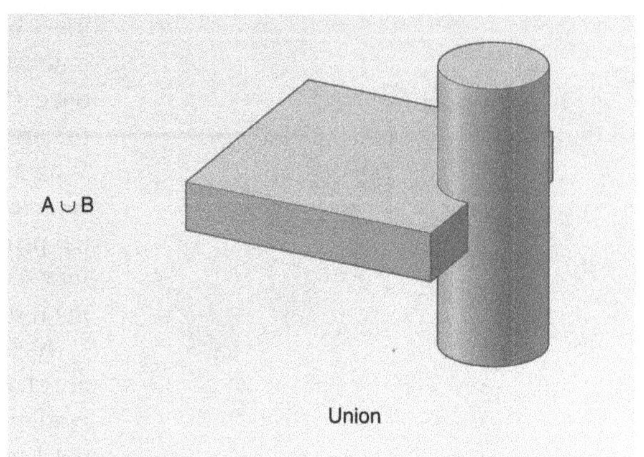

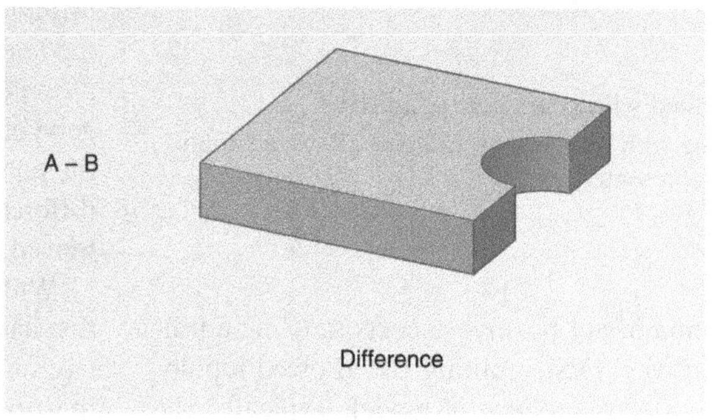

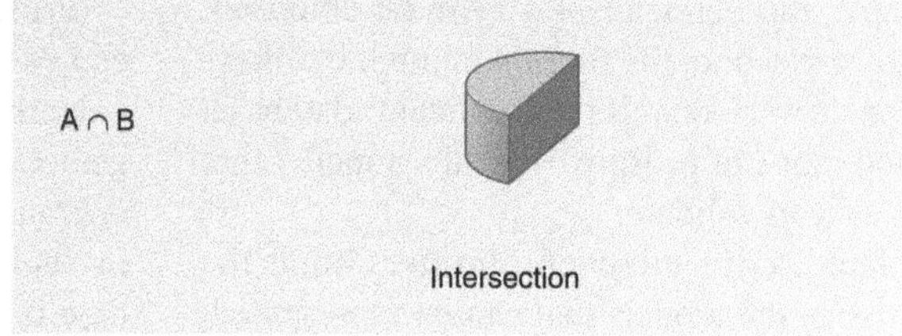

Figure 9.21

The three Boolean operations: union, difference, and intersection

The three operations, using the same primitives in the same locations, create very different objects.

more flexibility in modeling. This technique is discussed in Section 9.6.

Practice Exercise 9.3

Using clay or foam, create three pairs of primitive shapes, such as cylinders and rectilinear prisms. Sketch a pictorial of two of the primitives overlapping in some way. With the model pairs, create a single object that reflects the three Boolean operations: union, difference, and intersection.

9.3.2 Boundary Representation (B-Rep) Modeling

Boundary representation (B-rep) modeling and CSG modeling are the two most popular forms of solid modeling. With CSG modeling, surfaces are represented indirectly through half-spaces; with B-rep modeling, the surfaces, or *faces,* are themselves the basis for defining the solid. The face of a B-rep model is fundamentally different from a face in a wireframe modeler. Although both include a set of edges connected at vertices, a B-rep face explicitly represents an oriented surface. There are two

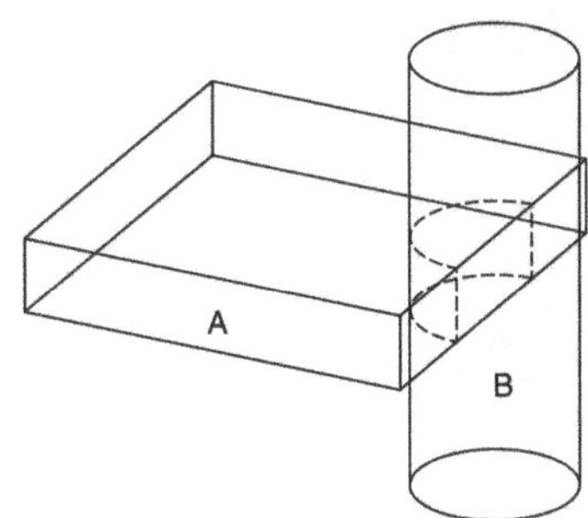

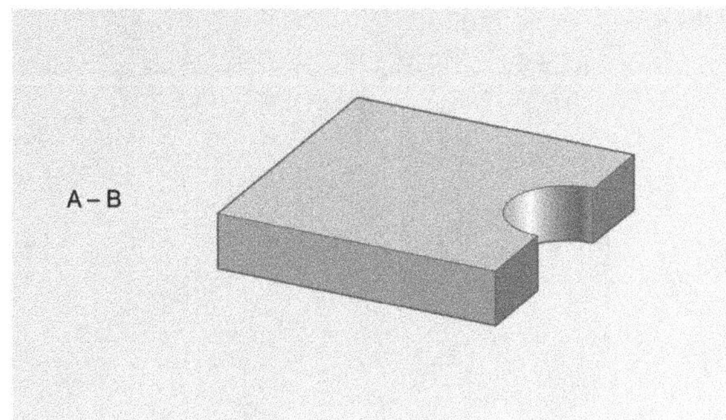

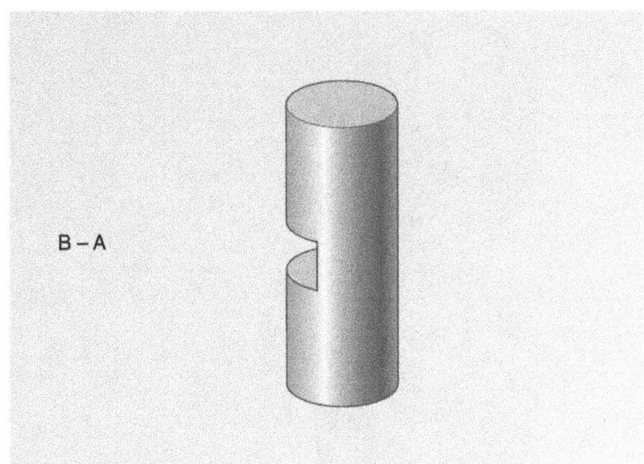

Figure 9.22

The effects of ordering of operands in a difference operation

Unlike the union operation, the difference operation is sensitive to the ordering of operations.

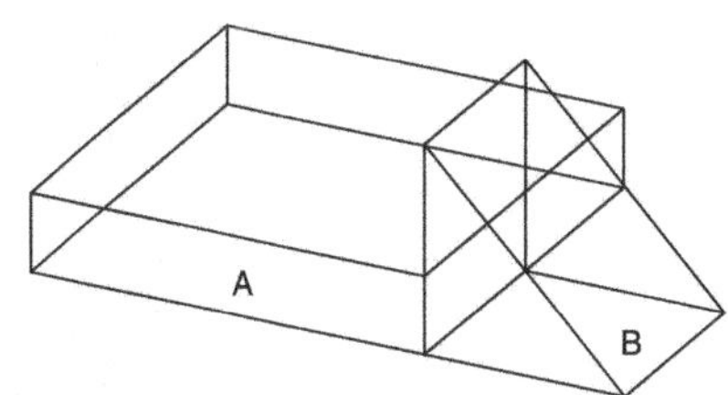

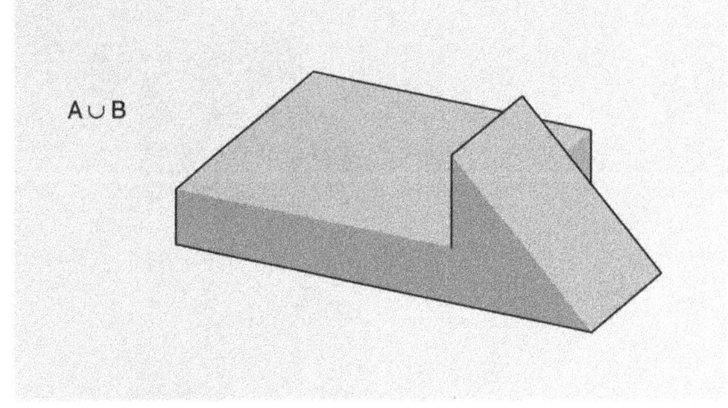

Figure 9.23

Boolean operations on adjoining primitives

Only the union operation is effective when primitives are adjoining but not overlapping.

sides to this surface: one is on the *inside* of the object (the solid side), and the other is on the *outside* of the object (the void side).

Also, like wireframe modelers, B-rep modelers have the capability of containing both linear and curved edges. Supporting curved edges also means supporting curved surfaces, which hinders model performance. For that reason, many modelers approximate curved surfaces with a series of planar ones. This is called *faceted* representation (Figure 9.25 on page 413).

The shape of a B-rep model is created using **Euler operations**. These operations are very similar to those used in mechanical drawing and wireframe model construction. The difference is that a solid bounded by faces is created. Building a solid model one vertex at a time is cumbersome.

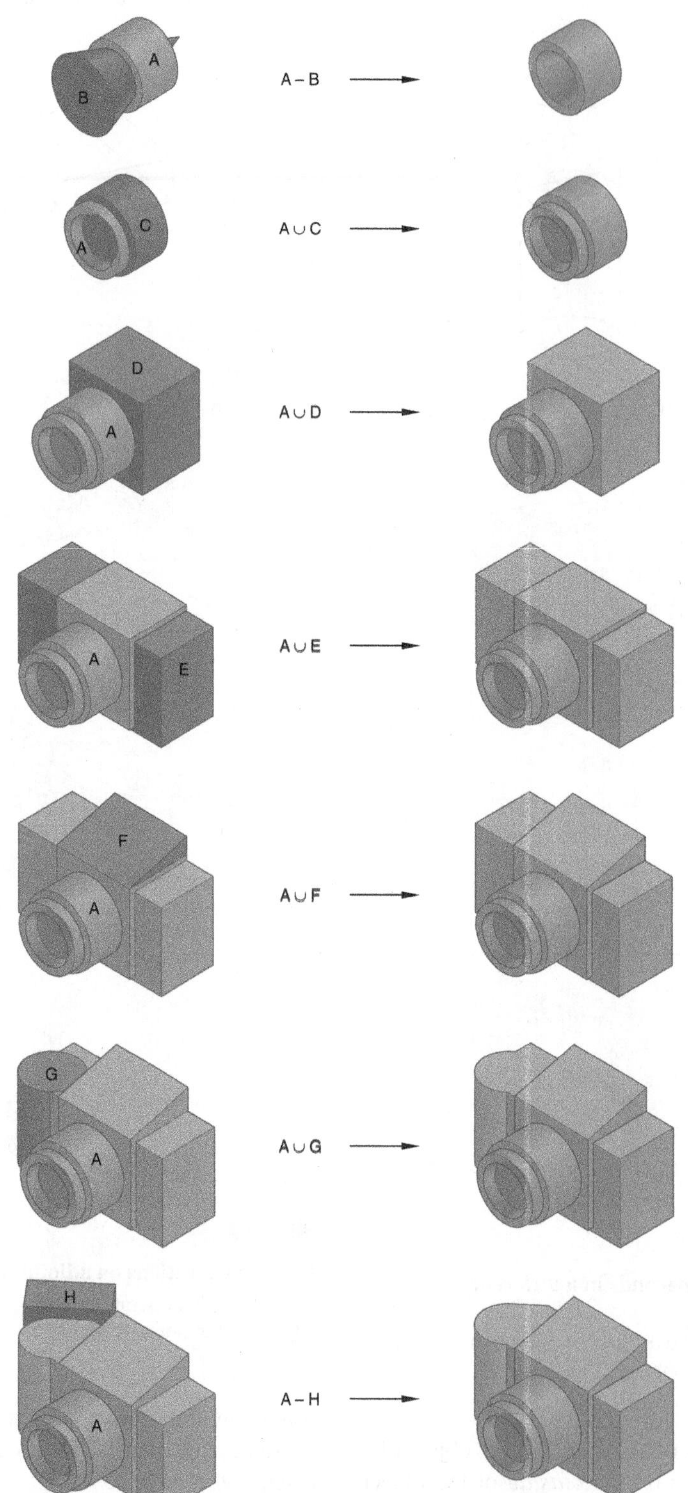

Figure 9.24

A camera described using CSG modeling

Boolean operations allow much more flexibility than just additive techniques with primitives.

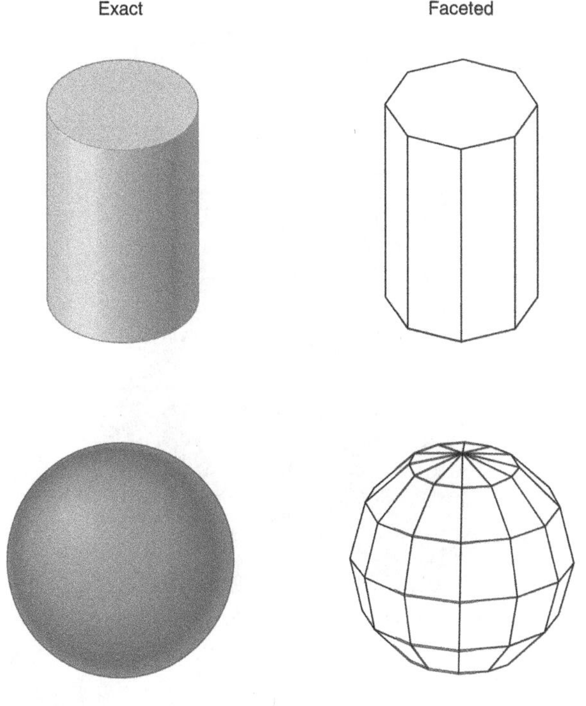

Figure 9.25

Exact versus faceted surfaces

Some modelers approximate curved surfaces with a series of planar ones called facets.

Therefore, in most modelers, B-rep primitives are often provided for use in creating or modifying groups of faces.

9.3.3 Hybrid Modeling

What the user sees and does at the system interface is usually very different from how the model information is stored and manipulated in the database. A command interpreter transforms the commands, which are designed for ease of use, into actions that are compatible with the data structure. For example, CSG-type commands are often used with B-rep modelers because they are easier to use than Euler operations. This translation also works in the reverse direction; CSG modelers often use a B-rep output for display because it is considerably easier to represent on the screen. However, because hidden line removal is time-consuming, the image on the screen often looks like a wireframe model. The lesson is, do not judge the capabilities of a modeler by what is represented on the screen or by what commands it provides. Careful exploration of a modeler's capabilities should reveal its basic underlying data structure.

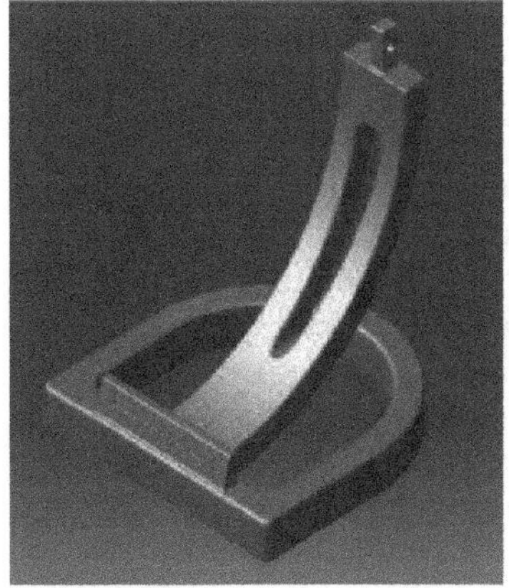

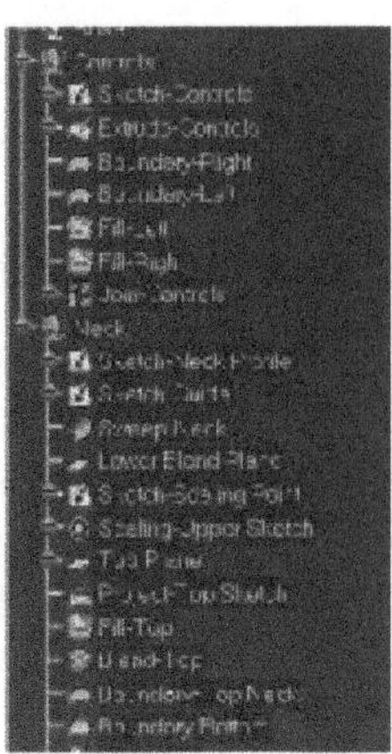

Figure 9.26

Hybrid model comprised of surface and solid geometry

Note that in the feature list shown, it includes both solid and surfaces brought together to create the object at left.

(© Nathan Hartman.)

Most modelers store their model data in multiple structures. Since no one model data structure is good for all purposes, systems will use a hybrid data structure. A true **hybrid modeler** combines fully functional CSG and B-rep databases. These types of solid modelers support Boolean operations, complex sculpted surfaces, and complete solids information on the model. The user can create either a single model using either CSG or B-rep tools or two parallel models using both techniques. The disadvantages of a hybrid modeler come in translating from one data structure to another. The translation may be inexact and contain subtle changes in the model. In many cases, certain information in the model must be kept in only one data structure, limiting the software tools available to work with that piece of the model.

Another method of hybrid modeling takes a more operational approach—the combination of both surface and solid geometry within the same model. By creating a model in this fashion, the engineer or designer is better able to capture the contours of many modern products. In any situation where an object has a combination of simple and complex shapes, the use of the hybrid technique is common. Since most contemporary CAD tools include the option of combining CSG and B-rep data structures in one model file, the ability to seamlessly integrate surface and solid geometry in the same file has given engineers and designers a great deal of flexibility in geometry creation (Figure 9.26). They have the ability to more accurately capture design intent and definition, without being forced to compromise due to lack of software functionality.

Historical Highlight
Ivan Sutherland (1938–)

Many people call Ivan Sutherland a modern-day pioneer. This engineer, professor, and entrepreneur has broken much new intellectual ground in the field of computers and continues to do so. His desire to know how things work and his love of problem solving have taken him far.

Sutherland's interest in computers started in high school in the 1950s, when he learned to program a relay-based computer. Computers of any kind were then rare; this was long before high-school students had access to them. Sutherland went on to study Electrical Engineering at Carnegie Tech, now Carnegie Mellon University; he received an M.S. from the California Institute of Technology (Caltech), and a Ph.D. from the Massachusetts Institute of Technology (MIT). His 1963 Ph.D. thesis, entitled "sketchpad, a Man Machine Graphical Communication System," made engineering drawing on a computer screen possible for the first time. For this work, Sutherland is often called the "father of computer graphics."

(Courtesy of Sun Microsystems, Inc.)

As a young Associate Professor at Harvard University, Sutherland developed a Head-Mounted Display system. The idea was simple. The computer shows the user exactly what he would see when facing in any direction. Today we call this idea "virtual reality." To build the first such system, Sutherland and his students had to invent everything from equipment to measure head position, to algorithms for eliminating material outside the user's field of view.

In 1968 Sutherland co-founded Evans and Sutherland (E&S, now a major manufacturer of very high performance displays. E&S supplies a majority of the displays used worldwide to train airline pilots. Sutherland was concurrently a part-time, tenured professor at the University of Utah. His students from that period have become today's major contributors to the international field of computer graphics.

In 1976, Sutherland became a professor at Caltech to start and head a Computer Science Department. By following the ideas of his co-founder, Carver Mead, and concentrating on design of integrated circuits, the small group at Caltech established integrated circuit design as an acceptable field for academic study.

Sutherland continues active work today in advanced hardware systems at Sun Microsystems.

9.4 Constraint-Based Modeling

Although the use of 3-D solid modeling grew steadily during the 1980s, companies were not realizing many of the productivity gains promised by CAD vendors. One of the reasons was that the process of creating a solid model was much more abstract than the process of designing real-world products. It wasn't until Parametric Technologies Corporation released Pro/ENGINEER in 1988 that many of the productivity tools now considered commonplace in modeling systems were brought together into a commercial software package.

Among the key innovations which Pro/ENGINEER and other packages have brought to 3-D solid modeling is the idea of having the model defined as a series of modifiable **features**. Each of these features was traditionally defined through operations (described in detail later in the chapter) which as closely as possible represented design or manufacturing features of the final product. While this direct link between design and manufacturing is not that simple in practice, modern CAD systems try to capture the intentions of the designer as much as possible. For example, a feature might be a hole bored through the model or a fillet added to an interior corner. Each of these features can be created independent of other features or linked so that modifications to one will update the others. The geometry of each of these features is controlled through modifiable constraints, creating a dynamic model that can be updated as the design requirements changed. This style of modeling extends to assemblies too. Constraints are also used to bring parts and subassemblies together to represent the final product assembly. Modifications to geometry in a feature are reflected in both the part containing the feature and assemblies containing this part, as well as any drawings that may reference the model in question.

9.5 Feature Analysis

A critical part of constraint-based modeling is planning that happens prior to building the model. Because much of the power of constraint-based modeling comes from the ability of the user to modify and otherwise manipulate the features that make up a part, careful planning is needed up front. Careful planning means that the model can be later modified by the person who created it or by others into a new design with a minimum of effort. What constitutes a feature and how it is defined are discussed in detail later in the chapter.

One of the critical early questions to ask before creating the model is where is the model data coming from and how is the model data going to be used—both in the short term and in the long run. For example, the model might be used exclusively for the generation of exploratory design ideas in the ideation stage of the design process. If so, then there may not be the need to carefully construct the model using features that accurately represent the final manufacturing processes. In addition, the operator may be less concerned about constructing and documenting the model so that other operators are able to modify the model later on. On the other hand, the model might be of an iterative design of an existing product. If so, an existing model may be used and features on the model modified to represent the new design. In this case, the designer hopes that the model has been carefully constructed and documented so that the model *behaves* as expected when features are modified. This behavior should reflect the **design intent** of the product being modeled. That is, changes in geometry of a feature should create model feedback or further changes in the model which reflect design performance or manufacturing constraints of the product. In addition to considering design intent, it is important to consider the order of feature creation prior to the creation of geometry within the CAD system. Due to the relational nature of modern constraint-based CAD tools, each feature is based in some way on the features that were created before it, whether it is for size information or for location. An effective way to plan the creation of a model is to develop a modeling procedure (Figure 9.27). A modeling procedure is a sketch that shows the cross-sectional profile for the first feature in the model, and then a sketch used to depict the finished geometric form after the 3-D feature operation has been applied. This process is repeated until the major features on the object have been defined. Depending on the complexity of the model, the engineer or designer may want to include basic dimensional information in these sketches. As a user becomes more experienced at using the CAD tool, this planning process becomes less formal.

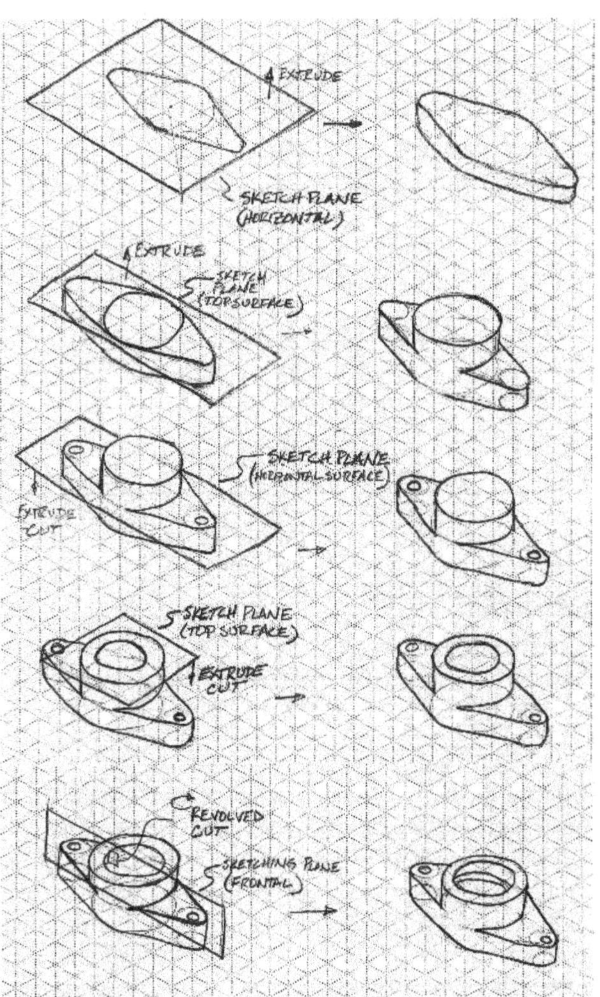

Figure 9.27

Modeling procedure for a part

(© Nathan Hartman.)

Capturing design intent in a model is a process of defining features and the relationship between features within a model. The goal is to make sure that information extracted

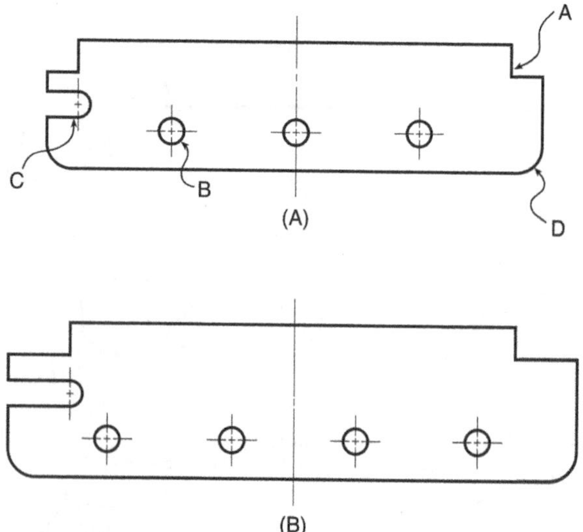

Figure 9.28

A part defined by features

Modification of part geometry is done by changing the size, location, and number of features in the part.

from the model or modified versions of the model for use in other parts of the product development process accurately reflects (as much as is possible) the original intent of the designers and engineers who specified the requirements of the product. 3-D modeling is a process of transforming product requirements into geometry. In a constraint-based model this geometry is dynamic, since the size and location of features in the model can easily be changed to alter the model's geometry.

The part in Figure 9.28 has embedded in it a number of design requirements through the constraints attached to features. Looking in Figure 9.28A, the notches on the top at either end (labeled A) are constrained horizontally symmetric in size and location. The holes (labeled B) are constrained to be equally spaced across the length of the part with the holes no farther than 4 cm apart. The slot (labeled C) is constrained a constant distance from the top of the part and has a depth equal to the depth of the notch. The radiused corners (labeled D) have a radius equal to one fifth the height of the part. A designer modifies the part in two ways: the overall length is increased from 20 cm to 23 cm, the height is increased from 5 cm to 6 cm, and the right-hand notch is doubled in depth. How does the constrained part model respond to these changes? The modified part (Figure 9.28B) shows a number of changes: First, the left-hand notch doubles in depth to match the notch on the right. Second, there are now four equally spaced holes instead of three. Third, the slot is still the same distance from the top of the part, but has increased in depth to match the new notch depth. Finally, the radii of the corners have increased to stay one-fifth the height of the part.

The example part in Figure 9.28 shows examples of a number of types of constraints that can be embedded in a single part. In reality, most parts exist as part of larger assemblies. Feature constraints can also be carried across parts in an assembly to make sure that changes in one part are accurately reflected in dependent parts. Figure 9.29 shows the same part seen in Figure 9.28 as part of an assembly. A change in the first part causes modification in the second part so that the two parts still fit together properly. Besides using the flat mating surfaces of the two parts, the line of symmetry down the middle of the part is used to help center the parts with respect to each other.

Decisions of how to capture design intent by constraining features begins with defining what geometry of the part will be contained within each feature. If the geometry of the part is already well defined, then the decision will largely be one of decomposing the part geometry into a series of smaller geometric elements that can be created with a single feature operation in the modeler (Figure 9.27). For the part seen in Figure 9.28, the notches, holes, slot, and radiused corners could all be defined as separate features in the part model. In this case, the building of the model would actually begin with a *base feature* represented by a rectangular prism. On this geometry, notches, holes, etc., would all be defined as features removing material from the base feature. At the other extreme, the final part seen in Figure 9.28 could be built all as one feature (you'll see how later on). Which is the right way of building the model? There is no easy answer to this question. In fact, depending on the situation, there may be a half dozen or more correct approaches to building this model.

How you define what geometry makes up a feature depends on a number of factors, including:

- How much of the final geometry of the part design has been decided on before you begin creating the model?
- What level of detail is needed in the model?
- What level of modification automation is going to be built into the model?
- What need is there to explore design alternatives that involve the addition and removal of geometric elements, rather than simply changing their sizes?
- Should the geometry be grouped according to the functional elements of the design?
- Should the geometry be grouped based on the manufacturing processes being used to produce the part?

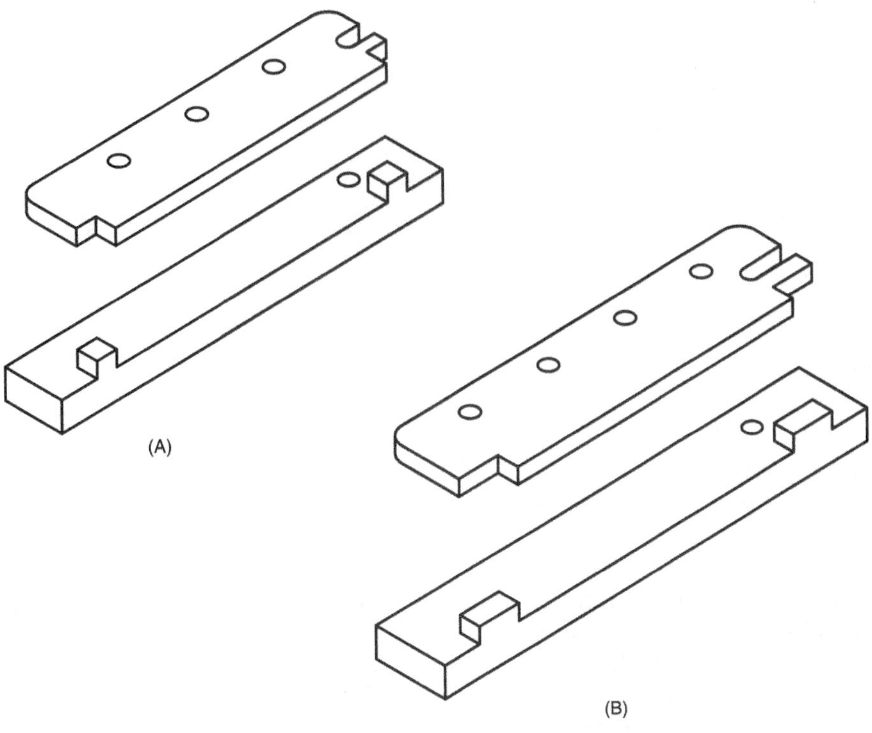

Figure 9.29

Features related across parts

Features in a part are often related to mating features on other parts in an assembly.

Often it is many of these factors that influence the decisions on feature definition.

9.6 Feature Definition

Knowing how to define features in the model begins with understanding how your modeler allows you to create and edit geometry. Though every constraint-based modeler has its own approaches to feature creation, there are ways of generalizing this process across modelers to understand some of the basic tools used in modeling. This first section will present an overview of this process. Each of these steps in the process will then be treated in greater depth in later sections.

9.6.1 Features from Generalized Sweeps

Many features in a model can be made through the use of **sweeping operations**. Most CAD systems use methods of automating solid feature generation. In a sweeping operation, a closed polygon, called a **profile**, is sketched on a plane and is translated or swept along a defined path for a defined length. Each swept profile can be visualized as a solid object. The first feature, the base feature, will look exactly like this visualized solid. Each successive feature after this will modify the existing geometry based on how the swept form intersects with it and whether the feature is to add or remove material from the part model.

In the simplest case, the path of the sweep is linear, and a prismatic solid is created (Figure 9.30 on page 418). If the linear path is coincident with the W axis, a right prism is created. If the path is at any other angle to the W axis, an oblique prism is created. An angle of 90 degrees is not allowed because it creates a form that is not three-dimensional; the path is parallel to the U–V plane. Another path a sweep could follow is circular (revolute). The specifications for a revolute path are more demanding than those for a linear path. With a revolute path, an axis of rotation must be defined in terms of both orientation and location. Figure 9.31 on page 419 shows examples of revolute sweeps.

If the features being created in Figures 9.30 and 9.31 were base features, then the resulting model would look exactly as the geometry is shown. If it is a later feature, then

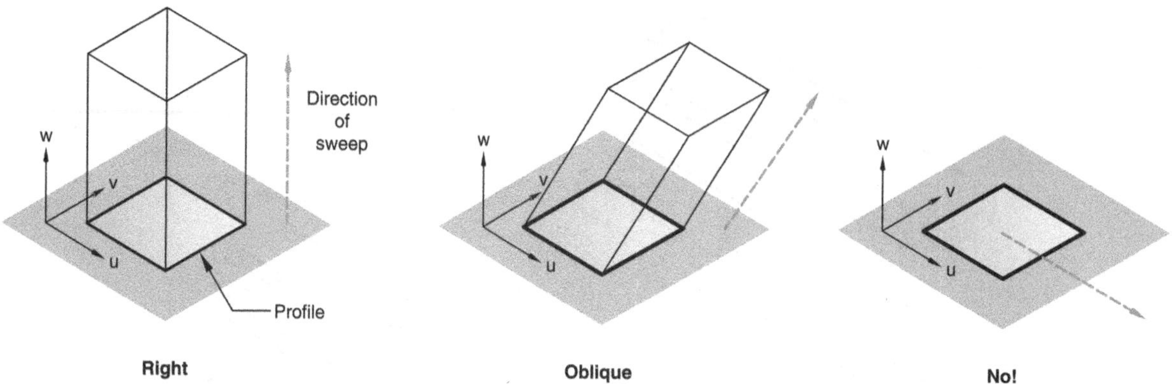

Figure 9.30

Types of linear sweeping operations

In some systems, linear sweeps are restricted to being perpendicular to the workplane.

whether the swept form is adding or subtracting volume from the current model has to be defined. With constructive solid geometry (CSG) modelers, Boolean operations would have defined the interaction between the existing model and the swept profile. With constraint-based modelers, the term Boolean is typically not used, though how Boolean operations are defined in Section 9.3.1 helps to understand how the geometry is being modified.

Creating a 3-D Model Using Sweeping Operations

Sweeping operations can be used to define many of the features in a model. Swept objects can represent both positive and negative geometry, and so can be used to either add or subtract volume from the model (Figure 9.32 on page 420).

Step 1. With a 2-D rectangular polygon defined on the workplane, determine the direction and distance for the sweep to produce the base feature.

Step 2. Using the top face of the initial solid as a guide, relocate the workplane, create a semicircle, then sweep it to create the half cylinder. Using an addition operation joins these two objects.

Step 3. Rather than using an existing face on the solid for orientation, rotate the workplane 90 degrees so that it is vertical, and create a triangle. Sweep the triangle to create a wedge, and unite it with the model.

Step 4. Translate the workplane so that it is on the front face of the object. Create a circle on the front face, and sweep it to the rear face of the object to form a cylinder. Using a subtraction operation, subtract the cylinder from the object to make a hole through the model.

Step 5. Do a final sweep with a rectangle following a circular path for 180 degrees. Using a subtraction operation to remove a portion of the bottom of the model.

9.6.2 Construction Geometry

All geometry in a model must be located and oriented relative to some default 3-D coordinate system. Depending on the modeling system, this **world coordinate system** can be explicitly defined and available for the operator to use in defining the location of geometry or implicit in other construction geometry used in model construction.

A **workplane** is the most common type of construction geometry used to support the creation of part geometry relative to the world coordinate system. Construction geometry does not represent any of the final geometry representing the part, but instead provides a framework for guiding the construction of this part geometry. Most current CAD tools use three default, mutually perpendicular planes as the starting point for modeling. All of these planes intersect at the default world coordinate system. (Figure 9.33A on page 420). These planes can be thought of as construction geometry used to support the creation of model feature geometry.

A workplane can be used in the same manner as a drawing surface. In a modeler, workplanes are typically used to orient the profile sketch used in feature generation. They also are used to position the first feature of the model in 3-D space. By adjusting the view of the model to be normal (perpendicular) to the workplane, the effect is that you can draw on the workplane as though you were looking

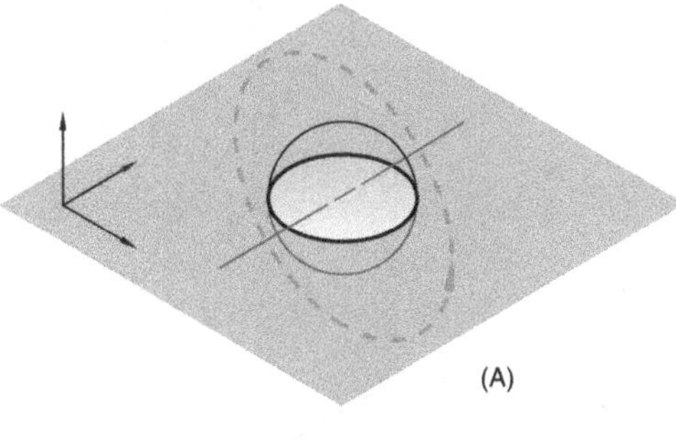
(A)

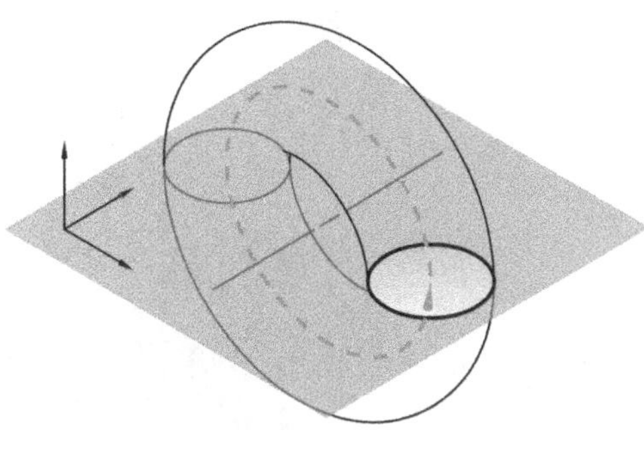
(B)

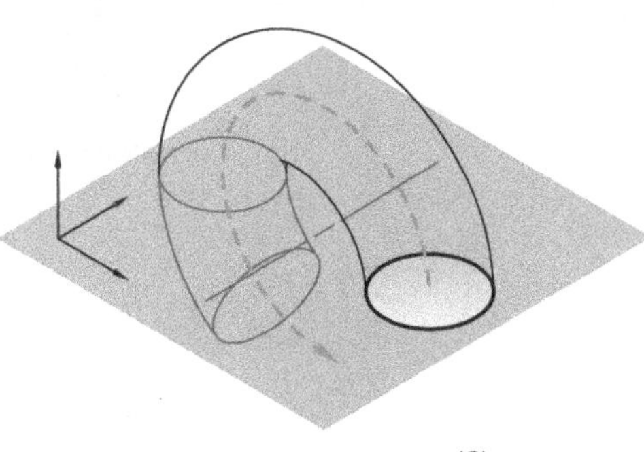
(C)

Figure 9.31

Examples of revolved sweeping operations

The resulting geometry is dependent on the location of the axis of rotation relative to the profile, and to the angular displacement.

directly down on a piece of paper. Figure 9.33B shows a sketch created on one of the workplanes. The workplane orients the sketch relative to the world coordinate system while dimensional constraints locate the sketch on the plane relative to the other two workplanes. This profile sketch might have been drawn in this pictorial view, or the view may have first been oriented normal to the workplane (Figure 9.33C).

Each of these infinitely large planes creates an implied *local,* or **relative coordinate system**. An alternative coordinate system is often used—for example U, V, W—to indicate the orientation of the plane relative to the world coordinate system. In Figure 9.34 on page 421, U and V are in the plane of the workplane while W is normal (perpendicular) to the workplane. As mentioned before, the location of sketch geometry on these planes is typically located relative to projections of construction geometry or part geometry onto this plane.

Once the base feature is created, workplanes are often oriented using geometry of the model being built. The simplest way to locate a workplane is to make it coplanar with an existing face of the model (Figure 9.35A on page 421). In addition, three vertices (V_1, V_2, V_3) can be specified to orient the workplane on the model. For example, the first vertex could be the origin, the second could show the direction of the U axis, and the third could be a point in the first quadrant of the U–V plane (Figure 9.35B). An alternative would be to specify an origin at a vertex and then the edges on the model to orient the plane.

Common methods for specifying the location and orientation of workplanes include (Figure 9.36 on page 422):

- Through
- Offset/parallel
- Angle
- Point or edge and orientation
- Tangent and orientation

Often one or more of these specifications needs to be used to unequivocally specify a new workplane.

In addition to workplanes, construction axes and construction points can also be created. Construction axes are often used to locate an axis of revolution or locate a point where the axis pierces a plane. Construction points can be used to locate a specific point along an infinitely long construction axis or a specific point on a construction plane or face of the model. Understanding of how the fundamentals of geometry are defined (see Chapter 8) is critical to understanding how construction geometry is created and manipulated.

9.6.3 Sketching the Profile

Many features on a part model begin as a **profile sketch** on a workplane. Once a workplane is chosen or created, a decision has to be made as to how to view the workplane while sketching on it. If a pictorial view is chosen to work in (Figure 9.33B), you have the opportunity to get an overall view of where the sketch is relative

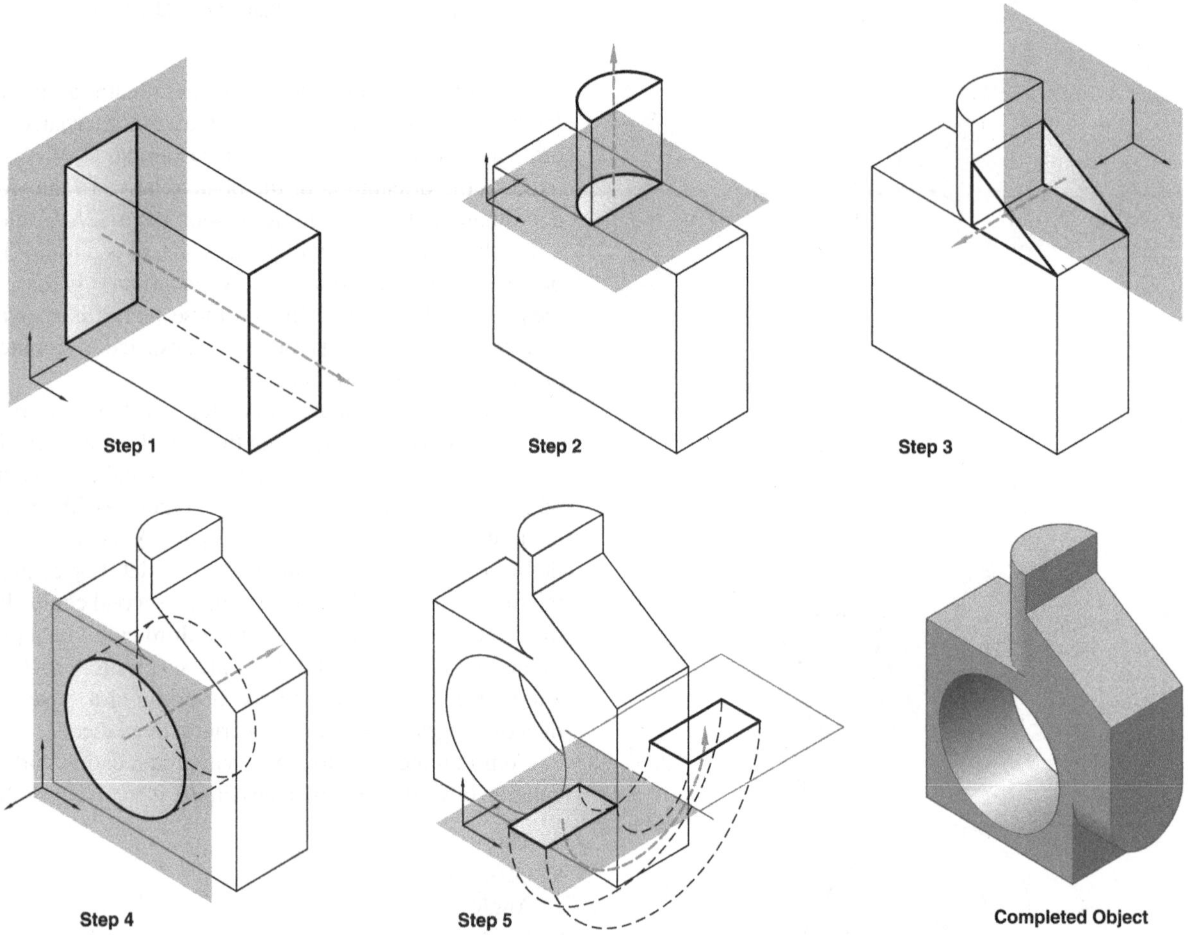

Step 1

Step 2

Step 3

Step 4

Step 5

Completed Object

Figure 9.32

Creating a solid model using sweeping and Boolean operations

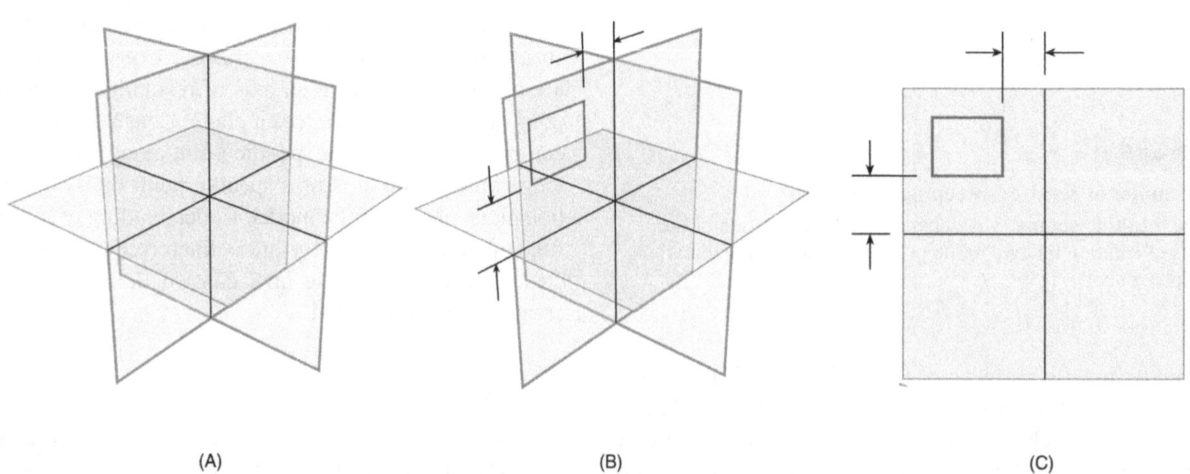

Figure 9.33

Mutually perpendicular workplanes

Three mutually perpendicular workplanes are often used as a starting point for defining the first feature of a part model.

to the other part geometry. On the other hand, a view normal to the workplane (Figure 9.33C) will likely give you a more precise view of how part geometry projects onto the sketched profile. For more complex profile sketches, you may want to shift between pictorial and normal views of the model and workplane.

If you choose a normal view of the workplane, you may also have the option of choosing the orientation of the workplane relative to the screen. That is, you can specify the rotation of the workplane about the normal axis. This is typically done by specifying a direction that construction or part geometry should point (up, down, right, or left). These directions are relative to the computer screen rather than the world coordinate system. Although, it is possible that the CAD system you choose will automatically produce a view normal to the workplane based on assumptions made by the software.

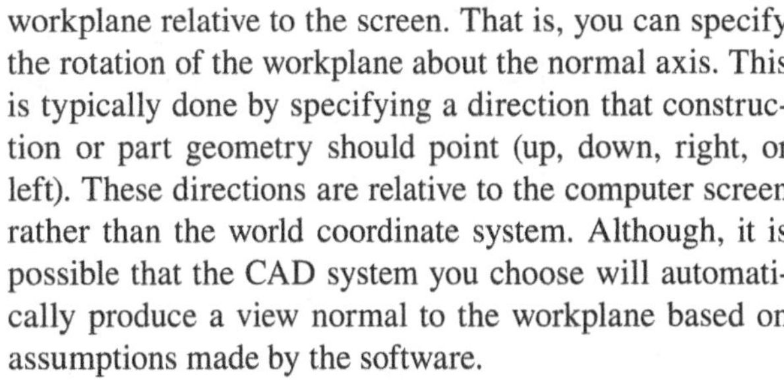

Once a view of the workplane is established, a profile sketch can be drawn on the workplane. This sketch will consist of a series of line elements such as straight lines, arcs, circles, or splines. Tools used for drawing this sketch will be very similar to the tools used for drawing such elements in a 2-D CAD system. One important difference concerns the accuracy with which the sketch needs to be drawn. Unlike a 2-D CAD drawing, the sketch does not need to be dimensionally accurate. Instead, the sketch represents the overall shape, the **topology**, of the profile, and the entities of the sketch should be proportional to each other. That is, the sketch should represent the total number of sides of the final profile, the basic shape of the elements (curved or straight), and the order in which the elements are connected together. The sketch should also represent the basic geometric relationships between the elements (parallel, tangent, etc.) within a reasonable level of accuracy. This level of accuracy will be discussed in the next section.

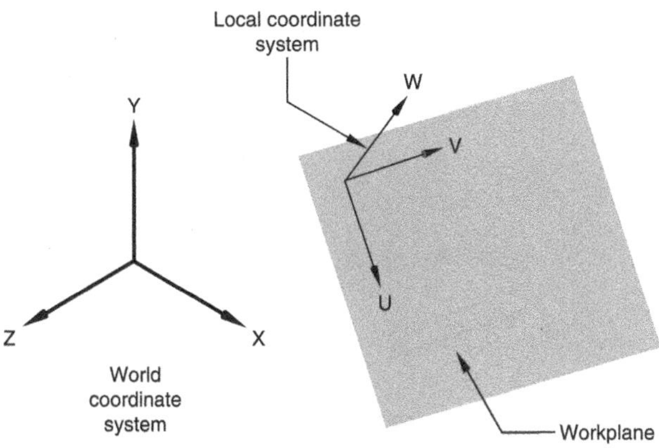

Figure 9.34

A local coordinate system attached to a workplane

Local coordinate systems are used to locate a workplane relative to the world coordinate system or the model.

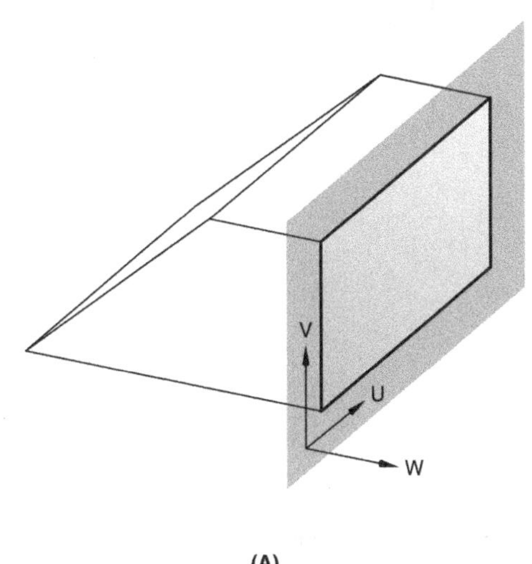

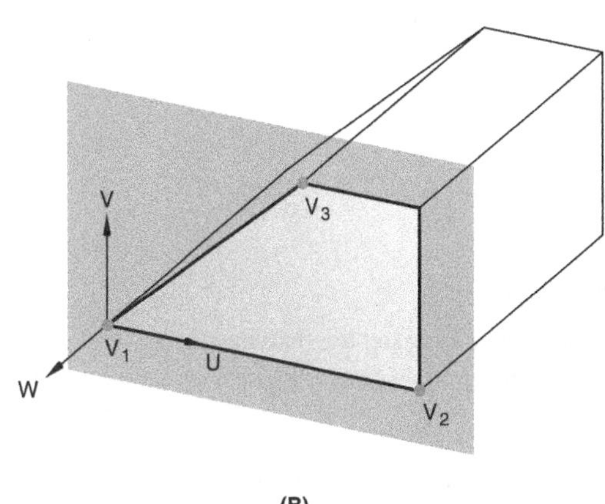

Figure 9.35

Locating a workplane by the features of the model

Both faces and individual vertices can be used to orient and locate workplanes.

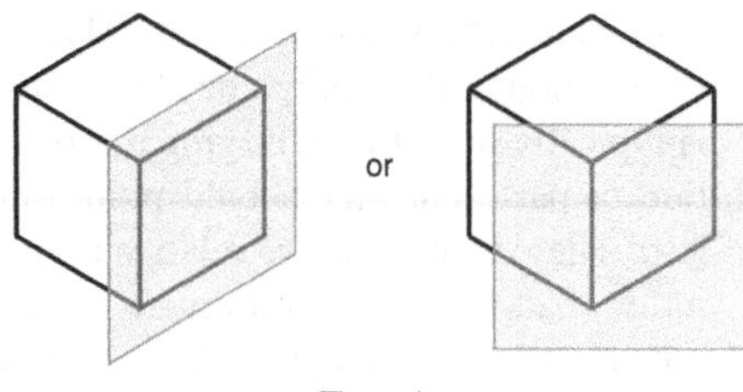

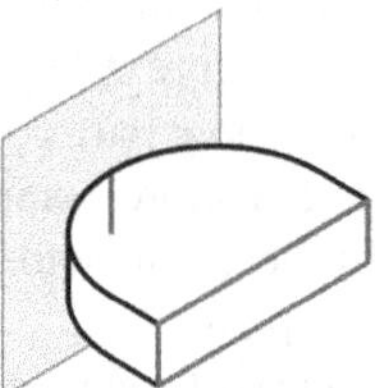

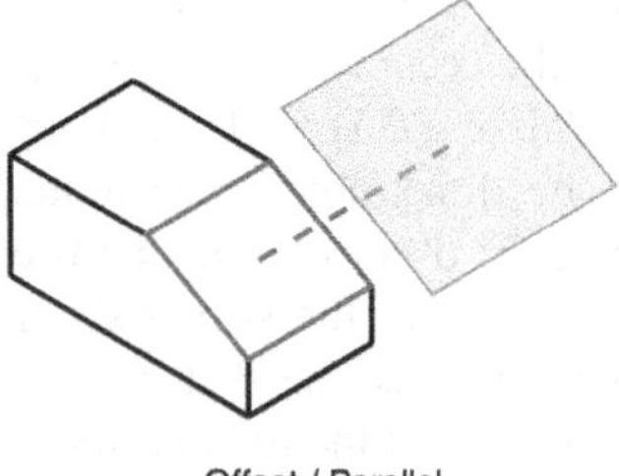

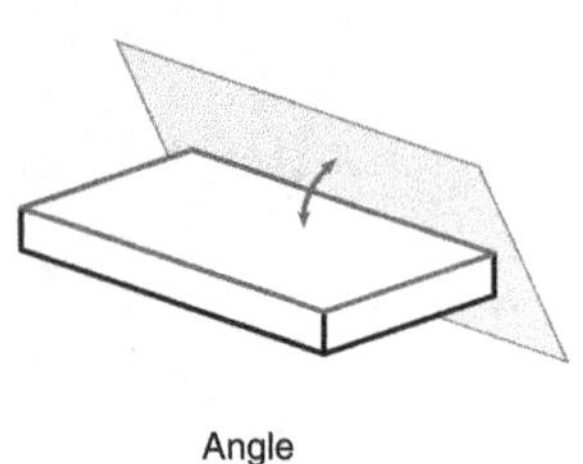

Figure 9.36

Common methods of creating new workplanes

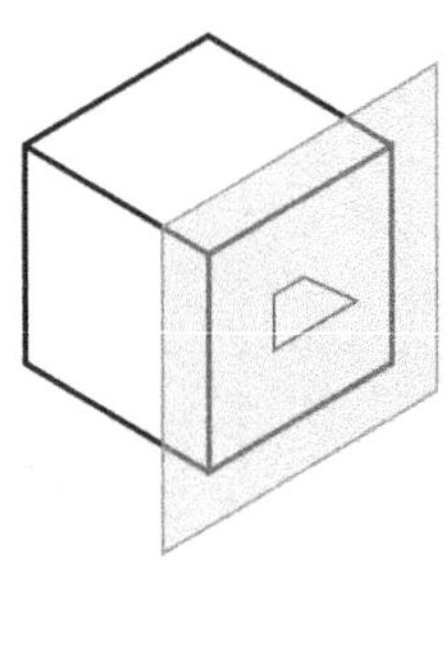

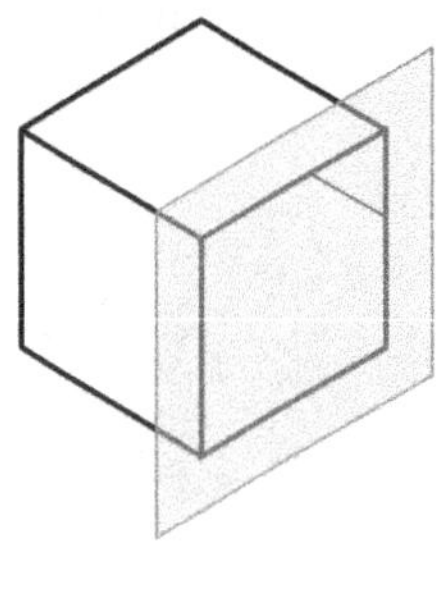

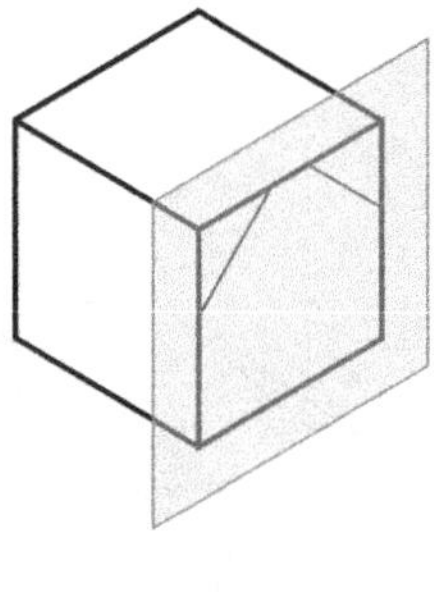

Figure 9.37

Closed and open loop profile sketches

Depending on the modeler, profile sketches can be either open or closed.

Depending on the type of modeler used, other characteristics of the profile may need to be considered. For example, the sketch might be either a **closed loop** or an open loop. A closed loop sketch has its last element connected with its first element to create a sealed path (Figure 9.37A). You could imagine that water poured inside of the loop would not leak out. An open loop sketch does not close back on itself and is used when fewer elements can clearly indicate the action of the sketch profile (Figure 9.37B). In this case, the endpoints of the open sketch entities typically will lie on the edge boundaries of the existing solid geometry. Whereas a closed loop implies

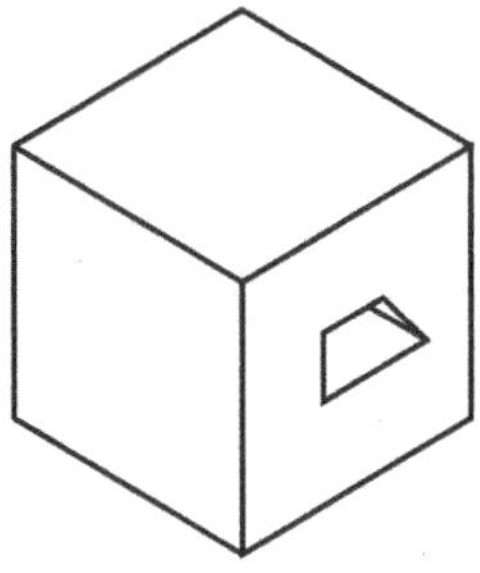

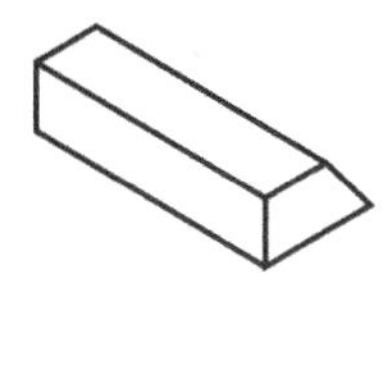

(A) (B)

Figure 9.38

Side of profile sketch

When subtracting material from a part, whether the inside or the outside of a profile sketch is chosen will make a difference to the end result.

an *inside* and *outside,* an open loop does not. When a profile sketch contains more than one loop, the loops usually all need to be closed to clearly indicate what is inside and outside (Figure 9.37C).

The definition of inside and outside is needed to specify how the profile is to interact with the existing geometry. For example, in Figure 9.38A, the material inside the loop is subtracted from the existing object, whereas in Figure 9.38B, the material on the outside of the loop is subtracted from the existing object.

9.6.4 Constraining the Profile

Going hand in hand with the sketching of the profile is applying *constraints.* Whereas the sketching defined the topology of the profile, constraining defines the **geometry** of the profile. This use of the word geometry refers to a more narrow definition of the term: the size, location, and orientation of geometric elements that give them an overall shape and form. The types of constraints applied to the sketch profile can be roughly divided into two categories: *explicit* and *implicit.* Operationally in a CAD system, explicit constraints often take the form of dimensions that the user adds to the sketch or by a specific geometric condition created between two sketched entities. Implicit constraints typically take the form of geometric relationships or automatic dimensions created by the software between entities in the sketch as the user is creating the geometry. These two types of constraints differ as to whether the modeling system *infers* the constraint based on the way the sketch was drawn, or whether the operator has to *explicitly* apply the constraint to the sketch.

Many systems create constraints based on the implied geometric relationships in the profile sketch. Common geometric relations for whom the system might create implied constraints include (Figure 9.39 on page 424):

- Closure (connected edges)
- Segment overlap
- Endpoint/line overlap
- Tangency
- Parallelism, perpendicularity
- Same size
- Coincident (but not touching)
- Concentric

These relationships are not only applied internally within the profile, but also between elements of the profile and existing geometric elements in the part model. For example, segment overlap is exclusively applied between a profile element and part geometry.

When a system applies these implicit constraints will be determined by a predefined tolerance. This tolerance will decide, for example, when two sketched lines are close enough to parallel that they should be constrained parallel. How does the system set this tolerance? In some cases it might be by predetermined values. Two lines would be inferred to be parallel or perpendicular if they were within 5 degrees of these respective orientations. Other systems use a tolerance based on view resolution based on the number of screen pixels between them. That is, if two lines look as though they are overlapping on the screen, then they will be constrained as such. Understanding how a system applies implied geometric constraints is important to devising a sketching strategy.

Though the profile does not need to be sketched dimensionally accurate, how you sketch it will influence how geometric constraints are applied. For example, if you have two lines that are to be 92 degrees relative to each other, trying to sketch this accurately will likely cause the system to apply an incorrect constraint of perpendicularity. What you would do instead is exaggerate the nonperpendicularity of the lines by sketching them at, say, 110 degrees and then later come back and apply a dimensional constraint to pull the segments back to 92 degrees. If implicit geometric constraints are applied which you do not want, there typically will be a function in the software for overriding or removing these constraints. Similarly, you may also have the ability to force the application of geometric constraints, which were not inferred by the system.

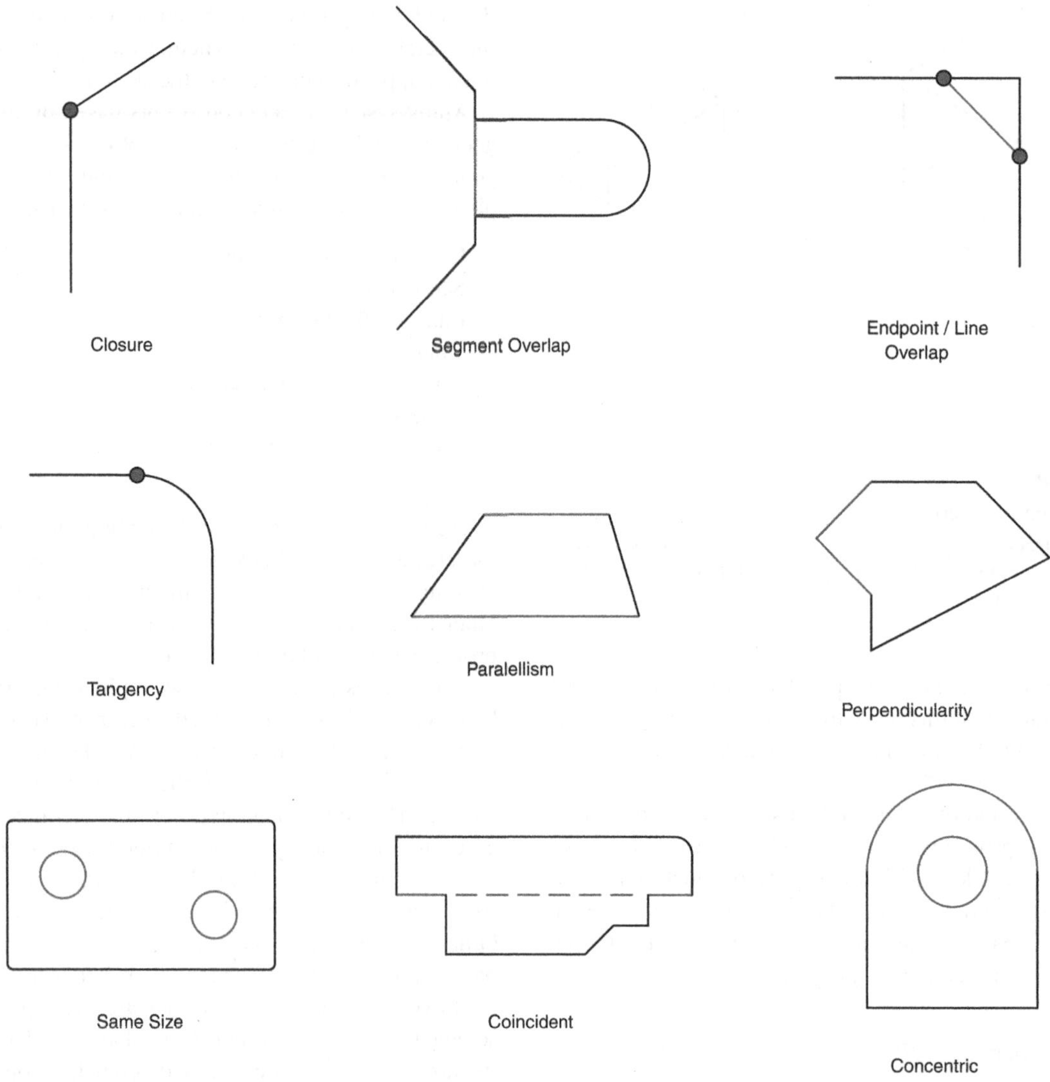

Figure 9.39

Common geometric relations for constraining a profile

Explicit constraints, unlike implicit constraints, are applied by the users to the profile sketch. The application of explicit constraints is very much like applying dimensions in a 2-D CAD system, yet they behave very differently. An explicit constraint indicates that a specific size or location of a profile element is going to be controlled by a variable, or parameter. With a traditional CAD modeler, geometric elements are created at a specific size and location (Figure 9.40A). For example, if a plate is to have a length equal to 32 mm and a width of half the length, a rectangle 32 mm long and 16 mm wide would be created. In a constraint-based modeler, constraints are assigned to geometric elements to control their size or location: the length would be defined as $P_1 = 32$ mm and the width defined as $P_2 = P_1 \div 2$ (Figure 9.40B). Though a profile element may be initially sketched a specific size (and a constraint assigned this as its initial value), the user can go back and change its size at any time. The power of this approach is seen when the model is modified. Instead of having to individually update all related dimensions,

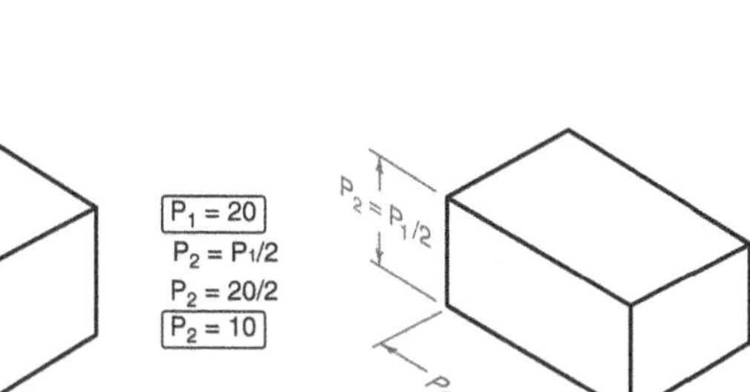

Figure 9.40

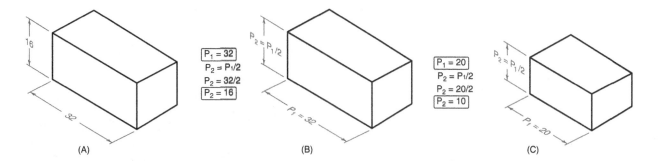

Traditional and constraint-based part definition

Traditional modelers define geometry directly while constraint-based modelers use parametric equations.

one dimension can be altered, and all dimensions linked through parameters automatically reflect the change. For example, if the length of the plate is reduced (P_1 = 20), the width automatically reduces by the appropriate amount to reflect the change in length (Figure 9.40C). As seen in this example, the constraint parameter may not be assigned a numeric value, but instead an algebraic relation tied to other constraint parameters.

Just as with dimensions in traditional engineering drawings, explicit, or dimensional, constraints specify either the location or size of a geometric element (Figure 9.41). The constraint may reference elements that are *internal* to the profile, or it may tie profile elements to *external* part or construction geometry. In Figure 9.41, dimension A represents an internal size constraint and dimension B represents an internal location constraint. Dimension C, on the other hand, is a location constraint with an external reference. When a profile element overlaps an external reference (indicated by D), the system may apply a locational constraint of value zero.

Explicit and implicit constraints should not be thought of as independent from each other. Figure 9.42 on page 426 shows how these two different kinds of constraints work together to create the final constrained profile. The initial profile (Figure 9.42A) is sketched to represent the appropriate geometric relations, such as parallelism between the top and bottom elements and tangency with the arc. With the implicit constraints applied, explicit dimensional constraints are applied to control the size of the profile elements (Figure 9.42B). Some of the constraint parameters, such as P_3, are controlled through algebraic relations by other parameters. Once applied, the explicit constraints can easily be altered to modify the shape and size of the profile (Figure 9.42C). Once constrained and parameter values are modified appropriately, the profile can be swept out (Figure 9.42D).

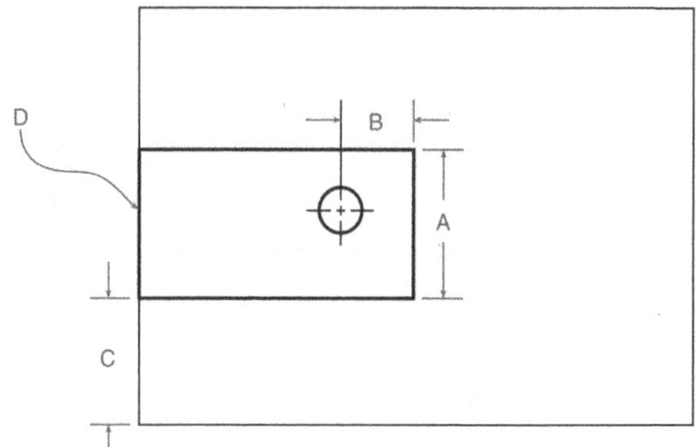

Figure 9.41

Explicit dimensional constraints

Dimensional constraints are used to locate and size feature elements.

Not all constraints easily fit into the categories of implicit or explicit. For example, a modeler may have an offset constraint (Figure 9.43 on page 426). This constraint allows you to select a group of existing geometric elements, specify a distance and side to offset, and create profile elements constrained to the originally selected elements. This constraint combines implicit geometric relations (the new profile elements stay parallel to the existing elements) with locational constraints (a constant offset distance). Size of the profile element ends up being determined indirectly through the connection points of the elements.

Central to developing a strategy for constraining a profile is knowing when the profile is fully constrained,

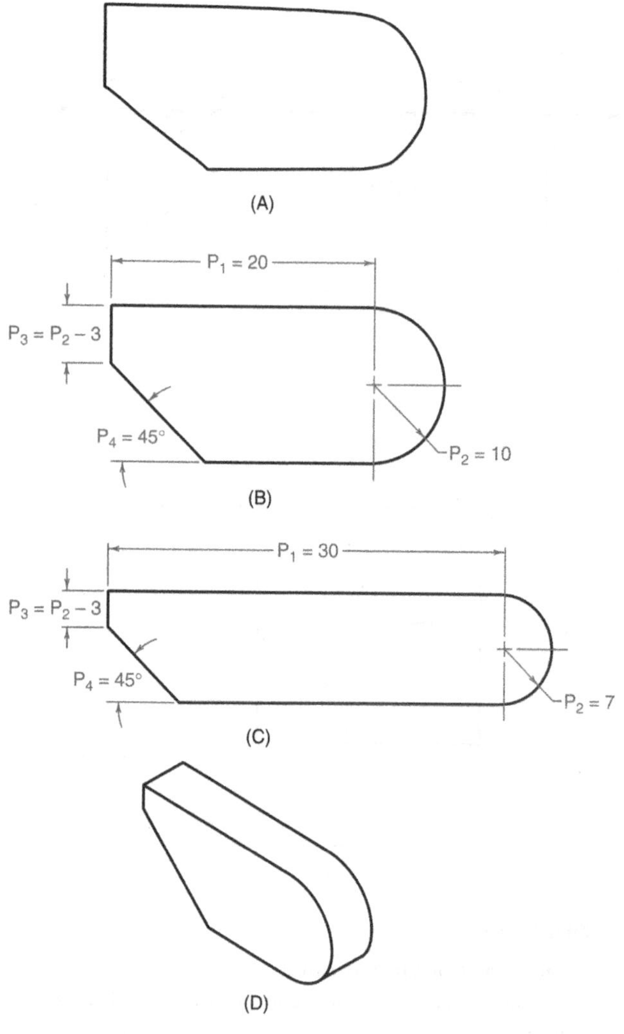

Figure 9.42

Creating a constrained model from a sketch profile

A rough sketch is constrained through implicit and explicit geometric constraints.

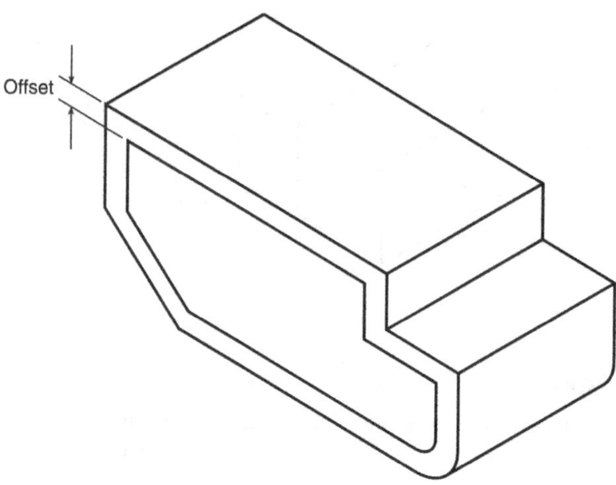

Figure 9.43

An offset constraint

Some constraints are not easily categorized as being either explicit or implicit.

underconstrained, or overconstrained. A *fully constrained* profile has completely specified the geometry of a profile. All elements are sized, located, and oriented relative to each other and to the part model (and, therefore, the world coordinate system). In many cases, the geometry of an element will be determined indirectly based on the size, location, orientation, and geometric relationship of other elements. In contrast, an underconstrained profile has one or more elements that have not been fully specified. Underconstrained elements will initially take on the geometric properties represented by the sketch: if it is sketched 94.3 cm long, then it will be represented that way. When constraints on the profile are later modified, the underconstrained elements will change (or not change) based on changes in other geometric elements rather than be driven by constraints within itself. This leads both to a freedom and to a certain degree of unpredictability when creating feature profiles. Profiles can also be overconstrained. This is generally an unwanted situation, since there are now constraints in conflict with each other with no clear indication as to which should take precedence. You would need to delete implicit or explicit constraints on the profile to resolve the overconstrained condition.

As was noted earlier in the section, dimensional constraint parameters can be set to something other than a constant value. The ability to link constraint parameters through algebraic equations or to control values based on logic statements provides tremendous power to the modeler to both embed design intent and automate modifications of the model.

A common type of algebraic formula to associate with a constraint is to have a parameter equal to another parameter plus or minus a constant. This type of *offset* formula can be seen in a constraint in Figure 9.42 where constraint P_3 will always be 3 less than P_2 no matter what the value of P_2. Another type of formula can be seen in Figure 9.40 where constraint P_2 is always a *ratio* of P_1. In this case, P_2 will always be one-half of P_1. It is often nec-

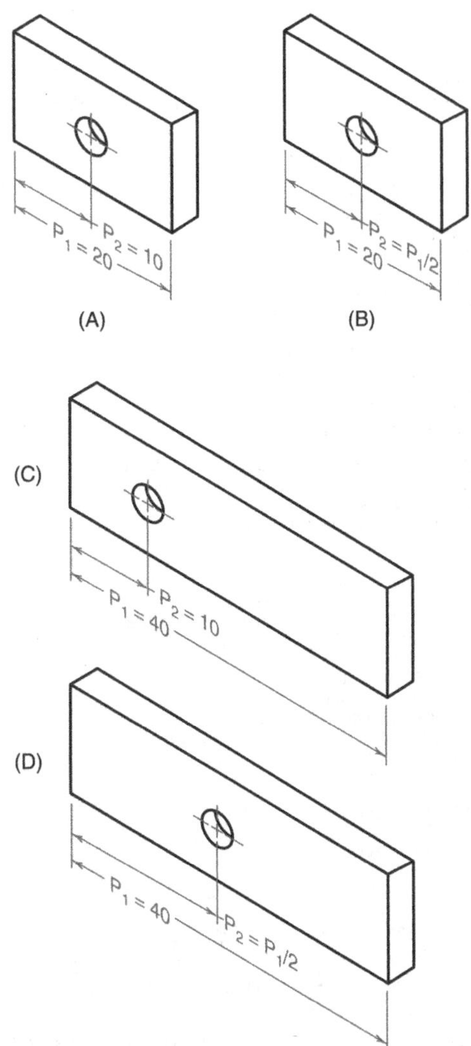

Figure 9.44

The effect of design intent on model changes

How a feature behaves when a part is modified depends on how it is constrained.

essary to look behind the current value for a constraint parameter to understand the design intent embedded in the constraint. In Figure 9.44A, two plates are created with holes and two different design intents. In the plate on the left, the hole was intended to be placed 10 mm from the left edge, while the plate on the right had the hole placed in the center. When the overall width is set to 20 mm, no difference is seen in the two models, but when the overall width is set to a different value, the difference in design intent is immediately seen (Figure 9.44B). With a traditional modeler, an engineer viewing the model in Figure 9.44A would not be able to tell what the design intent was and, therefore, how the hole should shift if the model was altered.

Figure 9.44 is an example of parameters being linked across features in a part. Here, the location of the hole feature is tied to the overall length of the base feature, the plate. In addition to linking parameters within and between features of a part, parameters can also be linked between parts in an assembly. Looking back on the assembly in Figure 9.29, the constraint parameter controlling the spread of the rectangular pins on the bottom piece needed to be linked to the overall length and notch cuts of the top plate. In complex assemblies, creating linkages between constraint parameters that reflect design intent can be very time-consuming. Figure 9.45 on page 428 shows just a portion of the constraint parameter relations written for a sofa assembly. Savings are seen, however, through increased accuracy and automated updating of parts when component parts in an assembly are modified throughout the design cycle.

9.6.5 Completing the Feature Definition

With the sweep profile drawn and constrained, there remain a few more elements of the sweep which need to be defined. Depending on the modeler, some or all of these definitions may take place prior to or after the creation of the constrained profile.

One part of the sweep definition that still needs to be defined is how the profile is going to sweep out to create a form in 3-D space. When the lines of the profile are swept out from the workplane, the profile creates a surface or set of surfaces. If the profile were an open loop consisting of a single element, say a straight line, and the profile were swept in linear direction, the resulting sweep would define a plane (Figure 9.46A on page 429). If the profile were a closed loop, say a circle, then a linear sweep would create a cylinder (Figure 9.46B). Depending on how the profile is defined, rather than capping the ends of the cylinder, the profile lines might be *thickened* to create a tube instead (Figure 9.46C). This thickness option can be used with both open and closed profiles and is used to define sheet metal and other *thin features*.

The direction of the linear sweep relative to the workplane will create different sets of extruded surfaces (see Figure 9.46). While a sweep of a closed loop profile normal to the workplane will create a right prism, an angle other than 90 degrees to the workplane will create an

```
/* CODING TABLE   SESSION ID   MODEL NAME
/* CODING TABLE    0    RAIL_BK_SKIRT.PRT
/* CODING TABLE    6    RAIL_BACK.PRT
/* CODING TABLE    2    POST_BACK.PRT
/* CODING TABLE    4    POST_BACK_MIR.PRT
/* CODING TABLE    8    RAIL_SIDE_SKIRT.PRT
/* CODING TABLE   12    POST_FRONT.PRT
/* CODING TABLE   10    RAIL_SIDE.PRT
/* CODING TABLE   14    RAIL_SIDE_SKIRT_MIR.PRT
/* CODING TABLE   16    RAIL_SIDE_MIR.PRT
/* CODING TABLE   18    RAIL_FRT_SKIRT.PRT
/* CODING TABLE   20    RAIL_FRONT.PRT
/* CODING TABLE   22    STRETCHER.PRT
/* CODING TABLE   24    RAIL_TOP.PRT
/* CODING TABLE   26    SUPPORT_RAIL_TOP.PRT
/* CODING TABLE   30    ARM_LEFT.PRT
/* CODING TABLE   32    ARM_UNDER.PRT
/* CODING TABLE   28    STUMP.PRT
/* CODING TABLE   36    ARM_RIGHT.PRT
/* CODING TABLE   38    ARM_UNDER_MIR.PRT
/* CODING TABLE   34    RAIL_SIDE_MEDIAN.PRT
/* CODING TABLE
/* global variables
seat_l = 73.5
seat_h = 11
seat_d = 25
splay =5
bo = .5
rail_h = 8
back_a = 14
arm_l = 20
/*set back rail lengths to sofa length
L:0 = seat_l
L:6 = seat_l
/* set front rails to sofa length, splay, and seat depth
L:18 = L:0 + 2*(seat_d * tan(splay))  - 1.516
L:20 = L:0 + 2*(seat_d * tan(splay))  - 1.516
/* set splay cuts on side rails
CUT_ANG1:10 = splay
CUT_ANG1:8 = splay
CUT_ANG1:14 = splay
CUT_ANG1:16 = splay
/* set side rails to sofa depth
L:10 = seat_d / cos (splay)
L:8 = seat_d / cos (splay)
L:14 = seat_d / cos (splay)
L:16 = seat_d / cos (splay)
/* set back skirt rail height
BORE_OFF4_L:2 = seat_h - bo
BORE_OFF3_L:2 = BORE_OFF4_L:2 -(BORE_OFF2_W:0 -
BORE_OFF1_W:0)
ORE_OFF4_L:4 = BORE_OFF4_L:2
ORE_OFF3_L:4 = BORE_OFF3_L:2
/* set side skirt rail height
ORE_OFF1_W:8 = BORE_OFF1_W:0
ore_off2_w:8 = BORE_OFF2_W:0
ORE_OFF1_W:14 = BORE_OFF1_W:0
ore_off2_w:14 = BORE_OFF2_W:0
ORE_OFF1_L:12 = BORE_OFF1_W:0
ORE_OFF2_L:12 = BORE_OFF2_W:0
L:12 = seat_h
/* set back rail height
BORE_OFF2_L:2 = rail_h - bo
BORE_OFF1_L:2 = BORE_OFF2_L:2 -(BORE_OFF2_W:6 -
BORE_OFF1_W:6)
ORE_OFF2_L:4 = BORE_OFF2_L:2
ORE_OFF1_L:4 = BORE_OFF1_L:2
/*set side rail height
BORE_OFF1_W:10 = BORE_OFF1_W:6
bore_off2_w:10 = BORE_OFF2_W:6
BORE_OFF1_W:16 = BORE_OFF1_W:6
bore_off2_w:16 = BORE_OFF2_W:6
BORE_OFF3_L:12 = BORE_OFF1_L:2
BORE_OFF4_L:12 = BORE_OFF2_L:2
/* set stretcher bores, width, and length
BORE_OFF1_L:20 = BORE_OFF1_L:6
BORE_OFF3_W:20 = BORE_OFF3_W:6
BORE_OFF1_W:22 = BORE_OFF3_W:6
W:22 = W:6
L:22 = seat_d + 2.662
/* set top rail length, bores
L:24 = seat_l
BORE_OFF6_L:2 = (W:24 - 2*BORE_OFF1_W:24) +
BORE_OFF5_L:2
BORE_OFF5_L:4 = BORE_OFF5_L:2
BORE_OFF6_L:4 = BORE_OFF6_L:2


/* set top rail support length, angle, bores
suph = BORE_OFF3_W:2 - BORE_OFF2_W:2
supv = L:2 - BORE_OFF4_L:2 - BORE_OFF6_L:2 -
BORE_OFF1_W:0 - BORE_OFF1_W:24
sup_ang = atan( suph / supv)
CUT_ANG1:26 = 90 - sup_ang
L:26 = supv * cos(sup_ang)
/* set arm/back post join - cut angles
BACK_ANG:2 = back_a
BACK_ANG:4 = back_a
CUT_ANG1:30 = back_a
CUT_ANG1:32 = back_a
CUT_ANG2:30 = splay
CUT_ANG2:32 = splay
CUT_ANG1:36 = back_a
CUT_ANG1:38 = back_a
CUT_ANG2:36 = splay
CUT_ANG2:38 = splay
/* set arm/back post join - post bore heights
BORE_OFF11_L:2 = L:12 + L:28 - CUT1_L:28
BORE_OFF10_L:2 = BORE_OFF11_L:2 - (T:30/2 + W:32/2)
BORE_OFF11_L:4 = BORE_OFF11_L:2
BORE_OFF10_L:4 = BORE_OFF10_L:2
/* set arm/back post join - arm length
back_a_off =( (BORE_OFF11_L:2 - BACK_ANG_L:2) + T:30/2) *
tan(BACK_ANG:2)
BORE_OFF3_L:10 = L:10 - arm_l
CUT_OFF1_L:30 = back_a_off + arm_l - ( T:28/2)
L:34 = arm_l + 2.25
BORE_OFF3_L:16 = BORE_OFF3_L:10
CUT_OFF1_L:36 = CUT_OFF1_L:30
```

Figure 9.45

Dimensional constraints controlled through parametric equations

oblique prism. The only angle not allowed is zero degrees to the workplane. In addition to linear sweeps, sweeps can also be circular (revolved) (see Figure 9.31). With a circular sweep, an axis of rotation has to be defined. The location of this axis relative to the profile can greatly affect the resulting sweep. Figure 9.31A and B shows two different circular sweeps, each with a different placement for the axis of rotation. In addition, angular displacements of other than 360 degrees can be specified (Figure 9.31C). With both linear and circular sweeps, the sweep can be defined as *one-sided* or *two-sided*. With a one-sided sweep, the profile is swept out only one direction from the

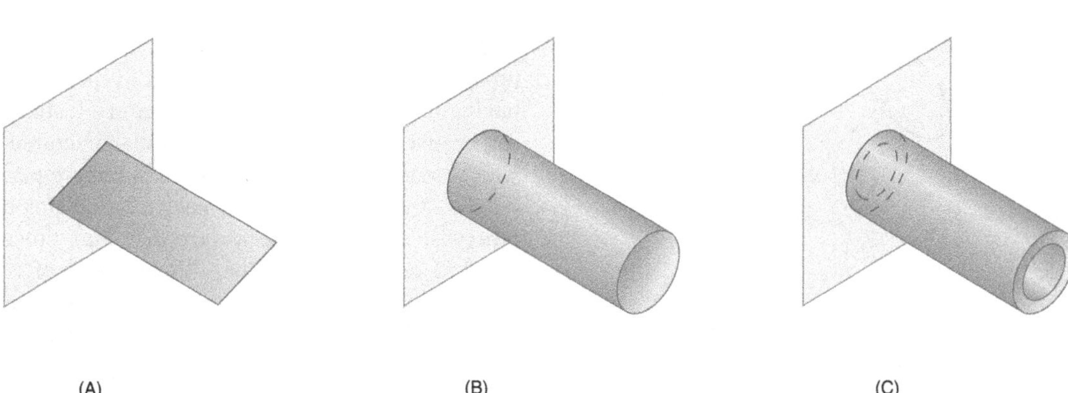

Figure 9.46

Thin versus solid features

Depending on how the profile is interpreted, either a thin or solid feature can be created from a profile.

workplane (Figure 9.47A). With a two-sided sweep, the profile is swept out both directions from the workplane (Figure 9.47B).

A less commonly used definition is a path-based sweep (Figure 9.48A on page 430). With a path-based sweep, the profile is swept along a path defined either by an existing edge on the part model or by a path drawn by the operator. If the operator draws the path, it will typically have to be sketched and constrained just as a profile would have to be. Finally, some systems will allow you to define multiple profiles on different workplanes. A swept form is then created by connecting surfaces between elements on the different profiles (Figure 9.48B). These blend sweeps typically have restrictions concerning the orientation of the profiles relative to each other, how they are ordered, and how elements on the different profiles are related to each other.

The distance that a profile is swept can be determined in a number of ways. A **blind** sweep indicates that a finite value is given for the sweep distance (Figure 9.49A on page 431). For a linear, one-sided sweep, this is a linear distance from the workplane to the end of the sweep. For a circular sweep, this distance is given as an angular displacement. For a two-sided sweep, the distance could be given for each side of the sweep separately, or one value could indicate the total distance of the sweep, evenly divided on either side of the workplane. The opposite of a finite (blind) sweep is an infinite through all sweep (Figure 9.49B). Sweep distances can also be specified relative to geometry on the part model. A **through next** sweep passes through the next *inside* region, but stops when it hits *outside* (Figure 9.49C). A **to next** (or to surface) sweep passes through an *outside* region, but stops when it hits *inside* (Figure 9.49D).

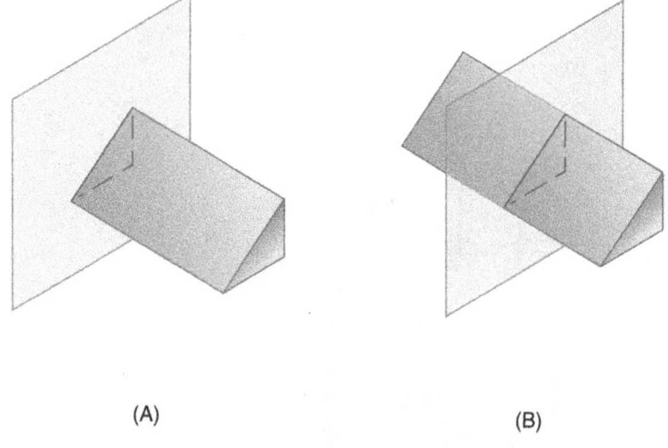

Figure 9.47

One-sided versus two-sided sweeps

A central element to all sweeping operations is defining how the swept form will interact with the existing part model. If the sweep is the first part geometry created, then it is the base feature and no operations have to be defined. All subsequent features have to either add or remove material from the model. If an open loop profile is going to remove material from the part model, then the *removal side* has to be defined (Figure 9.50 on page 431). An open loop profile which is not removing material will either be defined as a thin feature or will be attached to surfaces on the part model in a way which allows the new surfaces to form a closed form with the part (Figure 9.51 on page 432). A

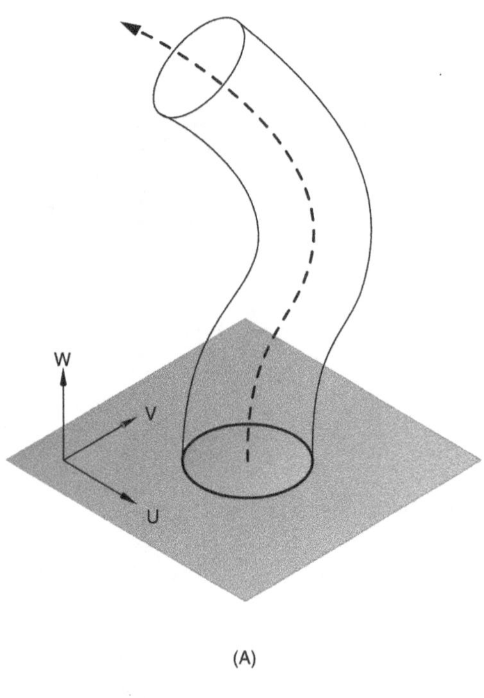

(A)

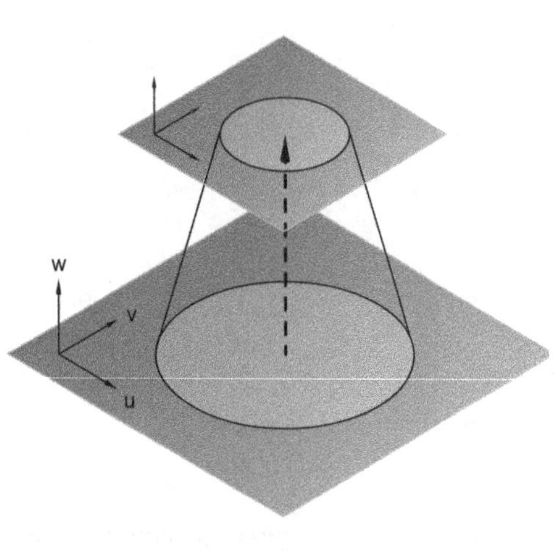

(B)

Figure 9.48

Advanced sweeping techniques

A path-based sweep moves the profile along a predefined curved path while a blend sweep interpolates between multiple profiles laid out in space.

closed profile clearly defines the inside and outside. When the profile is used for adding material, the addition is done on the inside of the profile. When the profile is used for subtracting material, the user has to specify whether the inside or outside is being removed (see Figure 9.38).

Most constraint-based modelers have tools that speed up the definition of commonly used features. Rather than having to define every variable of every feature, options can be given for common design or manufactured features which either have predefined certain feature parameters, bundled variables together in easy to use dialog boxes, or otherwise automated the feature definition process (Figure 9.52 on page 432). The ultimate goal, of course, is to make modeling a more efficient process more in tune with how designers and engineers actually work. Feature-based modeling bundles commands together to automate the process of creating and modifying features that represent common manufacturing operations. Usually implemented in modelers that also have constraint capabilities, feature-based modeling systems use special dialog boxes or other interface elements that allow users to input all of the variables needed to create a common manufactured feature.

Examples of manufactured features created through special feature-based dialog boxes include the following:

- Blind and through holes
- Counterbores and countersinks
- Slots
- Bosses

The hole dialog box shown in Figure 9.52 is a good example of automating the process of creating features in a model. The feature is broken down into its essential variables, with each variable represented by an input in the dialog box. Variables such as the hole's diameter have a value typed in, while the depth can be set to "through" by clicking a button or set to a finite value.

The variables entered through the dialog box largely define the shape and size. Once these variables of the feature are defined, the location is defined. A feature such as a blind hole is located by indicating its orientation to a face and distance from two edges (Figure 9.53 on page 432). In a constraint-based modeler, all of the variables of the feature—its shape, size, and location—are parametrically controlled and can be updated at any time. In addition, the parameters defining the feature can also be linked to other parameters defining the part. So, for example, the depth of a hole might be related to the overall thickness of the base part.

9.6.6 Feature Planning Strategies

Though it is impossible to come up with a definitive list of "rules" which should be followed when planning the modeling of every part, there are still certain characteristics of the part geometry that should be evaluated and

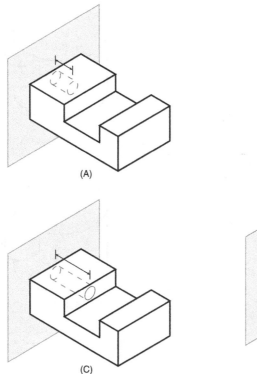

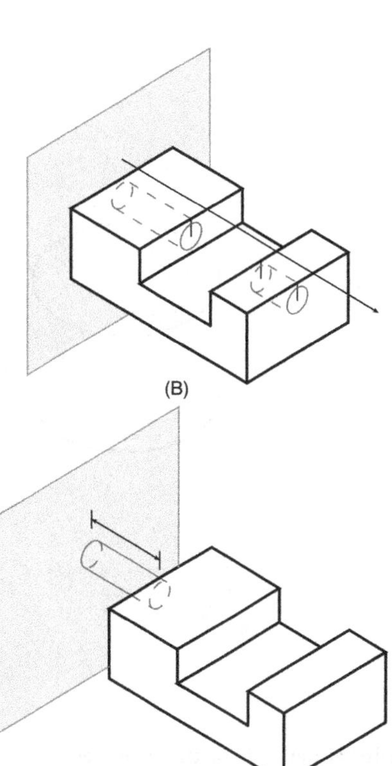

Figure 9.49

Defining sweep distance

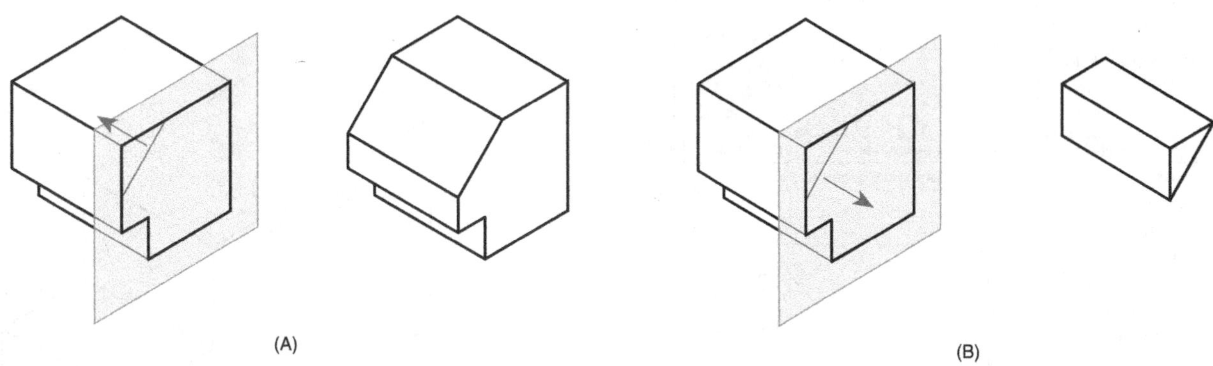

Figure 9.50

Determining the removal side of a sweep

Depending on which side of a profile is chosen, different material can be removed from the part.

decisions that have to be made for most parts during the planning process.

One of the more important considerations is whether the parts contain lines of symmetry. For example, the best way to leverage the symmetric aspects of the part depicted in Figure 9.54A and B (page 433) would be to construct the base feature with one of the datums along the line of symmetry. Not only will this assist in the construction of the base feature, but also it will allow mirror commands to be used to duplicate features across the plane of symmetry. Establishing this plane of symmetry, and tying many of the dimensional constraints to this plane, a design intent

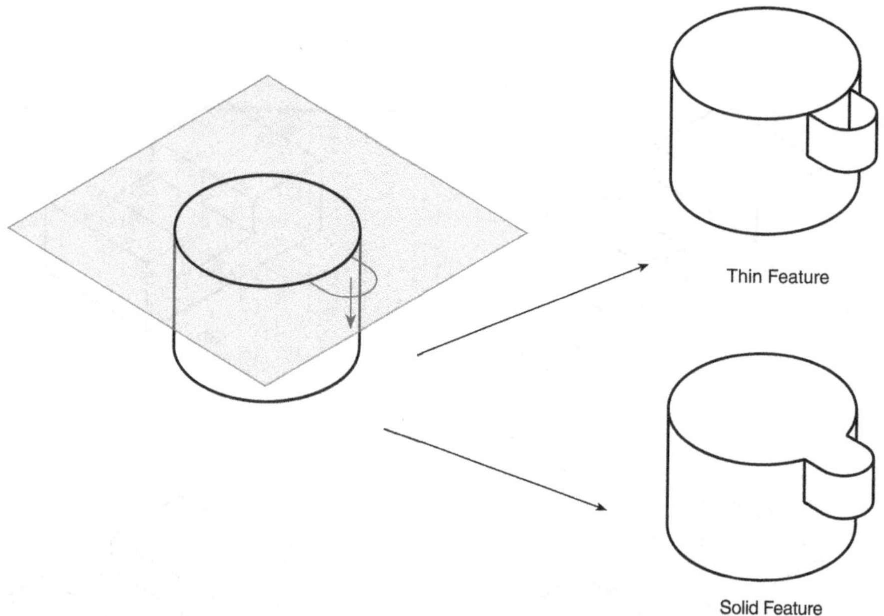

Figure 9.51

Open loops can define either solid or thin features

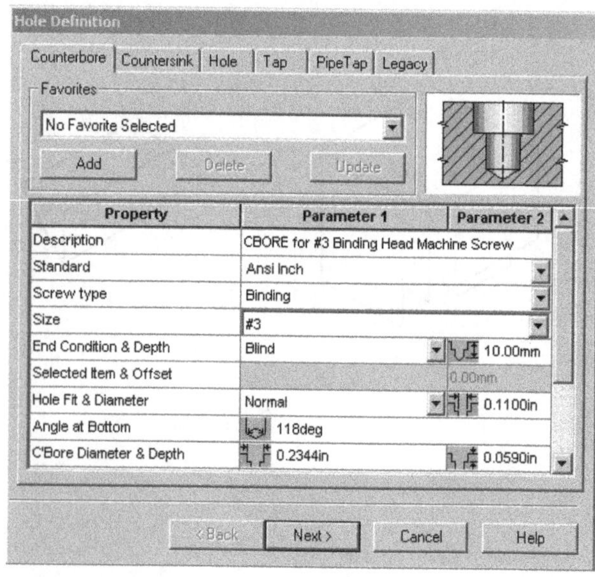

Figure 9.52

Example of a feature definition dialog box

The dialog contains all key parameters needed to define commonly used features, such as holes.

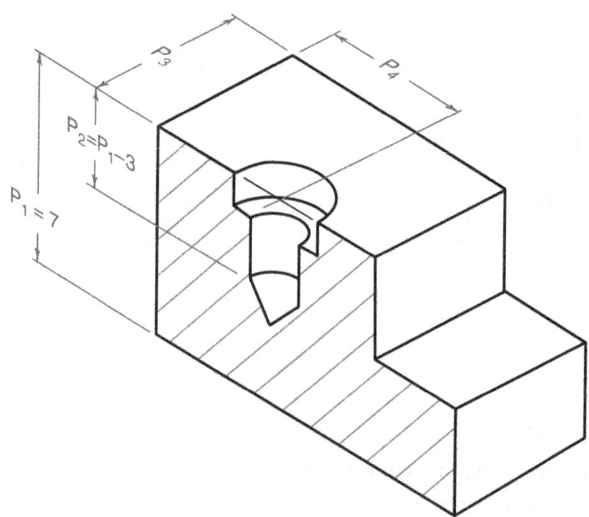

Figure 9.53

Locating a feature on the base part

Features such as this counterbore can also be defined relative to the existing part geometry.

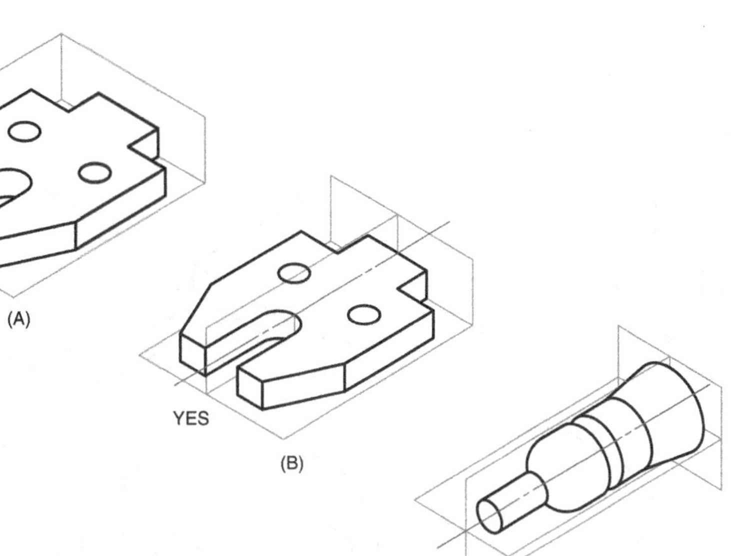

Figure 9.54

Using symmetry in feature definition

Construction planes can be used to help define symmetric features.

has been established that this plane of symmetry should be maintained as the part dimensions are modified. This plane of symmetry makes it easier to establish implicit and explicit constraints that preserve the symmetry of the part. With two-way symmetry, such as that seen in the turned shaft in Figure 9.54C, the base feature is established with its axis of rotation at the intersection of two datum planes. Again, this strategy makes it much easier to maintain a constant location for the axis as dimensions on the shaft are modified.

Another decision, which usually has to be made, is how geometric features are distributed across part features of the model. For example, the part seen in Figure 9.54A and B could be created with a single profile (Figure 9.55A on page 434) or it could be divided into a series of feature operations (Figure 9.55B). What would be the advantages or disadvantages of each approach? Generally speaking, the more complex the geometry is in a feature profile sketch, the harder it is to apply the desired implicit and explicit constraints. Also, geometry, which may not exist in all design variations of the part, should be broken out as separate features. This way, the features can be either suppressed or permanently deleted from the model with a minimum amount of disturbance to other feature profiles. On the other hand, there is no sense in needlessly decomposing geometry into the simplest possible profiles and thus creating an unnecessarily large number of features in the part. Large numbers of overly simplistic features can make management of the model difficult. Ultimately, the level of complexity of feature profile geometry comes down to what is a *logical* decomposition of the part geometry. (Refer to the modeling procedure in Section 9.5.) This logic is driven by how features are defined in the design and manufacturing process.

One way to logically decompose the geometry of a part is to divide features into *primary* and *detail* features. Primary features would define the overall functional form of the part while detail features would create geometry necessary for particular manufacturing process, fastener attachment, or tactile/visual qualities of the part. Whereas primary features might define the mass of a part within 10 percent of its final form, detail features might add fillets and rounds, through holes or mount points for assembly, or knurling on a surface. Generally speaking, you would want to create the primary features first with their constraints defined based on the larger functional design characteristics of the part. Detail features should be tied to either construction geometry located high (early) on the feature tree or to primary features.

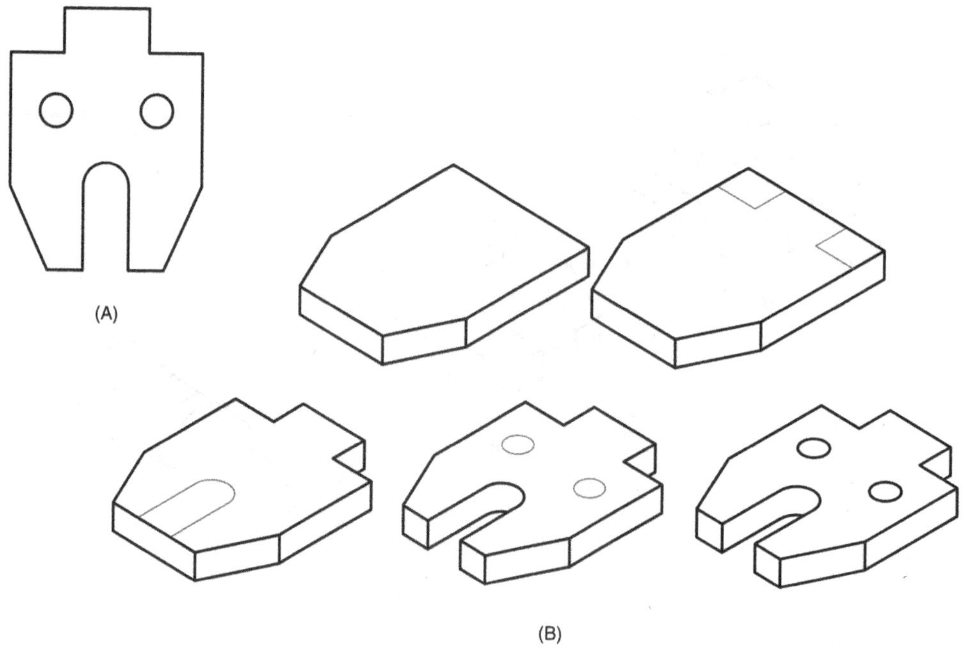

Figure 9.55

Geometric decomposition for features
How geometry is decomposed into features depends on an overall strategy for model use.

If detail features are tied to each other, then this should be done in a way that represents logical design or manufacturing groupings. For example, all of the fillets and rounds may be logically grouped together in the feature tree so that they can be easily suppressed as a group. The ability to turn detail feature "on and off" is important for some end uses of the model. For example, noncritical detail features may add considerable time to finite element analysis without adding noticeable improvement in accuracy. Similarly, unnecessary detail may bog down the refresh rates of large assemblies on the computer screen without adding appreciably to one's understanding of it.

Finally, good modeling practice calls for the user to avoid certain types of feature operation in order to preserve the integrity of the model geometry and to allow for easier management of the model. To begin with, a single feature should be created by a single feature operation, if at all possible. For example, the notch in Figure 9.56A could have easily been created with a single operation. Now two model features have to be manipulated to make changes in the logical geometric feature. At the other end, don't use a feature operation to create two logical parts when, in fact, the modeler still considers it one part model. Figure 9.56B shows an operation allowed by most modelers. This creates what looks to be two parts, but is in fact still one part model.

When creating geometry, the internal standards developed by your company need to be followed. Just as with 2-D CAD drawings, models made to standard will be easier, the value of the 3-D constraint based model increases considerably if it can be easily modified by anyone who needs to generate alternative designs from the model. Standards for modeling may include what geometry should be grouped together to define a feature, in what order should features be created, how the features should be linked together, and how automation features should be documented. Similarly, new or modified features that are added to an existing model should be equally well constructed and integrated so that the next operator who uses the model can also easily update it.

9.7 Editing Part Features

Once one or more features have been created on the model, the designer can go back and modify parameters used to define the features. The most common parame-

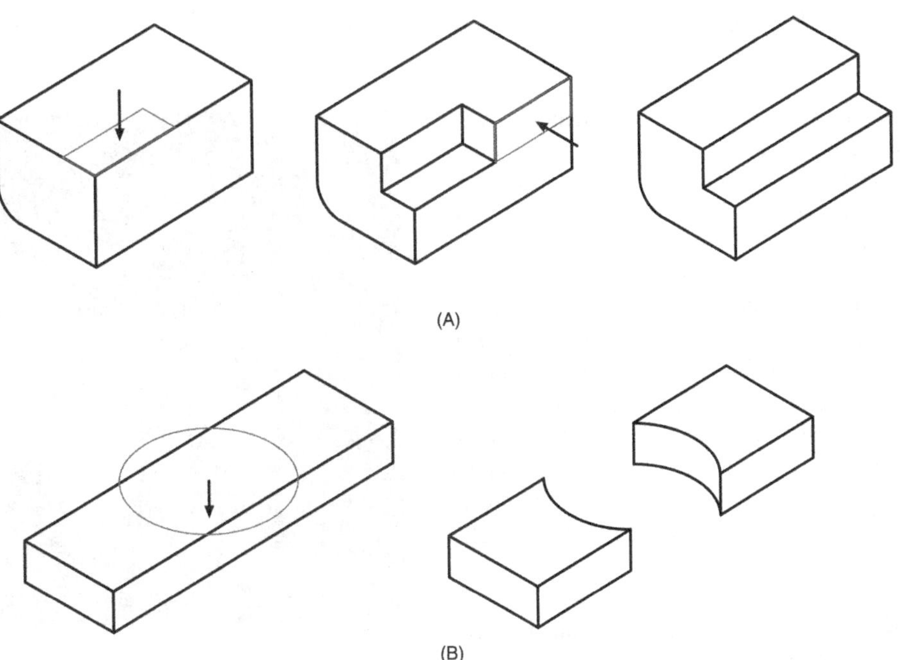

Figure 9.56

Examples of poor feature definition

ter to redefine is dimensional constraints. The dynamic nature of a constraint-based modeler makes it easy to modify the size, shape, and location of feature geometry on-the-fly. Constraint-based modelers were designed with the understanding that designing parts is a continual, ongoing process of modification.

The ability to successfully redefine a feature will depend, in part, on how sound the planning was that guided the development of the initial features. This section of the chapter will examine a few common elements related to the model-planning process. These items typically enable future editing of the model.

9.7.1 Understanding Feature Order

Most constraint-based modelers record the features created for a part in a *tree.* This tree may or may not be directly visible to the operator of the system. Many modelers have a window that depicts the features in a part model (Figure 9.57). Features, as they are created, are placed at the bottom of the feature tree. If a new feature is created as a copy or instance of another feature in the part model, the new feature on the tree may reference the original feature. Because features can be moved to other

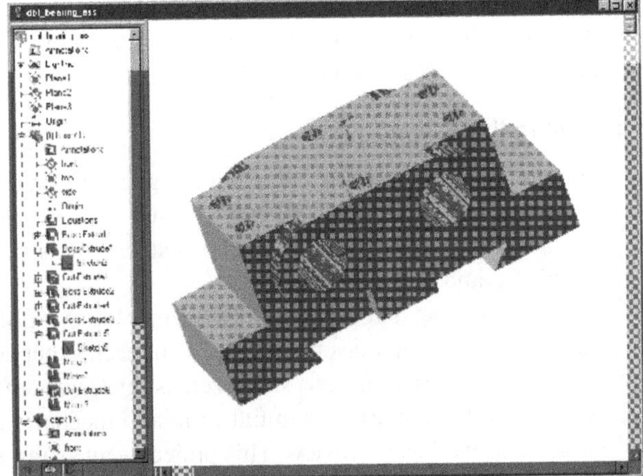

Figure 9.57

Example of a part feature tree

locations up and down the feature tree, the tree cannot be considered an exact *history* of feature creation. With many modelers, however, the order in the tree is the order in which features are applied to the construction of the model. Each time a new feature is added to the model,

Design in Industry

A Design with Heart

This case study presents the design of a medical device produced through collaboration with multiple companies. The medium for communication was the 3-D model, which was used for things such as design documentation and rapid prototyping.

On the whole, product designers enjoy their work—after all, it's fun to create a sleek new cover for an electronics device or an innovative children's toy. But their job gets even more satisfying when they're able to design something that makes the world a better place by saving lives. Such was the case for the designers at Strategix Vision, a product design and development company based in Bozeman, Montana, when they were asked to develop a device to make heart surgery safer and less invasive.

That device, the Embrace Heart Stabilizer, holds the heart and coronary artery in position during coronary bypass surgery, allowing a surgeon to bypass the blocked artery without having to stop the heart and maintain the patient on a heart-lung machine.

Strategix Vision developed the Embrace in conjunction with strategic product development company Herbst LaZar Bell, which provided human factors analysis and other design input, as well as with CardioVations, a division of Ethicon, a Johnson & Johnson company. The device is now marketed by CardioVations.

Laying the Groundwork

Strategix Vision employs industrial designers, mechanical and electrical engineers, and user researchers who work together to design and develop medical, industrial, scientific, and consumer products.

About a year before work on the Embrace even began, the two companies cooperated with each other on designs for a different heart stabilizer, using design software from SolidWorks for initial form and mechanical studies, as well as for review. This project went as far as the creation of working prototypes that were reviewed by cardio-thoracic surgeons.

New Kind of Heart Stabilizer

The impetus for the Embrace, according to Strategix Vision design engineering director Marty Albini, was to improve on an existing product by making it smaller and more ergonomic. "The idea was to free up some of the space it took up in the operating theater and reduce the effort it took [for surgeons] to operate. We also wanted to make the device more intuitive to use," he says.

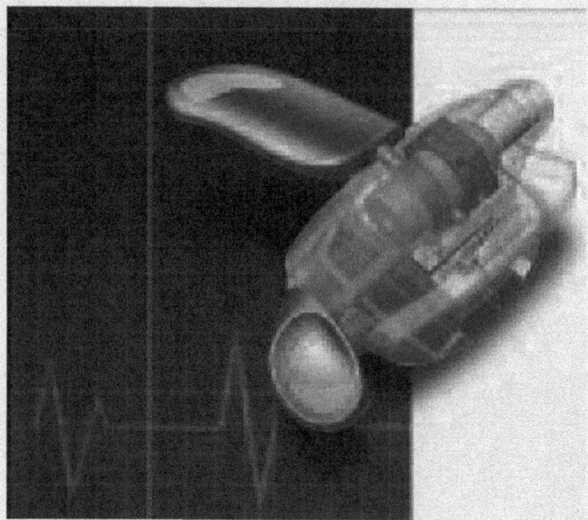

(Courtesy of Strategix Vision.)

Because both CardioVations and Strategix Vision are SolidWorks users, says Albini, their team members were able to share files to review and develop the design. For other proects, he notes, Strategix Vision often uses the e-drawings module of SolidWorks, which allows non-CAD experts to review and rotate models in 3-D without having to know the intricacies of the full SolidWorks package.

Whatever the project and whatever the package, says Svendseid, close collaboration is part of the Strategix Vision work ethic. "Designers work closely with the engineers in our company. We try to have an open structure where everyone can have an opinion, so we had many discussions around computers and projected images in order to set direction and quickly work through new ideas," says Swendseid. "The great thing about all the visualization tools we have at hand—from sketches to CAD—is that they allow us to understand each other in a common language. I don't know exactly how to be an engineer, but I can certainly understand what an en-

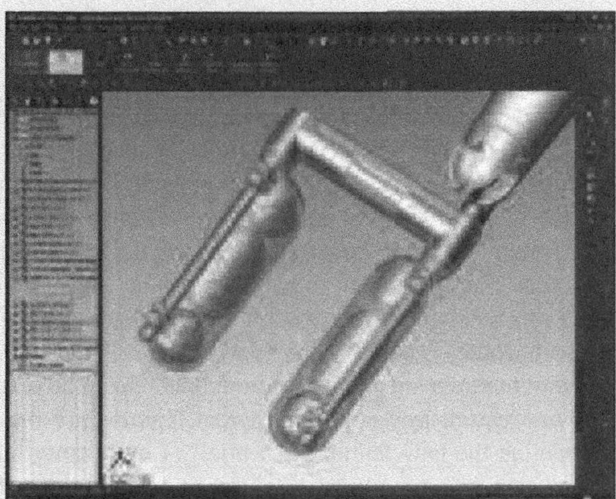

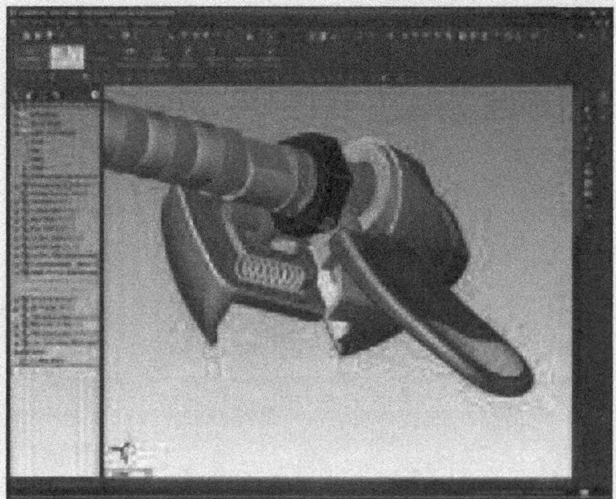

Both teams were experienced SolidWorks users, so designs and revisions for features such as the "toes" (left) that make contact with the heart could be reviewed in the same software. Levers and other controls (right) were designed to work as intuitively as possible. (Courtesy of Strategix Vision.)

gineer means and what that implies to a design when I can see it."

Meeting Challenges

Even with Strategix Vision's pre-established culture of collaboration, and even though the project was not radically different from the work the company typically performs, notes Swendseid, "the Embrace did present unique problems in ergonomics, mechanics, usability, and a specific user scenario." That last factor—the user scenario—involved a full understanding of who would be using the product, as well as how, and why. It is a vital ingredient of how designers "get it right" when creating products that people want to use.

After the design had progressed to the point of general approval, it was then tuned with rapid prototypes made in-house at Strategix Vision. "We use a variety of tools, including video projectors, to get a detailed view of what we're working on," explains Albini. "And there are some cool visualization tools that have emerged since the Embrace was designed that are helping us now as well, like RealView, a real-time texture-map visualization feature in SolidWorks that lets you dress up the models with realistic-looking surfaces." (RealView, says fielder Hiss, manager of product management for SolidWorks, was developed by SolidWorks in conjunction with Nvidia, and involves "almost photorealistic, real-time graphics." Designers can see the reflection of metal or the look of wood while they work, without having to wait for the file to render out.)

With or without such helpful eye candy, Albini says that at a certain juncture it's important for designers and potential users alike to have a physical prototype to hold.

Success

When surgeons saw one of the first Embrace units at a trade show and reacted extremely positively, the folks at Strategix Vision and CardioVations knew they had a success on their hands. This was confirmed by an IDEA award for the design from BusinessWeek magazine last year. The unit is now in production and in use.

"We can always be proud of our work as designers," says Albini, "but you can't fool someone who uses these things every day. If they like it, it's good. Product design is hard. There are always problems to solve, competing goals to balance, and late nights spent making it all work. A project like this makes all that worthwhile."

From Donelan, J., "A Design with Heart," *Computer Graphics World*, 30, 2007.

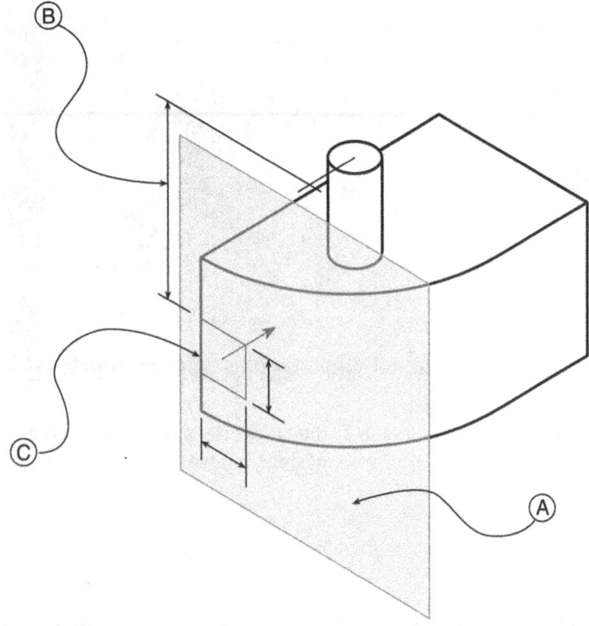

Figure 9.58

Feature interdependencies

Parent/child relationships are established when new features reference existing geometry.

the user explicitly rebuilds/regenerates the model, or the modeler is otherwise triggered to do a rebuild, the feature tree is traversed from top to bottom, building the part model through a succession of feature operations. Regeneration of a model's features also can occur when a feature has been modified, typically from that point in the model through each subsequent feature.

Closely related to the idea of feature ordering is the concept of parent-child relationships between features. As in a real parent-child relationship, the child feature is dependent on the existence of its parent feature. How is this dependency established? Every feature consists of constraints that both establish shape and size, but also locate it. Though all of the shape and size constraints may internally reference other elements of the feature profile, at least some of the location constraints must reference external features in order to locate it in 3-D space (Figure 9.58). This external referencing begins with the selection of a sketching plane. Whatever construction plane or model surface that is chosen as a sketch plane is considered a parent of the new feature. Whenever a profile sketch is located on the sketch plane by pulling a dimensional constraint from an edge on an existing feature, this feature now becomes a parent of the new feature. Similarly, if an element in a feature profile is constrained through overlap with an existing feature edge, that feature also becomes a parent of the new feature. It follows that parent features must exist before (above) the child feature in the feature tree since the parent features are needed to define the new feature. Essentially, any feature that is used as a reference to size, locate, or orient another feature would be considered as a parent feature during the feature creation process.

When creating a model, you must always be aware of feature dependencies, both when you create the model and when you edit it. Deleting a parent feature means that you must either also delete the child feature that depends on it or redefine the child feature so that it no longer depends on the feature to be deleted. Changing the geometry of a parent feature may also alter the geometry or location of the child feature. For example, if the top shaft in Figure 9.58 were lengthened, then the child feature would have to move up in order to keep the value of the dimensional constraint between them constant. Besides deleting a feature, changing the topology of a parent feature may also invalidate the child feature. The dependency with the parent feature is typically not to the parent feature as a whole but, rather, with specific geometry in the parent feature. If, in Figure 9.58, the edge of the parent feature that the child profile overlaps were to be rounded, then there would no longer be an edge to overlap with.

When planning the construction of your model, there are a number of items to consider to make sure that feature dependencies are used to your advantage. In general, create dependencies with existing features as early in (far up) the feature tree as is logical. Linking locational dimensional constraints or overlap constraints with the initial three datums or the base feature will mean that the deletion or modification of a later feature is unlikely to disturb the new feature. A corollary to this is create all the features which are likely to become parent features as early as possible.

In more complex models it may be neither possible nor wise to place all dependencies high up on the tree. Instead, dependencies may be linked based on the logical grouping of design or manufacturing features. For example, an injection molded part may require the creation of a geometrically complex fastening feature on the surface of the part.

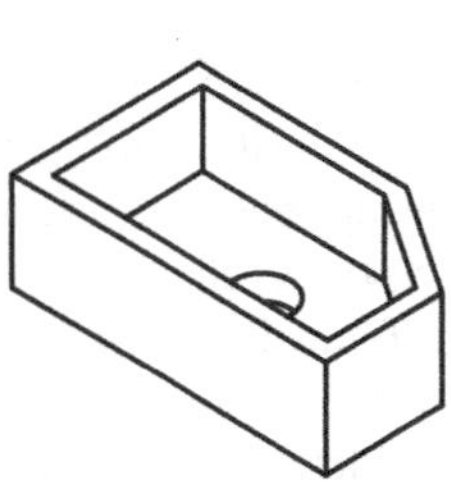

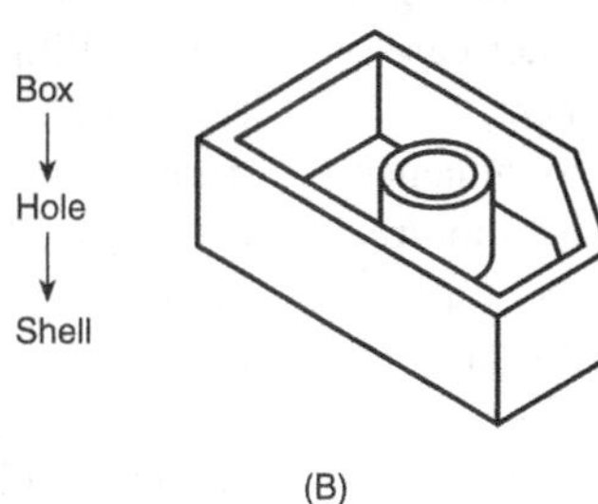

Figure 9.59

Feature ordering affects final geometry

The order in which features reside in the feature tree can affect the final part geometry.

Rather than trying to tie all the features of this fastener directly back to early features in the tree, a new datum plane and datum axis can be created from the original datums. From these new datums, a new *local* base feature is created from which other subfeatures of the fastener are made. With this setup, moving the new datums will move all of the features related to the fastener. Similarly, suppressing or deleting the new datums will also suppress/delete the fastener features without disturbing any other features.

Editing the order of features means moving features up or down in the feature tree. Dependencies between features means that features can't be moved to every possible position on the feature tree. Child features, for example, cannot be moved above any of their parent features on the tree. Prior to reordering any features, it is important to know the extent to which the feature in question is involved in parent-child relationships. Current CAD systems typically provide functionality, which allows a user to query the model for such information. The fewer parent features a child has, the more flexibility there is likely to be in moving the feature. Alternately, a feature can be redefined to change the parent feature, providing new possibilities for reordering features. Why would you want to reorder features? To begin with, you may be trying to more logically group features within the tree or you may be reordering as the result of deleting another feature. Reordering features also gives the operator a powerful tool for redefining the end resulting geometry of the model. Figure 9.59 shows a part with three model geometry features: a box, a shell, and a hole. When the features are created in this order, the sequence may look like that seen in Figure 9.59A. What happens when the hole operation happens before the shell operation? The end result is a very different model (Figure 9.59B).

9.7.2 Editing Feature Properties

In addition to changing the order of features within the feature tree, many of the parameters that initially defined the feature can be edited at a later time. If an error is made in defining a feature, it is often quicker to correct a feature parameter than it is to start the feature over from scratch. Since the sketch profile of a feature is considered a child of the plane on which it is defined, movement of the sketch plane—whether it is a construction plane or a face of another feature—will also move the sketch profile with it. Similarly, you may also be able to assign the sketch profile to another plane, creating an alternate parent-child relationship. Again, it is critical to examine the existing parent-child relationships before trying to alter them.

Within the sketch profile, elements of the profile can be deleted or modified. Typically, constraints associated with those deleted elements will also disappear. Alternately, all of the elements can be left alone, but the constraints associated with them altered. Explicit dimensional constraints are usually the easiest to delete and create, but implicit constraints can also be modified. In some cases an implicit constraint might simply be *suppressed,* allowing a new explicit constraint to take its place. In other cases, constraint elements, explicit constraint placement, or dimensional constraint values may be modified to influence what implicit constraints are applied at regeneration/rebuild. Probably the most common modification of a feature is the values associated with dimensional constraints. Often this type of modification is facilitated by special software interface elements since it is so common.

Other parameters besides the sketch profile can also be altered. The possible parameters that might be modifiable are:

- The type of sweep path
- The distance of the sweep
- Whether the sweep is one- or two-sided
- The direction of a one-sided sweep
- The side of the profile a removal operates on

Often the type of operation—removal or addition—cannot be changed. In addition, features that automate steps of the generalized sweep will have more limited options. For example, you probably can't change the circular profile in a Hole feature to a square, since in most CAD systems, the cross section of a Hole feature is always circular.

9.8 Duplicating Part Features

The ability to duplicate geometric elements is a powerful attribute of all CAD programs. Constraint-based modelers typically allow the user to duplicate geometry at the feature level. Often, the level of dependency between the original and newly copied feature can vary. At least initially, the topology of the profile will be the same as will the primary feature parameters such as direction and distance of the sweep and whether it is a material addition or removal operation. Whether all of the dimensional constraints are maintained between the parent and the child copy is often determined by the options chosen. For example, it may be that the size of a copied hole is independent of its parent hole. Locational constraints are often modified as part of the copying process. For a general copy, any of the following might be set independent of the parent feature:

- The value of locational constraints
- The model geometry to which locational constraints are attached
- The plane on which the feature profile resides

Often the copying process, especially if the copying involves the creation of more than one child, is automated to some degree. A common tool is an *array* (or pattern) option. With a **linear array** the parent feature is copied in one or two dimensions with specifications given for distances between copies and the total number of copies (Figure 9.60A). Alternately, a total number of copies might be specified along with a distance within which the copies are to be evenly distributed. With a **radial array**, an axis of revolution is specified along with a radius, angular displacement, and total number of copies (Figure 9.60B). Another common copying process is a **mirror**. In this case a mirror plane is specified along with features to be copied/mirrored. Often with a mirror copy, most of the constraints cannot be set independent of the parent feature since the design intent is to keep the child a mirror image of its parent. Moving the mirror plane, however, will alter the location of the child parts. The purpose of such duplication operations is to maintain design intent within the model. By capturing the desired geometry and topology of the parent feature, the engineer or designer is able to create a more efficient model in terms of downstream operations. Editing the model can also be faster and easier, provided the user is aware of the embedded parent/child references.

Sources of model data vary greatly from company to company and project to project. If the model is of a brand new design, then all the model data that exists may be rough sketches created by the modeler or another designer. If the company has recently switched over from a 2-D CAD system, then 2-D CAD drawings may be the source of model building data. In this case, you have accurate dimensional information, but often very little of the actual electronic data in the CAD file can be reused to create the model. If the company has switched 3-D modeling systems, then there may be an existing model, but it may be that little of the feature definition or constraint information can be carried over. The best situation, of course, is if you are able to reuse a model created in the same modeling system you are currently using.

The reuse of existing models is an important benefit to using a constraint-based modeler. Quite often, the time

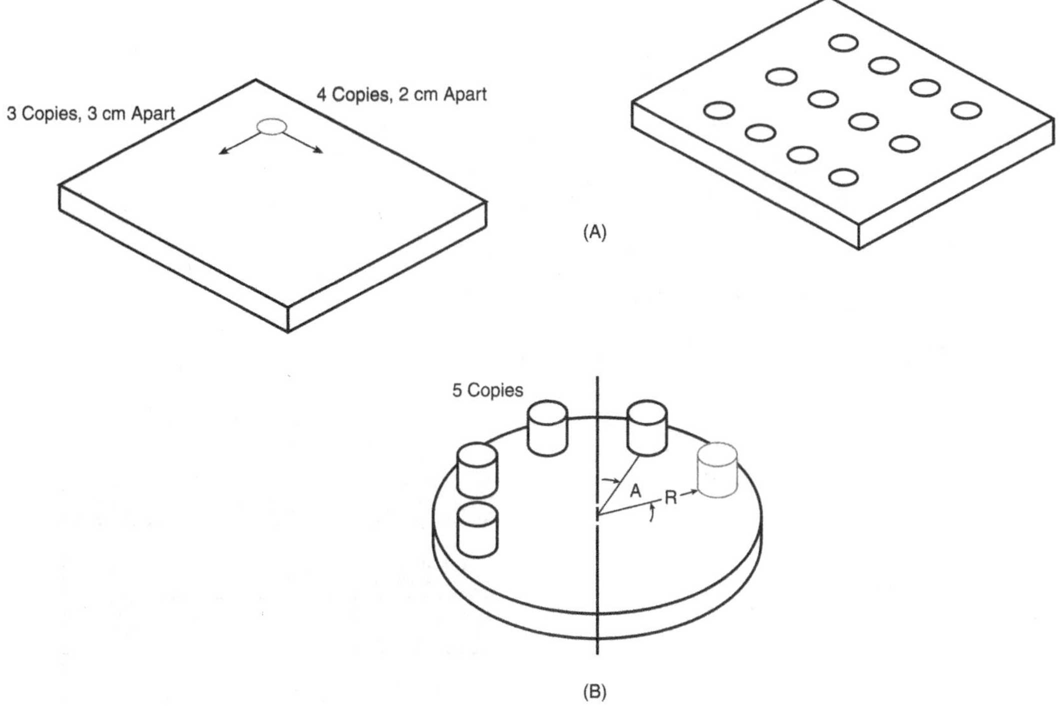

Figure 9.60

Linear and radial arrays

that it takes to build a model of the part from scratch is no quicker than it would be to create a set of 2-D CAD drawings of the part. If the model is constructed in such a way as to link dimensions of features together to automate modification of the model, then the time it takes to build the model increases. This time put into model construction will pay off only if you are able to create the model as a dynamic product data source, which provides a high degree of automation to the creation of alternative designs, This automation is not just within individual parts, but also between parts in an assembly.

9.9 Assembly Modeling

Rarely does a new or revised product consist of only a single part represented by a single solid. Most products consist of numerous parts (sometimes even hundreds or thousands). If a computer model of this product is to be constructed, facilities will be needed to coordinate the various parts of the model, as well as the different people assigned to develop those parts. Full integration of the design team and the 3-D computer model demands a database and a modeler that can keep track of many parts at many levels of design development.

Nonhierarchical Organization Most 2-D CAD systems support the concept of layers. **Layering** is a facility that allows the various graphics elements of a drawing to be grouped together in the database. This facility is used most often to control what is seen and/or editable on the screen and what is printed or plotted. Layering in most systems is *nonhierarchical;* that is, no one layer has precedence over another.

Hierarchical Organization Often, groups of objects must be brought into assemblies (Figure 9.61 on page 442). Such assemblies usually reflect the grouping of elements in the final product. For example, solids representing nuts and bolts might be grouped together in a hardware assembly. The most natural way to create these assemblies uses a **hierarchical** approach in which the real relationships of parts in an assembly are reflected. In the example, the hardware assembly would be a subassembly of the final product.

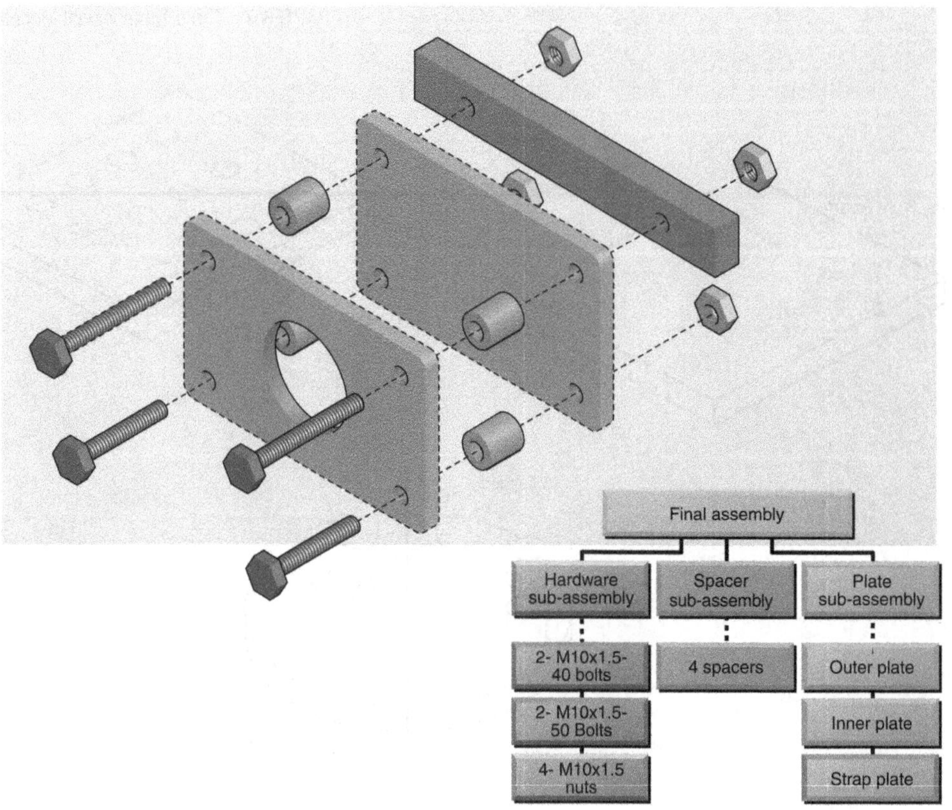

Figure 9.61

Hierarchical parts structure of an assembly

An assembly usually consists of a hierarchy of parts, some of them brought in as multiple instances.

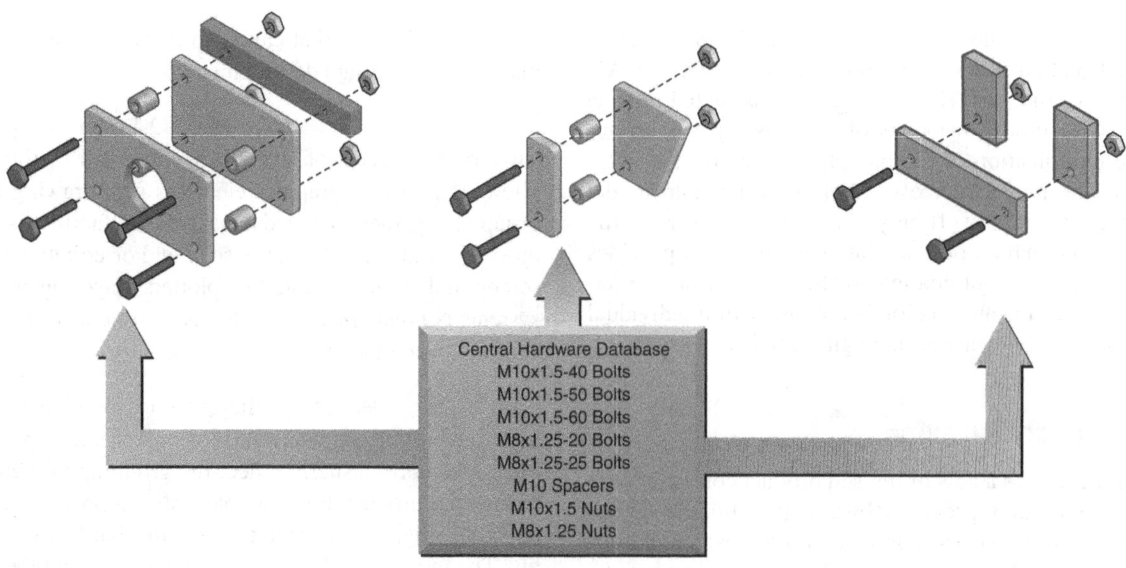

Figure 9.62

Shared common parts

Standard components can be instanced and shared across multiple assemblies.

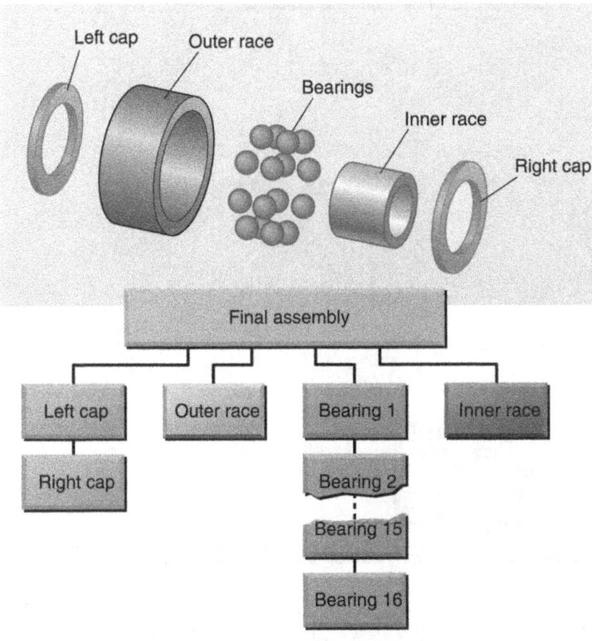

Figure 9.63

Creating a bearing assembly using instancing
Assemblies can contain single or multiple instances of objects.

Networked Hierarchical Organization The use of standardized parts to improve manufacturing efficiency is a technique that goes back to the 19th century. To assist this manufacturing goal, 3-D modeling systems must share common parts, both within an assembly and with other assemblies. This sharing across assemblies constitutes a **networked hierarchy** (Figure 9.62) in which parts exist in several hierarchical trees. The basic geometries of standard parts are stored in a central database and are never changed. When a variation on a standard part is needed, the geometry is copied, and the *copy* is modified.

A solid model can be shared in multiple **instances** in a model, where an instance shows the same form at new locations/orientations but does not duplicate the object in the database (Figure 9.63). Each instance has a unique name, location, and orientation. The information also contains a database address where the common geometry and topology shared by a group of instances is found.

This approach is considerably more efficient than duplicating the object four times. If the shape of the original object changes, all instances can be automatically updated. Most systems allow instances to be grouped together into assemblies. An assembly may be a group of instances made from the same solid, but more typically it is made of instances from different solids (Figure 9.63). In addition, assemblies can also bring in instances of other assemblies as a subassembly. A final assembly is made by gathering the appropriate number of instances of all of the solid parts. This way, all the parts of the assembly can be manipulated and loaded into the system as a group or individually.

The assembly of parts into larger models uses many of the same techniques and concepts used in part modeling. In an assembly model, **components** are brought together to define a larger, more complex product representation. A component is either a part or another assembly brought into an assembly model and associated with other components (Figure 9.62). Assemblies, when brought in as components, are now considered subassemblies in the new larger assembly. These subassemblies, in turn, are made up of components themselves. Any assembly can be thought of as a hierarchy of subassemblies and/or parts and can be represented in a *tree structure* much like the features in a part. A part or subassembly can be brought in multiple times to an assembly, creating multiple *instances* of the component (Figure 9.64 on page 444). Instancing of components does not add appreciably to the size of the assembly model since all of the instances refer back to a single part model (or part models of a subassembly). The same part or subassembly also can be used across multiple assembly models. Common hardware, fasteners, and other parts used in multiple designs by a company can be kept in networked component repositories for use by engineers and designers all over the company (Figure 9.62). Care is needed to manage this repository since change in a part here may affect multiple assemblies referencing it.

Constructing an assembly begins with bringing in a *base component.* As with the construction of a base feature in a part, a base component usually will be selected because of its central role in defining the overall assembly. Each successive component brought in needs to be oriented and located relative to other components in the assembly. Location and orientation is achieved by defining geometric relations between geometric elements of a component in the assembly and the elements of components being brought in. These elements may be part model geometry or construction geometry associated with the component. Directionality of the geometric elements is often as issue in orienting the new component. A face on a part model will have an *outside* and *inside,* often with the positive direction defined with a vector on the outside surface pointing away from the model. Construction planes do not have a natural inside and outside, so the directional vector usually has to be defined on the

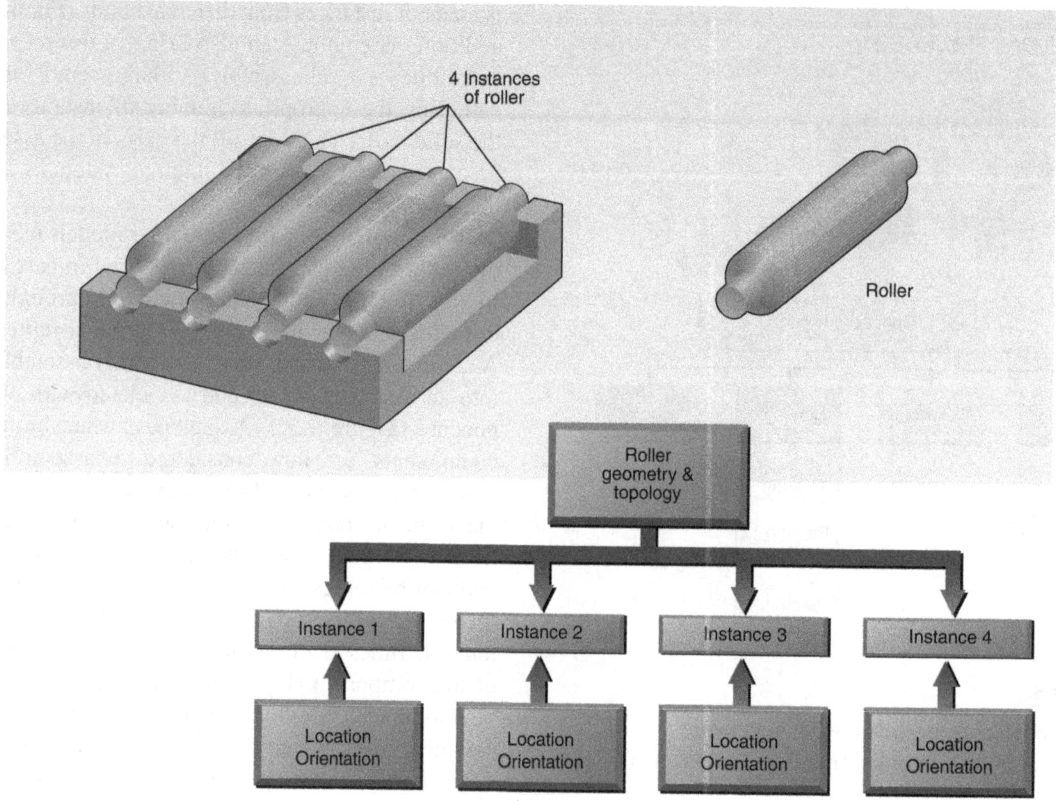

Figure 9.64

Creating multiple instances of a roller

Part components can be instanced multiple times in an assembly to help with management.

fly. Edges on the part models and construction axes may or may not have directionality to them. Coordinate systems, both global and local, can also be used to orient and locate components.

Defining these geometric relations primarily is done with two basic tools (Figure 9.65).

- Mate. Two part surfaces/construction planes are set coplanar with the directional vectors opposing each other.
- Align. Two part surfaces/construction planes are set coplanar with the directional vectors pointing the same direction. Alternately, two edges/construction axes are set collinear.

A modifier for both mate and align is *offset,* where an offset distance for surfaces is defined. The surfaces continue to be parallel to each other. In addition to mate and align, there may also be tools to define:

- Parallelism (without specifying distance)
- Tangency
- Perpendicularity
- Surface intersecting an edge/axis
- Edge/axis intersecting a point/vertex
- Angles of surfaces/planes to each other
- Relationship of geometry to a coordinate system

The assembly modeler also may allow the creation of construction geometry or coordinate systems on the fly as components within the assembly to help with the construction process. Establishment of these geometric relations between components creates parent-child relationships between the existing components and the new components coming in. Operators want to heed the same strategic principles in establishing parent-child relationships between components in an assembly as they did with features in a part model.

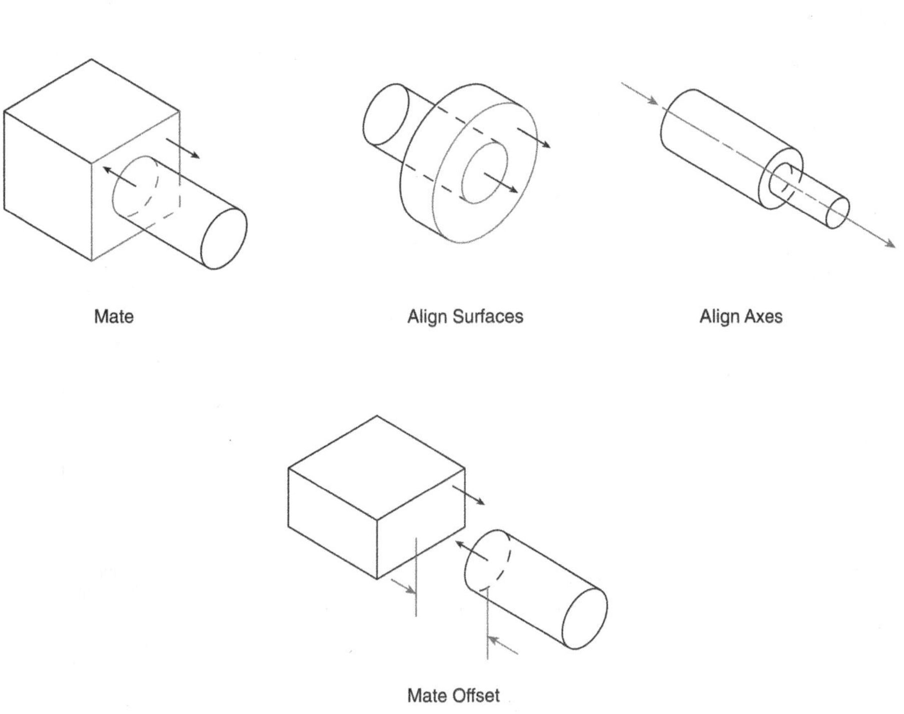

Figure 9.65

Methods for joining parts in an assembly

Mating and aligning are the most common methods for relating parts to each other in an assembly.

An assembly modeler tracks the relationship between components through *degrees of freedom.* The establishment of each geometric relationship between two components reduces the degrees of freedom components have to move relative to one another. Degrees of freedom are either rotational or linear, with a fully free 3-D part having six degrees of freedom: three rotational and three linear. When component parts have Zero degrees of freedom relative to each other, they are considered *fixed.* Figure 9.66 on page 446 shows the process of restricting the degrees of freedom of two component parts. Depending on the modeler, component parts may or may not be allowed to be left with degrees of freedom. If the assembly model is going to be used in kinematic or dynamic analysis, then degrees of freedom representing how the component parts are actually going to move in the assembly will need to be represented in the model.

Just as there often are limited ways in which part models can be modified within drawings, part models often can be modified within assembly models too. If the assembly modeler has bidirectional associativity with the part modeler, then dimensional constraints on parts can be modified in the assembly with the results reflected in both the assembly model and the individual part model. Simply typing in a new number can make modifications to constraint values through parametric equations. Just as equations can be used to link constraints across features in a part, equations also can be used to link constraints across part models in an assembly. These *assembly-level equations* must reference both a constraint parameter and the part that the constraint is associated with. This technique can be an extremely powerful tool to make sure that interacting features across parts—such as pins, holes, notches, etc.—continue to stay aligned and the proper size.

A particularly useful tool found in many assembly modelers is the ability to remove material from a component part, not with a feature operation, but with geometry from another component. For example, a Boolean subtraction operation can be performed between two parts in an assembly with the resultant material removal being represented as a new feature on the part. This can be a valuable technique for modifying a part to conform to a particularly complex fit in an assembly. Note that because of the dynamic associativity between part and assembly, the modified part now will be dependent on both the other part and the assembly model to define the new feature.

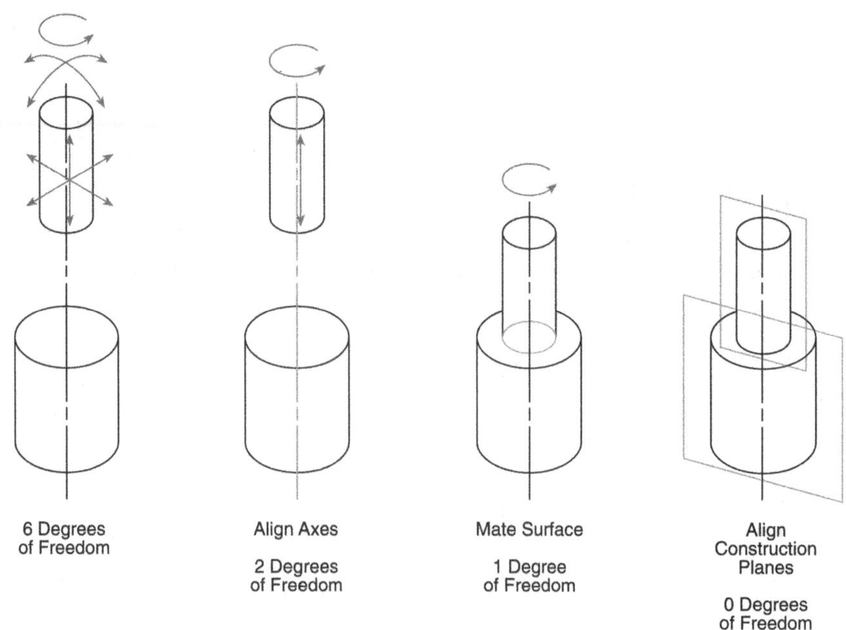

Figure 9.66

Degrees of freedom between components in an assembly

Modification of dimensional constraints and performing geometry removal within the assembly modeler are both examples of **top-down design**, where the final geometry of the parts has not been defined before bringing them in as components within the assembly. Often, assemblies are the best place to evaluate design goals for a product, so the final geometry of a part may not be decided until it is fit with other parts in their near-final configuration. The reverse of this approach would be **bottom-up design**, where all of the part geometry is defined before it is brought into an assembly. Though it may be possible to model parts from scratch within the assembly modeler, most part design uses a combination of both top-down and bottom-up design. Basic geometry for a part is established first; then it is brought into an assembly where it can be further refined, as necessary.

Just as individual parts can be documented, assemblies can also be brought into the document module of a modeler. The same techniques used to bring in a single piece are used for the assembly. As is the case with more traditional engineering drawing practices, what views are used and how they are notated is often different for an assembly than it is for individual parts. One additional tool that is very useful when documenting assemblies is the ability to create an **exploded view**. Often a default exploded view can be created automatically by having the model components move away from each other along the lines of the geometric constraints applied in the assembly. The location and orientation of the parts then can be adjusted to create a more optimal view. Flow lines then can be added between the part components. In addition to exploded views, tools to create bills of materials and to attach part codes with balloons and leaders are also standard in most document models. More information on paper notation of documentation can be found in Chapter 20.

9.10 Geometric Transformations

Solids can be modified in several ways. **Geometric transformations** include (Figure 9.67):

Translation—moving the solid linearly from one location to another along an axis.
Scaling—reducing or enlarging the object.
Shearing—moving selected vertices linearly along an axis.
Rotation—rotating the solid about an axis.
Reflection—transforming the solid into a mirror image across an axis.

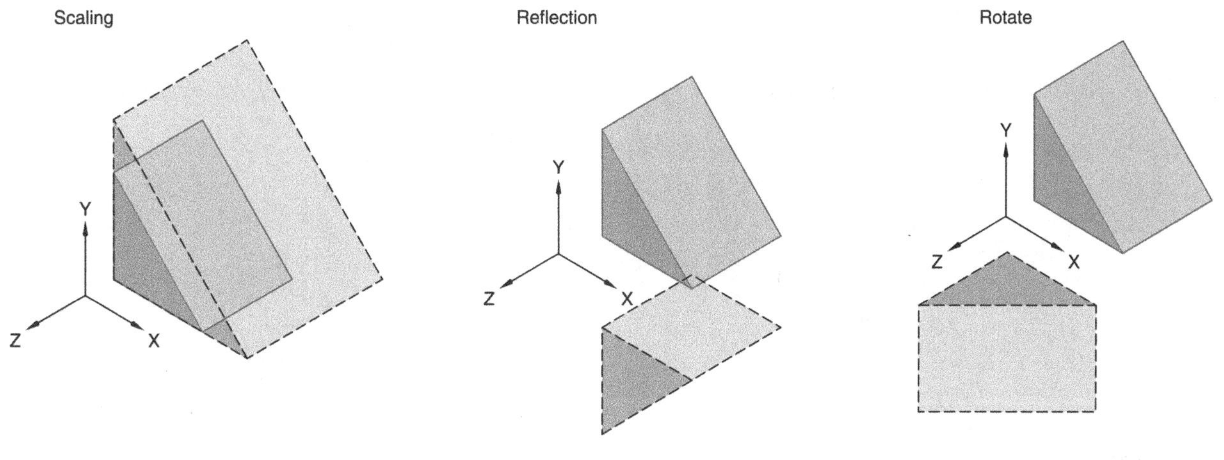

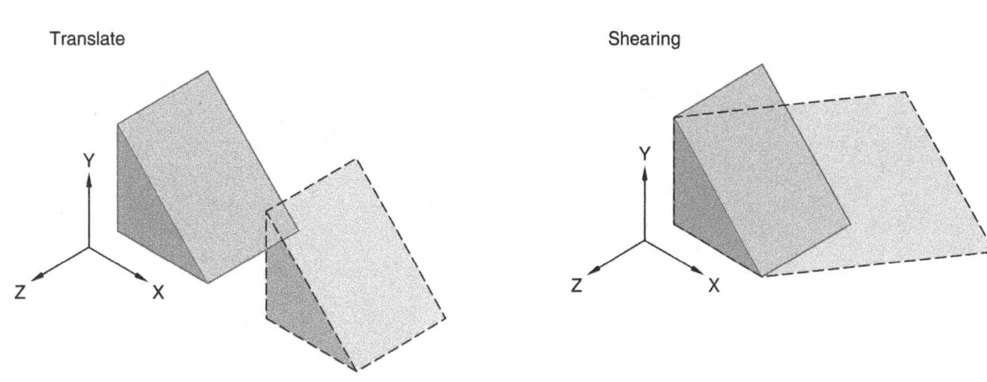

Figure 9.67

Common geometric transformations

Transformations can modify the location, orientation, or shape of an object.

Reflection, translation, and rotation are **rigid-body transformations**; they do not distort the shape of the solid. Scaling can be applied uniformly or nonuniformly to the three dimensions of the solid. If applied nonuniformly, face distortion will occur, but the edges will remain parallel. With shearing, distortion of some faces occurs, but parallelism is still preserved.

Of all the transformations, translation and rotation are the most important. Both play a central role in the creation and modification of solids. They are used for the two most common sweeping functions, linear and revolute, and for changing the viewpoint of a view camera.

Translations can be specified in terms of either *absolute* or *relative coordinates* (Figure 9.68 on page 448). For an absolute coordinates move, *from* and *to* coordinates are given. Alternatively, relative coordinates can be used to express the total move as a single coordinate change. A coordinate indicating a translation is a vector or axis whose size and orientation reflect the change in coordinate values.

A rotation is specified in terms of an axis of rotation and a degree of rotation. Although a primary axis, such as X or Y, can be used as the axis of rotation, this is the exception rather than the rule. Rotational transformations are more sensitive than translations to the location of the axis. The location of the axis of rotation relative to the solid markedly influences the resulting location of the solid (Figure 9.69 on page 448). The amount of rotation is

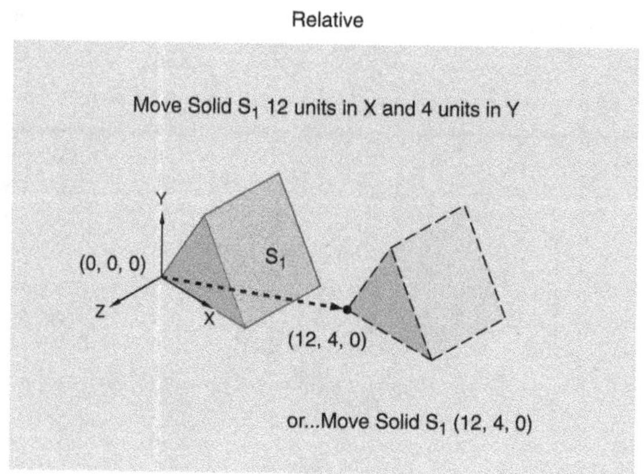

Figure 9.68

Absolute and relative translation transformations

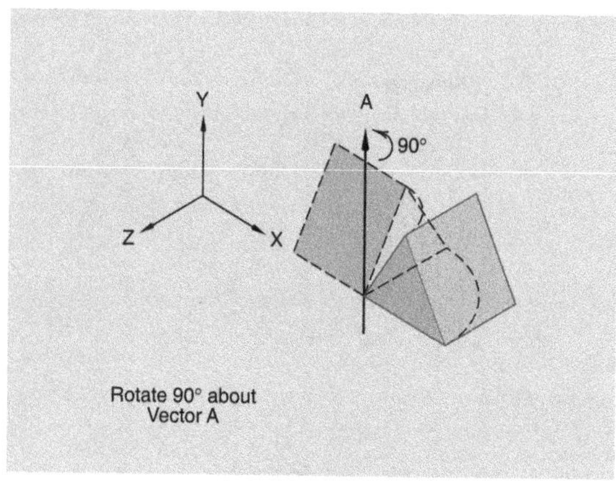

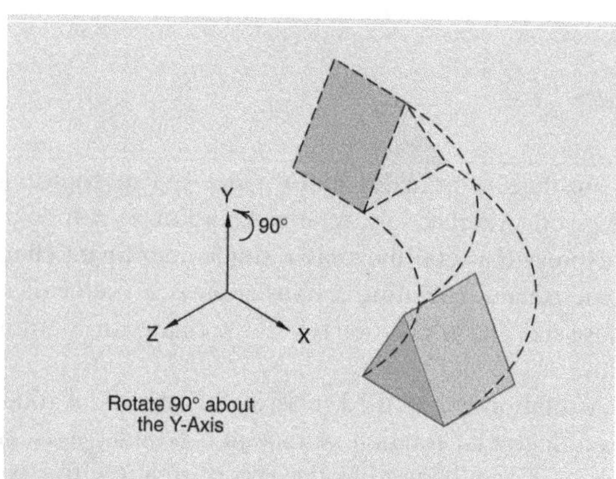

Figure 9.69

Effect of axis location on rotation transformations

Unlike translation operations, rotations are sensitive to both the orientation and location of the axis.

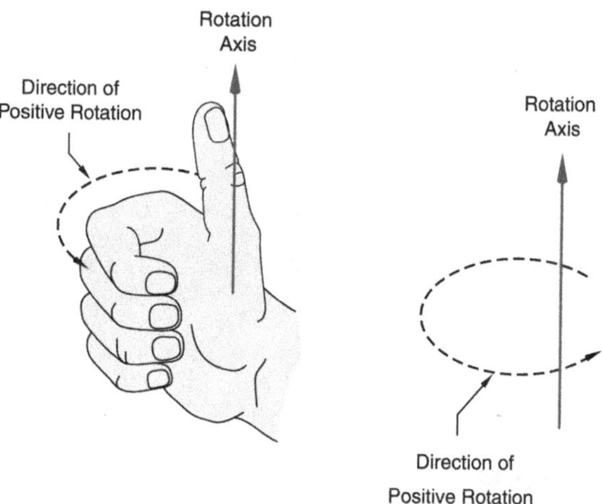

Figure 9.70

Right-hand rule

The direction of the axis specifies the direction of positive rotation.

specified as a scalar value (i.e., number of degrees), and on most systems, the direction of rotation is specified using the *righthand rule* (Figure 9.70).

An important distinction between translation and rotation is their effects on the geometric values for the solid. Translation changes the location of the solid; all of the vertices of the solid move the same amount. However, the orientation of the solid remains unchanged. With rotation, both location and orientation are affected. Because rotation is a rigid-body transformation, change in orientation is applied uniformly to all faces. However, the change in location of individual vertices depends on the position of the rotational axis. Figure 9.69 shows an example of how locational change can be affected by rotational axis placement. The closer the rotational axis is to the solid, the smaller the locational change of any given vertex. In fact, any vertex that is on the rotational axis (notice the one that lies on vector A) will not change location.

Another difference between the two transformations is that, with translation, any move with an absolute value greater than zero will change the location of the entire solid; with rotation, some values—360 degrees, for example—will result in no change to the solid, no matter where the rotational axis is placed.

All of the transformations can be specified through declarative statements indicating specific coordinates in space, features on the solid, or construction geometry. For example, for a translation, the *from* coordinate can be an existing vertex on the solid, and the *to* coordinate can be either a feature on a solid or a construction point in space. Indirect, procedural commands can also be used in some situations, depending in part on the flexibility of the system and the sensitivity of the transformation to absolute position specifications. For example, a command such as, "Have face F_1 of solid S_1 adjoin face F_2 of solid S_2," may be possible and may involve a combination of translational and rotational transformations.

9.11 3-D Viewing Techniques

The techniques used for viewing 3-D models are based on the principles of projection theory described earlier in this text. (See Chapter 7.) The computer screen, like a sheet of paper, is two-dimensional. Therefore, 3-D forms must be projected into 2-D. For review, the primary elements in creating a projection are the *model* (object), the *viewer,* and an *image (view) plane* (Figure 9.71). A coordinate system is attached to each of these elements and is used to define the spatial relationship between the elements. The world and any associated local coordinate systems define the model. The viewing coordinate system also has three axes, which are defined by the viewer's orientation in space: vertical, horizontal, and depth. Even though it would be convenient to associate the computer screen with the image plane coordinate system, that could lead to incorrect assumptions. Therefore, it is best at this time to imagine a 2-D plane in 3-D space, similar to a workplane.

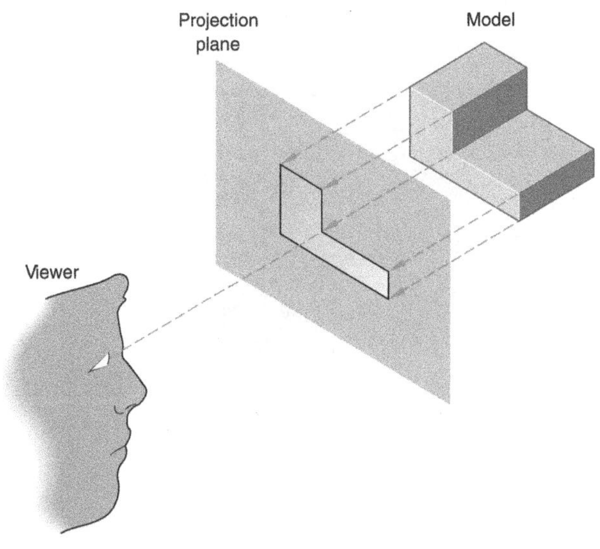

Figure 9.71

Elements of a projection system

9.11.1 The View Camera

The **view camera** is a metaphor used to describe the viewing process with respect to 3-D models in various CAD systems. Some systems support more than one view of the model at a time. For each view, there is a camera, and there is an image plane onto which the model is projected (Figure 9.72 on page 450). The camera records the image on the plane and broadcasts that image to the computer screen. The broadcasted image is contained within a viewport on the screen, and viewports may be resizable and relocatable or fixed, depending on the system. In addition, the limit to the number of active viewports, and therefore the number of cameras active at one time, also varies.

In nearly all cases, the image plane is oriented such that the viewing direction is perpendicular to the image plane, creating an orthographic projection. For the most part, oblique projections are not allowable with 3-D modeling systems. The vertical axis of the camera is also usually fixed relative to viewplane. Rotating the camera such that the vertical axis is no longer "up" also rotates the view in the port. Rotating the vertical axis 90 degrees would be like picking up your television set and turning it on its side. This is not how you normally perceive objects in space and it is therefore only done for special effects.

View cameras are used during model construction, as well as after the model is built. Active workplanes can be attached to the viewplane of the camera so that what you

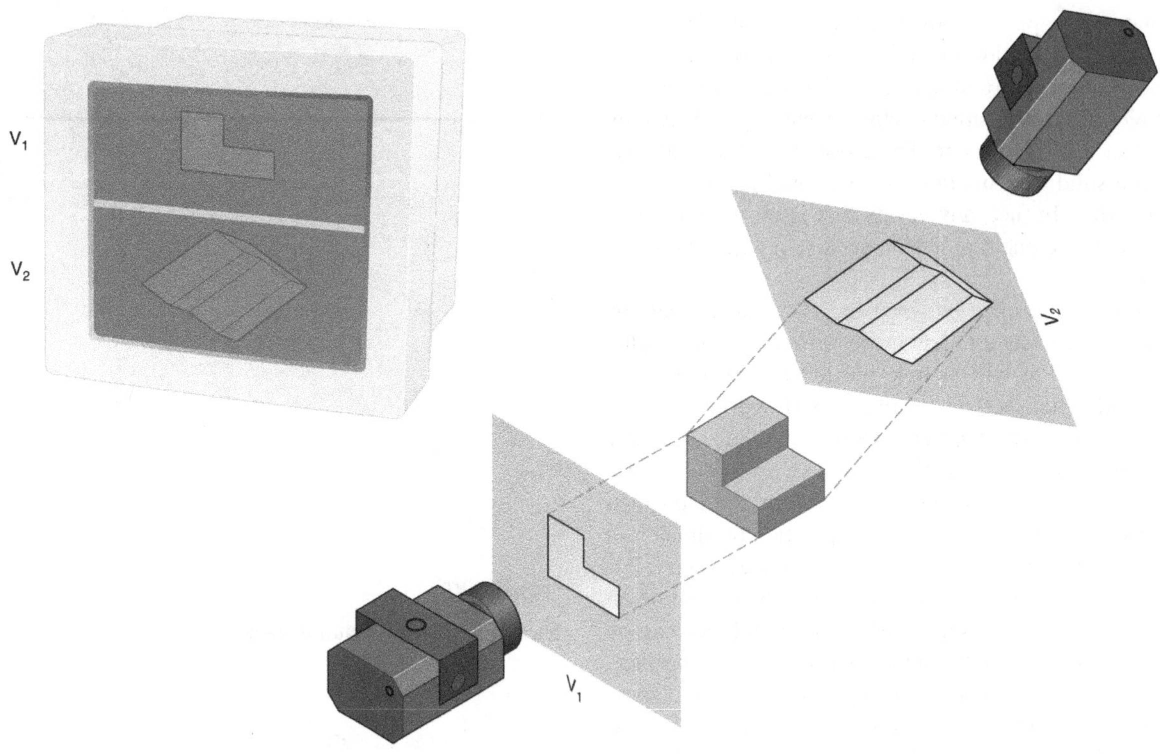

Figure 9.72

The view camera

The view camera captures a projection of the model on the image plane.

draw is seen on the screen port without distortion. With this arrangement, the u and v axes of the workplane correspond to the horizontal and vertical axes of the screen viewport, respectively (Figure 9.73). Each active workplane has its own local u,v coordinate system and its own orientation to the X, Y, Z world coordinate system. Ideally, the w axis of the workplane, the depth axis of the view camera, and an axis perpendicular to the screen are all kept parallel. This is an intuitive alignment that eases the difficult job of maneuvering in 3-D space.

The orientation of any particular view camera with respect to the world coordinate system can vary considerably during the course of model building. This lack of fixed orientation can often be disconcerting. The fact that view cameras are moving all around the model while you are firmly seated in front of the computer screen also contributes to the disorientation. If the camera is rotated in one direction about a model, the object itself appears to rotate in the opposite direction on the screen. An important distinction must be made between the two actions. If you rotate the model, its orientation to the world coordinate system changes, as will its geometry in the database. If you move the view camera, however, the camera has changed location relative to the world system, but the geometry of the model has remained untouched. Preserving the location and orientation of a model can be critical when multiple parts in an assembly are being coordinated. To get a new view of a part, rotate the camera and not the part.

9.11.2 View Camera Operation

Once a view camera has been oriented and a projection calculated, a number of auxiliary commands can be used to manipulate the view of the model (Figure 9.74). When a view is calculated, the projection of the model is stored in a buffer, and any change in the view that does not change the viewing direction can be done quickly and efficiently. Such commands include zoom in, zoom out, and pan, which can be done faster than, say, rotating the view about the object.

Most systems also default to setting the view camera infinitely far away from the model, creating a parallel projection. Changing a parallel projection to a perspective

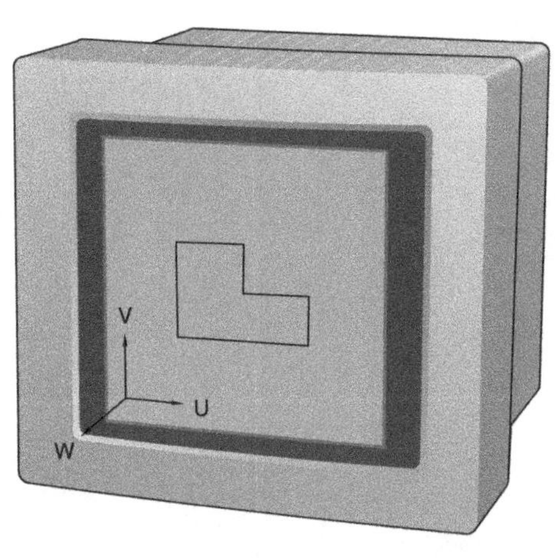

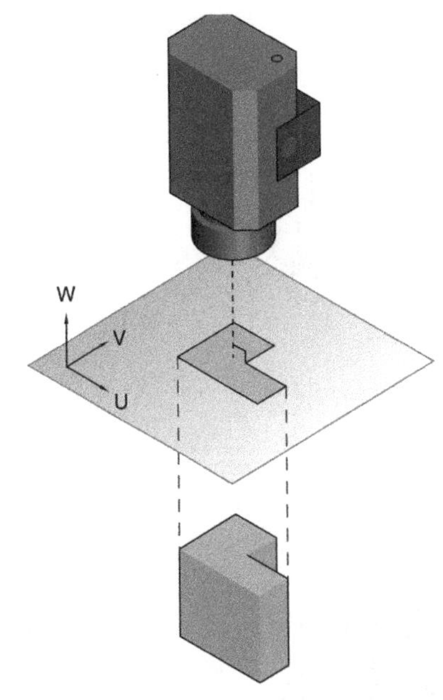

Figure 9.73

Orienting the workplane coincident with the viewplane
Workplanes are often used to orient the view camera.

Figure 9.74

View commands that do not involve changing the viewpoint
Pan and zoom commands do not change the projection of the model.

projection is usually a matter of setting the view camera distance to something other than infinite. The closer the camera is to the model, the wider the view angle required (Figure 9.75 on page 452). Some systems allow the view angle to be manipulated, while others change the viewing distance. In either case, the effect is a change in the convergence of any parallel edges on the model, from nearly parallel to extremely convergent.

A related issue in view specification is how to display the geometry of the model. The most common methods, shown in Figure 9.76 on page 453, are:

- Wireframe
- Hidden lines rendered
- Hidden lines removed
- Shaded

Camera View

What Is Seen

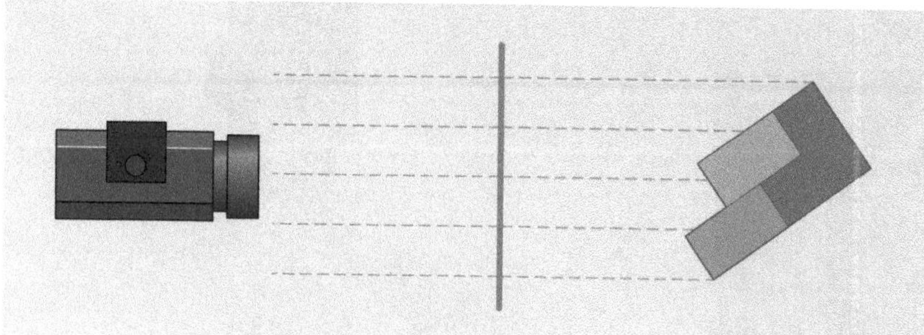

Parallel Projection

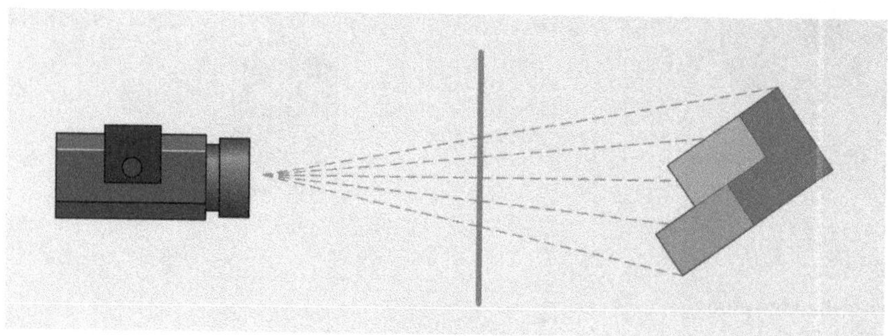

Perspective Projection

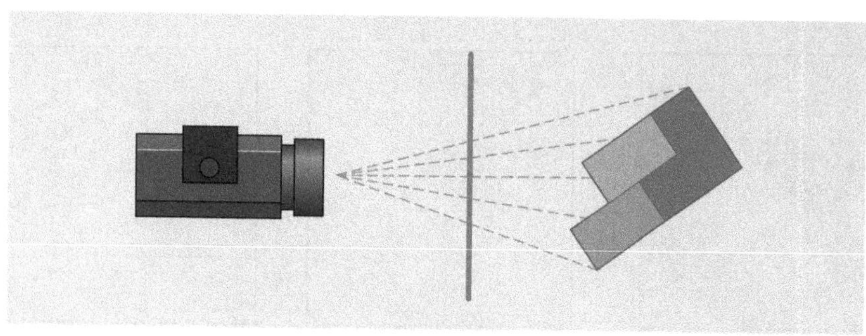

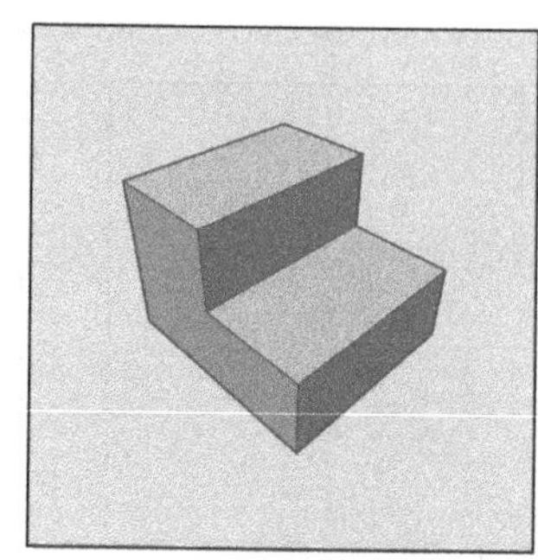

Perspective Projection

Figure 9.75

Parallel versus perspective projection

The closer the camera is to the object, the wider the angle of view and the more severe the convergence.

In addition, the lines representing tangency can be:

- Hidden
- Displayed solid
- Displayed as an alternate linetype

Exactly how the model is rendered can change numerous times during the construction of the model. Each rendering mode has its own advantages, with the decision of which mode to use often based on balancing the need to minimize the number of lines shown on the screen with having access to tangencies and hidden features. It is important to note that a model can be displayed in wireframe and still contain solid model information in the database. The rendering of the model is independent of the underlying geometric database.

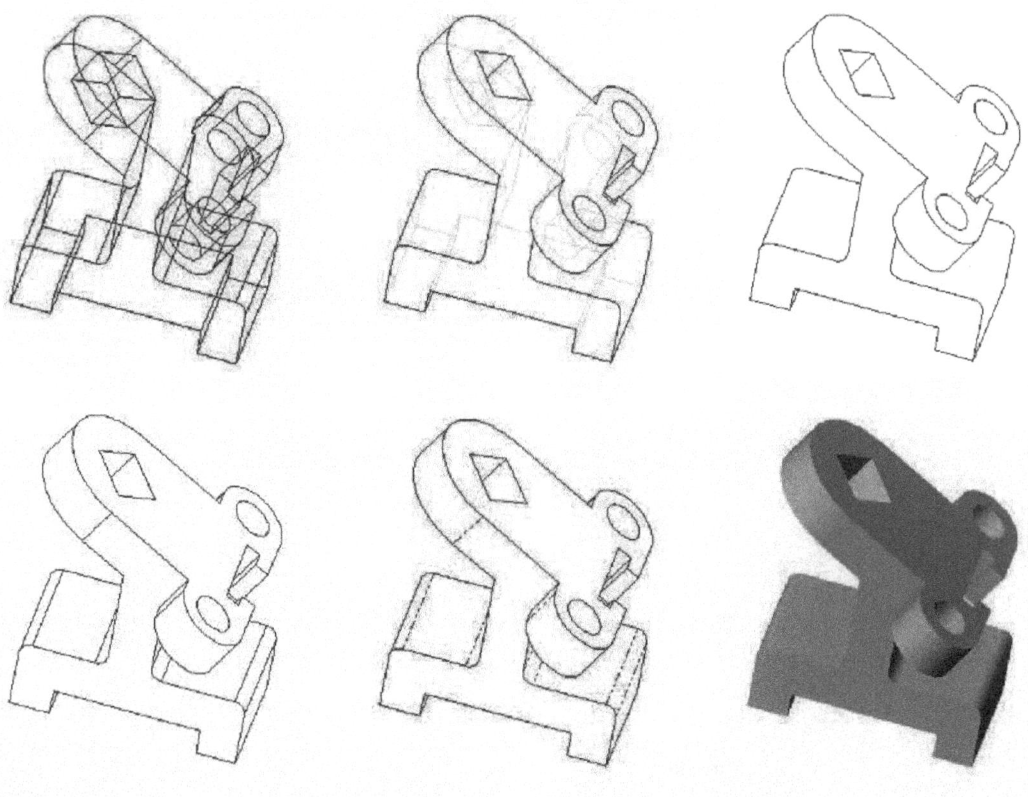

Figure 9.76

Different options for rendering a model

There are many options for how to depict hidden edges and tangents.

9.11.3 View Camera Strategy

Projection calculations are not sensitive to the point of view; a traditional front view of the object is as easy to calculate as an isometric pictorial view. This is not the case with 2-D CAD or mechanical drafting. The implication is that, except for the occasional need to conform to a standard view, there is no reason to stick solely to the traditional views when working with 3-D modelers.

Viewpoints should be chosen on the basis of the task to be performed. With multiple viewports, the views are often distributed between those used strictly for viewing and those used for constructing the model. A pictorial view of the model is useful for observing the progress of the overall construction. The pictorial is often an axonometric view oriented such that the features currently being worked on are seen with a minimum amount of foreshortening. Pictorial views are a compromise that allows all three major dimensions of the model to be seen. With 3-D modelers, dimetric and trimetric pictorials are as much an option as isometric pictorials. Rather than being limited to a certain pictorial view, the user can interactively orient the model to depict the features to the best advantage.

During model construction, traditional multiviews are available. The workplane is aligned to an existing face on the model, or along a global axis, and the resulting view matches a traditional front, side, or top view.

To choose viewpoints for construction, or for viewing a completed model, use the same rules as for sketching or drawing, as follows:

- Avoid views that are close but not quite a standard orthographic view (Figure 9.77A on page 454). Such views would have the features along one primary dimension severely foreshortened and therefore very distorted.
- Clearly identify the features of interest, and orient the view camera to depict those features (Figure 9.77B). If there are important features along all three primary dimensions, an isometric or near isometric view may be appropriate.

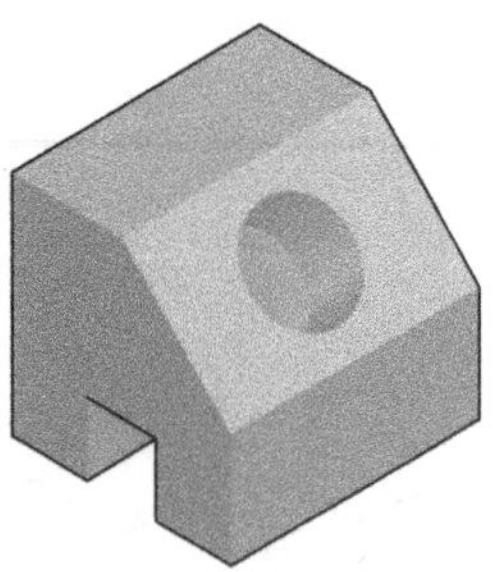

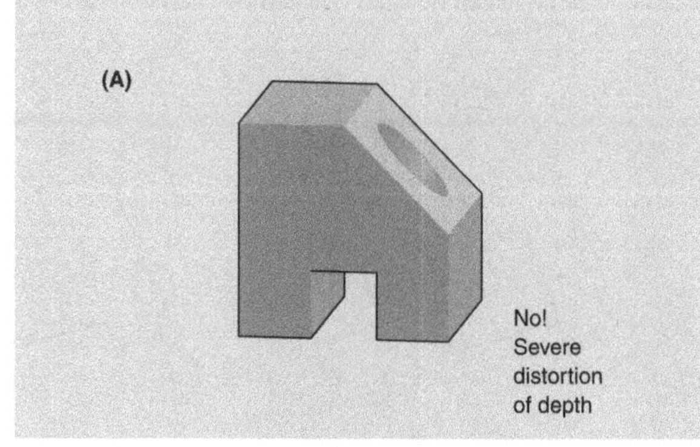

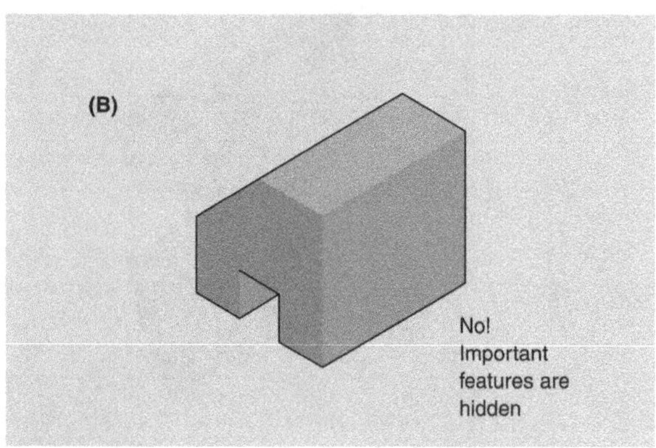

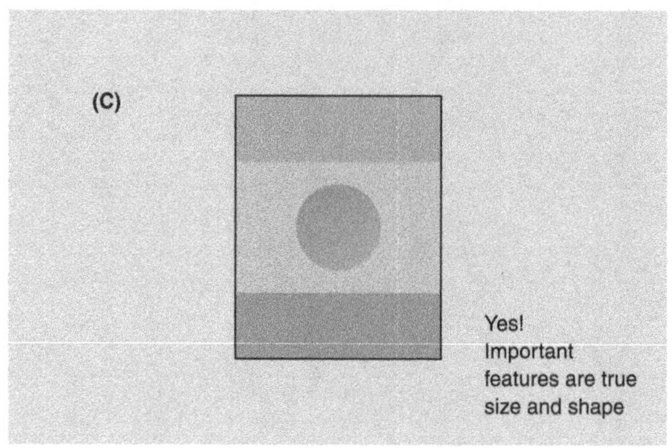

Figure 9.77

Good and poor viewing practice for modeling

The choice of view should be feature driven. Which view best depicts the hole and inclined plane?

- If most of the features of interest are along only two of the three primary dimensions, choose a view that favors those two; however, retain the third dimension. If there are features on more than three sides of the model, another viewport with a view from the opposite side of the model may be required.
- For features that must be carefully analyzed, choose a view where the applicable faces can be seen in their true size and shape (Figure 9.77C).

Practice Exercise 9.4

Select a small object with features on at least three faces. Use a small sheet of clear plastic as an image (view) plane. Use your eyes as the camera behind the image plane. Move the image plane about the object to find three orthographic views that capture most of the important features of the object. Move the view plane to one of the views and use a water-based marker to sketch the projection of the object on the plastic. On a sheet of tracing paper divide it into four quadrants. Each quadrant represents a viewport. Each viewport should be the size of the plastic viewplane. Place the plastic under one sheet of tracing paper, and transfer the projection drawn into the viewport. Repeat this process until the other two orthographic views and a pictorial view are transferred to the viewports on the tracing paper. This process mimics the process of creating views in viewports using a 3-D modeling system.

9.13 3-D Modeling and the Design Process

CAD was introduced into most businesses as an automated drafting tool and was then defined as computer-aided drafting. The introduction of 3-D modeling systems has transformed CAD into computer-aided *design*.

CAD 3-D modeling plays an important role in many newly emerging manufacturing techniques, includ-

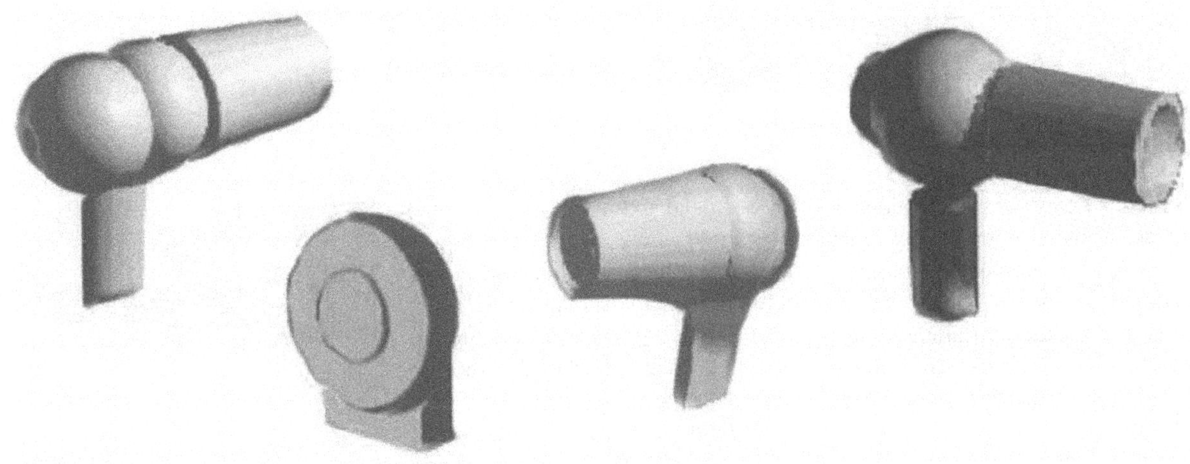

Figure 9.78

Form refinement of a hair dryer

3-D modeling tools can be used for designs at all stages of development.

ing computer-aided manufacturing (CAM), computer-integrated manufacturing (CIM), concurrent engineering, and design for manufacturability (DFM). All of these manufacturing techniques are aimed at shortening the design cycle, minimizing material and labor expenditures, raising product quality, and lowering the cost of the final product. Central to these goals is better communications within a company. By sharing the 3-D database of the proposed product, more people can be working simultaneously on various aspects of the design problem. The graphics nature of the database has convinced many that 3-D modeling is a superior method of communicating many of the design intents.

Another important part of the model planning process is understanding how the model data is going to be used once it is created. If you are going to use analysis tools such as finite element analysis (FEA), you will need to make sure that the critical features you have earmarked for careful analysis are modeled in enough detail to give accurate results. Similarly, if you are going to be creating physical prototypes using rapid prototyping tools for visual analysis, careful attention will need to be paid to the visible exterior surfaces. Models used to generate CNC or related manufacturing data will need to accurately represent the geometry of the final manufactured parts, inside and out. For example, internal ribs, bosses, fillets, or draft angles that might not have been of importance to evaluating its external appearance are critical when cutting injection molds.

9.12.1 Sketch Modeling

Early in the design process, during the idea generation phase, models must be constructed quickly so that the design ideas can be tested. Because speed is more important than accuracy at this stage, modelers designed for this purpose are called **sketch modelers**.

The initial computer models are often developed using simple primitives (Figure 9.78). The more promising designs are refined to provide a better idea of how the final product may look. In these early stages, many designs may be developed simultaneously and then compared. The comparison process may mean visual inspection of the designs, requiring that alternative designs be brought up simultaneously on the computer screen. Alternatively, prints or plots of the models can be made. Rendering techniques, such as shading and coloring, can be used to enhance the visual comparisons (Figure 9.78).

9.12.2 Prototyping

Even with the capability of developing virtual models, physical mockups are often needed as the design progresses. Prototyping techniques allow physical models to be made directly from a 3-D database. With some systems, the outer surface of the model is translated into a series of paths traced by cutter heads on a milling machine (Figure 9.79 on the next page). This technique can be used for high-precision manufacturing of the final product, or for lower-precision production of prototypes made from

Dream **High Tech** Job

Designing Snowboards

The engineering design process is used in many types of jobs from the design of consumer product packaging to the design of snowboards and related equipment. An understanding of the design process and 3-D solid modeling—along with formal education in a field of engineering—can lead to exciting job opportunities, such as the one described here of an engineer who worked on the design of snowboards.

Snow Sports

"When I was a kid, we called my grandfather 'Fix-it Grandpa.' He could fix anything, and I often followed him around asking questions about everything. I was always fascinated when he took everything apart; only, if I did it, I couldn't always get it back together. Neither of my parents were mechanically inclined, so, when I needed something fixed, I either had to call Grandpa or fix it myself.

"When I was graduating from high school, I wanted to go to college at University of California, Santa Barbara. My dad and I were looking through the college catalog and ran across a picture of a Human Powered Vehicle under the mechanical engineering section. We both agreed that it looked interesting, and I felt confident that I could study mechanical engineering because I enjoyed math, science, and physics.

"Because of my engineering education, I feel that I can solve any problem and can do whatever I want with my life. The education gave me a set of tools to have a successful life.

"To make extra money, I worked for Joyride Snowboards as a college sales rep. I had been an avid snowboarder for the last 12 years so it seemed like a good fit to use my engineering skills to further the sport of snowboarding.

"My employment at K2 started as an internship after graduation and eventually became a full-time gig. At K2, I designed snowboard footprints, profiles, and constructions with an emphasis on women's boards. I also organized and led on-snow tests on Mt. Hood for prototype testing. My design, the K2 Mix, is still in production and was ranked in the Top 5 Women's boards in the 2002 Transworld Buyers Guide. In fact, Gretchen Bleiler, the winner of the Women's Super-pipe in the 2003 X-Games and the Women's U.S. Open Half-pipe Championships, rides my board!"

STACIE GLASS
Former Snowboard Design Engineer, K2 Snowboards
(Courtesy of Stacie Shannon Glass.)

Skis and Snowboards

Engineers who love to ski and snowboard naturally gravitate toward work in the snow sports industry. Traditionally, when an idea for a new ski or snowboard design came along, engineers would build a prototype, perform laboratory tests for stiffness, and test it on the slopes. Based on the test experience, engineers would make design changes and retest the equipment. This method of design resulted in a slow and tedious process. In addition, the perfectly crafted ski or snowboard is not perfect for everyone. The needs of a 5′2″ female snowboarder are much different than the needs of a 6′0″ male snowboarder. The snowboard's height, weight, and skill level, as well as the snow conditions and the angle of the slope, all need to be taken into consideration when trying to fit the perfect board to the enthusiast.

Snowboards are made out of several layers of materials, along with glue and paint. Snowboarders believe that the edge design, or effective edge, is the most important part of the design. Edge design determines how the snowboard will turn. The more surface area the edge has, the more control and, hence, the sharper the turns that can be made. Structural strength of the snowboard is also very important. Engineers determine the strength by figuring out the acceleration of the rider.

To accommodate these various conditions, engineers from manufacturers such as K2 and Head are designing intelligent technology that will enable skiers and snowboarders to go faster and have more control.

Reprinted with permission from Baine, Celeste, *High Tech Hot Shots,* 2004, NSPE, hightechhotshots.com.

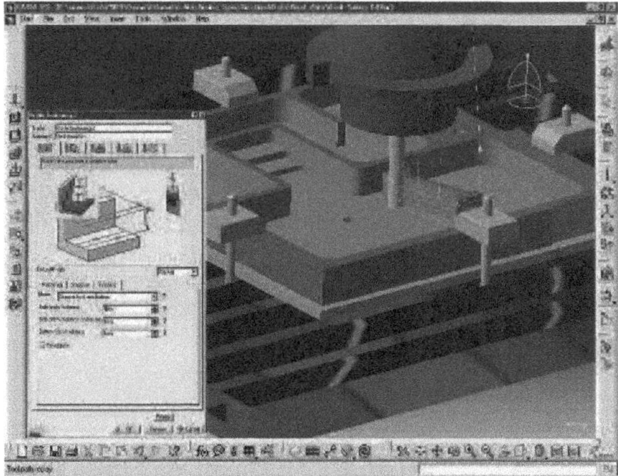

Figure 9.79

Cutter paths on a surface model

Milling machines driven by computer controllers can automate the process of creating physical prototypes.

(Photo courtesy of Dassault Systemes.)

Figure 9.81

Virtual reality technology

This technology allows a more complete use of the senses to explore and evaluate design concepts.

(Reprinted Courtesy of Caterpillar, Inc.)

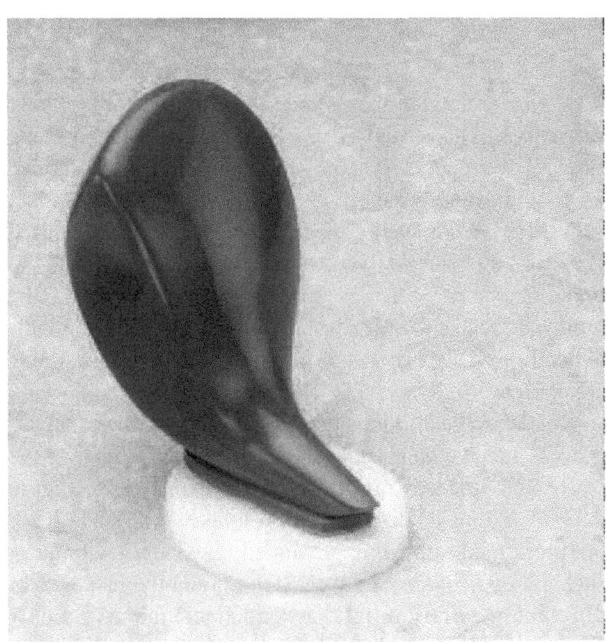

Figure 9.80

Rapid prototyping machine used to create this golf club head

Rapid prototyping technologies allow complex geometries to be transformed quickly and accurately from 3-D computer models into real models.

inexpensive materials, such as wax or foam blocks. A more expensive technique called **stereolithography** uses light beams to trace the surface, avoiding the limitations of mechanical cutter heads (Figure 9.80). In stereolithography, the model is decomposed into a series of very thin layers. Each layer is a 2-D profile with a nominal thickness in the third dimension. Two light beams move a focal point around in a vat of photosensitive polymer, tracing an outline of one of the layers. Once a layer of polymer has been hardened by the light beams, the next layer up is traced. Stereolithography is one of several *rapid prototyping techniques*. Models of considerable complexity can thus be created.

In some cases, it is not practical to make a prototype because of size or cost. In other cases, the prototype would not respond the way the actual product would. For these situations, as well as others, **virtual reality (VR)** systems offer a viable analysis approach (Figure 9.81). VR systems use the principles of perception to develop completely *immersive* environments in which the user can interact with the object through some or all of the senses. In such an environment, the user has the feeling of actually interacting with the virtual model.

VR technology requires models that correspond closely to the real object. Also, the system must be able to monitor all actions taken by the user. This includes changing the point of view when the user's head position changes or depicting a virtual hand when the user is

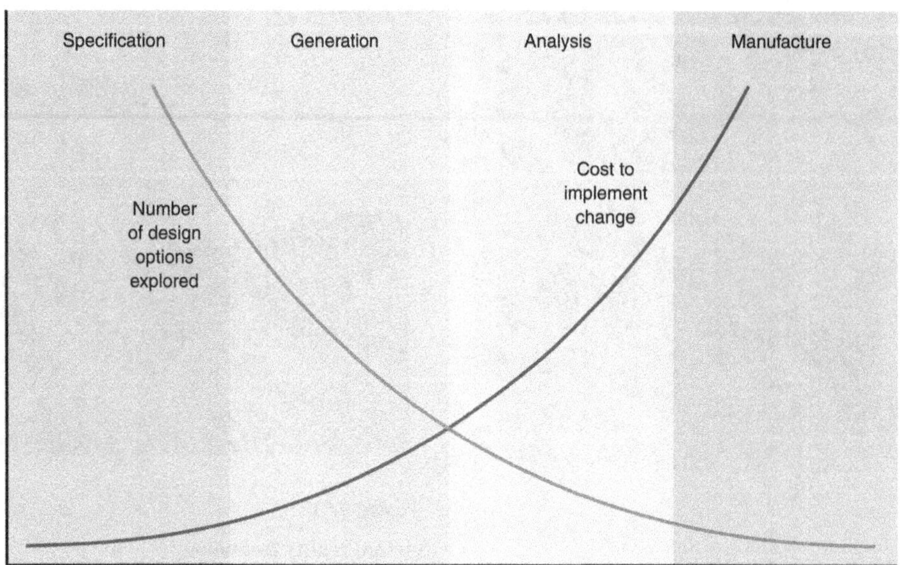

Figure 9.82

Changes in cost factors over the design cycle

As the design becomes finalized and moves toward production, changes to the design become increasingly expensive to implement.

reaching out and grasping the virtual object. In addition, the user needs to receive feedback that closely mimics the environment's responses to the user's actions. The visual and auditory fields must be completely controlled by the system, and this is often done with headsets. State-of-the-art technology that would provide kinesthetic feedback is being developed. The virtual model would feel like it has weight when it is being moved around by the user.

9.12.3 Analysis

The specification phase of the design process establishes the requirements for the needed product. Periodically, the various design concepts being developed should be evaluated against these requirements. As the design process progresses, changes become more expensive to implement, and fewer design options can affordably be explored (Figure 9.82). However, evaluations take time and resources, and they should not be done unnecessarily. Selecting the right analysis method is as important as determining when or how often evaluations must or should be done. Some computer evaluation techniques are very time-consuming, while others are quick and can be done essentially on a continuous basis as the design evolves.

Visual Inspection **Visual inspection** is an evaluation technique that is quick and easy, although very subjective. The visual inspection may involve making sure all the necessary parts are in an assembly model. Technicians and engineers familiar with the end product can often make well-educated design decisions based purely on a visual analysis. Visual analysis is also used to make aesthetic decisions concerning the "look" of the model. Industrial designers and marketing professionals depend heavily on visual analysis to judge aesthetic appearance.

Rendering techniques that enhance the visual analysis process involve steps ranging from simply removing the edges and surfaces normally hidden from view (Figure 9.83) to adding shading or color to make some surfaces or features stand out. More advanced rendering techniques, such as *ray tracing,* can accurately model the response of different materials to light rays. Such techniques not only assist in aesthetic design decisions but also in safety decisions where reflected light (glare) could pose problems.

Kinematics Kinematics is an analysis technique used to evaluate the design of a **mechanism**, that is, an assembly of multiple parts, some of which move with

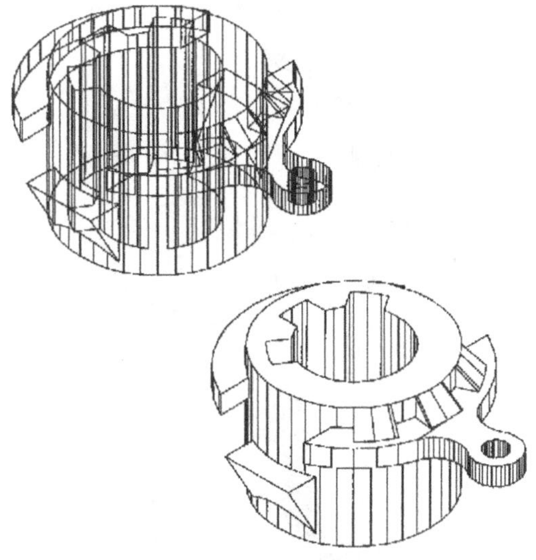

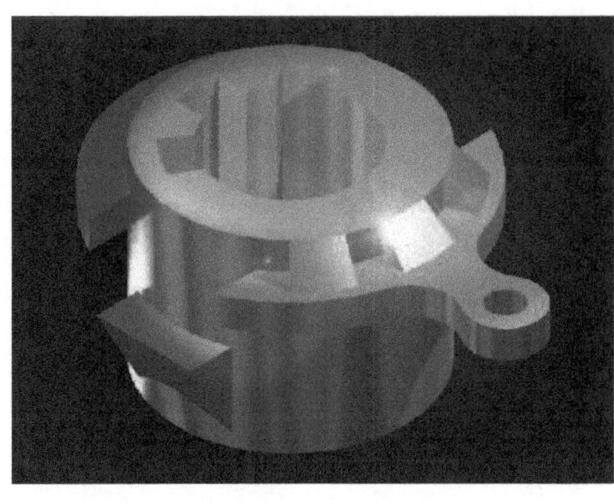

Figure 9.83

Wireframe, hidden line removed (HLR), and rendered model of a part

Different types of rendering will give the designers different information about the model.

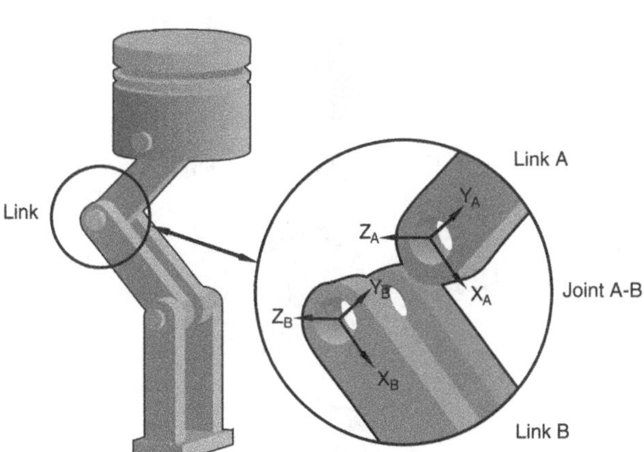

Figure 9.84

Components of a kinematic mechanism

Links in a mechanism are related to each other through local coordinate systems composing the joint.

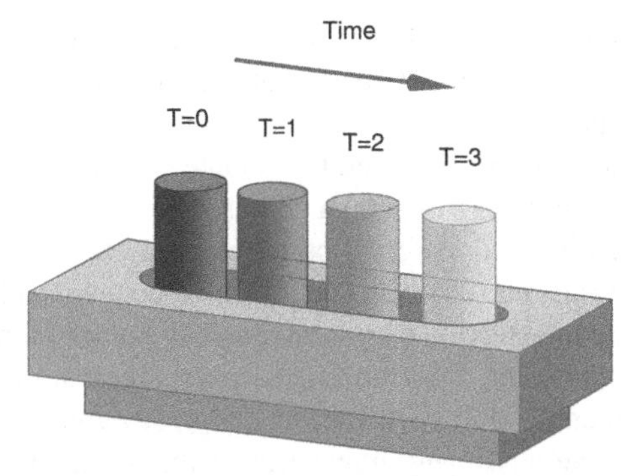

Figure 9.85

Representing the fourth dimension of time as discrete geometry

Modification tools in 3-D modeling systems can be used to represent the change in a part over time.

respect to other parts. A mechanism contains two main components: the solids themselves, which represent the **links**, and the **joints**, which describe how the links can move relative to each other (Figure 9.84). Joints constrain movement to either translational or rotational, or a combination of the two.

Linking parts together into a kinematic model allows the designer to evaluate the paths of motion of various parts. This movement requires the addition of a fourth dimension, *time*, to the computer model. The time dimension specifies the orientation or location of a given part at a given time (Figure 9.85). The movement paths can be represented as discrete solids, or can be depicted by the

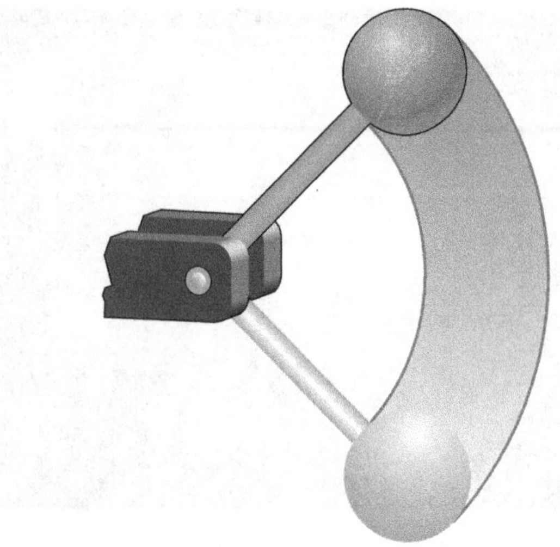

Figure 9.86

Representing a moving part as a swept path

Sweeping tools in the 3-D modeler can be used to represent the path of a part.

sweeping technique. In Figure 9.86, a new solid is created to show the volume of space that the part passes through over time.

Kinematics is also used to evaluate whether any parts, movable or otherwise, **clash**, that is, whether the volumes representing two different parts intersect each other. Although this analysis can sometimes be done visually, the Boolean intersection operation provides a much more precise assessment. Boolean intersections taken at different time intervals will show the exact topology and geometry of any overlap during movement of the mechanism. For example, a redesign of the base in Figure 9.87 could be performed by representing the movement of the arm as a swept solid and then performing a Boolean difference operation on the base. This would remove from the base a volume exactly matching the path of the arm (Figure 9.88).

Mass Properties Analysis Additional information about the model can be obtained by performing a **mass properties analysis**. With those 3-D modeling systems capable of calculating the volume of a solid, density values can be added to calculate the overall mass of the solid (Figure 9.89). In addition, the centers of gravity (centroids) and the internal properties can also be calculated. Such calculations are used either on a single solid of uniform density or on a complete assembly containing parts of varying materials and densities. A simple but important application of

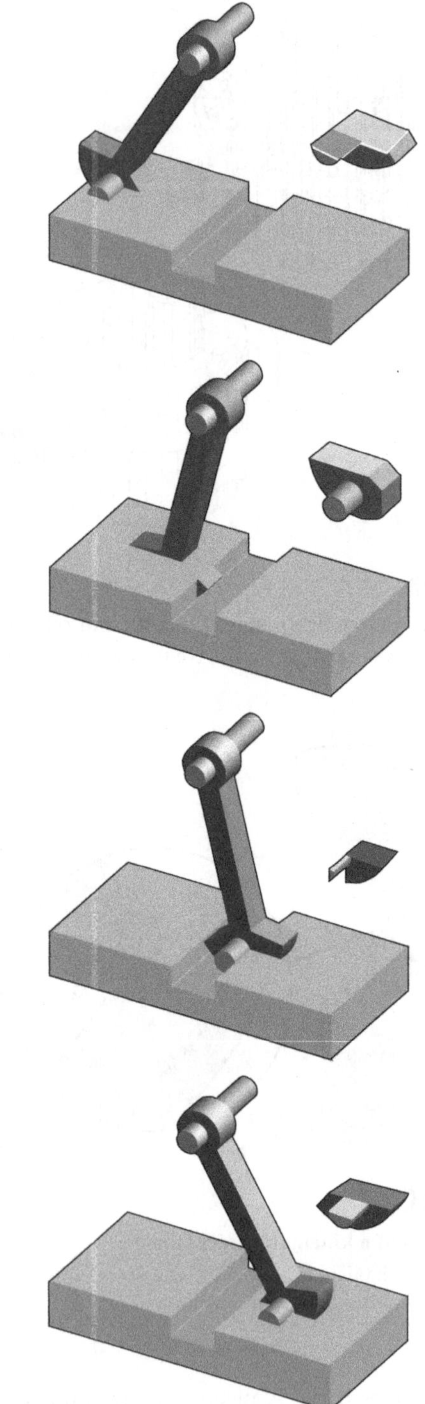

Figure 9.87

Calculating the clash between parts using an intersection Boolean operation

As parts move relative to each other, their intersection can be evaluated.

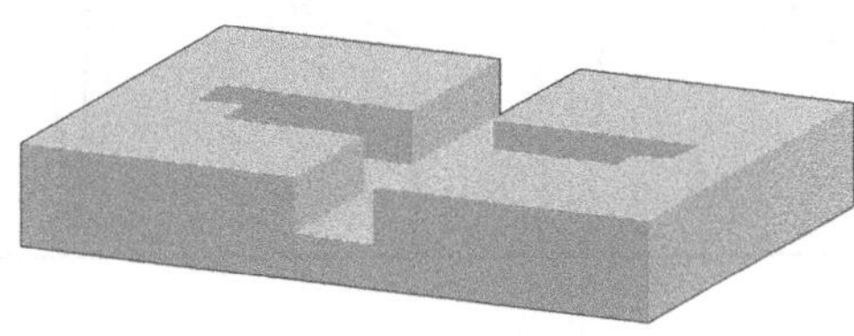

Figure 9.88

Redesigning a part to avoid interference

The swept path of the arm can be subtracted from the base using the Boolean difference operation.

this analysis involves calculating the final shipping weight of a product.

When mass properties analysis is combined with kinematic information, a more sophisticated technique called a **dynamic analysis** can be performed on the model. Straight kinematic analysis assumes that all parts are moving at a constant velocity and that no forces are acting on the parts. However, for a mechanism, forces are acting on the parts at all times. Forces are needed to start and stop a mechanism and, because of friction, to keep it going. The distribution of mass of a part plays a central role in these calculations. For example, it takes much more power or force to get a truck moving from a dead stop than it does to get a motorcycle moving; it is also much harder to get a moving truck to stop.

Finite Element Analysis Mass information helps calculate the forces acting on a part but not necessarily how the part responds to those forces. A real-world object is a continuous mass that responds in a very complex manner to forces acting upon it. Currently, only the responses of very simple geometric shapes are clearly understood. A process called *discretization* divides more complex geometries into simpler forms so that the response of a solid to

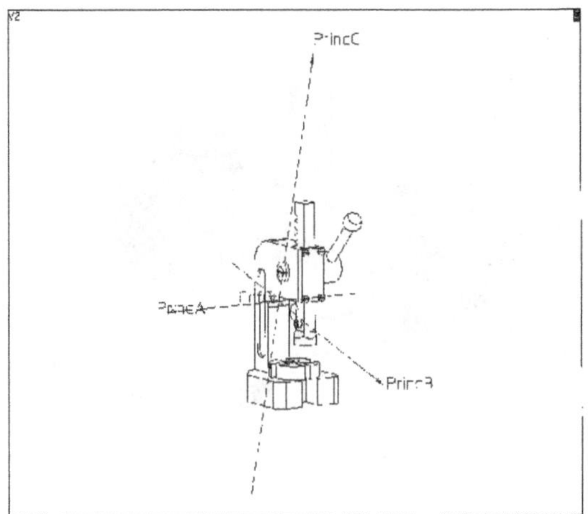

VOLUME	133969.7108		
MASS	133969.7108		
CENTROID	Xbar	Ybar	Zbar
	0.2439426889	26.03605442	93.66152808
PARALLEL CENTROID AXES			
Moment of Inertia	Ixx	Iyy	Izz
	312232716.3	262236625.6	64632247.74
Radius of Gyration	Kxx	Kyy	Kzz
	48.27651301	44.24287738	21.96449992
Product of Inertia	Iyz	Ixz	Ixy
	–59194625.5	–1089532.317	–964951.745
PRINCIPAL AXES THROUGH CENTROID			
Moment of Inertia	IXX	IYY	IZZ
	312251349	278599864.1	48250376.48
Radius of Gyration	KXX	KYY	KZZ
	48.27795346	45.60234125	18.97785147
Principal Axes			
PrincA	0.9998070774	–0.01963977285	0.0002955702916
PrincB	0.01900740565	0.9636017962	–0.2666651399
PrincC	0.004952430712	0.2666193122	0.9637891968

Figure 9.89

Sample property analysis

Mass properties analysis gives information such as its volume and inertial properties.

forces can be estimated. The process of creating a model of primitive geometries is called *finite element modeling (FEM),* and the analysis done on the resulting model is **finite element analysis (FEA)**.

A virtual model can be designed to exhibit the same thermal or elastic properties as the material from which the product will be made (Figure 9.90 on page 462). Instead of having real forces exerted on real models, hypothetical forces can be applied to a virtual model, avoiding the often-destructive results for a physical prototype. Working with virtual models saves the time and expense of fabricating one-of-a-kind prototypes.

Ergonomics **Ergonomics** examines the interaction between technology and humans. The point of interaction could be the hand grip on a vacuum cleaner, the

Figure 9.90

Finite element analysis of a product

Powerful desktop computers not only allow the simulation of loads on a design but also coding the values in color for easy visualization.

(Image by COSMOSWorks, the integrated design validation tool in SolidWorks.)

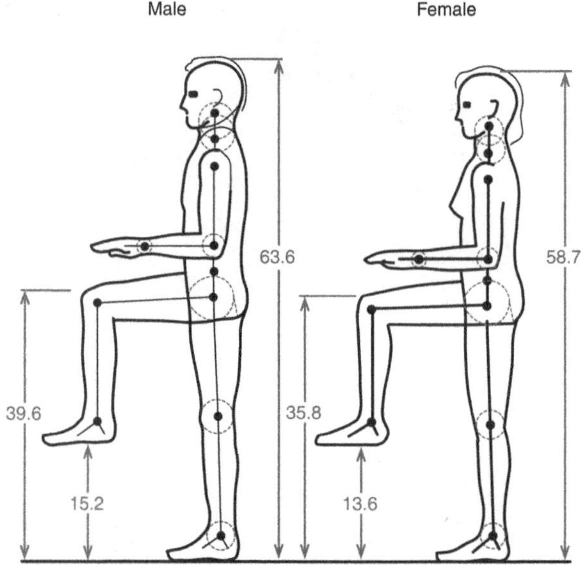

Figure 9.91

Human proportion 95th percentile chart

Body dimensions of various population segments can be used to model their interaction in work environments.

seat in a car, or a control panel in a nuclear power plant. Ergonomic analyses revolve around the concepts of comfort, efficiency, and safety. Using virtual models, both the products and the human operators can be modeled.

Some types of interactions may be related to the physical characteristics of the human body (Figure 9.91), dimensions of which vary considerably from one person to another. Values have been established to reflect the percentage of certain populations that fall within a given range. Body dimensions must be analyzed when items such as seating are designed to accommodate a full range of sizes. Designing a seated computer workstation is a good example: for the largest, there must be adequate leg room; for the smallest, their feet must still be able to touch the ground.

More sophisticated human modelers allow various anatomical components to be modeled as separate parts and linked to a kinematic model. These models are manipulated to mimic how a human would walk, bend, crawl, etc., through a given space or to evaluate whether certain controls are too far away to reach (Figure 9.92). *Reach envelopes* can be swept for human limbs in the same way they are for mechanical parts. Other geometric solids are created to represent other limits of human capability. For example, a right-angled cone is used to represent the *cone of vision* of an aircraft pilot. The intersection of this cone with the cockpit model indicates the controls that can be seen by the pilot at that moment.

9.13 Computer-Aided Manufacturing (CAM)

Three-dimensional modeling techniques can be combined with **computer-aided manufacturing (CAM)** capabilities to ensure that a product design satisfies the desired manufacturability requirements as closely as possible.

Three-dimensional models and their associated databases ease the transition from design to manufacturing by reducing or eliminating the need for traditional working or production drawings (Figure 9.93). In many instances, the computer-generated model and database can be translated directly to the computer system controlling the CAM operation.

The first step in the manufacturing of a product is **process planning** (Figure 9.94 on page 464), in which the most efficient approach for producing the product is determined. Since individual parts are manufactured separately, the product, and therefore the model, is divided along its natural hierarchical structure. The parts can also be separated between those parts that are ready-made and those to be fabricated on site. For those that are to be fab-

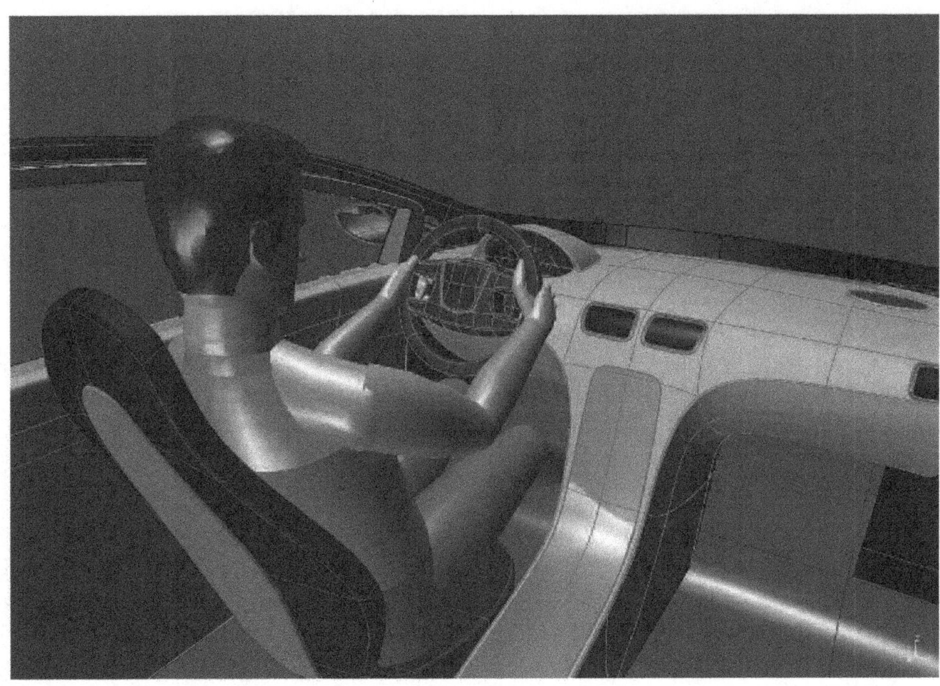

Figure 9.92

Human interaction and ergonomic simulation within a 3-D car

(Courtesy of Dassault Systemes.)

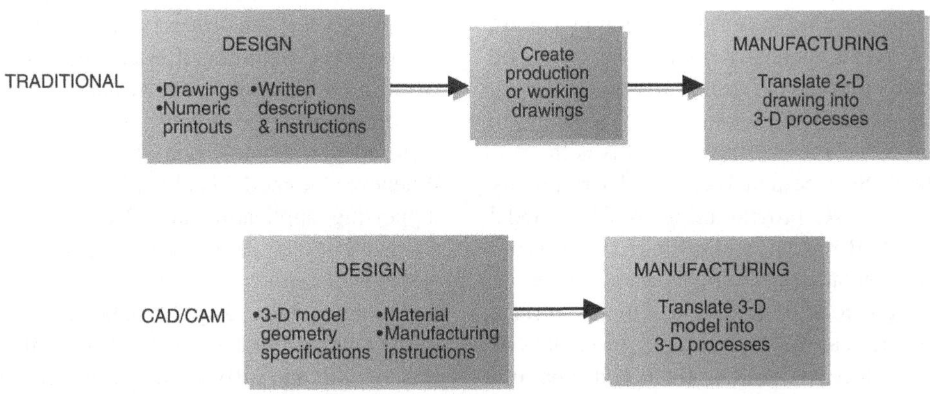

Figure 9.93

Design to manufacture, with and without 3-D computer models

Modern CAD/CAM techniques use 3-D model databases to minimize the need to produce and interpret 2-D drawings of a design.

ricated on site, models can be made showing what each part will look like at each stage of the manufacturing process (Figure 9.95 on page 465). These models provide information used to determine how much time, material, and labor would be required to manufacture the product as modeled. If special types of tooling (e.g., cutters, jigs, etc.) are required, 3-D models can also be made for them.

Increasingly, the machinery used for fabrication is programmed using the computer models of each part. The information related to the model is translated into

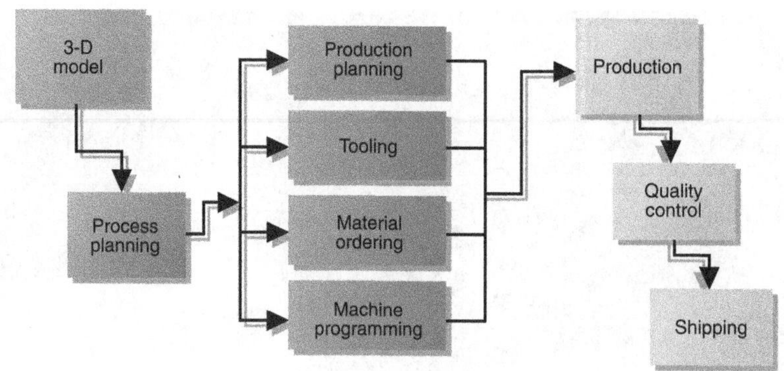

Figure 9.94

The manufacturing process using a 3-D computer model

The 3-D model database contains information used in every phase of the manufacturing process.

manufacturing operations by specialized programs. These programs control the machine tools through a process called **numeric control (NC)** (Figure 9.96). Originally, information was provided to NC machines by punched tapes. Improvements in technology have led to the full-scale integration of computers with machine tools, and the development of **computer numeric control (CNC)**. The use of CNC means less translation and less chance for error. In the current generation of CNC technology, simulations of the tool cutting action are created and tested on virtual models before actual materials and equipment are used (Figure 9.97). This cuts down on material waste and reduces troubleshooting time, freeing up the equipment for greater use in production.

An important factor in planning tool paths is the surface of the model. Surface and B-rep modelers readily lend themselves to CNC programming. A CSG model must be converted to B-rep data and is limited to the types of analytic surface geometry the modeler can represent. The parametric equations describing a sculpted surface in a surface modeler can be used directly to create NC code (Figure 9.98 on page 466). As the u and v parameters are incremented, cutter paths are generated as either discrete points or curved paths. Even with CNC milling machines, sculpted surfaces can be very time-consuming to cut. However, the CNC milling machine can be used to make a master mold or die that, in turn, is used to quickly form plastic or metal for the final product.

9.14 Data Associativity

Often, the 3-D modeling system is the primary generator of engineering data for the product being designed. From 3-D model data, analyses such as FEA and kinematics are performed, 2-D production drawings are generated, and images are rendered for visual inspection. To cut down on development time, there is a need to move information from the modeler to these support applications as quickly and accurately as possible. In a concurrent engineering environment where many people are working on a design simultaneously, there is a great risk that not all team members have up-to-date information to perform their jobs. On one hand, they do not want to extract model information too soon if the model specifications are still changing, yet if the process of extracting model information is time-consuming, they cannot leave this step for the last minute. Data associativity addresses this dilemma by creating a dynamic linkage of information between the 3-D model database and the supporting applications. Whenever the model is altered, the associated data in the supporting application are also automatically updated, giving all design team members the most current information to work with.

The dynamic linkage of data can be established in a number of different ways. First the linkage can all take place within one software package, which contains multiple discrete applications. Links can be established between different applications running on a single workstation using standard technology such as Microsoft's Object Linking and Embedding (OLE). With the assistance of networking and Product Data Management (PDM) tools (see Section 2.3), data can also be dynamically linked across networks to all users working on the same design project. Links made between the 3-D model and supporting applications can be either *unidirectional* or *bidirectional.* With unidirectional associativity, the supporting application's data can be altered by changing the 3-D model, but not vice versa. With bidirectional associativity, changes

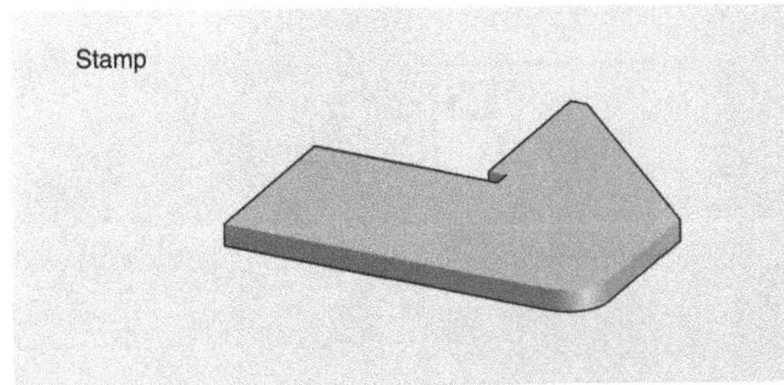

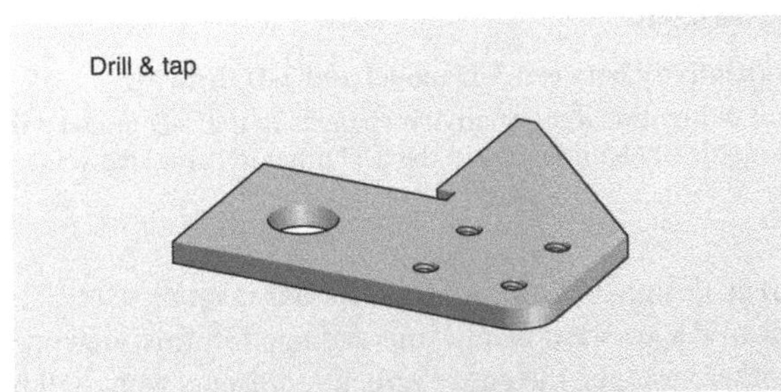

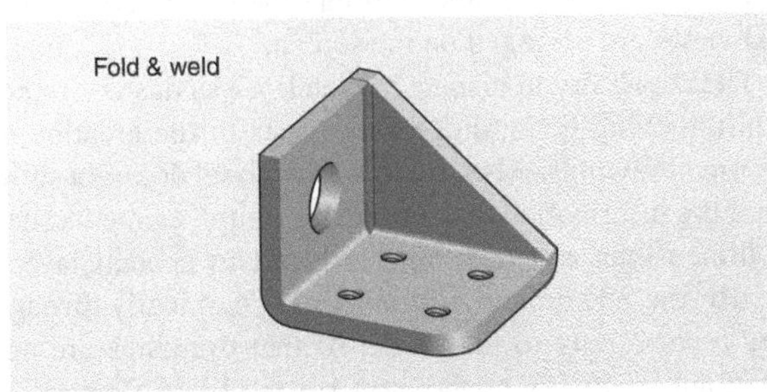

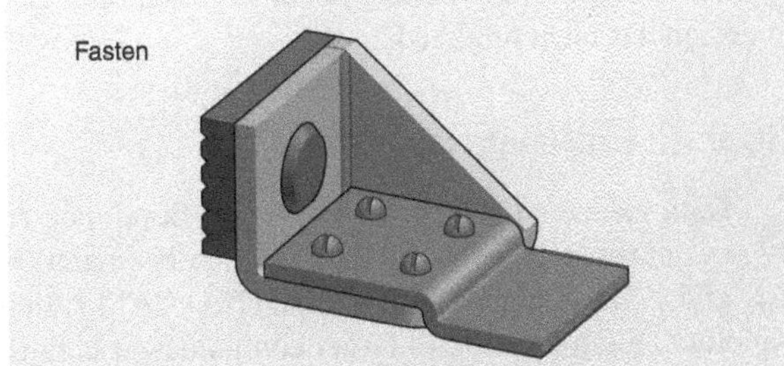

Figure 9.95

Modeling the incremental fabrication of a part

Virtual 3-D models can be used to simulate the manufacturing process.

```
T%
00590 (URG, THREAD SS-DENUDER TUBES)
N00G00
N10T1010 (TT TRIANGLE)
N20G97S1400M03
N25G00X1.35Z.1
/1M08
G01X.875F.010
N30G01Z0F.002
X1.025F.005
G03X1.125Z-.050F.003R.050
G01Z-.157
X1.25Z-.187
X1.255Z-.250M09
G00X2.0Z3.0
T100
N90M00

N91G00
T1111 (60 DEGREE CHAMFER (3/8 DIA.))
G97S300M03
G00X.90Z.050
/1M08
G00Z0
G01Z-.060F.005
G04U.3
G00Z0M09
G00X2.0Z2.0
T1100
M01

....
....
....
```

Figure 9.96

Generating machine instructions for an NC milling machine

3-D models simplify the process of generating NC code for manufacturing.

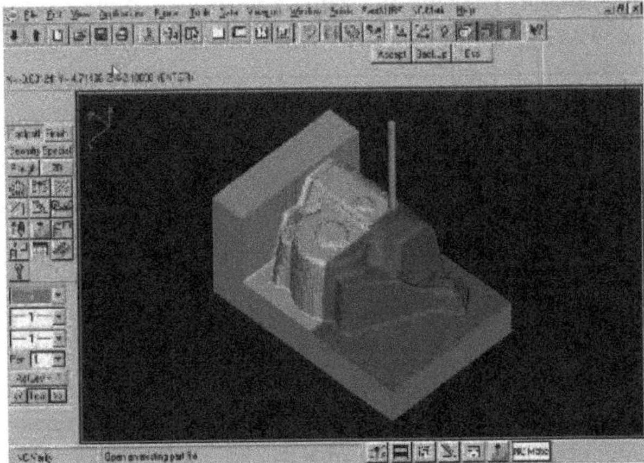

Figure 9.97

Planning tool paths using a virtual 3-D model

Tool paths can be troubleshot on virtual models without risk of damaging expensive tooling.

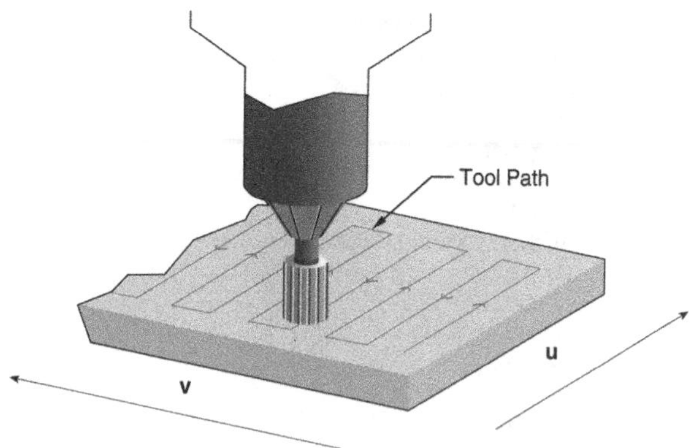

Figure 9.98

Translating a surface patch into a tool path
Surface model databases are easily translated into machining instructions.

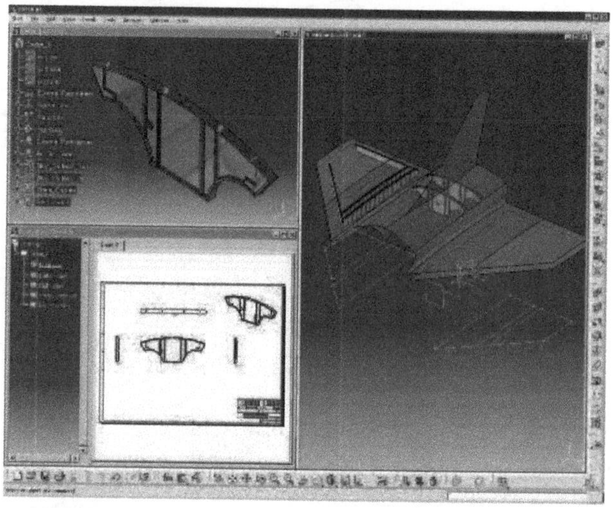

Figure 9.99

Associativity between 3-D model and 2-D drawing
With bidirectional associativity, changes in the 3-D model will automatically be reflected in the 2-D drawing, and vice versa.
(Courtesy of Dassault Systemes.)

in either the 3-D model or data in the supporting application will affect the other. In addition to the direction of the data flow, the updating can be set to be done automatically whenever there is a change, or done manually when an update command is chosen.

One of the most common types of data associativity is between the 3-D model and a 2-D production drawing. For example, if the 3-D modeling system also has a 2-D drafting module, then links can be set up between the model and the views represented in the production drawing (Figure 9.99). In a modeling system in which this is implemented, the views in the production drawing can be thought of as live projections of the 3-D model from different points of view. Typically, a *base view* of the model (such as a front view) is anchored in the production drawing. Then, principal and auxiliary views are established relative to this base view. In addition, sections and details can usually be created. What cannot be added, however, are those standard conventions drafters usually use that violate true projections of the object. For example, aligned sections and conventional breaks to shorten elongated parts are not typically allowed. Although hidden lines may be turned off altogether, selective removal of unwanted hidden lines usually is not.

When 2-D documentation of a product is needed, it is relatively easy to generate. Traditional multiview projections of an object can typically be captured directly from the projection of the 3-D model in the viewport. Many 3-D modeling systems also contain a 2-D drafting component. When the model has been properly positioned, the view is captured and projected on the image plane as 2-D line information. With some systems, a special viewport is designated as two dimensional (Figure 9.99). The captured views are placed and arranged in this viewport. In other systems, the entire screen represents what will be seen on the drawing, and multiple viewports containing 3-D views are arranged on the screen.

The capability to display hidden lines as dashes, rather than removing them altogether, assists in the creation of the final drawings. Also, since a 3-D model does not show all of the information that a drawing would, elements such as dimensions and text can be added in special layers. Ideally, the 2-D drawings are linked dynamically through data associativity to the model so that drawings are updated automatically as the model is modified. The safest approach is to generate the 2-D documentation only after the design has been finalized.

9.15 Data Exchange Standards

Data exchange standards have been developed for the purpose of allowing databases to be shared by CAD and CAM systems and from one CAD/CAM system to another (Figure 9.100). In larger companies, it is fairly common to have more than one CAD system, and the resulting data must be exchanged with the company's CAM systems. In addition, data from the CAD/CAM systems of outside vendors supplying standardized parts must be integrated with the company's systems.

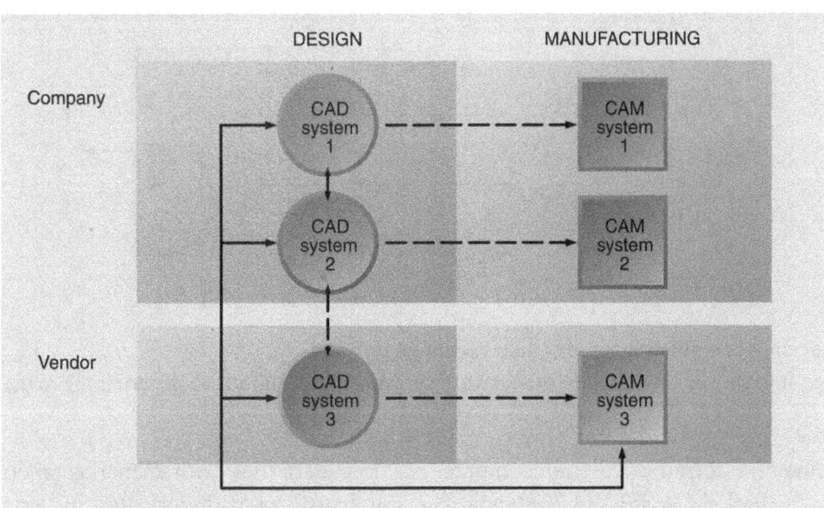

Figure 9.100

Data exchange between various CAD and CAM systems

Reliable data exchange tools are a must for coordinating the manufacturing activities within the company and by outside contractors.

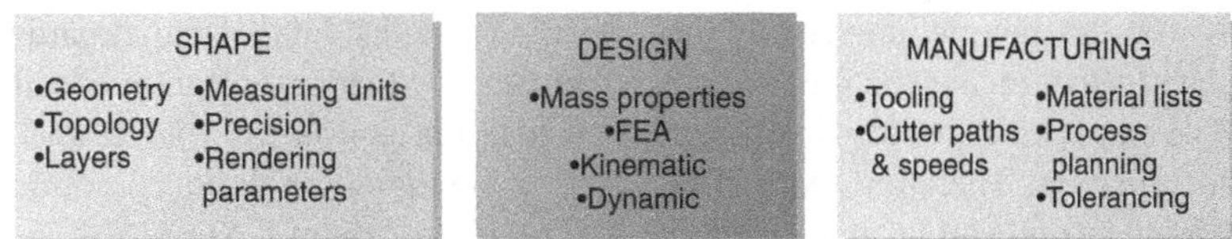

Figure 9.101

Types of CAD/CAM Data

Modern CAD/CAM systems allow information on every phase of the design and manufacturing process to be stored in a database.

There are many types of data that can potentially be exchanged between CAD/CAM databases (Figure 9.101). The data can be divided roughly into shape, design, and manufacturing information. Shape data can be divided into geometry, topology, font, color, measuring units, and level of precision. Design data can include the results of mass properties analyses and FEA. Manufacturing data would include material lists, tolerancing, process planning, etc. While early data-exchange standards focused on data formats (how information would be displayed), later formats focused on the data model (specific information to be displayed). Through this evolutionary process, data exchange standards have come to support increasingly complex information. However, CAD software vendors have been reluctant to adopt and implement some of the newer standards definitions and specifications, which has left a void in the pipeline of communicating model data between CAD systems.

Drawing Exchange Format (DXF) **Drawing exchange format (DXF)** is a standard originally developed by Autodesk, the developers of AutoCAD (Figure 9.102 on the next page). Due to the longevity and dominance of AutoCAD in the microcomputer market, DXF has become a de facto standard in this market. DXF is an ASCII text file containing both 2-D and 3-D geometric and topological information, in addition to such information as layer, line color, and text.

Initial Graphics Exchange Specification (IGES) In the 1970s, the U.S. government, specifically the Air Force, and the large defense contractors began work on a data ex-

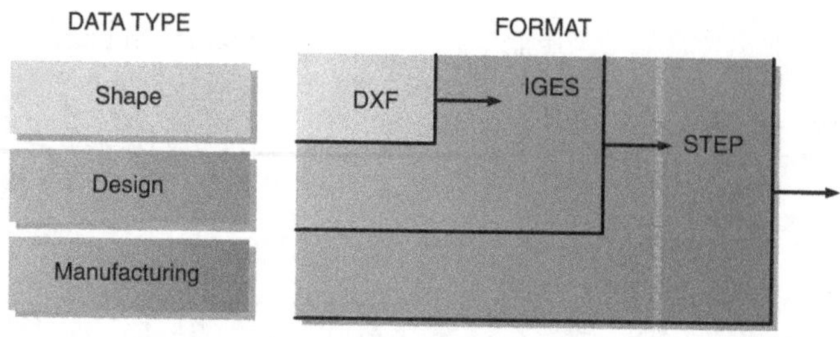

Figure 9.102

Type of information or data contained in neutral data exchange formats

Different data exchange standards are designed to support differing amounts of information pertaining to the design and manufacture of a product.

change format for their mainframe and minicomputer CAD/CAM systems. In 1980, the ANSI Y14.26 standards committees voted to adopt **Initial Graphics Exchange Specification (IGES)** Version 1.0 as part of its standards on digital product data. IGES initially supported only 2-D data, version 2.0 supported finite element data, version 4.0 supports 3-D CSG model information, and version 5.0 will support B-rep model data.

Like DXF, IGES was originally designed to write to an ASCII text file. However, the generic, universally descriptive nature of the data format means the files are not very concise. Also, ASCII text is an especially inefficient way of saving digital information. Therefore, both DXF and IGES ASCII files tend to be quite large, usually many times larger than the same information stored in its original format. IGES version 3.0 was developed with compression schemes to reduce file sizes by a third.

Although IGES and DXF do not explicitly contain manufacturing data, both standards are still used extensively for the exchange of data between CAD and CAM systems. The shape data in the exchange file are translated from CAD to CAM, where they are augmented with manufacturing information, entered manually. However, as constraint-based CAD tools have developed, the IGES standard has been unable to incorporate parameters, constraints, and construction history from these models.

DXF continues to be dominant in the PC market, and IGES is used extensively in mainframe, minicomputer, and workstation systems. As PC CAD packages such as AutoCAD and CADKEY have migrated to workstations, support for both standards has increased. Users should still be aware that some elements native to a particular system may not be supported by either neutral format. In addition, the method of information translation is subject to interpretation. All translators should be thoroughly tested with benchmark files before being used for production. Part files with planar geometry, oblique surfaces, and surfaces with curvature in two directions work well as test cases. Assembly models with varying numbers of components work well also for testing the translation of CAD data in any format.

Product Data Exchange using STEP (PDES) In the mid-1980s, the development of a new data-exchange format was begun—Standard for the Exchange of Product (STEP) model data—by an organization known as PDES. Eventually that organization became PDES Incorporated, whose mission is to promote the development of STEP as a standard for digitally communicating design data through the use of CAD, CAM, and PDM systems. STEP finally evolved into a sanctioned standard in 1994 and currently is being maintained by technical committees within the International Organization for Standardization (ISO). Currently, STEP is widely known as ISO 10303, which is a data-exchange standard that encompasses data related to geometry, dimensioning, manufacturing, and support. Unlike IGES, the STEP file format includes information regarding shape (3-D by default), design, manufacturing, quality assurance, testing, maintenance, etc. The STEP standard is becoming increasingly viable for companies as a mechanism to communicate and store design information as product lifecycles continue to increase, in some cases lasting as long as 50 years. In order to maintain data for such a long period of time and across diverse industries and markets, the STEP file format has remained open to the public domain and can be edited to reflect the needs of a specific company or product. Hence, it is evolving into a neutral file format capable of being a repository for much of the data necessary to design, manufacture, and support a product. Future releases of the STEP standard are likely to address product data structure, construction history, and parameters and constraints, all of which are found in modern CAD systems. In doing so, the communication of product data throughout an enterprise may become easier (Figure 9.100).

In an effort to promote communication between companies and their suppliers, CAD software vendors are examining and developing other neutral data formats that eventually may become industry standards. Technologies such as JT, 3DXML, and 3D PDF are allowing companies the ability to share 3-D CAD data in a fashion that currently is not done using IGES or STEP. In particular, 3DXML and 3D PDF both are based on technologies that have the benefit of being *defacto* industry standards in domains other than engineering design. As such, they have been able to integrate into corporate documentation procedures without a great deal of additional planning or difficulty. To support collaboration across the enterprise and across the supply chain (Figure 9.100), software vendors have developed these "lightweight" 3-D file formats used for viewing a 3-D model without requiring the native CAD software to be installed on the local workstation. The receiver need only have a model viewing utility (typically made by the CAD software vendor) on their machine so that the 3-D geometry may be viewed. In addition to viewing the model, many of these applications support the ability to search, measure, and create cross sections through the geometry being viewed. It has been argued that with advances in the development of these types of 3-D data communication techniques, the creation and use of 2-D technical drawings will be minimized.

9.16 Summary

Three-dimensional modeling is becoming the standard method in engineering for developing product designs for many industries. The advantages of using 3-D modeling versus 2-D drafting are numerous. New technical design methods require the use of intelligent graphics, that is, graphics, such as surface and solid models, that contain important information beyond the basic geometric shapes. The more information contained in the model, the more useful the model is for designing, manufacturing, marketing, and servicing a product or structure.

Online Learning Center (OLC) Features

There are a number of Online Learning Center features listed below that you can use to supplement your text reading to improve your understanding and retention of the material presented in this chapter at www.mhhe.com/bertoline.

- Learning Objectives
- Chapter Outline
- Questions for Review
- Multiple Choice Quiz
- True or False Questions
- Flashcards
- Website Links
- Animations
- Related Readings
- Stapler Design Problem

Questions for Review

1. What is a fundamental difference between 2-D and 3-D CAD systems? Is there any overlap between the two types of CAD systems?
2. What are some of the different types of computer hardware platforms used for running CAD software? During what periods in history were each of these platforms in common usage?
3. What is the minimum information needed to define a true wireframe model? Is there enough information in a wireframe model to determine which edges are hidden?
4. What are the advantages and disadvantages of the three types of curves used to make surface patches?
5. Can you depict a hole in an object using a primitive-based solid modeler? What other types of solid modelers could be used?
6. Define the three types of Boolean operations, and sketch examples of each one. Can you derive the same final object using different Boolean operations and/or primitives?
7. Describe the differences and similarities of B-rep models and CSG models; do the same for wireframe models and B-rep models.
8. What is "design intent"? Why does this play a role in planning the construction of a constraint-based model?
9. What are the basic elements of a generalized sweep? Describe the major types of generalized sweeps used in feature creation.
10. What are workplanes used for? What are five ways a workplane can be defined?

11. What is the difference between implicit and explicit constraints? Give examples of four types of implicit geometric constraints.
12. Give an example of a parent-child relationship. How is a feature tree used to identify parent-child relationships?
13. What are the two primary types of duplication methods? What input parameters are needed to define each one?
14. Describe the relationship of the view camera to the workplane and to the viewport.
15. List the rules of thumb for choosing a good viewpoint. Do all of these rules apply when you are using either parallel or perspective projection?
16. Will a translation operation always change the global coordinate location of all vertices on the object? What about a rotation operation?
17. Draw or describe a dialog box which would create bosses in a feature-based modeler.
18. Explain the advantages and disadvantages of using a virtual model over a real model when designing a product.
19. Name and briefly describe four different analysis techniques and give an application of each on a real-world product.
20. Describe the connection of CAD to computer-aided manufacturing (CAM). How does the CAD/CAM relationship alter the role of 2-D CAD documents?
21. What are the differences between IGES and STEP?
22. Describe the role of viewable neutral file formats in the product lifecycle.
23. Discuss the impact that Ivan Sutherland has had on the field of engineering graphics.

Further Reading

Anand, V. *Computer Graphics and Geometric Modeling for Engineers.* New York: John Wiley, 1993.

Bolluyt, James E. *Design Modeling with Pro/Engineer.* Shawnee-Mission, KS: Schroff Development Corp., 1998.

Kidd, Paul T. *Agile Manufacturing: Forging New Frontiers,* Edited by J. Browne, Series in Manufacturing Systems. Reading, MA: Addison-Wesley, 1994.

LaCourse, Donald, ed. *Solid Modeling Handbook.* NY: McGraw-Hill, 1996.

Machover, Carl. *CAD/CAM Handbook.* NY: McGraw-Hill, 1996.

IGES Home page (http://www.nist.gov/iges/).

Introduction to the STEP file standard (http://strategis.ic.gc.ca/epic/site/adad.nsf/en/ad03581e.html).

PDES, Inc. (Promoting the Development and Implementation of the STEP Standard) (http://pdesinc.aticorp.org/).

Problems

9.1 Given the vertex, edge, and face information found in Table 9.1, create a wireframe or B-rep model using CAD or hand tools. Using the same vertex information, create at least one different object by altering the topology of the model (i.e., create new connections between the vertices).

9.2 Given the following list of procedural instructions for generating edges, create a wireframe or B-rep model using CAD or sketching. (Note: *move* means relocate cursor without drawing an edge; *go* means create an edge.)

E1: move to 0,2,0 and go +3 in X
E2: go +2 in Y
E3: go −3 in X
E4: go −2 in Y
E5: go −4 in Z
E6: go −2 in Y
E7: go 5 in X
E8: go 4 in Y
E9: go −3 in X
E10: go −2 in Y
E11: go −2 in X
E12: move 3 in X and go +4 in Z
E13: move 2 in Y and go −4 in Z
E14: move –3 in X, move +4 in Z, and go −8 in Z
E15: go 11 in X
E16: go −6 in X and −5 in Z (to draw diagonal line)
E17: go −1 in Z
E18: move −4 in Y and go +1 in Z
E19: move 4 in Y and go −4 in Z
E20: go 6 in X and −5 in Z (to draw diagonal)
E21: go 4 in Y
E22: move −4 in Y and go −11 in X
E23: go 4 in Z
E24: move −4 in Z and go 4 in Y

Add up all of the *move's* and *go's*. What is the net change in X, Y, and Z? How does that correspond to where you started and ended in building your model?

9.3 (Figure 9.103) Create wireframe or solid models by sweeping the profiles shown in the figure using a scale assigned by your instructor.

Do the following with each of the profiles:

a. Sweep linearly 5 units along the +Z axis.
b. Sweep linearly along the vector (2,–3,5).
c. Sweep 360° about the Y axis.
d. Sweep 360° about the X axis.
e. Sweep 90° about the +X axis.
f. Sweep 270° about the –Y axis.

Table 9.1 **Vertex, Edge, and Face Information for Problem 9.1**

Vertices	Edges	Faces
V1: 0,0,0	E1: V1,V2	F1: E1,E2,E3,E4,E5,E6, E7,E8,E9,E10,E11, E12
V2: 2,0,0	E2: V2,V3	
V3: 2,2,0	E3: V3,V4	
V4: 10,2,0	E4: V4,V5	F2: E13,E14,E15,E16, E17,E18,E19,E20, E21, E22,E23,E24
V5: 10,0,0	E5: V5,V6	
V6: 12,0,0	E6: V6,V7	
V7: 12,8,0	E7: V7,V8	F3: E1,E26,E13,E25
V8: 8,8,0	E8: V8,V9	F4: E2,E27,E14,E26
V9: 8,5,0	E9: V9,V10	F5: E3,E28,E15,E27
V10: 4,5,0	E10: V10,V11	F6: E4,E29,E16,E28
V11: 4,8,0	E11: V11,V12	F7: E5,E30,E17,E29
V12: 0,8,0	E12: V12,V13	F8: E6,E31,E18,E30
V13: 0,0,6	E13: V13,V14	F9: E7,E32,E19,E31
V14: 2,0,6	E14: V14,V15	F10: E8,E33,E20,E32
V15: 2,2,6	E15: V15,V16	F11: E9,E34,E21,E33
V16: 10,2,6	E16: V16,V17	F12: E10,E35,E22,E34
V17: 10,0,6	E17: V17,V18	F13: E11,E36,E23,E35
V18: 12,0,6	E18: V18,V19	F14: E12,E26,E24,E36
V19: 12,8,6	E19: V19,V20	
V20: 8,8,6	E20: V20,V21	
V21: 8,5,6	E21: V21,V22	
V22: 4,5,6	E22: V22,V23	
V23: 4,8,6	E23: V23,V24	
V24: 0,8,6	E24: V24,V13	
	E25: V1,V13	
	E26: V2,V14	
	E27: V3,V15	
	E28: V4,V16	
	E29: V5,V17	
	E30: V6,V18	
	E31: V7,V19	
	E32: V8,V20	
	E33: V9,V21	
	E34: V10,V22	
	E35: V11,V23	
	E36: V12,V24	

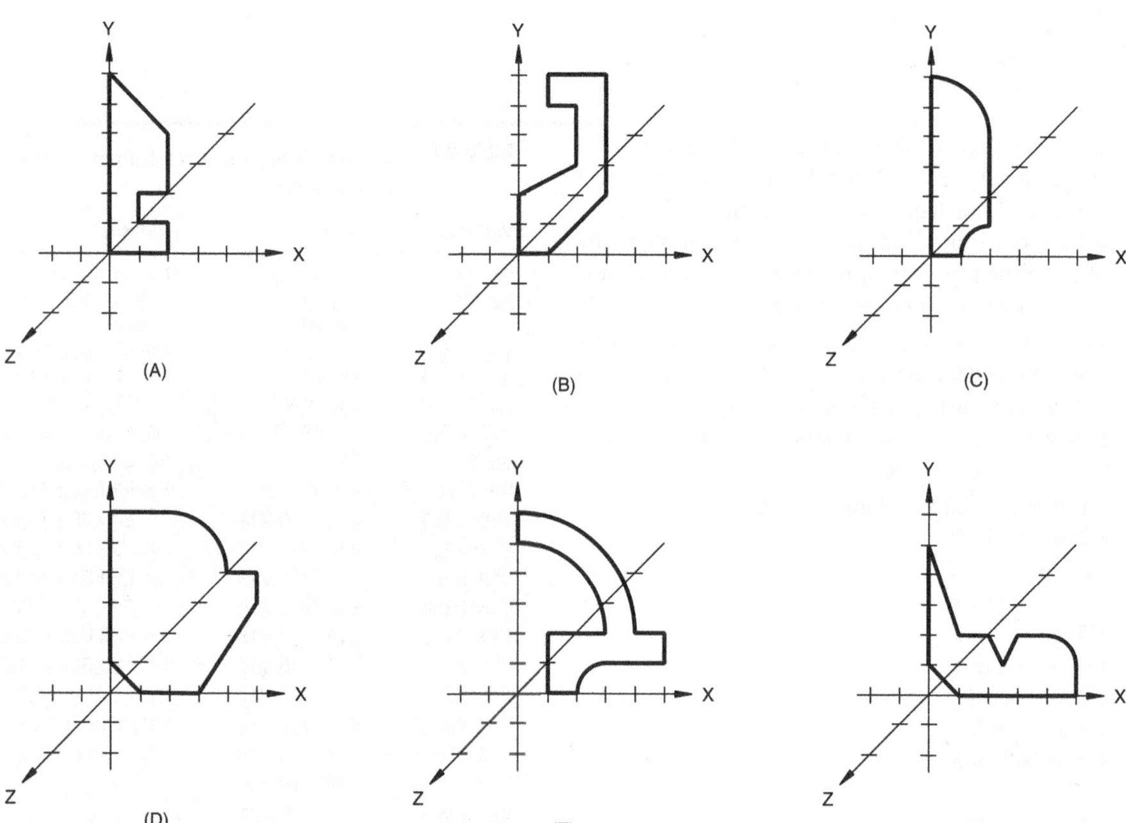

Figure 9.103
Profiles to be swept

g. Sweep 360° about a Y axis offset 2 units in +X direction.

h. Sweep 180° about an X axis offset 3 units in +Y direction.

i. Sweep the profile about 2 different axes to create two objects. Combine the two objects to create a new single object.

9.4 Create a coffee mug, using sweep operations. In a sketch, clearly define the profile shapes to be used and the axes about which they will be swept.

9.5 Problem 9.3 demonstrated that the same profile turned about different axes will create markedly different shapes. In Figure 9.104, there are 12 objects swept, using 12 different profiles. Match the objects with the same profile used to create 3-D objects. (Hint: Unlike Problem 9.3, the profiles may not always be swept at axes perpendicular to each other.)

9.6 Model the primitives in Figure 9.105A, using either general modeling techniques or specialized parametric primitive modeling tools and a scale assigned by your instructor.

a. Using purely additive techniques, combine the primitives to create the objects in Figure 9.99B.

b. Create at least five other objects, using combinations of the primitives. Use five or more primitives in each of the new objects.

9.7 Figures 9.106A through C contain groups of three overlapping primitives shown in wireframe. On separate sheets of isometric grid paper, sketch the objects resulting from the following Boolean operations:

Figure 9.106A:

a. $(A \cup B) \cup C$

b. $(A \cup B) - C$

c. $(A - B) - C$

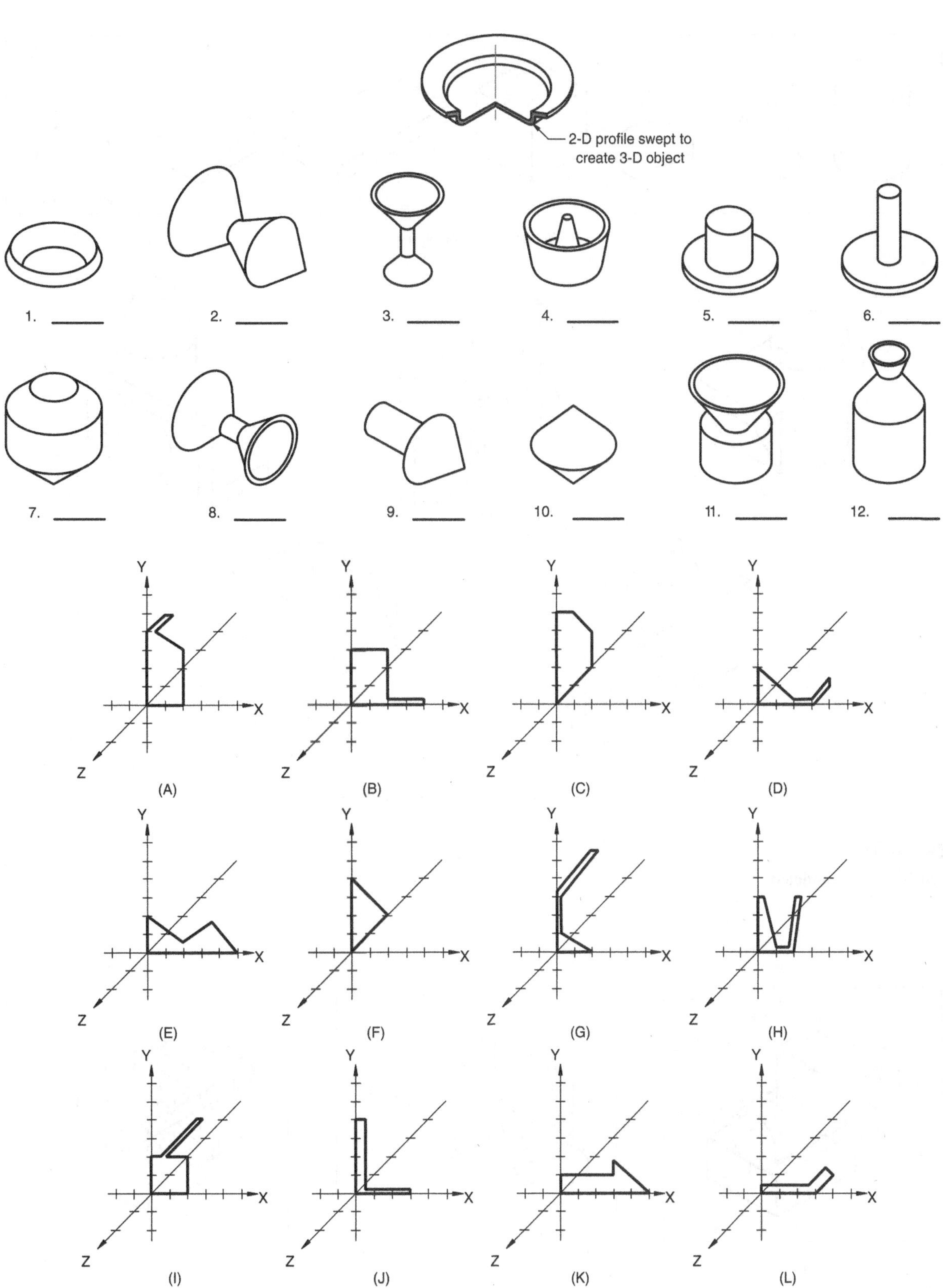

Figure 9.104

Match 2-D profiles to 3-D objects

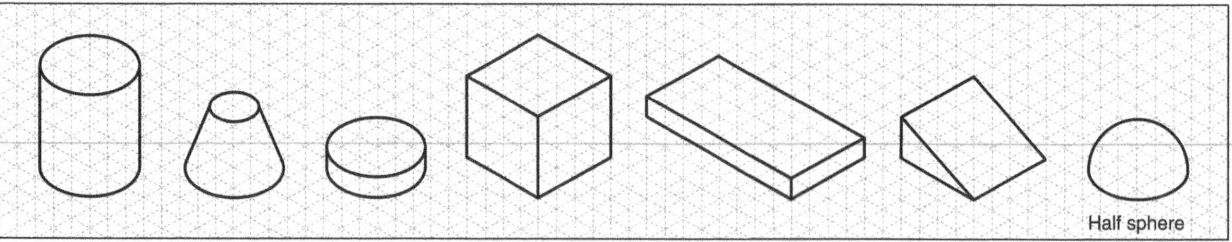

(A) Model these primitives

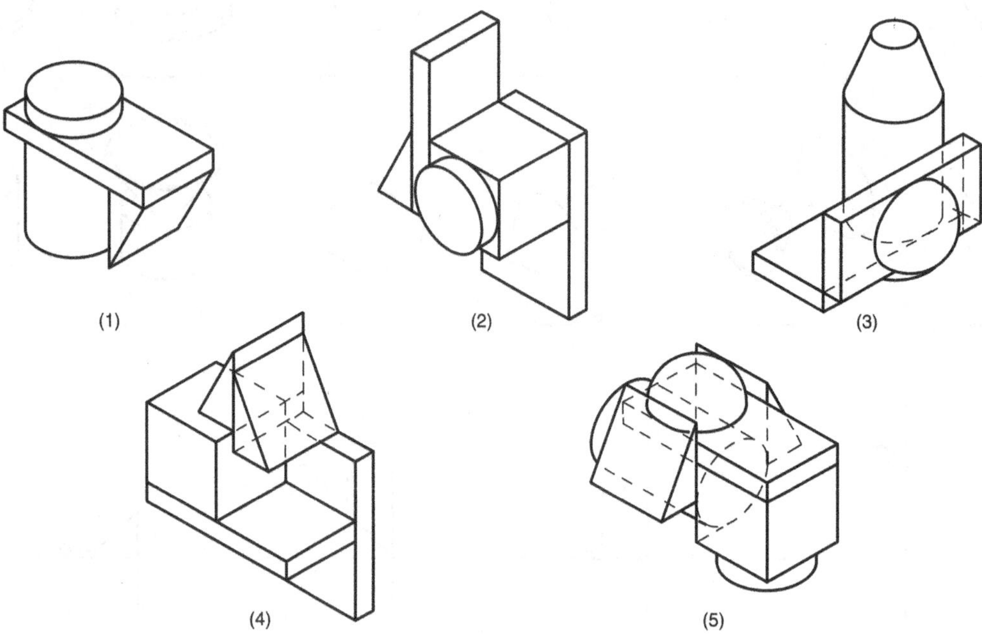

(B) Combine the primitives to make these objects

Figure 9.105

Primitives to be modeled

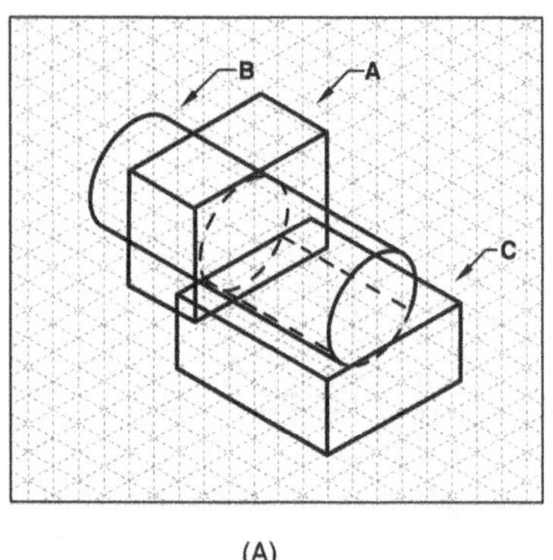

(A)

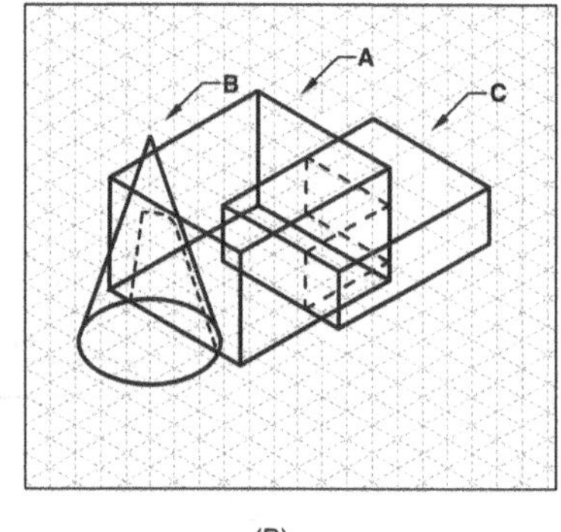

(B)

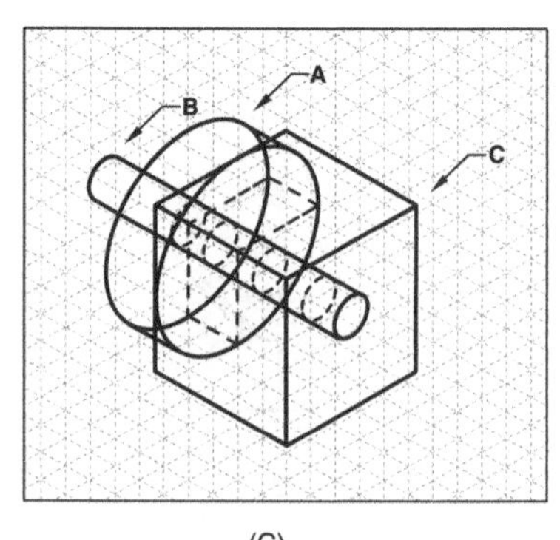

(C)

Figure 9.106

Groups of three overlapping primitives shown in wireframe

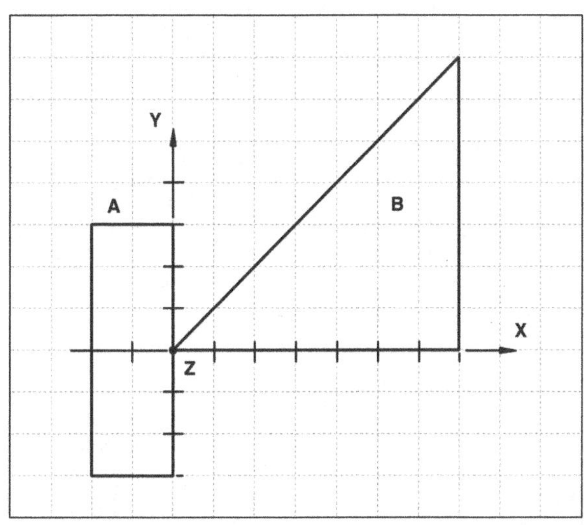

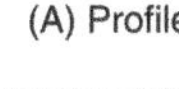
(A) Profile

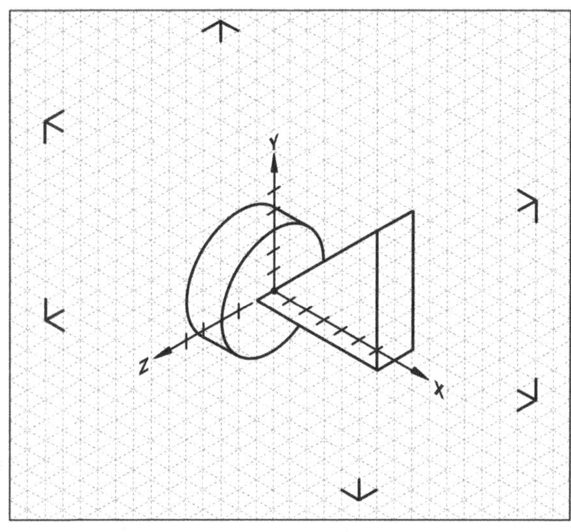

(A)

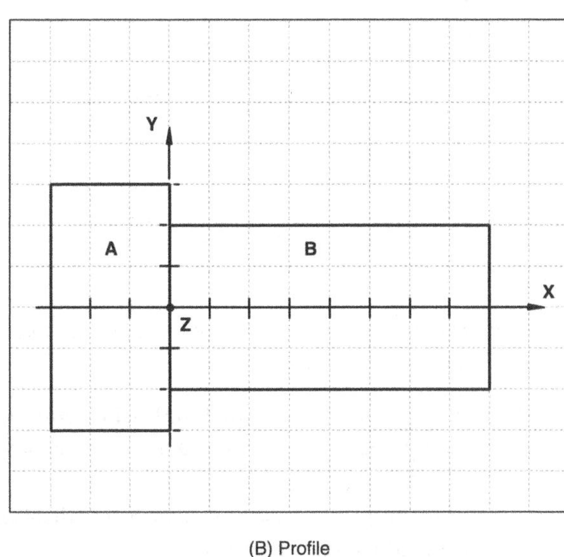

(B) Profile

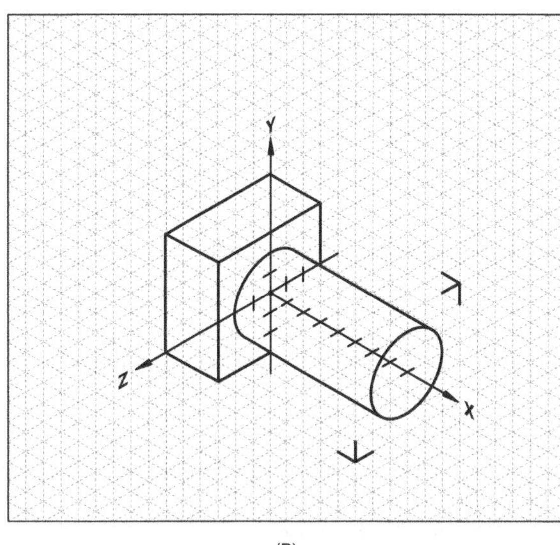

(B)

Figure 9.107

Primitive objects to be modeled

Figure 9.106B.

a. (A − B) − C

b. (A ∪ B) ∪ C

c. B − (A ∪ C)

Figure 9.106C.

a. (C − A) − B

b. (A ∪ C) − B

c. (A ∩ C) − B

9.8 Model the primitives in the positions shown in Figures 9.107A and B. Create new objects by first performing the following transformations and then performing the Boolean operation A − B on primitive A. For example, in part (*a*), translate primitive B zero units in the +X direction. Next do a Boolean subtraction of B from A.

Figure 9.107A.

a. Translate 0 units in +X.

b. Translate 3 units in −X.

c. Translate 5 units in −X.

d. Rotate 45° about +Z.

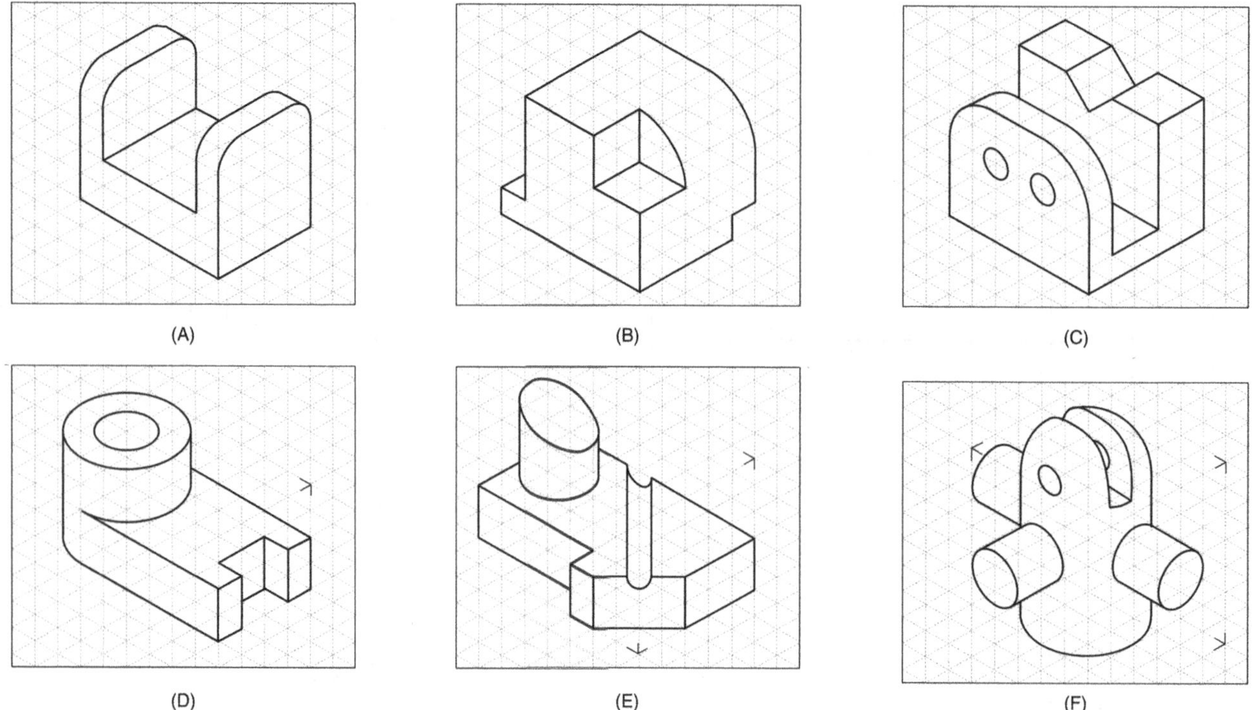

Figure 9.108

Create 3-D models of the objects. All holes are through.

e. Rotate 90° about +Z.

f. Rotate 45° about +Z, translate 1 unit in –X.

Figure 9.107B.

a. Translate 1 unit in –X.

b. Translate 2 units in +Y and translate 2 units in –X.

c. Rotate 90° about +Z.

d. Rotate 45° about +Z and translate 1 unit in –X.

e. Translate 4 units in –X and rotate 90° about +Z.

f. Translate 4 units in +X and rotate 90° about +Z.

9.9 Create the objects in Figure 9.108, using wireframe or solid modeling techniques and a scale assigned by your instructor.

a. Print or plot an isometric pictorial, displayed as a wireframe.

b. Print or plot an isometric pictorial, with hidden lines removed.

c. Capture both standard orthographic views and an isometric view of the object. Organize these views in a standard border with a title block, and print or plot the drawing.

d. Same as (*c*) except add dimensions and notes to the drawing.

9.10 Create the objects in Figure 9.109, using wireframe or solid modeling techniques and a scale assigned by your instructor.

a. Print or plot an isometric pictorial displayed with hidden lines removed.

b. Capture both standard orthographic views and an isometric view of the object. Use auxiliary and section views as appropriate. Organize these views in a standard border with a title block and print or plot the drawing.

c. Same as (*b*) except add dimensions and notes to the drawing.

9.11 Model the assembly shown in Figure 9.110.

a. Organize an exploded assembly from the parts. Capture the following views of the object, place the captured views in a standard border with a title block, and notate appropriately.

(i) Axonometric view.

(ii) Axonometric view, rendered with color to code the parts.

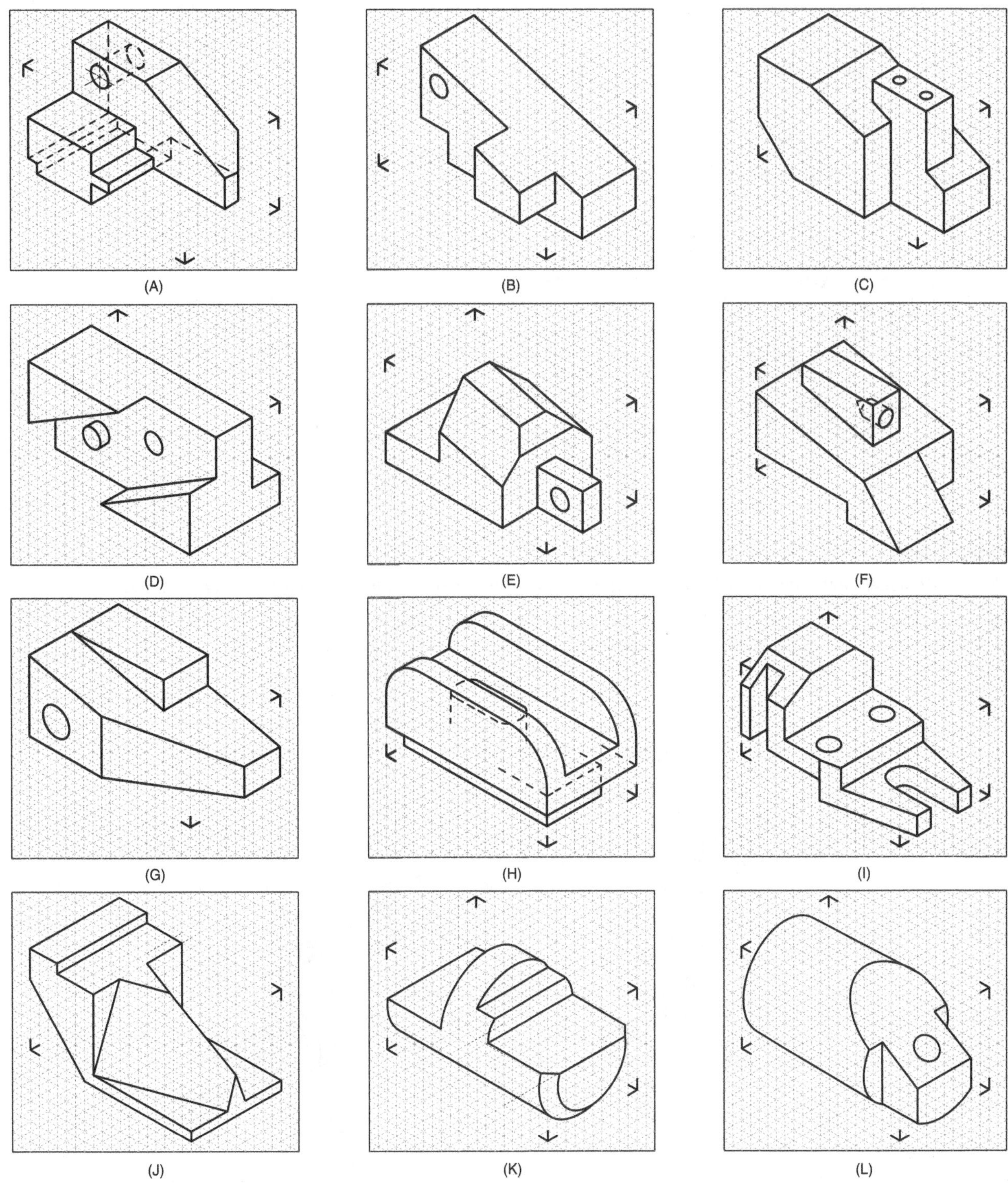

Figure 9.109

Create 3-D models of the objects. All holes are through unless otherwise indicated with dashed lines.

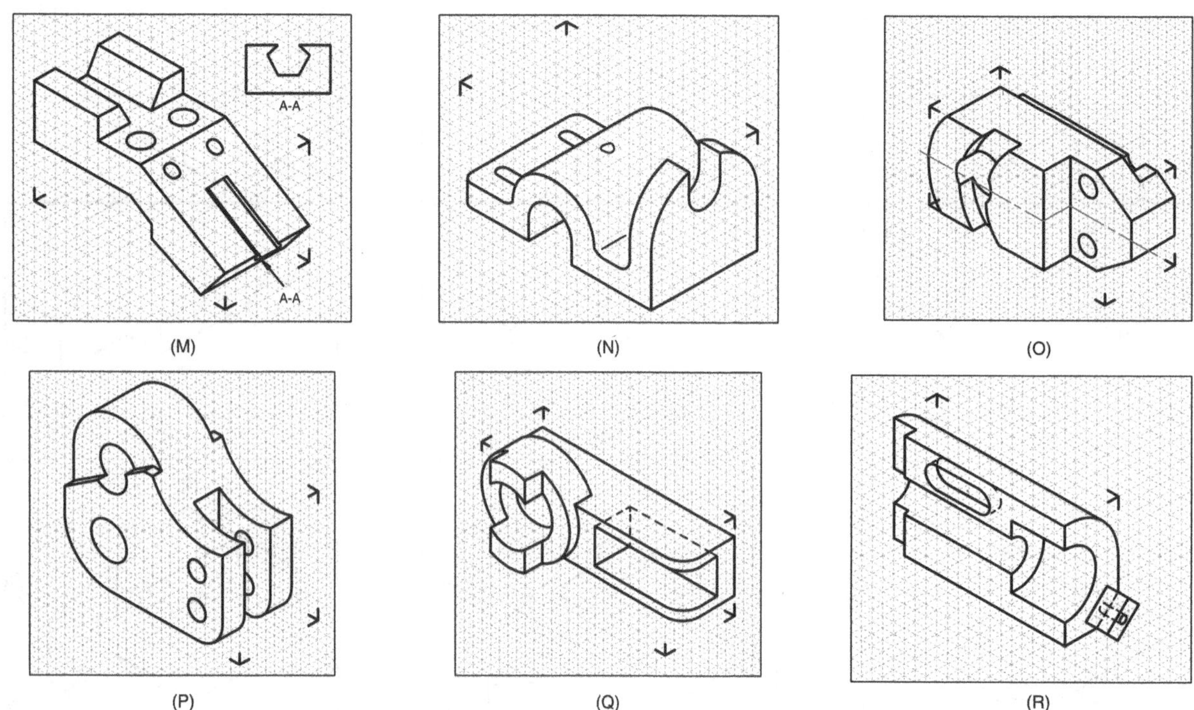

Figure 9.109

Create 3-D models of the objects. All holes are through unless otherwise indicated with dashed lines. (Continued)

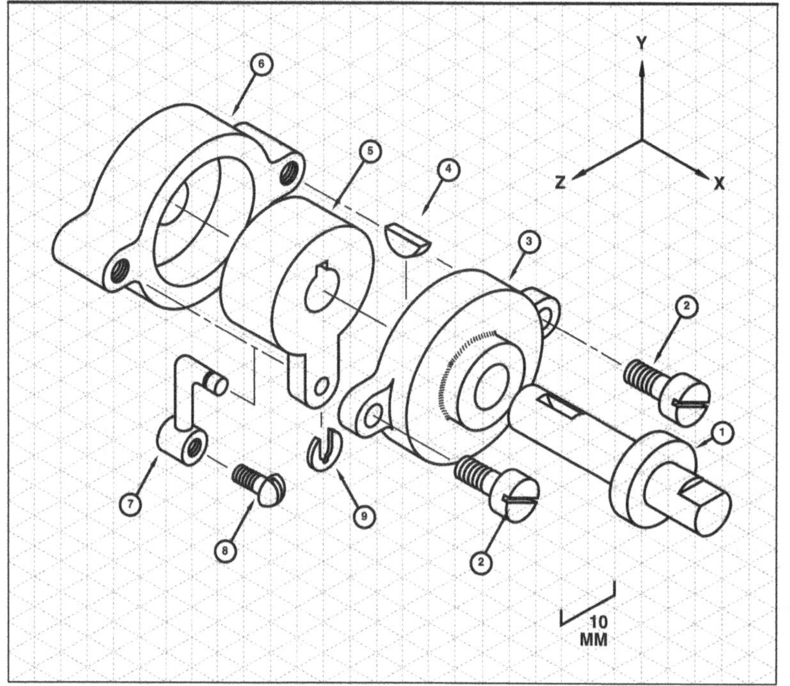

Figure 9.110

Assembly to be modeled

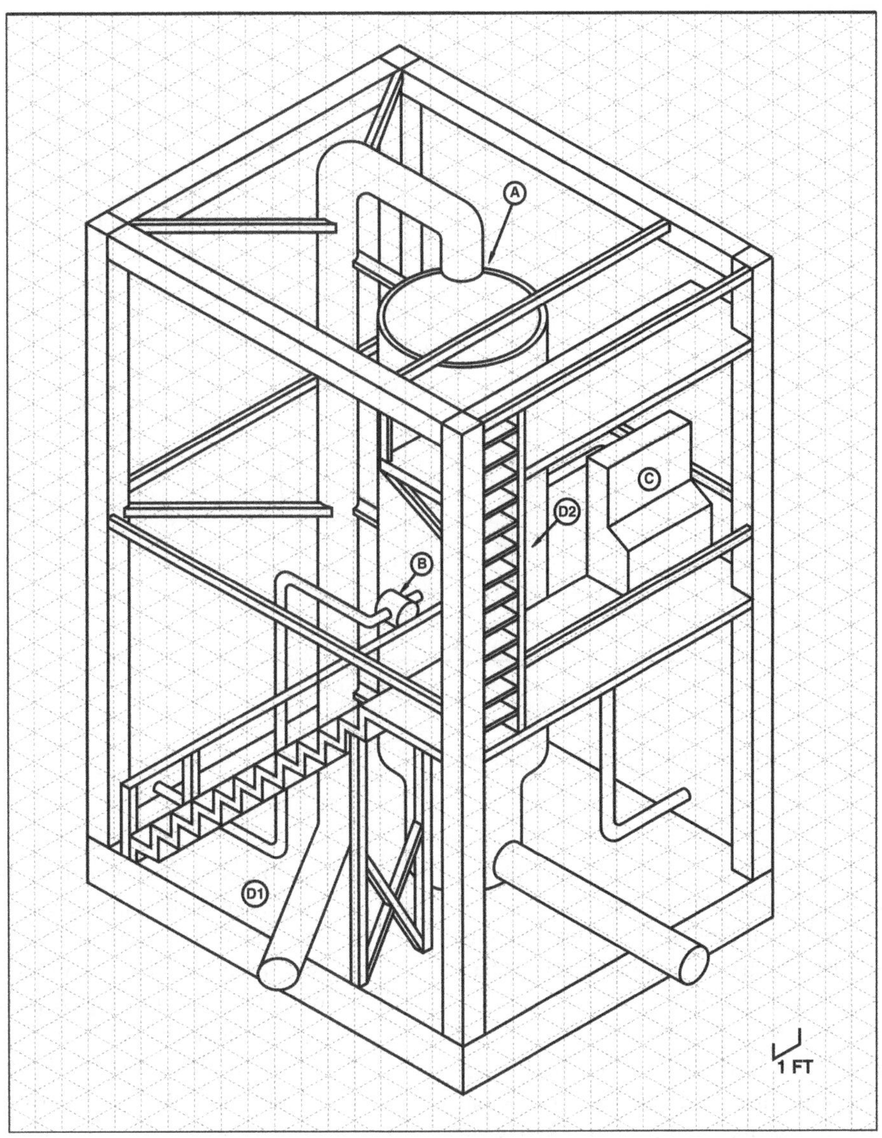

Figure 9.111

Create a 3-D model of this production facility

b. Organize the parts in their assembled position. Capture the following views of the object, place the captured views in a standard border with a title block, and notate appropriately.
   (i) Axonometric pictorial view.
   (ii) Front orthographic view, sectioned.
   (iii) Axonometric pictorial view, rendered and using transparency techniques to reveal interior detail.

c. With the front and back housing (parts 3 and 6) fixed, the shaft (1) rotates the cylinder (5), which, in turn, actuates the "L" pin (7). The screw (8) attaches the "L" pin to a vertical slider (not pictured). Analyze how far the shaft would have to rotate in order to move the vertical slider 5 mm. The "L" pin is vertical when the cylinder is in the position shown in the figure. Represent this analysis as follows:

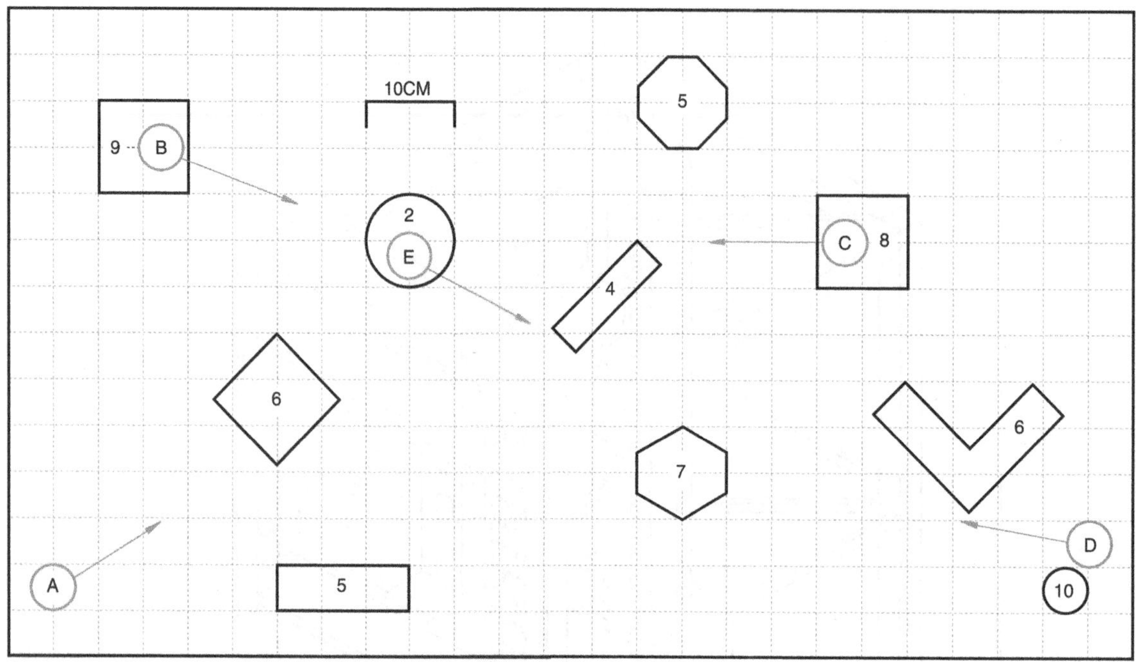

Figure 9.112

Plan (top) view of a collection of polygonal prisms on a base

(i) As an axonometric pictorial, using phantom lines to show the movement.

(ii) As a pair of orthographic views looking down the primary axis, showing the mechanism in its two positions.

(iii) As a computer animation.

9.12 Model the production facility shown in Figure 9.111. Before beginning the modeling process on the computer, divide the facility into a series of logical parts, giving each one a name. You may find it helpful to create sketches of the individual parts. Using the completed model, do the following:

a. Render with color to code the parts.

b. By manipulating the view control of the modeling software, create a "walkthrough" that simulates a worker walking around the base of the platform, up the stairs, and to the front of the control panel (labeled C).

c. Using the view control, analyze whether a worker standing at control panel C could see the following:

(i) Material leaving the input pipe at A.

(ii) The pressure indicator B.

Capture the views as seen by the worker. In addition, create orthographic views showing the line of sight of the worker. Assume 5.75 feet from floor to eye level and a 35° cone of vision. Print or plot a set of drawings depicting this analysis.

d. Do an analysis similar to the one done in (*c*), except evaluate how far down into the main reactor tank a worker can see when standing on the upper catwalk.

e. A new 0.5-foot diameter pipe has to be run from the base at D1 into the side of the reactor tank at D2. The pipe carries a material at high temperatures. Design a path for the pipe which maximizes the distance from worker traffic and other pipes. The pipe needs a minimum 1-foot clearance from workers or other pipes if it is to be uninsulated. Evaluate how much of the pipe needs to be insulated. Print or plot a set of drawings depicting this analysis.

9.13 Figure 9.112 shows a plan (top) view of a collection of polygonal prisms on a base. The number in the middle of each prism indicates height, in 10-cm units. By manipulating the view control, create a series of views looking horizontally from the vectors A through E. Those letters that are over a prism are assumed to be at the top of it. Perform the following changes to the view control, and capture the result using either wireframe, hidden line removal, or shading:

a. Parallel projection.

b. Perspective projection with the default angle of view.

c. Perspective projection with the widest and then the narrowest angle of view.

d. A shaded model and an infinite light source held at a constant location.

e. Same as (*d*), except with shadow casting.

9.14 (Figures 9.113 through 9.116) Assign different Boolean operations to the eight assembled primitive parts, then do the following:

a. Sketch the resulting composite solids.

b. Use a solid modeling software to create the primitives with the given dimensions, then verify your sketches by performing the same Boolean operations on the computer.

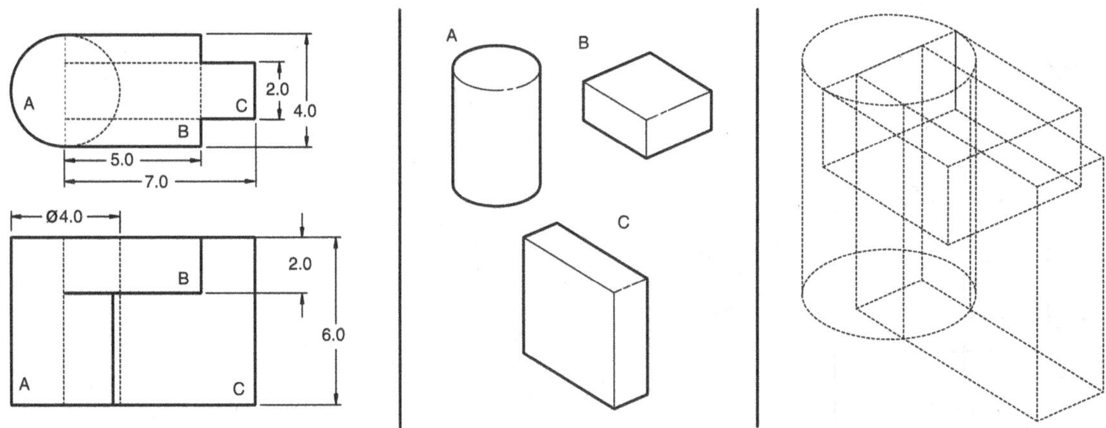

Figure 9.113

Assembled primitive parts for Boolean operations

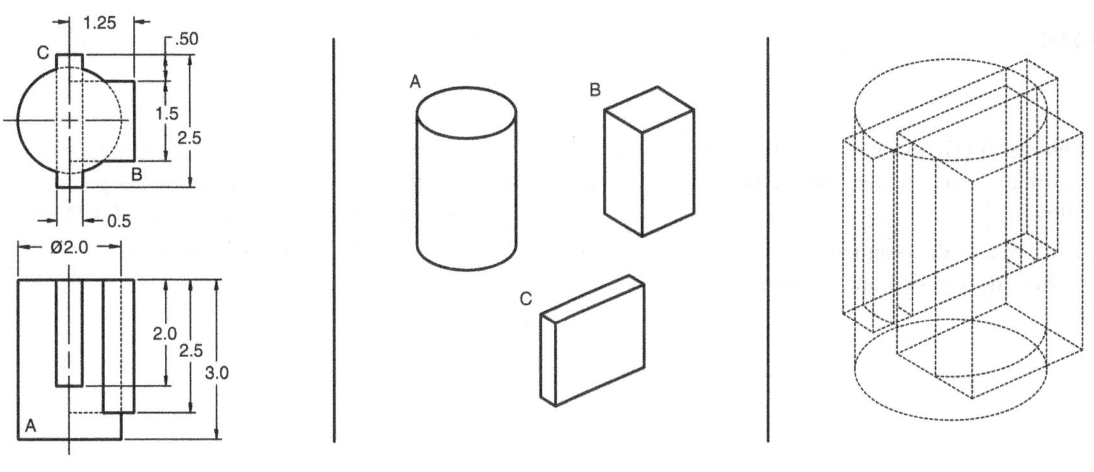

Figure 9.114

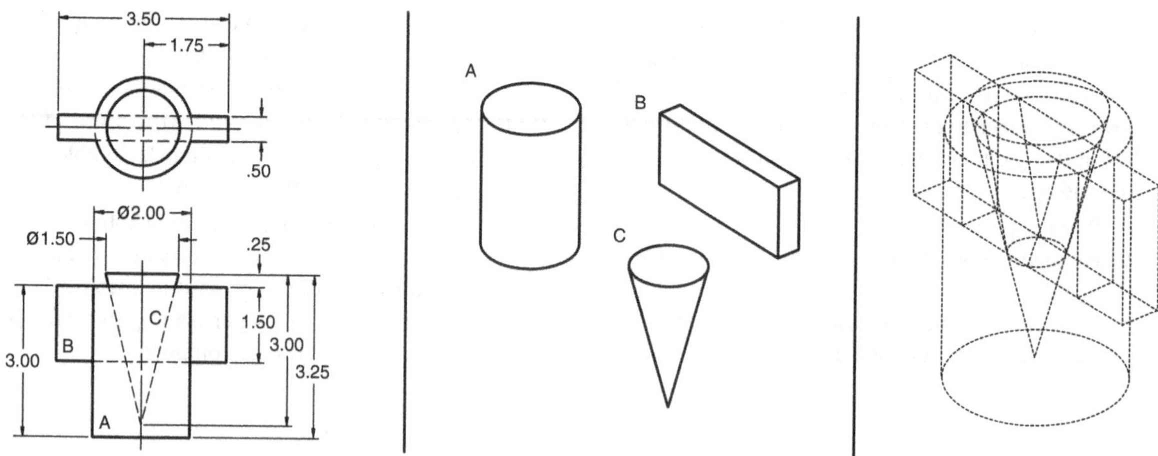

Figure 9.115

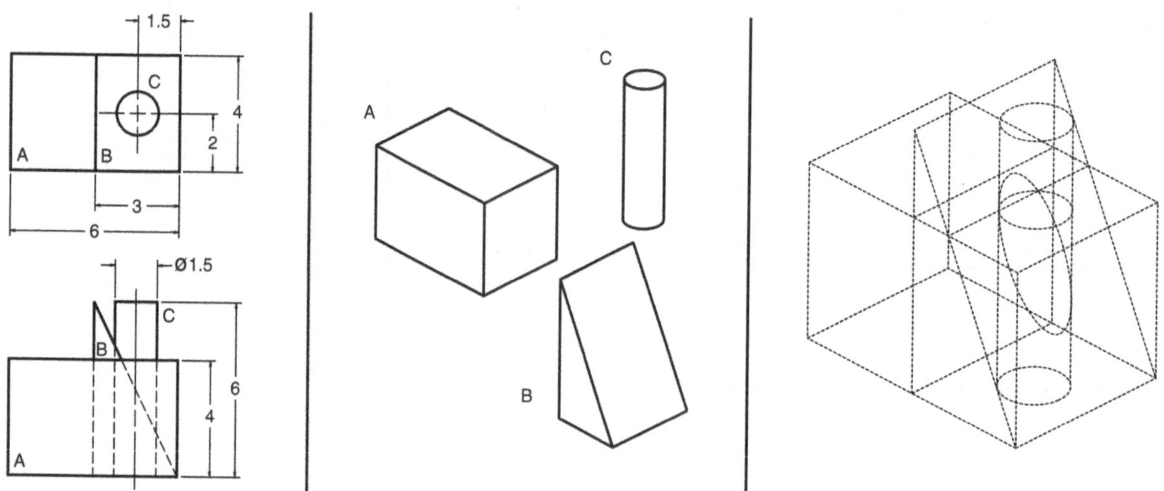

Figure 9.116

9.15 (Figures 9.117 through 9.126) Using the given information for feature-based modeling, do the following:

a. Using a scale assigned by your instructor, measure the profiles and workpiece. On isometric grid paper, sketch the resulting workpiece after the feature-based modeling is performed.

b. Do the same operations with CAD and compare the results with your sketch.

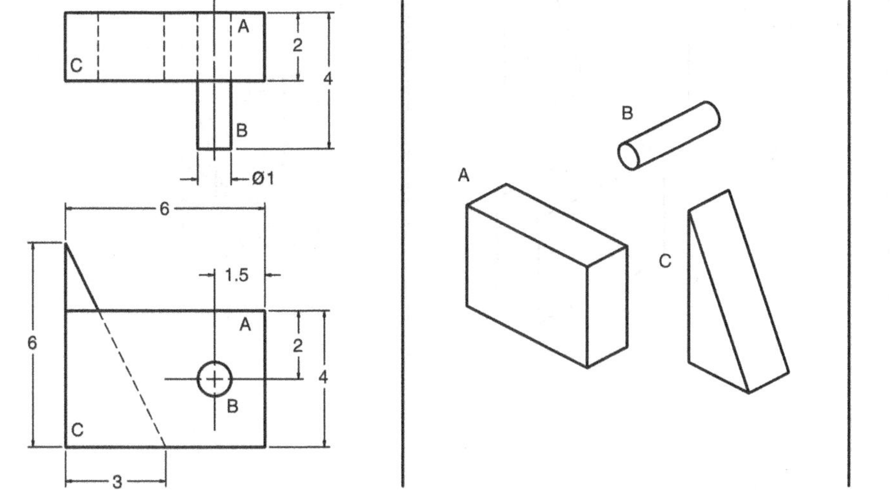

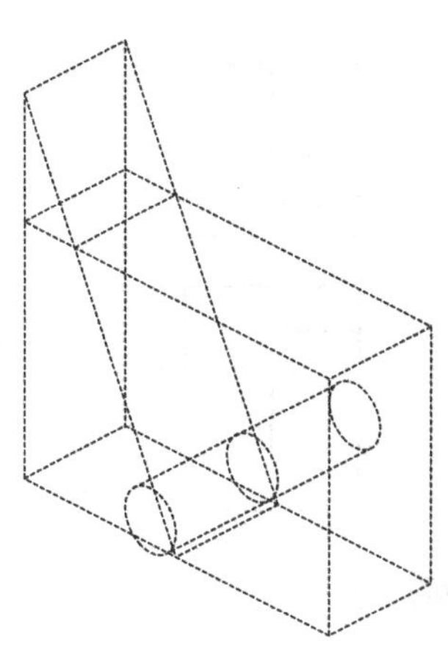

Figure 9.117

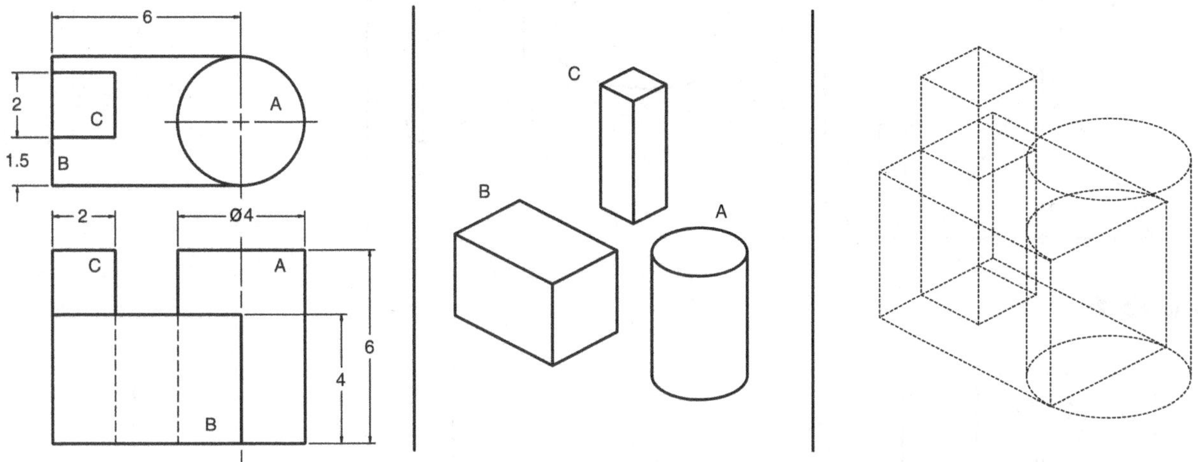

Figure 9.118

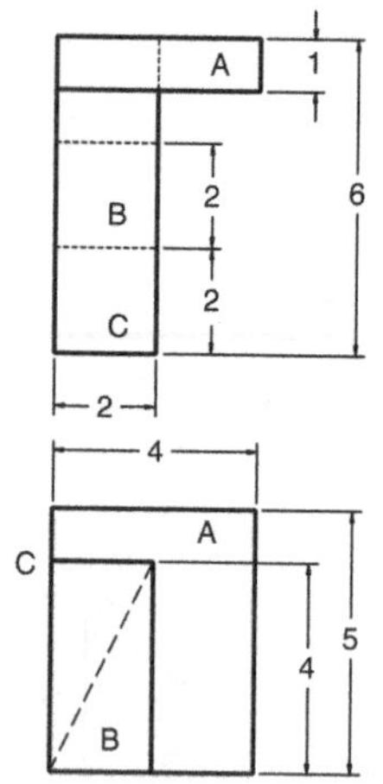

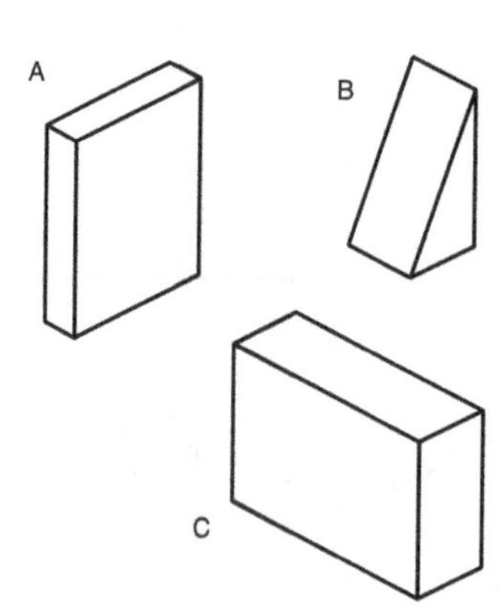

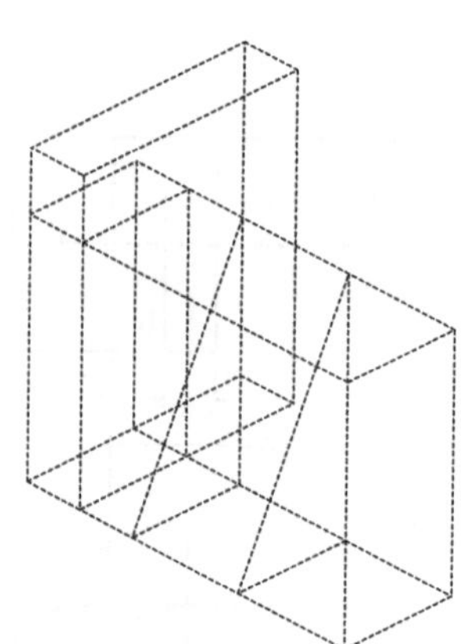

Figure 9.119

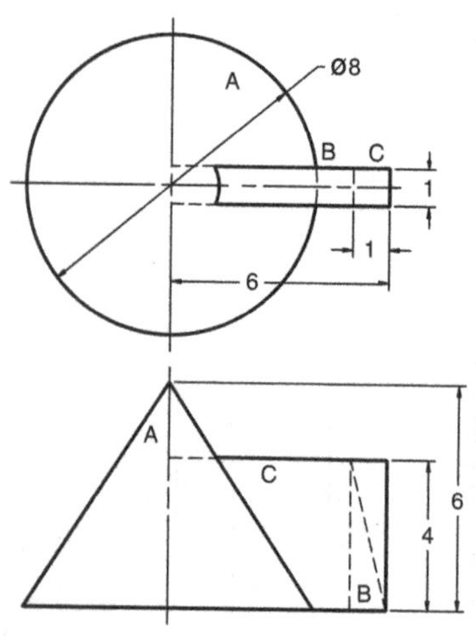

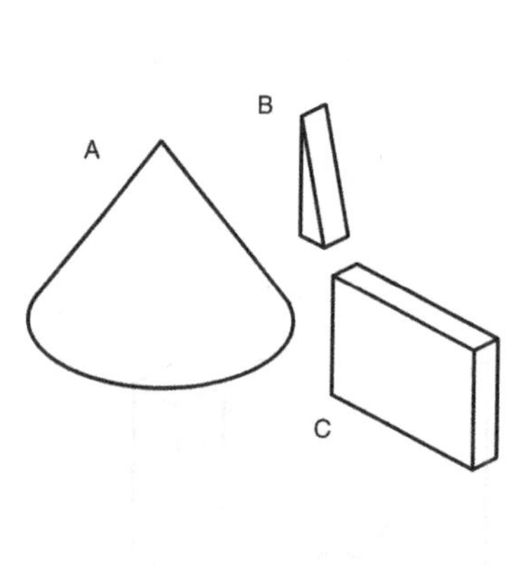

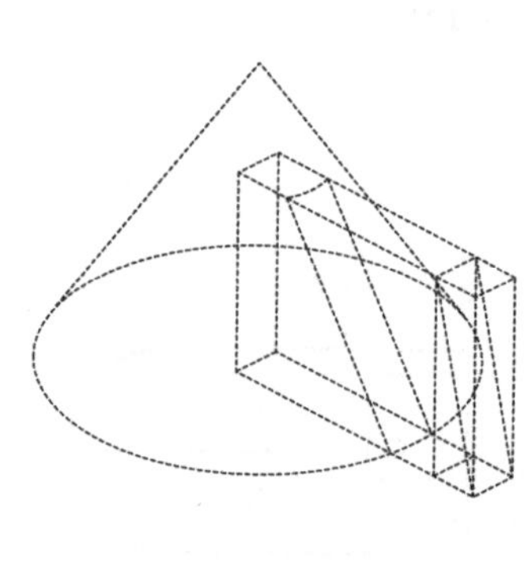

Figure 9.120

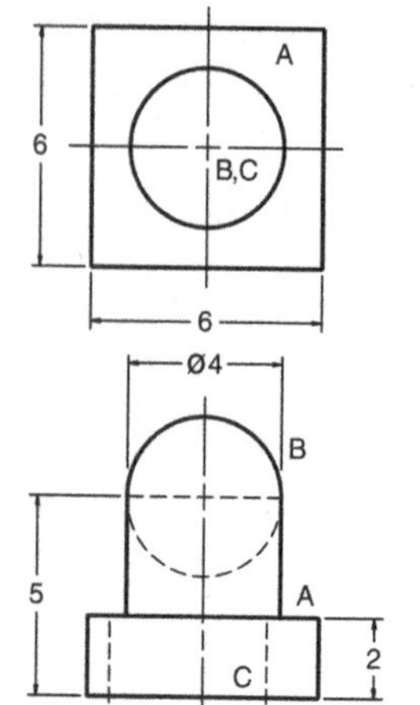

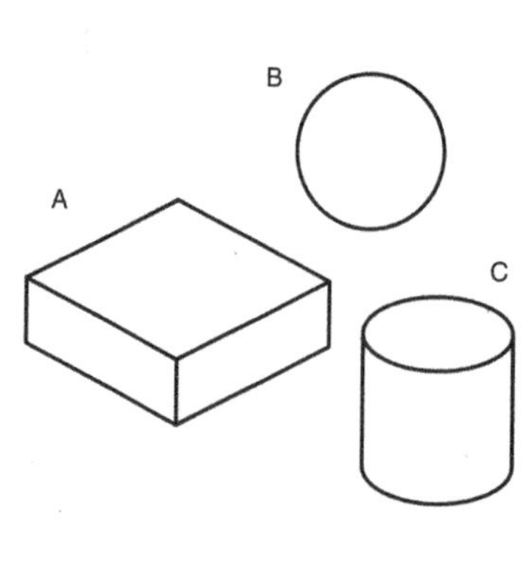

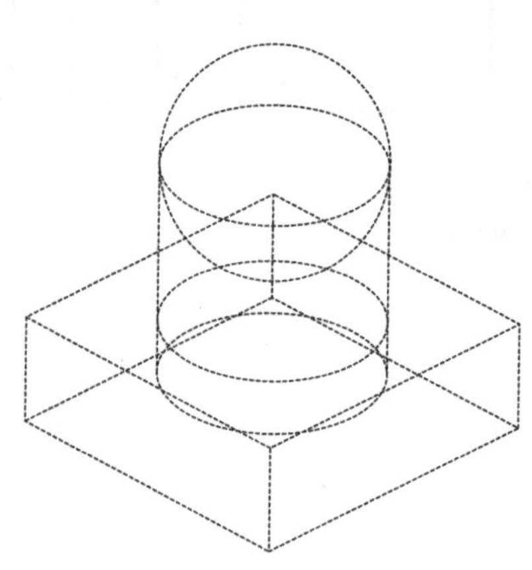

Figure 9.121

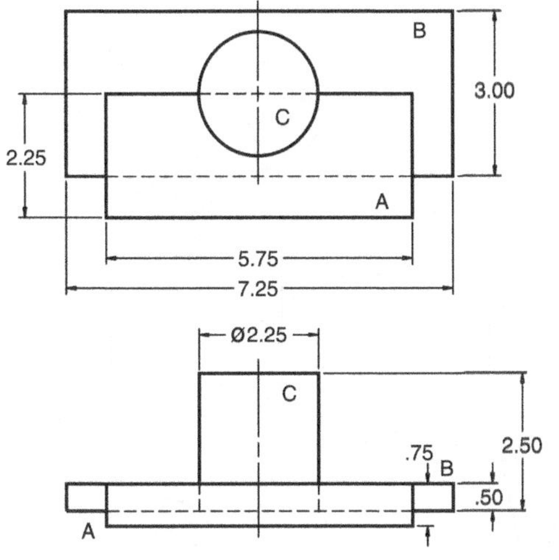

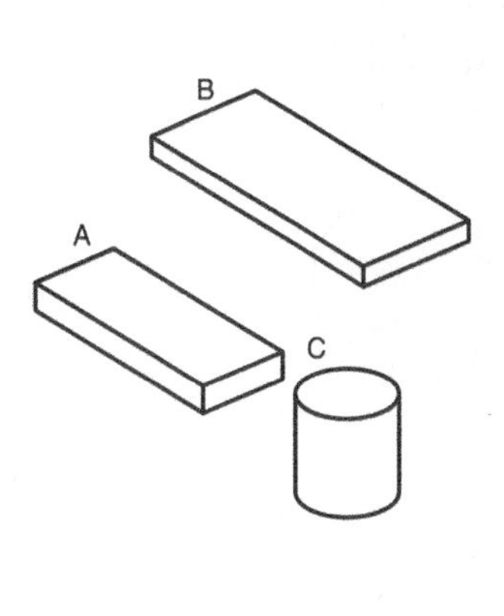

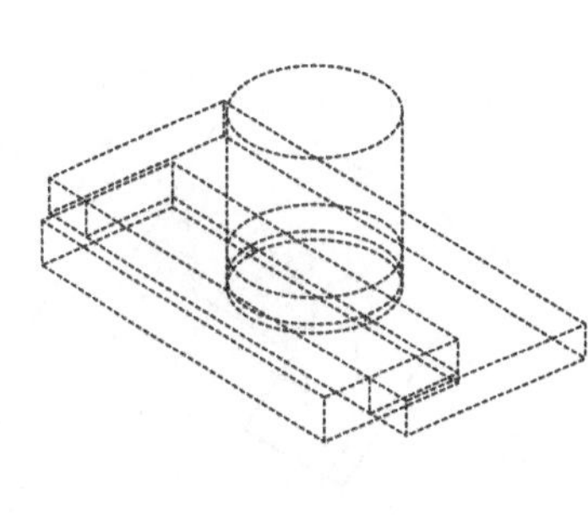

Figure 9.122

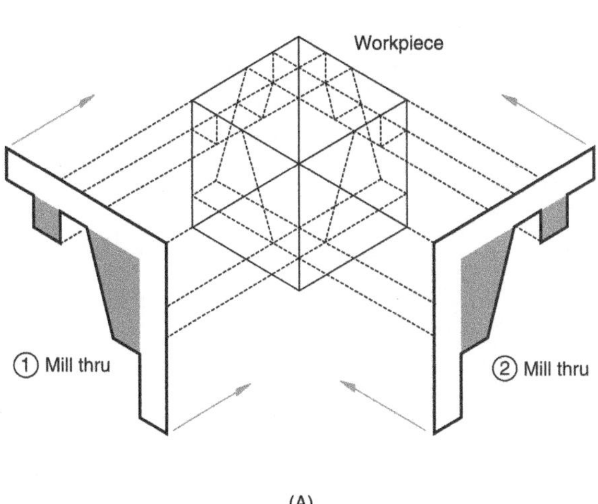

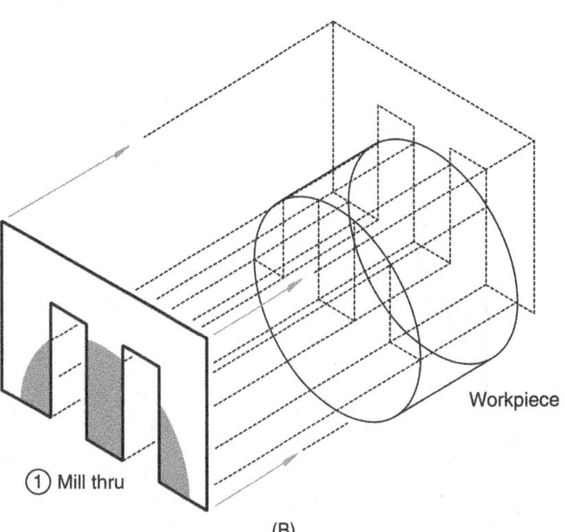

Figure 9.123

Feature-based modeling information

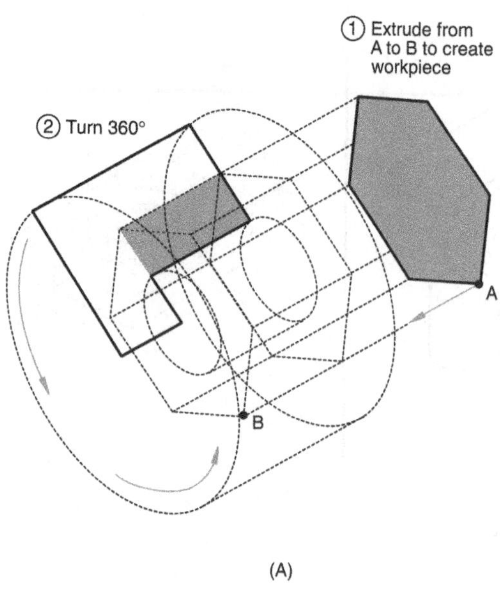

(A)

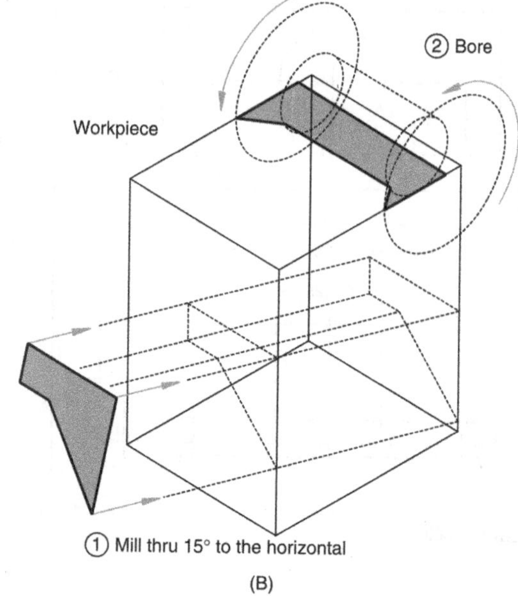

(B)

Figure 9.124

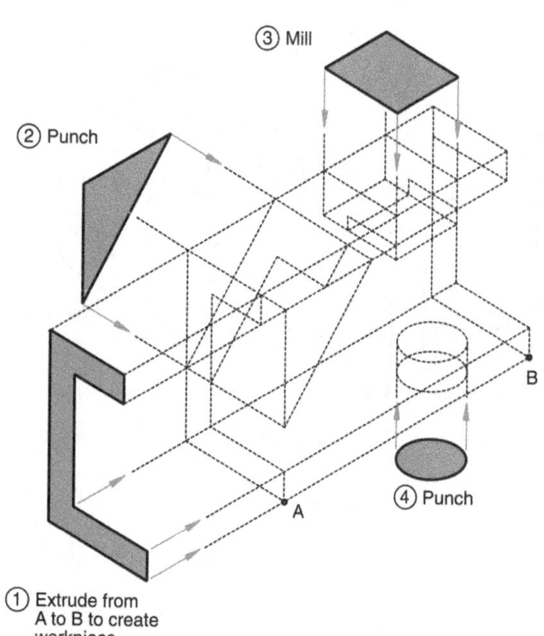

Figure 9.125

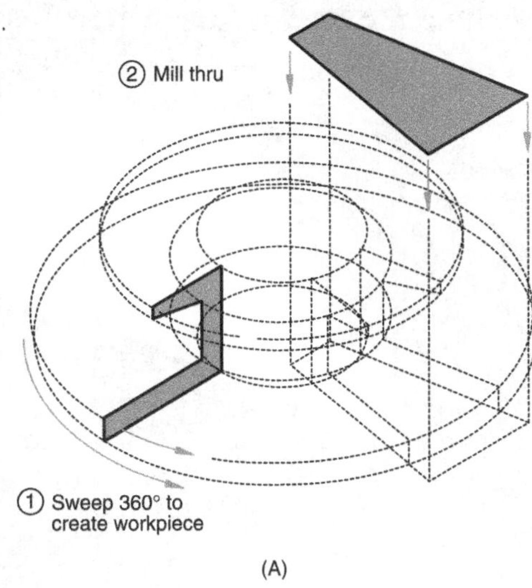

(A)

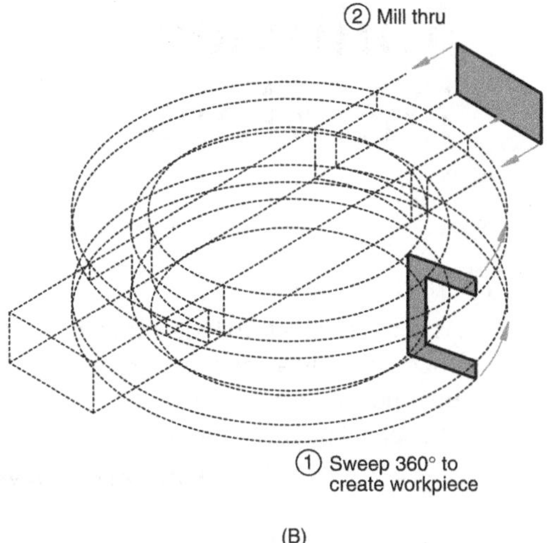

(B)

Figure 9.126

Chapter Ten

Chapter Ten

Multiview Drawings

As lines, so loves oblique, may well
Themselves in every angle greet;
But ours, so truly parallel,
Though infinite, can never meet.

—Andrew Marvell

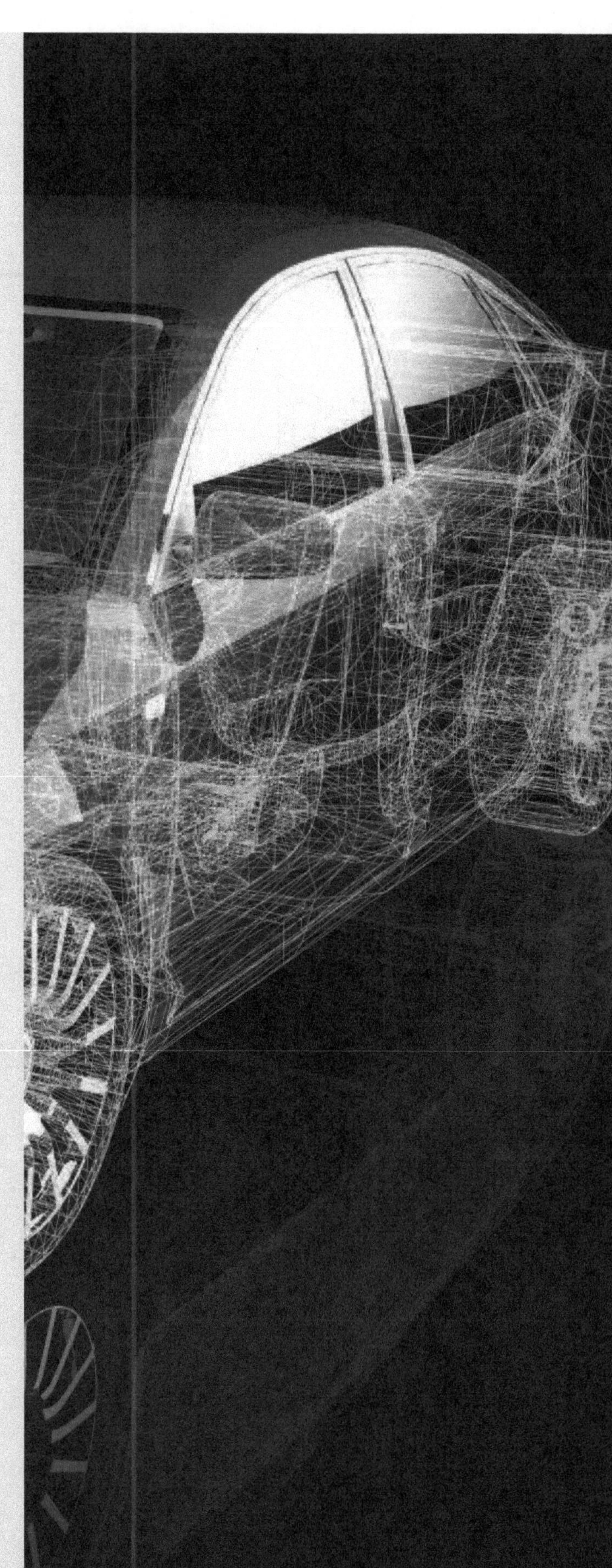

Objectives

After completing this chapter, you will be able to:

1. Explain orthographic and multiview projection.
2. Identify frontal, horizontal, and profile planes.
3. Identify the six principal views and the three space dimensions.
4. Apply standard line practices to multiview drawings.
5. Create a multiview drawing using hand tools or CAD.
6. Identify normal, inclined, and oblique planes in multiview drawings.
7. Represent lines, curves, surfaces, holes, fillets, rounds, chamfers, runouts, and ellipses in multiview drawings.
8. Apply visualization by solids and surfaces to multiview drawings.
9. Explain the importance of multiview drawings.
10. Identify limiting elements, hidden features, and intersections of two planes in multiview drawings.

Introduction

Chapter 10 introduces the theory, techniques, and standards of multiview drawings, which are standard methods for representing engineering designs. The chapter describes how to create one-, two-, and three-view drawings with traditional tools and CAD. Also described are standard practices for representing edges, curves, holes, tangencies, and fillets and rounds. The foundation of multiview drawings is orthographic projection, based on parallel lines of sight and mutually perpendicular views.

10.1 Projection Theory

Engineering and technical graphics are dependent on projection methods. The two projection methods primarily used are perspective and parallel (Figure 10.1). Both methods are based on projection theory, which has taken many years to evolve the rules used today.

Projection theory comprises the principles used to graphically represent 3-D objects and structures on 2-D media. An example of one of the methods developed to accomplish this task is shown in Figure 10.2 on page 491, which is a pictorial drawing with shades and shadows to give the impression of three dimensions.

All projection theory is based on two variables: line of sight and plane of projection. These variables are described briefly in the following paragraphs.

10.1.1 Line of Sight (LOS)

Drawing more than one face of an object by rotating the object relative to your *line of sight* helps in understanding the 3-D form (Figure 10.3 on page 491). A **line of sight (LOS)** is an imaginary ray of light between an observer's eye and an object. In perspective projection, all lines of sight start at a single point (Figure 10.4 on page 492); in parallel projection, all lines of sight are parallel (Figure 10.5 on page 492).

10.1.2 Plane of Projection

A **plane of projection** (i.e., an image or picture plane) is an imaginary flat plane upon which the image created by the lines of sight is projected. The image is produced by connecting the points where the lines of sight pierce the projection plane. (See Figure 10.5.) In effect, the 3-D object is transformed into a 2-D representation (also called a projection). The paper or computer screen on which a sketch or drawing is created is a plane of projection.

10.1.3 Parallel versus Perspective Projection

If the distance from the observer to the object is infinite (or essentially so), then the *projectors* (i.e., projection lines) are parallel and the drawing is classified as a parallel projection. (See Figure 10.5.) **Parallel projection** requires that the object be positioned at infinity and viewed from multiple points on an imaginary line parallel to the object. If the distance from the observer to the object is finite, then the projectors are not parallel and the drawing is classified as a perspective projection. (See Figure 10.4.) **Perspective projection** requires that the object be positioned at a finite distance and viewed from a single point (station point).

Perspective projections mimic what the human eye sees; however, perspective drawings are difficult to create. Parallel projections are less realistic, but they are easier to draw. This chapter will focus on parallel projection. Perspective drawings are covered in Chapter 12.

Orthographic projection is a parallel projection technique in which the plane of projection is positioned between the observer and the object and is perpendicular to the parallel lines of sight. The orthographic projection technique can produce either pictorial drawings that show all three dimensions of an object in one view or multiviews that show only two dimensions of an object in a single view (Figure 10.6 on page 493).

10.2 Multiview Projection Planes

Multiview projection is an orthographic projection for which the object is behind the plane of projection, and the object is oriented such that only two of its dimensions are shown (Figure 10.7 on page 493). As the parallel lines of sight pierce the projection plane, the features of the part are outlined.

Multiview drawings employ multiview projection techniques. In multiview drawings, generally three views of an object are drawn, and the features and dimensions in each view accurately represent those of the object. Each view is a 2-D flat image, as shown in Figure 10.8 on page 493. The views are defined according to the positions of the planes of projection with respect to the object.

10.2.1 Frontal Plane of Projection

The *front view* of an object shows the *width* and *height* dimensions. The views in Figures 10.7 and 10.8 are front views. The **frontal plane of projection** is the plane onto which the front view of a multiview drawing is projected.

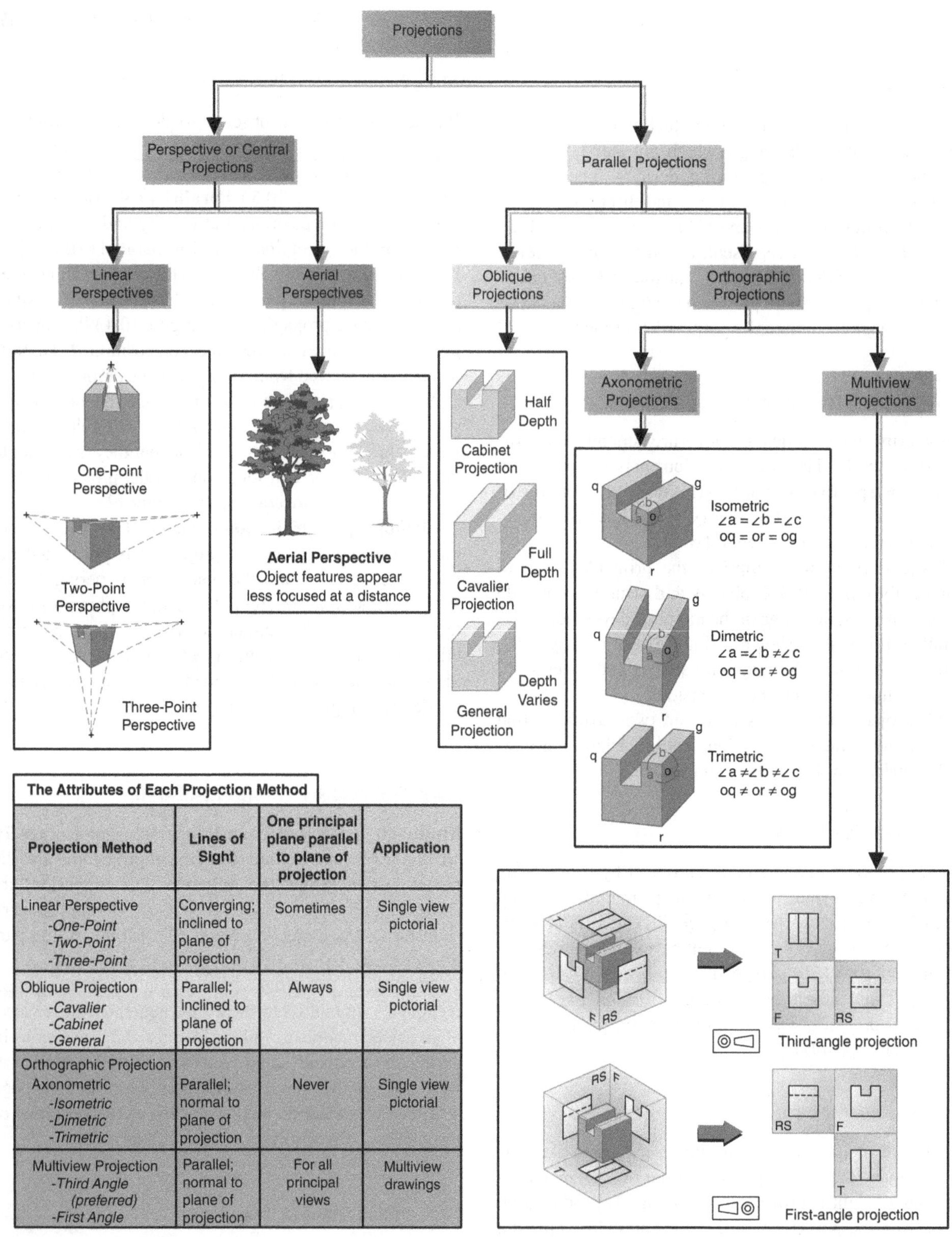

The Attributes of Each Projection Method

Projection Method	Lines of Sight	One principal plane parallel to plane of projection	Application
Linear Perspective *-One-Point* *-Two-Point* *-Three-Point*	Converging; inclined to plane of projection	Sometimes	Single view pictorial
Oblique Projection *-Cavalier* *-Cabinet* *-General*	Parallel; inclined to plane of projection	Always	Single view pictorial
Orthographic Projection Axonometric *-Isometric* *-Dimetric* *-Trimetric*	Parallel; normal to plane of projection	Never	Single view pictorial
Multiview Projection *-Third Angle (preferred)* *-First Angle*	Parallel; normal to plane of projection	For all principal views	Multiview drawings

Figure 10.1

Projection methods

Projection techniques developed along two lines: parallel and perspective.

Figure 10.2

Pictorial illustration

This is a computer-generated pictorial illustration with shades and shadows. These rendering techniques help enhance the 3-D quality of the image.

(© Courtesy of Zagato Centrostile.)

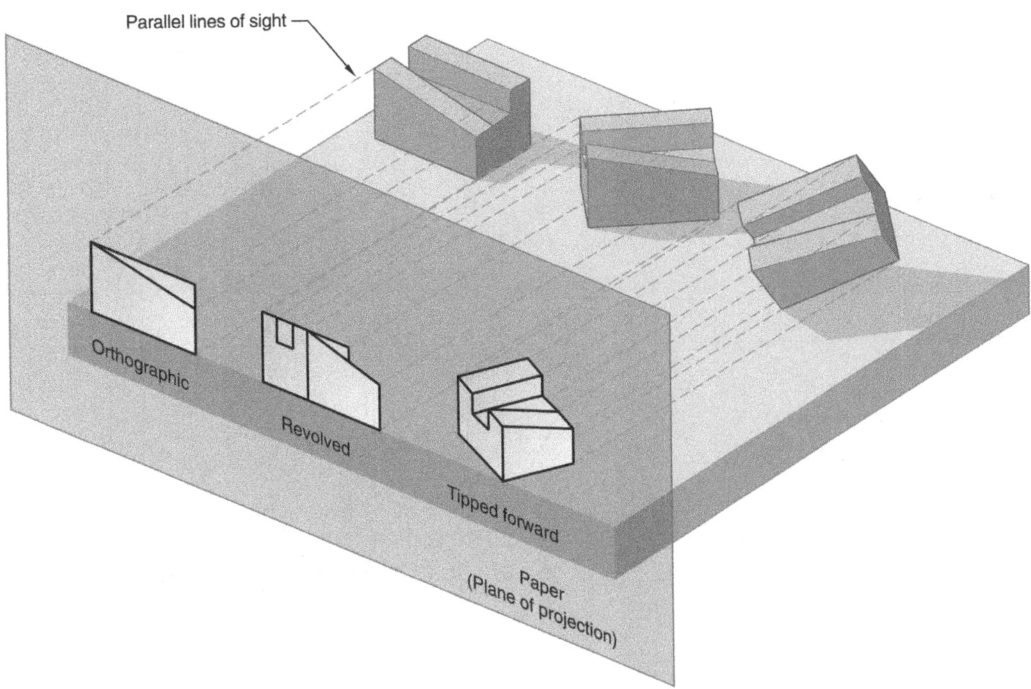

Figure 10.3

Changing viewpoint

Changing the position of the object relative to the line of sight creates different views of the same object.

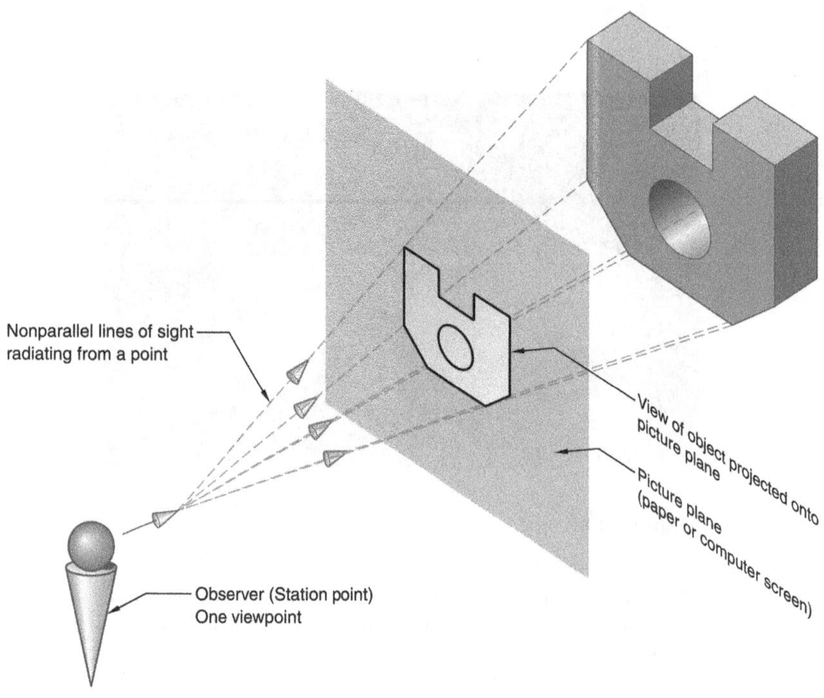

Figure 10.4

Perspective projection

Radiating lines of sight produce a perspective projection.

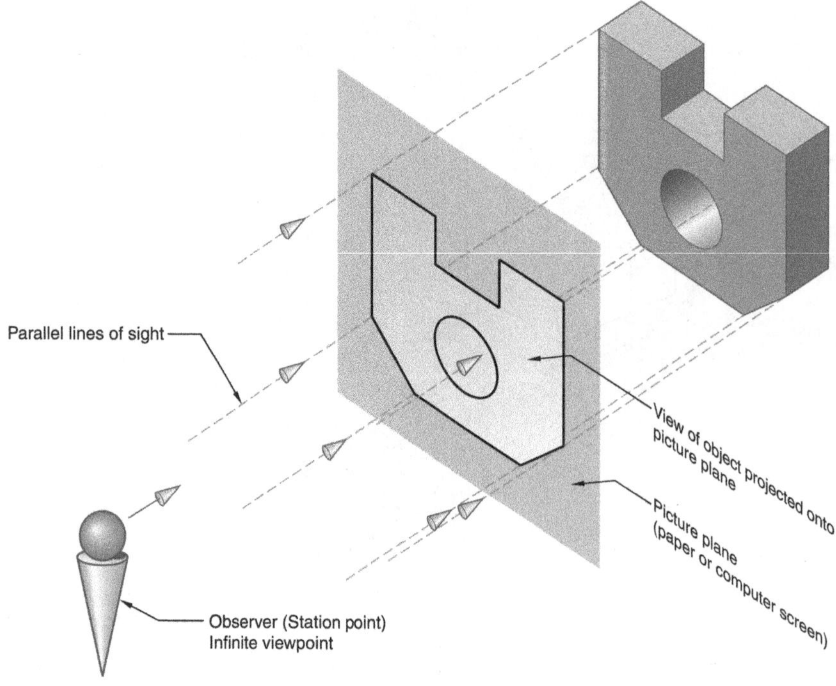

Figure 10.5

Parallel projection

Parallel lines of sight produce a parallel projection.

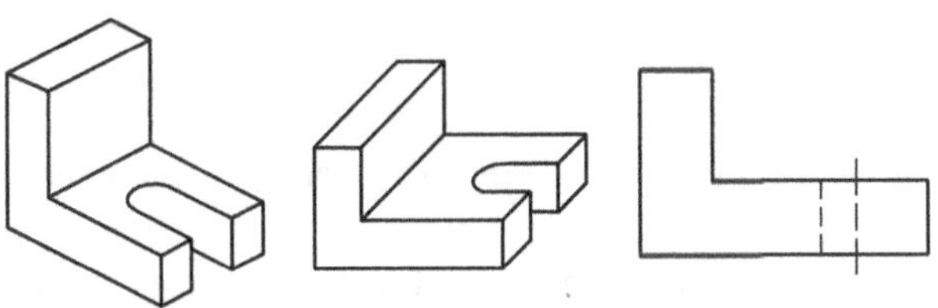

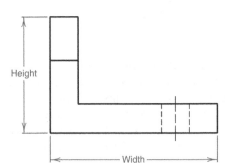

Figure 10.6

Parallel projection

Parallel projection techniques can be used to create multiview or pictorial drawings.

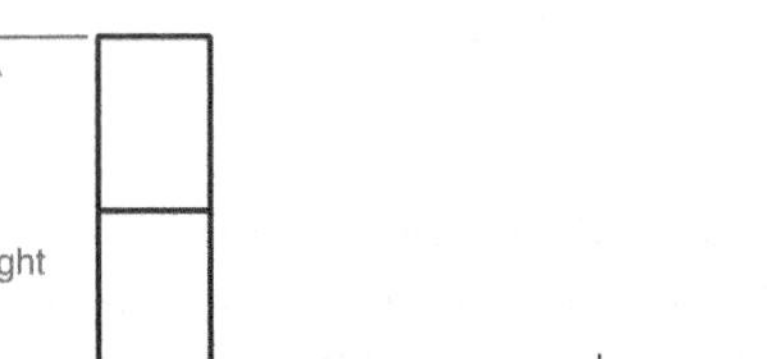

Figure 10.8

Single view

A single view, in this case the front view, drawn on paper or computer screen makes the 3-D object appear 2-D; one dimension, in this case the depth dimension, cannot be represented since it is perpendicular to the paper.

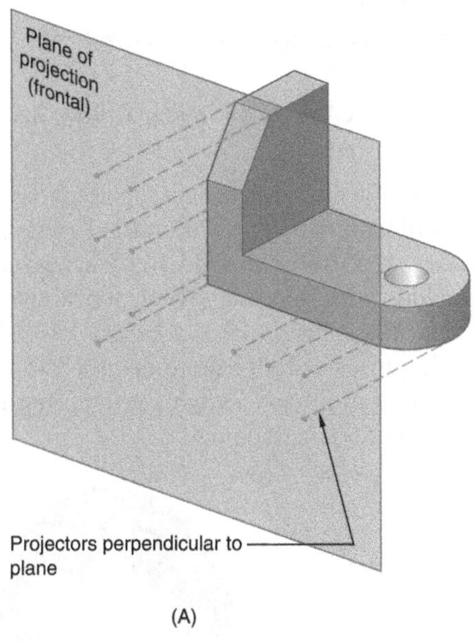

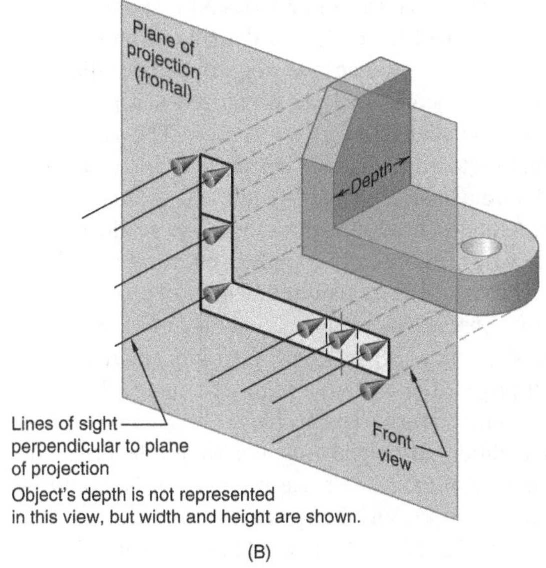

Figure 10.7

Orthographic projection

Orthographic projection is used to create this front multiview drawing by projecting details onto a projection plane that is parallel to the view of the object selected as the front.

10.2.2 Horizontal Plane of Projection

The *top view* of an object shows the *width* and *depth* dimensions (Figure 10.9 on page 495). The top view is projected onto the **horizontal plane of projection**, which is a plane suspended above and parallel to the top of the object.

10.2.3 Profile Plane of Projection

The *side view* of an object shows the *depth* and *height* dimensions. In multiview drawings, the right side view is the standard side view used. The right side view is projected onto the right **profile plane of projection**, which

Design in Industry

Motorola NFL Headset Generation II

This case study describes the design of headsets made specifically for NFL coaches by Motorola using 3-D modeling and CAD. In this case study, you will see examples of how the design process is used and the importance of 3-D modeling in the design process to improve on the design and visual appeal of a product that is worn by NFL coaches.

The Motorola NFL Headset Generation II is a high-tech wireless communication device that serves the communication needs of NFL coaches while heightening consumer awareness of the Motorola brand. Operating procedure is intuitive, and the single ear version may be used on either ear by swiveling the boom around.

This project first was conceived when Motorola became an official sponsor of the NFL (National Football League). The project presented a unique branding opportunity for Motorola. Unlike previous NFL sponsors who simply imprinted their logo on the side of an existing headset, Motorola wanted to leverage their capabilities as a major manufacturer to create an entirely new product.

Design challenges were numerous: The television medium required a dramatic design that would support the Motorola image and multi-year brand awareness program. A modest headset with a subtle logo would get lost in the fast-paced, visually complex context of a football game. Product details required a high degree of bold elements, special color palettes, and logo treatments that would show up effectively on TV. Colors and materials had to project the Motorola high-tech image, but also compliment the various team colors.

In addition to heightening the Motorola brand, it was important that the device respond to the communication, comfort, and image needs of NFL coaches. Motorola's marketing efforts wouldn't be achieved if the NFL coaches were uncomfortable and wouldn't wear the newly designed headsets. All of these issues were at stake when placed against a looming, non-flexible release date: kick-off of the NFL Season.

The modified Motorola NFL Headset Generation II supports and showcases Motorola consumer product-design efforts. Projecting a high-tech, rugged, and cool appearance, this headset represents the leading edge of wireless communication devices.

The overall appearance of the Motorola NFL Headset offers superior elements and a daring new profile to stand out against the backdrop of vivid team colors and a myriad of screaming fans. Design details include:

- Product cues that tie in with other Motorola branded products
- Customized shapes—bold color contrast for TV zoom
- High-impact logo placement on five different angles
- Soft, comfortable mesh-foam headband
- Variety of sizes ensures comfort—fit for any head size
- Redesigned earphone with temple support to maximize "wearability"
- Bi-directional orientation allows placement on either side of head
- Elongated form to spread pressure across head
- Temple pad inserts to achieve balance and further reduce pressure
- Positive clamping force over ears with top able to lift away from head
- Floating structure to promote airflow and add to comfort

The result of this project is a high-tech headset for the new millennium that provides visual excitement and awareness of the Motorola brand. Introducing such a new dramatic look with such a high-tech appeal into a tradition-bound atmosphere, such as football, was risky—but it paid off as this new design represents the latest in wireless communication devices without ignoring the mud and guts of professional football.

Double-ear version

(© Motorola, Inc.)

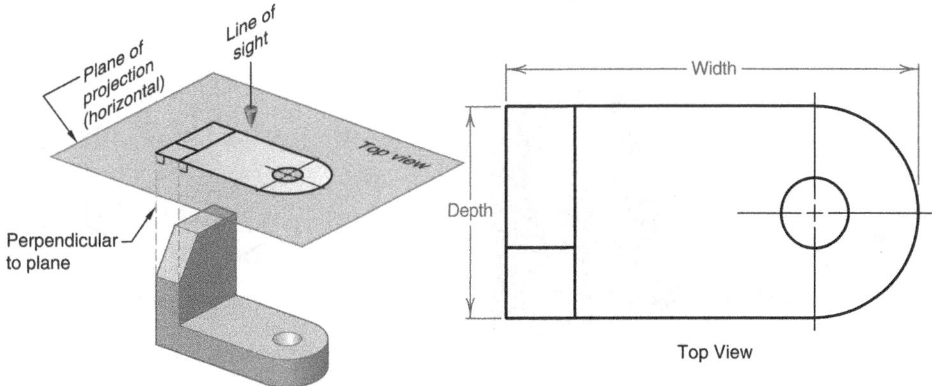

Figure 10.9

Top view

A top view of the object is created by projecting onto the horizontal plane of projection.

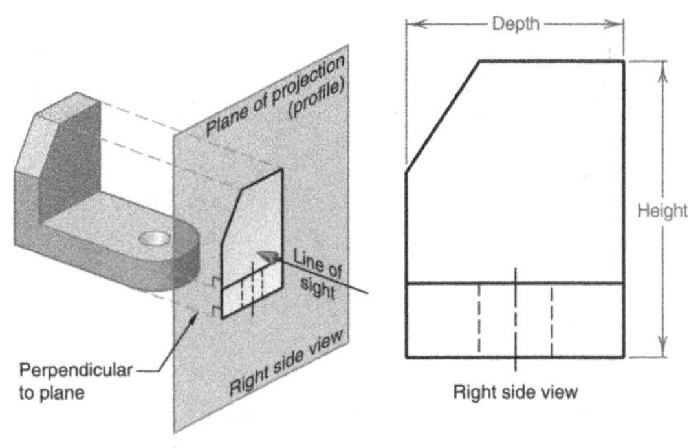

Figure 10.10

Profile view

A right side view of the object is created by projecting onto the profile plane of projection.

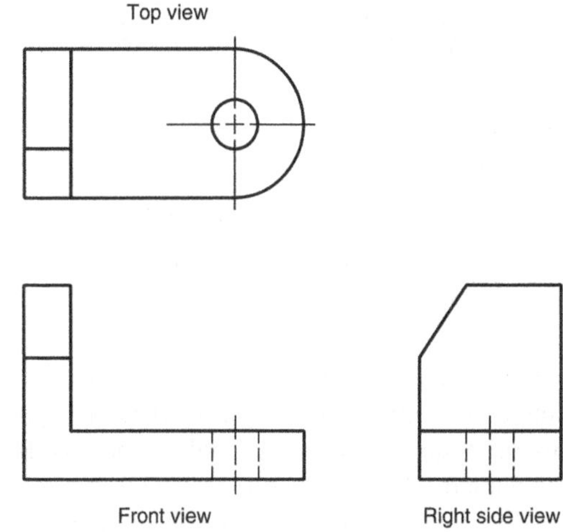

Figure 10.11

Multiview drawing of an object

For this object three views are created: front, top, and right side. The views are aligned so that common dimensions are shared between views.

is a plane that is parallel to the right side of the object (Figure 10.10 on page 495).

10.2.4 Orientation of Views from Projection Planes

The views projected onto the three planes are shown together in Figure 10.11. The top view is always positioned above and aligned with the front view, and the right side view is always positioned to the right of and aligned with the front view, as shown in the figure.

10.3 Advantages of Multiview Drawings

In order to produce a new product, it is necessary to know its true dimensions, and true dimensions are not adequately represented in most pictorial drawings. To illustrate, the photograph in Figure 10.12 on the next page is a pictorial perspective image. The image distorts true distances, which are essential in manufacturing and construction. Figure 10.13 on the next page demonstrates how a perspective projection distorts measurements. Note that the two width dimensions in the front view of the block appear different in length; equal distances do not appear equal on a perspective drawing.

In the pictorial drawings in Figure 10.14 (next page), angles are also distorted. In the isometric view, right angles are not shown as 90 degrees. In the oblique view, only the front

Figure 10.12

Perspective image

The photograph shows the road in perspective, which is how cameras capture images. Notice how the telephone poles appear shorter and closer together off in the distance.

(Photo courtesy of Anna Anderson.)

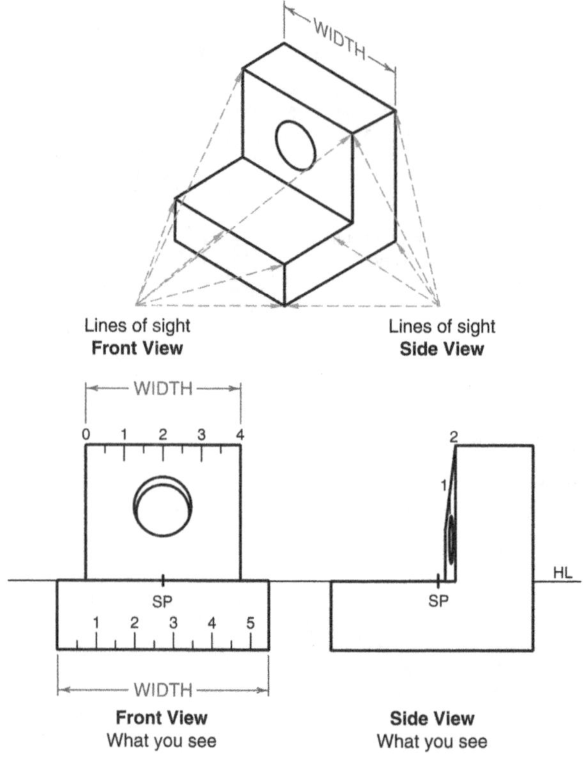

Figure 10.13

Distorted dimensions

Perspective drawings distort true dimensions.

surfaces and surfaces parallel to the front surface show true right angles. In isometric drawings, circular holes appear as ellipses; in oblique drawings, circles also appear as ellipses, except on the front plane and surfaces parallel to the front surface. Changing the position of the object will minimize the distortion of some surfaces, but not all.

Since engineering and technology depend on exact size and shape descriptions for designs, the best approach is to use the parallel projection technique called orthographic projection to create views that show only two of the three dimensions (width, height, depth). If the object is correctly positioned relative to the projection planes, the dimensions of features will be represented in true size in one or more of the views (Figure 10.15). Multiview drawings provide the most accurate description of three-dimensional objects and structures for engineering, manufacturing, and construction requirements.

In the computer world, 3-D models replace the multiview drawing as the source of information about the geometry. These models are interpreted directly from the database, without the use of dimensioned drawings (Figure 10.16). See Chapter 9.

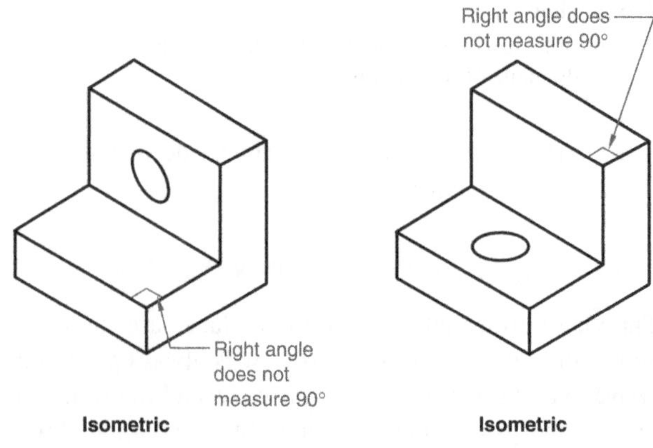

Figure 10.14

Distorted angles

Angular dimensions are distorted on pictorial drawings.

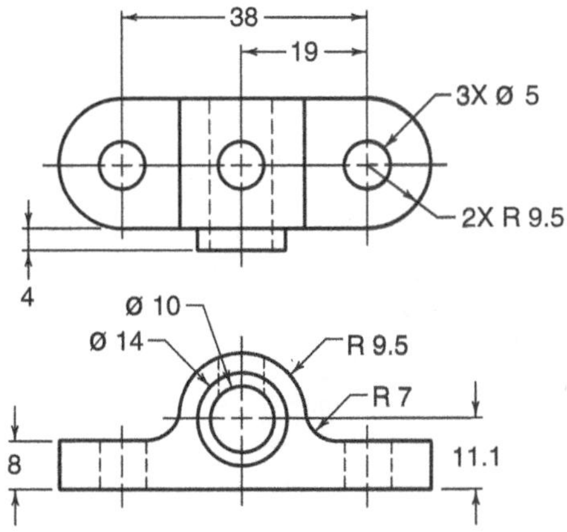

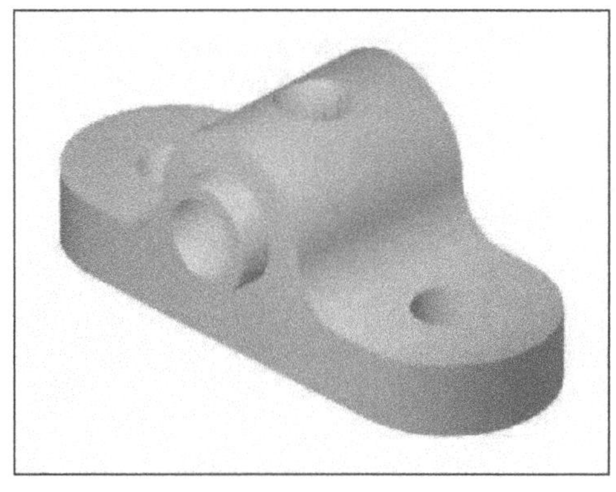

Figure 10.15

Multiview drawing

Multiview drawings produce true-size features, which can be used for dimensionally accurate representations.

Figure 10.16

CAD data used directly by machine tool

This computer-numeric-control (CNC) machine tool can interpret and process 3-D CAD data for use in manufacturing, to create dimensionally accurate parts.

(Courtesy of Intergraph Corporation.)

10.4 The Six Principal Views

The plane of projection can be oriented to produce an infinite number of views of an object. However, some views are more important than others. These **principal views** are the six mutually perpendicular views that are produced by six mutually perpendicular planes of projection. If you imagine suspending an object in a glass box with major surfaces of the object positioned so that they are parallel to the sides of the box, the six sides of the box become projection planes showing the six views (Figure 10.17 on the next page). The six principal views are front, top, left side, right side, bottom, and rear. To draw these views on 2-D media, that is, a piece of paper or a computer monitor, imagine putting hinges on all sides of the front glass plane and on one edge of the left profile plane. Then cut along all the other corners, and flatten out the box to create a six-view drawing, as shown in Figure 10.18 on page 499.

The following descriptions are based on the X, Y, and Z coordinate system. In CAD, *width* can be assigned the X axis, *height* assigned the Y axis, and *depth* assigned the Z axis. This is not universally true for all CAD systems but is used as a standard in this text.

The **front view** is the one that shows the most features or characteristics. All other views are based on the orientation chosen for the front view. Also, all other views, except the rear view, are formed by rotating the lines of sight 90 degrees in an appropriate direction from the front view. With CAD, the front view is the one created by looking down the Z axis (in the negative Z viewing direction), perpendicular to the X and Y axes.

The **top view** shows what is the top of the object once the position of the front view is established. With CAD, the top view is created by looking down the Y axis (in the negative Y viewing direction), perpendicular to the Z and X axes.

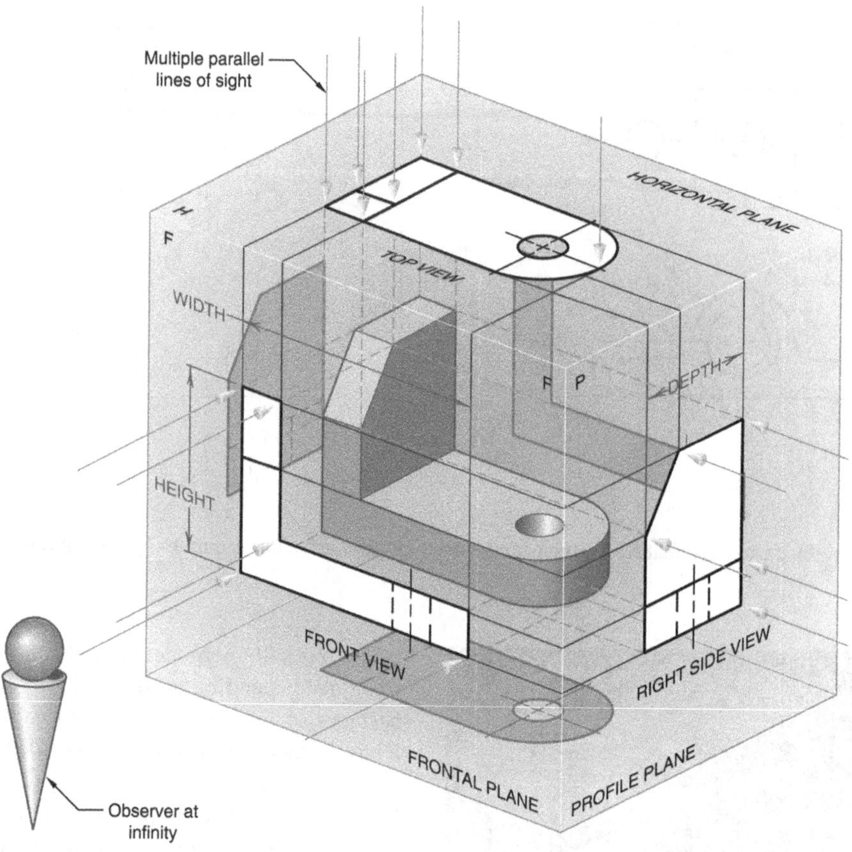

Figure 10.17

Object suspended in a glass box, producing the six principal views
Each view is perpendicular to and aligned with the adjacent views.

The **right side view** shows what is the right side of the object once the position of the front view is established. With CAD, the right side view is created by looking down the X axis from the right (in the negative X viewing direction), perpendicular to the Z and Y axes.

The **left side view** shows what is the left side of the object once the position of the front view is established. The left side view is a mirror image of the right side view, except that hidden features are different. With CAD, the left side view is created by looking down the X axis from the left (in the positive X viewing direction), perpendicular to the Z and Y axes.

The **rear view** shows what becomes the rear of the object once the front view is established. The rear view is at 90 degrees to the left side view and is a mirror image of the front view, except that hidden features are different. With CAD, the rear view is created by looking down the Z axis from behind the object (in the positive Z viewing direction), perpendicular to the Y and X axes.

The **bottom view** shows what becomes the bottom of the object once the front view is established. The bottom view is a mirror image of the top view, except that hidden features are different. With CAD, the bottom view is created by looking down the Y axis from below the object (positive Y viewing direction), perpendicular to the Z and X axes.

The concept of laying the views flat by "unfolding the glass box," as shown in Figure 10.18, forms the basis for two important multiview drawing standards:

1. Alignment of views
2. Fold lines

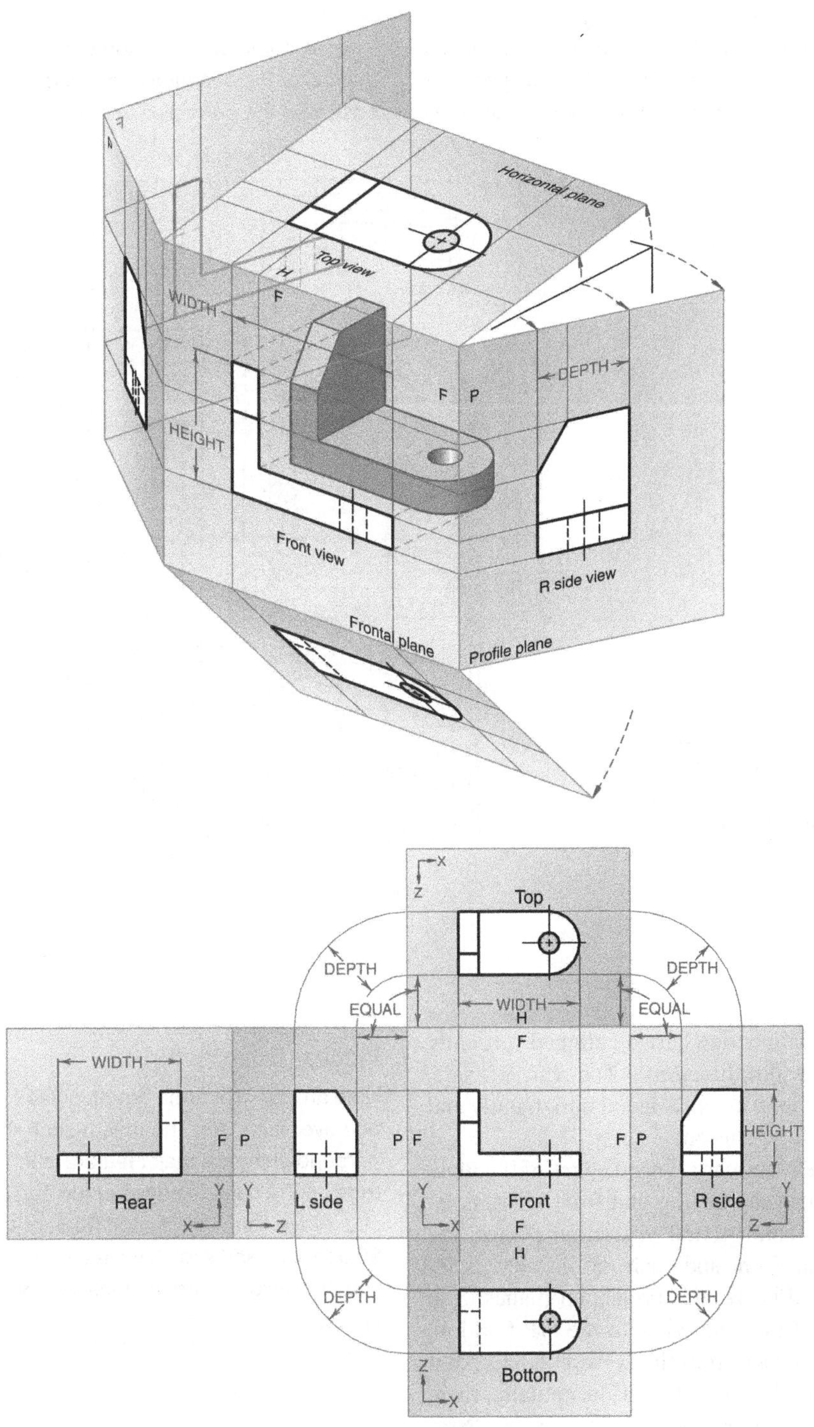

Figure 10.18

Unfolding the glass box to produce a six-view drawing

Historical Highlight
Multiview Drawings

Rudimentary plan views of buildings have been used since ancient times. See Figure 1.15. However, elevations or multiviews of buildings would take many more years before they were in common use. Albrecht Dürer (1471–1528) is known mainly for his beautiful engravings (Figure 1.17) but he demonstrated the principles of multiview drawings in a book that

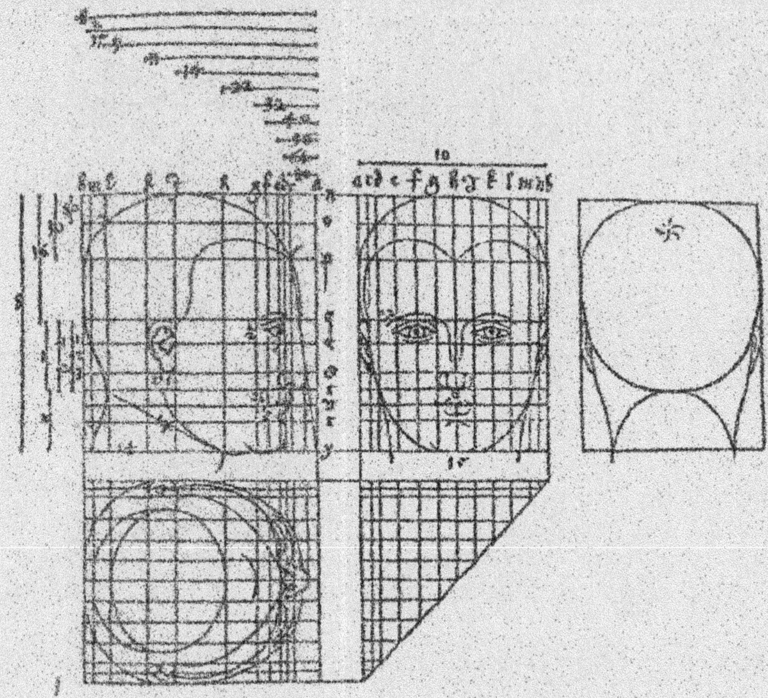

(a) Dürer's systematic use of orthographic projection to define the human head and its features' proportions. Most of the dimensions given should be read as their reciprocals, taking the whole man's height as unity.

The top, front, and bottom views are all aligned vertically and share the same width dimension. The rear, left side, front, and right side views are all aligned horizontally and share the same height dimension.

Fold lines are the imaginary hinged edges of the glass box. The fold line between the top and front views is labeled *H/F,* for horizontal/frontal projection planes; the fold line between the front and each profile view is labeled *F/P,* for frontal/horizontal projection planes. The distance from a point in a side view to the F/P fold line is the same as the distance from the corresponding point in the top view to the H/F fold line. Conceptually, then, the fold lines are edge-on views of reference planes. Normally, fold lines or reference planes are not shown in engineering drawings. However, they are very important for auxiliary views and spatial geometry construction, covered in Chapters 13 and 14.

Practice Exercise 10.1

Hold an object at arm's length or lay it on a flat surface. Close one eye, then view the object such that your line of sight is perpendicular to a major feature, such as a flat side. Concentrate on the outside edges of the object and sketch what you see. Move your line of sight 90 degrees, or rotate the object 90 degrees, and sketch what you see. This process will show you the basic procedure necessary to create the six principal views.

10.4.1 Conventional View Placement

The three-view multiview drawing is the standard used in engineering and technology, because many times the other three principal views are mirror images and do did not have much appeal to those who would have benefited most from his work. Toward the end of his life he wrote a book on geometry that was mainly a summary of what was already known but did contain some interesting drawings. In this book were elementary drawings such as sections through cones and the principles of orthographic projection.

Dürer began another series of books on geometry titled *The Four Books on Human Proportions*, published posthumously in 1528. For this book he made careful measurements of the proportions of human figures, then averaged them before recording his findings. The problem he faced was how to graphically represent these human proportions. Dürer chose to use orthogonal multiview drawings to represent human proportions as shown in Figure 1. His drawings bear a lot of similarity to multiview drawings used today, but it was very new at his time. Although Dürer demonstrated the usefulness of orthogonal multiview drawings, they were not widely practiced until Gaspard Monge refined this projection system in 1795.

Excerpted from *The History of Engineering Drawing*, by Jeffrey Booker, Chatto & Windus, London, England, 1963.

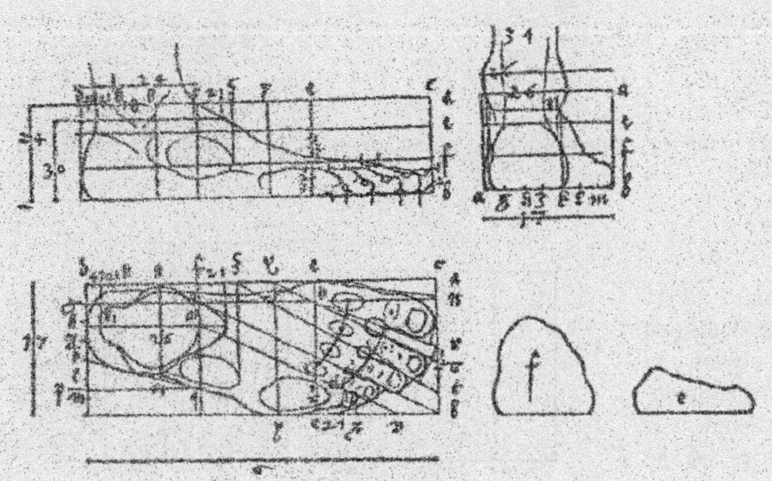

(b) A foot defined in terms of its three orthographic projections systematically arranged. Notice that Dürer arranged these in "first angle" while his heads in (a) are in "third angle." The two shapes "f" and "e" to the right are vertical sections through the foot at *f* and *e* in the elevation and plan.

not add to the knowledge about the object. The standard views used in a three-view drawing are the *top, front,* and *right side* views, arranged as shown in Figure 10.19. The width dimensions are aligned between the front and top views, using vertical projection lines. The height dimensions are aligned between the front and profile views, using horizontal projection lines. Because of the relative positioning of the three views, the depth dimension cannot be aligned using projection lines. Instead, the depth dimension is measured in either the top or right side view and transferred to the other view, using either a scale, miter line, compass, or dividers (Figure 10.20 on page 502).

The arrangement of the views may only vary as shown in Figure 10.21 on page 502. The right side view can be placed adjacent to the top view because both views share the depth dimension. Note that the side view is rotated so that the depth dimension in the two views is aligned.

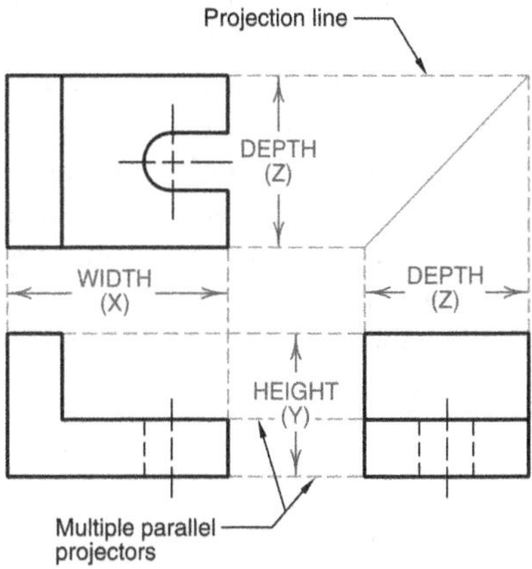

Figure 10.19

Three space dimensions

The three space dimensions are width, height, and depth. A single view on a multiview drawing will only reveal two of the three space dimensions. The 3-D CAD systems use X, Y, and Z to represent the three dimensions.

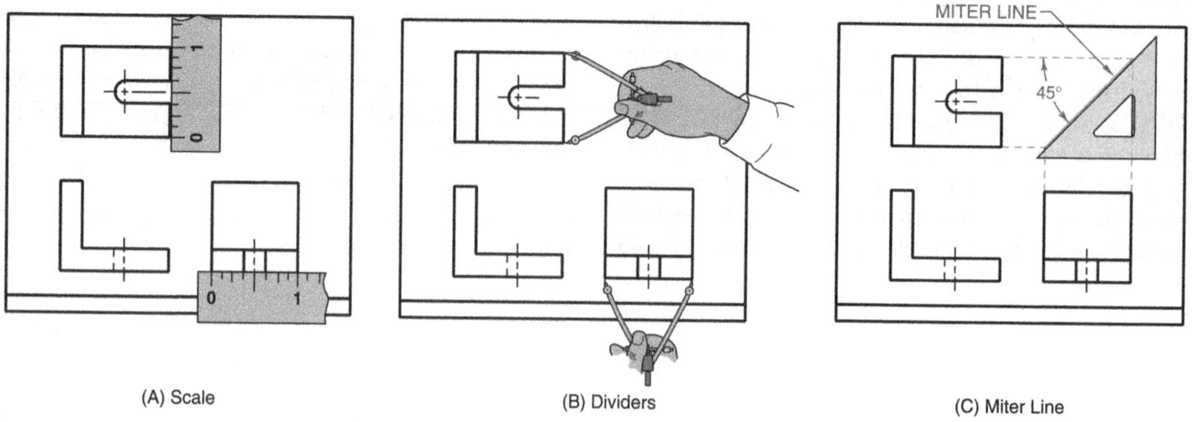

Figure 10.20

Transferring depth dimensions from the top view to the right side view, using a scale, dividers, or a 45-degree triangle and a miter line

10.4.2 First- and Third-Angle Projection

Figure 10.22A shows the standard arrangement of all six views of an object, as practiced in the United States and Canada. The ANSI standard third-angle symbol shown in the figure commonly appears on technical drawings to denote that the drawing was done following third-angle projection conventions. Europe and other countries use the first-angle projection and a different symbol, as shown in Figure 10.22B. To understand the difference between first- and third-angle projection, refer to Figure 10.23 on page 504, which shows the *orthogonal planes.* Orthographic projection can be described using these planes. If the first quadrant is used for a multiview drawing, the results will be very different from those of the third quadrant (Figure 10.24 on page 505). Familiarity with both first- and third-angle projection is valuable because of the global nature of business in our era. As an example, Figure 10.25 on page 506 shows an engineering drawing produced in the United States for a German-owned company, using first-angle projection.

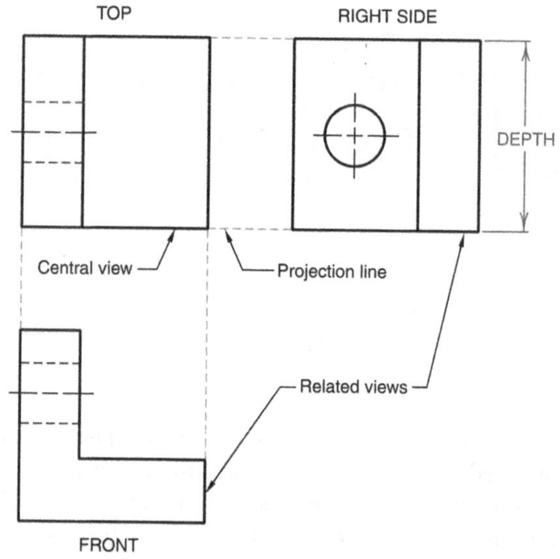

Figure 10.21

Alternate view arrangement

In this view arrangement, the top view is considered the central view.

10.4.3 Adjacent Views

Adjacent views are two views separated by 90 degrees of viewing rotation. In adjacent views two orthographic views are placed next to each other such that the dimension they share in common is aligned, using parallel projectors. The top and front views share the width dimension; therefore, the top view is placed directly above the front view, and vertical parallel projectors are used to ensure alignment of the shared width dimension. The right side and front views share the height dimension; therefore, the right side view is placed directly to the right of the front view, and horizontal parallel projectors are used to ensure alignment of the shared height dimension.

The manner in which adjacent views are positioned illustrates the first rule of orthographic projection: Every

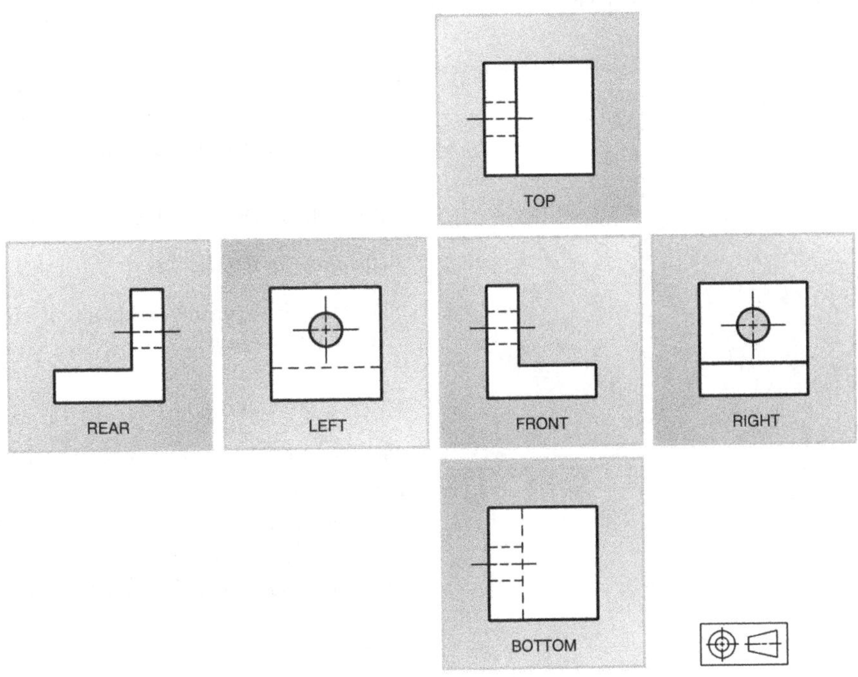

(A) U.S. Standard Third-Angle Projection

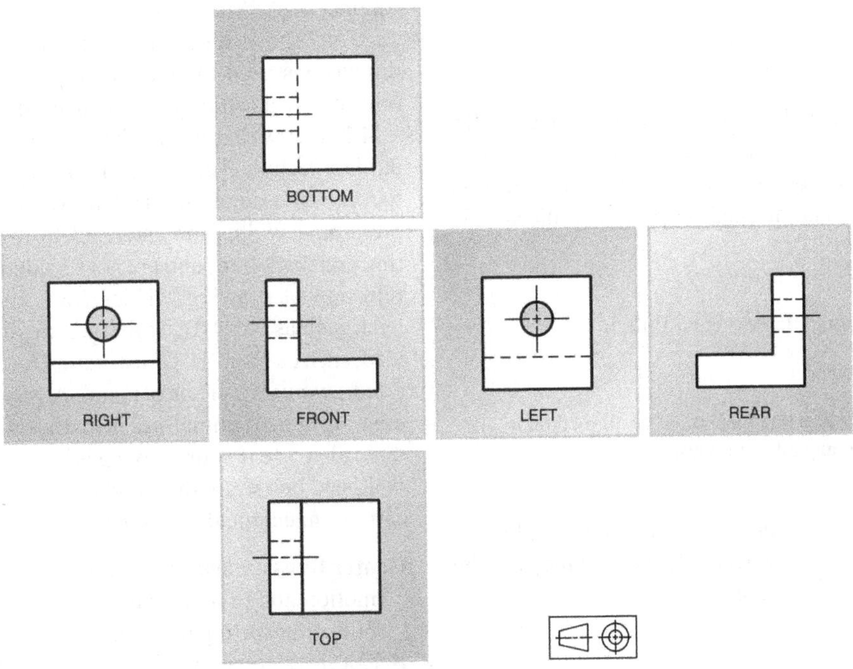

(B) ISO Standard First-Angle Projection

Figure 10.22

Standard arrangement of the six principal views for third- and first-angle projection

Third- and first-angle drawings are designated by the standard symbol shown in the lower right corner of parts (A) and (B). The symbol represents how the front and right-side views of a frustum of a cone would appear in each standard.

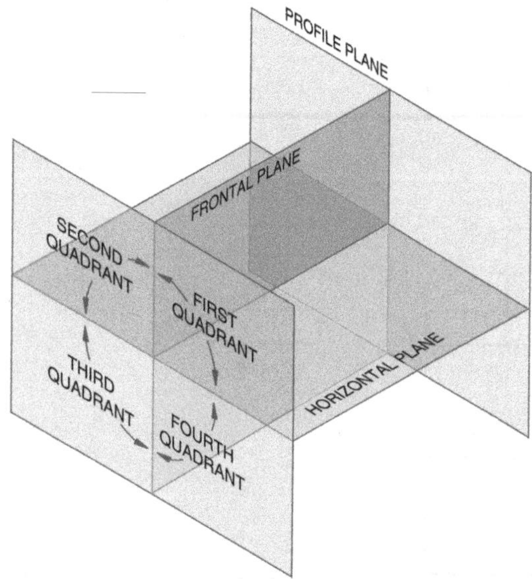

Figure 10.23

The principal projection planes and quadrants used to create first- and third-angle projection drawings

These planes are used to create the six principal views of first- and third-angle projection drawings.

point or feature in one view must be aligned on a parallel projector in any adjacent view. In Figure 10.26 on page 506, the hole in the block is an example of a feature shown in one view and aligned on parallel projectors in the adjacent view.

> Principles of Orthographic Projection Rule 1:
>
> ***Alignment of Features***
>
> Every point or feature in one view must be aligned on a parallel projector in any adjacent view.

The distance *between* the views is not fixed, and it can vary according to the space available on the paper and the number of dimensions to be shown.

10.4.4 Related Views

Two views that are adjacent to the same view are called **related views**; in related views, distances between common features are equal. In related views the two views are separated by two 90-degree viewing rotations. In Figure 10.26, for example, the distance between surface 1 and surface 2 is the same in the top view as it is in the right side view; therefore, the top and right side views are related views. The front and right side views in the figure are also related views, relative to the top view.

> Principles of Orthographic Projection Rule 2:
>
> ***Distances in Related Views***
>
> Distances between any two points of a feature in related views must be equal.

10.4.5 Central View

The view from which adjacent views are aligned is the **central view**. In Figure 10.26, the front view is the central view. In Figure 10.21, the top view is the central view. Distances and features are projected or measured from the central view to the adjacent views.

10.4.6 Line Conventions

The **alphabet of lines** is a set of standard linetypes established by the American Society of Mechanical Engineers (ASME) for technical drawing. Figure 10.27 on page 507 shows the alphabet of lines, and the approximate dimensions used to create different linetypes, which are referred to as *linestyles* when used with CAD. ASME Y14.2M–1992 has established these linetypes as the standard for technical drawings. Two line weights are sufficient to follow the standards, a 0.6 mm and a 0.3 mm. These approximate widths are intended to differentiate between thin and thick lines and are not for control of acceptance or rejection of drawings. Thick lines are drawn using soft lead, such as F or HB. Thin lines are drawn using a harder lead, such as H or 2H. Construction lines are very light and are drawn using 4H or 6H lead. A good rule of thumb for creating construction lines is to draw them so that they are difficult to see if your drawing is held at arm's length.

Listed below are the standard linetypes and their applications in technical drawings:

Center lines are used to represent symmetry and paths of motion and to mark the centers of circles and the axes of symmetrical parts, such as cylinders and bolts.

Break lines come in two forms: a freehand thick line and a long, ruled thin line with zigzags. Break lines are used to show where an object is broken to save drawing space or reveal interior features.

Dimension and extension lines are used to indicate the sizes of features on a drawing.

Section lines are used in section views to represent surfaces of an object cut by a cutting plane.

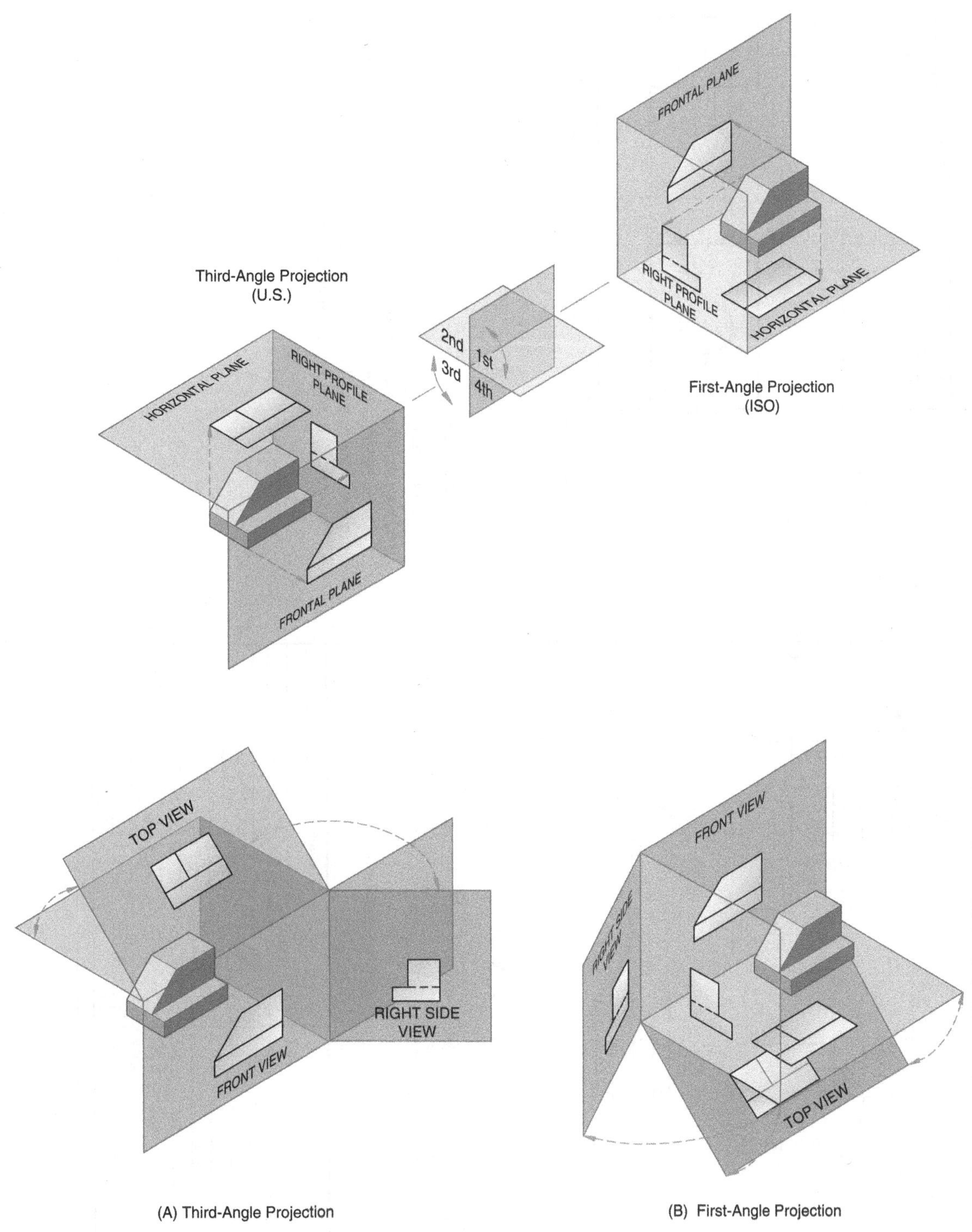

Figure 10.24

Pictorial comparison between first- and third-angle projection techniques

Placing the object in the third quadrant puts the projection planes between the viewer and the object. When placed in the first quadrant, the object is between the viewer and the projection planes.

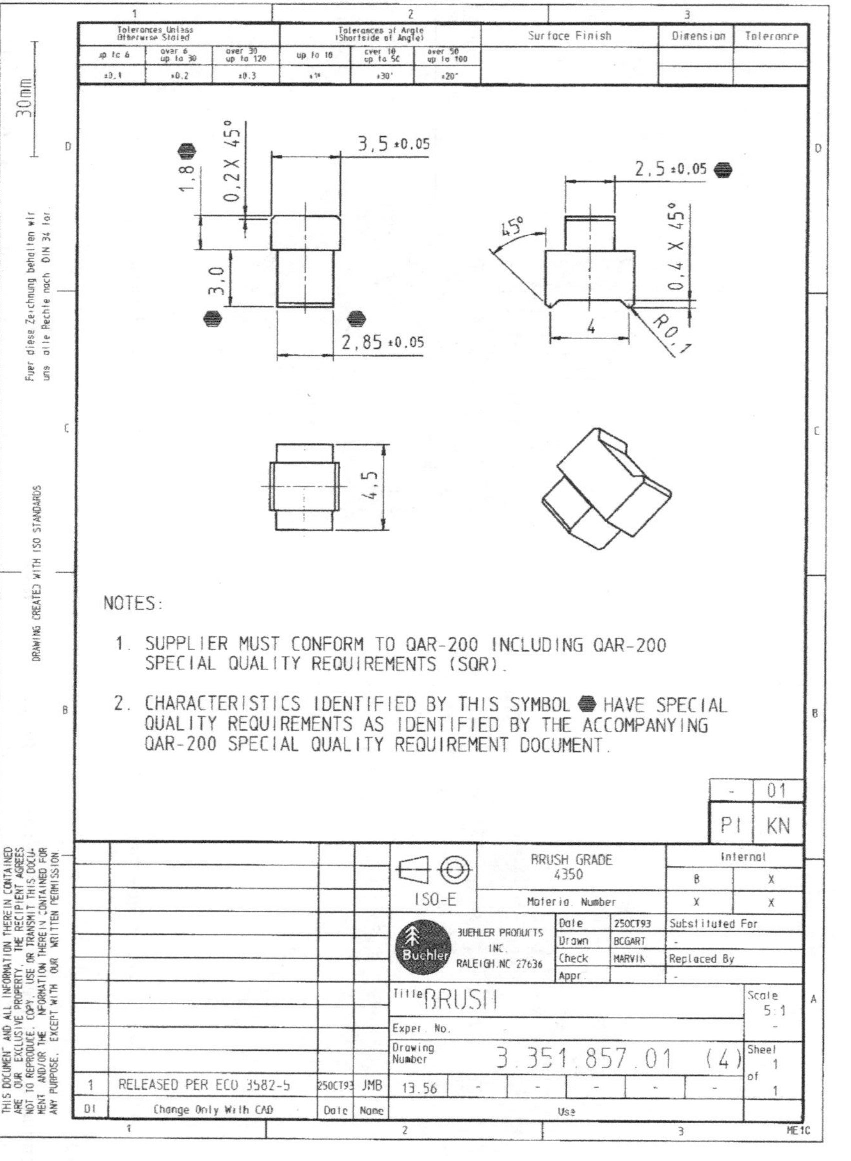

Figure 10.25

First-angle projection engineering drawing produced in the United States for a European company

(Courtesy of Buehler Motor, Inc.)

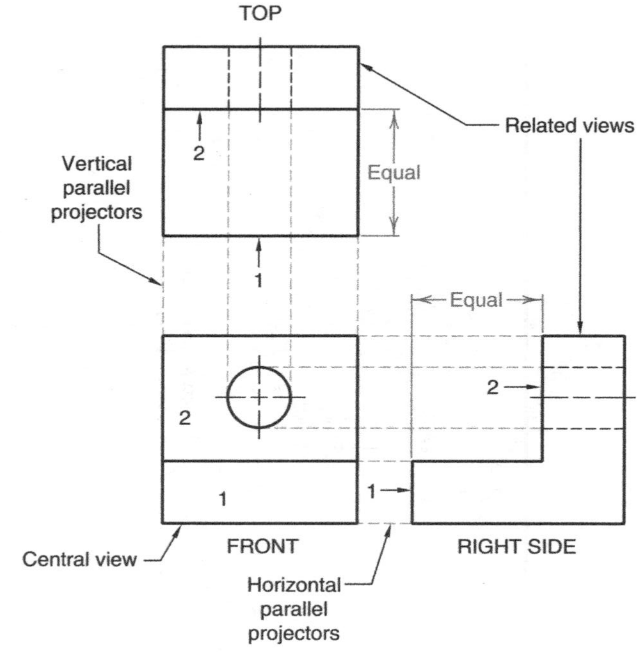

Figure 10.26

Alignment of views

Three-view drawings are aligned horizontally and vertically on engineering drawings. In this view arrangement, the front view is the central view. Also notice that surfaces 1 and 2 are the same distance apart in the related views: top and right side.

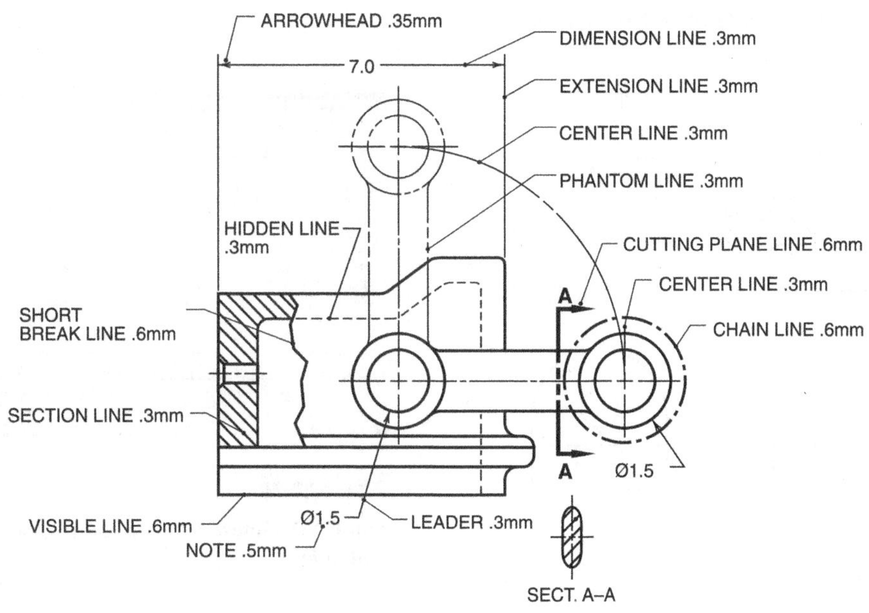

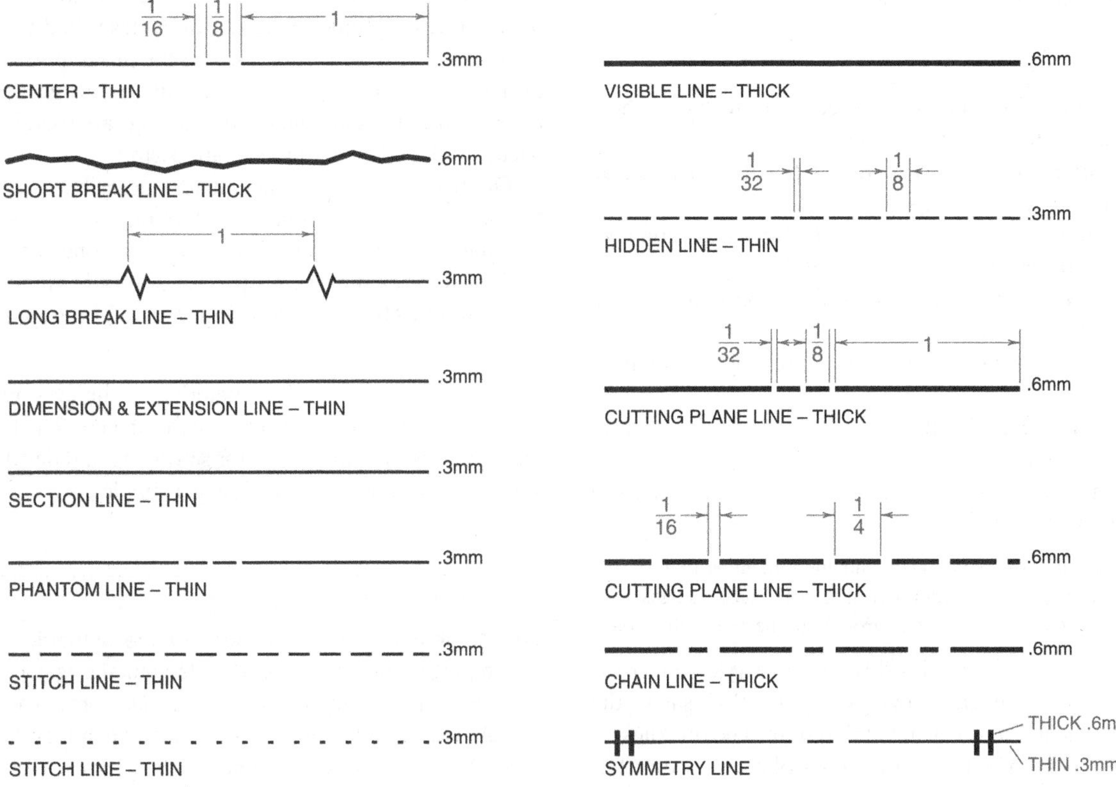

Figure 10.27

The alphabet of lines

The alphabet of lines is a set of ASME standard linetypes used on technical drawings. The approximate dimensions shown on some linetypes are used as guides for drawing them with traditional tools. The technical drawing at the top shows how different linetypes are used in a drawing.

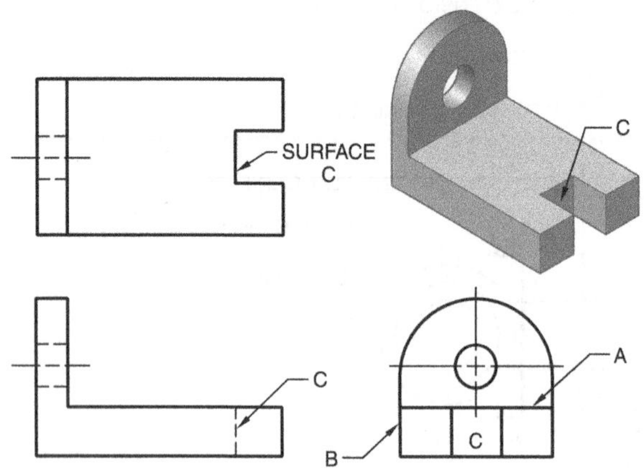

Figure 10.28

Hidden features

The dashed lines on this drawing indicate hidden features. The vertical dashed line in the front view shows the location of plane C. The horizontal dashed lines in the front and top views show the location of the hole.

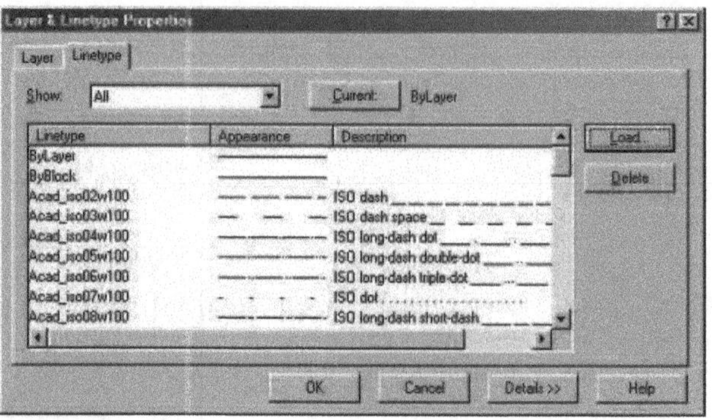

Figure 10.29

AutoCAD's linestyle menu showing some of the linetypes available

Cutting plane lines are used in section drawings to show the locations of cutting planes.

Visible lines are used to represent features that can be seen in the current view.

Hidden lines are used to represent features that cannot be seen in the current view (Figure 10.28).

Phantom lines are used to represent a moveable feature in its different positions.

Stitch lines are used to indicate a sewing or stitching process.

Chain lines are used to indicate that a surface is to receive additional treatment.

Symmetry lines are used as an axis of symmetry for a particular view.

> It is important that you understand and remember these different linetypes and their definitions and uses, because they are referred to routinely throughout the rest of this book.

CAD software provides different linestyles for creating standard technical drawings. Figure 10.29 shows the linestyle menu for a typical CAD system. The thicknesses of lines on a CAD drawing are controlled by two different means: (1) controlling the thickness of the lines drawn on the display screen and (2) controlling the plotted output of lines on pen plotters by using different pen numbers for different linestyles, where different pen numbers have different thicknesses, such as a 0.7 mm and 0.3 mm. Figure 10.30 is a CAD produced drawing showing many different linestyles.

One- and Two-View Drawings Some objects can be adequately described with only one view (Figure 10.31). A sphere can be drawn with one view because all views will be a circle. A cylinder or cube can be described with one view if a note is added to describe the missing feature or dimension. Other applications include a thin gasket or a printed circuit board. One-view drawings are used in electrical, civil, and construction engineering.

Other objects can be adequately described with two views. Cylindrical, conical, and pyramidal shapes are examples of such objects. For example, a cone can be described with a front and a top view. A profile view would be the same as the front view (Figure 10.32 on page 510).

Three-View Drawings The majority of objects require three views to completely describe the objects. The following steps describe the basics for setting up and developing a three-view multiview drawing of a simple part.

Creating a Three-View Drawing

Step 1. In Figure 10.33 on page 510, the isometric view of the part represents the part in its natural position; it appears to be resting on its largest surface area. The front, right side, and top views are selected such that the fewest hidden lines would appear on the views.

Step 2. The spacing of the views is determined by the total width, height, and depth of the object. Views are carefully spaced to center the drawing within the working area of the drawing sheet. Also, the distance between views can vary, but enough space should be left so that dimensions can be placed between the views. A good rule of thumb is to allow about 1.5″ (36 mm) between views. For this

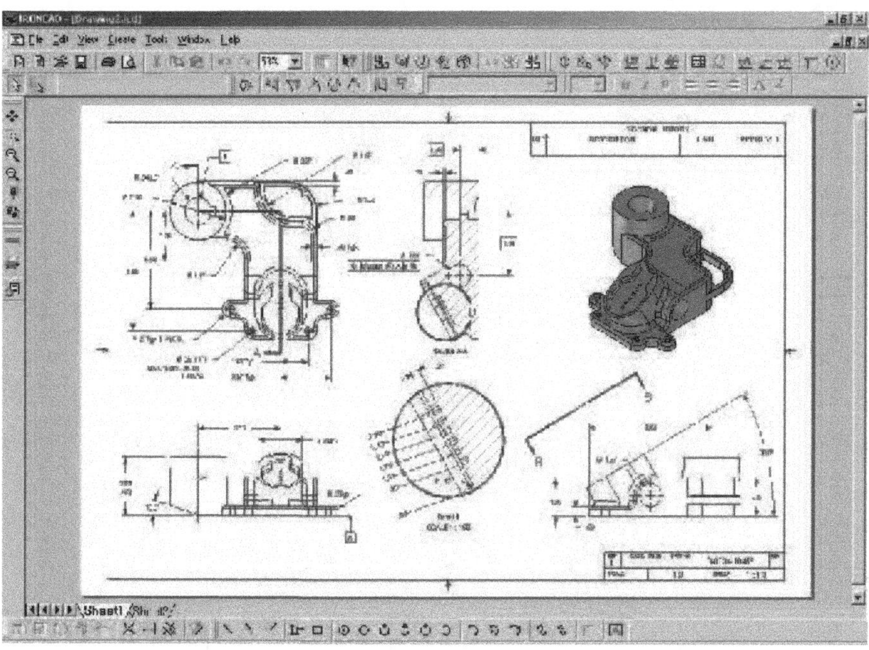

Figure 10.30

Linestyles represented on a CAD drawing

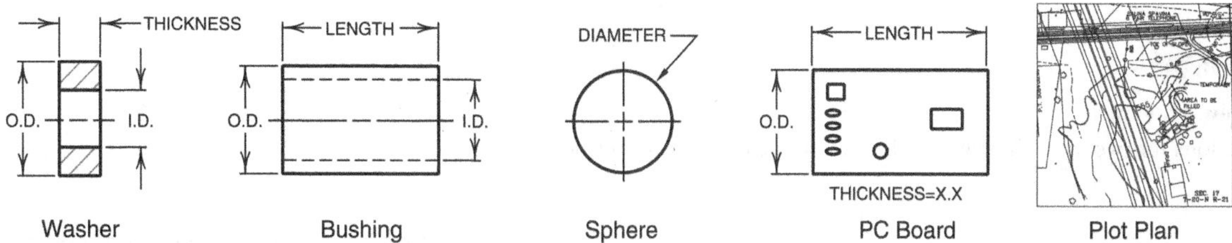

Figure 10.31

One-view drawings

Applications for one-view drawings include some simple cylindrical shapes, spheres, thin parts, and map drawings.

example, use an object with a width of 4″, height of 3″, and a depth of 3″. To determine the total amount of space necessary to draw the front and side views in alignment, add the width (4″) of the front view and the depth (3″) of the side view. Then add 1.5″ to give 8.5″ as the total amount of space needed for the front and side views and the space between. If the horizontal space on the paper is 10″, subtract 8.5″ to get 1.5″; divide the result by 2 to get 0.75″, which is the space left on either side of the two views together. These distances are marked across the paper, as shown in Figure 10.34A on page 511.

In a similar manner, the vertical positioning is determined by adding the height of the front view (3″) to the depth of the top view (3″) and then adding 1.5″ for the space between the views. The result is 7.5″. The 7.5″ is subtracted from the working area of 9″; the result is divided by 2 to get 0.75″, which is the distance across the top and bottom of the sheet (Figure 10.34B).

Step 3. Using techniques described previously in this text, locate the center lines in each view, and lightly draw the arc and circles (Figure 10.34C).

Step 4. Locate other details, and lightly draw horizontal, vertical, and inclined lines in each view. Normally, the front view is constructed first because it has the most details. These details are then projected to the other views using construction lines. Details that cannot be projected

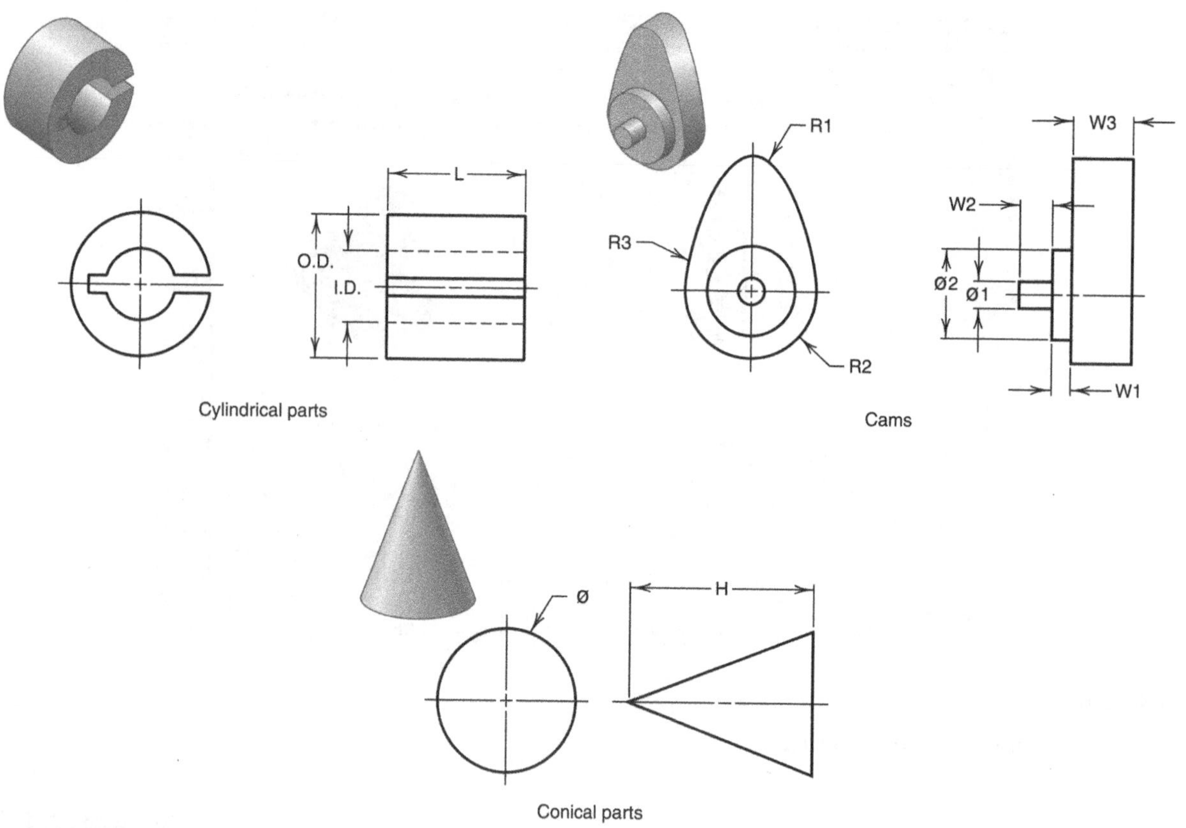

Figure 10.32

Two-view drawings

Applications for two-view drawings include cylindrical and conical shapes.

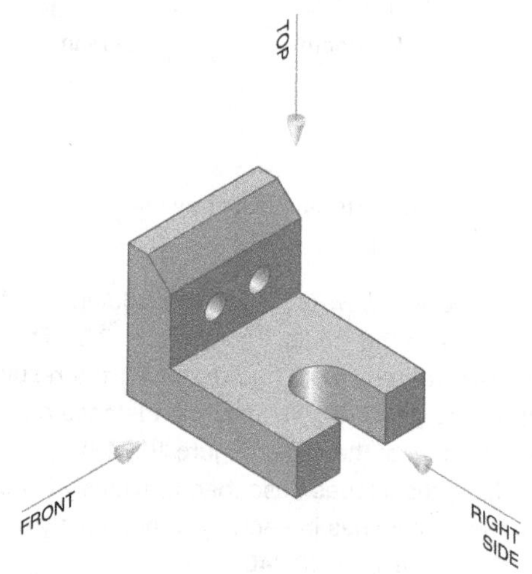

Figure 10.33

Selecting the views for a multiview drawing

The object should be oriented in its natural position, and views chosen should best describe the features.

directly must be measured and transferred or projected using a miter line. For example, dividers can be used to measure and transfer details from the top view to the right side view (Figure 10.34D). A miter line can also be constructed by drawing a 45-degree line from the intersection of the top and side view and drawing the projection lines as shown in Figure 10.34C.

Step 5. Locate and lightly draw hidden lines in each view. For this example, hidden lines are used to represent the limiting elements of the holes.

Step 6. Following the alphabet of lines, darken all object lines by doing all horizontal, then all vertical, and finally all inclined lines, in that order. Darken all hidden and center lines. Lighten or erase any construction lines that can be easily seen when the drawing is held at arm's length. The same basic procedures can be used with 2-D CAD. However, construction lines do not have to be erased. Instead, they can be placed on a separate layer, then turned off.

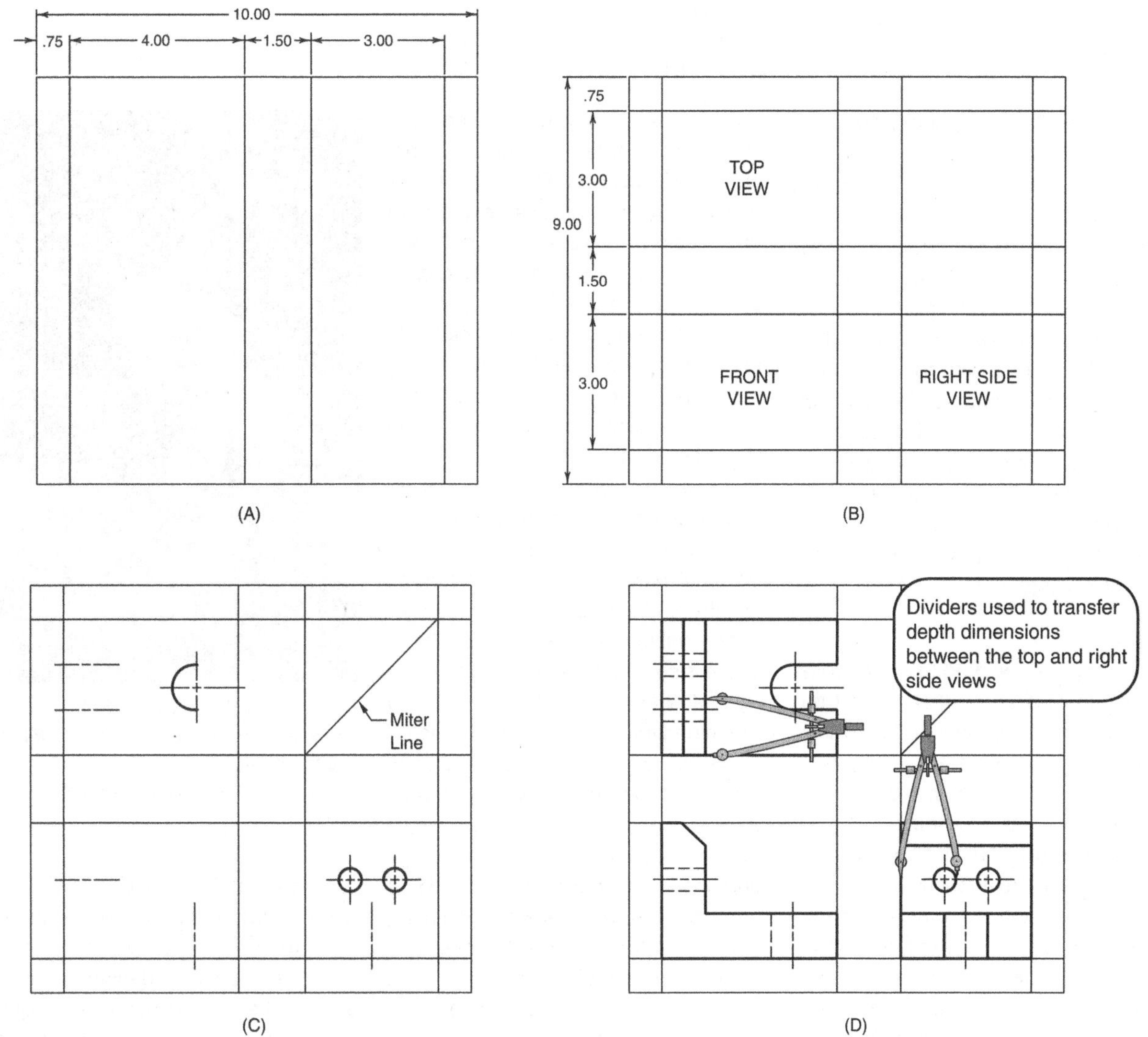

Figure 10.34

Steps to center and create a three-view multiview drawing on an A-size sheet

10.4.7 Multiviews from 3-D CAD Models

The computer screen can be used as a projection plane displaying the 2-D image of a 3-D CAD model. The user can control the line of sight and the type of projection (parallel or perspective). Most 3-D CAD software programs have automated the task of creating multiview drawings from 3-D models. With these CAD systems, the 3-D model of the object is created first (see Figure 10.33). Most CAD programs have predefined viewpoints that correspond to the six principal views (Figure 10.35 on page 514). The views that will best represent the object in multiview are selected, the viewpoint is changed, a CAD command converts the projection of the 3-D model into a 2-D drawing, and the first view is created (Figure 10.36 on page 514). This view is then saved as a block or symbol. The second view is created by changing the viewpoint again and then converting the new projection to a 2-D drawing of the object (Figure 10.37 on page 515). These steps are repeated for as many views as are necessary for the multiview drawing.

After the required number of 2-D views are created, the views are arranged on a new drawing by retrieving the blocks or symbols created earlier. Care must be taken to

Dream **High Tech** Job

Designing Tennis Equipment

The engineering design process is used in many types of jobs from the design of consumer product packaging to the design of tennis gear. An understanding of the design process, multiview drawings, and visualization along with formal education in a field of engineering can lead to exciting job opportunities, such as the one described here of an engineer who started off at a sporting goods company as a co-op student and became their primary performance tennis racket engineer.

Tennis

"Growing up, I wanted to design roller coasters. It was my dream. As I began researching how to get there, I learned it would take a degree in engineering to fulfill this dream. My grandfather was an engineer, so I felt I already knew a little bit about what it would take to be an engineer.

"During my freshman year at Purdue University, a required class dealing with all the various disciplines of engineering introduced me to my major, mechanical engineering. Mechanical seemed to be the most versatile form of engineering, and that really appealed to me.

"At Purdue, the top one-third of the class is offered the opportunity to be in a cooperative education (co-op) program. Following your freshman year, a student can enroll in the co-op program and alternate semesters between working at a company and going to school; basically, turning a four-year program into a five-year program, but you graduate with valuable work experience. Wilson Sporting Goods was my first choice, because tennis has always been one of my passions. I played competitively through high school and worked as an assistant tennis professional giving lessons at a local country club. My tennis experience and knowledge of racquets, along with my performance in the classroom at Purdue, helped me get the Wilson co-op position.

"As a co-op student, I was involved in the testing and analyzing of racquets and tennis balls. I measured the physical properties, such as length, weight, and inertia, to determine how a new design was going to perform. There is so much to learn in this industry that I was constantly fascinated by the dynamics of the design process.

DONALD LOEFFLER, EIT
Performance Racquet Design Engineer, Wilson Sporting Goods.
(Courtesy of Karl Weatherly/Getty Images.)

"After receiving my degree from Purdue I began working full-time as a design engineer in January of 2003. Wilson employs three design engineers: the performance racquet engineer, an accessories engineer, and an indoor sports (racquetball/badminton/squash) engineer. On any given day, I often combine the knowledge I acquired at school with the skills I learned while working as a co-op, to arrive at the best answer or solution. Only 18 months after graduation, I am now Wilson's primary performance racquet engineer. Performance racquets are the racquets sold in sporting goods stores and pro shops without strings. These racquets are typically more expensive and used by serious recreational players or professionals. I give my input regarding the design from start to finish, watching the design process from prototype through production."

If tennis is your passion, as an engineer, you can design racquets, strings, balls, and other new equipment to advance the game and reduce injuries. Every year, manufacturers come out with multiple racquet designs to make the game better for the professionals and more enjoyable for the recreational players. String materials made from cow gut to synthetics are designed to give more power or greater control, and more than 70 million tennis balls are manufactured and sold in stores every year. There is a wealth of opportunity in the tennis industry.

Tennis Balls

In tennis, ball design is a complex subject. Professional players can hit serves as fast as 135 mph. When a ball is hit with that much force, an engineer must understand what happens during the impact. How does the ball deform and how does that affect its resulting performance characteristics? After considerable deformation, can the ball be used the next day? Will it offer the same spin ability or, more important, will it impact the present match?

To answer some of these questions, the United States Tennis Association (USTA) uses a Stevens machine to compress the tennis balls. Each ball is squash-tested, or compressed, for 10 seconds and then checked for deformation. If the ball does not return to a round shape, it is rejected by the USTA.

Engineers often test tennis ball aerodynamics in a wind tunnel, which blows air over the tennis ball to determine how the forces act on it. For example, if the tunnel blows air over the tennis ball at 135 mph, it simulates a ball served at 135 mph. Wind tunnels are fascinating and provide the engineer with important aerodynamic data that would be close to impossible to obtain any other way.

To understand the basic physics of tennis and to learn how speed, spin, height, and altitude determine the flight of a tennis ball, visit http://wings.avkids.com. This interactive software program is part of the Aeronautics Internet Textbook and offers a wealth of information on all things aeronautical, from tennis ball trajectories to careers that use aeronautics.

Tennis Racquets

To a person who doesn't play tennis, a racquet is a device to hit a tennis ball over the net. To a tennis racquet designer, a tennis racquet is a work of art that presents a constant challenge in creating the "perfect" racquet for each level of player ability. Many years ago, the average racquet weighed two to three pounds. A few years ago, the average racquet weighed 11–12 ounces. Today, racquets made with high-tech alloys weigh only seven or eight ounces. What do you think happens to the player and to the game when the weight is lowered or redistributed? More mass or weight usually equals more power. How would you maintain the power of a stroke despite a lower racquet weight?

The answer to the problem lies in determining the correct string tension. The strings on a racquet are another feat of science and engineering in racquet design. By changing the position of the strings or by designing different string geometry configurations, the "sweet spot" can be enlarged and more power can be delivered to off-center hits. An average or low-strength player can still whack the ball proficiently with a well-designed racket.

Engineers Who Do This:

- **Aeronautical/Aerospace Engineers**—May design tennis balls and/or racquets and research the aerodynamics of tennis play.
- **Civil Engineers**—May design courts and other tennis venues.
- **Materials Engineers**—May look for new materials to make the game more fun or challenging, such as racquet components (e.g., strings and grips) or balls (cores and cover materials), and may work with civil engineers to design new court surfaces that reduce injury while also slowing or speeding up the game.
- **Mechanical Engineers**—May design tennis racquets or the machines that produce them, or be involved in the manufacturing processes of racquets, ball launchers, or line-call systems that determine whether a ball is hit in or out of play.

This tennis racquet by Head is made of lightweight magnesium.
(Courtesy of Jules Frazier/Getty Images.)

More Resources:

- Aeronautics Internet Textbook—http://wings.avkids.com
- International Sports Engineering Association—www.sports-engineering.co.uk
- International Tennis Federation—www.itftennis.com
- Racquet Research—www.racquetresearch.com
- Tennis Server—www.tennisserver.com
- United States Tennis Association—www.usta.com
- United States Racquet Stringers Association—www.tennisone.com

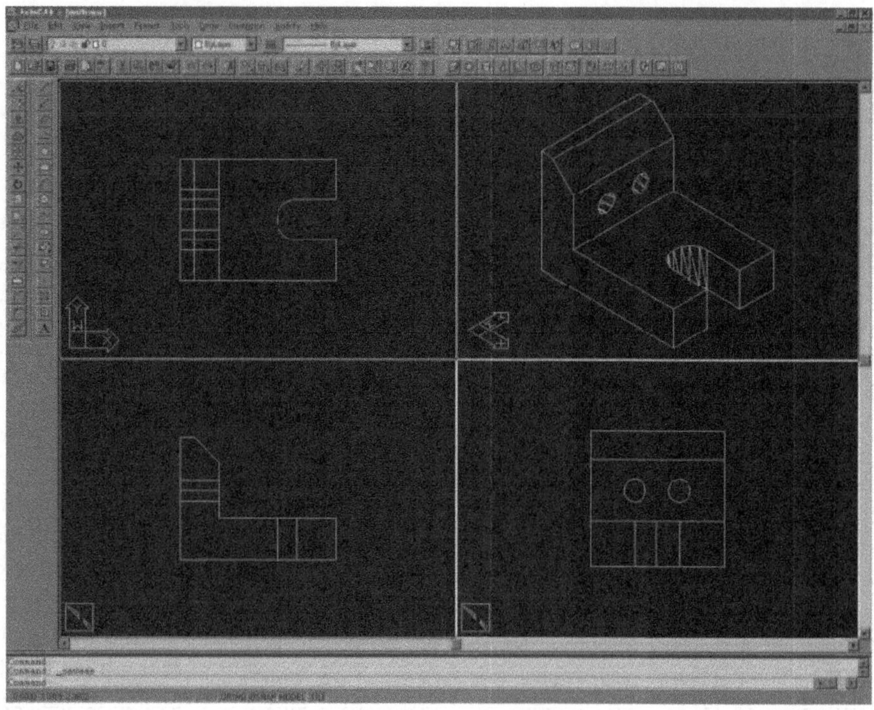

Figure 10.35

Predefined multiviews on a CAD system

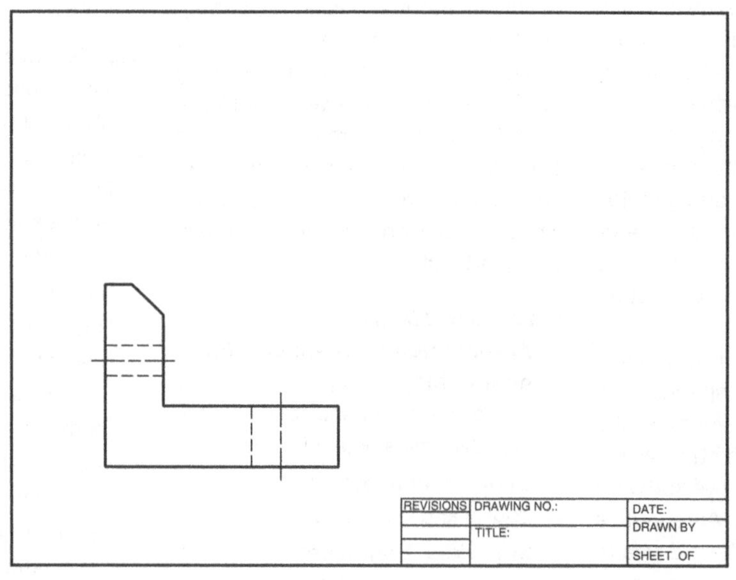

Figure 10.36

Changing the viewpoint on a 3-D CAD model to create a front view

This view is captured, then placed in a title block and border line.

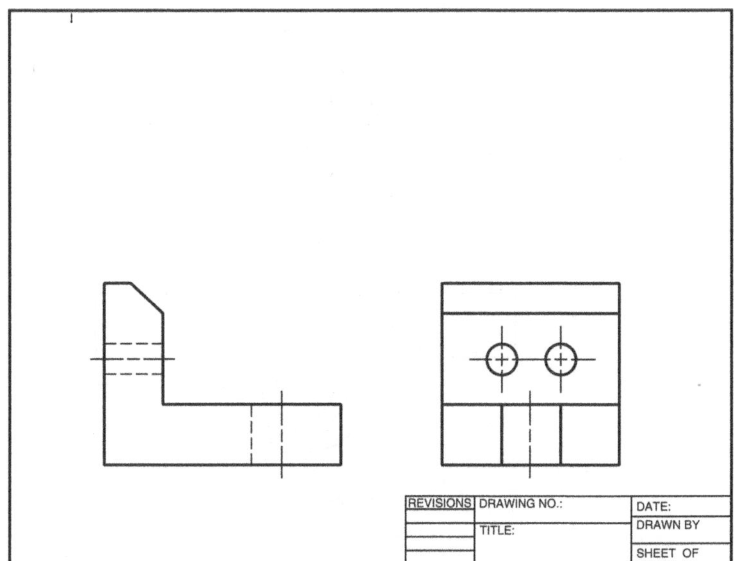

Figure 10.37

Changing the viewpoint on the 3-D model to create a right side view

This view is captured, then placed in a title block and border line.

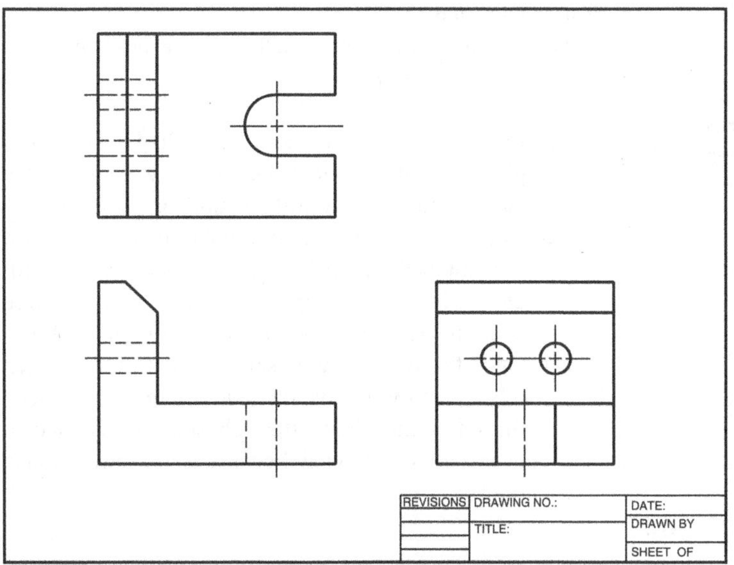

Figure 10.38

Creating a multiview drawing of the 3-D model

The previously captured views are brought together with a standard border and title block to create the final drawing.

bring the views in at the proper scale and correct alignment. The views must then be edited to change solid lines to hidden lines and to add center lines. Other changes may be required so that the views are drawn to accepted standards (Figure 10.38).

10.5 View Selection

Before a multiview drawing is created, the views must be selected. Four basic decisions must be made to determine the best views:

1. Determine the best position of the object. The object must be positioned within the imaginary glass box such that the surfaces of major features are either perpendicular or parallel to the glass planes (Figure 10.39 on page 516). This will create views with a minimum number of hidden lines. Figure 10.40 on page 516 shows an example of poor positioning: the surfaces of the object are not parallel to the glass planes, resulting in many more hidden lines.
2. Define the front view. The front view should show the object in its natural or assembled state and be

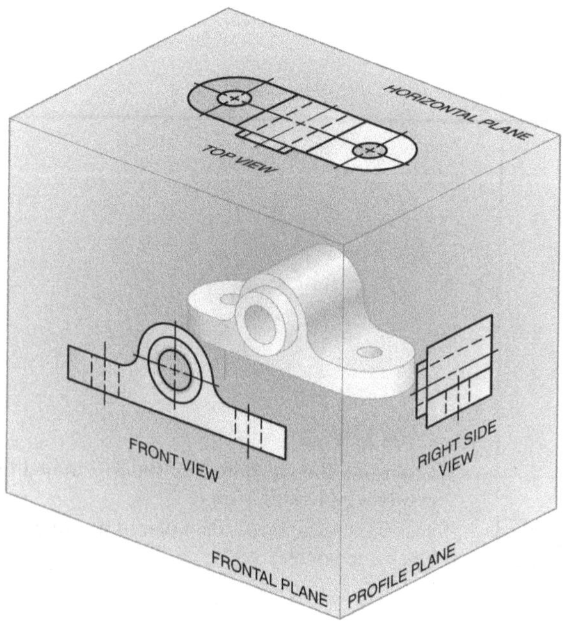

Figure 10.39

Good orientation

Suspend the object in the glass box such that major surfaces are parallel or perpendicular to the sides of the box (projection planes).

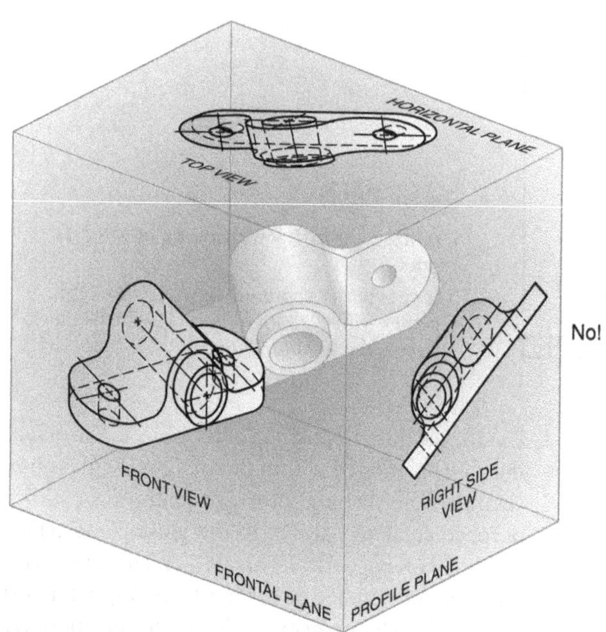

Figure 10.40

Poor orientation

Suspending the object such that surfaces are not parallel to the sides of the glass box produces views with many hidden lines.

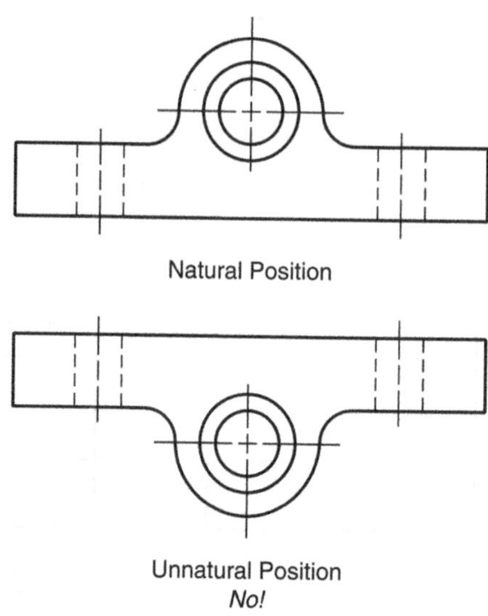

Figure 10.41

Natural position

Always attempt to draw objects in their natural position.

the most descriptive view (Figure 10.41). For example, the front view of an automobile would show the automobile in its natural position, on its wheels.

3. Determine the minimum number of views needed to completely describe the object so it can be produced. For our example, three views are required to completely describe the object (Figure 10.42).
4. Once the front view is selected, determine which other views will have the fewest number of hidden lines. In Figure 10.43, the right side view is selected over the left side view because it has fewer hidden lines.

Practice Exercise 10.2

Using any of the objects in Figure 10.94 in the back of this chapter, generate three multiview sketches. Each sketch should use a different view of the object as the front view. What features of the object become hidden or visible as you change the front view?

10.6 Fundamental Views of Edges and Planes

In multiview drawings, there are *fundamental views* for edges and planes. These fundamental views show the edges or planes in true size, not foreshortened, so that

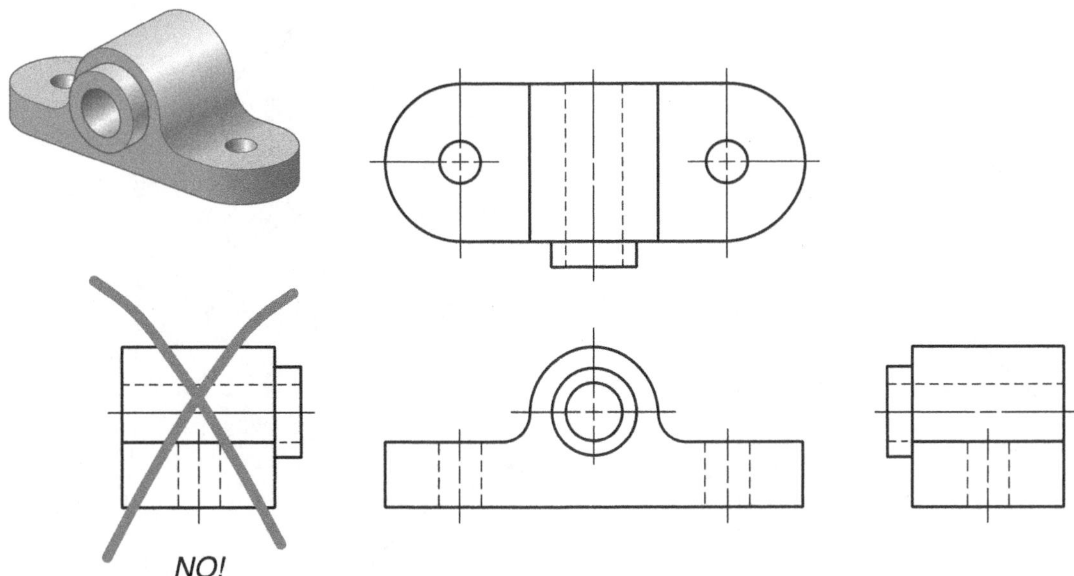

Figure 10.42

Minimum number of views

Select the minimum number of views needed to completely describe an object. Eliminate views that are mirror images of other views.

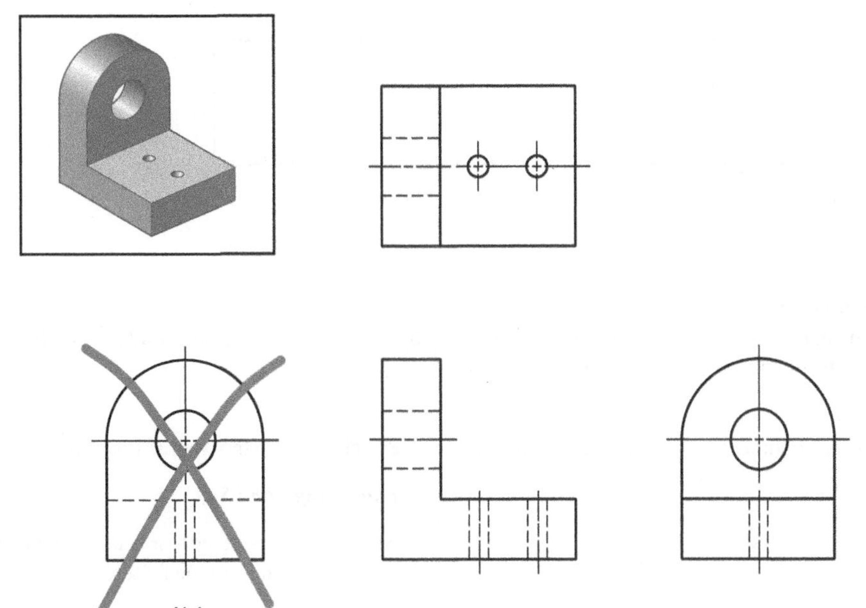

Figure 10.43

Most descriptive views

Select those views which are the most descriptive and have the fewest hidden lines. In this example, the right side view has fewer hidden lines than the left side view.

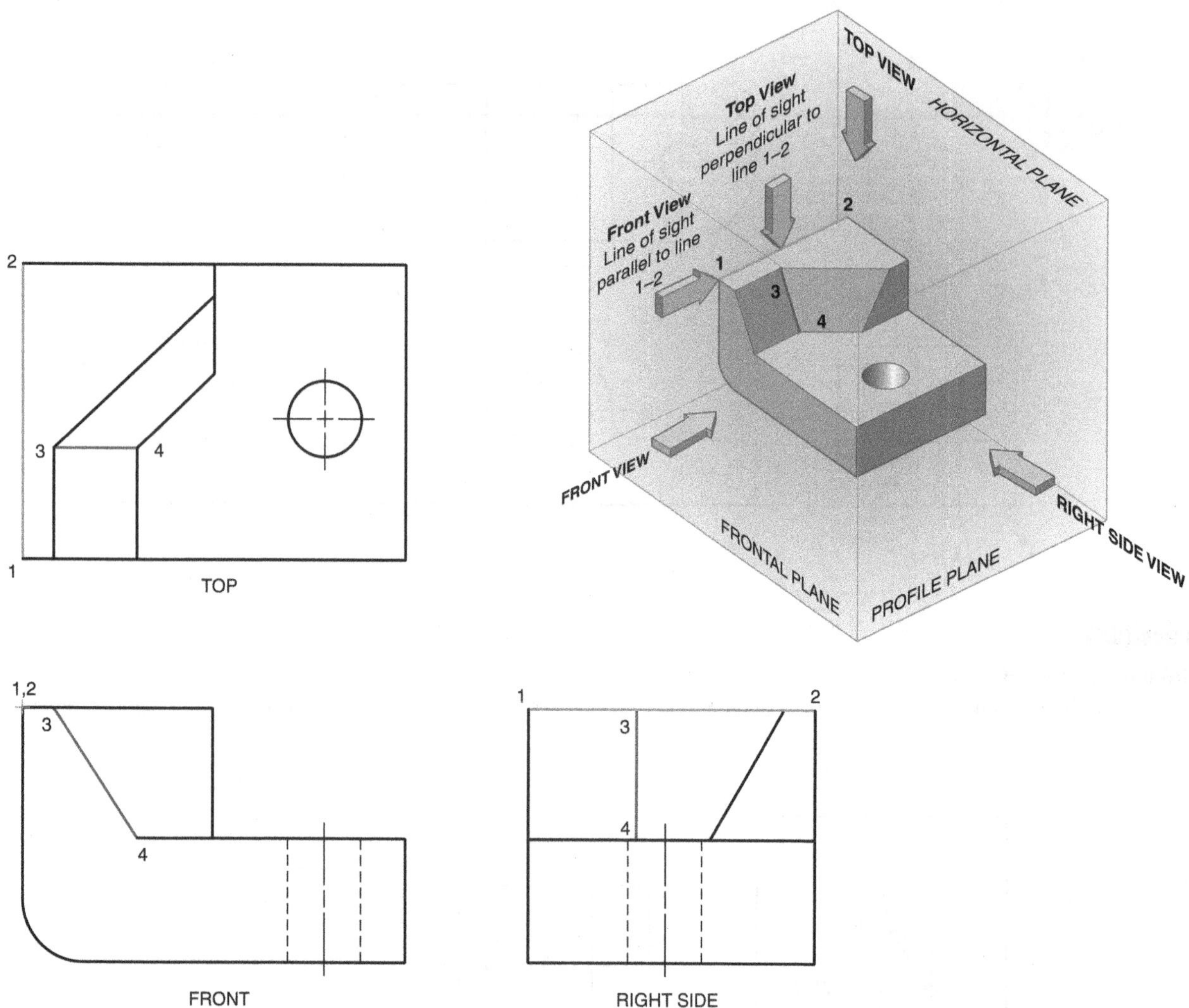

Figure 10.44

Fundamental views of edges

Determine the fundamental views of edges on a multiview drawing by the position of the object relative to the current line of sight and the relationship of the object to the planes of the glass box.

true measurements of distances, angles, and areas can be made.

10.6.1 Edge Lines

An **edge line** is the intersection of two planes and is represented as a line on multiview drawings. A **normal line**, or **true-length line**, is an edge line that is parallel to a plane of projection and thus perpendicular to the line of sight. In Figure 10.44, edge line 1–2 in the top and right side views is a normal edge.

Principles of Orthographic Projection Rule 3:

True Length and Size

Features are true length or true size when the lines of sight are perpendicular to the feature.

An edge line appears as a point in a plane of projection to which it is perpendicular. Edge line 1–2 is a point in the front view of Figure 10.44. The edge line appears as a point because it is parallel to the line of sight used to create the front view.

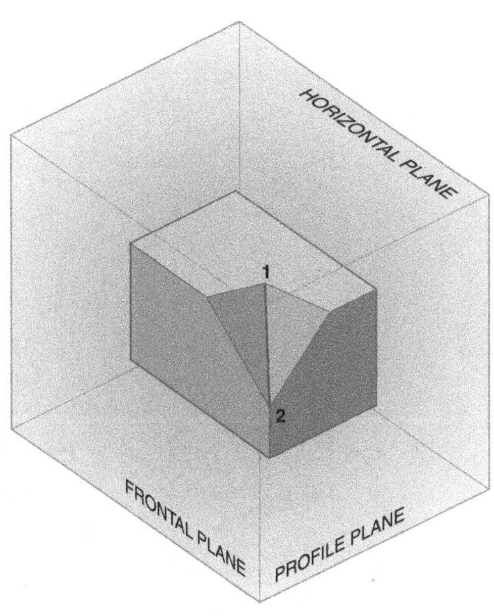

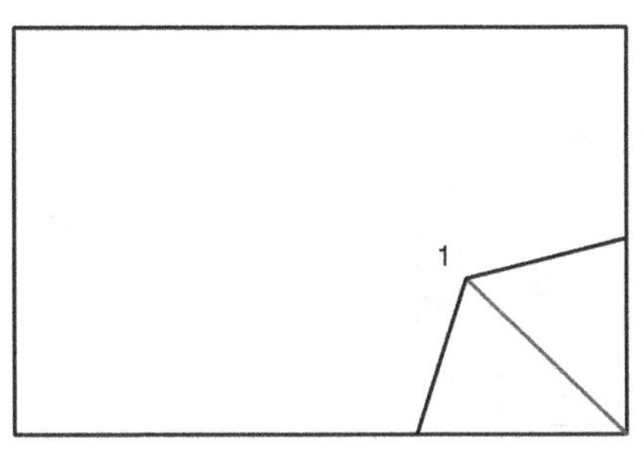

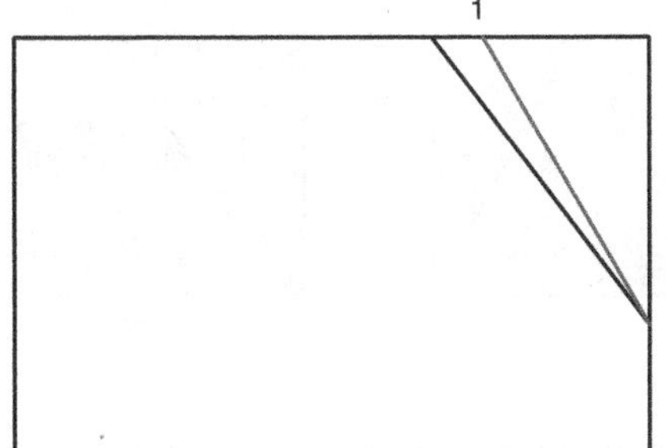

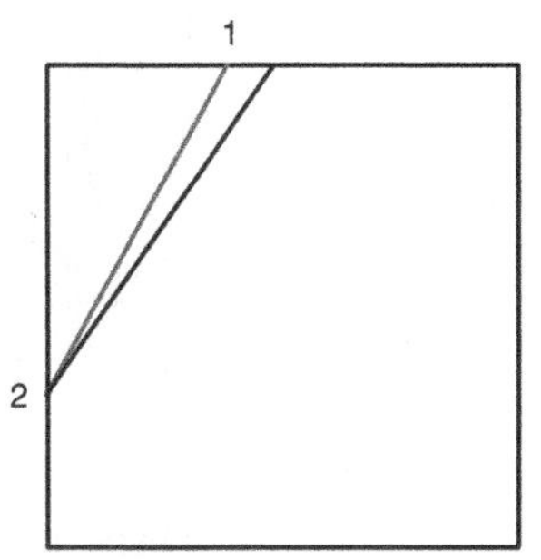

Figure 10.45

Oblique line

Oblique line 1–2 is not parallel to any of the principal planes of projection of the glass box.

An **inclined line** is parallel to a plane of projection but inclined to the adjacent planes, and it appears foreshortened in the adjacent planes. In Figure 10.44, line 3–4 is inclined and foreshortened in the top and right side view, but is true length in the front view because it is parallel to the frontal plane of projection.

An **oblique line** is not parallel to any principal plane of projection; therefore, it never appears as a point or in true length in any of the six principal views. Instead, an oblique edge will be foreshortened in every view and will always appear inclined. Line 1–2 in Figure 10.45 is an oblique edge.

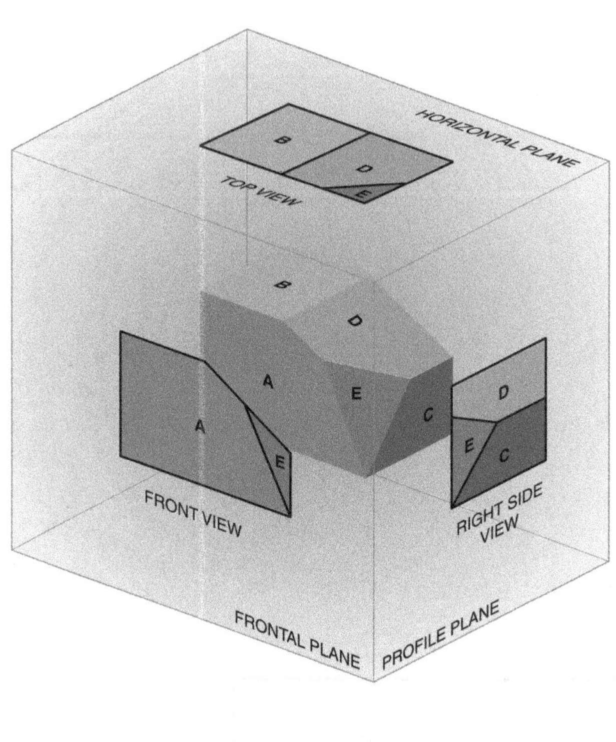

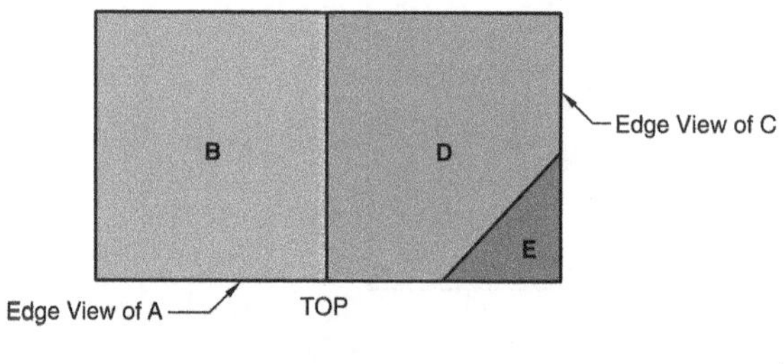

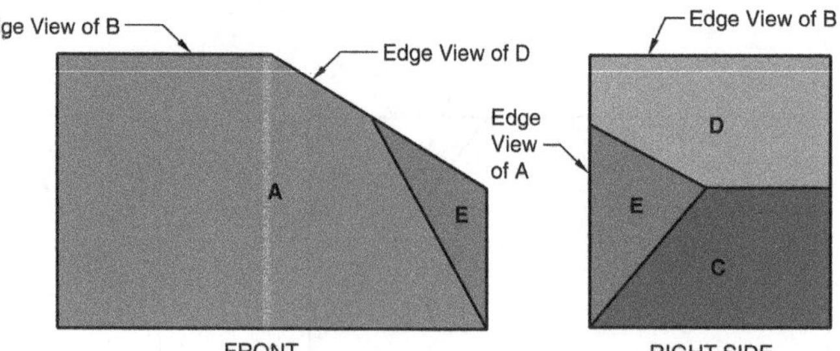

Figure 10.46

Fundamental views of surfaces

Surface A is parallel to the frontal plane of projection. Surface B is parallel to the horizontal plane of projection. Surface C is parallel to the profile plane of projection. Surface D is an inclined plane and is on edge in one of the principal views (the front view). Surface E is an oblique plane and is neither parallel nor on edge in any of the principal planes of projection.

Principles of Orthographic Projection Rule 4:

Foreshortening

Features are foreshortened when the lines of sight are not perpendicular to the feature.

10.6.2 Principal Planes

A **principal plane** is parallel to one of the principal planes of projection and is therefore perpendicular to the line of sight. A principal plane or surface will be true size and shape in the view where it is parallel to the projection plane and will appear as a horizontal or vertical line in the adjacent views. In Figure 10.46, surface A is parallel to the frontal projection plane and is therefore a principal plane. Because surface A appears true size and shape in the front view, it is sometimes referred to as a **normal plane** in that view. In this figure, surface A appears as a horizontal edge in the top view and as a vertical edge in the right side view. This edge representation is an important characteristic in multiview drawings. Principal planes are categorized by the view in which the plane appears true size and shape: frontal, horizontal, or profile.

A **frontal plane** is parallel to the front plane of projection and is true size and shape in the front view. A frontal plane appears as a horizontal edge in the top view and a vertical edge in the profile views. In Figure 10.46, surface A is a frontal plane.

A **horizontal plane** is parallel to the horizontal planes of projection and is true size and shape in the top (and bottom) view. A horizontal plane appears as a horizontal edge in the front and side views. In Figure 10.46, surface B is a horizontal plane.

A **profile plane** is parallel to the profile (right or left side) planes of projection and is true size and shape in the profile views. A profile plane appears as a vertical edge in the front and top views. In Figure 10.46, surface C is a profile plane.

10.6.3 Inclined Planes

An **inclined plane** is perpendicular to one plane of projection and inclined to adjacent planes and cannot be viewed in true size and shape in any of the principal views. An inclined plane appears as an edge in the view where it is perpendicular to the projection plane and as a foreshortened surface in the adjacent views. In Figure 10.46, plane D is an inclined surface. To view an inclined plane in its true size and shape, create an auxiliary view, as described in Chapter 13.

10.6.4 Oblique Planes

An **oblique plane** is not parallel to any of the principal planes of projection. In Figure 10.46, plane E is an oblique surface. An oblique surface does not appear in its true size and shape, or as an edge, in any of the principal views; instead, an oblique plane always appears as a foreshortened plane in the principal views. A secondary auxiliary view must be constructed, or the object must be rotated, in order to create a normal view of an oblique plane. (See Chapter 14.)

Practice Exercise 10.3

Using stiff cardboard, cut out the following shapes:

- Rectangle
- Circle
- Trapezoid
- Irregular shape with at least six sides, at least two of which are parallel to each other

Sketch the following multiviews of each shape:

- The line of sight perpendicular to the face
- Rotated 45 degrees about the vertical axis
- Rotated 90 degrees about the vertical axis
- Rotated 45 degrees about the horizontal axis
- Rotated 90 degrees about the horizontal axis
- Rotated 45 degrees about both the vertical and horizontal axes

Which views represent true-size projections of the surface? In what views is the surface inclined, oblique, or on edge? What is the shape of a circle when it is foreshortened? For the inclined projections, how many primary dimensions of the surface appear smaller than they are in true-size projection? What is the relationship between the foreshortened dimension and the axis of rotation? Identify the parallel edges of the surface in the true-size projection. Do these edges stay parallel in the other views? Are these edges always seen in true length?

10.7 Multiview Representations

Three-dimensional solid objects are represented on 2-D media as points, lines, and planes. The solid geometric primitives are transformed into 2-D geometric primitives. Being able to identify 2-D primitives and the 3-D primitive solids they represent is important in visualizing and creating multiview drawings. Figure 10.47 on the next page shows multiview drawings of common geometric solids.

10.7.1 Points

A **point** represents a specific position in space and has no width, height, or depth. A point can represent

The *end view of a line.*
The *intersection of two lines.*
A *specific position in space.*

Even though a point does not have width, height, or depth, its position must still be marked. On technical drawings, a point marker is a small symmetrical cross. (See Chapter 8.)

10.7.2 Planes

A plane can be viewed from an infinite number of vantage points. A plane surface will always project as either a line or an area. Areas are represented in true size or are foreshortened and will always be similar in configuration (same number of vertices and edges) from one view to another, unless viewed as an edge. For example, surface B

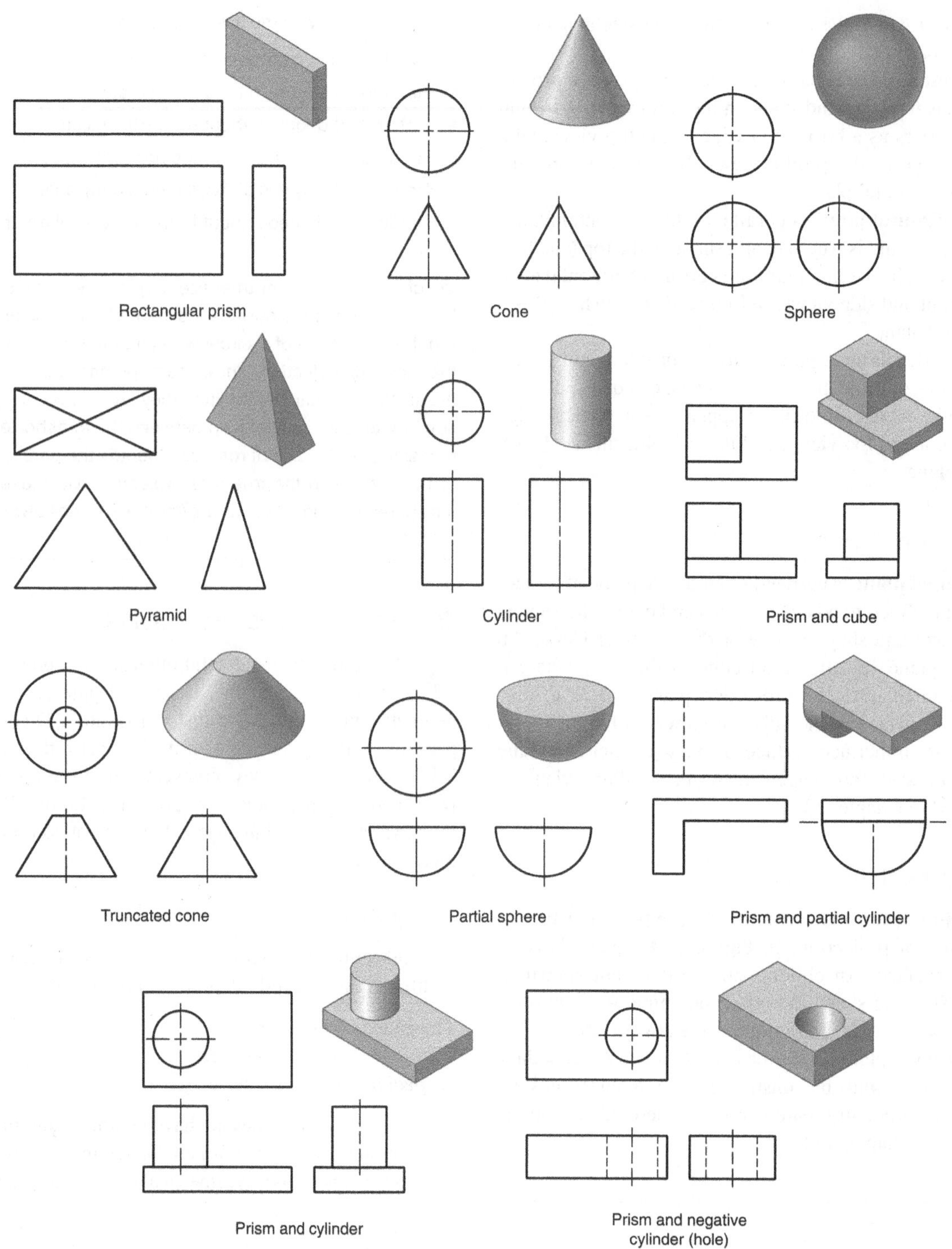

Figure 10.47

Multiview drawings of solid primitive shapes

Understanding and recognizing these shapes will help you understand their application in technical drawings. Notice that the cone, sphere, and cylinder are adequately represented with fewer than three views.

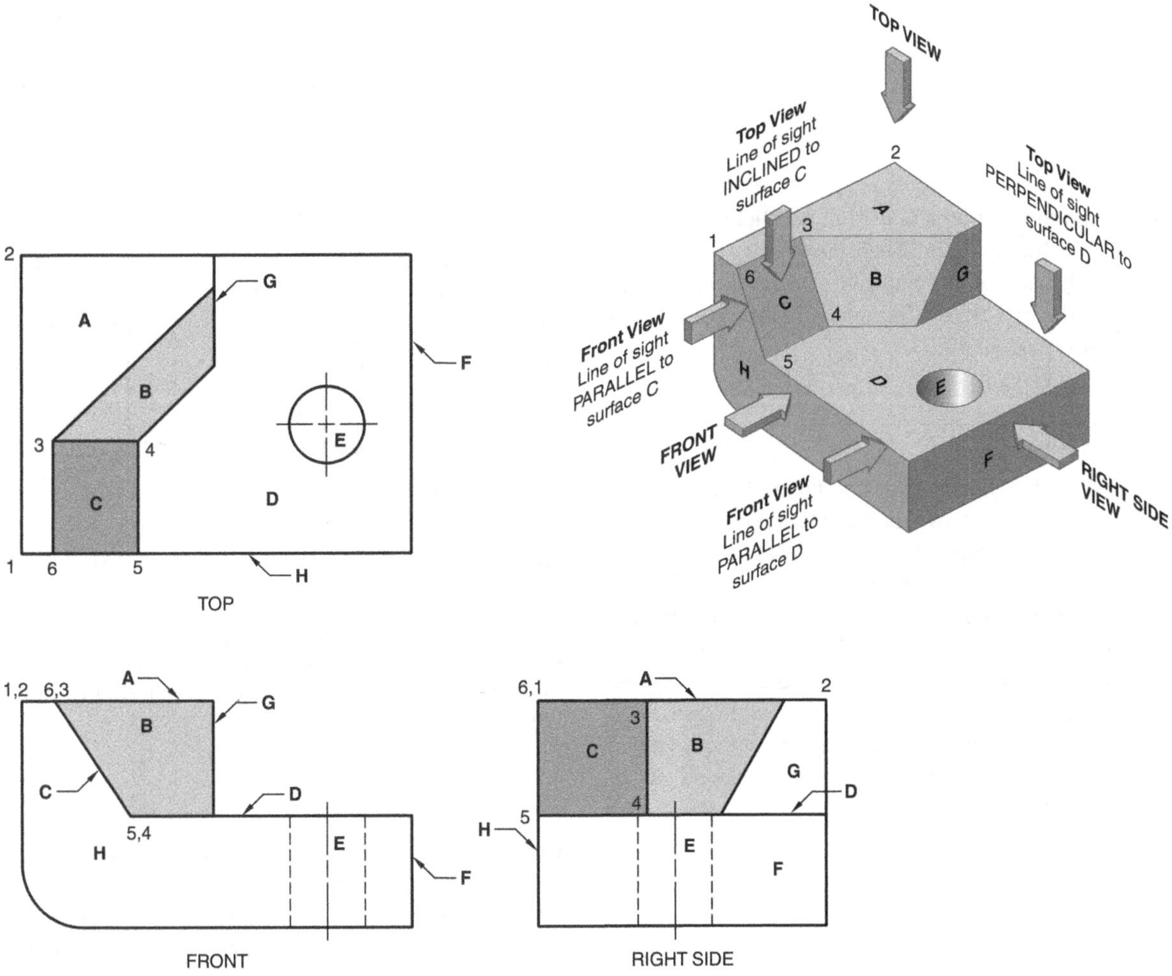

Figure 10.48

Rule of configuration of planes

Surface B is an example of the Rule of Configuration of Planes. The edges of surface C, 3–4 and 5–6, are examples of the Rule of Parallel Features.

in Figure 10.48 is always an irregular four-sided polygon with two parallel sides (a trapezoid), in all the principal views. Since surface B is seen as a foreshortened area in the three views, it is an oblique plane.

> Principles of Orthographic Projection Rule 5:
>
> ***Configuration of Planes***
>
> Areas that are the same feature will always be similar in configuration from one view to the next, unless viewed on edge.

In contrast, area C in Figure 10.48 is similar in shape in two of the orthographic views and is on edge in the third. Surface C is a regular rectangle, with parallel sides labeled 3, 4, 5, and 6. Sides 3–6 and 4–5 are parallel in both the top view and the right side view. Also, lines 3–4 and 5–6 are parallel in both views. Parallel features will always be parallel, regardless of the viewpoint.

> Principles of Orthographic Projection Rule 6:
>
> ***Parallel Features***
>
> Parallel features will always appear parallel in all views.

A plane appears as an **edge view** or *line* when it is parallel to the line of sight in the current view. In the front view of Figure 10.48, surfaces A and D are shown as edges.

Principles of Orthographic Projection Rule 7:

Edge Views

Surfaces that are parallel to the lines of sight will appear as lines or edge views.

A **foreshortened plane** is neither parallel nor perpendicular to the line of sight. There are two types of foreshortened planes, oblique and inclined, as described in Sections 10.6.3 and 10.6.4. Surface B is foreshortened in all views of Figure 10.48.

Practice Exercise 10.4

Hold an object that has at least one flat surface (plane) at arm's length. Close one eye, and rotate the object so that your line of sight is perpendicular to the flat surface. What you see is a true-size view of the plane. Slowly rotate the object while focusing on the flat plane. Notice that the flat plane begins to foreshorten. As you continue to rotate the object slowly, the plane will become more foreshortened until it disappears from your line of sight and appears as a line or edge. This exercise demonstrates how a flat plane can be represented on paper in true size, foreshortened, or as a line.

10.7.3 Change of Planes (Edge Lines)

A change of planes, or **edge lines**, occurs when two nonparallel surfaces meet, forming a corner, line, or edge (Figure 10.48, Line 3–4). Whenever there is a change in plane, a line must be drawn to represent that change. The lines are drawn as solid or continuous if visible in the current view or dashed if they are hidden.

10.7.4 Angles on Planes

An angle is represented in true size when it is in a normal plane. If an angle is not in a normal plane, then the angle will appear either larger or smaller than true size. For example, in Figure 10.49A, the 135-degree angle is measured as 135 degrees in the front view, which is parallel to the plane containing the angle. In Figure 10.49B, the angle is measured as less than true size in the front view because the plane containing the angle is not parallel to the frontal plane and is foreshortened. Right angles can be measured as 90° in a foreshortened plane if one line is true length (Figure 10.49C).

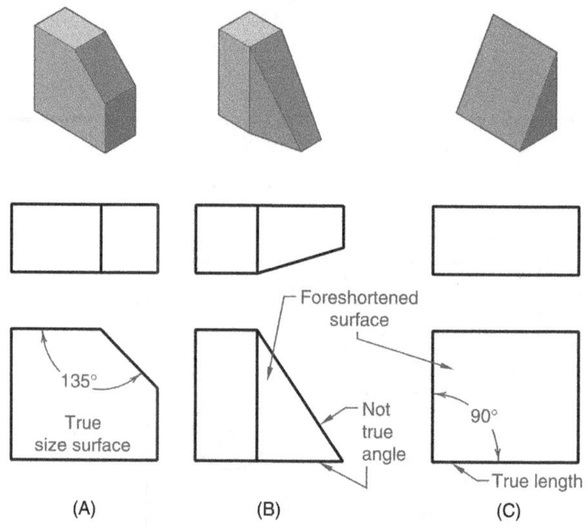

Figure 10.49

Angles

Angles other than 90 degrees can only be measured in views where the surface that contains the angle is perpendicular to the line of sight. A 90-degree angle can be measured in a foreshortened surface if one edge is true length.

10.7.5 Curved Surfaces

Curved surfaces are used to round the ends of parts and to show drilled holes and cylindrical features. Cones, cylinders, and spheres are examples of geometric primitives that are represented as curved surfaces on technical drawings.

Only the far outside boundary, or limiting element, of a curved surface is represented in multiview drawings. For example, the curved surfaces of the cone and cylinder in Figure 10.50 are represented as lines in the front and side views. Note that the bases of the cone and cylinder are represented as circles when they are positioned perpendicular to the line of sight.

Practice Exercise 10.5

Hold a 12-ounce can of soda at arm's length so that your line of sight is perpendicular to the axis of the can. Close one eye; the outline of the view should be a rectangle. The two short sides are edge views of the circles representing the top and bottom of the can. The two long sides represent the limiting elements of the curved surface. Hold the can at arm's length such that your line of sight is perpendicular to the top or bottom. Close one eye; the outline should look like a circle.

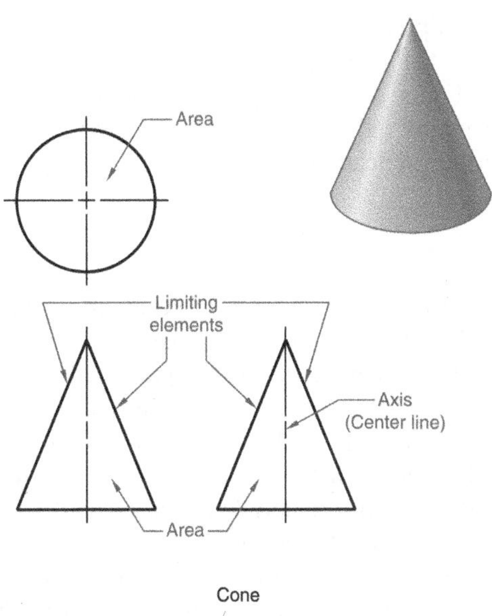

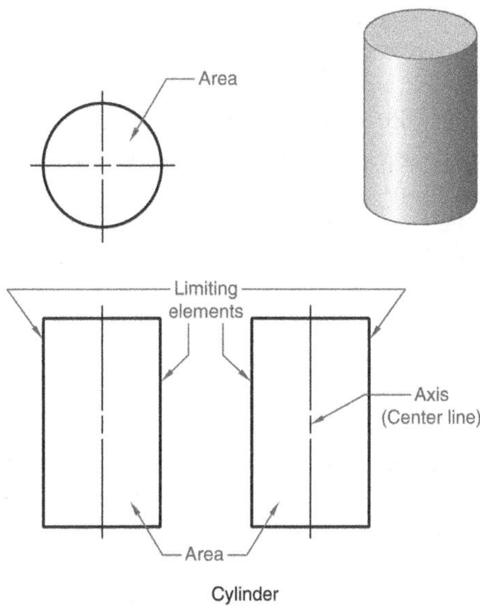

Figure 10.50

Limiting elements

In technical drawings, a cone is represented as a circle in one view and a triangle in the other. The sides of the triangle represent limiting elements of the cone. A cylinder is represented as a circle in one view and a rectangle in the other.

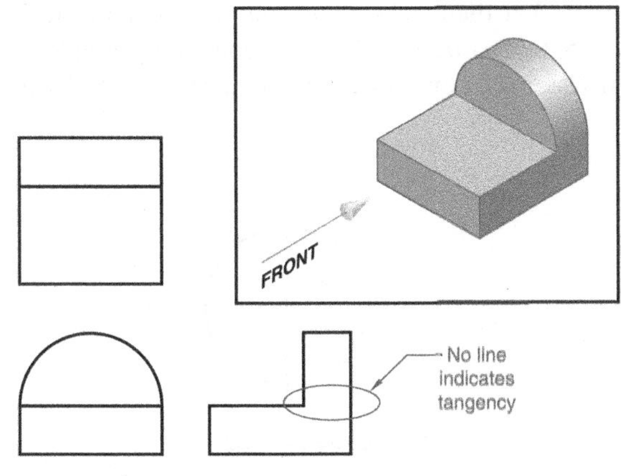

Figure 10.51

Tangent partial cylinder

A rounded-end, or partial, cylinder is represented as an arc when the line of sight is parallel to the axis of the partial cylinder. No line is drawn at the place where the partial cylinder becomes tangent to another feature, such as the vertical face of the side.

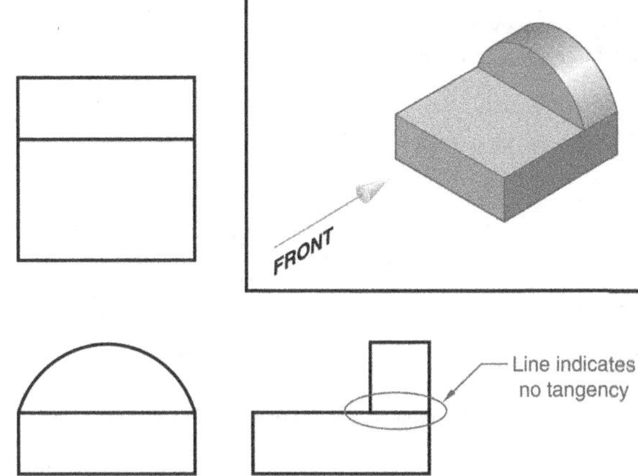

Figure 10.52

Nontangent partial cylinder

When the transition of a rounded end to another feature is not tangent, a line is used at the point of intersection.

Partial cylinders result in other types of multiview representations. For example, the rounded end of the object in Figure 10.51 is represented as an arc in the front view. In the adjacent views, it is a rectangle because the curve is tangent to the sides of the object. If the curve were not tangent to the sides, then a line representing a change of planes would be needed in the profile and top views (Figure 10.52).

An ellipse is used to represent a hole or circular feature that is viewed at an angle other than perpendicular or parallel. Such features include handles, wheels, clock faces, and ends of cans and bottles. Figure 10.53 shows the end of a cylinder, viewed first with a perpendicular line of sight and then with a line of sight at 45 degrees. For the perpendicular view, the center lines are true length, and the figure is represented as a circle (Figure 10.54). However, when the view is tilted, one of the center lines is foreshortened and becomes the minor axis of an ellipse. The center line that remains true length becomes the major axis of the ellipse. As the viewing angle relative to the circle increases, the length of the minor axis is further foreshortened (Figure 10.54). Ellipses are also produced by planes intersecting right circular cones and circular cylinders, as described in Section 8.6.

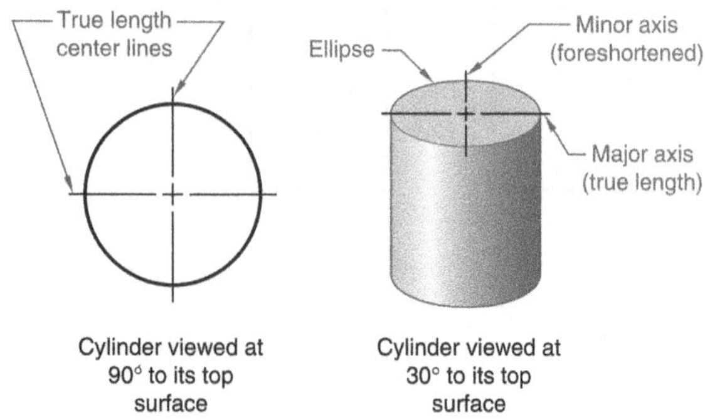

Figure 10.53

Elliptical representation of a circle

An elliptical view of a circle is created when the circle is viewed at an oblique angle.

10.7.6 Holes

Figure 10.55 shows how to represent most types of machined holes. *A through hole,* that is, a hole that goes all the way through an object, is represented in one view as two parallel hidden lines for the limiting elements and is shown as a circle in the adjacent view (Figure 10.55A). A **blind hole**, that is, one that is not drilled all the way through the material, is represented as shown in Figure 10.55B. The bottom of a drilled hole is pointed because all drills used to make such holes are pointed. The depth of the blind hole is measured to the flat, as shown, then 30-degree lines are added to represent the drill tip.

A drilled and *counterbored hole* is shown in Figure 10.55C. Counterbored holes are used to allow the heads of bolts to be flush with or below the surface of the part. A drilled and countersunk hole is shown in Figure 10.55D. *Countersunk holes* are commonly used for flathead fasteners. Normally, the countersink is represented

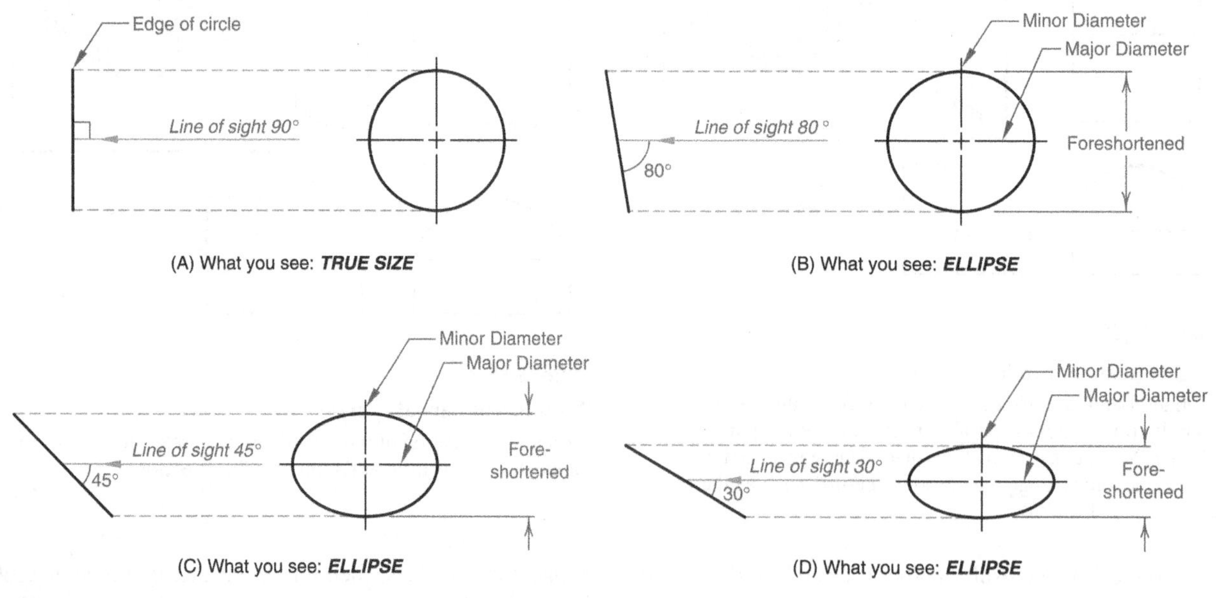

Figure 10.54

Viewing angles for ellipses

The size or exposure of an ellipse is determined by the angle of the line of sight relative to the circle.

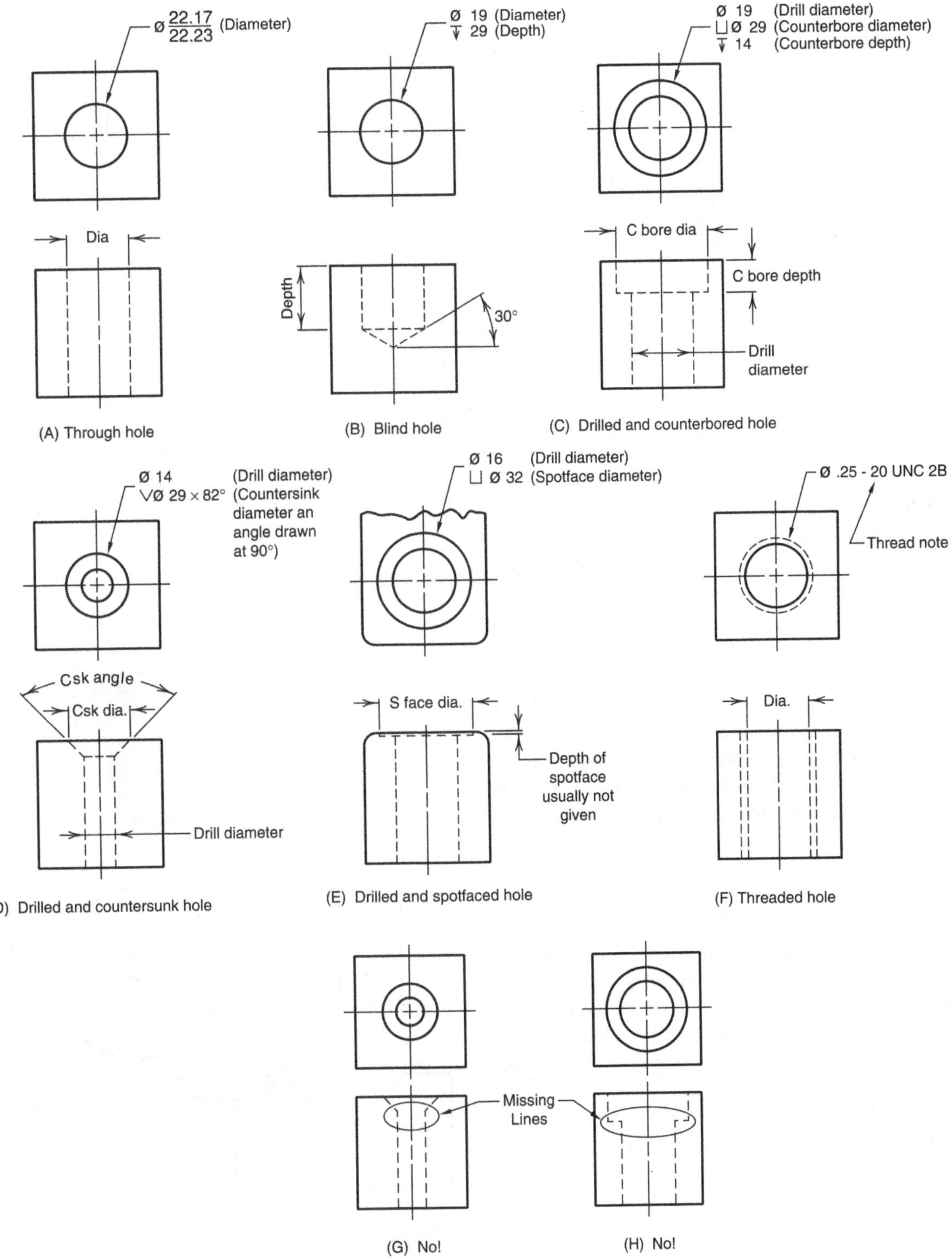

Figure 10.55

Representation of various types of machined holes

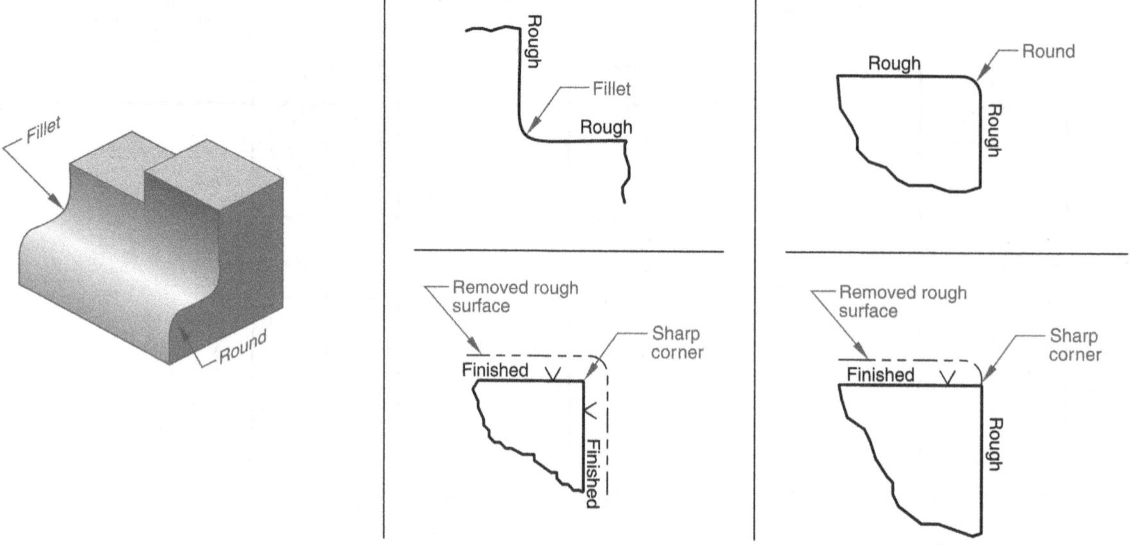

Figure 10.56

Representation of fillets and rounds

Fillets and rounds indicate that surfaces of metal objects have not been machine finished; therefore, there are rounded corners.

by drawing 45-degree lines. A *spotfaced hole* is shown in Figure 10.55E. A spotfaced hole provides a place for the heads of fasteners to rest, to create a smooth surface on cast parts. For countersunk, counterbored, and spotfaced holes, a line must be drawn to represent the change of planes that occurs between the large diameter and the small diameter of the hole. Figure 10.55F shows a threaded hole, with two hidden lines in the front view and a solid and a hidden line in the top view.

10.7.7 Fillets, Rounds, Finished Surfaces, and Chamfers

A **fillet** is a rounded *interior* corner, normally found on cast, forged, or plastic parts. A **round** is a rounded *exterior* corner, normally found on cast, forged, or plastic parts. A fillet or round can indicate that both intersecting surfaces are not machine finished (Figure 10.56). A fillet or round is shown as a small arc.

With CAD, corners are initially drawn square, then fillets and rounds are added using a FILLET command.

Fillets and rounds eliminate sharp corners on objects; therefore, there is no true change of planes at these places on the object. However, on technical drawings, only corners, edge views of planes, and limiting elements are represented. Therefore, at times it is necessary to add lines to represent rounded corners for a clearer representation of an object (Figure 10.57). In adjacent views, lines are added to the filleted and rounded corners by projecting

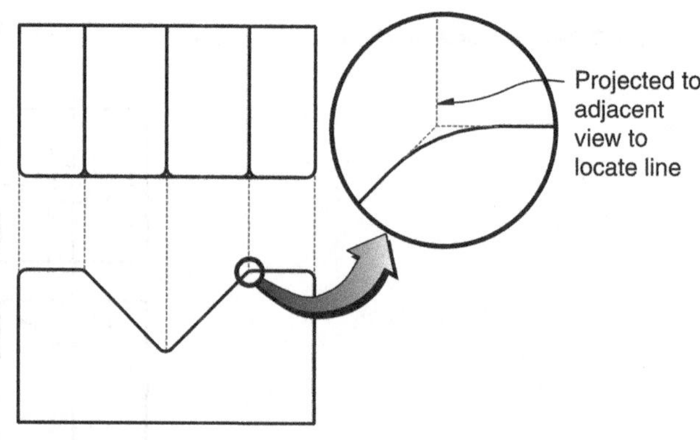

Figure 10.57

Representing fillet and rounded corners

Lines tangent to a fillet or round are constructed and then extended, to create a sharp corner. The location of the sharp corner is projected to the adjacent view to determine where to place representative lines indicating a change of planes.

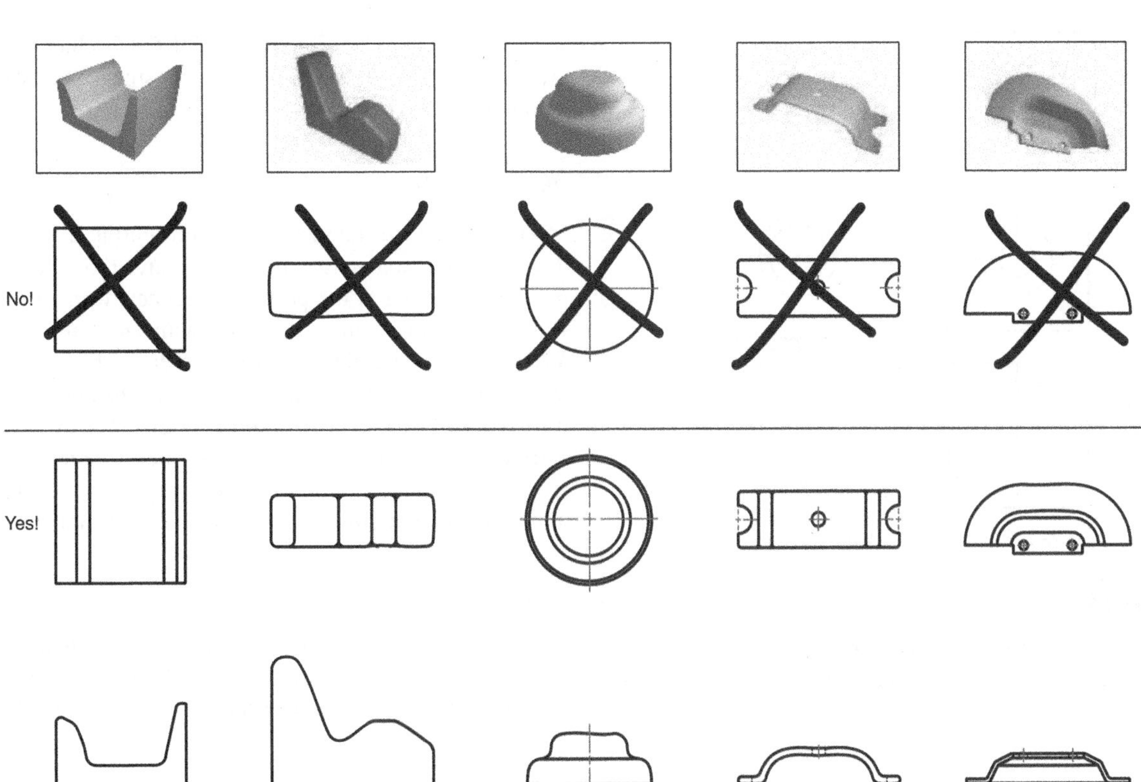

Figure 10.58

Examples representing fillet and rounded corners

Lines are added to parts with fillets and rounds, for clarity. Lines are used in the top views of these parts to represent changes of planes that have fillets or rounds at the corners.

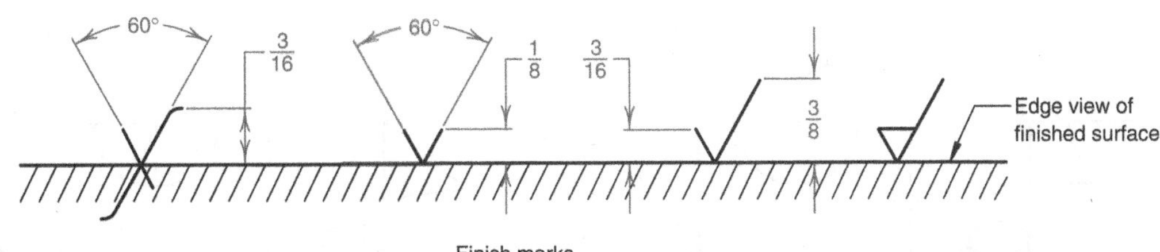

Figure 10.59

Finish mark symbols

Finish marks are placed on engineering drawings to indicate machine finished surfaces.

from the place where the two surfaces would intersect if the fillets or rounds were not used (Figure 10.58). This is a conventional practice used to give more realistic representation of the object in a multiview drawing.

When a surface is to be machined to a finish, a *finish mark* in the form of a small v is drawn on the edge view of the surface to be machined, that is, the *finished surface*. Figure 10.59 shows different methods of representing finish marks and the dimensions used to draw them.

A **chamfer** is a beveled corner used on the openings of holes and the ends of cylindrical parts, to eliminate sharp corners (Figure 10.60 on the next page). Chamfers are represented as lines or circles to show the change of plane. Chamfers can be internal or external and are specified by a

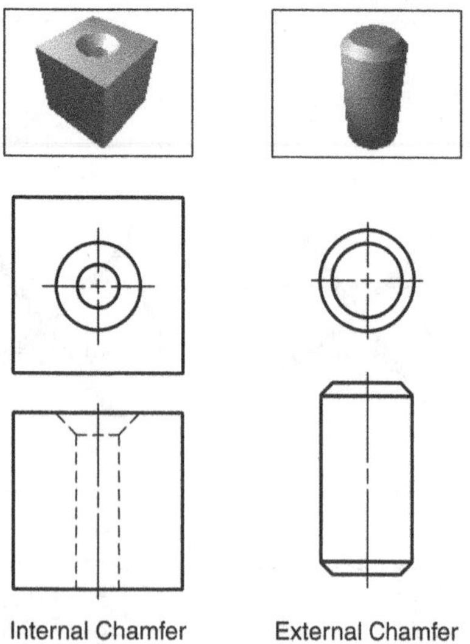

Figure 10.60

Examples of internal and external chamfers

Chamfers are used to break sharp corners on ends of cylinders and holes.

linear and an angular dimension. With CAD, chamfers are added automatically to square corners using a CHAMFER command.

10.7.8 Runouts

A **runout** is a special method of representing filleted surfaces that are tangent to cylinders (Figure 10.61). A runout is drawn starting at the point of tangency, using a radius equal to that of the filleted surface with a curvature of approximately one-eighth the circumference of a circle. Examples of runout uses in technical drawings are shown in Figure 10.62. If a very small round intersects a cylindrical surface, the runouts curve *away* from each other (Figure 10.62A). If a large round intersects a cylindrical surface, the runouts curve *toward* each other (Figure 10.62C).

10.7.9 Elliptical Surfaces

If a right circular cylinder is cut at an acute angle to the axis, an ellipse is created in one of the multiviews (Figure 10.63 on page 532). The major and minor diameters

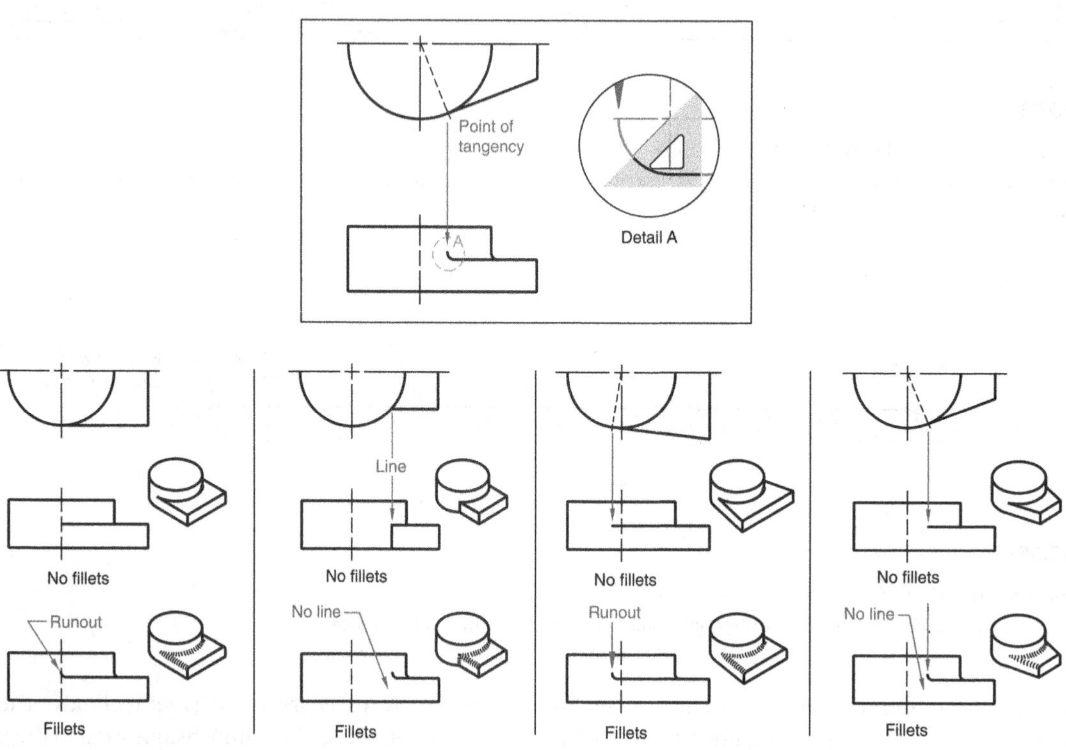

Figure 10.61

Runouts

Runouts are used to represent corners with fillets that intersect cylinders. Notice the difference in the point of tangency with and without the fillets.

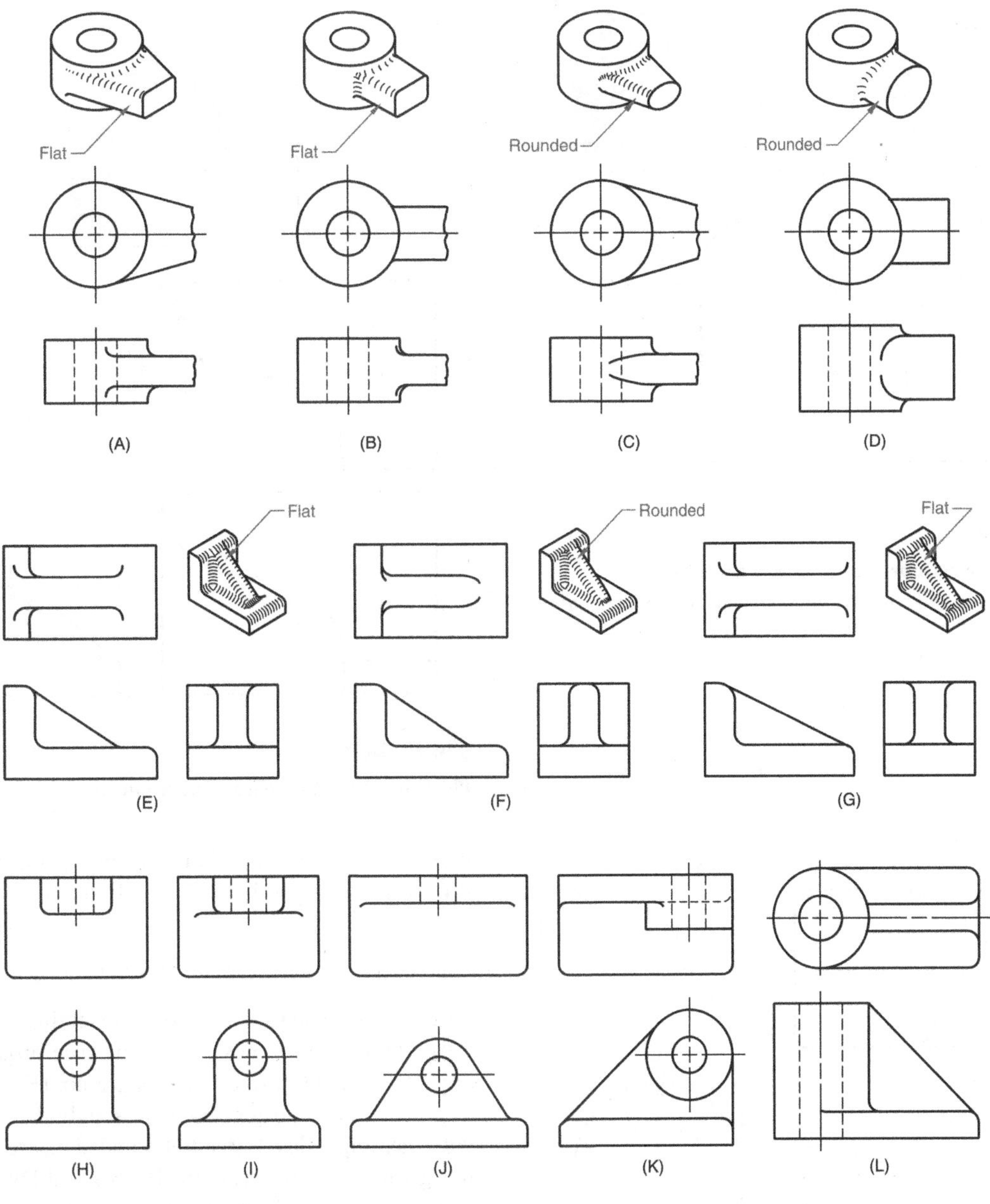

Figure 10.62

Examples of runouts in multiview drawings

can be projected into the view that shows the top of the cylinder as an ellipse. The ellipse can then be constructed using the methods described in Section 8.6.3 (Figure 10.64 on the next page).

10.7.10 Irregular or Space Curves

Irregular or space curves are drawn by plotting points along the curve in one view and then transferring or projecting those points to the adjacent views (Figure 10.65 on the next page). The intersections of projected points locate the path of the space curve, which is drawn using an irregular curve. With CAD, a SPLINE command is used to draw the curve.

10.7.11 Intersecting Cylinders

When two dissimilar shapes meet, a line of intersection usually results. The conventional practices for representing intersecting surfaces on multiview drawings are

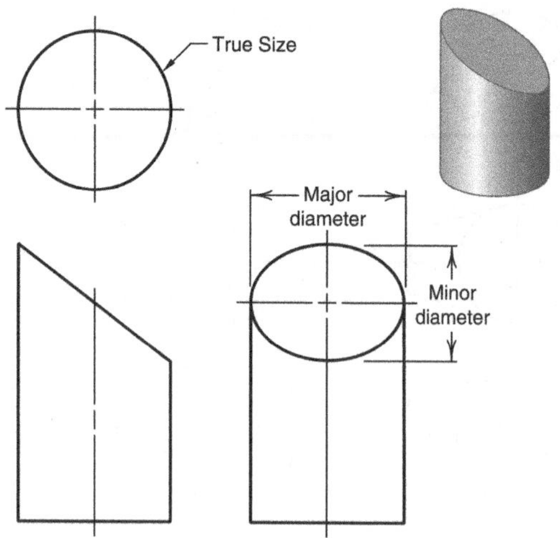

Figure 10.63

Right circular cylinder cut to create an ellipse

An ellipse is created when a cylinder is cut at an acute angle to the axis.

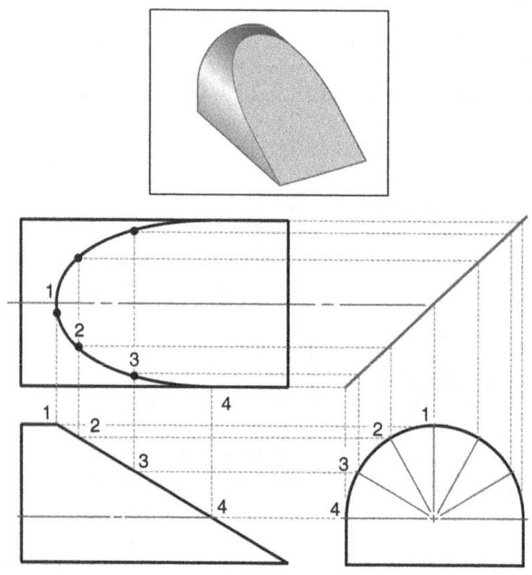

Figure 10.64

Creating an ellipse by plotting points

One method of drawing an ellipse is to plot points on the curve and transfer those points to the adjacent views.

demonstrated in Figure 10.66, which shows two cylinders intersecting. When one of the intersecting cylinders is small, true projection is disregarded (Figure 10.66A). When one cylinder is slightly smaller than the other, some construction is required (Figure 10.66B). When both cylinders are of the same diameter, the intersecting surface is drawn as straight lines (Figure 10.66C).

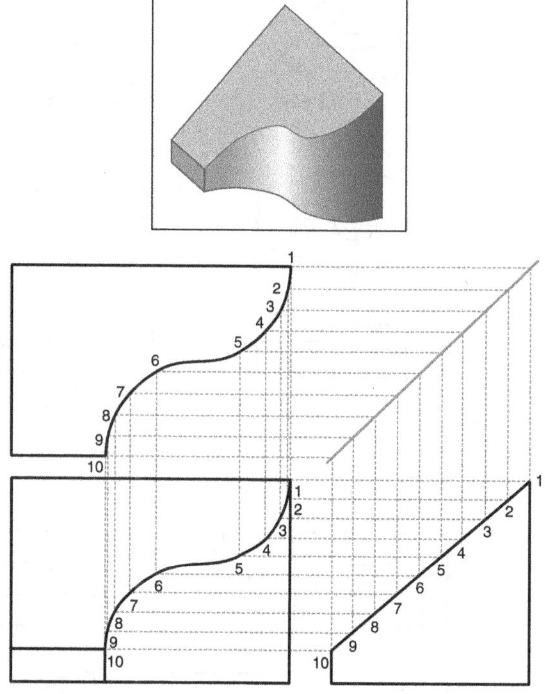

Figure 10.65

Plotting points to create a space curve

10.7.12 Cylinders Intersecting Prisms and Holes

Figure 10.67 shows cylinders intersecting with prisms. Large prisms are represented using true projection (Figure 10.67B and C); small prisms are not (Figure 10.67A). Figure 10.68 on page 534 shows cylinders intersected with piercing holes. Large holes and slots are represented using true projection (Figure 10.68B and D); small holes and slots are not (Figure 10.68A and C).

10.8 Multiview Drawing Visualization

With sufficient practice, it is possible to learn to *read* 2-D engineering drawings, such as the multiview drawings in Figure 10.69 on page 535, and to develop mental 3-D images of the objects. Reading a drawing means being able to look at a two- or three-view multiview drawing and form a clear mental image of the three-dimensional object. A corollary skill is the ability to create a multiview drawing from a pictorial view of an object. Going from

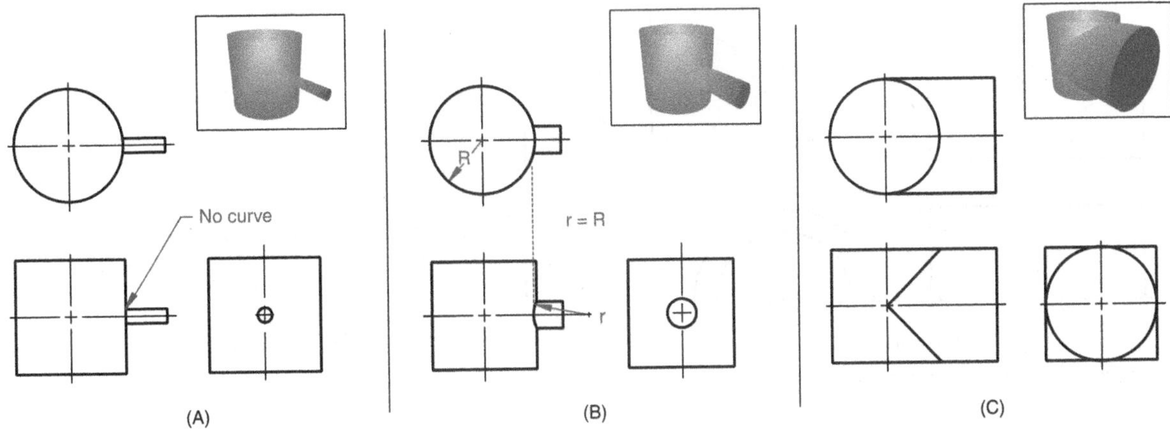

Figure 10.66

Representing the intersection of two cylinders

Representation of the intersection of two cylinders varies according to the relative sizes of the cylinders.

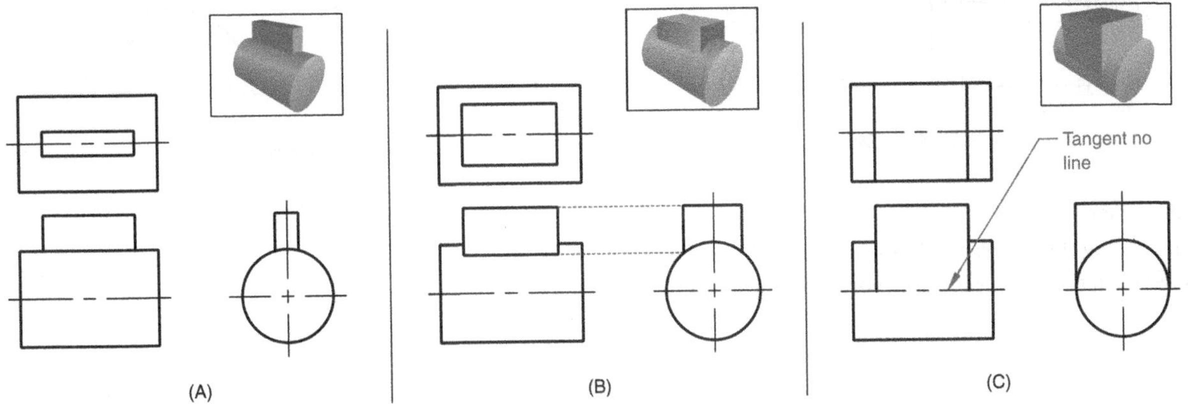

Figure 10.67

Representing the intersection between a cylinder and a prism

Representation of the intersection between a cylinder and a prism depends on the size of the prism relative to the cylinder.

pictorial to multiview and multiview to pictorial is an important process performed every day by technologists. The following sections describe various techniques for improving your ability to visualize multiview drawings. Additional information on visualizing 3-D objects is found in Chapter 5.

10.8.1 Projection Studies

One technique that will improve multiview drawing visualization skills is the study of completed multiviews of various objects, such as those in Figure 10.69. Study each object for orientation, view selection, projection of visible and hidden features, tangent features, holes and rounded surfaces, inclined and oblique surfaces, and dashed line usage.

10.8.2 Physical Model Construction

The creation of physical models can be useful in learning to visualize objects in multiview drawings. Typically, these models are created from modeling clay, wax, or Styrofoam. The two basic techniques for creating these models are cutting the 3-D form out of a rectangular

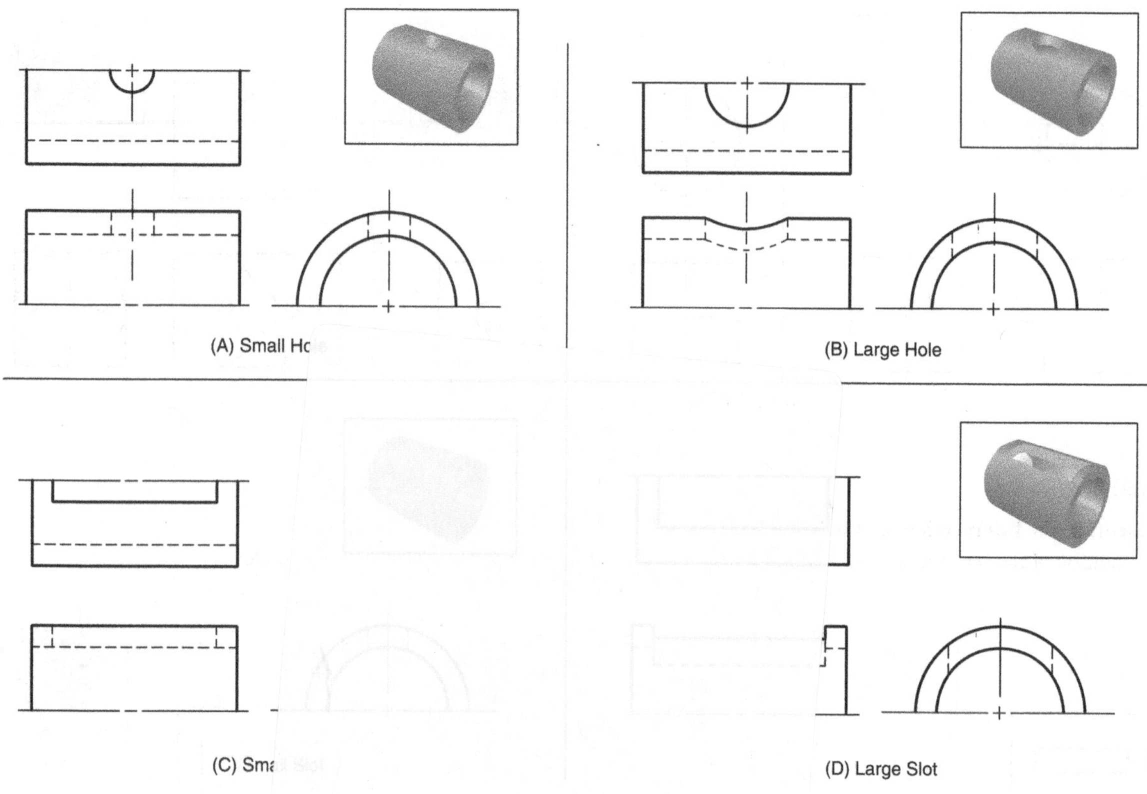

Figure 10.68

Representing the intersection between a cylinder and a hole

Representation of the intersection between a cylinder and a hole or slot depends on the size of the hole or slot relative to the cylinder.

shape (Figure 10.70 on page 536) and using analysis of solids (Figure 10.71 on page 536) to divide the object into its basic geometric primitives and then combining these shapes. (See Section 10.8.8 for more information on analysis of solids.)

Practice Exercise 10.6

Figure 10.70 shows the steps for creating a physical model from a rectangular block of modeling clay, based on a multiview drawing.

Step 1. Create a rectangular piece of clay that is proportional to the width, height, and depth dimensions shown on the multiview drawing.

Step 2. Score the surface of the clay with the point of the knife to indicate the positions of the features.

Step 3. Remove the amount of clay necessary to leave the required L-shape shown in the side view.

Step 4. Cut along the angled line to remove the last piece of clay.

Step 5. Sketch a multiview drawing of the piece of clay. Repeat these steps to create other 3-D geometric forms.

10.8.3 Adjacent Areas

Given the top view of an object, as shown in Figure 10.72 on page 538, sketch isometric views of several possible 3-D forms. Figure 10.73 on page 538 shows just four of the solutions possible and demonstrates the importance of understanding adjacent areas when reading multiview drawings. **Adjacent areas** are surfaces that reside next to each other. The boundary between the surfaces

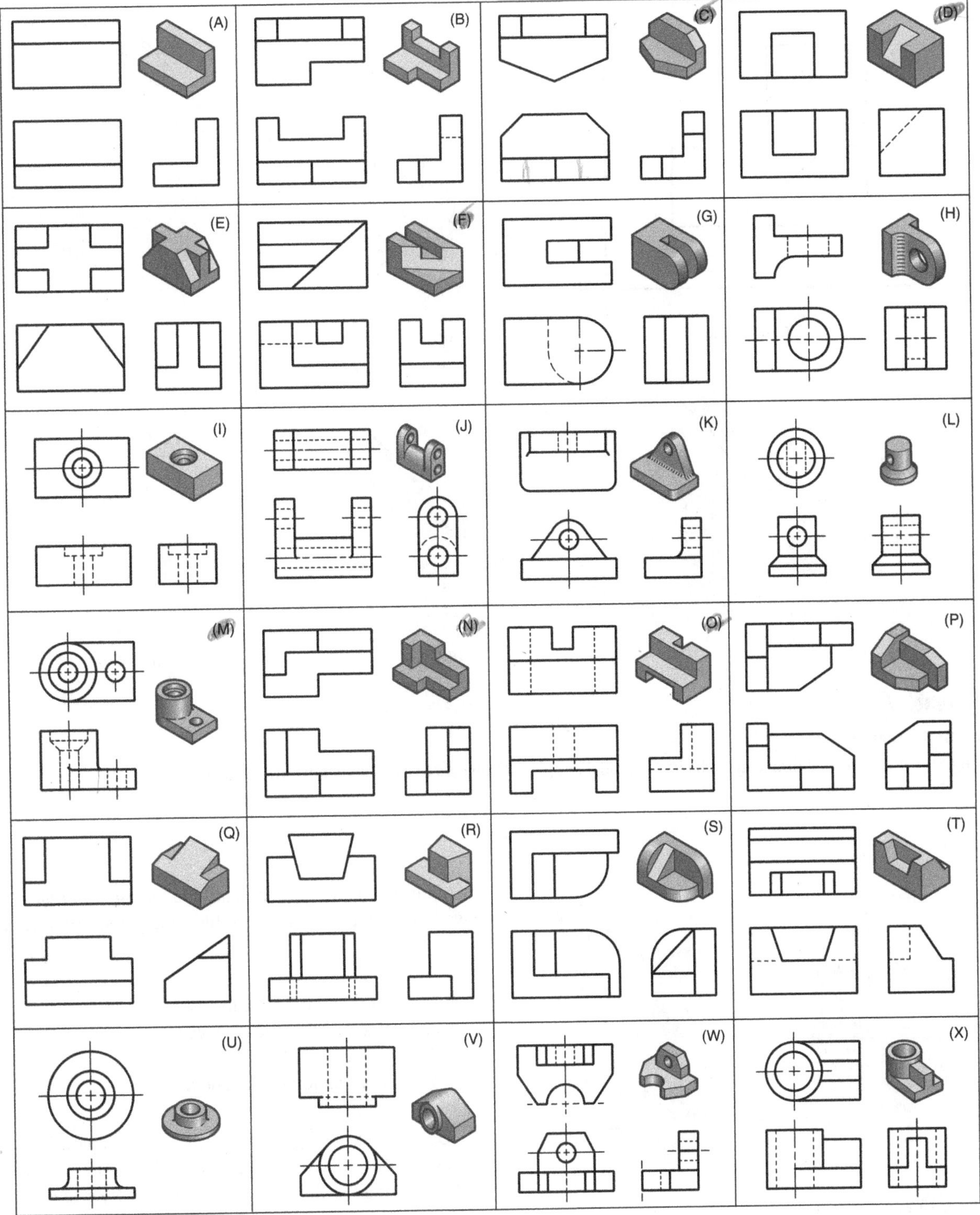

Figure 10.69

Examples of the standard representations of various geometric forms

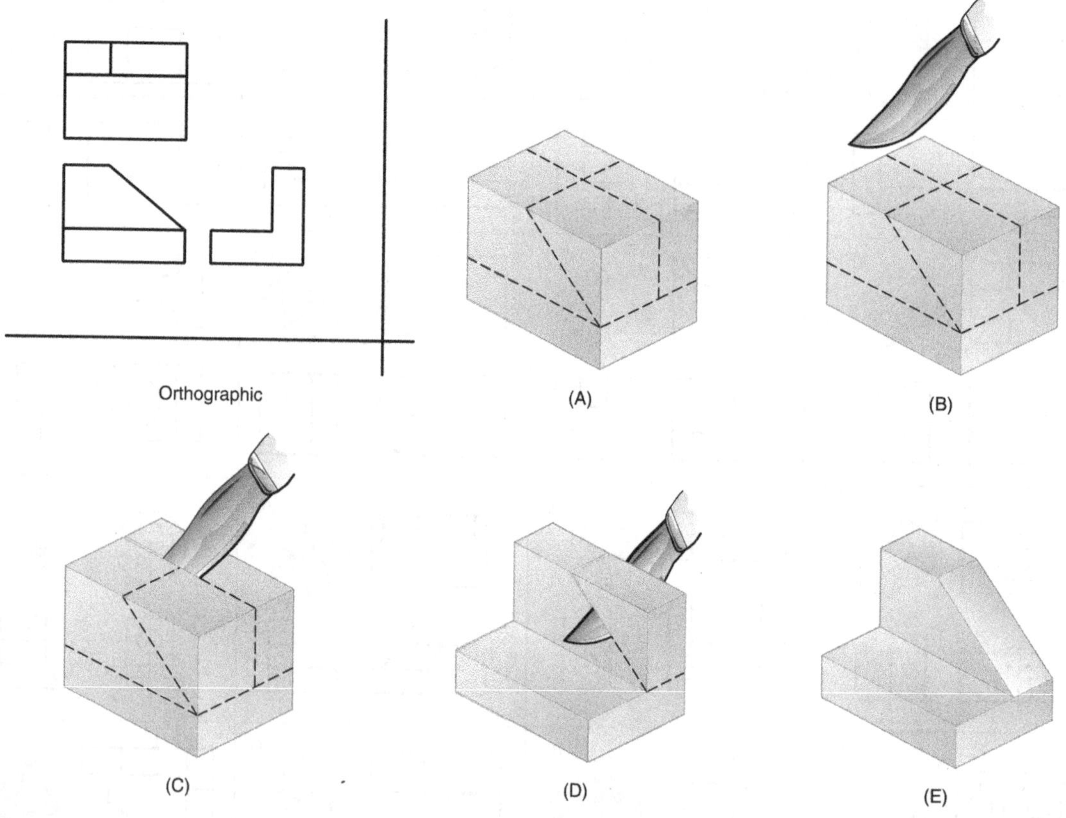

Figure 10.70

Creating a real model

Using Styrofoam or modeling clay and a knife, model simple 3-D objects to aid the visualization process.

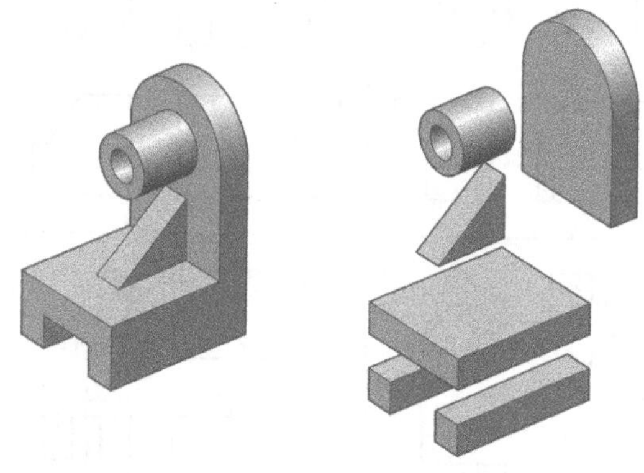

Figure 10.71

Analysis of solids

A complex object can be visualized by decomposing it into simpler geometric forms.

is represented as a line indicating a *change in planes.* No two adjacent areas can lie in the same plane. Adjacent areas represent

1. Surfaces at different levels
2. Inclined or oblique surfaces
3. Cylindrical surfaces
4. A combination of the above

Going back to Figure 10.72, the lines separating surfaces A, B, and C represent three different surfaces at different heights. Surface A may be higher or lower than surfaces B and C; surface A may also be inclined or cylindrical. This ambiguity emphasizes the importance of using more than one orthographic view to represent an object clearly.

Practice Problem 10.1

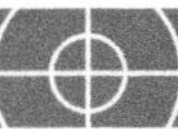

Create a three-view sketch of the object using the grid. The front, top, and right side views have been blocked in for you.

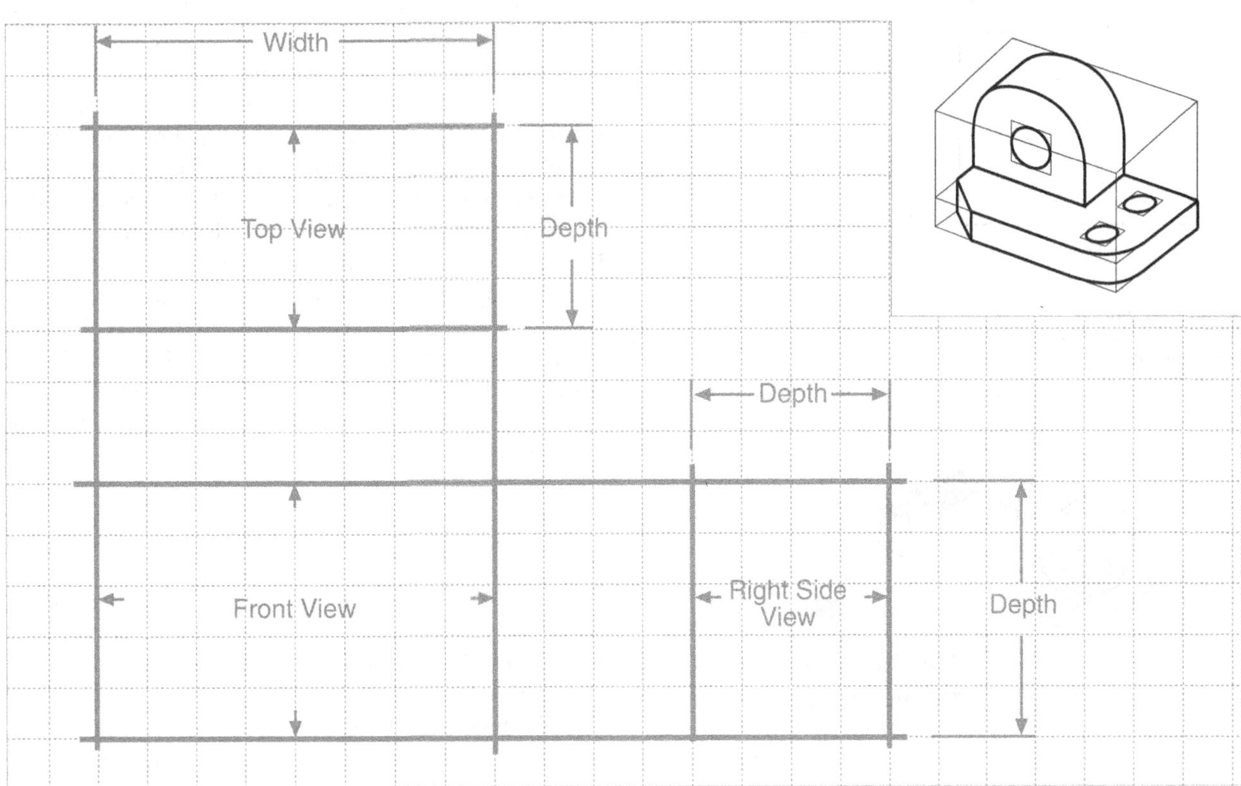

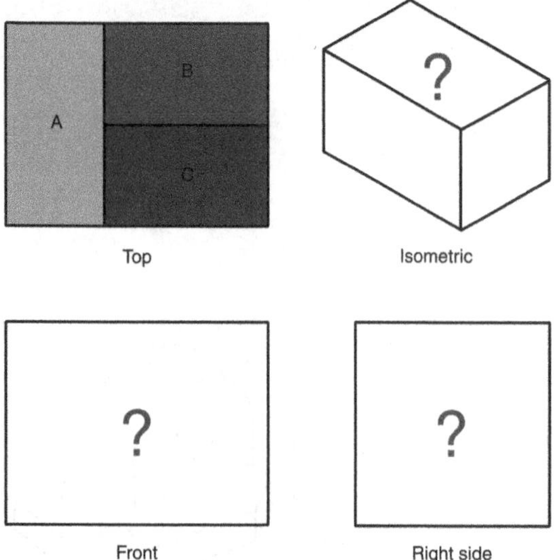

Figure 10.72

Adjacent areas

Given the top view, make isometric sketches of possible 3-D objects.

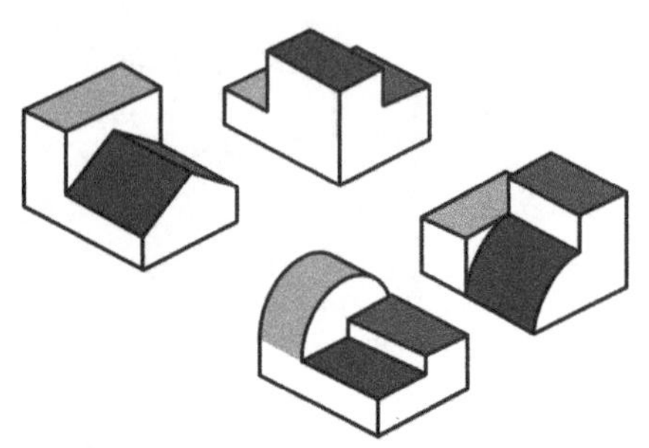

Figure 10.73

Possible solutions to Figure 10.72

10.8.4 Similar Shapes

One visualization technique involves identifying those views in which a surface has a similar configuration and number of sides. (See Section 10.7.2, Rule 5, configuration of planes, and Rule 6, parallel features.) Similar shape or configuration is useful in visualizing or creating multiview drawings of objects with inclined or oblique surfaces. For example, if an inclined surface has four edges with opposite edges parallel, then that surface will appear with four sides with opposite edges parallel in any orthographic view, unless viewing the surface on edge. By remembering this rule you can visually check the accuracy of an orthographic drawing by comparing the configuration and number of sides of surfaces from view to view. Figure 10.74 shows objects with shaded surfaces that can be described by their shapes. In Figure 10.74A, the shaded surface is L-shaped and appears similar in the top and front views, but is an edge in the right side view. In Figure 10.74B, the shaded surface is U-shaped and is configured similarly in the front and top views. In Figure 10.74C, the shaded surface is T-shaped in the top and front views. In Figure 10.74D, the shaded surface has eight sides in both the front and top views.

10.8.5 Surface Labeling

When multiview drawings are created from a given pictorial view, surfaces are labeled to check the accuracy of the solution. The surfaces are labeled in the pictorial view and then in each multiview, using the pictorial view as a guide. Figure 10.75 is the pictorial view of an object, with the visible surfaces labeled with a number; for example, the inclined surface is number 5, the oblique sur-

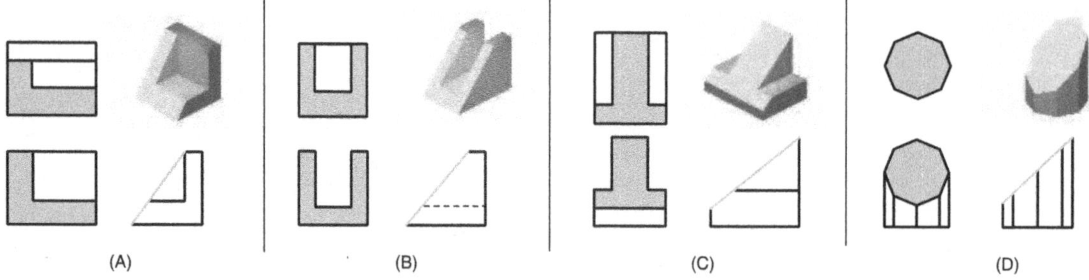

Figure 10.74

Similar-shaped surfaces

Similar-shaped surfaces will retain their basic configuration in all views, unless viewed on edge. Notice that the number of edges of a face remains constant in all the views and that edges parallel in one view will remain parallel in other views.

face is number 8, and the hole is number 4. The multiview drawing is then created, the visible surfaces in each view are labeled, and the results are checked against the pictorial.

10.8.6 Missing Lines

Another way of becoming more proficient at reading and drawing multiviews is by solving missing-line problems. Figure 10.76 is a multiview drawing with at least one line missing. Study each view, then add any missing lines to the incomplete views. Lines may be missing in more than one of the views. It may be helpful to create a rough isometric sketch of the object when trying to determine the location of missing lines.

Locating Missing Lines in an Incomplete Multiview Drawing

Step 1. Study the three given views in Figure 10.76.

Step 2. Use analysis by solids or analysis by surfaces, as described earlier in this text, to create a mental image of the 3-D form.

Step 3. If necessary, create a rough isometric sketch of the object to determine the missing lines.

Step 4. From every corner of the object, sketch construction lines between the views. Because each projected corner should align with a feature in the adjacent view, this technique may reveal missing details. For the figure, corner A in the right side view does not align with any feature in the front view, thus revealing the location of the missing line.

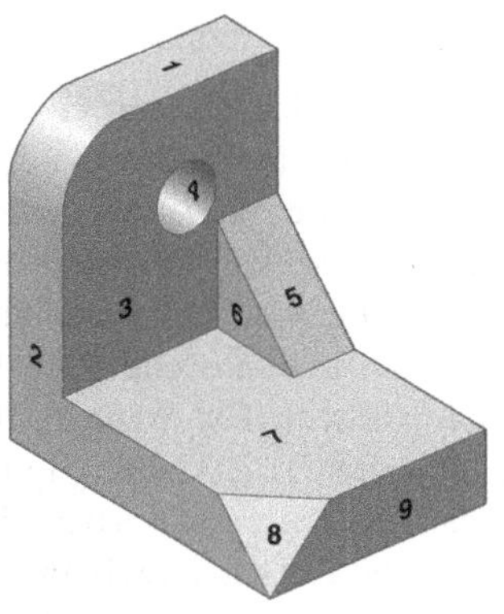

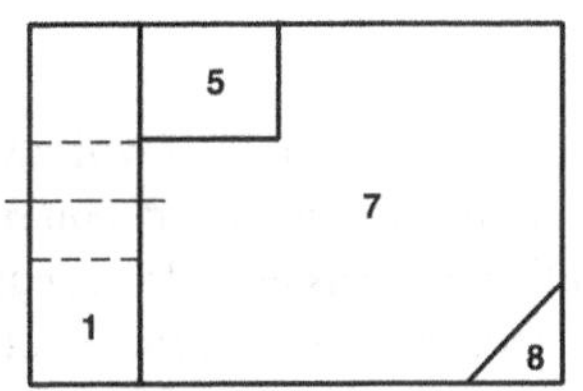

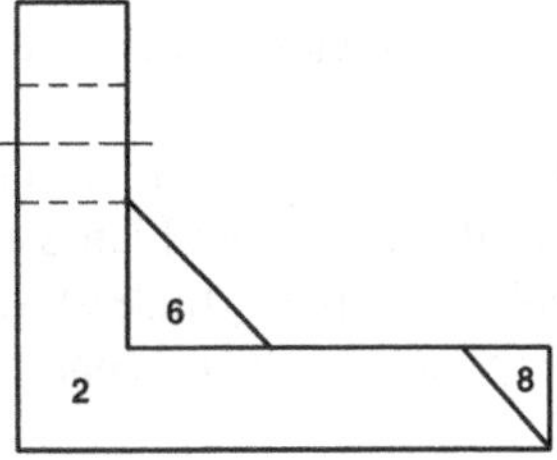

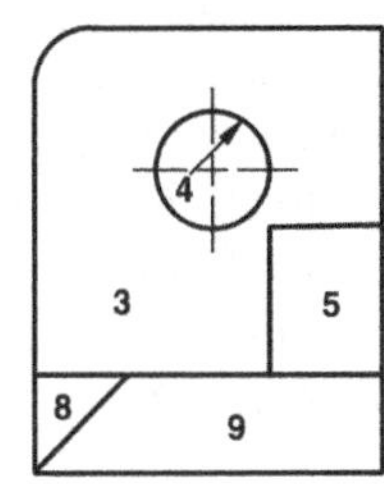

Figure 10.75

Surface labeling

To check the accuracy of multiview drawings, surfaces can be labeled and compared to those in the pictorial view.

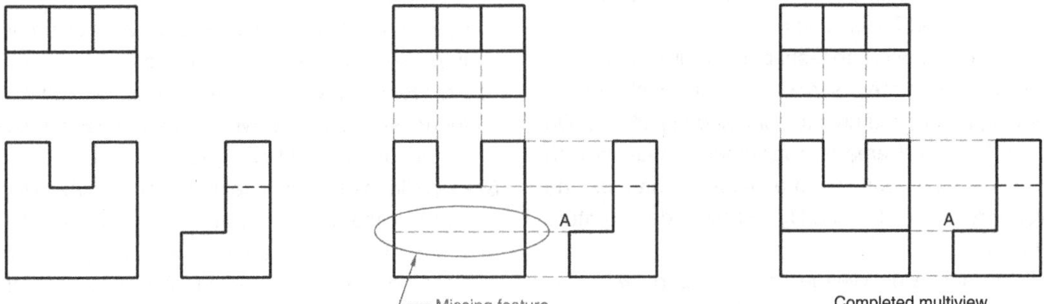

Figure 10.76

Missing line problems

One way to improve your proficiency is to solve missing-line problems. A combination of holistic visualization skills and systematic analysis is used to identify missing features.

10.8.7 Vertex Labeling

It is often helpful to label the vertices of the isometric view as a check for the multiview drawing. In the isometric view in Figure 10.77, the vertices, including hidden ones, are labeled with numbers; then the corresponding vertices in the multiviews are numbered. In the multiviews, hidden vertices are lettered to the right of the numbered visible vertices. For example, the vertices of surface A are numbered 1, 2, 3, and 4. In the front view, surface A appears on edge, and vertices 1 and 4 are in front of vertices 3 and 2. Therefore, in the front view, the vertices of surface A are labeled 4, 3 and 1, 2.

10.8.8 Analysis by Solids

A common technique for analyzing multiview drawings is *analysis by solids,* in which objects are decomposed into solid geometric primitives such as cylinders, negative cylinders (holes), square and rectangular prisms, cones, spheres, etc. These primitives are shown in Figure 10.47 earlier in this chapter. Their importance in the understanding and visualization of multiview drawings cannot be overemphasized.

Figure 10.78 is a multiview drawing of a 3-D object. Important features are labeled in each view. Planes are labeled with a P subscript, holes (negative cylinders) with an H subscript, and cylinders (positive) with a C subscript.

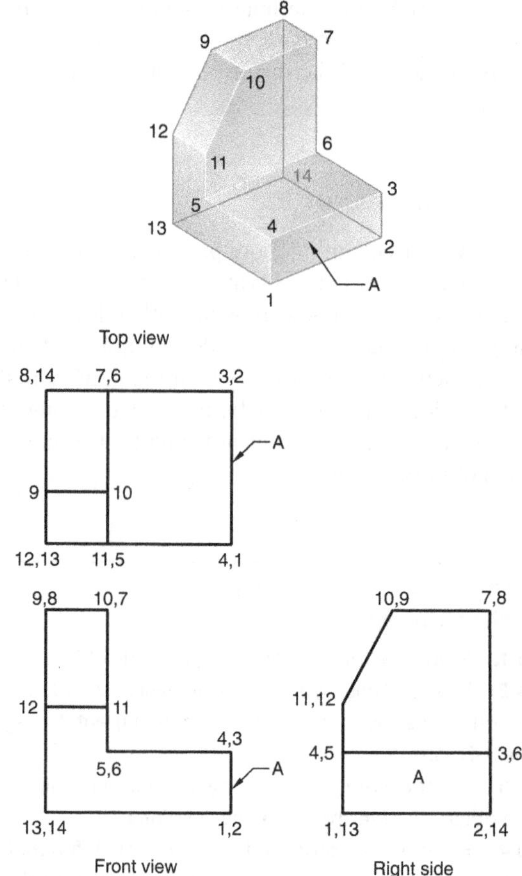

Figure 10.77

Numbering the isometric pictorial and the multiviews to help visualize an object

Analysis by Solids

Step 1. Examine all three views in Figure 10.78 as a whole and then each view in detail. In the top view is a rectangular shape labeled AP and three circles labeled G_H, H_C, and I_H. On the left end of the rectangular area are dashed lines representing hidden features. These hidden features are labeled D_P, E_C, and F_H.

Step 2. In the front view is an L-shaped feature labeled B_P. At opposite ends of the L-shaped area are dashed lines representing hidden features and labeled G_H and F_H. On top of the L-shaped area is a rectangular feature with dashed lines representing more hidden features. The rectangular feature is labeled H_c and the hidden feature is labeled I_H.

Step 3. In the right side view are two rectangular areas, and a U-shaped area with a circular feature. The rectangular feature adjacent to and above the U-shaped area is labeled C_P and has hidden lines labeled G_H. The rectangular feature above C_P is labeled H_C and contains dashed lines labeled I_H. The U-shaped area is labeled D_P, and the arc is labeled E_C. The circular feature in the U-shaped area is labeled F_H.

This general examination of the views reveals some important information about the 3-D form of the object. Adjacent views are compared with each other, and parallel projectors are drawn between adjacent views to help further analysis of the object.

Step 4. In the top view, rectangular area A_P extends the full width of the drawing, can only be aligned with area B_P in the front view, and appears as an edge in the front and right side views. Area B_P in the front view is aligned with area C_P in the right side view. B_P appears as a vertical edge in the right side view and a horizontal edge in the top view. The conclusion is that areas A_P, B_P, and C_P are top, front, and right side views, respectively, of a rectangular prism, which is the main body of the part.

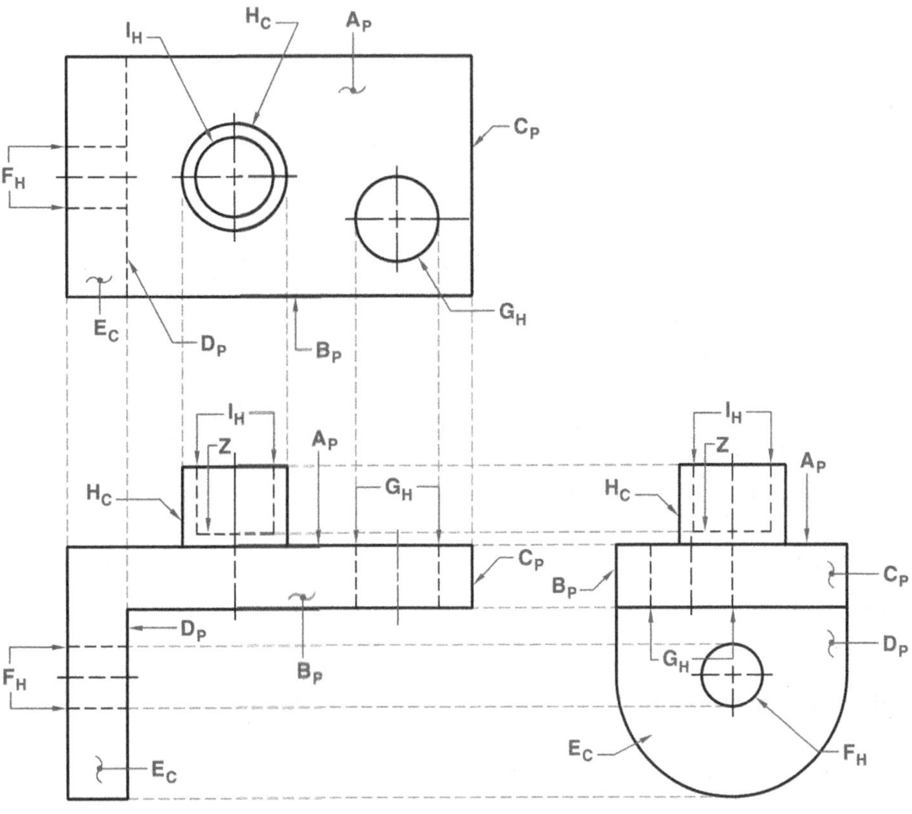

Figure 10.78

Visualizing a multiview drawing using analysis by solids

Step 5. Circular area G_H in the top view is aligned with the hidden lines labeled G_H in the front view. Because these hidden lines go from top to bottom in the front view, it is concluded that the circle represents a hole. This can be verified by the dashed lines G_H in the right side view.

Step 6. In the front view, rectangular area H_C projects above the main body of the part; therefore, it should be visible in the top view. This rectangular area is in alignment with circular area H_C in the top view and with rectangular area H_C in the right side view. The conclusion is that area H_C is a cylinder because it appears as a circle in one view and as a rectangle in the other two views.

Step 7. The circle I_H in the top view is aligned with dashed lines I_H in the front view and is inside cylinder H_C. This indicates that circle I_H in the top view is a negative cylinder (hole) centered within cylinder H_C. The dashed line labeled Z in the front and right side views shows the depth of the negative cylinder I_H.

Step 8. In the top view, the dashed lines at the left end of rectangular area A_P represent one or more feature(s) below the main body of the part. Hidden line D_P in the top view is aligned with visible line D_P in the front view, and dashed lines F_H in the top view are directly above dashed lines F_H in the front view. Area E_C in the top view is aligned with area E_C in the front view. So the features hidden in the top view must be D_P and E_C in the front view.

D_P and E_C in the front view are aligned with D_P and E_C in the right side view. The right side view appears to be the most descriptive view of these features. In this view, area E_C is a partial cylinder represented by arc E_C. The side view also reveals that dashed lines F_H in the top and front views represent the diameter of hole F_H. Therefore, area D_P and partial cylinder E_C are a U-shaped feature with a hole whose width is revealed in the front and top views.

Analysis by solids should result in a clear mental image of the 3-D form represented in a 2-D multiview drawing.

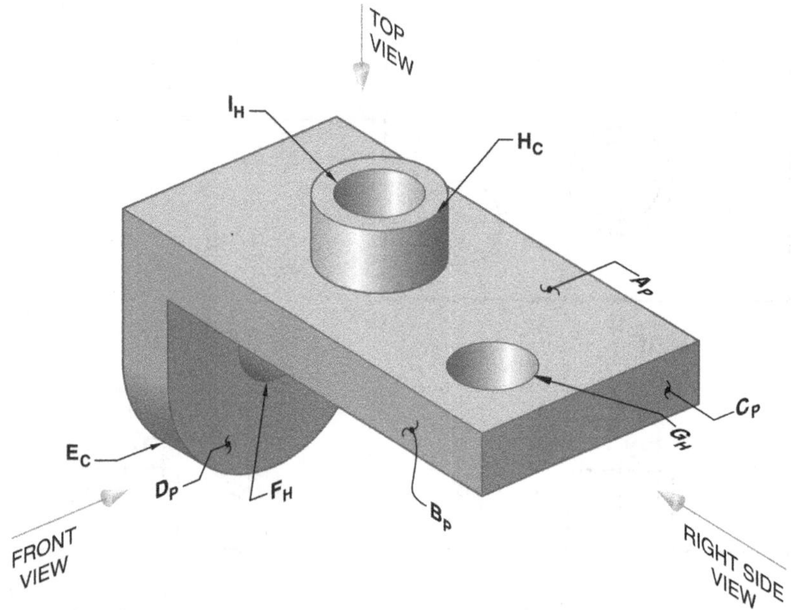

Figure 10.79

A pictorial view of the multiview drawing in Figure 10.78, revealing its three-dimensional form

Figure 10.79 is a pictorial view of the object in the multiview drawing, and it should be similar to the mental image created after following the preceding eight steps.

10.8.9 Analysis by Surfaces

Figure 10.79 lends itself to analysis by solids because there are no inclined or oblique surfaces. With inclined and oblique surfaces, such as those shown in Figure 10.80, *analysis by surfaces* may be more useful.

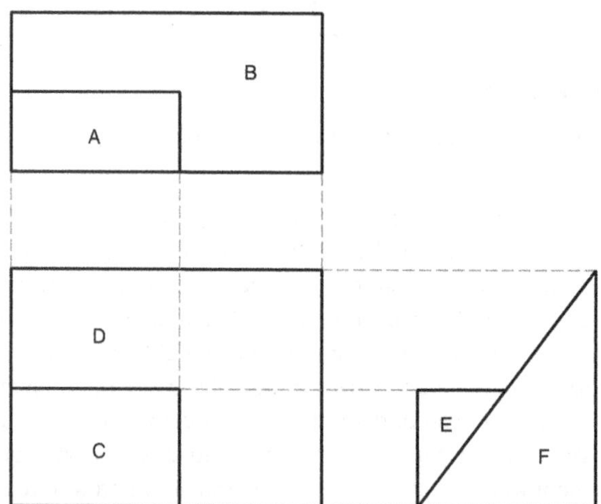

Figure 10.80

Visualizing a multiview drawing using analysis by surfaces

Analysis by Surfaces

Step 1. Examine all three views in Figure 10.80. There are no circular or elliptical features; therefore, all the areas must be bounded by planar surfaces. In the top view, areas A and B are separated by lines; therefore, they are not in the same plane. The same is true for areas C and D in the front view and areas E and F in the right side view. The reason for this is that no two contiguous (adjacent) areas can lie in the same plane. If they were in the same plane, a line would not be drawn to separate them. This is an example of Rule 8.

Step 2. The lines of projection between the top and front views indicate that area B corresponds to area D. Areas B and D are also similar in shape in that they both have six sides, thus reinforcing the possibility that areas B and D are the same feature. Similarly, areas A and C are aligned and are similar in shape, so they could be the same feature. However, before accepting these two possibilities, the side view must be considered.

Step 3. Area D aligns with area F, but they are not similar in shape; area F is three-sided and area D is six-sided.

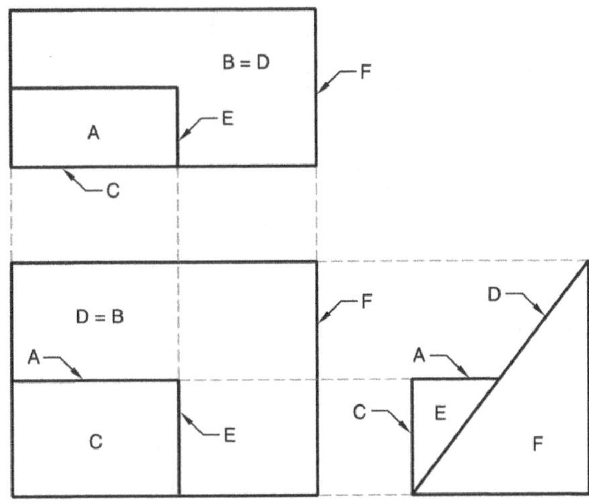

Figure 10.81

Conclusions drawn about Figure 10.80

Therefore, areas D and F are not the same feature. In the right side view, area D must be represented as an edge view separating areas E and F; therefore, area D is the inclined plane in the right side view. Area C aligns with area E, but they are not similar in shape; area C is four-sided, and area E is three-sided. In the right side view, area C must be represented as an edge view and is the vertical line on the left side of the view.

Step 4. Areas E and F are not represented in the top or front views; therefore, areas E and F are edge views in the front and top views (Figure 10.81). Because areas E and F are visible in the right side view, they are at the right end of the front and top views. Therefore, they must be located at the right end of the object.

Step 5. Based on alignment and similarity of shape, surfaces B and D must be the same surface.

Step 6. Area A in the top view is an edge view represented as a horizontal line in the front and side views. Area C in the front view is a horizontal edge view in the top view and a vertical edge view in the right side view. Areas A and C are therefore not the same.

Figure 10.82 is a pictorial view of the object. Areas B and D are the same inclined plane, area A is a horizontal plane, and areas C, E, and F are vertical planes.

Principles of Orthographic Projection Rule 8:

Contiguous Areas

No two contiguous areas can lie in the same plane.

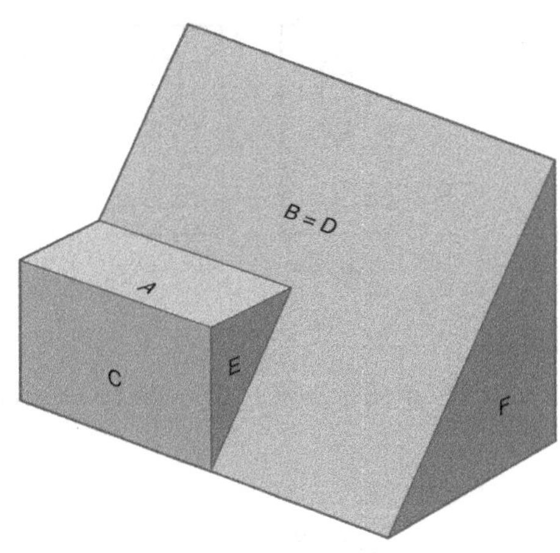

Figure 10.82

A pictorial view of Figure 10.80, revealing its three-dimensional form

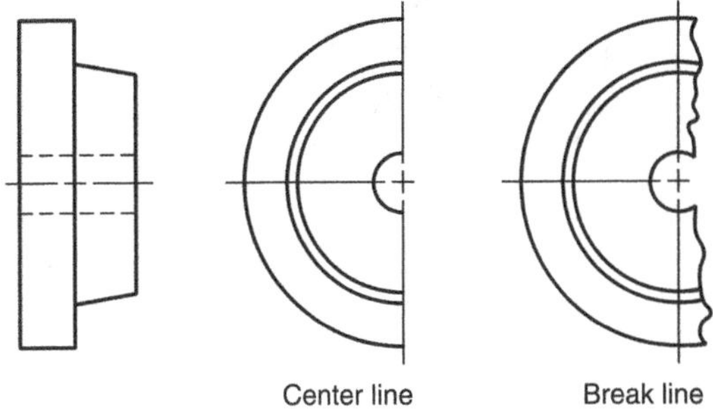

Figure 10.83

A partial view used on a symmetrical object

The partial view is created along a center line or a break line.

10.9 ANSI Standards for Multiview Drawings

Standards form the common language used by engineers and technologists for communicating information. The standard view representations developed by ANSI for multiview drawings are described in the following paragraphs.

10.9.1 Partial Views

A **partial view** shows only what is necessary to completely describe the object. Partial views are used for symmetrical objects, for some types of auxiliary views, and for saving time when creating some types of multiview drawings. A break line (shown as a jagged line) or center line for symmetrical objects may be used to limit the partial view (Figure 10.83). If a break line is used, it

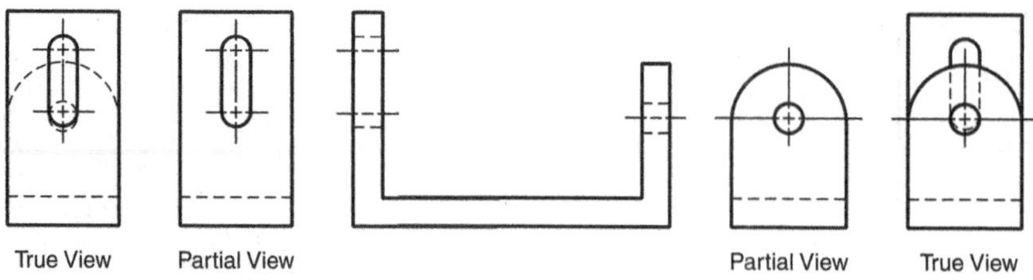

Figure 10.84

Use of two partial profile views to describe an object and eliminate hidden lines

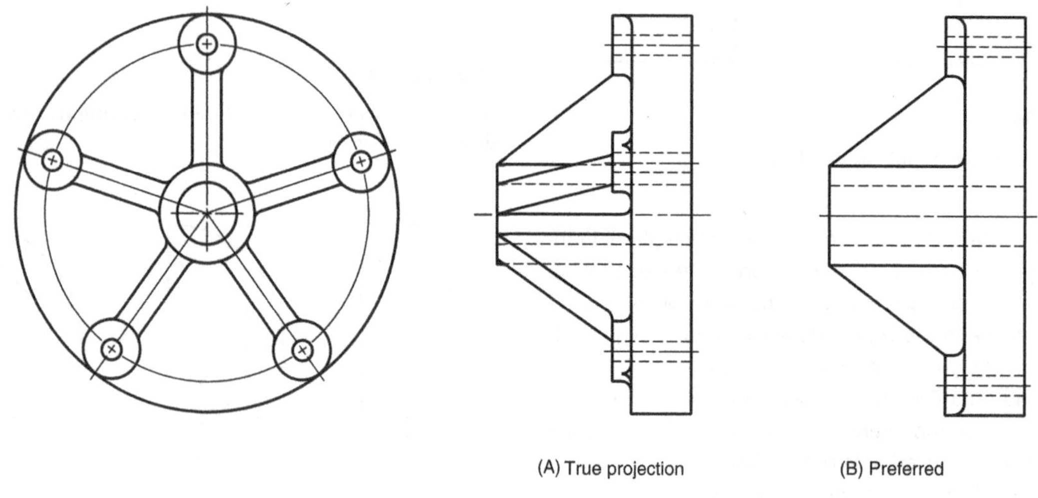

Figure 10.85

Revolution conventions used to simplify the representation of ribs and webs

is placed where it will not coincide with a visible or hidden line.

Partial views are used to eliminate excessive hidden lines that would make reading and visualizing a drawing difficult. At times it may be necessary to supplement a partial view with another view. For example, in Figure 10.84, two partial profile views are used to describe the object better. What has been left off in the profile views are details located behind the views.

10.9.2 Revolution Conventions

At times, a normal multiview drawing will result in views that are difficult to visualize and read. This is especially true of objects with ribs, arms, or holes that are not aligned with horizontal and vertical center lines. Figure 10.85 shows an object with ribs and holes that are equally spaced, with the two bottom holes not aligned with the center line of the object. True projection produces an awkward profile view that is difficult to draw because all but one rib are foreshortened (Figure 10.85A). ANSI standard **revolution conventions** allow the profile view to be drawn as shown in Figure 10.85B. You must visualize the object as if the ribs are revolved into alignment with the vertical center line in the front view. This will produce a profile view that is easier to visualize and draw.

Revolution conventions can also be used on parts that have *bolt circles.* Figure 10.86 shows the true projection of a plate with a bolt circle. Notice that the profile view becomes difficult to read because of so many hidden lines. As shown in Figure 10.86, revolution conventions dictate that only two of the bolt circle holes must be represented

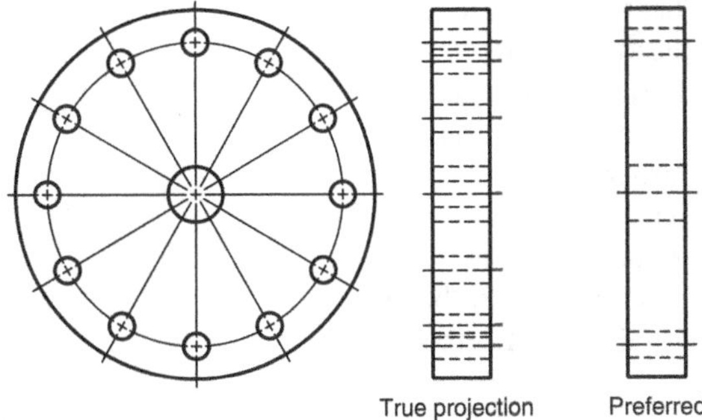

Figure 10.86

Revolution conventions used on objects with bolt circles to eliminate hidden lines and improve visualization

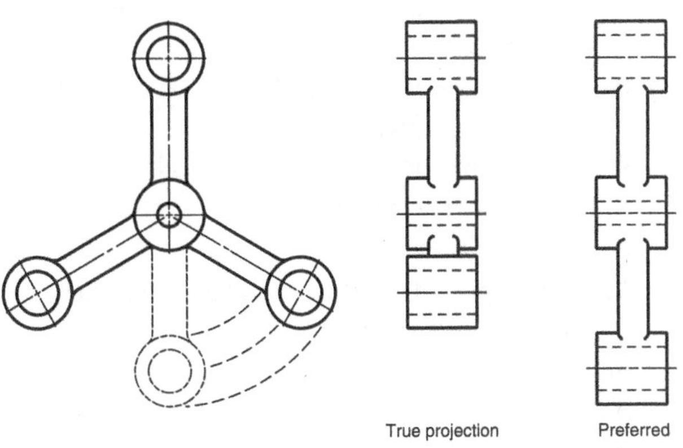

Figure 10.87

Revolution conventions used to simplify the representation of arms

in the profile view. These two bolt circle holes are aligned with the vertical center line in the front view and are then represented in that position in the profile view.

Figure 10.87 shows another example of revolution conventions. The inclined arms in the figure result in a foreshortened profile view, which is difficult and time consuming to draw. Revolution conventions allow the arms to be shown in alignment with the vertical center line of the front view to create the profile view shown in the figure.

Objects similar to those described in the preceding paragraphs are frequently represented as section views. When revolution techniques are used with section views, the drawings are called *aligned sections*. (See Chapter 16.)

Revolution conventions were developed before CAD. With the advent of 3-D CAD and the ability to extract views automatically, it is possible to create a true-projection view, such as that shown in Figure 10.87, quickly and easily. You are cautioned that, even though a view can be automatically produced by a CAD system, this does not necessarily mean that the view will be easy to visualize by the user.

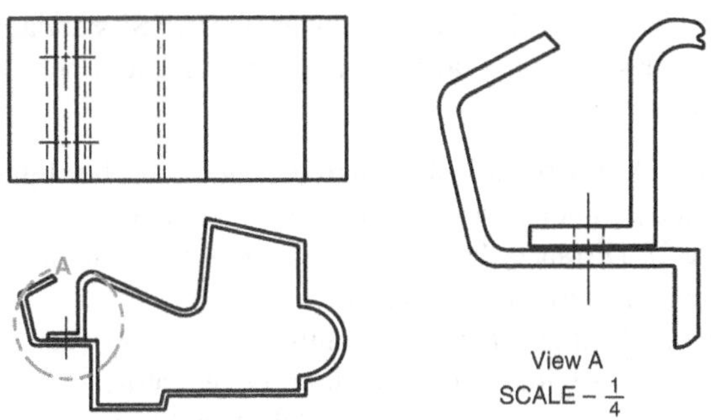

Figure 10.88

A scaled removed view (view A)

Practice Exercise 10.7

In Figures 10.85 through 10.87, a new revolved view was created to replace a true projection in the profile view. This was done in order to represent the features of the object more clearly. Sketch new front views as if the new profile views represented true projections.

10.9.3 Removed Views

At times, it is important to highlight or enlarge part of a multiview. A new view is drawn that is not in alignment with one of the principal views, but is removed and placed at a convenient location on the drawing sheet. A **removed view** is a complete or partial orthographic view that shows details more clearly. A new viewing plane is used to define the line of sight used to create the removed view, and both the viewing plane and the removed view are labeled, as shown in Figure 10.88.

10.10 Summary

Multiview drawings are an important part of technical graphics. Creating multiview drawings takes a high degree of visualization skill and considerable practice. Multiview drawings are created by closely following orthographic projection techniques and ANSI standards. The rules of orthographic projection are listed here for your reference.

Rule 1: Every point or feature in one view must be aligned on a parallel projector in any adjacent view.
Rule 2: Distances between any two points of a feature in related views must be equal.
Rule 3: Features are true length or true size when the lines of sight are perpendicular to the feature.
Rule 4: Features are foreshortened when the lines of sight are not perpendicular to the feature.
Rule 5: Areas that are the same feature will always be similar in configuration from one view to the next, unless viewed as an edge.
Rule 6: Parallel features will always appear parallel in all views.
Rule 7: Surfaces that are parallel to the lines of sight will appear as lines or edge views.
Rule 8: No two contiguous areas can lie in the same plane.

Online Learning Center (OLC) Features

There are number of Online Learning Center features listed below that you can use to supplement your text reading to improve your understanding and retention of the material presented in this chapter at www.mhhe.com/bertoline.

- Learning Objectives
- Chapter Outline
- Chapter Overview
- Questions for Review
- Multiple Choice Quiz
- True or False Questions
- Flashcards
- Website Links
- Animations
- Stapler Design Problem
- Visualization Exercises

Questions for Review

1. Define orthographic projection.
2. How is orthographic projection different from perspective projection? Use a sketch to highlight the differences.
3. Define multiview drawings. Make a simple multiview sketch of an object.
4. Define frontal, horizontal, and profile planes.
5. List the six principal views.
6. Define fold lines.
7. List the space dimensions found on a front view, top view, and profile view.
8. Define a normal plane.
9. Define an inclined plane.
10. Define an oblique plane.
11. List the eight rules of orthographic projection.

Problems

10.1 (Figure 10.89) Draw or sketch the front, top, and right side views of the object shown in the pictorial. Number each visible surface in each of the multiviews to correspond to the numbers given in the pictorial view.

10.2 (Figure 10.90) Draw or sketch the front, top, and right side views of the object shown in the pictorial. Number each visible surface in each of the multiviews to correspond to the numbers given in the pictorial view.

10.3 (Figure 10.91) Given the front view shown in the figure, design at least six different solutions. Sketch your solutions in pictorial and in front and side views.

10.4 (Figure 10.92) Given the two views of a multiview drawing of an object, sketch or draw the given views, freehand or using instruments or CAD, and then add the missing view. As an additional exercise, create a pictorial sketch of the object.

10.5 (Figure 10.93) Given three incomplete views of a multiview drawing of an object, sketch or draw the given views, freehand or using instruments or CAD, and then add the missing line or lines. As an additional exercise, create a pictorial sketch of the object.

10.6 (Figure 10.94) Sketch, or draw with instruments or CAD, multiviews of the objects shown in the pictorials.

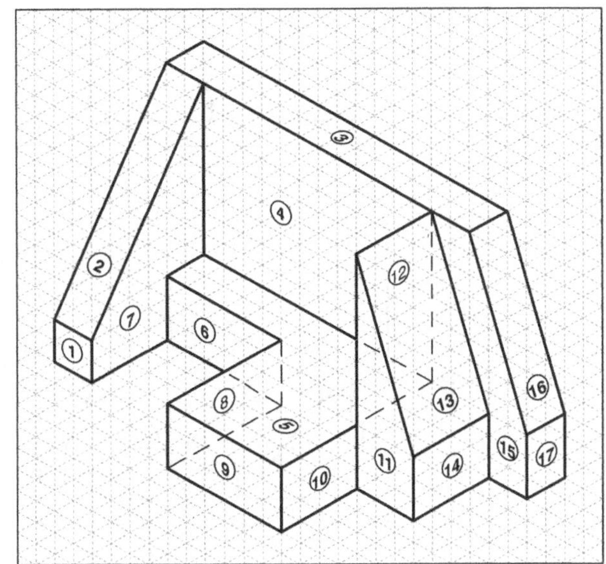

Figure 10.89

Solid object for Problem 10.1

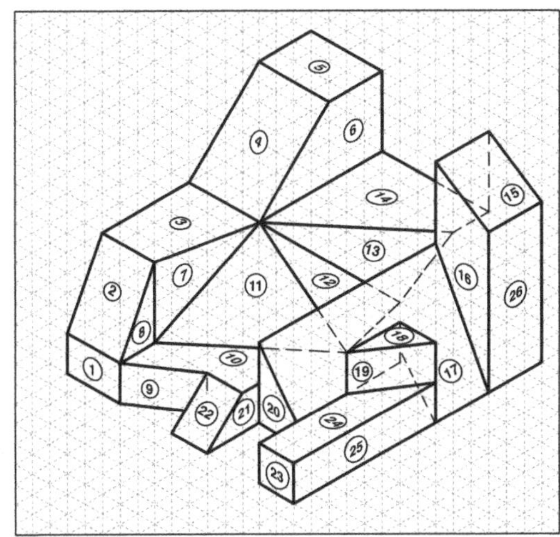

Figure 10.90

Solid object for Problem 10.2

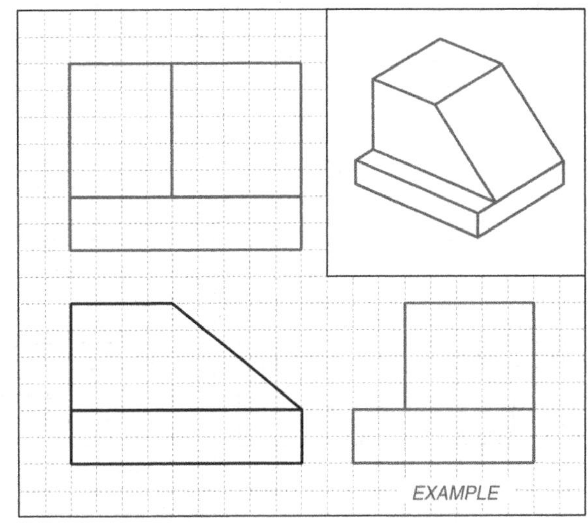

Figure 10.91

Front view for Problem 10.3

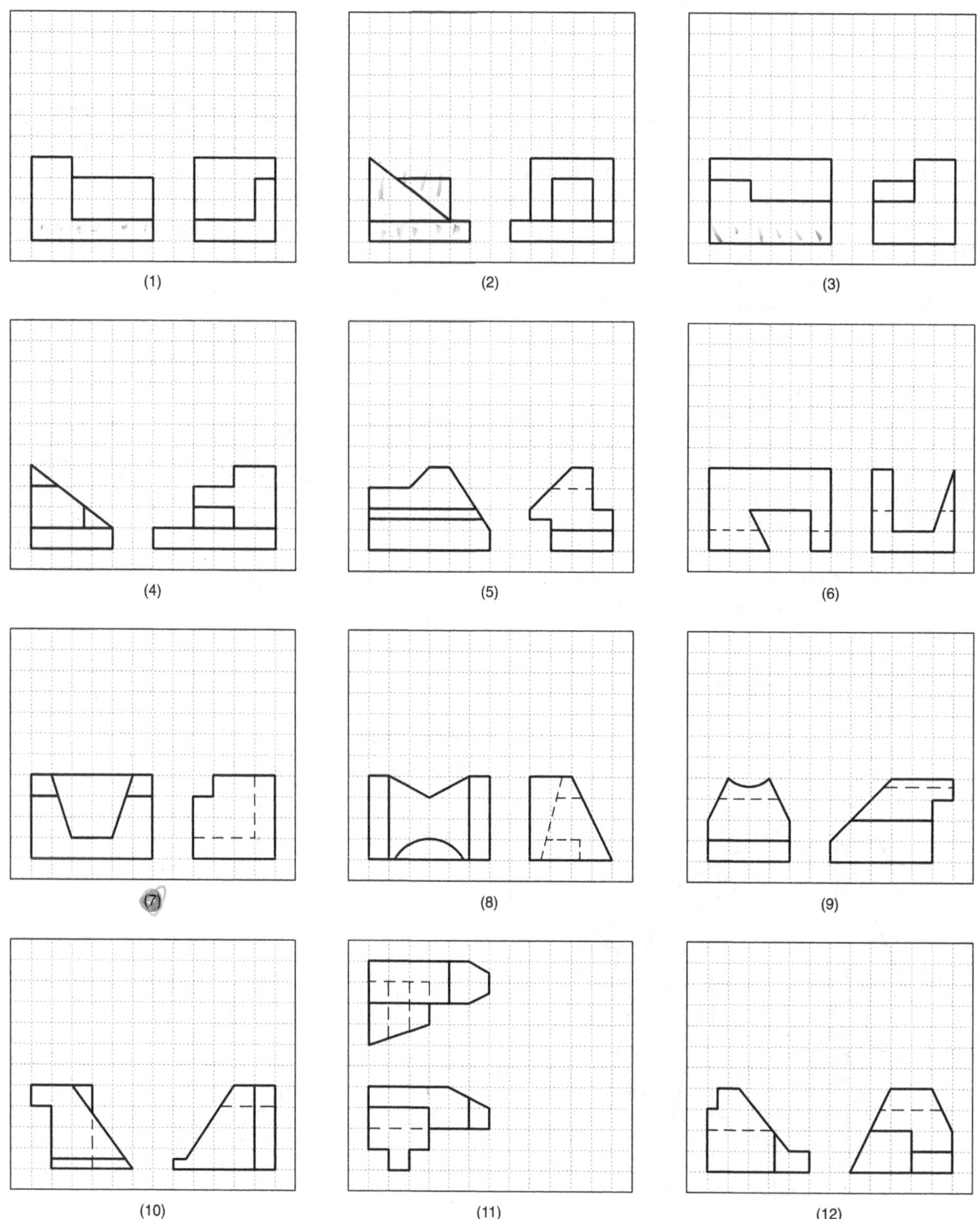

Figure 10.92

Two-view drawings of several objects for Problem 10.4

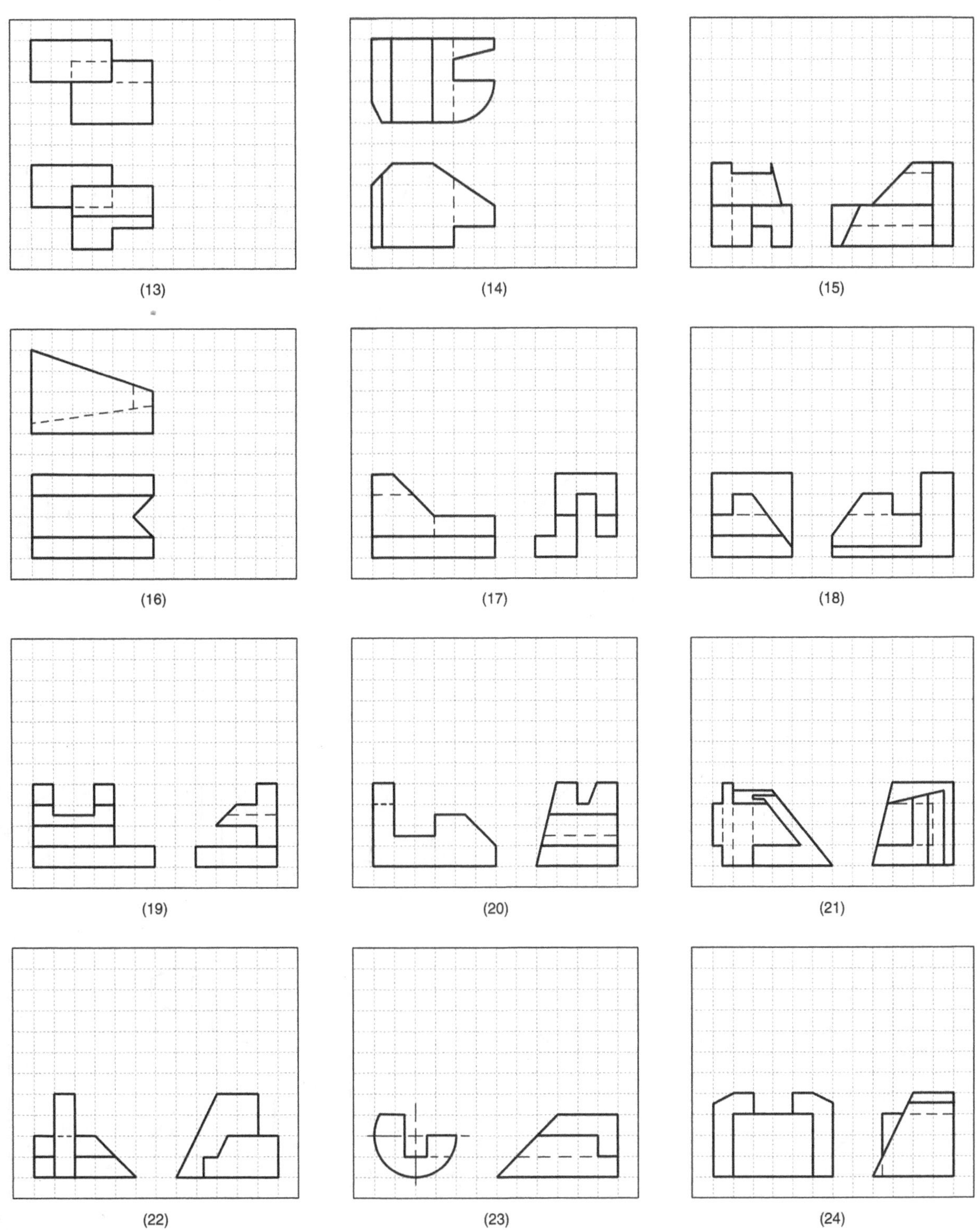

Figure 10.92

Two-view drawings of several objects for Problem 10.4 (Continued)

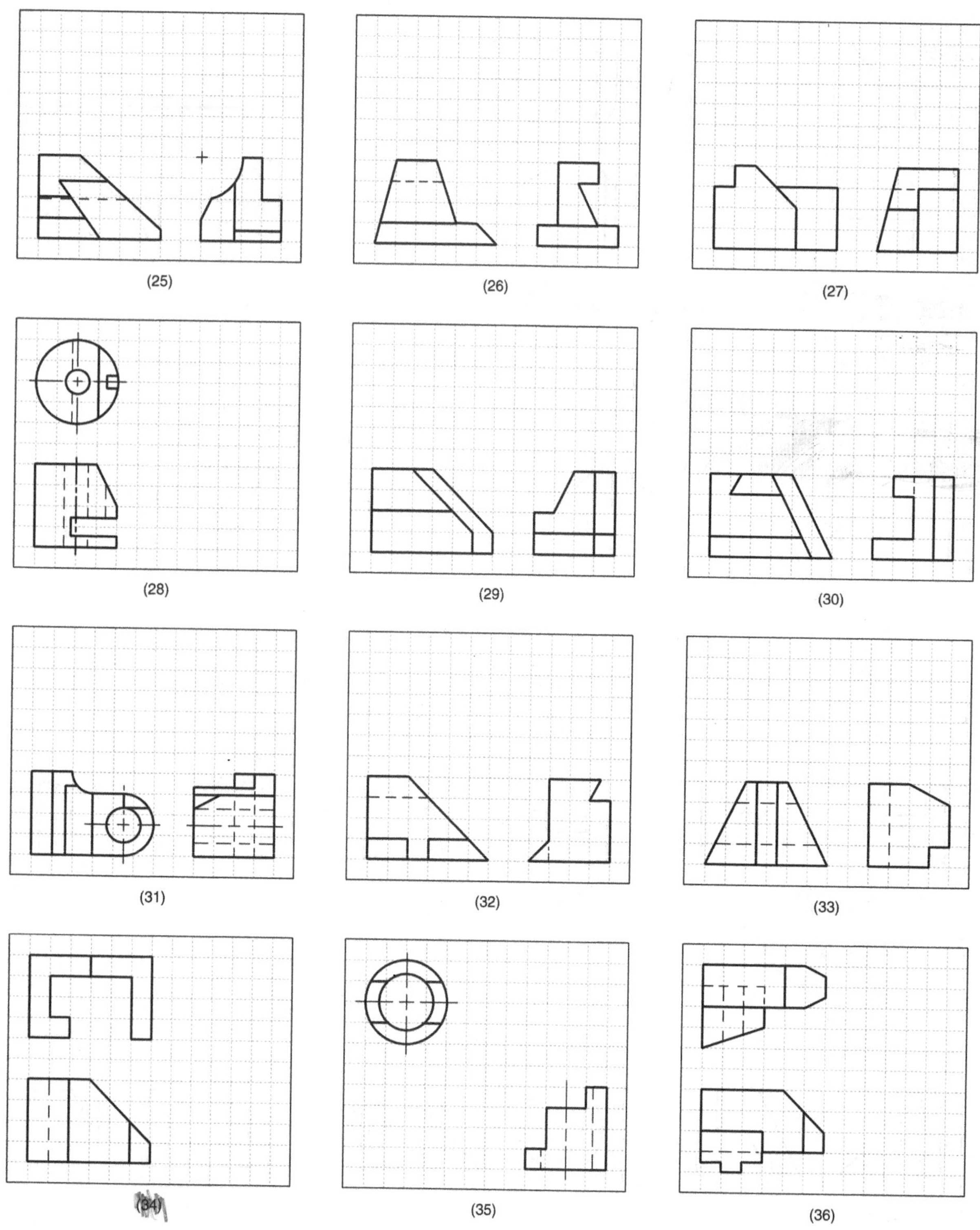

Figure 10.92

Two-view drawings of several objects for Problem 10.4 (Continued)

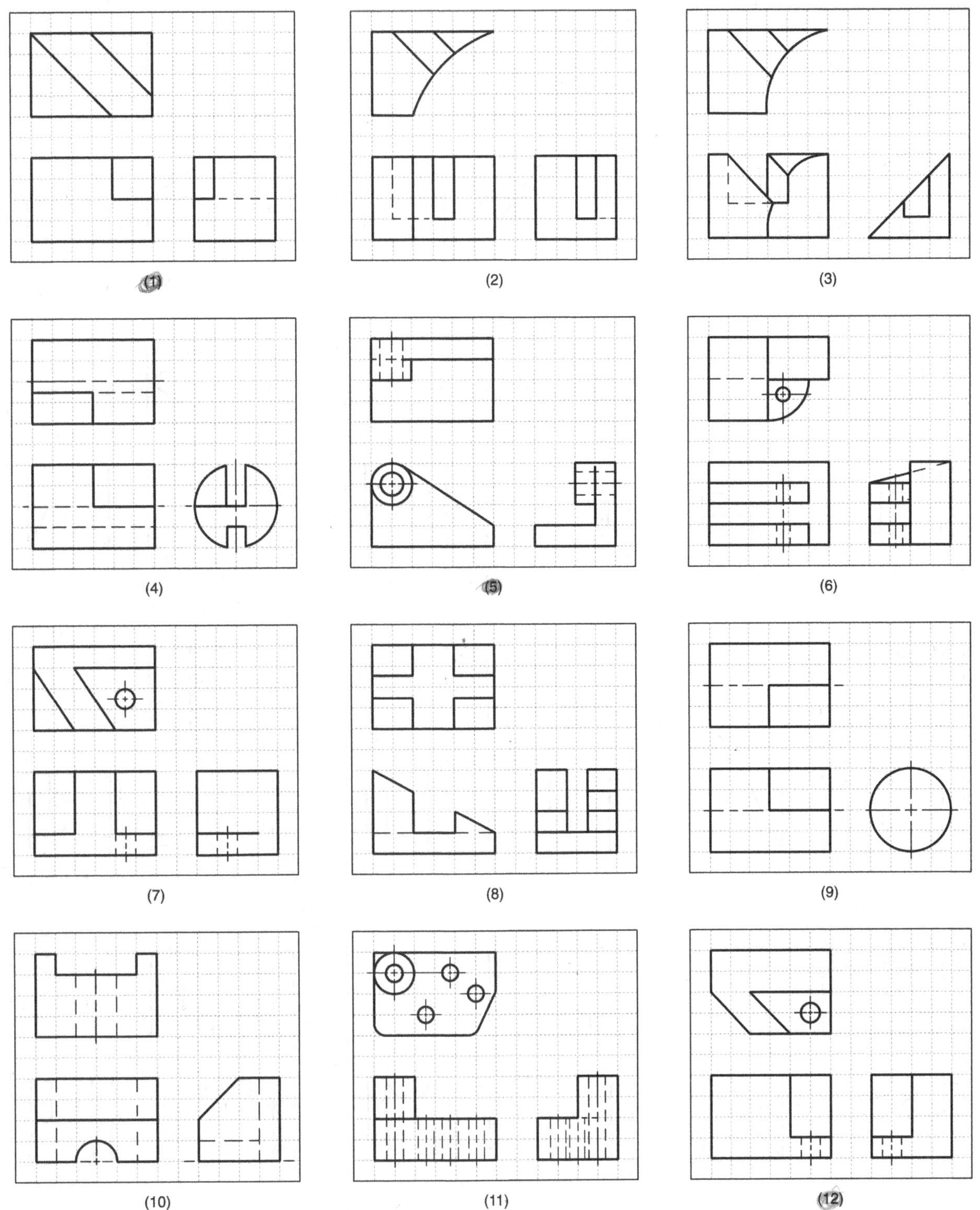

Figure 10.93

Three incomplete views of a multiview drawing of an object for Problem 10.5

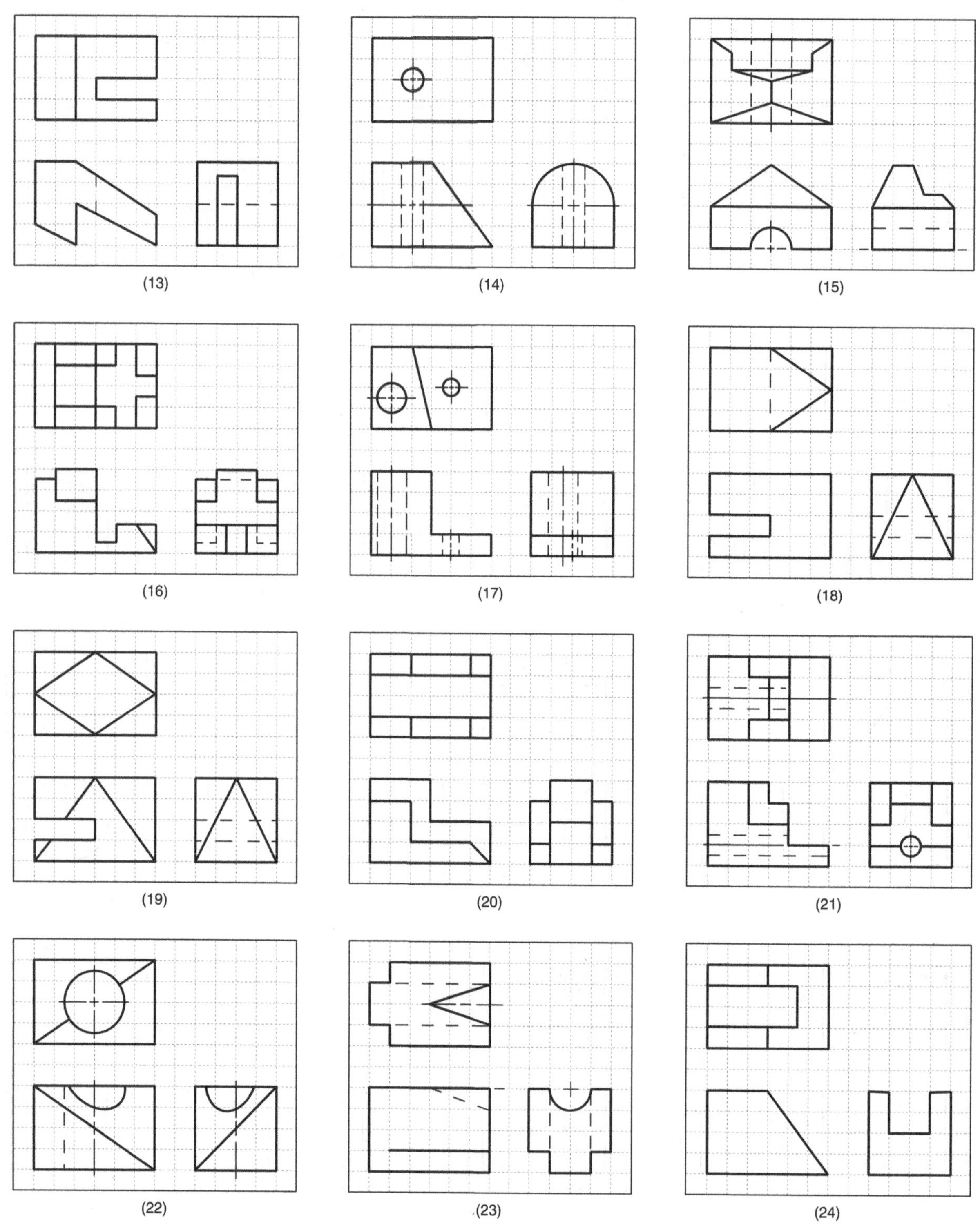

Figure 10.93

Three incomplete views of a multiview drawing of an object for Problem 10.5 (Continued)

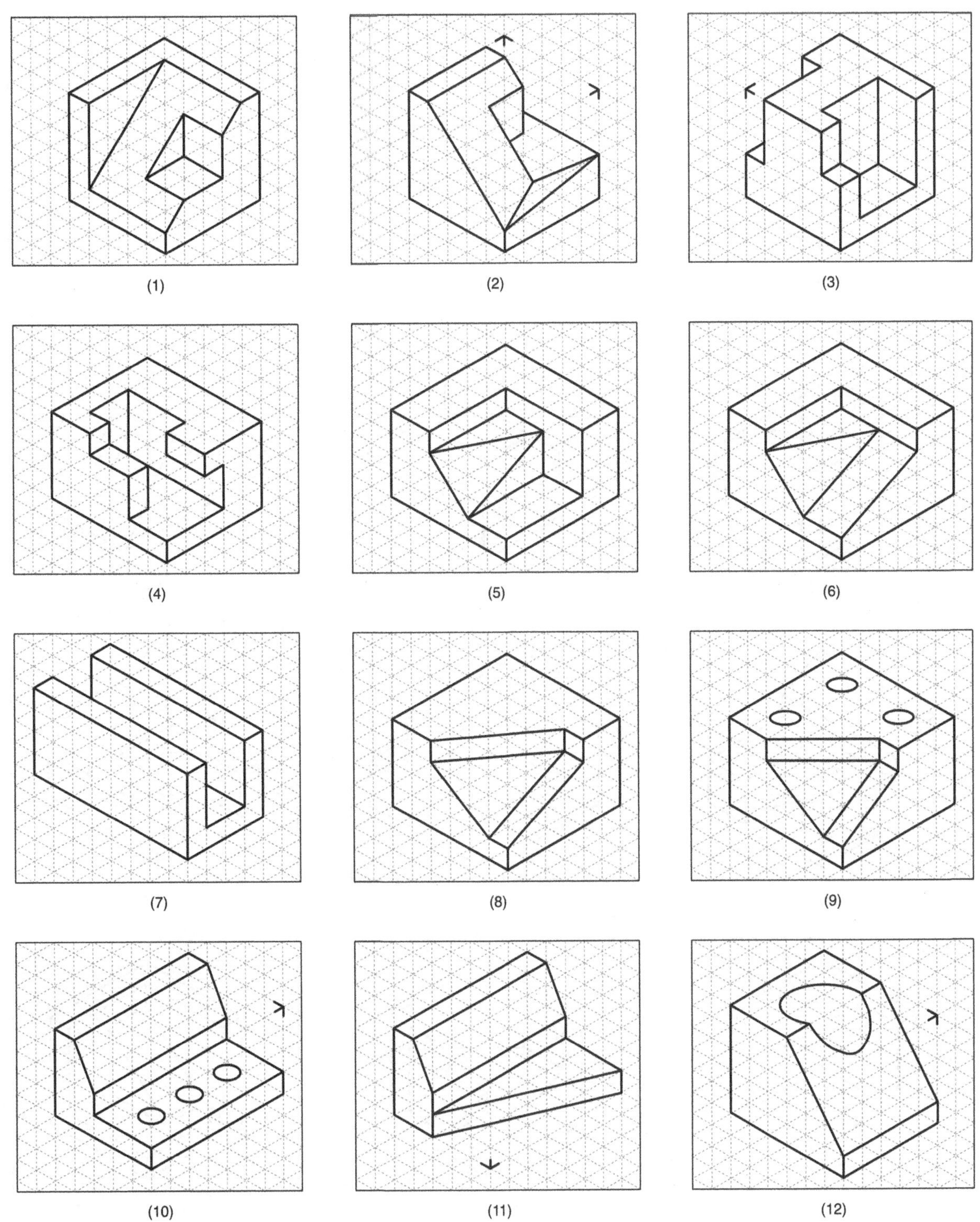

Figure 10.94

Pictorials of several objects for Problems 10.6 and 10.13

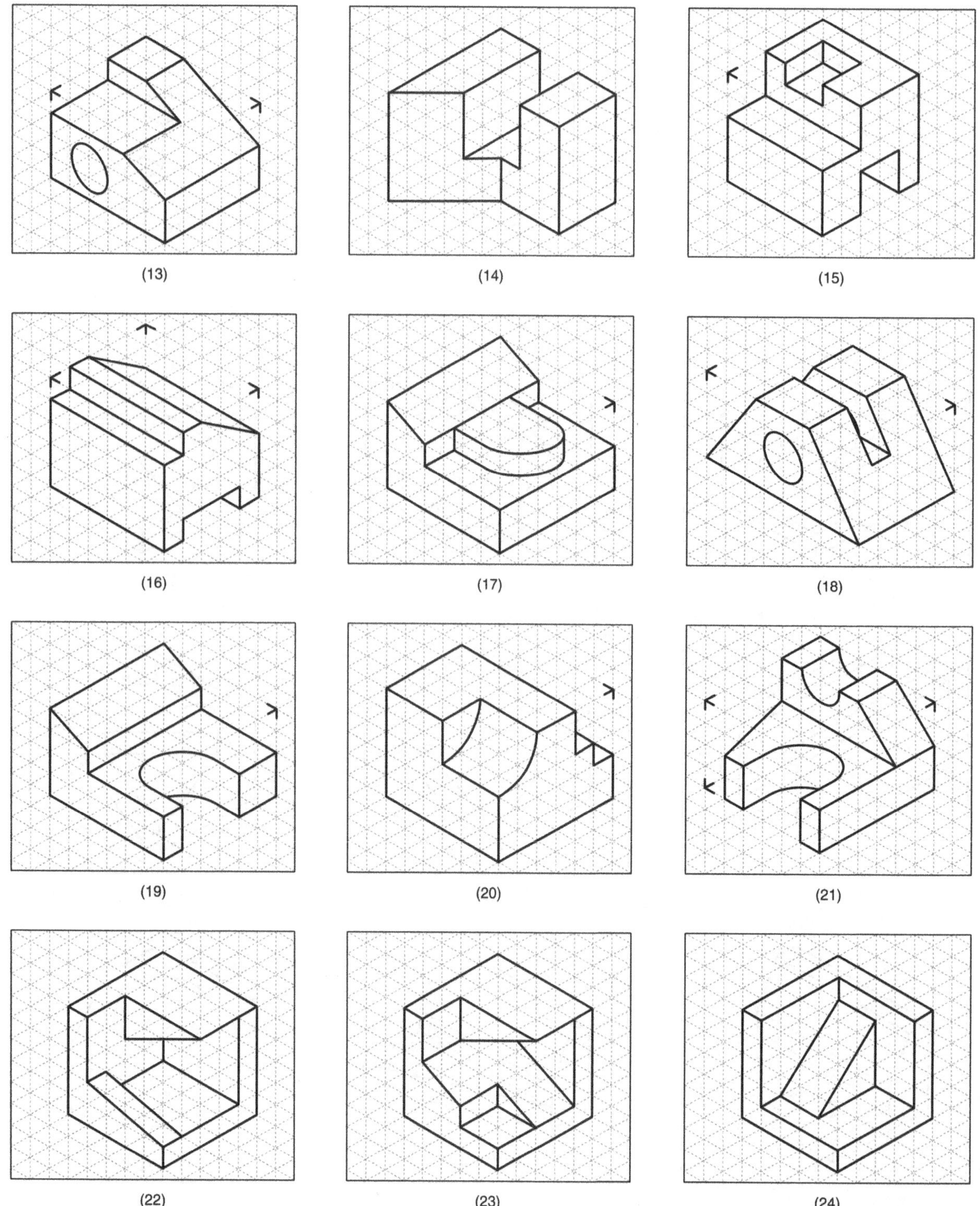

Figure 10.94

Pictorials of several objects for Problems 10.6 and 10.13 (Continued)

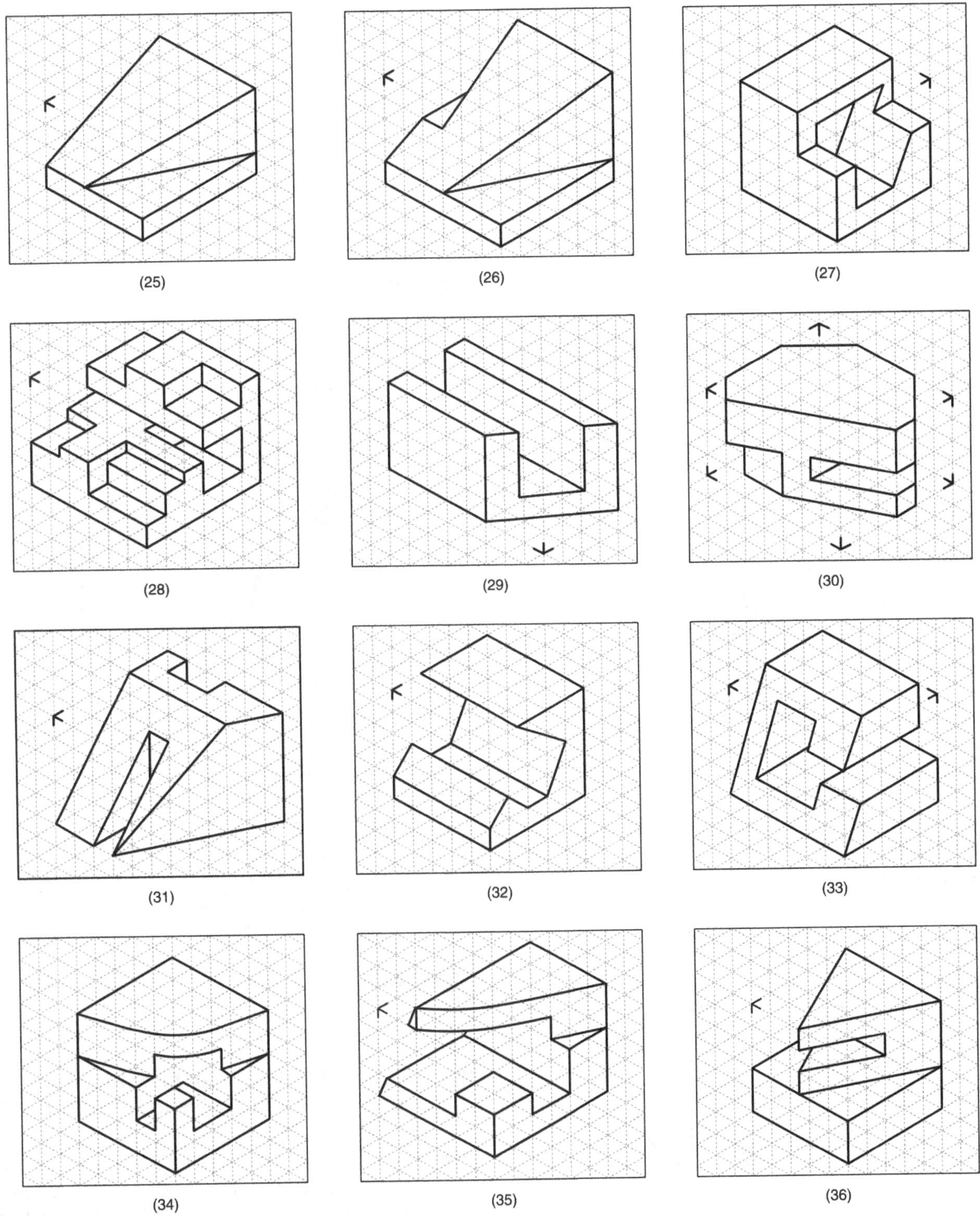

Figure 10.94

Pictorials of several objects for Problems 10.6 and 10.13 (Continued)

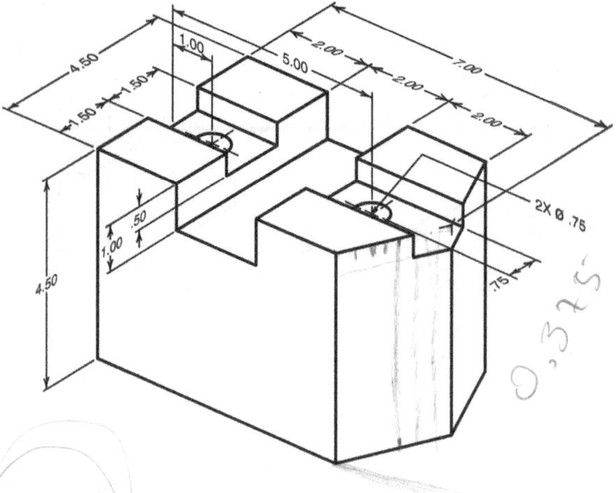

Figure 10.95

Tool block

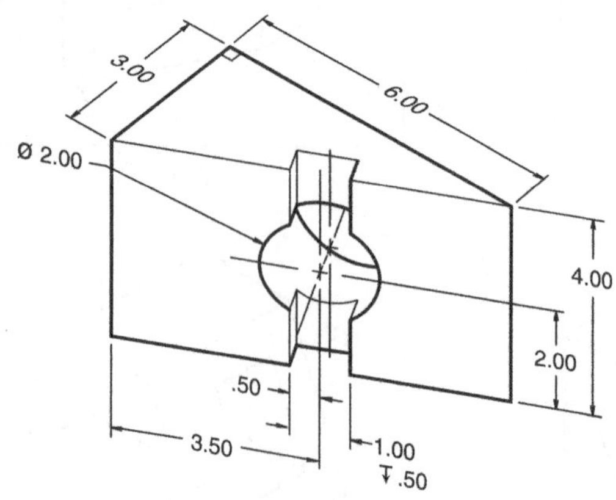

Figure 10.96

Wedge support

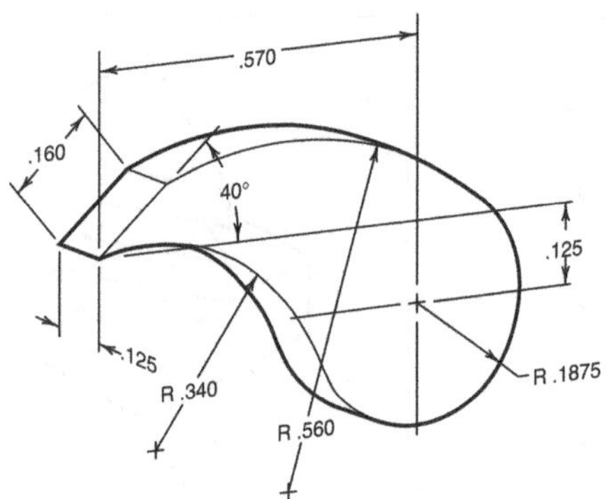

Figure 10.97

Ratchet stop

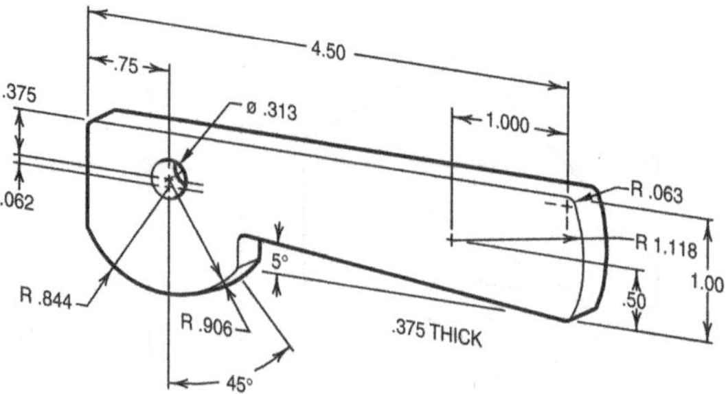

Figure 10.98

Lever

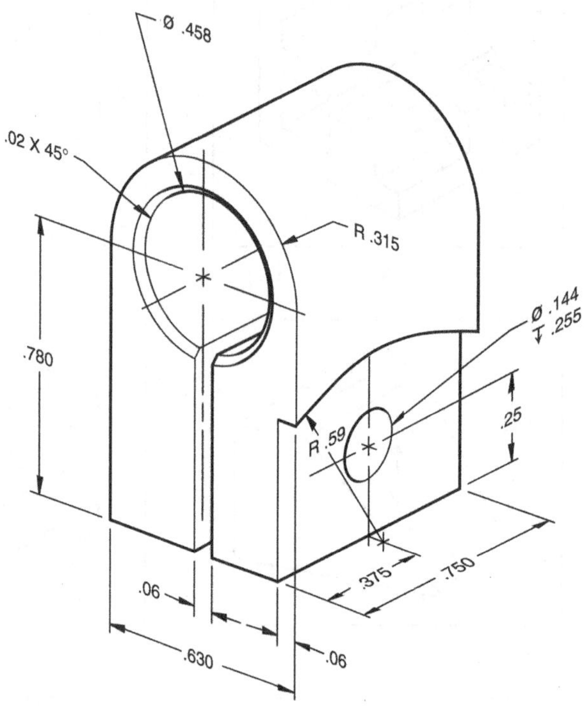

Figure 10.99

Coupling

10.7 (Figures 10.95 through 10.154) Sketch, draw with instruments or CAD, or create 3-D CAD models for the parts shown.

10.8 On square grid paper, sketch a series of multiviews of a cube, at least eight squares on a side. Visualize the following modifications to the cube and draw the resulting multiviews:

a. Looking at the front view, drill a hole 3 squares in diameter and parallel to the line of sight.

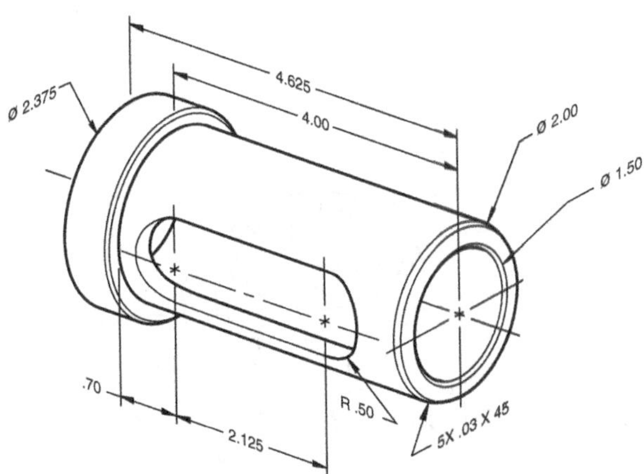

Figure 10.100

Retainer

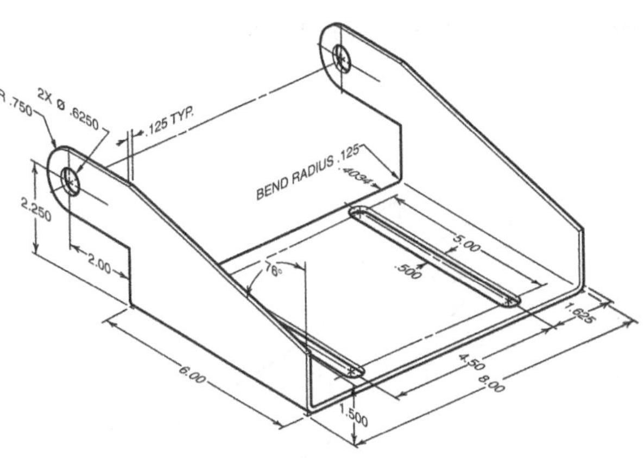

Figure 10.103

Top bracket

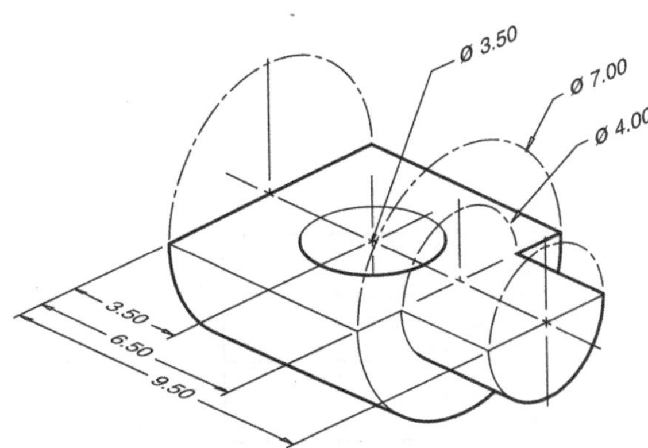

Figure 10.101

Half pin

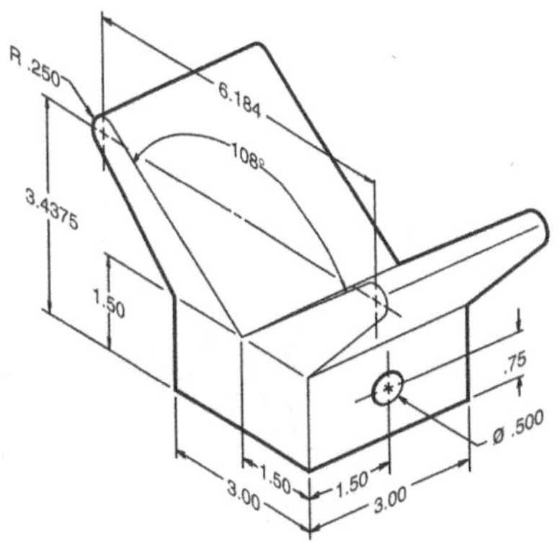

Figure 10.104

Snubber

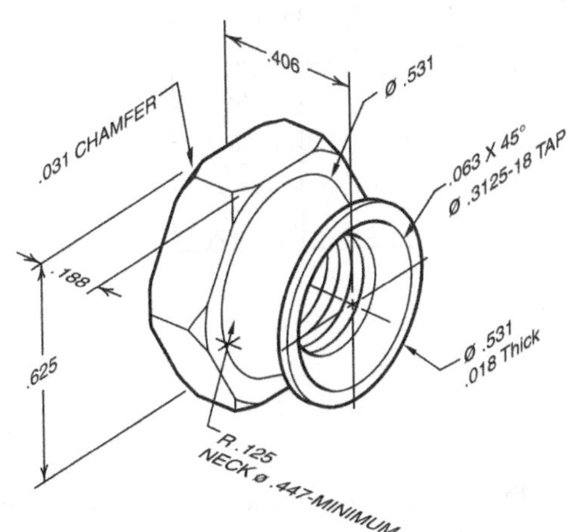

Figure 10.102

Latch nut

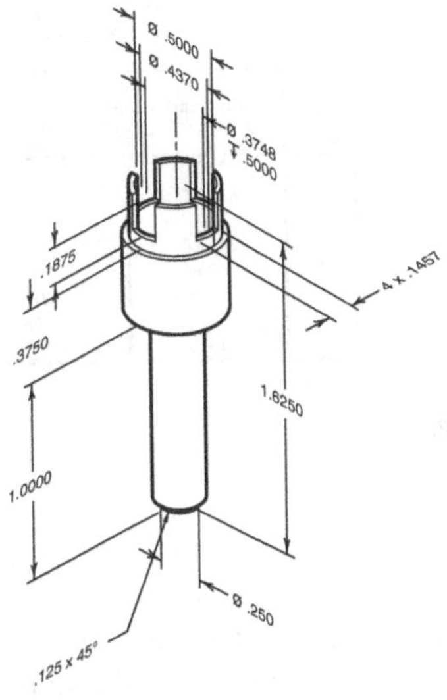

Figure 10.105

Dial extension

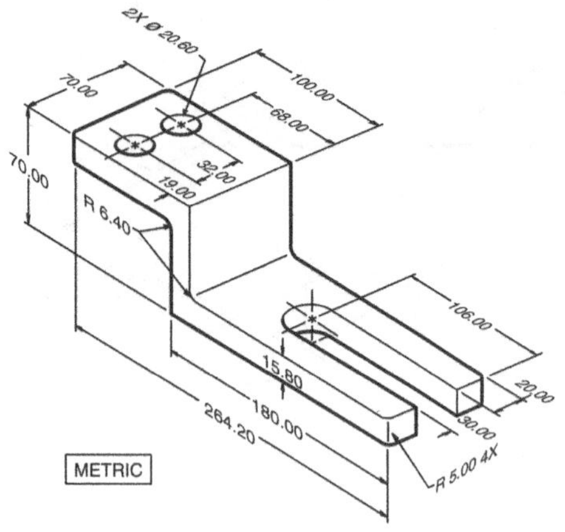

Figure 10.106

Motor plate

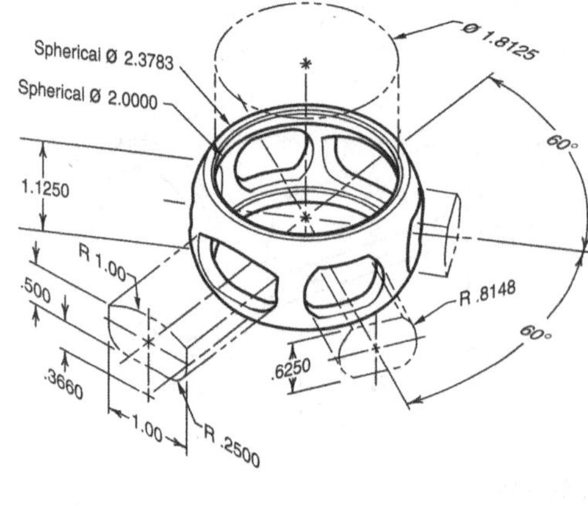

Figure 10.107

Release

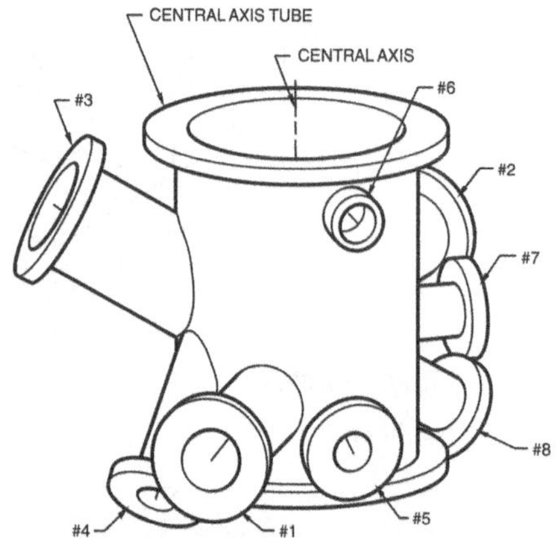

Central axis tube height = 11.000"
Central axis tube I.D. = 7.250"
Central axis tube O.D. = 8.000"
Central axis tube flange dia = 10.000"
Central axis tube flange width = .500"
All flange diameters = tube diameter + 1.5"
All flange widths = .500"
All tube I.D.'s = Tube diameter - .500"

Tube #	Elevation from base (on the central axis)	Azimuth angle from tube #1 (around central axis)	Offset distance from central axis	Angle of elevation from the base of the part	Length of tube from end of flange to apparent intersection with central axis	Outer diameter of tube
1	4.000"	0°	0.000"	0°	14.000"	3.000"
2	7.000"	180°	0.000"	0°	11.000"	2.500"
3	7.000"	110°	0.000"	30°	9.250"	3.500"
4	4.000"	70°	2.000"	-45°	9.500"	1.750"
5	2.750"	310°	0.500"	-10°	5.000"	1.750"
6	9.125"	310°	0.750"	0°	5.500"	1.750"
7	4.625"	205°	0.125"	0°	6.000"	1.750"
8	4.500"	230°	0.250"	-30°	7.500"	1.750"

Figure 10.108

Evaporator

b. Take the result of (*a*) and drill another hole 2 squares in diameter to the right of the first hole.

c. Take the result of (*a*) and drill another hole 3 squares in diameter above the first hole.

d. Take the result of (*a*) and drill a hole 5 squares in diameter in the same location as the first hole, but only half-way through the cube.

e. Instead of drilling a 3-square diameter hole through the object, create a cylinder projecting

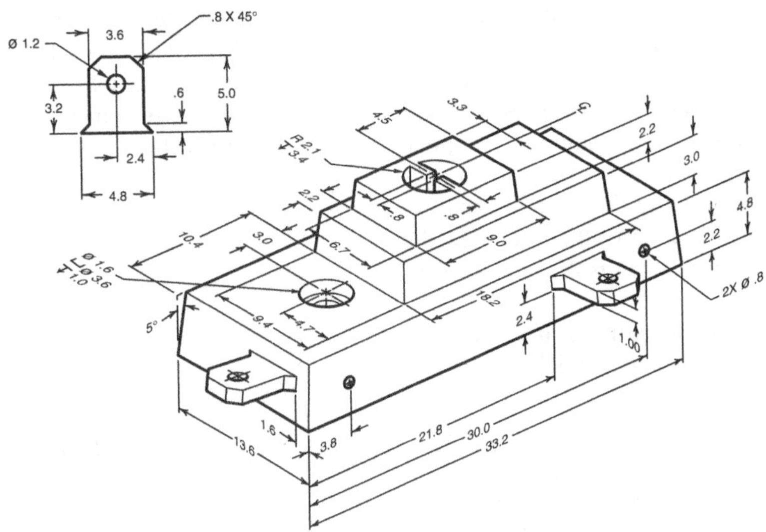

Figure 10.109

Manifold

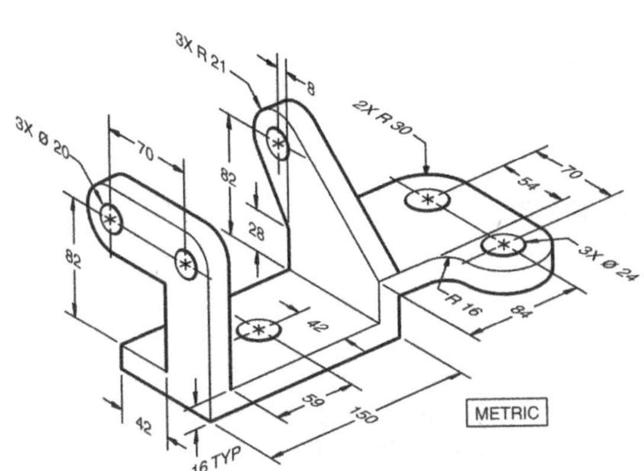

Figure 10.110

Cutoff

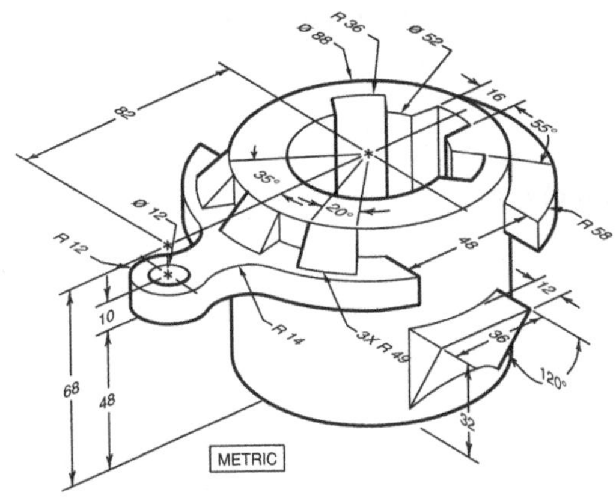

Figure 10.111

Spline pilot

2 squares out of the cube and parallel to the line of sight of the front view. Compare this with the views in (*a*).

f. Same as (*e*), except raise the cylinder along the line of sight of the top view.

g. Same as (*a*), except remove a square feature rather than a round hole. Compare this with the views in (*a*).

h. Same as (*a*), except place the center 2 squares to the right. Enlarge the drill to a diameter of 5 squares; 7 squares; 9 squares.

i. Find the midpoints of the top and right side edges of the front view. Draw a line connecting these points and project it along the line of sight for the front view to create a cutting plane. Remove this corner of the cube.

j. Same as (*i*), except rotate the cutting plane to be 15 degrees, 30 degrees, 60 degrees, and 75 degrees to the horizontal. Compare the dimensions of the inclined surface projections at each of these angles (including the original 45-degree angle).

k. Same as (*i*), except move the cutting plane toward the lower left corner of the front view, in 2-square increments. When is the inclined surface the largest?

l. Same as (*i*), except the cutting plane is defined by the midpoints of the top and right side edges of the front view and the midpoint of the top edge of the right side view.

m. Same as (*l*), except move the cutting plane in 2-square increments toward the opposite corner of the cube.

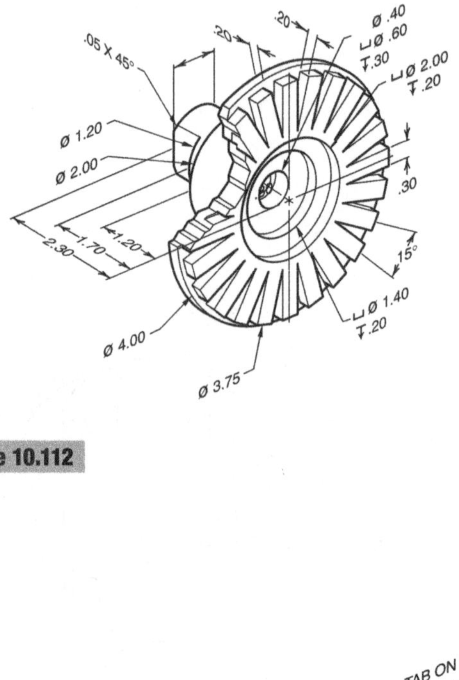

Figure 10.112
Index

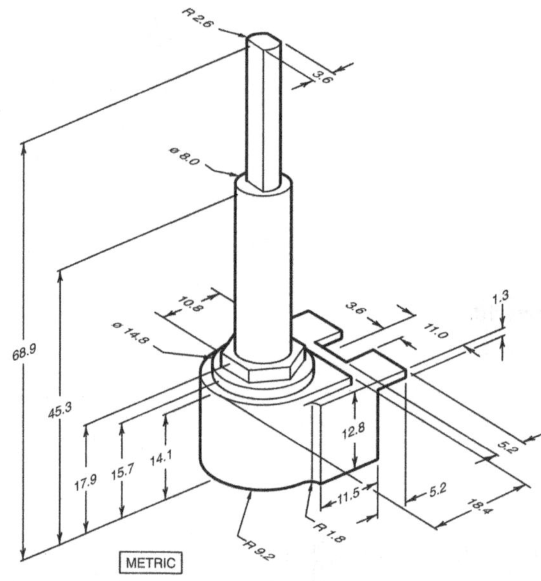

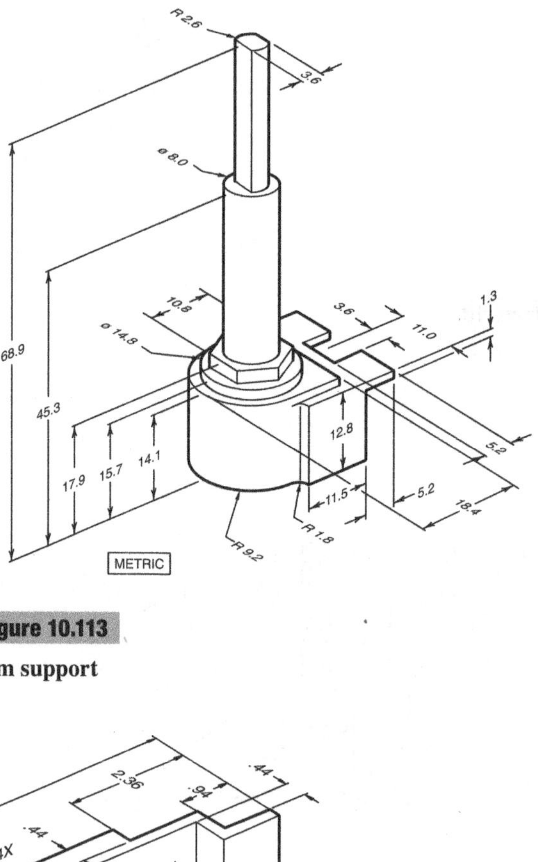

Figure 10.113
Arm support

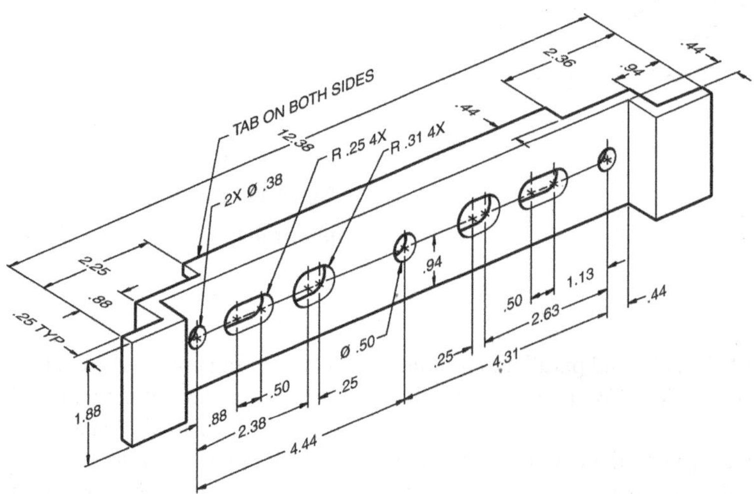

Figure 10.114
Control back

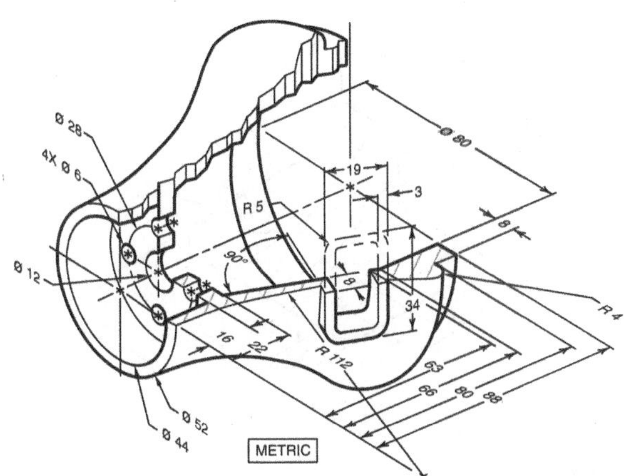

Figure 10.115

Inlet

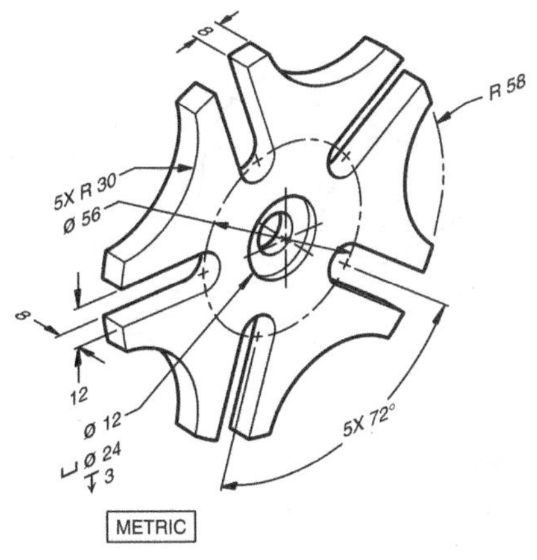

Figure 10.116

Gear index

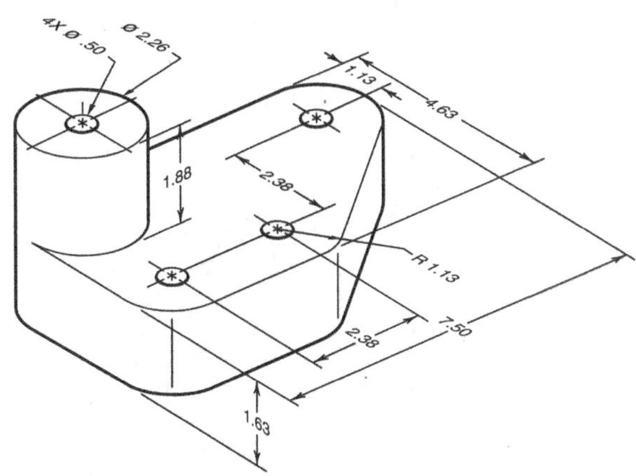

Figure 10.117

Speed spacer

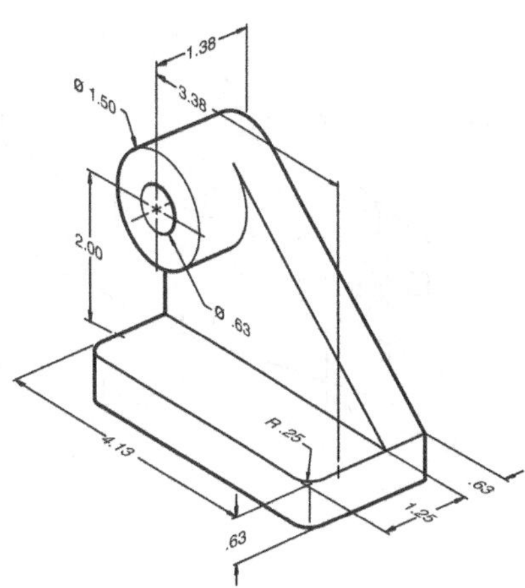

Figure 10.118

Shaft support

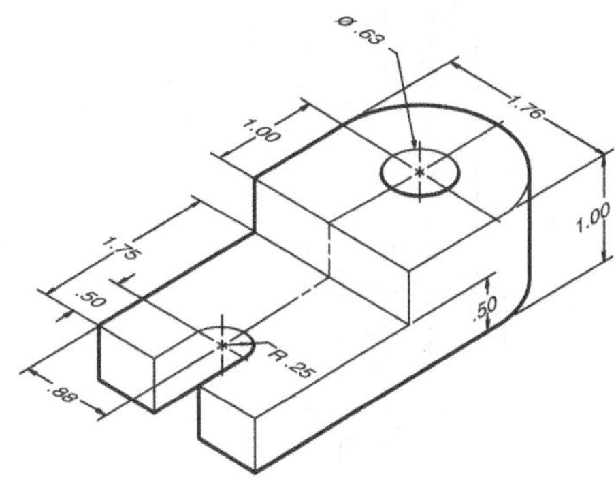

Figure 10.119

Stop base

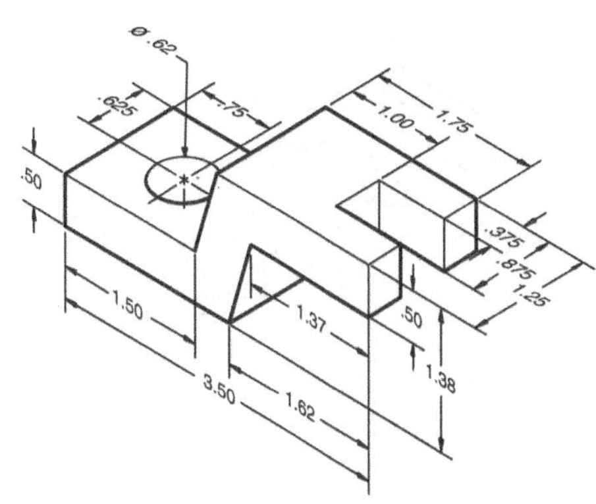

Figure 10.120

Tool holder

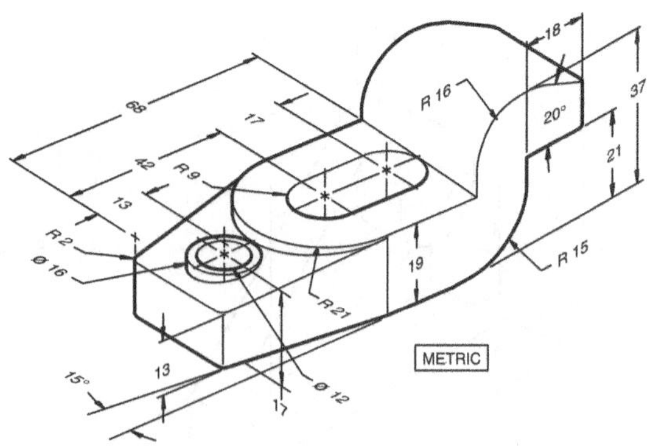

Figure 10.121

CNC clamp

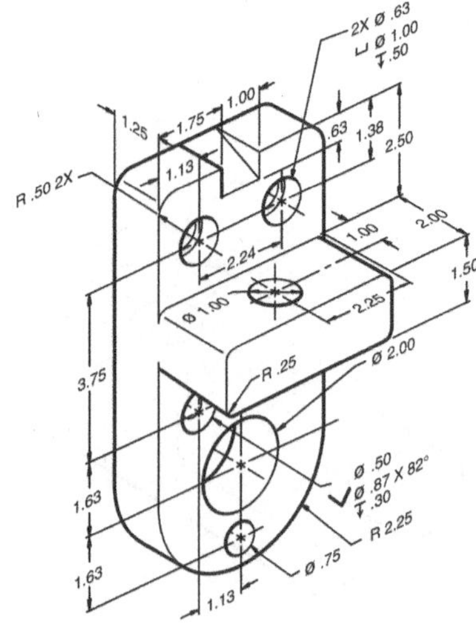

Figure 10.122

Pen block

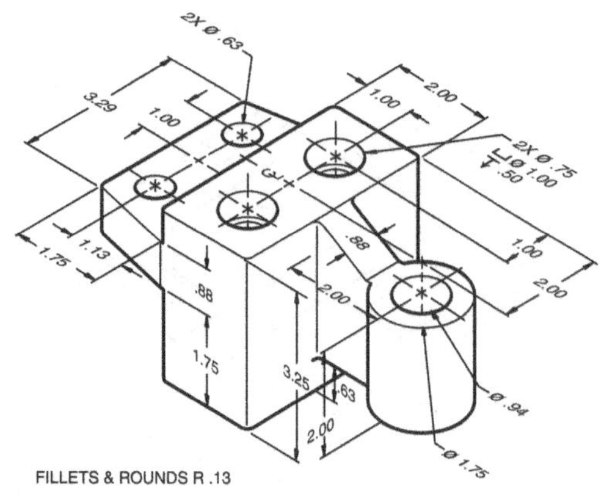

Figure 10.123

Cover guide

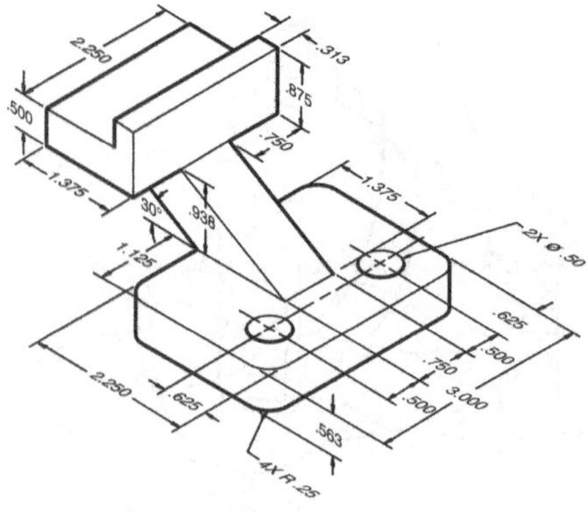

Figure 10.124

Dial bracket

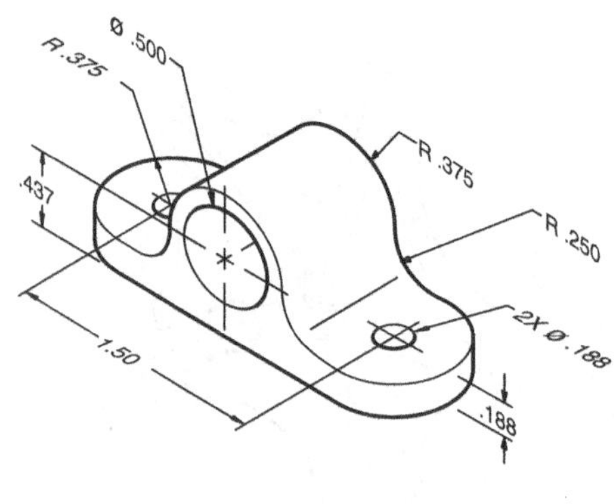

Figure 10.125

Bearing block

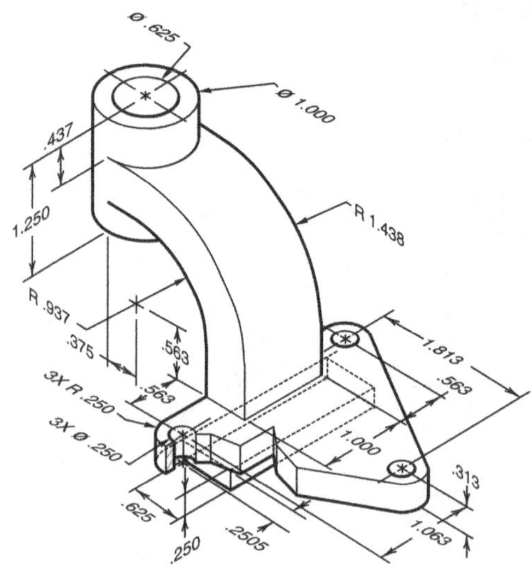

Figure 10.126

Pulley support

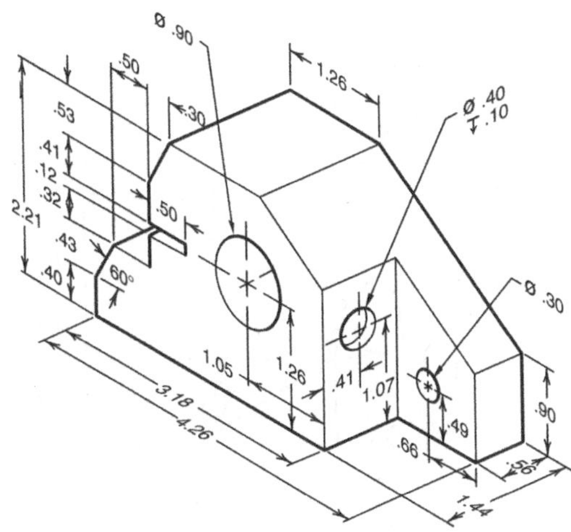

Figure 10.127

Centering clip

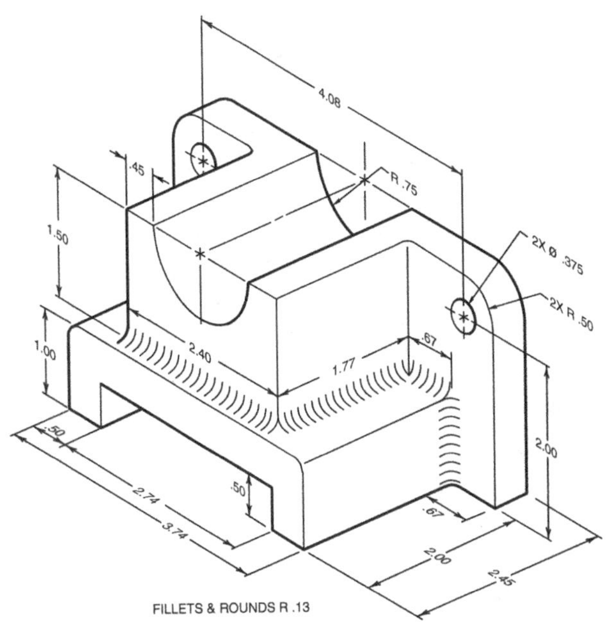

Figure 10.129

Auger support

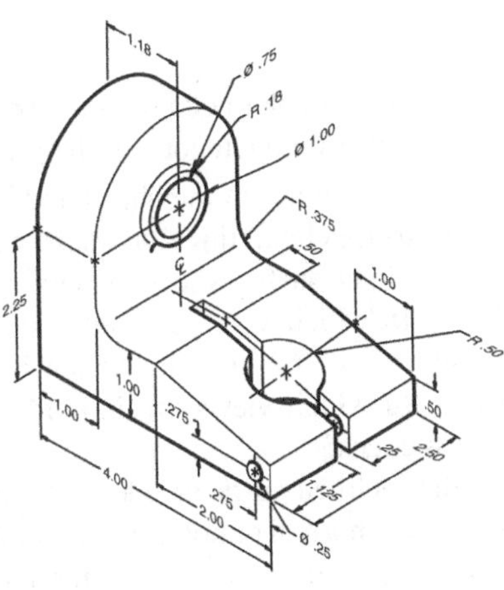

Figure 10.128

Adjustable guide

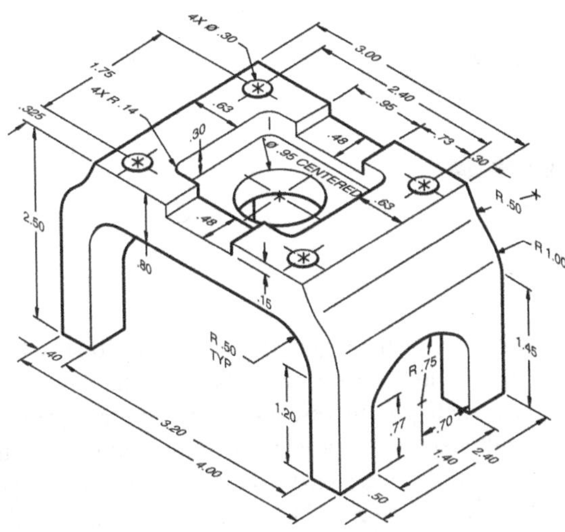

Figure 10.130

Dryer clip

10.9 Same as 10.8 (*a* through *k*), except use a cylinder 8 squares in diameter, 8 squares deep, and seen in its circular form in the front view.

10.10 Using any of the objects shown in the exercises in the back of this chapter, decompose the objects into primitive geometric shapes. Color code these shapes to show whether they represent positive material added to the object or negative material removed from it. This can be done by:

- Drawing isometric pictorial sketches of the objects.
- Overdrawing on top of photocopies of the drawings.
- Tracing over the drawings.

10.11 Using either a photocopy or a tracing of the object in Figure 10.89, color, number, or letter each face

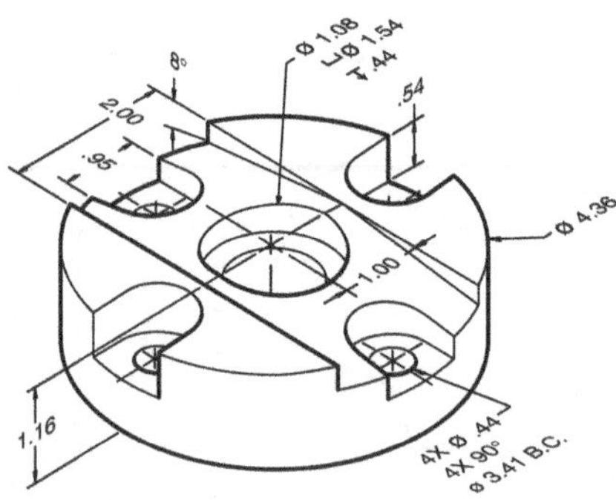

Figure 10.131

Retaining cap

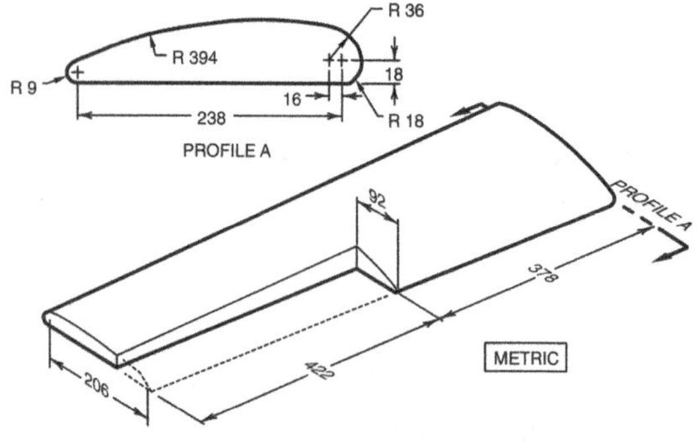

Figure 10.132

Air foil

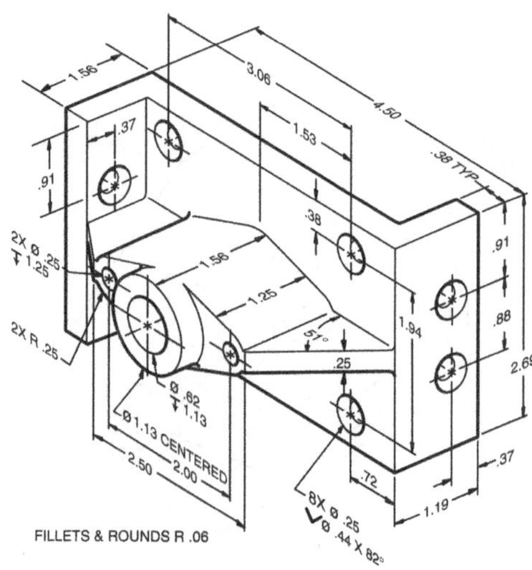

Figure 10.133

Locating base

(surface) of the object. Pick a surface that will be seen in its true size and shape in the front view and sketch its representation in the three primary multiviews. Use projection lines to align the surface in all three views. Label it the same as you did in the pictorial. Then, pick another surface that shares an edge with the one you just sketched, and sketch the new surface in the three views. Repeat the process until you have sketched all the faces contiguous with the original one. How many of these faces are contiguous with each other? How many are also seen in their true size and shape in the front view? In other views?

10.12 Using the object in Figure 10.89, identify the normal, inclined, and oblique planar surfaces. Either letter, number, or color code the surfaces on a tracing paper copy or a photocopy of the pictorial.

a. Create a multiview of the object and identify the same surfaces in all three views. In which views are individual surfaces seen in their true size and shape? In which views are individual surfaces foreshortened? (Which dimension is foreshortened?) In which views are individual features seen as edges?

b. For the inclined surfaces, identify which edges show up as normal or non-normal (angled) edges on normal surfaces. How does the inclined surface appear in the view where a non-normal edge is present?

c. For the oblique surfaces, are there any normal edges? Is there any view in which any of these surfaces are seen as edges?

d. Visualize a view which would allow an inclined or oblique surface to be seen in its true size and shape, and try to sketch that view. What happens to the surfaces which were normal in the principal views?

10.13 Using any of the objects from Figure 10.94, sketch them on tracing paper or make a photocopy. Sketch cutting planes which would divide all or part of each object into symmetrical halves. Sketch multiviews of each half of each object.

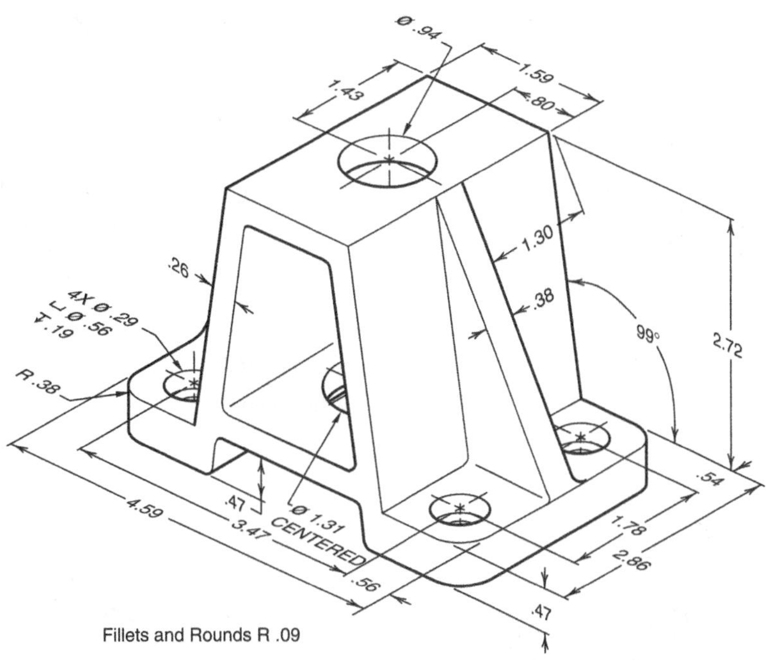

Figure 10.134

Anchor base

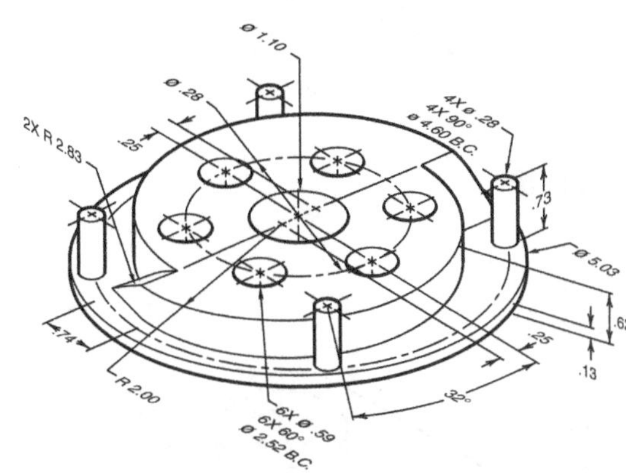

Figure 10.135

Evaporator cover

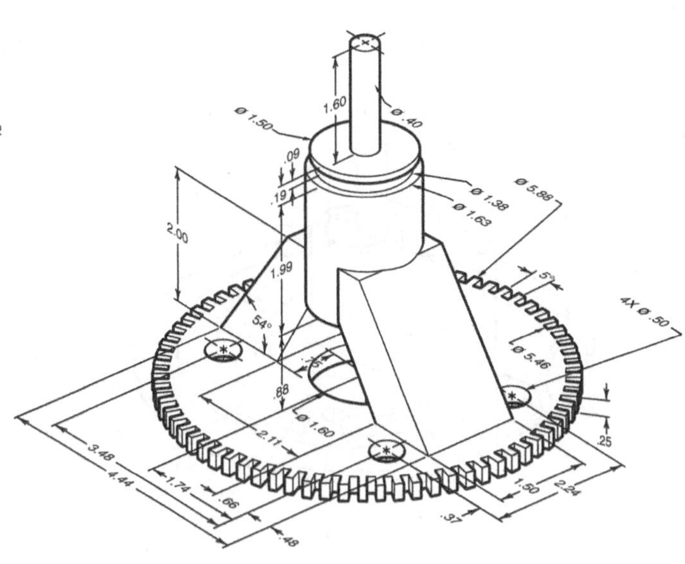

Figure 10.136

Dryer gear

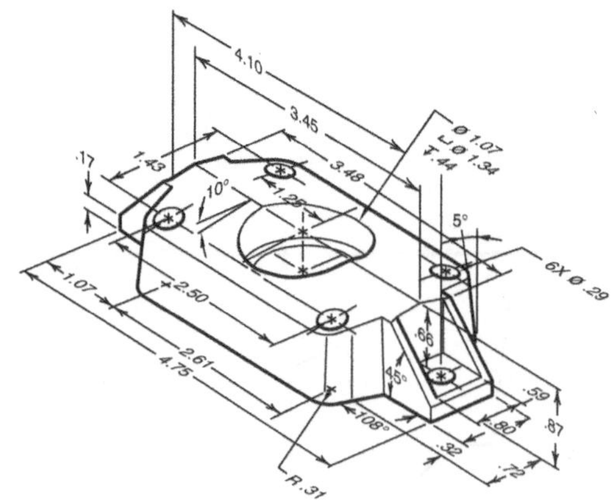

Figure 10.137

Heater clip

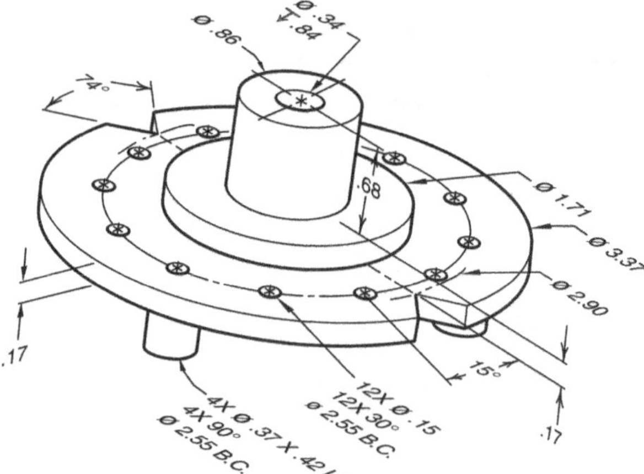

Figure 10.138

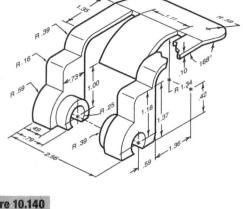

Relay clip

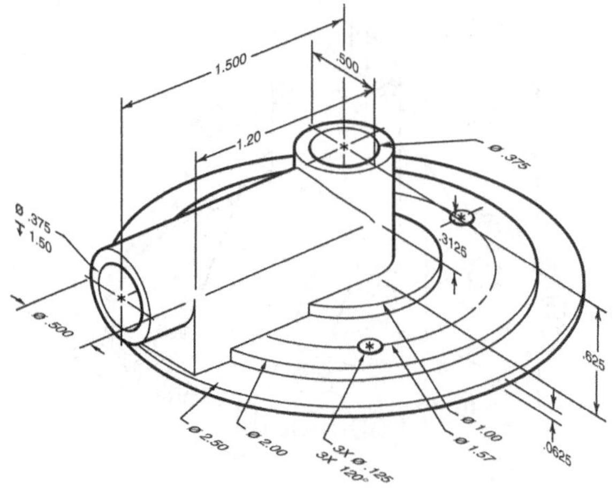

Figure 10.139

Clip release

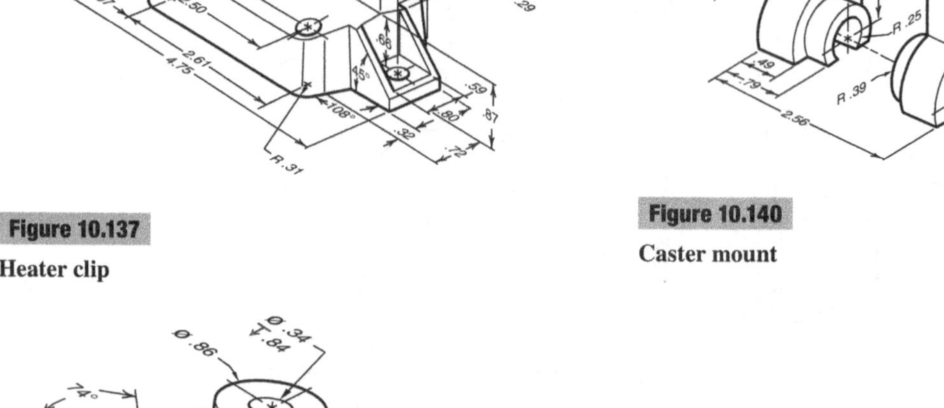

Figure 10.140

Caster mount

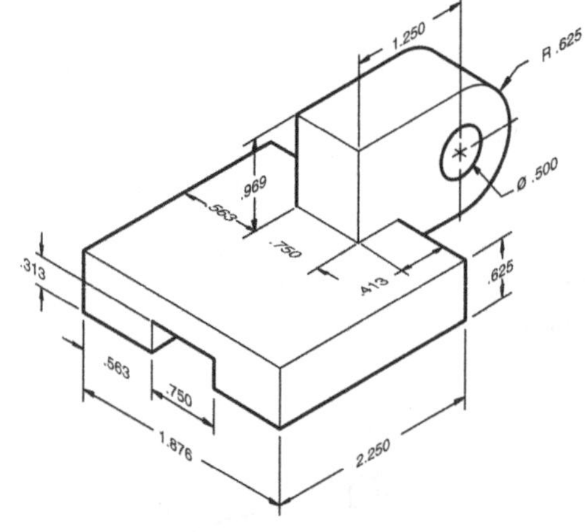

Figure 10.141

Slide base

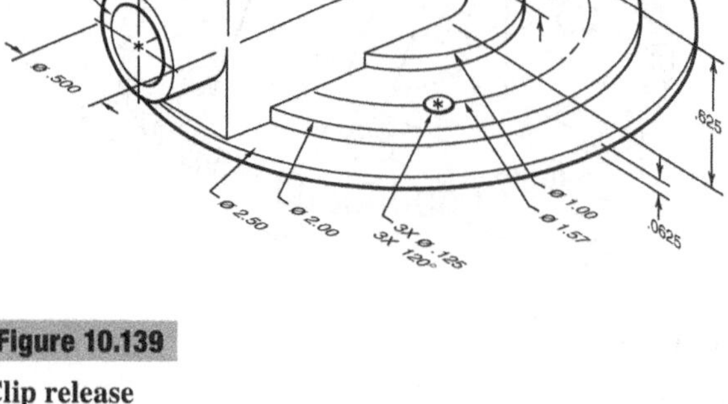

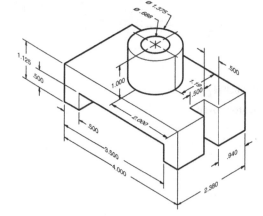

Figure 10.142

Retainer clip

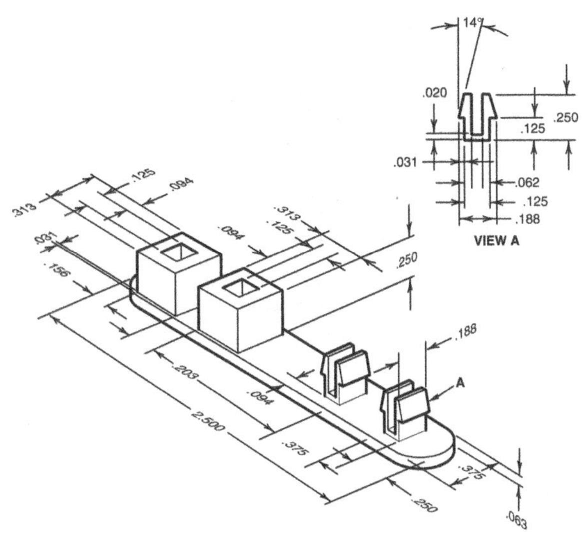

Figure 10.143

Lens clip

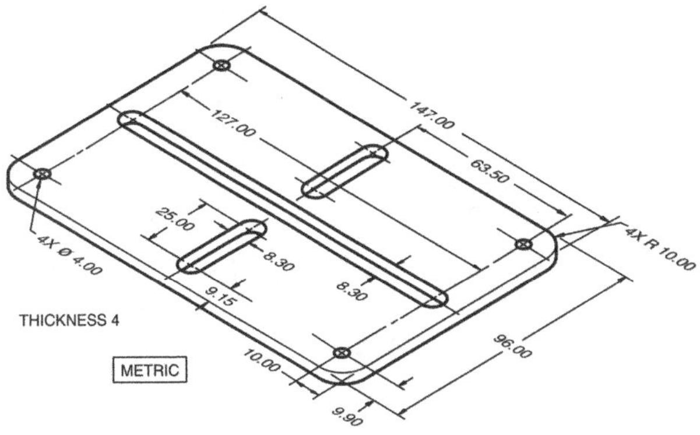

THICKNESS 4

METRIC

Figure 10.145

Offset plate

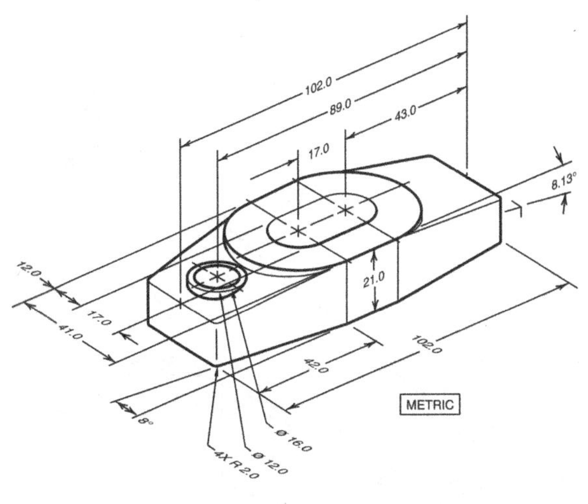

Figure 10.146

Clamp down

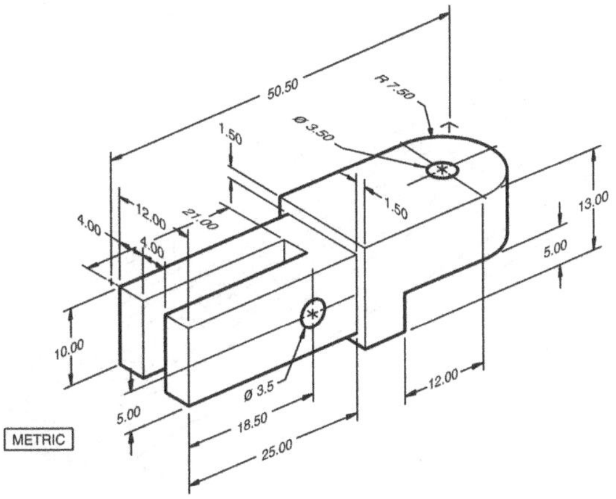

METRIC

Figure 10.144

Strike arm

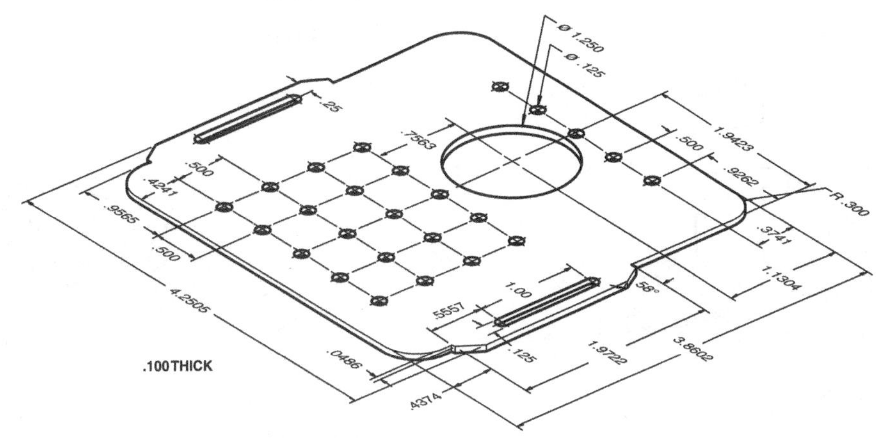

Figure 10.147

Manifold plate

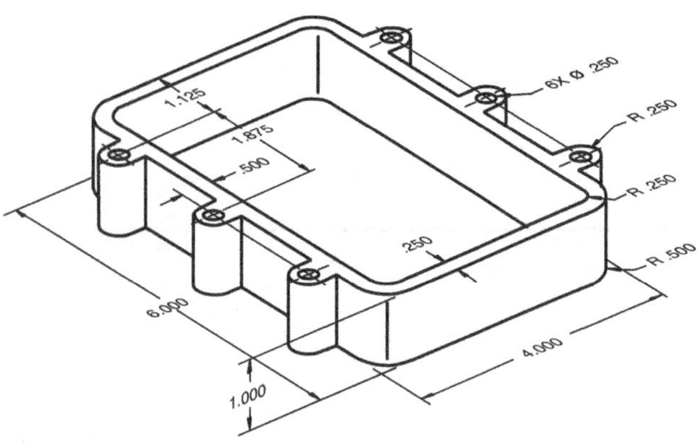

Figure 10.148

Protector

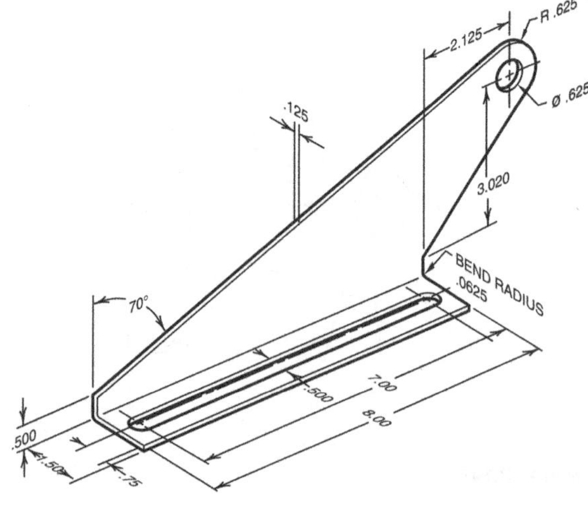

Figure 10.149

Angled support

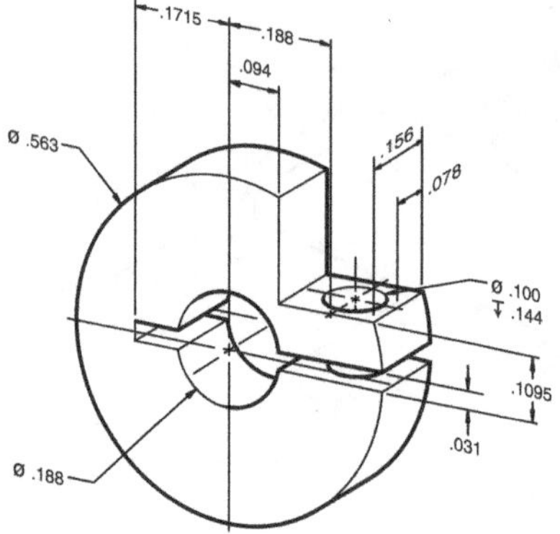

Figure 10.150

Drive collar

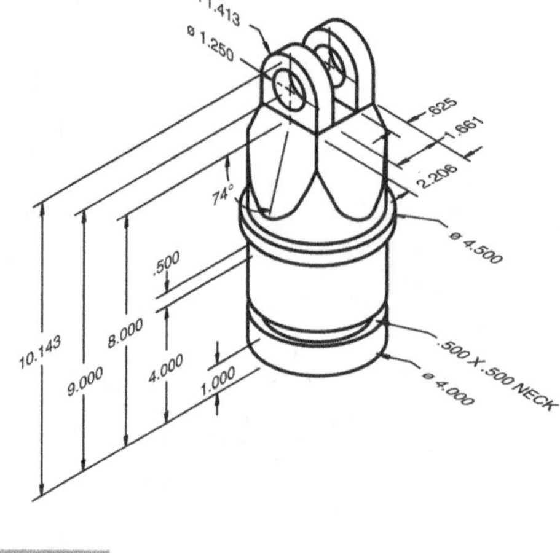

Figure 10.151

Elevator guide

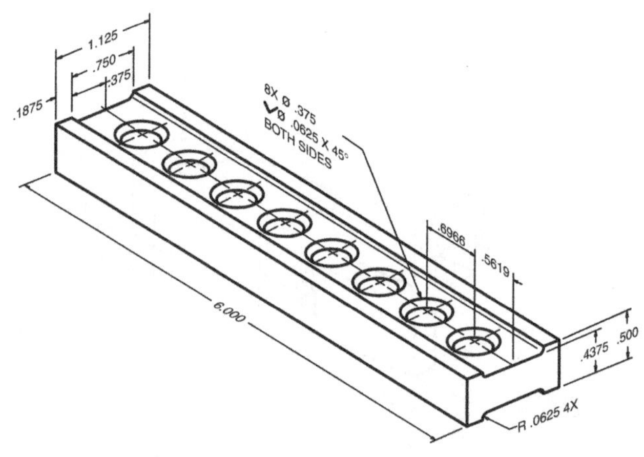

Figure 10.152

Burner cap

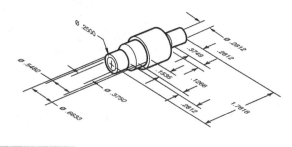

Figure 10.153

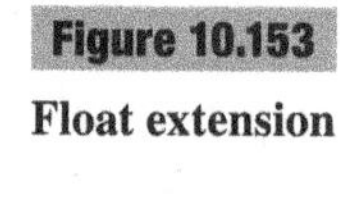

Float extension

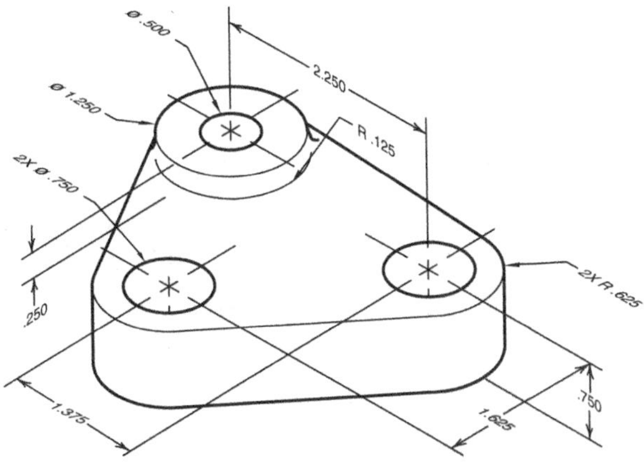

Figure 10.154

Drive base

Classic Problems

The following classic problems were taken from *Engineering Drawing & Graphic Technology,* 14th Edition, by Thomas E. French, Charles J. Vierck, and Robert Foster. All fillets and rounds .125" or 2 mm unless otherwise indicated. Figure 10.155

1. Pieces to be drawn freehand in orthographic projection.
2. Draw three views of the bearing rest. Figure 10.156
3. Draw three views of the swivel yoke. Figure 10.157
4. Draw three views of the wire thimble. Figure 10.158
5. Make a unit-assembly working drawing of the wing-nose rib. Figure 10.159

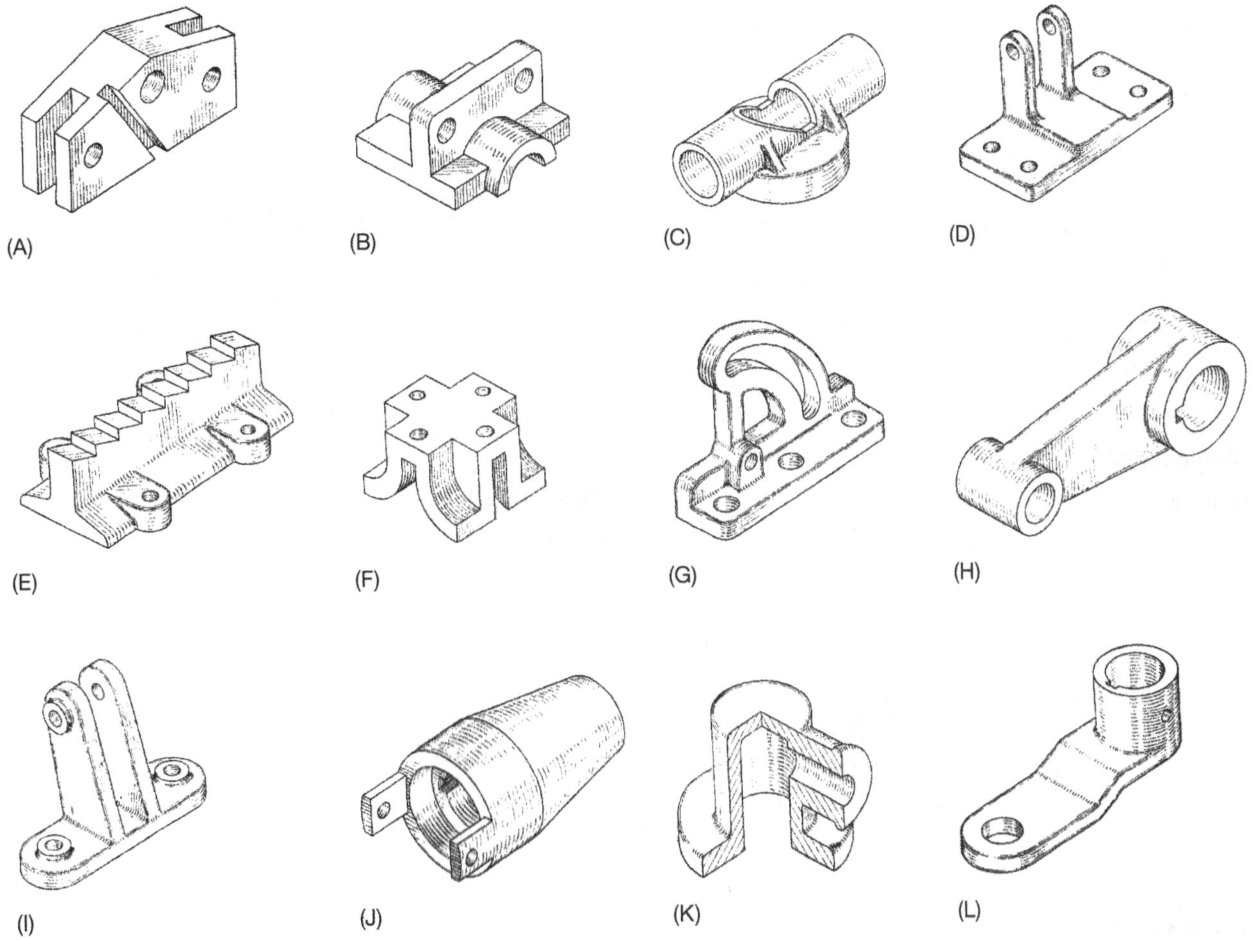

(A) (B) (C) (D)

(E) (F) (G) (H)

(I) (J) (K) (L)

Figure 10.155

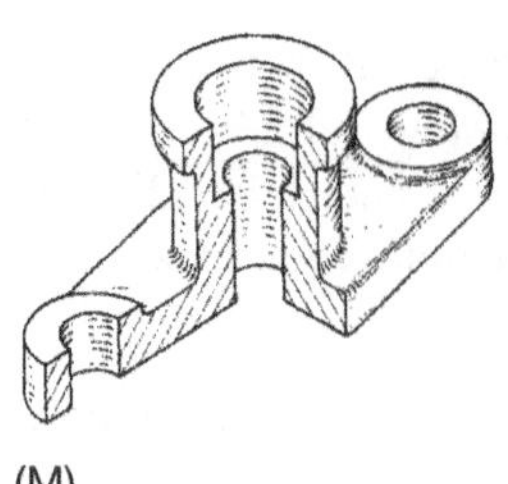

(M)

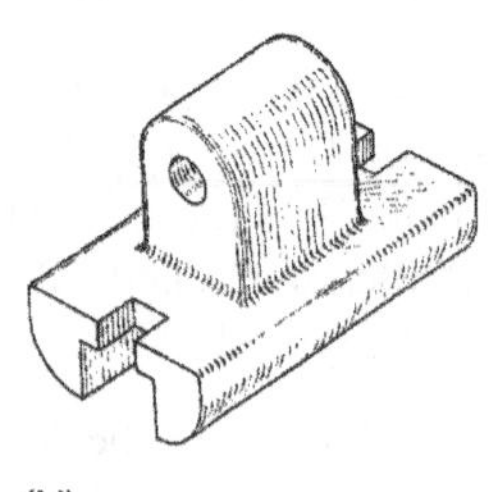

(N)

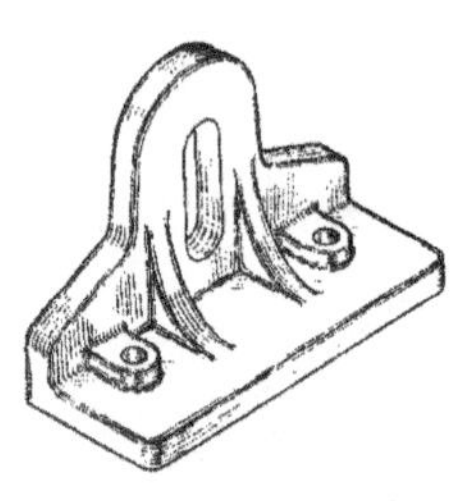

(O)

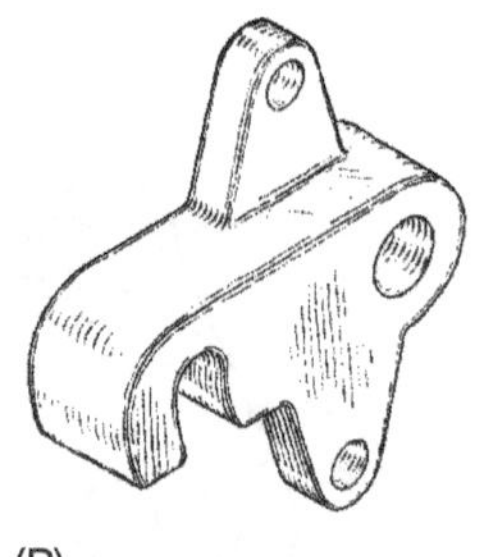

(P)

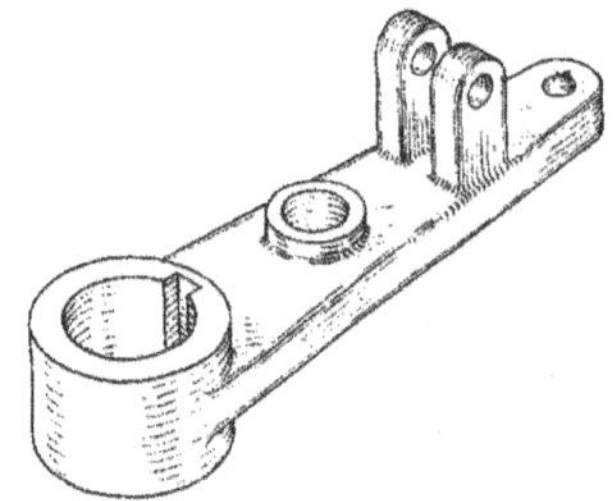

(Q)

Figure 10.155

Continued

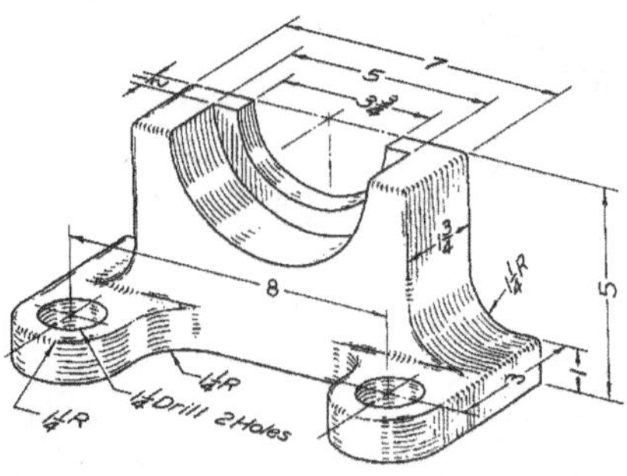

Figure 10.156

Bearing rest

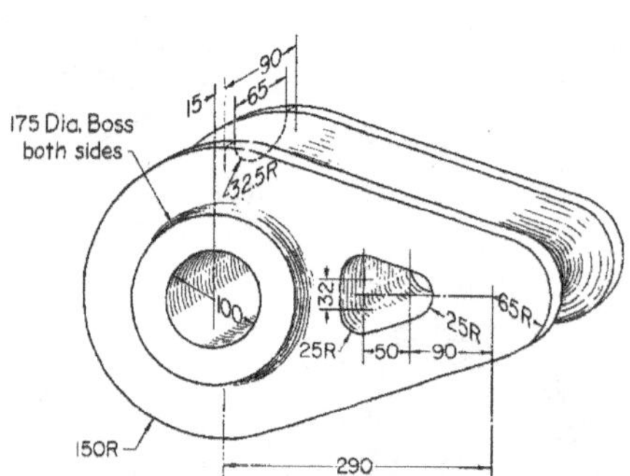

Figure 10.158

Wire thimble

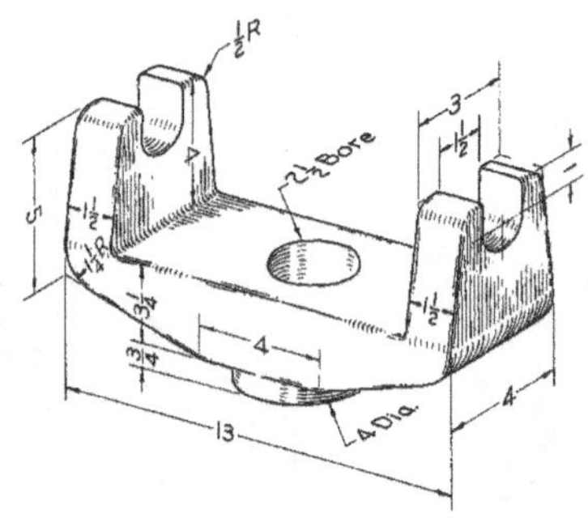

Figure 10.157

Swivel yoke

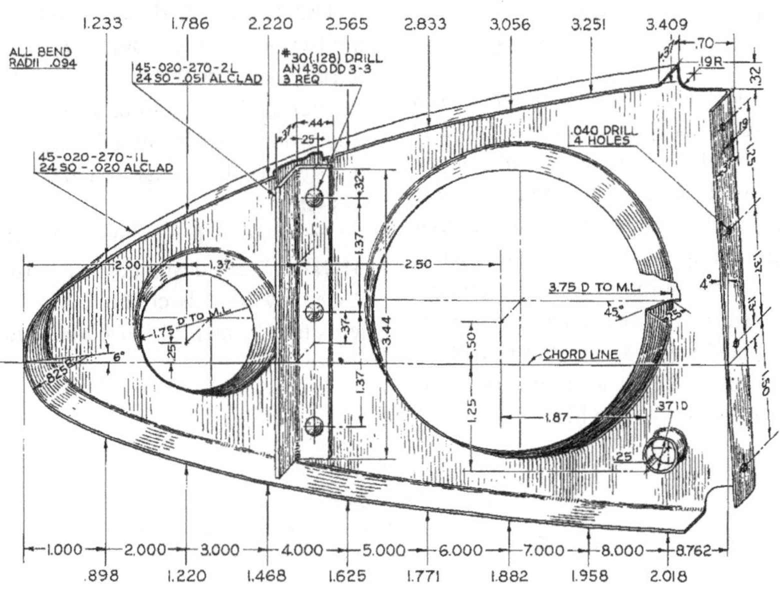

Figure 10.159

Wing-nose rib

3-D Solid Part Models and Multiview Documentation from Technical Sketches

The technical sketches in Figures 10.160 through 10.168 are designed to be used to construct fully constrained 3-D solid part models. Any available parametric solid modeling software may be used. Refer to Chapter 9 *Three-Dimensional Modeling* as needed for a review of construction or datum plane set up, profiles, and part bodies using standard extrusion, revolution, or lofting methods. Use appropriate geometric and dimensional constraints to fully constrain each part. Apply 3-D features, such as holes, fillets, chamfers, ribs, and thin wall operations (as required) to create a logical, easy to edit history tree.

Use the finished part model to generate associated multiview drawings containing appropriate drawing views to fully describe the part (ie; front, top, right side, isometric views). As an option, make parametric changes to key dimensions and features in the part model and use these revisions to the model to update the associated multiview drawing.

Problems designated **"FOR 3-D ASSEMBLY MODEL"** are designed to be used as parts within 3-D Assembly Models contained at the end of chapter problems for Chapter 20 *Working Drawings*.

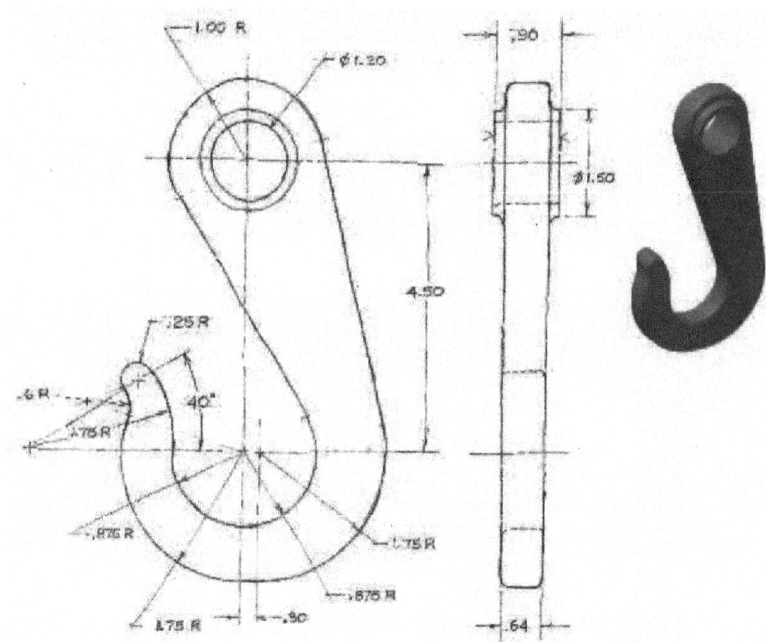

Figure 10.160

Hoist Hook

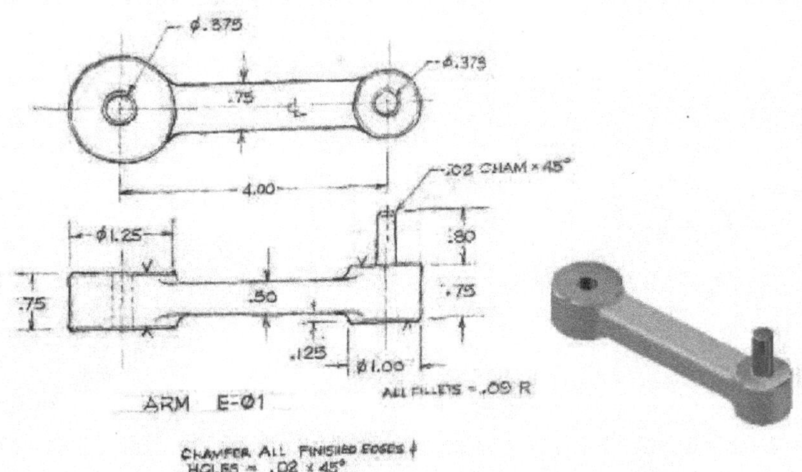

Figure 10.161

Robotic Arm E-01—for 3-D assembly model

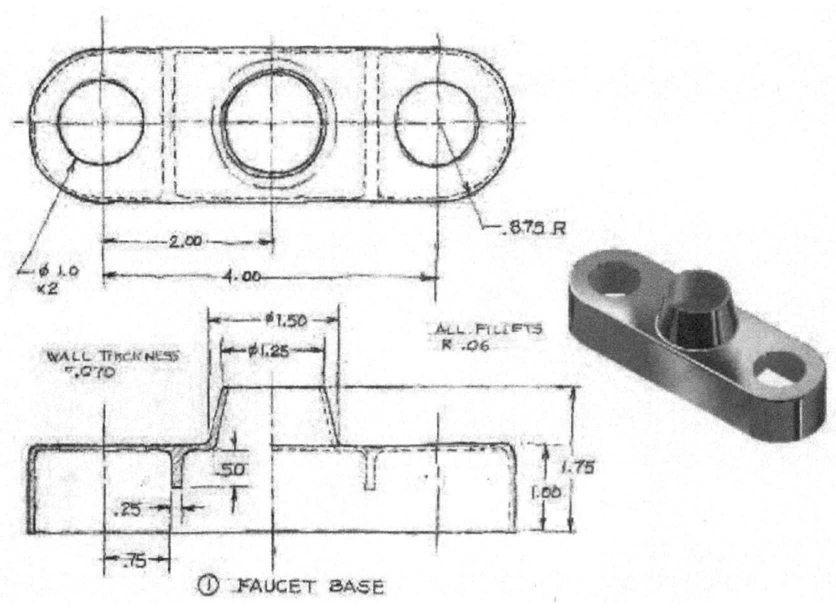

Figure 10.162

Faucet Base—for 3-D assembly model

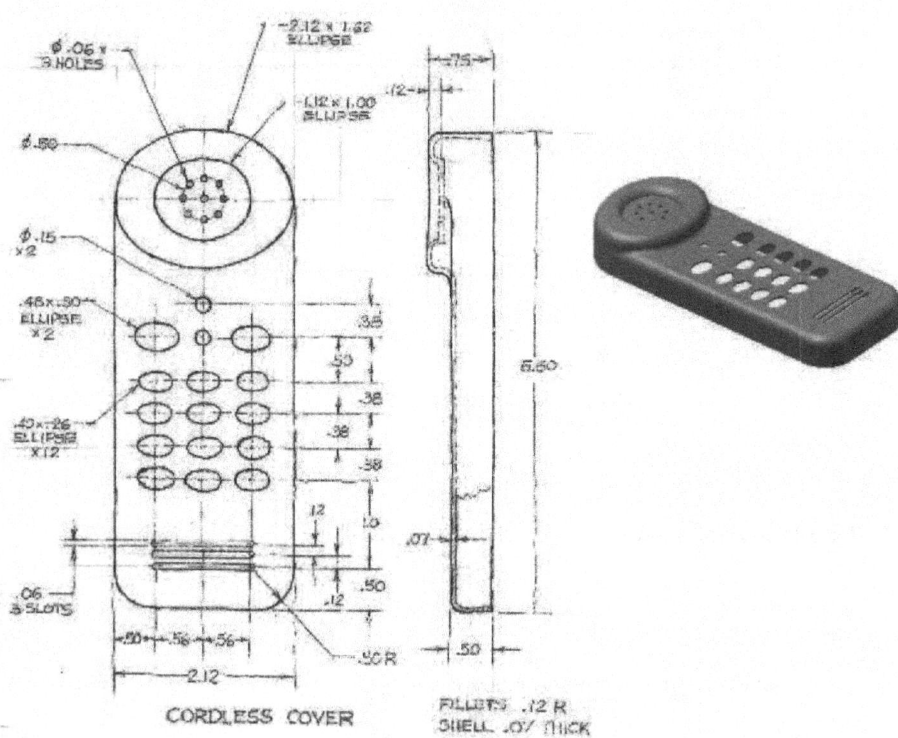

Figure 10.163

Cordless Cover

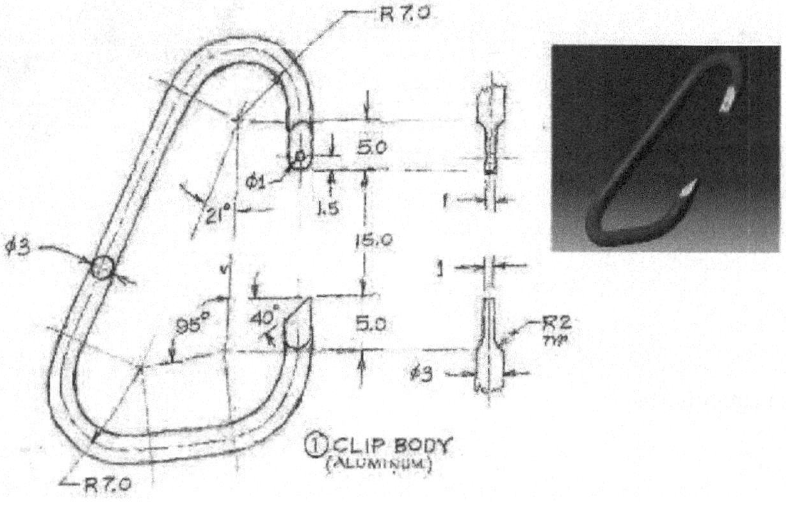

Figure 10.164

Carabiner Clip Body

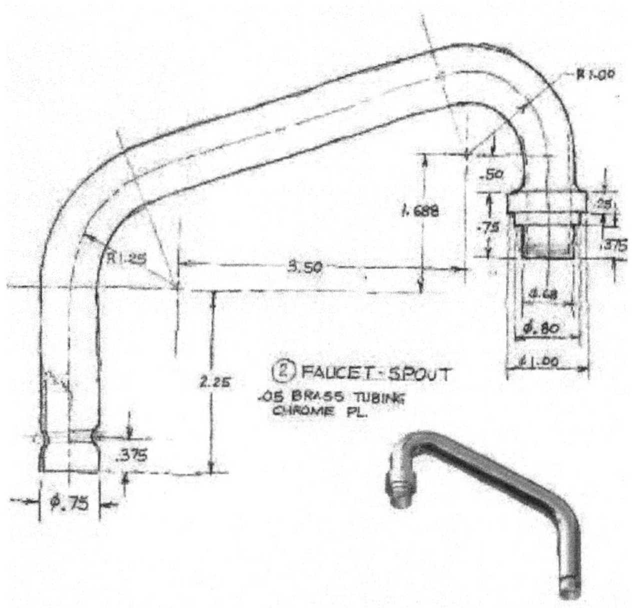

Figure 10.165

Faucet Tube—for 3-D assembly model

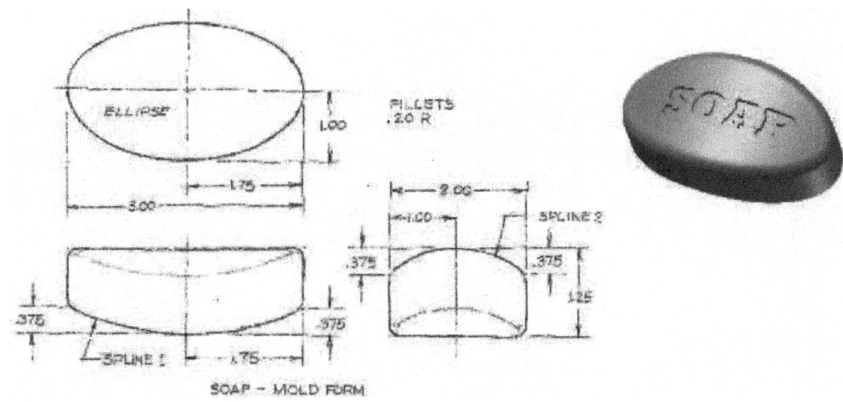

Figure 10.166

Soap Mold Form

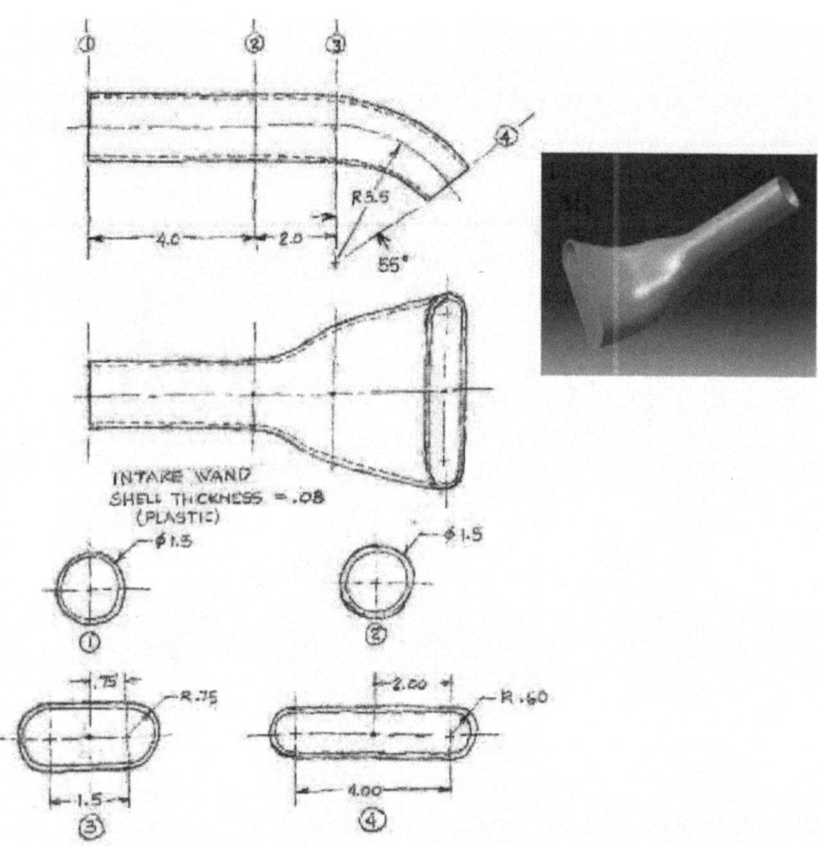

Figure 10.167

Intake Wand

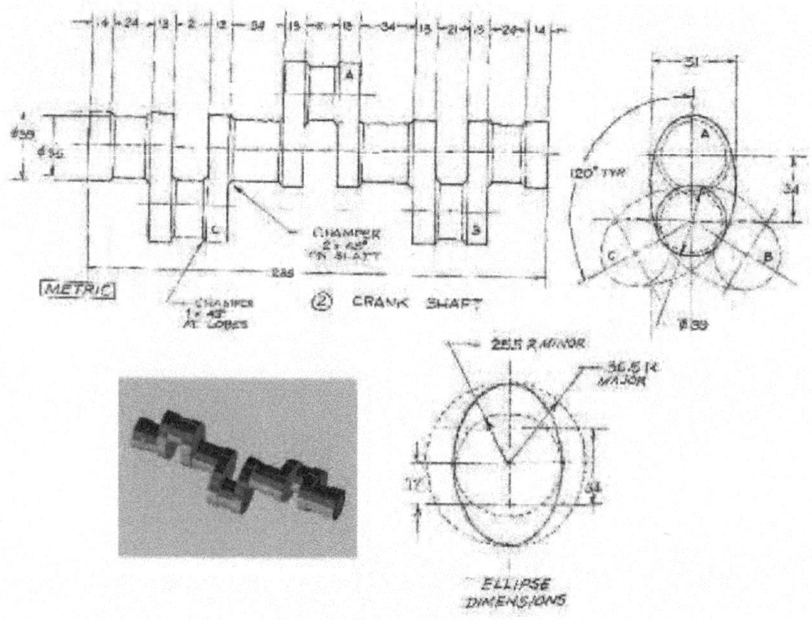

Figure 10.168

Crank Shaft—for 3-D assembly model